PEARSON

ALWAYS LEARNING

Jane B. Reece • Lisa A. Urry • Michael L. Cain
Steven A. Wasserman • Peter V. Minorsky • Robert B. Jackson

Campbell Biology

Custom Edition for University of Minnesota

Taken from:
Campbell Biology, Tenth Edition
by Jane B. Reece, Lisa A. Urry, Michael L. Cain, Steven A. Wasserman,
Peter V. Minorsky, and Robert B. Jackson

Cover Art: Courtesy of Pearson Learning Solutions.

Taken from:

Campbell Biology, Tenth Edition
by Jane B. Reece, Lisa A. Urry, Michael L. Cain, Steven A. Wasserman, Peter V. Minorsky, and Robert B. Jackson
Copyright © 2014, 2011, 2008 by Pearson Education, Inc.
Boston, Massachusetts 02116

This special edition published in cooperation with Pearson Learning Solutions.

All trademarks, service marks, registered trademarks, and registered service marks are the property of their respective owners and are used herein for identification purposes only.

Pearson Learning Solutions, 501 Boylston Street, Suite 900, Boston, MA 02116
A Pearson Education Company
www.pearsoned.com

Printed in the United States of America

10 17

000200010271886331

CN

ISBN 10: 1-269-88545-6
ISBN 13: 978-1-269-88545-4

The Tenth Edition author team's contributions reflect their biological expertise as researchers and their teaching sensibilities gained from years of experience as instructors at diverse institutions. The team's highly collaborative style continues to be evident in the cohesiveness and consistency of the Tenth Edition.

Jane B. Reece

Jane Reece was Neil Campbell's longtime collaborator, and she has participated in every edition of CAMPBELL BIOLOGY. Earlier, Jane taught biology at Middlesex County College and Queensborough Community College. She holds an A.B. in biology from Harvard University, an M.S. in microbiology from Rutgers University, and a Ph.D. in bacteriology from the University of California, Berkeley. Jane's research as a doctoral student at UC Berkeley and postdoctoral fellow at Stanford University focused on genetic recombination in bacteria. Besides her work on CAMPBELL BIOLOGY, she has been a coauthor on Campbell Biology in Focus, Campbell Biology: Concepts & Connections, Campbell Essential Biology, and The World of the Cell.

Lisa A. Urry

Lisa Urry is Professor of Biology and Chair of the Biology Department at Mills College in Oakland, California, and a Visiting Scholar at the University of California, Berkeley. After graduating from Tufts University with a double major in biology and French, Lisa completed her Ph.D. in molecular and developmental biology at the Massachusetts Institute of Technology (MIT) in the MIT/Woods Hole Oceanographic Institution Joint Program. She has published a number of research papers, most of them focused on gene expression during embryonic and larval development in sea urchins. Lisa has taught a variety of courses, from introductory biology to developmental biology and senior seminar. As a part of her mission to increase understanding of evolution, Lisa also teaches a nonmajors course called Evolution for Future Presidents and is on the Teacher Advisory Board for the Understanding Evolution website developed by the University of California Museum of Paleontology. Lisa is also deeply committed to promoting opportunities in science for women and underrepresented minorities. Lisa is also a coauthor of Campbell Biology in Focus.

Michael L. Cain

Michael Cain is an ecologist and evolutionary biologist who is now writing full-time. Michael earned a joint degree in biology and math at Bowdoin College, an M.Sc. from Brown University, and a Ph.D. in ecology and evolutionary biology from Cornell University. As a faculty member at New Mexico State University and Rose-Hulman Institute of Technology, he taught a wide range of courses, including introductory biology, ecology, evolution, botany, and conservation biology. Michael is the author of dozens of scientific papers on topics that include foraging behavior in insects and plants, long-distance seed dispersal, and speciation in crickets. In addition to his work on CAMPBELL BIOLOGY and Campbell Biology in Focus, Michael is the lead author of an ecology textbook.

Steven A. Wasserman

Steve Wasserman is Professor of Biology at the University of California, San Diego (UCSD). He earned his A.B. in biology from Harvard University and his Ph.D. in biological sciences from MIT. Through his research on regulatory pathway mechanisms in the fruit fly *Drosophila*, Steve has contributed to the fields of developmental biology, reproduction, and immunity. As a faculty member at the University of Texas Southwestern Medical Center and UCSD, he has taught genetics, development, and physiology to undergraduate, graduate, and medical students. He currently focuses on teaching introductory biology. He has also served as the research mentor for more than a dozen doctoral students and more than 50 aspiring scientists at the undergraduate and high school levels. Steve has been the recipient of distinguished scholar awards from both the Markey Charitable Trust and the David and Lucile Packard Foundation. In 2007, he received UCSD's Distinguished Teaching Award for undergraduate teaching. Steve is also a coauthor of *Campbell Biology in Focus*.

Peter V. Minorsky

Peter Minorsky is Professor of Biology at Mercy College in New York, where he teaches introductory biology, evolution, ecology, and botany. He received his A.B. in biology from Vassar College and his Ph.D. in plant physiology from Cornell University. He is also the science writer for the journal *Plant Physiology*. After a postdoctoral fellowship at the University of Wisconsin at Madison, Peter taught at Kenyon College, Union College, Western Connecticut State University, and Vassar College. His research interests concern how plants sense environmental change. Peter received the 2008 Award for Teaching Excellence at Mercy College. Peter is also a coauthor of *Campbell Biology in Focus*.

Robert B. Jackson

Rob Jackson is the Douglas Professor of Environment and Energy in the Department of Environmental Earth System Science at Stanford University. Rob holds a B.S. in chemical engineering from Rice University, as well as M.S. degrees in ecology and statistics and a Ph.D. in ecology from Utah State University. While a biology professor at Duke University, Rob directed the university's Program in Ecology and was Vice President of Science for the Ecological Society of America. He has received numerous awards, including a Presidential Early Career Award in Science and Engineering from the National Science Foundation. Rob is a Fellow of both the Ecological Society of America and the American Geophysical Union. He also enjoys popular writing, having published a trade book about the environment, *The Earth Remains Forever*, and two books of poetry for children, *Animal Mischief* and *Weekend Mischief*. Rob is also a coauthor of *Campbell Biology in Focus*.

Neil A. Campbell

Neil Campbell (1946–2004) combined the investigative nature of a research scientist with the soul of an experienced and caring teacher. He earned his M.A. in zoology from the University of California, Los Angeles, and his Ph.D. in plant biology from the University of California, Riverside, where he received the Distinguished Alumnus Award in 2001. Neil published numerous research articles on desert and coastal plants and how the sensitive plant (*Mimosa*) and other legumes move their leaves. His 30 years of teaching in diverse environments included introductory biology courses at Cornell University, Pomona College, and San Bernardino Valley College, where he received the college's first Outstanding Professor Award in 1986. Neil was a visiting scholar in the Department of Botany and Plant Sciences at the University of California, Riverside.

We are honored to present the Tenth Edition of *CAMPBELL BIOLOGY*. For the last quarter century, *CAMPBELL BIOLOGY* has been the leading college text in the biological sciences. It has been translated into more than a dozen languages and has provided millions of students with a solid foundation in college-level biology. This success is a testament not only to Neil Campbell's original vision but also to the dedication of thousands of reviewers, who, together with editors, artists, and contributors, have shaped and inspired this work. Although this Tenth Edition represents a milestone, science and pedagogy are not static—as they evolve, so does *CAMPBELL BIOLOGY*.

Our goals for the Tenth Edition include:

- helping students **make connections visually** across the diverse topics of biology
- giving students a strong foundation in **scientific thinking and quantitative reasoning skills**
- inspiring students with the excitement and relevance of modern biology, particularly in the realm of **genomics**

Our starting point, as always, is our commitment to crafting text and visuals that are accurate, are current, and reflect our passion for teaching and learning about biology.

New to This Edition

Here we provide an overview of the new features that we have developed for the Tenth Edition; we invite you to explore pages x–xxvi for more information and examples.

- Make Connections Figures draw together topics from different chapters to show how they are all related in the "big picture." By reinforcing fundamental conceptual connections throughout biology, these figures help overcome students' tendencies to compartmentalize information.
- Scientific Skills Exercises in every chapter use real data and guide students in learning and practicing data interpretation, graphing, experimental design, and math skills. All 56 Scientific Skills Exercises have assignable, automatically graded versions in **MasteringBiology®**.

- Interpret the Data Questions throughout the text engage students in scientific inquiry by asking them to interpret data presented in a graph, figure, or table. The Interpret the Data Questions can be assigned and automatically graded in **MasteringBiology**.
- The impact of genomics across biology is explored throughout the Tenth Edition with examples that reveal how our ability to rapidly sequence DNA and proteins is transforming all areas of biology, from molecular and cell biology to phylogenetics, physiology, and ecology. Chapter 5 provides a launching point for this feature in a new Key Concept, "Genomics and proteomics have transformed biological inquiry and applications." Illustrative examples are distributed throughout later chapters.
- Synthesize Your Knowledge Questions at the end of each chapter ask students to synthesize the material in the chapter and demonstrate their big-picture understanding. A striking photograph with a thought-provoking question helps students see how material they learned in the chapter connects to their world and provides insight into natural phenomena.
- The Tenth Edition provides a range of new practice and assessment opportunities in **MasteringBiology.** Besides the Scientific Skills Exercises and Interpret the Data Questions, Solve It Tutorials in MasteringBiology engage students in a multistep investigation of a "mystery" or open question. Acting as scientists, students must analyze real data and work through a simulated investigation. In addition, Adaptive Follow-Up Assignments provide coaching and practice that continually adapt to each student's needs, making efficient use of study time. Students can use the Dynamic Study Modules to study anytime and anywhere with their smartphones, tablets, or computers.
- Learning Catalytics™ allows students to use their smartphones, tablets, or laptops to respond to questions in class.
- As in each new edition of *CAMPBELL BIOLOGY*, the Tenth Edition incorporates **new content** and **organizational improvements**. These are summarized on pp. viii–ix, following this Preface.

Our Hallmark Features

Teachers of general biology face a daunting challenge: to help students acquire a conceptual framework for organizing an ever-expanding amount of information. The hallmark features of CAMPBELL BIOLOGY provide such a framework, while promoting a deeper understanding of biology and the process of science.

To help students distinguish the "forest from the trees," each chapter is organized around a framework of three to seven carefully chosen **Key Concepts**. The text, Concept Check Questions, Summary of Key Concepts, and MasteringBiology all reinforce these main ideas and essential facts.

CAMPBELL BIOLOGY also helps students organize and make sense of what they learn by emphasizing **evolution and other unifying themes** that pervade biology. These themes are introduced in Chapter 1 and are integrated throughout the book. Each chapter includes at least one Evolution section that explicitly focuses on evolutionary aspects of the chapter material, and each chapter ends with an Evolution Connection Question and a Write About a Theme Question.

Because text and illustrations are equally important for learning biology, **integration of text and figures** has been a hallmark of this text since the First Edition. In addition to the new Make Connections Figures, our popular Exploring Figures on selected topics epitomize this approach: Each is a learning unit of core content that brings together related illustrations and text. Another example is our Guided Tour Figures, which use descriptions in blue type to walk students through complex figures as an instructor would. Visual Organizer Figures highlight the main parts of a figure, helping students see key categories at a glance. And Summary Figures visually recap information from the chapter.

To encourage **active reading** of the text, CAMPBELL BIOLOGY includes numerous opportunities for students to stop and think about what they are reading, often by putting pencil to paper to draw a sketch, annotate a figure, or graph data. Active learning questions include Make Connections Questions, What If? Questions, Figure Legend Questions, Draw It Questions, Summary Questions, and the new Synthesize Your Knowledge and Interpret the Data Questions.

Finally, CAMPBELL BIOLOGY has always featured **scientific inquiry**, an essential component of any biology course. Complementing stories of scientific discovery in the text narrative and the unit-opening interviews, our standard-setting Inquiry Figures deepen the ability of students to understand how we know what we know. Scientific Inquiry Questions give students opportunities to practice scientific thinking, along with the new Scientific Skills Exercises and Interpret the Data Questions.

MasteringBiology®

MasteringBiology, the most widely used online assessment and tutorial program for biology, provides an extensive library of homework assignments that are graded automatically. In addition to the new Scientific Skills Exercises, Interpret the Data Questions, Solve It Tutorials, Adaptive Follow-Up Assignments, and Dynamic Study Modules, MasteringBiology offers BioFlix® Tutorials with 3-D Animations, Experimental Inquiry Tutorials, Interpreting Data Tutorials, BLAST Tutorials, Make Connections Tutorials, Video Tutor Sessions, Get Ready for Biology, Activities, Reading Quiz Questions, Student Misconception Questions, 4,500 Test Bank Questions, and MasteringBiology Virtual Labs. MasteringBiology also includes the CAMPBELL BIOLOGY eText, Study Area, and Instructor Resources. See pages xviii–xxi and www.masteringbiology.com for more details.

Our Partnership with Instructors and Students

A core value underlying our work is our belief in the importance of a partnership with instructors and students. One primary way of serving instructors and students, of course, is providing a text that teaches biology well. In addition, Pearson Education offers a rich variety of instructor and student resources, in both print and electronic form (see pp. xviii–xxiii). In our continuing efforts to improve the book and its supplements, we benefit tremendously from instructor and student feedback, not only in formal reviews from hundreds of scientists, but also via e-mail and other avenues of informal communication.

The real test of any textbook is how well it helps instructors teach and students learn. We welcome comments from both students and instructors. Please address your suggestions to any of us:

Jane Reece
    janereece@cal.berkeley.edu
Lisa Urry (Chapter 1 and Units 1–3)
    lurry@mills.edu
Michael Cain (Units 4 and 5)
    mcain@bowdoin.edu
Peter Minorsky (Unit 6)
    pminorsky@mercy.edu
Steven Wasserman (Unit 7)
    stevenw@ucsd.edu
Rob Jackson (Unit 8)
    rob.jackson@stanford.edu

This section highlights selected new content and organizational changes in CAMPBELL BIOLOGY, Tenth Edition.

CHAPTER 1

Evolution, the Themes of Biology, and Scientific Inquiry

To help students focus on the big ideas of biology, we now emphasize five themes: Organization, Information, Energy and Matter, Interactions, and the core theme of Evolution. The new Figure 1.8 on gene expression equips students from the outset with an understanding of how gene sequences determine an organism's characteristics. Concept 1.3 has been reframed to more realistically reflect the scientific process, including a new figure on the complexity of the practice of science (Figure 1.23). A new case study in scientific inquiry (Figures 1.24 and 1.25) deals with evolution of coloration in mice.

1 The Chemistry of Life

New chapter-opening photos and introductory stories engage students in learning this foundational material. Chapter 2 has a new Evolution section on radiometric dating. In Chapter 5, there is a new Key Concept section, "Genomics and proteomics have transformed biological inquiry and applications" (Concept 5.6), and a new Make Connections Figure, "Contributions of Genomics and Proteomics to Biology" (Figure 5.26).

2 The Cell

Our main goal for this unit was to make the material more accessible to students. We have streamlined coverage of the cytoskeleton in Chapter 6 and historical aspects of the membrane model in Chapter 7. We have revised the photosynthesis summary figure (Figure 10.22) to incorporate a big-picture view of photosynthesis. The new Make Connections Figure 10.23 integrates the cellular activities covered in Chapters 5–10 in the context of a single plant cell. Concept 12.3 has been streamlined, with a new Figure 12.17 that covers the M checkpoint as well as the G_1 checkpoint.

3 Genetics

In Chapters 13–17, we have incorporated changes that help students make connections between the more abstract concepts of genetics and their molecular underpinnings. For example, Chapter 13 includes a new figure (Figure 13.9) detailing the events of crossing over during prophase. Figure 14.4, showing alleles on chromosomes, has been enhanced to show the DNA sequences of both alleles, along with their biochemical and phenotypic consequences. A new figure on sickle-cell disease also connects these levels (Figure 14.17). In Chapter 17, material on coupled transcription and translation in bacteria has been united with coverage of polyribosomes.

Chapters 18–21 are extensively updated, driven by exciting new discoveries based on high-throughput sequencing. Chapter 18 includes a new figure (Figure 18.15) on the role of siRNAs in chromatin remodeling. A new Make Connections Figure (Figure 18.27) describes four subtypes of breast cancer that have recently been proposed, based on gene expression in tumor cells. In Chapter 20, techniques that are less commonly used have been pruned, and the chapter has been reorganized to emphasize the important role of sequencing. A new figure (Figure 20.4) illustrates next-generation sequencing. Chapter 21 has been updated to reflect new research, including the ENCODE project, the Cancer Genome Atlas, and the genome sequences of the gorilla and bonobo. A new figure (Figure 21.15) compares the 3-D structures of lysozyme and α-lactalbumin and their amino acid sequences, providing support for their common evolutionary origin.

4 Mechanisms of Evolution

One goal of this revision was to highlight connections among fundamental evolutionary concepts. Helping meet this goal, new material connects Darwin's ideas to what can be learned from phylogenetic trees, and a new figure (Figure 25.13) and text illustrate how the combined effects of speciation and extinction determine the number of species in different groups of organisms. The unit also features new material on nucleotide variability within genetic loci, including a new figure (Figure 23.4) that shows variability within coding and noncoding regions of a gene. Other changes enhance the storyline of the unit. For instance, Chapter 25 includes new text on how the rise of large eukaryotes in the Ediacaran period represented a monumental transition in the history of life—the end of a microbe-only world. Updates include revised discussions of the events and underlying causes of the Cambrian explosion and the Permian mass extinction, as well as new figures providing fossil evidence of key evolutionary events, such as the formation of plant-fungi symbioses (Figure 25.12). A new Make Connections Figure (Figure 23.17) explores the sickle-cell allele and its impact from the molecular and cellular levels to organisms to the evolutionary explanation for the allele's global distribution in the human population.

UNIT 5 The Evolutionary History of Biological Diversity

In keeping with our Tenth Edition goals, we have expanded the coverage of genomic and other molecular studies and how they inform our understanding of phylogeny. Examples include a new Inquiry Figure (Figure 34.49) on the Neanderthal genome and presentation of new evidence that mutualistic interactions between plants and fungi are ancient. In addition, many phylogenies have been revised to reflect recent miRNA and genomic data. The unit also contains new material on tree-thinking, such as a new figure (Figure 26.11) that distinguishes between paraphyletic and polyphyletic taxa. We continue to emphasize evolutionary events that underlie the diversity of life on Earth. For example, a new section in Chapter 32 discusses the origin of multicellularity in animal ancestors. A new Make Connections Figure (Figure 33.9) explores the diverse structural solutions for maximizing surface area that have evolved across different kingdoms.

UNIT 6 Plant Form and Function

In developing the Tenth Edition, we have continued to provide students with a basic understanding of plant anatomy and function while highlighting dynamic areas of plant research and the many important connections between plants and other organisms. To underscore the relevance of plant biology to society, there is now expanded coverage of plant biotechnology and the development of biofuels in Chapter 38. Other updates include expanded coverage of bacterial components of the rhizosphere (Figure 37.9), plant mineral deficiency symptoms (Table 37.1), evolutionary trends in floral morphology (Chapter 38), and chemical communication between plants (Chapter 39). The discussion of plant defenses against pathogens and herbivores has been extensively revised and now includes a Make Connections Figure that examines how plants deter herbivores at numerous levels of biological organization, ranging from the molecular level to the community level (Figure 39.27).

UNIT 7 Animal Form and Function

In revising this unit, we strove to enhance student appreciation of the core concepts and ideas that apply across diverse organisms and varied organ systems. For example, a new Make Connections Figure (Figure 40.22) highlights challenges common to plant and animal physiology and presents both shared and divergent solutions to those challenges; this figure provides both a useful summary of plant physiology and an introduction to animal physiology. To help students recognize the central concept of homeostasis, figures have been revised across six chapters to provide a consistent organization that facilitates interpretation of individual hormone pathways as well as the comparison of pathways for different hormones. Homeostasis and endocrine regulation are highlighted by new and engaging chapter-opening photos and stories on the desert ant (Chapter 40) and on sexual dimorphism (Chapter 45), a revised presentation of the variation in target cell responses to a hormone (Figure 45.8), and a new figure integrating art and text on human endocrine glands and hormones (Figure 45.9). Many figures have been reconceived to emphasize key information, including new figures introducing the classes of essential nutrients (Figure 41.2) and showing oxygen and carbon dioxide partial pressures throughout the circulatory system (Figure 42.29). A new Make Connections Figure (Figure 44.17) demonstrates the importance of concentration gradients in animals as well as all other organisms. Throughout the unit, new state-of-the-art images and material on current and compelling topics—such as the human stomach microbiome (Figure 41.18) and the identification of the complete set of human taste receptors (Chapter 50)—will help engage students and encourage them to make connections beyond the text.

UNIT 8 Ecology

For the Tenth Edition, the ecology unit engages students with new ideas and examples. Chapter 52 highlights the discovery of the world's smallest vertebrate species. New text and a figure use the saguaro cactus to illustrate how abiotic and biotic factors limit the distribution of species (Figure 52.15). Greater emphasis is placed on the importance of disturbances, such as the effects of Hurricane Katrina on forest mortality. Chapter 53 features the loggerhead turtle in the chapter opener, Concept 53.1 (reproduction), and Concept 53.4 (evolution and life history traits). The chapter also includes new molecular coverage: how ecologists use genetic profiles to estimate the number of breeding loggerhead turtles (Figure 53.7) and how a single gene influences dispersal in the Glanville fritillary. In Chapter 54, new text and a figure highlight the mimic octopus, a recently discovered species that illustrates how predators use mimicry (Figure 54.6). A new Make Connections Figure ties together population, community, and ecosystem processes in the arctic tundra (Figure 55.13). Chapter 55 also has a new opening story on habitat transformation in the tundra. Chapter 56 highlights the emerging fields of urban ecology and conservation biology, including the technical and ethical challenges of resurrecting extinct species. It also examines the threat posed by pharmaceuticals in the environment. The book ends on a hopeful note, charging students to use biological knowledge to help solve problems and improve life on Earth.

See the Big Picture

KEY CONCEPTS

Each chapter is organized around a framework of 3 to 7 Key Concepts that focus on the big picture and provide a context for the supporting details.

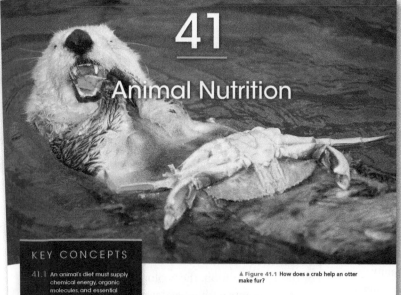

41

Animal Nutrition

KEY CONCEPTS

41.1 An animal's diet must supply chemical energy, organic molecules, and essential nutrients

41.2 The main stages of food processing are ingestion, digestion, absorption, and elimination

41.3 Organs specialized for sequential stages of food processing form the mammalian digestive system

41.4 Evolutionary adaptations of vertebrate digestive systems correlate with diet

41.5 Feedback circuits regulate digestion, energy storage, and appetite

▲ Figure 41.1 How does a crab help an otter make fur?

The Need to Feed

Dinnertime has arrived for the sea otter in Figure 41.1 (and for the crab, though in quite a different sense). The muscles and other organs of the crab will be chewed into pieces, broken down by acid and enzymes in the otter's digestive system, and finally absorbed as small molecules into the body of the otter. Such a process is what is meant by animal **nutrition**: food being taken in, taken apart, and taken up.

Although dining on fish, crabs, urchins, and abalone is the sea otter's specialty, all animals eat other organisms—dead or alive, piecemeal or whole. Unlike plants, animals must consume food for both energy and the organic molecules used to assemble new molecules, cells, and tissues. Despite this shared need, animals have diverse diets. **Herbivores**, such as cattle, sea slugs, and caterpillars, dine mainly on plants or algae. **Carnivores**, such as sea otters, hawks, and spiders, mostly eat other animals. Rats and other **omnivores** (from the Latin *omnis*, all) don't in fact eat everything, but they do regularly consume animals as well as plants or algae. We humans are typically omnivores, as are cockroaches and crows.

The terms *herbivore, carnivore,* and *omnivore* represent the kinds of food an animal usually eats. Keep in mind, however, that most animals are opportunistic feeders, eating foods outside their standard diet when their usual foods aren't available.

▲ The List of Key Concepts introduces the big ideas covered in the chapter.

◀ Every chapter opens with a visually dynamic photo accompanied by an intriguing question that invites students into the chapter.

After reading a Key Concept section, students can check their understanding using the Concept Check Questions.

◀ Questions throughout the chapter encourage students to read the text actively.

Make Connections Questions ▶ ask students to relate content in the chapter to material presented earlier in the course.

What if? Questions ask students ▶ to apply what they've learned.

CONCEPT CHECK 41.1

1. All 20 amino acids are needed to make animal proteins. Why aren't they all essential to animal diets?

2. **MAKE CONNECTIONS** Considering the role of enzymes in metabolic reactions (see Concept 8.4), explain why vitamins are required in very small amounts in the diet.

3. **WHAT IF?** If a zoo animal eating ample food shows signs of malnutrition, how might a researcher determine which nutrient is lacking in its diet?

The **Summary of Key Concepts** refocuses students on the main points of the chapter.

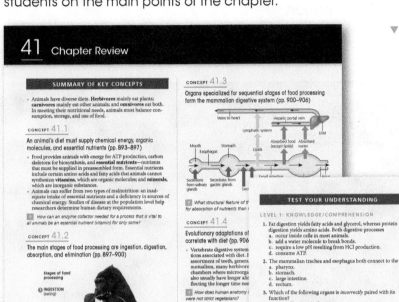

▲ **Summary Figures** recap key information in a visual way. **Summary of Key Concepts Questions** check students' understanding of a key idea from each concept.

▼ **Test Your Understanding Questions** at the end of each chapter are organized into three levels based on **Bloom's Taxonomy**:

- Level 1: Knowledge/Comprehension
- Level 2: Application/Analysis
- Level 3: Synthesis/Evaluation

Test Bank questions and multiple-choice questions in MasteringBiology® are also categorized by Bloom's Taxonomy.

◄ **NEW!** **Synthesize Your Knowledge Questions** ask students to apply their understanding of the chapter content to explain an intriguing photo.

THEMES

To help students focus on the big ideas of biology, five **themes** are introduced in Chapter 1 and woven throughout the text:

- Evolution
- Organization
- Information
- Energy and Matter
- Interactions

Every chapter has a section ▶ explicitly relating the chapter content to evolution, the fundamental theme of biology.

▲ To reinforce the themes, every chapter ends with an **Evolution Connection Question** and a **Write About a Theme Question**.

The Evolutionary Origins of Mitochondria and Chloroplasts

EVOLUTION Mitochondria and chloroplasts display similarities with bacteria that led to the **endosymbiont theory**, illustrated in **Figure 6.16**. This theory states that an early ancestor of eukaryotic cells engulfed an oxygen-using nonphotosynthetic prokaryotic cell. Eventually, the engulfed

Make Connections Visually

NEW! Make Connections Figures pull together content from different chapters, providing a visual representation of "big picture" relationships.

Make Connections Figures include:

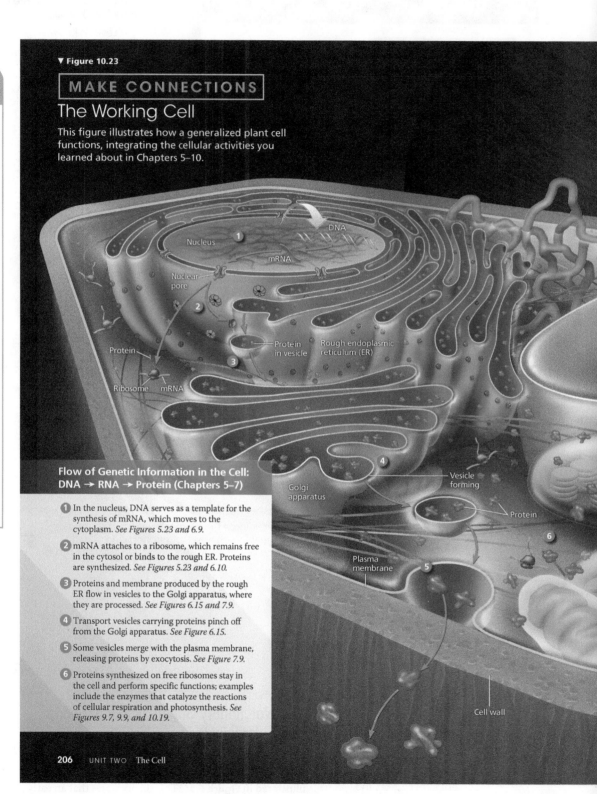

▼ Figure 10.23

MAKE CONNECTIONS

The Working Cell

This figure illustrates how a generalized plant cell functions, integrating the cellular activities you learned about in Chapters 5–10.

Flow of Genetic Information in the Cell: DNA → RNA → Protein (Chapters 5–7)

1. In the nucleus, DNA serves as a template for the synthesis of mRNA, which moves to the cytoplasm. *See Figures 5.23 and 6.9.*

2. mRNA attaches to a ribosome, which remains free in the cytosol or binds to the rough ER. Proteins are synthesized. *See Figures 5.23 and 6.10.*

3. Proteins and membrane produced by the rough ER flow in vesicles to the Golgi apparatus, where they are processed. *See Figures 6.15 and 7.9.*

4. Transport vesicles carrying proteins pinch off from the Golgi apparatus. *See Figure 6.15.*

5. Some vesicles merge with the plasma membrane, releasing proteins by exocytosis. *See Figure 7.9.*

6. Proteins synthesized on free ribosomes stay in the cell and perform specific functions; examples include the enzymes that catalyze the reactions of cellular respiration and photosynthesis. *See Figures 9.7, 9.9, and 10.19.*

Labels on figure: DNA, Nucleus, mRNA, Nuclear pore, Protein, Ribosome, mRNA, Protein in vesicle, Rough endoplasmic reticulum (ER), Golgi apparatus, Vesicle forming, Protein, Plasma membrane, Cell wall

206 UNIT TWO   The Cell

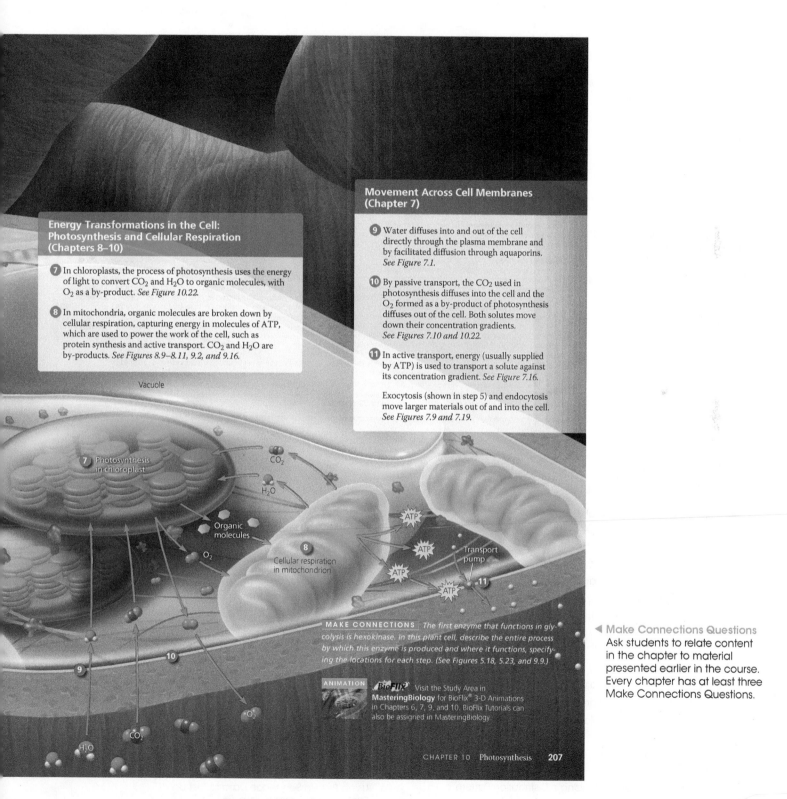

Energy Transformations in the Cell: Photosynthesis and Cellular Respiration (Chapters 8–10)

7 In chloroplasts, the process of photosynthesis uses the energy of light to convert CO_2 and H_2O to organic molecules, with O_2 as a by-product. *See Figure 10.22.*

8 In mitochondria, organic molecules are broken down by cellular respiration, capturing energy in molecules of ATP, which are used to power the work of the cell, such as protein synthesis and active transport. CO_2 and H_2O are by-products. *See Figures 8.9–8.11, 9.2, and 9.16.*

Vacuole

Movement Across Cell Membranes (Chapter 7)

9 Water diffuses into and out of the cell directly through the plasma membrane and by facilitated diffusion through aquaporins. *See Figure 7.1.*

10 By passive transport, the CO_2 used in photosynthesis diffuses into the cell and the O_2 formed as a by-product of photosynthesis diffuses out of the cell. Both solutes move down their concentration gradients. *See Figures 7.10 and 10.22.*

11 In active transport, energy (usually supplied by ATP) is used to transport a solute against its concentration gradient. *See Figure 7.16.*

Exocytosis (shown in step 5) and endocytosis move larger materials out of and into the cell. *See Figures 7.9 and 7.19.*

7 Photosynthesis in chloroplast

CO_2

H_2O

Organic molecules

O_2

8 Cellular respiration in mitochondrion

ATP
ATP
ATP
ATP

Transport pump

11

10

9

O_2

H_2O

CO_2

MAKE CONNECTIONS *The first enzyme that functions in glycolysis is hexokinase. In this plant cell, describe the entire process by which this enzyme is produced and where it functions, specifying the locations for each step. (See Figures 5.18, 5.23, and 9.9.)*

ANIMATION **BioFlix** Visit the Study Area in **MasteringBiology** for BioFlix® 3-D Animations in Chapters 6, 7, 9, and 10. BioFlix Tutorials can also be assigned in MasteringBiology.

◄ Make Connections Questions
Ask students to relate content in the chapter to material presented earlier in the course. Every chapter has at least three Make Connections Questions.

Make Connections Visually

NEW! Scientific Skills Exercises in every chapter use real data to build key skills needed for biology, including data interpretation, graphing, experimental design, and math skills.

▼ Photos provide visual interest and context.

Each Scientific Skills Exercise ▶ is based on an experiment related to the chapter content.

Most Scientific Skills Exercises ▶ use data from published research.

Questions build in difficulty, ▶ walking students through new skills step by step and providing opportunities for higher-level critical thinking.

SCIENTIFIC SKILLS EXERCISE

Interpreting a Scatter Plot with a Regression Line

How Does the Carbonate Ion Concentration of Seawater Affect the Calcification Rate of a Coral Reef? Scientists predict that acidification of the ocean due to higher levels of atmospheric CO_2 will lower the concentration of dissolved carbonate ions, which living corals use to build calcium carbonate reef structures. In this exercise, you will analyze data from a controlled experiment that examined the effect of carbonate ion concentration ($[CO_3^{2-}]$) on calcium carbonate deposition, a process called calcification.

How the Experiment Was Done The Biosphere 2 aquarium in Arizona contains a large coral reef system that behaves like a natural reef. For several years, a group of researchers measured the rate of calcification by the reef organisms and examined how the calcification rate changed with differing amounts of dissolved carbonate ions in the seawater.

Data from the Experiment The black data points in the graph form a scatter plot. The red line, known as a linear regression line, is the best-fitting straight line for these points.

Interpret the Data

1. When presented with a graph of experimental data, the first step in analysis is to determine what each axis represents. (a) In words, explain what is being shown on the x-axis. Be sure to include the units. (b) What is being shown on the y-axis (including units)? (c) Which variable is the independent variable—the variable that was *manipulated* by the researchers? (d) Which variable is the dependent variable—the variable that responded to or depended on the treatment, which was *measured* by the researchers? (For additional information about graphs, see the Scientific Skills Review in Appendix F and in the Study Area in MasteringBiology.)

2. Based on the data shown in the graph, describe in words the relationship between carbonate ion concentration and calcification rate.

3. (a) If the seawater carbonate ion concentration is 270 µmol/kg, what is the approximate rate of calcification, and approximately how many days would it take 1 square meter of reef to accumulate 30 mmol of

calcium carbonate ($CaCO_3$)? (b) If the seawater carbonate ion concentration is 250 µmol/kg, what is the approximate rate of calcification, and approximately how many days would it take 1 square meter of reef to accumulate 30 mmol of calcium carbonate? (c) If carbonate ion concentration decreases, how does the calcification rate change, and how does that affect the time it takes coral to grow?

4. (a) Referring to the equations in Figure 3.11, determine which step of the process is measured in this experiment. (b) Are the results of this experiment consistent with the hypothesis that increased atmospheric $[CO_2]$ will slow the growth of coral reefs? Why or why not?

(MB) A version of this Scientific Skills Exercise can be assigned in MasteringBiology.

Data from C. Langdon et al., Effect of calcium carbonate saturation state on the calcification rate of an experimental coral reef, *Global Biogeochemical Cycles* 14:639–654 (2000).

▲ Each Scientific Skills Exercise cites the published research.

Every chapter has a Scientific Skills Exercise

NEW! All **56** Scientific Skills Exercises from the text have assignable, interactive versions in MasteringBiology® that are automatically graded.

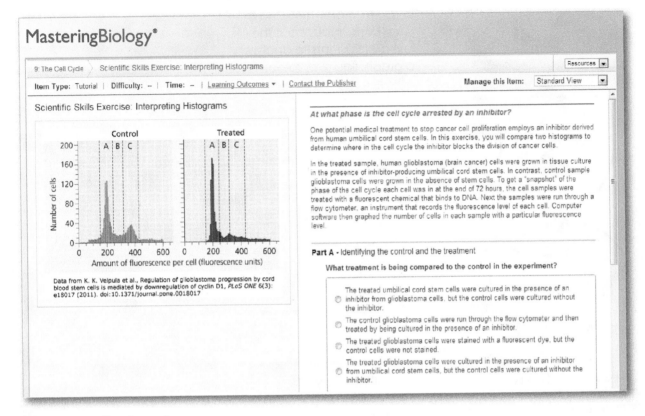

MasteringBiology®

To learn more, visit www.masteringbiology.com

CAMPBELL BIOLOGY, Tenth Edition, and MasteringBiology®
offer a wide variety of ways for students to move beyond
memorization and **think like a scientist**.

▲ **Figure 56.25 Biological magnification of PCBs in a Great
Lakes food web.** (ppm = parts per million)

INTERPRET THE DATA *If a typical smelt weighs 225 g, what is the
total mass of PCBs in a smelt in the Great Lakes? If an average lake trout
weighs 4,500 g, what is the total mass of PCBs in a trout in the Great
Lakes? Assume that a lake trout from an unpolluted source is introduced
into the Great Lakes and smelt are the only source of PCBs in the trout's
diet. The new trout would have the same level of PCBs as the existing
trout after eating how many smelt? (Assume that the trout retains 100%
of the PCBs it consumes.)*

◄ **NEW!** Interpret the Data
Questions throughout the
text ask students to analyze
a graph, figure, or table.

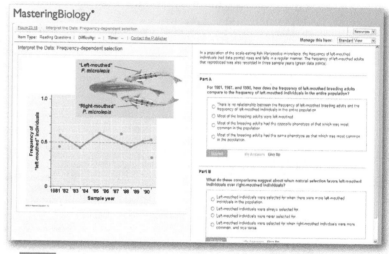

▲ **NEW!** Every Interpret the
Data Question from the text is
assignable in MasteringBiology.

MasteringBiology®

Learn more at
www.masteringbiology.com

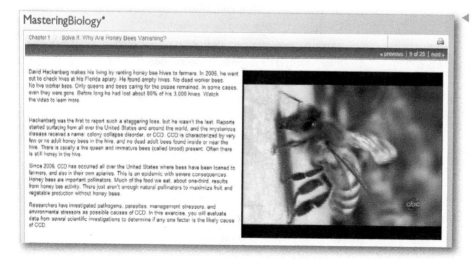

◄ **NEW!** Solve It Tutorials engage
students in a multi-step investigation of
a "mystery" or open question in which
they must analyze real data. These are
assignable in MasteringBiology.

Topics include:

- Is It Possible to Treat Bacterial Infections Without
  Traditional Antibiotics?
- Are You Getting the Fish You Paid For?
- Why Are Honey Bees Vanishing?
- Which Biofuel Has the Most Potential to Reduce
  our Dependence on Fossil Fuels?
- Which Insulin Mutations May Result in Disease?
- What is Causing Episodes of Muscle Weakness
  in a Patient?

NEW! Throughout the Tenth Edition, new examples show students how our ability to sequence DNA and proteins rapidly and inexpensively is transforming every subfield of biology, from cell biology to physiology to ecology.

◄ This new Make Connections Figure in Chapter 5 previews some examples of how genomics and proteomics have helped shed light on diverse biological questions. These examples are explored in greater depth later in the text.

Selected Scientific Skills Exercises involve working with DNA or protein sequences. ▶

SCIENTIFIC SKILLS EXERCISE

► Human   ► Rhesus monkey   ► Gibbon

Analyzing Polypeptide Sequence Data

Are Rhesus Monkeys or Gibbons More Closely Related to Humans? DNA and polypeptide sequences from closely related species are more similar to each other than are sequences from more distantly related species. In this exercise, you will look at amino acid sequence data for the β polypeptide chain of hemoglobin, often called β-globin. You will then interpret the data to hypothesize whether the monkey or the gibbon is more closely related to humans.

How Such Experiments Are Done Researchers can isolate the polypeptide of interest from an organism and then determine the amino acid sequence. More frequently, the DNA of the relevant gene is sequenced, and the amino acid sequence of the polypeptide is deduced from the DNA sequence of its gene.

Data from the Experiments In the data below, the letters give the sequence of the 146 amino acids in β-globin from humans, rhesus

monkeys, and gibbons. Because a complete sequence would not fit on one line here, the sequences are broken into three segments. The sequences for the three different species are aligned so that you can compare them easily. For example, you can see that for all three species, the first amino acid is V (valine) and the 146th amino acid is H (histidine).

Interpret the Data

1. Scan the monkey and gibbon sequences, letter by letter, circling any amino acids that do not match the human sequence. (a) How many amino acids differ between the monkey and the human sequences? (b) Between the gibbon and human?

2. For each nonhuman species, what percent of its amino acids are identical to the human sequence of β-globin?

3. Based on these data alone, state a hypothesis for which of these two species is more closely related to humans. What is your reasoning?

4. What other evidence could you use to support your hypothesis?

(🖥) A version of this Scientific Skills Exercise can be assigned in MasteringBiology.

Data from Human: http://www.ncbi.nlm.nih.gov/protein/AAA21113.1; rhesus monkey: http://www.ncbi.nlm.nih.gov/protein/122634; gibbon: http://www.ncbi.nlm.nih.gov/protein/122616

Species	Alignment of Amino Acid Sequences of β-globin
Human	1 VHLTPEEKSA VTALWGKVNV DEVGGEALGR LLVVYPWTQR FFESFGDLST
Monkey	1 VHLTPEEKNA VTTLWGKVNV DEVGGEALGR LLLVYPWTQR FFESFGDLSS
Gibbon	1 VHLTPEEKSA VTALWGKVNV DEVGGEALGR LLVVYPWTQR FFESFGDLST
Human	51 PDAVMGNPKV KAHGKKVLGA FSDGLAHLDN LKGTFATLSE LHCDKLHVDP
Monkey	51 PDAVMGNPKV KAHGKKVLGA FSDGLNHLDN LKGTFAQLSE LHCDKLHVDP
Gibbon	51 PDAVMGNPKV KAHGKKVLGA FSDGLAHLDN LKGTFAQLSE LHCDKLHVDP
Human	101 ENFRLLGNVL VCVLAHHFGK EFTPPVQAAY QKVVAGVANA LAHKYH
Monkey	101 ENFKLLGNVL VCVLAHHFGK EFTPQVQAAY QKVVAGVANA LAHKYH
Gibbon	101 ENFRLLGNVL VCVLAHHFGK EFTPQVQAAY QKVVAGVANA LAHKYH

Study Anytime, Anywhere

MasteringBiology®

eTEXT

Access the complete
textbook online!

▲ The Pearson eText gives students access to the text whenever and wherever
they can access the Internet. The eText can be viewed on PCs, Macs, and
tablets, including iPad® and Android.® The eText includes powerful interactive
and customization functions:

- Write notes
- Highlight text
- Bookmark pages
- Zoom

- Click hyperlinked words to view definitions
- Search
- Link to media activities and quizzes

Instructors can even write notes for the class and highlight important materials
using a tool that works like an electronic pen on a whiteboard.

STUDY AREA

Students can access the Study Area for
use on their own or in a study group.

BioFlix® 3-D Animations ▶
explore the most
difficult biology topics,
reinforced with tutorials,
quizzes, and more.

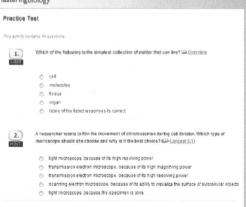

▲ Get Ready for Biology helps
students get up to speed for
their course by covering study
skills, basic math, terminology,
chemistry, and biology basics.

◀ Practice Tests help students
assess their understanding of
each chapter, providing feedback
for right and wrong answers.

The Study Area also includes:
Cumulative Test, MP3 Tutor
Sessions, Videos, Activities,
Investigations, Lab Media, Audio
Glossary, Word Roots, Key Terms,
Flashcards, and Art.

DYNAMIC STUDY MODULES

NEW! Dynamic Study Modules, designed to enable students to study effectively on their own, help students quickly access and learn the information they need to be more successful on quizzes and exams.

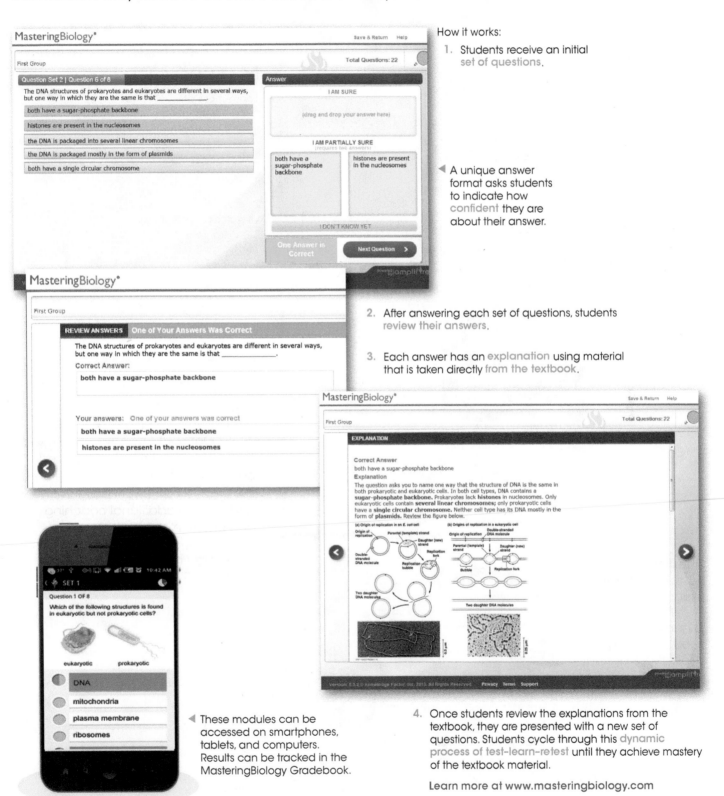

How it works:

1. Students receive an initial set of questions.

◄ A unique answer format asks students to indicate how confident they are about their answer.

2. After answering each set of questions, students review their answers.

3. Each answer has an explanation using material that is taken directly from the textbook.

◄ These modules can be accessed on smartphones, tablets, and computers. Results can be tracked in the MasteringBiology Gradebook.

4. Once students review the explanations from the textbook, they are presented with a new set of questions. Students cycle through this dynamic process of test-learn-retest until they achieve mastery of the textbook material.

Learn more at www.masteringbiology.com

Instructors can assign **self-paced MasteringBiology®️ tutorials** that provide students with individualized coaching with specific hints and feedback on the toughest topics in the course.

MasteringBiology®️

Learn more at
www.masteringbiology.com

1. If a student gets stuck ...

2. specific wrong-answer feedback appears in the purple feedback box.

3. Hints coach the student to the correct response.

4. **NEW!** Optional Adaptive Follow-Up Assignments are based on each student's performance on the original homework assignment and provide additional coaching and practice as needed.

Question sets in the Adaptive Follow-Up Assignments continuously adapt to each student's needs, making efficient use of study time.

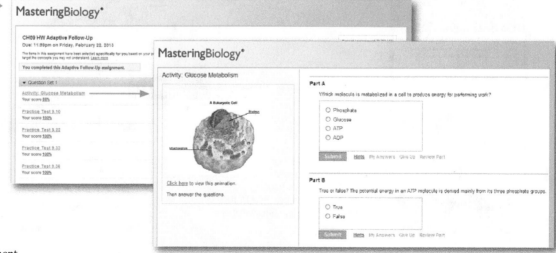

The **MasteringBiology®** Gradebook provides instructors with quick results and easy-to-interpret insights into student performance. Every assignment is automatically graded. Shades of red highlight vulnerable students and challenging assignments.

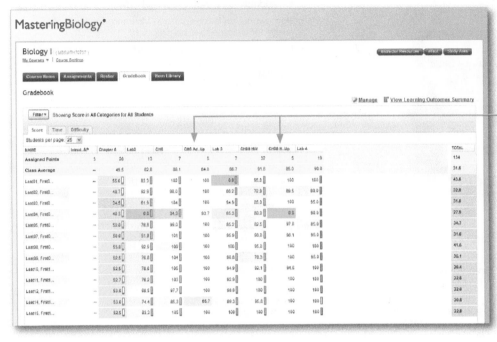

NEW! Student scores on the optional Adaptive Follow-Up Assignments are recorded in the gradebook and offer additional diagnostic information for instructors to monitor learning outcomes and more.

MasteringBiology offers a wide variety of tutorials that can be assigned as homework. For example, BioFlix Tutorials use 3-D, movie-quality Animations and coaching exercises to help students master tough topics outside of class. Animations can also be shown in class.

BioFlix Tutorials and 3-D Animations include:

- A Tour of the Animal Cell
- A Tour of the Plant Cell
- Membrane Transport
- Cellular Respiration
- Photosynthesis
- Mitosis
- Meiosis
- DNA Replication
- Protein Synthesis
- Mechanisms of Evolution
- Water Transport in Plants
- Homeostasis: Regulating Blood Sugar
- Gas Exchange
- How Neurons Work
- How Synapses Work
- Muscle Contraction
- Population Ecology
- The Carbon Cycle

FOR INSTRUCTORS

NEW! Learning Catalytics™ allows students to use their smartphone, tablet, or laptop to respond to questions in class. Visit www.learningcatalytics.com.

Instructor's Resource DVD (IRDVD) Package
978-0-321-83494-2 / 0-321-83494-1

The instructor resources for **CAMPBELL BIOLOGY, Tenth Edition,** are combined into one chapter-by-chapter resource that includes DVDs of all chapter visual resources. Assets include:

- Editable figures (art and photos) and tables from the text in PowerPoint®
- Prepared PowerPoint Lecture Presentations for each chapter, with lecture notes, editable figures, tables, and links to animations and videos
- 250+ Instructor Animations and Videos, including BioFlix® 3-D Animations and *ABC News* Videos

- JPEG Images, including labeled and unlabeled art, photos from the text, and extra photos
- Digital Transparencies
- Clicker Questions in PowerPoint
- Quick Reference Guide
- Test Bank questions in TestGen® software and Microsoft® Word

Instructor Resources Area in MasteringBiology®

This area includes:

- Art and Photos in PowerPoint
- PowerPoint Lecture Presentations
- Videos and Animations, including BioFlix®
- JPEG Images
- Digital Transparencies
- Clicker Questions
- Test Bank Files
- Lecture Outlines
- Learning Objectives

- Pre-Tests, Post-Tests, and Strategies for Overcoming Common Student Misconceptions
- Instructor Guides for Supplements
- Rubric and Tips for Grading Short-Answer Essays
- Suggested Answers for Scientific Skills Exercises and Short-Answer Essay Questions
- Lab Media

▲ Clicker Questions can be used to stimulate effective classroom discussions (for use with or without clickers).

Instructor Resources for Flipped Classrooms

- Lecture videos can be posted on MasteringBiology for students to view before class.
- Homework can be assigned in MasteringBiology so students come to class prepared.
- In-class resources: Learning Catalytics, Clicker Questions, Student Misconception Questions, end-of-chapter essay questions, and activities and case studies from the student supplements.

Chloroplasts: The Sites of Photosynthesis in Plants

- Leaves are the major locations of photosynthesis
- Their green color is from **chlorophyll,** the green pigment within chloroplasts
- Light energy absorbed by chlorophyll drives the synthesis of organic molecules in the chloroplast
- CO_2 enters and O_2 exits the leaf through microscopic pores called **stomata**

▲ Customizable PowerPoints provide a jumpstart for each lecture.

▲ All of the art, graphs, and photos from the book are provided with customizable labels. More than 1,600 photos from the text and other sources are included.

Printed Test Bank
978-0-321-82371-7 / 0-321-82371-0

This invaluable resource contains more than 4,500 questions, including scenario-based questions and art, graph, and data interpretation questions. In addition to a print version, the Test Bank is available electronically in MasteringBiology, on the Instructor's Resource DVD Package, within the Blackboard course management system, and at www.pearsonhighered.com.

Course Management Systems

Content is available in **Blackboard**. Also, **MasteringBiology New Design** offers the usual Mastering features plus:

- Blackboard integration with single sign-on
- Temporary access (grace period)
- Discussion boards

- Email
- Chat and class live (synchronous whiteboard presentation)
- Submissions (Dropbox)

FOR STUDENTS

Study Guide, Tenth Edition
by Martha R. Taylor, *Ithaca, New York*
978-0-321-83392-1 / 0-321-83392-9
This popular study aid provides concept maps, chapter summaries, word roots, and a variety of interactive activities including multiple-choice, short-answer essay, art labeling, and graph-interpretation questions.

Inquiry in Action: Interpreting Scientific Papers, Third Edition*
by Ruth Buskirk, *University of Texas at Austin,* and Christopher M. Gillen, *Kenyon College*
978-0-321-83417-1 / 0-321-83417-8
This guide helps students learn how to read and understand primary research articles. Part A presents complete articles accompanied by questions that help students analyze the article. Related Inquiry Figures are included in the supplement. Part B covers every part of a research paper, explaining the aim of the sections and how the paper works as a whole.

Practicing Biology: A Student Workbook, Fifth Edition*
by Jean Heitz and Cynthia Giffen, *University of Wisconsin, Madison*
978-0-321-87705-5 / 0-321-87705-5
This workbook offers a variety of activities to suit different learning styles. Activities such as modeling and concept mapping allow students to visualize and understand biological processes. Other activities focus on basic skills, such as reading and drawing graphs.

Biological Inquiry: A Workbook of Investigative Cases, Fourth Edition*
by Margaret Waterman, *Southeast Missouri State University,* and Ethel Stanley, *BioQUEST Curriculum Consortium and Beloit College*
978-0-321-83391-4 / 0-321-83391-0
This workbook offers ten investigative cases. Each case study requires students to synthesize information from multiple chapters of the text and apply that knowledge to a real-world scenario as they pose hypotheses, gather new information, analyze evidence, graph data, and draw conclusions. A link to a student website is in the Study Area in MasteringBiology.

Study Card, Tenth Edition
978-0-321-83415-7 / 0-321-83415-1
This quick-reference card provides students with an overview of the entire field of biology, helping them see the connections among topics.

Spanish Glossary, Tenth Edition
by Laura P. Zanello, *University of California, Riverside*
978-0-321-83498-0 / 0-321-83498-4
This resource provides definitions in Spanish for glossary terms.

Into the Jungle: Great Adventures in the Search for Evolution
by Sean B. Carroll, *University of Wisconsin, Madison*
978-0-321-55671-4 / 0-321-55671-2
These nine short tales vividly depict key discoveries in evolutionary biology and the excitement of the scientific process. Online resources available at www.aw-bc.com/carroll.

Get Ready for Biology
978-0-321-50057-1 / 0-321-50057-1
This engaging workbook helps students brush up on important math and study skills and get up to speed on biological terminology and the basics of chemistry and cell biology.

A Short Guide to Writing About Biology, Eighth Edition
by Jan A. Pechenik, *Tufts University*
978-0-321-83386-0 / 0-321-83386-4
This best-selling writing guide teaches students to think as biologists and to express ideas clearly and concisely through their writing.

An Introduction to Chemistry for Biology Students, Ninth Edition
by George I. Sackheim, *University of Illinois, Chicago*
978-0-8053-9571-6 / 0-8053-9571-7
This text/workbook helps students review and master all the basic facts, concepts, and terminology of chemistry that they need for their life science course.

FOR LAB

Investigating Biology Laboratory Manual, Eighth Edition
by Judith Giles Morgan, *Emory University,* and M. Eloise Brown Carter, *Oxford College of Emory University*
978-0-321-83899-5 / 0-321-83899-8
Now in full color! With its distinctive investigative approach to learning, this best-selling laboratory manual is now more engaging than ever, with full-color art and photos throughout. As always, the lab manual encourages students to participate in the process of science and develop creative and critical-reasoning skills.

The Eighth Edition includes major revisions that reflect new molecular evidence and the current understanding of phylogenetic relationships for plants, invertebrates, protists, and fungi. A new lab topic, "Fungi," has been added, providing expanded coverage of the major fungi groups. The "Protists" lab topic has been revised and expanded with additional examples of all the major clades. In the new edition, population genetics is covered in one lab topic with new problems and examples that connect ecology, evolution, and genetics.

Annotated Instructor Edition for Investigating Biology Laboratory Manual, Eighth Edition
by Judith Giles Morgan, *Emory University,* and M. Eloise Brown Carter, *Oxford College of Emory University*
978-0-321-83497-3 / 0-321-83497-6

Preparation Guide for Investigating Biology Laboratory Manual, Eighth Edition
by Judith Giles Morgan, *Emory University,* and M. Eloise Brown Carter, *Oxford College of Emory University*
978-0-321-83445-4 / 0-321-83445-3

Symbiosis: The Pearson Custom Laboratory Program for the Biological Sciences
www.pearsoncustom.com/database/symbiosis/bc.html

MasteringBiology® Virtual Labs
www.masteringbiology.com
This online environment promotes critical thinking skills using virtual experiments and explorations that may be difficult to perform in a wet lab environment due to time, cost, or safety concerns. Designed to supplement or substitute for existing wet labs, this product offers students unique learning experiences and critical thinking exercises in the areas of microscopy, molecular biology, genetics, ecology, and systematics.

*An Instructor Guide is available for download in the Instructor Resources Area in MasteringBiology.

Make Connections Figures

Exploring Figures

Inquiry Figures

Research Method Figures

*The Inquiry Figure, original research paper, and a worksheet to guide you through the paper are provided in *Inquiry in Action: Interpreting Scientific Papers*, Third Edition.
†A related Experimental Inquiry Tutorial can be assigned in MasteringBiology.®

The authors wish to express their gratitude to the global community of instructors, researchers, students, and publishing professionals who have contributed to the Tenth Edition of CAMPBELL BIOLOGY.

As authors of this text, we are mindful of the daunting challenge of keeping up to date in all areas of our rapidly expanding subject. We are grateful to the many scientists who helped shape this text by discussing their research fields with us, answering specific questions in their areas of expertise, and sharing their ideas about biology education. We are especially grateful to the following, listed alphabetically: Monika Abedin, John Archibald, Chris Austin, Kristian Axelsen, Jamie Bascom, Ethan Bier, Barbara Bowman, Daniel Boyce, Jean DeSaix, Amy Dobberteen, Ira Greenbaum, Ken Halanych, Robert Hebbel, Erin Irish, Duncan Irschick, Azarias Karamanlidis, Patrick Keeling, Nikos Kyrpides, Teri Liegler, Gene Likens, Tom Owens, Kevin Peterson, Michael Pollock, Amy Rappaport, Andrew Roger, Andrew Roth, Andrew Schaffner, Thomas Schneider, Alastair Simpson, Doug Soltis, Pamela Soltis, Anna Thanukos, Elisabeth Wade, Phillip Zamore, and Christine Zardecki. In addition, the biologists listed on pages xxviii–xxxi provided detailed reviews, helping us ensure the text's scientific accuracy and improve its pedagogical effectiveness. We thank Marty Taylor, author of the Study Guide, for her many contributions to the accuracy, clarity, and consistency of the text; and we thank Carolyn Wetzel, Ruth Buskirk, Joan Sharp, Jennifer Yeh, and Charlene D'Avanzo for their contributions to the Scientific Skills Exercises.

Thanks also to the other professors and students, from all over the world, who contacted the authors directly with useful suggestions. We alone bear the responsibility for any errors that remain, but the dedication of our consultants, reviewers, and other correspondents makes us confident in the accuracy and effectiveness of this text.

Interviews with prominent scientists have been a hallmark of CAMPBELL BIOLOGY since its inception, and conducting these interviews was again one of the great pleasures of revising the book. To open the eight units of this edition, we are proud to include interviews with Venki Ramakrishnan, Haifan Lin, Charles Rotimi, Hopi Hoekstra, Nicole King, Jeffery Dangl, Ulrike Heberlein, and Monica Turner.

The value of CAMPBELL BIOLOGY as a learning tool is greatly enhanced by the supplementary materials that have been created for instructors and students. We recognize that the dedicated authors of these materials are essentially writing mini (and not so mini) books. We appreciate the hard work and creativity of all the authors listed, with their creations, on page xxiii. We are also grateful to Kathleen Fitzpatrick and Nicole Tunbridge (PowerPoint® Lecture Presentations); Scott Meissner, Roberta Batorsky, Tara Turley Stoulig, Lisa Flick, and Bryan Jennings (Clicker Questions); Ed Zalisko, Melissa Fierke, Rebecca Orr, and Diane Jokinen (Test Bank); Natalie Bronstein, Linda Logdberg, Matt McArdle, Ria Murphy, Chris Romero, and Andy Stull (Dynamic Study Modules); and Eileen Gregory, Rebecca Orr, and Elena Pravosudova (Adaptive Follow-up Assignments).

MasteringBiology® and the other electronic accompaniments for this text are invaluable teaching and learning aids. We thank the hardworking, industrious instructors who worked on the revised and new media: Beverly Brown, Erica Cline, Willy Cushwa, Tom Kennedy, Tom Owens, Michael Pollock, Frieda Reichsman, Rick Spinney, Dennis Venema, Carolyn Wetzel, Heather Wilson-Ashworth, and Jennifer Yeh. We are also grateful to the many other people— biology instructors, editors, and production experts—who are listed in the credits for these and other elements of the electronic media that accompany the text.

CAMPBELL BIOLOGY results from an unusually strong synergy between a team of scientists and a team of publishing professionals.

Our editorial team at Pearson Education again demonstrated unmatched talents, commitment, and pedagogical insights. Our Senior Acquisitions Editor, Josh Frost, brought publishing savvy, intelligence, and a much appreciated level head to leading the whole team. The clarity and effectiveness of every page owe much to our extraordinary Supervising Editors Pat Burner and Beth Winickoff, who worked with a top-notch team of Developmental Editors in Mary Ann Murray, John Burner, Matt Lee, Hilair Chism, and Andrew Recher (Precision Graphics). Our unsurpassed Executive Editorial Manager Ginnie Simione Jutson, Executive Director of Development Deborah Gale, Assistant Editor Katherine Harrison-Adcock, and Editor-in-Chief Beth Wilbur were indispensable in moving the project in the right direction. We also want to thank Robin Heyden for organizing the annual Biology Leadership Conferences and keeping us in touch with the world of AP Biology.

You would not have this beautiful text if not for the work of the production team: Director of Production Erin Gregg; Managing Editor Michael Early; Project Manager Shannon Tozier; Senior Photo Editor Donna Kalal; Photo Researcher Maureen Spuhler; Copy Editor Joanna Dinsmore; Proofreader Pete Shanks; Text Permissions Project Managers Alison Bruckner and Joe Croscup; Text Permissions Manager Tim Nicholls; Senior Project Editor Emily Bush, Paging Specialist Donna Healy, and the rest of the staff at S4Carlisle; Art Production Manager Kristina Seymour, Artist Andrew Recher, and the rest of the staff at Precision Graphics; Design Manager Marilyn Perry; Art/Design Specialist Kelly Murphy; Text Designer tani hasegawa; Cover Designer Yvo Riezebos; and Manufacturing Buyer Jeffery Sargent. We also thank those who worked on the text's supplements: Susan Berge, Brady Golden, Jane Brundage, Phil Minnitte, Katherine Harrison-Adcock, Katie Cook, Melanie Field, Kris Langan, Pete Shanks, and John Hammett. And for creating the wonderful package of electronic media that accompanies the text, we are grateful to Tania Mlawer (Director of Content Development for MasteringBiology), Sarah Jensen, J. Zane Barlow, Lee Ann Doctor, Caroline Ross, Taylor Merck, and Brienn Buchanan, as well as Director of Media Development Lauren Fogel and Director of Media Strategy Stacy Treco.

For their important roles in marketing the text and media, we thank Christy Lesko, Lauren Harp, Scott Dustan, Chris Hess, Jane Campbell, Jessica Perry, and Jennifer Aumiller. For her market development support, we thank Michelle Cadden. We are grateful to Paul Corey, President of Pearson Science, for his enthusiasm, encouragement, and support.

The Pearson sales team, which represents CAMPBELL BIOLOGY on campus, is an essential link to the users of the text. They tell us what you like and don't like about the text, communicate the features of the text, and provide prompt service. We thank them for their hard work and professionalism. David Theisen, national director for Key Markets, tirelessly visits countless instructors every year, providing us with meaningful editorial guidance. For representing our text to our international audience, we thank our sales and marketing partners throughout the world. They are all strong allies in biology education.

Finally, we wish to thank our families and friends for their encouragement and patience throughout this long project. Our special thanks to Paul, Dan, Maria, Armelle, and Sean (J.B.R.); Lillian Alibertini Urry and Ross, Lily, and Alex (L.A.U.); Debra and Hannah (M.L.C.); Harry, Elga, Aaron, Sophie, Noah, and Gabriele (S.A.W.); Natalie (P.V.M.); and Sally, Will, David, and Robert (R.B.J.). And, as always, thanks to Rochelle, Allison, Jason, McKay, and Gus.

Jane B. Reece, Lisa A. Urry, Michael L. Cain,
Steven A. Wasserman, Peter V. Minorsky, and Robert B. Jackson

Tenth Edition Reviewers

John Alcock, *Arizona State University*
Rodney Allrich, *Purdue University*
Teri Balser, *University of Wisconsin, Madison*
David Bos, *Purdue University*
Scott Bowling, *Auburn University*
Beverly Brown, *Nazareth College*
Warren Burggren, *University of North Texas*
Dale Burnside, *Lenoir-Rhyne University*
Mickael Cariveau, *Mount Olive College*
Jung Choi, *Georgia Institute of Technology*
Steve Christensen, *Brigham Young University*
Reggie Cobb, *Nashville Community College*
Sean Coleman, *University of the Ozarks*
Deborah Dardis, *Southeastern Louisiana University*
Melissa Deadmond, *Truckee Meadows Community College*
Jean DeSaix, *University of North Carolina, Chapel Hill*
Jason Douglas, *Angelina College*
Anna Edlund, *Lafayette College*
Kurt Elliott, *North West Vista College*
Rob Erdman, *Florida Gulf Coast College*
Dale Erskine, *Lebanon Valley College*
Margaret Folsom, *Methodist College*
Robert Fowler, *San Jose State University*
Kim Fredericks, *Viterbo University*
Craig Gatto, *Illinois State University*
Kristen Genet, *Anoka Ramsey Community College*
Phil Gibson, *University of Oklahoma*
Eric Gillock, *Fort Hayes State University*
Edwin Ginés-Candelaria, *Miami Dade College*
Eileen Gregory, *Rollins College*
Bradley Griggs, *Piedmont Technical College*
Edward Gruberg, *Temple University*
Carla Guthridge, *Cameron University*
Carla Haas, *Pennsylvania State University*
Pryce Pete Haddix, *Auburn University*
Heather Hallen-Adams, *University of Nebraska, Lincoln*
Monica Hall-Woods, *St. Charles Community College*
Bill Hamilton, *Washington & Lee University*
Dennis Haney, *Furman University*
Jean Hardwick, *Ithaca College*
Luke Harmon, *University of Idaho*
Chris Haynes, *Shelton State Community College*
Jean Heitz, *University of Wisconsin, Madison*
Albert Herrera, *University of Southern California*
Chris Hess, *Butler University*
Kendra Hill, *San Diego State University*
Laura Houston, *Northeast Lakeview College*
Harry Itagaki, *Kenyon College*
Kathy Jacobson, *Grinnell College*
Roishene Johnson, *Bossier Parish Community College*
The-Hui Kao, *Pennsylvania State University*
Judy Kaufman, *Monroe Community College*
Thomas Keller, *Florida State University*
Janice Knepper, *Villanova University*
Charles Knight, *California Polytechnic State University*
Jacob Krans, *Western New England University*
Barb Kuemerle, *Case Western Reserve University*
Jani Lewis, *State University of New York*
Nancy Magill, *Indiana University*
Charles Mallery, *University of Miami*
Mark Maloney, *University of South Mississippi*
Darcy Medica, *Pennsylvania State University*
Mike Meighan, *University of California, Berkeley*
Jan Mikesell, *Gettysburg College*
Sarah Milton, *Florida Atlantic University*
Linda Moore, *Georgia Military College*
Karen Neal, *Reynolds University*
Ross Nehm, *Ohio State University*
Eric Nielsen, *University of Michigan*
Gretchen North, *Occidental College*
Margaret Olney, *St. Martin's College*
Rebecca Orr, *Spring Creek College*

Matt Palmtag, *Florida Gulf Coast University*
Eric Peters, *Chicago State University*
Larry Peterson, *University of Guelph*
Deb Pires, *University of California, Los Angeles*
Crima Pogge, *San Francisco Community College*
Michael Pollock, *Mount Royal University*
Jason Porter, *University of the Sciences, Philadelphia*
Elena Pravosudova, *University of Nevada, Reno*
Eileen Preston, *Tarrant Community College Northwest*
Pushpa Ramakrishna, *Chandler-Gilbert Community College*
David Randall, *City University Hong Kong*
Robert Reavis, *Glendale Community College*
Todd Rimkus, *Marymount University*
John Rinehart, *Eastern Oregon University*
Diane Robins, *University of Michigan*
Deb Roess, *Colorado State University*
Suzanne Rogers, *Seton Hill University*
Glenn-Peter Saetre, *University of Oslo*
Sanga Saha, *Harold Washington College*
Kathleen Sandman, *Ohio State University*
Andrew Schaffner, *Cal Poly San Luis Obispo*
Duane Sears, *University of California, Santa Barbara*
Joan Sharp, *Simon Fraser University*
Eric Shows, *Jones County Junior College*
John Skillman, *California State University, San Bernardino*
Doug Soltis, *University of Florida, Gainesville*
Mike Toliver, *Eureka College*
Victoria Turgeon, *Furman University*
Amy Volmer, *Swarthmore College*
James Wandersee, *Louisiana State University*
James Wee, *Loyola University*
Murray Wiegand, *University of Winnipeg*
Kimberly Williams, *Kansas State University*
Shuhai Xiao, *Virginia Polytechnic Institute*

Reviewers of Previous Editions

Kenneth Able, *State University of New York, Albany*; Thomas Adams, *Michigan State University*; Martin Adamson, *University of British Columbia*; Dominique Adriaens, *Ghent University*; Ann Aguanno, *Marymount Manhattan College*; Shylaja Akkaraju, *Bronx Community College of CUNY*; Marc Albrecht, *University of Nebraska*; John Alcock, *Arizona State University*; Eric Alcorn, *Acadia University*; George R. Aliaga, *Tarrant County College*; Richard Almon, *State University of New York, Buffalo*; Bonnie Amos, *Angelo State University*; Katherine Anderson, *University of California, Berkeley*; Richard J. Andren, *Montgomery County Community College*; Estry Ang, *University of Pittsburgh, Greensburg*; Jeff Appling, *Clemson University*; J. David Archibald, *San Diego State University*; David Armstrong, *University of Colorado, Boulder*; Howard J. Arnott, *University of Texas, Arlington*; Mary Ashley, *University of Illinois, Chicago*; Angela S. Aspbury, *Texas State University*; Robert Atherton, *University of Wyoming*; Karl Aufderheide, *Texas A&M University*; Leigh Auleb, *San Francisco State University*; Terry Austin, *Temple College*; P. Stephen Baenziger, *University of Nebraska*; Brian Bagatto, *University of Akron*; Ellen Baker, *Santa Monica College*; Katherine Baker, *Millersville University*; Virginia Baker, *Chipola College*; William Barklow, *Framingham State College*; Susan Barman, *Michigan State University*; Steven Barnhart, *Santa Rosa Junior College*; Andrew Barton, *University of Maine Farmington*; Rebecca A. Bartow, *Western Kentucky University*; Ron Basmajian, *Merced College*; David Bass, *University of Central Oklahoma*; Bonnie Baxter, *Westminster College*; Tim Beagley, *Salt Lake Community College*; Margaret E. Beard, *College of the Holy Cross*; Tom Beatty, *University of British Columbia*; Chris Beck, *Emory University*; Wayne Becker, *University of Wisconsin, Madison*; Patricia Bedinger, *Colorado State University*; Jane Beiswenger, *University of Wyoming*; Anne Bekoff, *University of Colorado, Boulder*; Marc Bekoff, *University of Colorado, Boulder*; Tania Beliz, *College of San Mateo*; Adrianne Bendich, *Hoffman-La Roche, Inc.*; Marilee Benore, *University of Michigan, Dearborn*; Barbara Bentley, *State University of New York, Stony Brook*; Darwin Berg, *University of California, San Diego*; Werner Bergen, *Michigan State University*; Gerald Bergstrom, *University of Wisconsin, Milwaukee*; Anna W. Berkovitz, *Purdue University*; Dorothy Berner, *Temple University*; Annalisa Berta, *San Diego State University*; Paulette Bierzychudek, *Pomona College*; Charles Biggers, *Memphis State University*; Kenneth Birnbaum, *New York University*; Catherine Black, *Idaho State University*; Michael W. Black, *California Polytechnic State University, San Luis Obispo*; William Blaker, *Furman University*; Robert Blanchard, *University of New Hampshire*; Andrew R. Blaustein, *Oregon State University*; Judy Bluemer, *Morton*

53 Population Ecology 1184

54 Community Ecology 1208

55 Ecosystems and Restoration Ecology 1232

56 Conservation Biology and Global Change 1254

1

Evolution, the Themes of Biology, and Scientific Inquiry

▲ Figure 1.1 **How is the dandelion adapted to its environment?**

Inquiring About Life

The dandelions shown in **Figure 1.1** send their seeds aloft for dispersal. A seed is an embryo surrounded by a store of food and a protective coat. The dandelion's seeds, shown at the lower left, are borne on the wind by parachute-like structures made from modified flower parts. The parachutes harness the wind, which carries such seeds to new locations where conditions may favor sprouting and growth. Dandelions are very successful plants, found in temperate regions worldwide.

An organism's adaptations to its environment, such as the dandelion seed's parachute, are the result of evolution. **Evolution** is the process of change that has transformed life on Earth from its earliest beginnings to the diversity of organisms living today. Because evolution is the fundamental organizing principle of biology, it is the core theme of this book.

Although biologists know a great deal about life on Earth, many mysteries remain. For instance, what processes led to the origin of flowering among plants such as the ones pictured above? Posing questions about the living world and seeking answers through scientific inquiry are the central activities of **biology**, the scientific study of life. Biologists' questions can be ambitious. They may ask how a single tiny cell becomes a tree or a dog, how the human mind works, or how the different

▼ **Order.** This close-up of a sunflower illustrates the highly ordered structure that characterizes life.

▲ **Evolutionary adaptation.** The appearance of this pygmy sea horse camouflages the animal in its environment. Such adaptations evolve over many generations by the reproductive success of those individuals with heritable traits that are best suited to their environments.

▲ **Regulation.** The regulation of blood flow through the blood vessels of this jackrabbit's ears helps maintain a constant body temperature by adjusting heat exchange with the surrounding air.

▼ **Reproduction.** Organisms (living things) reproduce their own kind.

▲ **Energy processing.** This butterfly obtains fuel in the form of nectar from flowers. The butterfly will use chemical energy stored in its food to power flight and other work.

▲ **Growth and development.** Inherited information carried by genes controls the pattern of growth and development of organisms, such as this oak seedling.

▲ **Response to the environment.** This Venus flytrap closed its trap rapidly in response to the environmental stimulus of a damselfly landing on the open trap.

▲ **Figure 1.2**
Some properties of life.

forms of life in a forest interact. Many interesting questions probably occur to you when you are out-of-doors, surrounded by the natural world. When they do, you are already thinking like a biologist. More than anything else, biology is a quest, an ongoing inquiry about the nature of life.

At the most fundamental level, we may ask: What is life? Even a child realizes that a dog or a plant is alive, while a rock or a car is not. Yet the phenomenon we call life defies a simple, one-sentence definition. We recognize life by what living things do. **Figure 1.2** highlights some of the properties and processes we associate with life.

While limited to a handful of images, Figure 1.2 reminds us that the living world is wondrously varied. How do biologists make sense of this diversity and complexity? This opening chapter sets up a framework for answering this question. The first part of the chapter provides a panoramic view of the biological "landscape," organized around some unifying themes. We then focus on biology's core theme, evolution, which accounts for life's unity and diversity. Next, we look at scientific inquiry—how scientists ask and attempt to answer questions about the natural world. Finally, we address the culture of science and its effects on society.

CONCEPT 1.1

The study of life reveals common themes

Biology is a subject of enormous scope, and exciting new biological discoveries are being made every day. How can you organize into a comprehensible framework all the information you'll encounter as you study the broad range of topics included in biology? Focusing on a few big ideas will

help. Here, we'll list five unifying themes—ways of thinking about life that will still hold true decades from now. These unifying themes are described in greater detail in the next few pages. We hope they will serve as touchstones as you proceed through this text:

- Organization
- Information
- Energy and Matter
- Interactions
- Evolution

▼ Figure 1.3
Exploring Levels of Biological Organization

◄ 1 The Biosphere

Even from space, we can see signs of Earth's life—in the green mosaic of the forests, for example. We can also see the scale of the entire biosphere, which consists of all life on Earth and all the places where life exists: most regions of land, most bodies of water, the atmosphere to an altitude of several kilometers, and even sediments far below the ocean floor.

◄ 2 Ecosystems

Our first scale change brings us to a North American forest with many deciduous trees (trees that lose their leaves and grow new ones each year). A deciduous forest is an example of an ecosystem, as are grasslands, deserts, and coral reefs. An ecosystem consists of all the living things in a particular area, along with all the nonliving components of the environment with which life interacts, such as soil, water, atmospheric gases, and light.

► 3 Communities

The array of organisms inhabiting a particular ecosystem is called a biological community. The community in our forest ecosystem includes many kinds of trees and other plants, various animals, mushrooms and other fungi, and enormous numbers of diverse microorganisms, which are living forms, such as bacteria, that are too small to see without a microscope. Each of these forms of life is called a *species*.

► 4 Populations

A population consists of all the individuals of a species living within the bounds of a specified area. For example, our forest includes a population of sugar maple trees and a population of white-tailed deer. A community is therefore the set of populations that inhabit a particular area.

▲ 5 Organisms

Individual living things are called organisms. Each of the maple trees and other plants in the forest is an organism, and so is each deer, frog, beetle, and other forest animals. The soil teems with microorganisms such as bacteria.

2

Theme: New Properties Emerge at Successive Levels of Biological Organization

ORGANIZATION In **Figure 1.3**, we zoom in from space to take a closer and closer look at life in a deciduous forest in Ontario, Canada. This journey shows the different levels of organization recognized by biologists: The study of life extends from the global scale of the entire living planet to the microscopic scale of cells and molecules. The numbers in the figure guide you through the hierarchy of biological organization.

Zooming in at ever-finer resolution illustrates an approach called *reductionism*, which reduces complex systems to simpler components that are more manageable to study. Reductionism is a powerful strategy in biology. For example, by studying the molecular structure of DNA that had been extracted from cells, James Watson and Francis Crick inferred the chemical basis of biological inheritance. However, although it has propelled many major discoveries, reductionism provides a necessarily incomplete view of life on Earth, as we'll discuss next.

▼ 6 Organs and Organ Systems

The structural hierarchy of life continues to unfold as we explore the architecture of more complex organisms. A maple leaf is an example of an organ, a body part that carries out a particular function in the body. Stems and roots are the other major organs of plants. The organs of complex animals and plants are organized into organ systems, each a team of organs that cooperate in a larger function. Organs consist of multiple tissues.

▶ 10 Molecules

Our last scale change drops us into a chloroplast for a view of life at the molecular level. A molecule is a chemical structure consisting of two or more units called atoms, represented as balls in this computer graphic of a chlorophyll molecule. Chlorophyll is the pigment molecule that makes a maple leaf green, and it absorbs sunlight during photosynthesis. Within each chloroplast, millions of chlorophyll molecules are organized into systems that convert light energy to the chemical energy of food.

Atoms
Chlorophyll molecule
Chloroplast

▶ 9 Organelles

Chloroplasts are examples of organelles, the various functional components present in cells. This image, taken by a powerful microscope, shows a single chloroplast.

1 μm

◀ 7 Tissues

50 μm

Cell   10 μm

Viewing the tissues of a leaf requires a microscope. Each tissue is a group of cells that work together, performing a specialized function. The leaf shown here has been cut on an angle. The honeycombed tissue in the interior of the leaf (left side of photo) is the main location of photosynthesis, the process that converts light energy to the chemical energy of sugar. The jigsaw puzzle–like "skin" on the surface of the leaf is a tissue called epidermis (right side of photo). The pores through the epidermis allow entry of the gas CO_2, a raw material for sugar production.

▲ 8 Cells

The cell is life's fundamental unit of structure and function. Some organisms are single cells, while others are multicellular. A single cell performs all the functions of life, while a multicellular organism has a division of labor among specialized cells. Here we see a magnified view of cells in a leaf tissue. One cell is about 40 micrometers (μm) across—about 500 of them would reach across a small coin. As tiny as these cells are, you can see that each contains numerous green structures called chloroplasts, which are responsible for photosynthesis.

Emergent Properties

Let's reexamine Figure 1.3, beginning this time at the molecular level and then zooming out. This approach allows us to see novel properties emerge at each level that are absent from the preceding level. These **emergent properties** are due to the arrangement and interactions of parts as complexity increases. For example, although photosynthesis occurs in an intact chloroplast, it will not take place in a disorganized test-tube mixture of chlorophyll and other chloroplast molecules. The coordinated processes of photosynthesis require a specific organization of these molecules in the chloroplast. Isolated components of living systems, serving as the objects of study in a reductionist approach to biology, lack a number of significant properties that emerge at higher levels of organization.

Emergent properties are not unique to life. A box of bicycle parts won't transport you anywhere, but if they are arranged in a certain way, you can pedal to your chosen destination. Compared with such nonliving examples, however, biological systems are far more complex, making the emergent properties of life especially challenging to study.

To explore emergent properties more fully, biologists today complement reductionism with **systems biology**, the exploration of a biological system by analyzing the interactions among its parts. In this context, a single leaf cell can be considered a system, as can a frog, an ant colony, or a desert ecosystem. By examining and modeling the dynamic behavior of an integrated network of components, systems biology enables us to pose new kinds of questions. For example, we can ask how a drug that lowers blood pressure affects the functioning of organs throughout the human body. At a larger scale, how does a gradual increase in atmospheric carbon dioxide alter ecosystems and the entire biosphere? Systems biology can be used to study life at all levels.

Structure and Function

At each level of the biological hierarchy, we find a correlation of structure and function. Consider the leaf shown in Figure 1.3: Its thin, flat shape maximizes the capture of sunlight by chloroplasts. More generally, analyzing a biological structure gives us clues about what it does and how it works. Conversely, knowing the function of something provides insight into its structure and organization. Many examples from the animal kingdom show a correlation between structure and function. For example, the hummingbird's anatomy allows the wings to rotate at the shoulder, so hummingbirds have the ability, unique among birds, to fly backward or hover

in place. While hovering, the birds can extend their long, slender beaks into flowers and feed on nectar. The elegant match of form and function in the structures of life is explained by natural selection, which we'll explore shortly.

The Cell: An Organism's Basic Unit of Structure and Function

In life's structural hierarchy, the cell is the smallest unit of organization that can perform all activities required for life. In fact, the actions of organisms are all based on the functioning of cells. For instance, the movement of your eyes as you read this sentence results from the activities of muscle and nerve cells. Even a process that occurs on a global scale, such as the recycling of carbon atoms, is the product of cellular functions, including the photosynthetic activity of chloroplasts in leaf cells.

All cells share certain characteristics. For instance, every cell is enclosed by a membrane that regulates the passage of materials between the cell and its surroundings. Nevertheless, we recognize two main forms of cells: prokaryotic and eukaryotic. The cells of two groups of single-celled microorganisms—bacteria (singular, *bacterium*) and archaea (singular, *archaean*)—are prokaryotic. All other forms of life, including plants and animals, are composed of eukaryotic cells.

A **eukaryotic cell** contains membrane-enclosed organelles (**Figure 1.4**). Some organelles, such as the DNA-containing nucleus, are found in the cells of all eukaryotes; other organelles are specific to particular cell types. For example, the chloroplast in Figure 1.3 is an organelle found

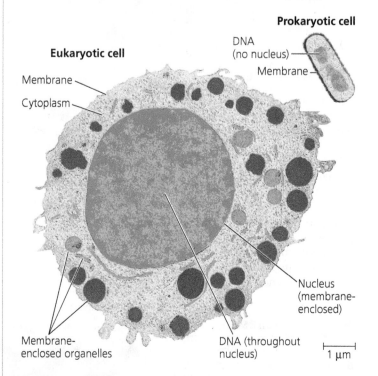

▲ **Figure 1.4 Contrasting eukaryotic and prokaryotic cells in size and complexity.**

only in eukaryotic cells that carry out photosynthesis. In contrast to eukaryotic cells, a **prokaryotic cell** lacks a nucleus or other membrane-enclosed organelles. Another distinction is that prokaryotic cells are generally smaller than eukaryotic cells, as shown in Figure 1.4.

Theme: Life's Processes Involve the Expression and Transmission of Genetic Information

INFORMATION Within cells, structures called chromosomes contain genetic material in the form of **DNA (deoxyribonucleic acid)**. In cells that are preparing to divide, the chromosomes may be made visible using a dye that appears blue when bound to the DNA (**Figure 1.5**).

25 μm

▲ **Figure 1.5 A lung cell from a newt divides into two smaller cells that will grow and divide again.**

DNA, the Genetic Material

Each time a cell divides, the DNA is first replicated, or copied, and each of the two cellular offspring inherits a complete set of chromosomes, identical to that of the parent cell. Each chromosome contains one very long DNA molecule with hundreds or thousands of **genes**, each a section of the DNA of the chromosome. Transmitted from parents to offspring, genes are the units of inheritance. They encode the information necessary to build all of the molecules synthesized within a cell, which in turn establish that cell's identity and function. Each of us began as a single cell stocked with DNA inherited from our parents. The replication of that DNA during each round of cell division transmitted copies of the DNA to what eventually became the trillions of cells of our body. As the cells grew and divided, the genetic information encoded by the DNA directed our development (**Figure 1.6**).

The molecular structure of DNA accounts for its ability to store information. A DNA molecule is made up of two long chains, called strands, arranged in a double helix. Each chain is made up of four kinds of chemical building blocks called nucleotides, abbreviated A, T, C, and G (**Figure 1.7**).

▲ **Figure 1.6 Inherited DNA directs development of an organism.**

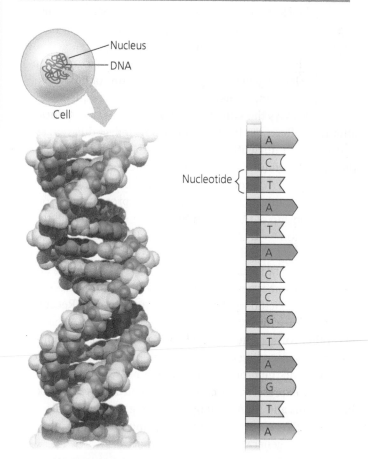

(a) **DNA double helix.** This model shows the atoms in a segment of DNA. Made up of two long chains (strands) of building blocks called nucleotides, a DNA molecule takes the three-dimensional form of a double helix.

(b) **Single strand of DNA.** These geometric shapes and letters are simple symbols for the nucleotides in a small section of one strand of a DNA molecule. Genetic information is encoded in specific sequences of the four types of nucleotides. Their names are abbreviated A, T, C, and G.

▲ **Figure 1.7 DNA: The genetic material.**

The way DNA encodes information is analogous to how we arrange the letters of the alphabet into words and phrases with specific meanings. The word *rat*, for example, evokes a rodent; the words *tar* and *art*, which contain the same letters, mean very different things. We can think of nucleotides as a four-letter alphabet. Specific sequences of these four nucleotides encode the information in genes.

Many genes provide the blueprints for making proteins, which are the major players in building and maintaining the cell and carrying out its activities. For instance, a given bacterial gene may specify a particular protein (an enzyme) required to break down a certain sugar molecule, while a human gene may denote a different protein (an antibody) that helps fight off infection.

Genes control protein production indirectly, using a related molecule called RNA as an intermediary (Figure 1.8). The sequence of nucleotides along a gene is transcribed into RNA, which is then translated into a linked series of protein building blocks called amino acids. These two stages result in a specific protein with a unique shape and function. The entire process, by which the information in a gene directs the manufacture of a cellular product, is called **gene expression**.

In translating genes into proteins, all forms of life employ essentially the same genetic code: A particular sequence of nucleotides says the same thing in one organism as it does in another. Differences between organisms reflect differences between their nucleotide sequences rather than between their genetic codes. Comparing the sequences in several species for a gene that codes for a particular protein can provide valuable information both about the protein and about the relationship of the species to each other, as you will see.

In addition to RNA molecules (called mRNAs) that are translated into proteins, some RNAs in the cell carry out other important tasks. For example, we have known for decades that some types of RNA are actually components of the cellular machinery that manufactures proteins. Recently, scientists have discovered whole new classes of RNA that play other roles in the cell, such as regulating the functioning of protein-coding genes. All of these RNAs are specified by genes, and the production of these RNAs is also referred to as gene expression. By carrying the instructions for making proteins and RNAs and by replicating with each cell division, DNA ensures faithful inheritance of genetic information from generation to generation.

Genomics: Large-Scale Analysis of DNA Sequences

The entire "library" of genetic instructions that an organism inherits is called its **genome**. A typical human cell has two similar sets of chromosomes, and each set has approximately 3 billion nucleotide pairs of DNA. If the one-letter abbreviations for the nucleotides of a set were written in letters the size of those you are now reading, the genetic text would fill about 700 biology textbooks.

(a) The lens of the eye (behind the pupil) is able to focus light because lens cells are tightly packed with transparent proteins called crystallin.

Lens cell

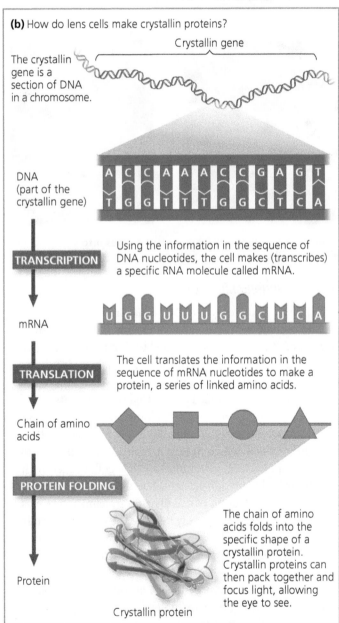

(b) How do lens cells make crystallin proteins?

Crystallin gene

The crystallin gene is a section of DNA in a chromosome.

DNA (part of the crystallin gene)

| A | C | C | A | A | A | C | C | G | A | G | T |
| T | G | G | T | T | T | G | G | C | T | C | A |

TRANSCRIPTION

Using the information in the sequence of DNA nucleotides, the cell makes (transcribes) a specific RNA molecule called mRNA.

mRNA

U G G U U U G G C U C A

TRANSLATION

The cell translates the information in the sequence of mRNA nucleotides to make a protein, a series of linked amino acids.

Chain of amino acids

PROTEIN FOLDING

Protein

The chain of amino acids folds into the specific shape of a crystallin protein. Crystallin proteins can then pack together and focus light, allowing the eye to see.

Crystallin protein

▲ Figure 1.8 Gene expression: The transfer of information from a gene results in a functional protein.

Since the early 1990s, the pace at which researchers can determine the sequence of a genome has accelerated at an astounding rate, enabled by a revolution in technology. The entire sequence of nucleotides in the human genome is now known, along with the genome sequences of many other organisms, including other animals and numerous plants, fungi, bacteria, and archaea. To make sense of the deluge of data from genome-sequencing projects and the growing catalog of known gene functions, scientists are applying a systems biology approach at the cellular and molecular levels. Rather than investigating a single gene at a time, researchers study whole sets of genes (or other DNA) in one or more species—an approach called **genomics**. Likewise, the term **proteomics** refers to the study of sets of proteins and their properties. (The entire set of proteins expressed by a given cell or group of cells is called a **proteome**).

Three important research developments have made the genomic and proteomic approaches possible. One is "high-throughput" technology, tools that can analyze many biological samples very rapidly. The second major development is **bioinformatics**, the use of computational tools to store, organize, and analyze the huge volume of data that results from high-throughput methods. The third development is the formation of interdisciplinary research teams—groups of diverse specialists that may include computer scientists, mathematicians, engineers, chemists, physicists, and, of course, biologists from a variety of fields. Researchers in such teams aim to learn how the activities of all the proteins and non-translated RNAs encoded by the DNA are coordinated in cells and in whole organisms.

Theme: Life Requires the Transfer and Transformation of Energy and Matter

ENERGY AND MATTER A fundamental characteristic of living organisms is their use of energy to carry out life's activities. Moving, growing, reproducing, and the various cellular activities of life are work, and work requires energy. The input of energy, primarily from the sun, and the transformation of energy from one form to another make life possible. A plant's leaves absorb sunlight, and molecules within the leaves convert the energy of sunlight to the chemical energy of food, such as sugars, produced during photosynthesis. The chemical energy in the food molecules is then passed along by plants and other photosynthetic organisms (**producers**) to consumers. **Consumers** are organisms, such as animals, that feed on producers and other consumers.

When an organism uses chemical energy to perform work, such as muscle contraction or cell division, some of that energy is lost to the surroundings as heat. As a result, energy flows one way *through* an ecosystem, usually entering as light and exiting as heat. In contrast, chemicals are recycled *within* an ecosystem **(Figure 1.9)**. Chemicals that a plant absorbs from the air or soil may be incorporated into the plant's body and then passed to an animal that eats the plant. Eventually, these chemicals will be returned to the environment by decomposers, such as bacteria and fungi, that break down waste products, leaf litter, and the bodies of dead organisms. The chemicals are then available to be taken up by plants again, thereby completing the cycle.

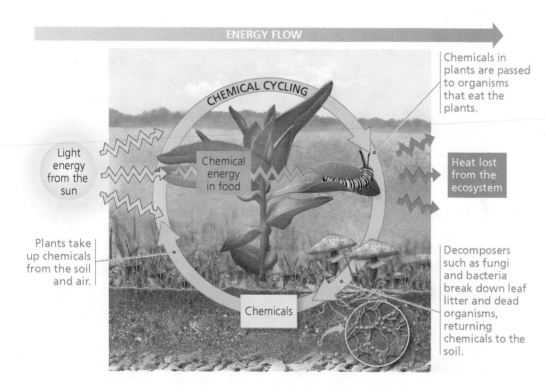

ENERGY FLOW

CHEMICAL CYCLING

Light energy from the sun

Chemical energy in food

Chemicals in plants are passed to organisms that eat the plants.

Heat lost from the ecosystem

Plants take up chemicals from the soil and air.

Chemicals

Decomposers such as fungi and bacteria break down leaf litter and dead organisms, returning chemicals to the soil.

◄ **Figure 1.9 Energy flow and chemical cycling.** There is a one-way flow of energy in an ecosystem: During photosynthesis, plants convert energy from sunlight to chemical energy (stored in food molecules such as sugars), which is used by plants and other organisms to do work and is eventually lost from the ecosystem as heat. In contrast, chemicals cycle between organisms and the physical environment.

Theme: From Ecosystems to Molecules, Interactions Are Important in Biological Systems

INTERACTIONS At any level of the biological hierarchy, interactions between the components of the system ensure smooth integration of all the parts, such that they function as a whole. This holds true equally well for the components of an ecosystem and the molecules in a cell; we'll discuss both as examples.

Ecosystems: An Organism's Interactions with Other Organisms and the Physical Environment

At the ecosystem level, each organism interacts with other organisms. For instance, an acacia tree interacts with soil microorganisms associated with its roots, insects that live on it, and animals that eat its leaves and fruit (Figure 1.10). In some cases, interactions between organisms are mutually beneficial. An example is the association between a sea turtle and the so-called "cleaner fish" that hover around it. The fish feed on parasites that would otherwise harm the turtle, while gaining a meal and protection from predators. Sometimes, one species benefits and the other is harmed, as when a lion kills and eats a zebra. In yet other cases, both species are harmed—for example, when two plants compete for a soil resource that is in short supply. Interactions among organisms help regulate the functioning of the ecosystem as a whole.

Organisms also interact continuously with physical factors in their environment. The leaves of a tree, for example, absorb light from the sun, take in carbon dioxide from the air, and release oxygen to the air (see Figure 1.10). The environment is also affected by the organisms living there. For instance, in addition to taking up water and minerals from the soil, the roots of a plant break up rocks as they grow, thereby contributing to the formation of soil. On a global scale, plants and other photosynthetic organisms have generated all the oxygen in the atmosphere.

Molecules: Interactions Within Organisms

At lower levels of organization, the interactions between components that make up living organisms—organs, tissues, cells, and molecules—are crucial to their smooth operation. Consider the sugar in your blood, for instance. After a meal, the level of the sugar glucose in your blood rises (Figure 1.11). The increase in blood glucose stimulates the pancreas to release insulin into the blood. Once it reaches liver or muscle cells, insulin causes excess glucose to be stored in the form of a very large carbohydrate called glycogen, reducing blood glucose level to a range that is optimal for bodily functioning. The lower blood glucose level that results no longer stimulates insulin secretion by pancreas cells. Some sugar is also used by cells for energy: When you exercise, your muscle cells increase their consumption of sugar molecules.

Interactions among the body's molecules are responsible for most of the steps in this process. For instance, like most chemical activities in the cell, those that either decompose or store sugar are accelerated at the molecular level (catalyzed) by proteins called enzymes. Each type of enzyme

▶ Figure 1.10 Interactions of an African acacia tree with other organisms and the physical environment.

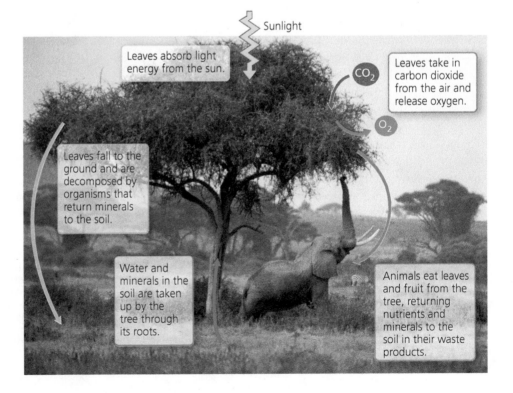

Sunlight

Leaves absorb light energy from the sun.

Leaves take in carbon dioxide from the air and release oxygen.

CO_2

O_2

Leaves fall to the ground and are decomposed by organisms that return minerals to the soil.

Water and minerals in the soil are taken up by the tree through its roots.

Animals eat leaves and fruit from the tree, returning nutrients and minerals to the soil in their waste products.

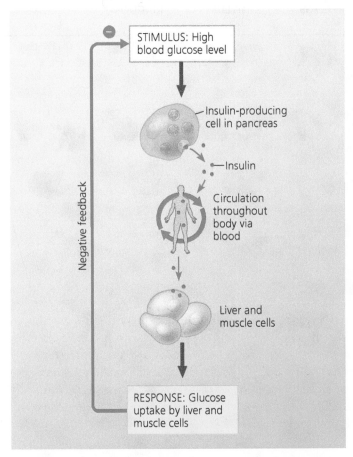

STIMULUS: High blood glucose level

Negative feedback

Insulin-producing cell in pancreas

Insulin

Circulation throughout body via blood

Liver and muscle cells

RESPONSE: Glucose uptake by liver and muscle cells

▲ **Figure 1.11 Feedback regulation.** The human body regulates the use and storage of glucose, a major cellular fuel derived from food. This figure shows negative feedback: The response (glucose uptake by cells) decreases the high glucose levels that provide the stimulus for insulin secretion, thus negatively regulating the process.

catalyzes a specific chemical reaction. In many cases, these reactions are linked into chemical pathways, each step with its own enzyme. How does the cell coordinate its various chemical pathways? In our example of sugar management, how does the cell match fuel supply to demand, regulating its opposing pathways of sugar consumption and storage? The key is the ability of many biological processes to self-regulate by a mechanism called feedback.

In **feedback regulation**, the output, or product, of a process regulates that very process. The most common form of regulation in living systems is *negative feedback*, a loop in which the response reduces the initial stimulus. As seen in the example of insulin signaling (see Figure 1.11), the uptake of glucose by cells (the response) decreases blood glucose levels, eliminating the stimulus for insulin secretion and thereby shutting off the pathway. Thus, the output of the process negatively regulates that process.

Though less common than processes regulated by negative feedback, there are also many biological processes regulated by *positive feedback*, in which an end product *speeds up* its own production. The clotting of your blood in response to injury is an example. When a blood vessel is

damaged, structures in the blood called platelets begin to aggregate at the site. Positive feedback occurs as chemicals released by the platelets attract *more* platelets. The platelet pileup then initiates a complex process that seals the wound with a clot.

Feedback is a regulatory motif common to life at all levels, from the molecular level through ecosystems and the biosphere. Interactions between organisms can affect system-wide processes like the growth of a population. And as we'll see, interactions between individuals not only affect the participants, but also affect how populations evolve over time.

Evolution, the Core Theme of Biology

Having considered four of the unifying themes that run through this text (organization, information, energy and matter, and interactions), let's now turn to biology's core theme—evolution. Evolution is the one idea that makes logical sense of everything we know about living organisms. As we will see in Units 4 and 5 of this text, the fossil record documents the fact that life has been evolving on Earth for billions of years, resulting in a vast diversity of past and present organisms. But along with the diversity are many shared features. For example, while sea horses, jackrabbits, hummingbirds, and giraffes all look very different, their skeletons are organized in the same basic way. The scientific explanation for this unity and diversity—as well as for the adaptation of organisms to their environments—is evolution: the concept that the organisms living on Earth today are the modified descendants of common ancestors. In other words, we can explain the sharing of traits by two organisms with the premise that the organisms have descended from a common ancestor, and we can account for differences with the idea that heritable changes have occurred along the way. Many kinds of evidence support the occurrence of evolution and the theory that describes how it takes place. In the next section, we'll consider the fundamental concept of evolution in greater detail.

CONCEPT CHECK 1.1

1. Starting with the molecular level in Figure 1.3, write a sentence that includes components from the previous (lower) level of biological organization, for example: "A molecule consists of *atoms* bonded together." Continue with organelles, moving up the biological hierarchy.

2. Identify the theme or themes exemplified by (a) the sharp quills of a porcupine, (b) the development of a multicellular organism from a single fertilized egg, and (c) a hummingbird using sugar to power its flight.

3. **WHAT IF?** For each theme discussed in this section, give an example not mentioned in the text.

For suggested answers, see Appendix A.

| SPECIES *Ursus americanus* | GENUS *Ursus* | FAMILY Ursidae | ORDER Carnivora | CLASS Mammalia | PHYLUM Chordata | KINGDOM Animalia | DOMAIN Eukarya |

▲ **Figure 1.12 Classifying life.** To help make sense of the diversity of life, biologists classify species into groups that are then combined into even broader groups. In the traditional "Linnaean" system, species that are very closely related, such as polar bears and brown bears, are placed in the same genus; genera (plural of genus) are grouped into families; and so on. This example classifies the species *Ursus americanus*, the American black bear. (Alternative classification schemes will be discussed in detail in Chapter 26.)

CONCEPT 1.2

The Core Theme: Evolution accounts for the unity and diversity of life

EVOLUTION There is consensus among biologists that evolution is the core theme of biology. The evolutionary changes seen in the fossil record are observable facts. Furthermore, as we'll describe, evolutionary mechanisms account for the unity and diversity of all species on Earth. To quote one of the founders of modern evolutionary theory, Theodosius Dobzhansky, "Nothing in biology makes sense except in the light of evolution."

In addition to encompassing a hierarchy of size scales from molecules to the biosphere, biology explores the great diversity of species that have ever lived on Earth. To understand Dobzhansky's statement, we need to discuss how biologists think about this vast diversity.

Classifying the Diversity of Life

Diversity is a hallmark of life. Biologists have so far identified and named about 1.8 million species. To date, this diversity of life is known to include at least 100,000 species of fungi, 290,000 plant species, 57,000 vertebrate species (animals with backbones), and 1 million insect species (more than half of all known forms of life)—not to mention the myriad types of single-celled organisms. Researchers identify thousands of additional species each year. Estimates of the total number of species range from about 10 million

to over 100 million. Whatever the actual number, the enormous variety of life gives biology a very broad scope. Biologists face a major challenge in attempting to make sense of this variety.

Grouping Species: The Basic Idea

There is a human tendency to group diverse items according to their similarities and their relationships to each other. For instance, we may speak of "squirrels" and "butterflies," though we recognize that many different species belong to each group. We may even sort groups into broader categories, such as rodents (which include squirrels) and insects (which include butterflies). Taxonomy, the branch of biology that names and classifies species, formalizes this ordering of species into groups of increasing breadth, based on the degree to which they share characteristics **(Figure 1.12)**. You will learn more about the details of this taxonomic scheme in Chapter 26. Here, we will focus on the big picture by considering the broadest units of classification, kingdoms and domains.

The Three Domains of Life

Historically, scientists have classified the diversity of life-forms into species and broader groupings by careful comparisons of structure, function, and other obvious features. In the last few decades, new methods of assessing species relationships, such as comparisons of DNA sequences, have led to an ongoing reevaluation of the number and boundaries of kingdoms. Researchers have proposed anywhere from six kingdoms to dozens of kingdoms. While debate continues at the kingdom level, biologists agree that the kingdoms of life can be grouped into three even higher levels of classification called domains. The three domains are named Bacteria, Archaea, and Eukarya **(Figure 1.13)**.

As you read earlier, the organisms making up two of the three domains—**Bacteria** and **Archaea**—are prokaryotic.

All the eukaryotes (organisms with eukaryotic cells) are now grouped in domain **Eukarya**. This domain includes three kingdoms of multicellular eukaryotes: kingdoms Plantae, Fungi, and Animalia. These three kingdoms are distinguished partly by their modes of nutrition. Plants produce their own sugars and other food molecules by photosynthesis, fungi absorb dissolved nutrients from their surroundings, and animals obtain food by eating and digesting other organisms. Animalia is, of course, the kingdom to which we belong. But neither plants, nor fungi, nor animals are as numerous or diverse as the single-celled eukaryotes we call protists. Although protists were once placed in a single kingdom, recent evidence shows that some protists are more closely related to plants, animals, or fungi than they are to other protists. Thus, the recent taxonomic trend has been to split the protists into several kingdoms.

▼ **Figure 1.13 The three domains of life.**

(a) Domain Bacteria

2 μm

Bacteria are the most diverse and widespread prokaryotes and are now classified into multiple kingdoms. Each rod-shaped structure in this photo is a bacterial cell.

(b) Domain Archaea

2 μm

Some of the prokaryotes known as **archaea** live in Earth's extreme environments, such as salty lakes and boiling hot springs. Domain Archaea includes multiple kingdoms. Each round structure in this photo is an archaeal cell.

(c) Domain Eukarya

◄ **Kingdom Animalia** consists of multicellular eukaryotes that ingest other organisms.

100 μm

▲ **Kingdom Plantae** consists of terrestrial multicellular eukaryotes (land plants) that carry out photosynthesis, the conversion of light energy to the chemical energy in food.

► **Kingdom Fungi** is defined in part by the nutritional mode of its members (such as this mushroom), which absorb nutrients from outside their bodies.

► **Protists** are mostly unicellular eukaryotes and some relatively simple multicellular relatives. Pictured here is an assortment of protists inhabiting pond water. Scientists are currently debating how to classify protists in a way that accurately reflects their evolutionary relationships.

Cross section of a cillum, as viewed with an electron microscope

5 µm

Cilia of *Paramecium*.
The cilia of the single-celled *Paramecium* propel the organism through pond water.

15 µm

0.1 µm

Cilia of windpipe cells.
The cells that line the human windpipe are equipped with cilia that help keep the lungs clean by sweeping a film of debris-trapping mucus upward.

▲ **Figure 1.14 An example of unity underlying the diversity of life: the architecture of cilia in eukaryotes.** Cilia (singular, *cilium*) are extensions of cells that function in locomotion. They occur in eukaryotes as diverse as *Paramecium* (found in pond water) and humans. Even organisms so different share a common architecture for their cilia, which have an elaborate system of tubules that is striking in cross-sectional views.

Unity in the Diversity of Life

As diverse as life is, it also displays remarkable unity. Earlier we mentioned both the similar skeletons of different vertebrate animals and the universal genetic language of DNA (the genetic code). In fact, similarities between organisms are evident at all levels of the biological hierarchy. For example, unity is obvious in many features of cell structure, even among distantly related organisms (Figure 1.14).

How can we account for life's dual nature of unity and diversity? The process of evolution, explained next, illuminates both the similarities and differences in the world of life. It also introduces another important dimension of biology: historical time.

Charles Darwin and the Theory of Natural Selection

The history of life, as documented by fossils and other evidence, is the saga of a changing Earth billions of years old, inhabited by an evolving cast of living forms (Figure 1.15). This evolutionary view of life came into sharp focus in November 1859, when Charles Robert Darwin published one of the most important and influential books ever written.

▼ **Figure 1.15 Digging into the past.** Paleontologists carefully excavate the hind leg of a long-necked dinosaur (*Rapetosaurus krausei*) from rocks in Madagascar.

▲ **Figure 1.16 Charles Darwin as a young man.** His revolutionary book *On the Origin of Species* was first published in 1859.

Entitled *On the Origin of Species by Means of Natural Selection*, Darwin's book was an immediate bestseller and soon made "Darwinism," as it was dubbed at the time, almost synonymous with the concept of evolution **(Figure 1.16)**.

On the Origin of Species articulated two main points. The first point was that contemporary species arose from a succession of ancestors that differed from them. Darwin called this process "descent with modification." This insightful phrase captured the duality of life's unity and diversity—unity in the kinship among species that descended from common ancestors and diversity in the modifications that evolved as species branched from their common ancestors **(Figure 1.17)**.

Darwin's second main point was his proposal that "natural selection" is an evolutionary mechanism for descent with modification.

Darwin developed his theory of natural selection from observations that by themselves were neither new nor profound. Others had described the pieces of the puzzle, but Darwin saw how they fit together. He started with the following three observations from nature: First, individuals in a population vary in their traits, many of which seem to be heritable (passed on from parents to offspring). Second, a population can produce far more offspring than can survive to produce offspring of their own. With more individuals than the environment is able to support, competition is inevitable. Third, species generally suit their environments—in other words, they are adapted to their environments. For instance, a common adaptation among birds that eat tough seeds as their major food source is that they have especially thick, strong beaks.

Making inferences from these three observations, Darwin arrived at his theory of evolution. He reasoned that individuals with inherited traits that are better suited to the local environment are more likely to survive and reproduce than less well-suited individuals. Over many generations, a higher and higher proportion of individuals in a population will have the advantageous traits. Evolution occurs as the unequal reproductive success of individuals ultimately leads to adaptation to their environment, as long as the environment remains the same.

Darwin called this mechanism of evolutionary adaptation **natural selection** because the natural environment "selects" for the propagation of certain traits among naturally occurring variant traits in the population. The example

◀ **European robin**

◀ **Figure 1.17 Unity and diversity among birds.** These three birds are variations on a common body plan. For example, each has feathers, a beak, and wings—although these features are highly specialized for the birds' diverse lifestyles.

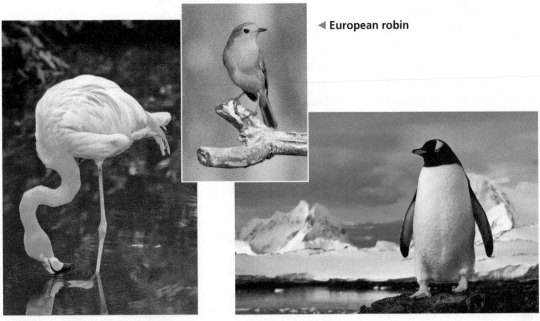

▲ **American flamingo**

▲ **Gentoo penguin**

① Population with varied inherited traits

② Elimination of individuals with certain traits

③ Reproduction of survivors

④ Increasing frequency of traits that enhance survival and reproductive success

▲ **Figure 1.18 Natural selection.** This imaginary beetle population has colonized a locale where the soil has been blackened by a recent brush fire. Initially, the population varies extensively in the inherited coloration of the individuals, from very light gray to charcoal. For hungry birds that prey on the beetles, it is easiest to spot the beetles that are lightest in color.

in **Figure 1.18** illustrates the ability of natural selection to "edit" a population's heritable variations in color. We see the products of natural selection in the exquisite adaptations of various organisms to the special circumstances of their way of life and their environment. The wings of the bat shown in **Figure 1.19** are an excellent example of adaptation.

The Tree of Life

Take another look at the skeletal architecture of the bat's wings in Figure 1.19. These wings are not like those of feathered birds; the bat is a mammal. The bat's forelimbs, though adapted for flight, actually have all the same bones, joints, nerves, and blood vessels found in other limbs as diverse as the human arm, the foreleg of a horse, and the flipper of a whale. Indeed, all mammalian forelimbs are anatomical variations of a common architecture, much as the birds in Figure 1.17 are variations on an underlying "avian" theme. Such examples of kinship connect life's unity in diversity to the Darwinian concept of descent with modification. In this view, the unity of mammalian limb anatomy reflects inheritance of that structure from a common

ancestor—the "prototype" mammal from which all other mammals descended. The diversity of mammalian forelimbs results from modification by natural selection operating over millions of generations in different environmental contexts. Fossils and other evidence corroborate anatomical unity in supporting this view of mammalian descent from a common ancestor.

Darwin proposed that natural selection, by its cumulative effects over long periods of time, could cause an ancestral species to give rise to two or more descendant species. This could occur, for example, if one population fragmented into several subpopulations isolated in different environments. In these separate arenas of natural selection, one species could gradually radiate into multiple species as the geographically isolated populations adapted over many generations to different sets of environmental factors.

The "family tree" of 14 finches in **Figure 1.20** illustrates a famous example of adaptive radiation of new species from a common ancestor. Darwin collected specimens of these birds during his 1835 visit to the remote Galápagos Islands, 900 kilometers (km) off the Pacific coast of South America. These relatively young, volcanic islands are home to many species of plants and animals found nowhere else in the world, though many Galápagos organisms are clearly related to species on the South American mainland. After volcanoes built up the Galápagos several million years ago, finches probably diversified on the various islands from an ancestral finch species that by chance reached the archipelago from elsewhere. Years after Darwin collected the Galapagos finches, researchers began to sort out the relationships among these finch species, first from anatomical and geographic data and more recently with the help of DNA sequence comparisons.

Biologists' diagrams of evolutionary relationships generally take treelike forms, though the trees are often turned

▲ **Figure 1.19 Evolutionary adaptation.** Bats, the only mammals capable of active flight, have wings with webbing between extended "fingers." Darwin proposed that such adaptations are refined over time by natural selection.

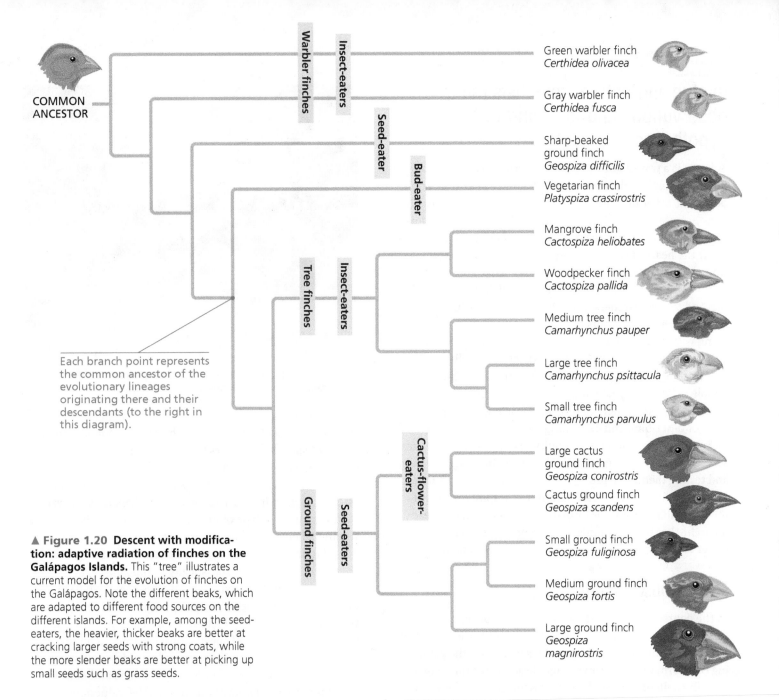

▲ **Figure 1.20 Descent with modification: adaptive radiation of finches on the Galápagos Islands.** This "tree" illustrates a current model for the evolution of finches on the Galápagos. Note the different beaks, which are adapted to different food sources on the different islands. For example, among the seed-eaters, the heavier, thicker beaks are better at cracking larger seeds with strong coats, while the more slender beaks are better at picking up small seeds such as grass seeds.

Each branch point represents the common ancestor of the evolutionary lineages originating there and their descendants (to the right in this diagram).

Green warbler finch
Certhidea olivacea

Gray warbler finch
Certhidea fusca

Sharp-beaked ground finch
Geospiza difficilis

Vegetarian finch
Platyspiza crassirostris

Mangrove finch
Cactospiza heliobates

Woodpecker finch
Cactospiza pallida

Medium tree finch
Camarhynchus pauper

Large tree finch
Camarhynchus psittacula

Small tree finch
Camarhynchus parvulus

Large cactus ground finch
Geospiza conirostris

Cactus ground finch
Geospiza scandens

Small ground finch
Geospiza fuliginosa

Medium ground finch
Geospiza fortis

Large ground finch
Geospiza magnirostris

sideways as in Figure 1.20. Tree diagrams make sense: Just as an individual has a genealogy that can be diagrammed as a family tree, each species is one twig of a branching tree of life extending back in time through ancestral species more and more remote. Species that are very similar, such as the Galápagos finches, share a common ancestor at a relatively recent branch point on the tree of life. But through an ancestor that lived much farther back in time, finches are related to sparrows, hawks, penguins, and all other birds. And birds, mammals, and all other vertebrates share a common ancestor even more ancient. Trace life back far enough, and we reach the early prokaryotes that inhabited Earth over 3.5 billion years ago. We can recognize their vestiges in our own cells—in the universal genetic code, for example. Indeed, all of life is connected through its long evolutionary history.

CONCEPT CHECK 1.2

1. How is a mailing address analogous to biology's hierarchical taxonomic system?

2. Explain why "editing" is an appropriate metaphor for how natural selection acts on a population's heritable variation.

3. **WHAT IF?** The three domains you learned about in Concept 1.2 can be represented in the tree of life as the three main branches, with three subbranches on the eukaryotic branch being the kingdoms Plantae, Fungi, and Animalia. What if fungi and animals are more closely related to each other than either of these kingdoms is to plants—as recent evidence strongly suggests? Draw a simple branching pattern that symbolizes the proposed relationship between these three eukaryotic kingdoms.

For suggested answers, see Appendix A.

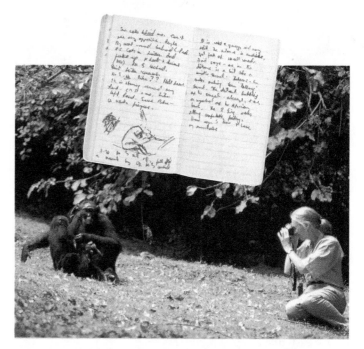

CONCEPT 1.3

In studying nature, scientists make observations and form and test hypotheses

Science is a way of knowing—an approach to understanding the natural world. It developed out of our curiosity about ourselves, other life-forms, our planet, and the universe. The word *science* is derived from a Latin verb meaning "to know." Striving to understand seems to be one of our basic urges.

At the heart of science is **inquiry**, a search for information and explanations of natural phenomena. There is no formula for successful scientific inquiry, no single scientific method that researchers must rigidly follow. As in all quests, science includes elements of challenge, adventure, and luck, along with careful planning, reasoning, creativity, patience, and the persistence to overcome setbacks. Such diverse elements of inquiry make science far less structured than most people realize. That said, it is possible to highlight certain characteristics that help to distinguish science from other ways of describing and explaining nature.

Scientists use a process of inquiry that includes making observations, forming logical, testable explanations (*hypotheses*), and testing them. The process is necessarily repetitive: In testing a hypothesis, more observations may inspire revision of the original hypothesis or formation of a new one, thus leading to further testing. In this way, scientists circle closer and closer to their best estimation of the laws governing nature.

Making Observations

In the course of their work, scientists describe natural structures and processes as accurately as possible through careful observation and analysis of data. Observation is the gathering of information, either through direct use of the senses or with the help of tools such as microscopes, thermometers, and balances that extend our senses. Observations can reveal valuable information about the natural world. For example, a series of detailed observations have shaped our understanding of cell structure, and another set of observations is currently expanding our databases of genomes of diverse species and of genes whose expression is altered in cancer and other diseases.

Recorded observations are called **data**. Put another way, data are items of information on which scientific inquiry is based. The term *data* implies numbers to many people. But some data are *qualitative*, often in the form of recorded descriptions rather than numerical measurements. For example, Jane Goodall spent decades recording her observations of chimpanzee behavior during field research in a Tanzanian jungle **(Figure 1.21)**. Along with these qualitative data, Goodall also enriched the field of animal behavior with

▲ **Figure 1.21 Jane Goodall collecting qualitative data on chimpanzee behavior.** Goodall recorded her observations in field notebooks, often with sketches of the animals' behavior.

volumes of *quantitative* data, such as the frequency and duration of specific behaviors for different members of a group of chimpanzees in a variety of situations. Quantitative data are generally expressed as numerical measurements and often organized into tables and graphs. Scientists analyze their data using a type of mathematics called statistics to test whether their results are significant or merely due to random fluctuations. (Note that all results presented in this text have been shown to be statistically significant.)

Collecting and analyzing observations can lead to important conclusions based on a type of logic called **inductive reasoning**. Through induction, we derive generalizations from a large number of specific observations. "The sun always rises in the east" is an example. And so is "All organisms are made of cells." Careful observations and data analyses, along with generalizations reached by induction, are fundamental to our understanding of nature.

Forming and Testing Hypotheses

Our innate curiosity often stimulates us to pose questions about the natural basis for the phenomena we observe in the world. What *caused* the different chimpanzee behaviors that Goodall observed in different situations? What *causes* the roots of a plant seedling to grow downward? In science, such inquiry usually involves the forming and testing of hypothetical explanations—that is, hypotheses.

In science, a **hypothesis** is a tentative answer to a well-framed question—an explanation on trial. It is usually a rational account for a set of observations, based on the available data and guided by inductive reasoning. A scientific hypothesis must lead to predictions that can be tested by

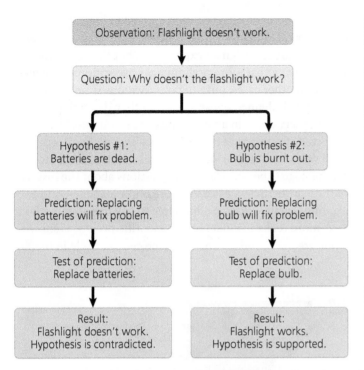

▲ **Figure 1.22 A simplified view of the scientific process.** The idealized process sometimes called the "scientific method" is shown in this flow chart, using a campground example of hypothesis testing.

making additional observations or by performing experiments. An *experiment* is a scientific test, carried out under controlled conditions.

We all use observations and develop questions and hypotheses in solving everyday problems. Let's say, for example, that your flashlight fails while you are camping. That's an observation. The question is obvious: Why doesn't the flashlight work? Two reasonable hypotheses based on your experience are that (1) the batteries in the flashlight are dead or (2) the bulb is burnt out. Each of these alternative hypotheses leads to predictions you can test with informal experiments. For example, the dead-battery hypothesis predicts that replacing the batteries will fix the problem. **Figure 1.22** diagrams this campground inquiry. Figuring things out like this, by systematic trial and error, is a hypothesis-based approach.

Sometimes we can't carry out an experiment but can test a hypothesis using observations. Let's say you don't have a spare bulb or spare batteries. How could you figure out which hypothesis is more likely? You could examine the bulb and see if it looks burnt out. You could also check the expiration date on the battery. Experiments are great ways to test hypotheses, but when experiments aren't possible, we can often test a hypothesis in other ways.

Deductive Reasoning

A type of logic called deduction is also built into the use of hypotheses in science. While induction entails reasoning from a set of specific observations to reach a general

conclusion, **deductive reasoning** involves logic that flows in the opposite direction, from the general to the specific. From general premises, we extrapolate to the specific results we should expect if the premises are true. In the scientific process, deductions usually take the form of predictions of results that will be found if a particular hypothesis (premise) is correct. We then test the hypothesis by carrying out experiments or observations to see whether or not the results are as predicted. This deductive testing takes the form of "*If ... then*" logic. In the case of the flashlight example: *If* the dead-battery hypothesis is correct, *then* the flashlight should work if you replace the batteries with new ones.

The flashlight inquiry demonstrates two other key points about the use of hypotheses in science. First, the initial observations may give rise to multiple hypotheses. The ideal plan is to design experiments to test all these candidate explanations. For instance, another of the many possible alternative hypotheses to explain our dead flashlight is that *both* the batteries *and* the bulb are bad, and you could design an experiment to test this.

Second, we can never *prove* that a hypothesis is true. Based on the experiments shown in Figure 1.22, the burnt-out bulb hypothesis stands out as the most likely explanation. The results support that hypothesis but do not absolutely prove it is correct. Perhaps the first bulb was simply loose, so it wasn't making electrical contact, and the new bulb was inserted correctly. We could attempt to test the burnt-out bulb hypothesis again by trying another experiment—removing the original bulb and carefully reinstalling it. If the flashlight still doesn't work, the burnt-out bulb hypothesis is supported by another line of evidence—but still not proven. For example, the bulb may have another defect not related to being burnt out. Testing a hypothesis in various ways, producing different sorts of data, can increase our confidence in it tremendously, but no amount of experimental testing can *prove* a hypothesis beyond a shadow of doubt.

Questions That Can and Cannot Be Addressed by Science

Scientific inquiry is a powerful way to learn about nature, but there are limitations to the kinds of questions it can answer. A scientific hypothesis must be *testable*; there must be some observation or experiment that could reveal if such an idea is likely to be true or false. The hypothesis that dead batteries are the sole cause of the broken flashlight could be (and was) tested by replacing the old batteries with new ones.

Not all hypotheses meet the criteria of science: You wouldn't be able to test the hypothesis that invisible campground ghosts are fooling with your flashlight! Because science only deals with natural, testable explanations for natural phenomena, it can neither support nor contradict the invisible ghost hypothesis, nor whether spirits, elves, or fairies, either benevolent or evil, cause storms, rainbows, illnesses, and cures. Such supernatural explanations, because they cannot be tested, are simply outside the bounds of science. For the same reason, science does not deal with religious matters, which are issues of personal faith. Science and religion are not mutually exclusive or contradictory, they are simply concerned with different issues.

The Flexibility of the Scientific Process

The flashlight example of Figure 1.22 traces an idealized process of inquiry sometimes called *the scientific method*. We can recognize the elements of this process in most of the research articles published by scientists, but rarely in such structured form. Very few scientific inquiries adhere rigidly to the sequence of steps prescribed by the "textbook"

scientific method, which is often applied in hindsight, after the experiment or study is completed. For example, a scientist may start to design an experiment, but then backtrack after realizing that more preliminary observations are necessary. In other cases, puzzling observations simply don't prompt well-defined questions until other research places those observations in a new context. For example, Darwin collected specimens of the Galápagos finches, but it wasn't until years later, as the idea of natural selection began to gel, that biologists began asking key questions about the history of those birds. Science is a lot more unpredictable—and exciting—than lock-step adherence to any five-step method.

A more realistic model of the scientific process is shown in **Figure 1.23.** The core activity (the central circle in the

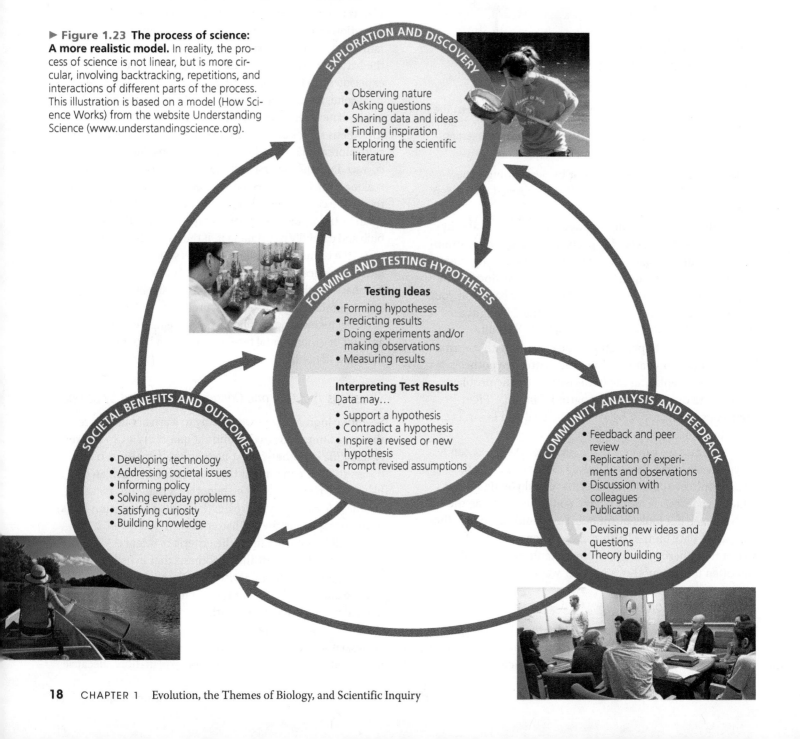

▶ **Figure 1.23 The process of science: A more realistic model.** In reality, the process of science is not linear, but is more circular, involving backtracking, repetitions, and interactions of different parts of the process. This illustration is based on a model (How Science Works) from the website Understanding Science (www.understandingscience.org).

EXPLORATION AND DISCOVERY

- Observing nature
- Asking questions
- Sharing data and ideas
- Finding inspiration
- Exploring the scientific literature

FORMING AND TESTING HYPOTHESES

Testing Ideas
- Forming hypotheses
- Predicting results
- Doing experiments and/or making observations
- Measuring results

Interpreting Test Results
Data may...
- Support a hypothesis
- Contradict a hypothesis
- Inspire a revised or new hypothesis
- Prompt revised assumptions

SOCIETAL BENEFITS AND OUTCOMES

- Developing technology
- Addressing societal issues
- Informing policy
- Solving everyday problems
- Satisfying curiosity
- Building knowledge

COMMUNITY ANALYSIS AND FEEDBACK

- Feedback and peer review
- Replication of experiments and observations
- Discussion with colleagues
- Publication

- Devising new ideas and questions
- Theory building

figure) is the forming and testing of hypotheses. This is the most fundamental aspect of science and is the reason that science does such a reliable job of explaining phenomena in the natural world. However, there is much more to the scientific process than just testing. The choice of ideas to test, the interpretation and evaluation of results, and the decision about which ideas to pursue for further study are influenced by three other arenas as well.

First, well-framed questions, new hypotheses, and good study designs do not spring to life out of thin air; they are inspired and nurtured by the sorts of endeavors associated with exploration and discovery (the upper circle in Figure 1.23). Second, testing is not performed in a social vacuum; community analysis and feedback play an important role (lower right circle). Interactions within the scientific community influence which hypotheses are tested and how, provoke reinterpretations of test results, provide independent assessments of the validity of study designs, and much more. Finally, the process of science is interwoven with the fabric of society (lower left circle). A societal need—for example, to understand the process of climate change—may inspire a flurry of hypotheses and studies. Similarly, well-supported hypotheses may wind up enabling an important technological innovation or encouraging a particular policy, which may, in turn, inspire new scientific questions. Though testing hypotheses and interpreting data are at the heart of science, these pursuits represent only part of the picture.

A Case Study in Scientific Inquiry: Investigating Coat Coloration in Mouse Populations

Now that we have highlighted the key features of scientific inquiry—making observations and forming and testing hypotheses—you should be able to recognize these features in a case study of actual scientific research.

The story begins with a set of observations and inductive generalizations. Color patterns of animals vary widely in nature, sometimes even among members of the same species. What accounts for such variation? An illustrative example is found in two populations of mice that belong to the same species (*Peromyscus polionotus*) but have different color patterns and reside in different environments **(Figure 1.24)**. The beach mouse lives along the Florida seashore, a habitat of brilliant white sand dunes with sparse clumps of beach grass. The inland mouse lives on darker, more fertile soil farther inland. Even a brief glance at the photographs in Figure 1.24 reveals a striking match of mouse coloration to its habitat. The natural predators of these mice, including hawks, owls, foxes, and coyotes, are all visual hunters (they use their

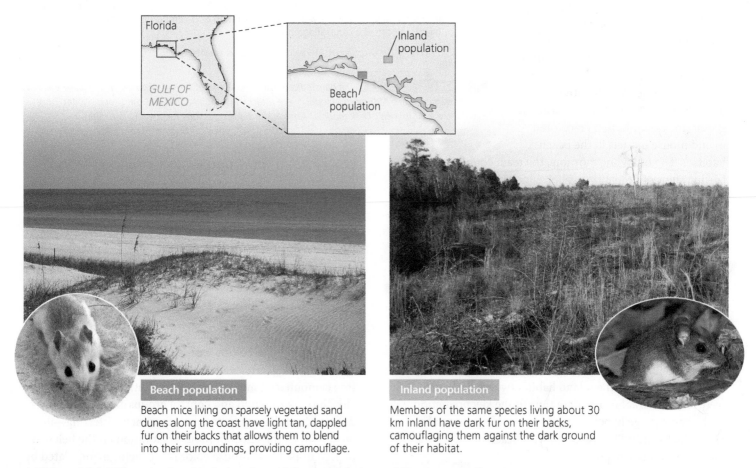

Beach population

Beach mice living on sparsely vegetated sand dunes along the coast have light tan, dappled fur on their backs that allows them to blend into their surroundings, providing camouflage.

Inland population

Members of the same species living about 30 km inland have dark fur on their backs, camouflaging them against the dark ground of their habitat.

▲ **Figure 1.24** **Different coloration in beach and inland populations of *Peromyscus polionotus*.**

eyes to look for prey). It was logical, therefore, for Francis Bertody Sumner, a naturalist studying populations of these mice in the 1920s, to form the hypothesis that their coloration patterns had evolved as adaptations that camouflage the mice in their native environments, protecting them from predation.

As obvious as the camouflage hypothesis may seem, it still required testing. In 2010, biologist Hopi Hoekstra of Harvard University and a group of her students headed to Florida to test the prediction that mice with coloration that did not match their habitat would be preyed on more heavily than the native, well-matched mice. **Figure 1.25** summarizes this field experiment.

The researchers built hundreds of plasticine models of mice and spray-painted them to resemble either beach mice (light colored) or inland mice (darker colored), so that the models differed only in their color patterns. The researchers placed equal numbers of these model mice randomly in both habitats and left them overnight. The mouse models resembling the native mice in the habitat were the *control* group (for instance, light-colored beach mouse models in the beach habitat), while the mouse models with the non-native coloration were the *experimental* group (for example, darker-colored inland mouse models in the beach habitat). The following morning, the team counted and recorded signs of predation events, which ranged from bites and gouge marks on some models to the outright disappearance of others. Judging by the shape of the predator's bites and the tracks surrounding the experimental sites, the predators appeared to be split fairly evenly between mammals (such as foxes and coyotes) and birds (such as owls, herons, and hawks).

For each environment, the researchers then calculated the percentage of predation events that targeted camouflaged mouse models. The results were clear: Camouflaged models experienced much less predation than those lacking camouflage in both the beach habitat (where light mice were less vulnerable) and the inland habitat (where dark mice were less vulnerable). The data thus fit the key prediction of the camouflage hypothesis. For more information about Hopi Hoekstra and her research with beach mice, see the interview before Chapter 22.

▼ **Figure 1.25** | Inquiry

Does camouflage affect predation rates on two populations of mice?

Experiment Hopi Hoekstra and colleagues wanted to test the hypothesis that coloration of beach and inland mice (*Peromyscus polionotus*) provides camouflage that protects them from predation in their respective habitats. The researchers spray-painted mouse models with either light or dark color patterns that matched those of the beach and inland mice and then placed models with both patterns in each of the habitats. The next morning, they counted damaged or missing models.

Results For each habitat, the researchers calculated the percentage of attacked models that were camouflaged or non-camouflaged. In both habitats, the models whose pattern did not match their surroundings suffered much higher "predation" than did the camouflaged models.

Conclusion The results are consistent with the researchers' prediction: that mouse models with camouflage coloration would be preyed on less often than non-camouflaged mouse models. Thus, the experiment supports the camouflage hypothesis.

Source: S. N. Vignieri, J. G. Larson, and H. E. Hoekstra, The selective advantage of crypsis in mice, *Evolution* 64:2153–2158 (2010).

INTERPRET THE DATA *The bars indicate the percentage of the attacked models that were either light or dark. Assume 100 mouse models were attacked in each habitat. For the beach habitat, how many were light models? Dark models? Answer the same questions for the inland habitat.*

Experimental Variables and Controls

Earlier in this section, we described an experiment as a scientific test carried out under controlled conditions. More specifically, an **experiment** involves manipulation of one factor in a system in order to see the effects of changing it. Both the factor that is manipulated and the effects that are measured are types of experimental **variables**—factors that vary in an experiment.

The mouse camouflage experiment described in Figure 1.25 is an example of a **controlled experiment**, one that is designed to compare an experimental group (the non-camouflaged mice, in this case) with a control group (the camouflaged mice normally resident in the area). Ideally, the experimental and control groups are designed to differ only in the one factor the experiment is testing—in our example, the effect of mouse coloration on the behavior of predators. Here, mouse color is the factor manipulated by the researchers; it is called the the **independent variable**. The amount of predation is the **dependent variable**, a factor that is measured in the experiment. Without the control group, the researchers would not have been able to rule out other factors as causes of the more frequent attacks on the non-camouflaged mice—such as different numbers of predators or different temperatures in the different test areas. The clever experimental design left coloration as the only factor that could account for the low predation rate on the camouflaged mice placed in their normal environment.

A common misconception is that the term *controlled experiment* means that scientists control the experimental environment to keep everything strictly constant except the one variable being tested. But that's impossible in field research and not realistic even in highly regulated laboratory environments. Researchers usually "control" unwanted variables not by *eliminating* them through environmental regulation, but by *canceling out* their effects by using control groups.

Theories in Science

Our everyday use of the term *theory* often implies an untested speculation: "It's just a theory!" But the term *theory* has a different meaning in science. What is a scientific theory, and how is it different from a hypothesis or from mere speculation?

First, a scientific **theory** is much broader in scope than a hypothesis. This is a hypothesis: "Fur coloration well-matched to their habitat is an adaptation that protects mice from predators." But *this* is a theory: "Evolutionary adaptations arise by natural selection." This theory proposes that natural selection is the evolutionary mechanism that accounts for an enormous variety of adaptations, of which coat color in mice is but one example.

Second, a theory is general enough to spin off many new, specific hypotheses that can be tested. For example, two researchers at Princeton University, Peter and Rosemary Grant, were motivated by the theory of natural selection to test the specific hypothesis that the beaks of Galápagos finches evolve in response to changes in the types of available food. (Their results supported their hypothesis; see the Chapter 23 overview.)

And third, compared with any hypothesis, a theory is generally supported by a much greater body of evidence. The theory of natural selection has been supported by a vast quantity of evidence, with more being found every day, and has not been contradicted by any scientific data. Other similarly supported theories include the theory of gravity and the theory that the Earth revolves around the sun. Those theories that become widely adopted in science explain a great range of observations and are supported by a vast accumulation of evidence. In fact, scrutiny of theories continues through testing of the specific hypotheses they generate.

In spite of the body of evidence supporting a widely accepted theory, scientists will modify or even reject theories when new research produces results that don't fit. For example, the theory of biological diversity that lumped bacteria and archaea together as a kingdom of prokaryotes began to erode when new methods for comparing cells and molecules made it possible to test some of the hypothetical relationships between organisms that were based on the theory. If there is "truth" in science, it is at best conditional, based on the preponderance of available evidence.

CONCEPT CHECK 1.3

1. Contrast inductive reasoning with deductive reasoning.
2. In the mouse camouflage experiment, what is the independent variable? The dependent variable? Explain.
3. Why is natural selection called a theory?
4. **WHAT IF?** In the deserts of the southwestern United States, the soils are mostly sandy, with occasional large regions of black rock derived from lava flows that occurred 1.7 million years ago. Mice are found in both sandy and rocky areas, and owls are known predators. What might you expect about coat color in these two mouse populations? Explain. How would you use this ecosystem to further test the camouflage hypothesis?

For suggested answers, see Appendix A.

CONCEPT 1.4

Science benefits from a cooperative approach and diverse viewpoints

Movies and cartoons sometimes portray scientists as loners working in isolated labs. In reality, science is an intensely social activity. Most scientists work in teams, which often include both graduate and undergraduate students. And to succeed in science, it helps to be a good communicator. Research results have no impact until shared with a community of peers through seminars, publications, and websites.

Building on the Work of Others

The great scientist Isaac Newton once said: "To explain all nature is too difficult a task for any one man or even for any one age. 'Tis much better to do a little with certainty, and leave the rest for others that come after you. . . ." Anyone who becomes a scientist, driven by curiosity about how nature works, is sure to benefit greatly from the rich storehouse of discoveries by others who have come before. In fact, Hopi Hoekstra's experiment benefited from the work of another researcher, D. W. Kaufman, 40 years earlier. You

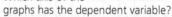

Interpreting a Pair of Bar Graphs

How Much Does Camouflage Affect Predation on Mice by Owls with and without Moonlight? D. W. Kaufman investigated the effect of prey camouflage on predation. Kaufman tested the hypothesis that the amount of contrast between the coat color of a mouse and the color of its surroundings would affect the rate of nighttime predation by owls. He also hypothesized that the color contrast would be affected by the amount of moonlight. In this exercise, you will analyze data from his owl-mouse predation studies.

How the Experiment Was Done Pairs of mice (*Peromyscus polionotus*) with different coat colors, one light brown and one dark brown, were released simultaneously into an enclosure that contained a hungry owl. The researcher recorded the color of the mouse that was first caught by the owl. If the owl did not catch either mouse within 15 minutes, the test was recorded as a zero. The release trials were repeated multiple times in enclosures with either a dark-colored soil surface or a light-colored soil surface. The presence or absence of moonlight during each assay was recorded.

Data from the Experiment

Interpret the Data

1. First, make sure you understand how the graphs are set up. Graph A shows data from the light-colored soil enclosure and graph B from the dark-colored enclosure, but in all other respects the graphs are the same. (a) There is more than one independent variable in these graphs. What are the independent variables, the variables that were tested by the researcher? Which axis of the graphs has the independent variables? (b) What is the dependent variable, the response to the variables being tested? Which axis of the graphs has the dependent variable?

2. (a) How many dark brown mice were caught in the light-colored soil enclosure on a moonlit night? (b) How many dark brown mice were caught in the dark-colored soil enclosure on a moonlit night? (c) On a moonlit night, would a dark brown mouse be more likely to escape predation by owls on dark- or light-colored soil? Explain your answer.

3. (a) Is a dark brown mouse on dark-colored soil more likely to escape predation under a full moon or with no moon? (b) A light brown mouse on light-colored soil? Explain.

4. (a) Under which conditions would a dark brown mouse be most likely to escape predation at night? (b) A light brown mouse?

5. (a) What combination of independent variables led to the highest predation level in enclosures with light-colored soil? (b) What combination of independent variables led to the highest predation level in enclosures with dark-colored soil? (c) What relationship, if any, do you see in your answers to parts (a) and (b)?

6. What conditions are most deadly for both light brown and dark brown mice?

7. Combining the data shown in both graphs, estimate the total number of mice caught in moonlight versus no-moonlight conditions. Which condition is optimal for predation by the owl on mice? Explain your answer.

(MB) A version of this Scientific Skills Exercise can be assigned in MasteringBiology.

Data from D. W. Kaufman, Adaptive coloration in *Peromyscus polionotus*: Experimental selection by owls, *Journal of Mammalogy* 55:271–283 (1974).

can study the design of Kaufman's experiment and interpret the results in the Scientific Skills Exercise.

Scientific results are continually vetted through the repetition of observations and experiments. Scientists working in the same research field often check one another's claims by attempting to confirm observations or repeat experiments. If experimental results cannot be repeated by scientific colleagues, this failure may reflect some underlying weakness in the original claim, which will then have to be revised. In this sense, science polices itself. Integrity and adherence to high professional standards in reporting results are central to the scientific endeavor. After all, the validity of experimental data is key to designing further lines of inquiry.

It is not unusual for several scientists to converge on the same research question. Some scientists enjoy the challenge of being first with an important discovery or key experiment, while others derive more satisfaction from cooperating with fellow scientists working on the same problem.

Cooperation is facilitated when scientists use the same organism. Often it is a widely used **model organism**—a species that is easy to grow in the lab and lends itself particularly well to the questions being investigated. Because all species are evolutionarily related, such an organism may be viewed as a model for understanding the biology of other species and their diseases. For example, genetic studies of the fruit fly *Drosophila melanogaster* have taught us a lot about how genes work in other species, even humans. Some other popular model organisms are the mustard plant *Arabidopsis thaliana*, the soil worm *Caenorhabditis elegans*, the zebrafish *Danio rerio*, the mouse *Mus musculus*, and the bacterium *Escherichia coli*. As you read through this book, note the many contributions that these and other model organisms have made to the study of life.

Biologists may approach interesting questions from different angles. Some biologists focus on ecosystems, while others study natural phenomena at the level of organisms or cells. This text is divided into units that look at biology at different levels. Yet any given problem can be addressed from many perspectives, which in fact complement each other. For example, Hoekstra's work uncovered at least one genetic mutation that underlies the differences between beach and inland mouse coloration. Her lab includes biologists specializing at different biological levels, allowing links to be made between the evolutionary adaptations she focuses on and their molecular basis in DNA sequences.

As a biology student, you can benefit from making connections between the different levels of biology. You can develop this skill by noticing when certain topics crop up again and again in different units. One such topic is sickle-cell disease, a well-understood genetic condition that is prevalent among native inhabitants of Africa and other warm regions and their descendants. Sickle-cell disease will appear in several units of the text, each time addressed at a new level. In addition, we have designed a number of figures that make connections between the content in different chapters, as well as questions that ask you to make the connections yourselves. We hope these features will help you integrate the material you're learning and enhance your enjoyment of biology by encouraging you to keep the big picture in mind.

Science, Technology, and Society

The research community is part of society at large, and the relationship of science to society becomes clearer when we add technology to the picture (see Figure 1.23). Though science and technology sometimes employ similar inquiry patterns, their basic goals differ. The goal of science is to understand natural phenomena, while that of **technology** is to *apply* scientific knowledge for some specific purpose. Biologists and other scientists usually speak of "discoveries," while engineers and other technologists more often speak of "inventions." Because scientists put new technology to work in their research, science and technology are interdependent.

The potent combination of science and technology can have dramatic effects on society. Sometimes, the applications of basic research that turn out to be the most beneficial come out of the blue, from completely unanticipated observations in the course of scientific exploration. For example, discovery of the structure of DNA by Watson and Crick 60 years ago and subsequent achievements in DNA science led to the technologies of DNA manipulation that are transforming applied fields such as medicine, agriculture, and forensics **(Figure 1.26)**. Perhaps Watson and Crick

▲ **Figure 1.26 DNA technology and crime scene investigation.** In 2011, forensic analysis of DNA samples from a crime scene led to the release of Michael Morton from prison after he had served nearly 25 years for a crime he didn't commit, the brutal murder of his wife. The DNA analysis linked another man, also charged in a second murder, to the crime. The photo shows Mr. Morton hugging his parents after his conviction was overturned. The details of forensic analysis of DNA will be described in Chapter 20.

envisioned that their discovery would someday lead to important applications, but it is unlikely that they could have predicted exactly what all those applications would be.

The directions that technology takes depend less on the curiosity that drives basic science than on the current needs and wants of people and on the social environment of the times. Debates about technology center more on "*should* we do it" than "*can* we do it." With advances in technology come difficult choices. For example, under what circumstances is it acceptable to use DNA technology to find out if particular people have genes for hereditary diseases? Should such tests always be voluntary, or are there circumstances when genetic testing should be mandatory? Should insurance companies or employers have access to the information, as they do for many other types of personal health data? These questions are becoming much more urgent as the sequencing of individual genomes becomes quicker and cheaper.

Ethical issues raised by such questions have as much to do with politics, economics, and cultural values as with science and technology. All citizens—not only professional scientists—have a responsibility to be informed about how science works and about the potential benefits and risks of technology. The relationship between science, technology, and society increases the significance and value of any biology course.

The Value of Diverse Viewpoints in Science

Many of the technological innovations with the most profound impact on human society originated in settlements along trade routes, where a rich mix of different cultures ignited new ideas. For example, the printing press, which helped spread knowledge to all social classes and ultimately led to the book in your hands, was invented by the German

Johannes Gutenberg around 1440. This invention relied on several innovations from China, including paper and ink. Paper traveled along trade routes from China to Baghdad, where technology was developed for its mass production. This technology then migrated to Europe, as did water-based ink from China, which was modified by Gutenberg to become oil-based ink. We have the cross-fertilization of diverse cultures to thank for the printing press, and the same can be said for other important inventions.

Along similar lines, science stands to gain much from embracing a diversity of backgrounds and viewpoints among its practitioners. But just how diverse a population are scientists in relation to gender, race, ethnicity, and other attributes?

The scientific community reflects the cultural standards and behaviors of the society around it. It is therefore not surprising that until recently, women and certain minorities have faced huge obstacles in their pursuit to become professional scientists in many countries around the world. Over the past 50 years, changing attitudes about career choices have increased the proportion of women in biology and some other sciences, so that now women constitute roughly half of undergraduate biology majors and biology Ph.D. students. The pace has been slow at higher levels in the profession, however, and women and many racial and ethnic groups are still significantly underrepresented in many branches of science. This lack of diversity hampers the progress of science. The more voices that are heard at the table, the more robust, valuable, and productive the scientific interchange will be. The authors of this text welcome all students to the community of biologists, wishing you the joys and satisfactions of this exciting field of science.

CONCEPT CHECK 1.4

1. How does science differ from technology?
2. **MAKE CONNECTIONS** The gene that causes sickle-cell disease is present in a higher percentage of residents of sub-Saharan Africa than among those of African descent living in the United States. This gene provides some protection from malaria, a serious disease that is widespread in sub-Saharan Africa. Discuss an evolutionary process that could account for the different percentages among residents of the two regions. (See Concept 1.2.)

For suggested answers, see Appendix A.

1 Chapter Review

SUMMARY OF KEY CONCEPTS

CONCEPT 1.1

The study of life reveals common themes (pp. 2–9)

Organization Theme: New Properties Emerge at Successive Levels of Biological Organization

- The hierarchy of life unfolds as follows: biosphere > ecosystem > community > population > organism > organ system > organ > tissue > cell > organelle > molecule > atom. With each step upward from atoms, new **emergent properties** result from interactions among components at the lower levels. In an approach called reductionism, complex systems are broken down to simpler components that are more manageable to study. In **systems biology**, scientists attempt to model the dynamic behavior of whole biological systems by studying the interactions among the system's parts.
- The structure and function of biological components are interrelated. The cell, an organism's basic unit of structure and function, is the lowest level of organization that can perform all activities required for life. Cells are either prokaryotic or eukaryotic. **Eukaryotic cells** contain membrane-enclosed organelles, including a DNA-containing nucleus. **Prokaryotic cells** lack membrane-enclosed organelles.

Information Theme: Life's Processes Involve the Expression and Transmission of Genetic Information

- Genetic information is encoded in the nucleotide sequences of **DNA**. It is DNA that transmits heritable information from parents to offspring. DNA sequences called **genes** program a cell's protein production by being transcribed into mRNAs and then translated into specific proteins, a process called **gene expression**. Gene expression also results in RNAs that are not translated into protein but serve other important functions. **Genomics** is the large-scale analysis of the DNA sequences of a species (its **genome**) as well as the comparison of genomes between species. **Bioinformatics** uses computational tools to deal with huge volumes of sequence data.

Energy and Matter Theme: Life Requires the Transfer and Transformation of Energy and Matter

- Energy flows through an ecosystem. All organisms must perform work, which requires energy. Producers convert energy from sunlight to chemical energy, some of which is then passed on to consumers. (The rest is lost as heat energy.) Chemicals cycle between organisms and the environment.

ENERGY FLOW

CHEMICAL CYCLING

Interactions Theme: From Ecosystems to Molecules, Interactions Are Important in Biological Systems

- Organisms interact continuously with physical factors. Plants take up nutrients from the soil and chemicals from the air and use energy from the sun. Interactions among plants, animals, and other organisms affect the participants in various ways.

- In **feedback regulation,** a process is regulated by its output or end product. In negative feedback, accumulation of the end product slows its production. In positive feedback, an end product speeds up its own production. Feedback is a type of regulation common to life at all levels, from molecules to ecosystems.

STIMULUS

Negative feedback

RESPONSE

Evolution, the Core Theme of Biology

- **Evolution**, the process of change that has transformed life on Earth, accounts for the unity and diversity of life. It also explains evolutionary adaptation—the match of organisms to their environments.

? *Why is evolution considered the core theme of biology?*

CONCEPT 1.2

The Core Theme: Evolution accounts for the unity and diversity of life (pp. 10–15)

- Biologists classify species according to a system of broader and broader groups. Domain **Bacteria** and domain **Archaea** consist of prokaryotes. Domain **Eukarya**, the eukaryotes, includes various groups of protists and the kingdoms Plantae, Fungi, and Animalia. As diverse as life is, there is also evidence of remarkable unity, which is revealed in the similarities between different kinds of organisms.

- Darwin proposed **natural selection** as the mechanism for evolutionary adaptation of populations to their environments.

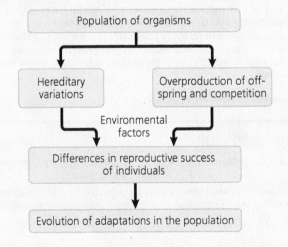

Population of organisms

Hereditary variations

Overproduction of offspring and competition

Environmental factors

Differences in reproductive success of individuals

Evolution of adaptations in the population

- Each species is one twig of a branching tree of life extending back in time through ancestral species more and more remote. All of life is connected through its long evolutionary history.

? *How could natural selection have led to the evolution of adaptations such as the parachute-like structure carrying a seed shown on the first page of this chapter?*

CONCEPT 1.3

In studying nature, scientists make observations and form and test hypotheses (pp. 16–21)

- In scientific **inquiry**, scientists make observations (collect **data**) and use **inductive reasoning** to draw a general conclusion, which can be developed into a testable **hypothesis**. **Deductive reasoning** makes predictions that can be used to test hypotheses. Hypotheses must be testable; science can address neither the possibility of supernatural phenomena nor the validity of religious beliefs. Hypotheses can be tested by experimentation or, when that is not possible, by making observations. In the process of science, the core activity is testing ideas. This endeavor is influenced by three arenas: exploration and discovery, community analysis and feedback, and societal benefits and outcomes. Testing ideas, in turn, affects each of these three pursuits as well.

- **Controlled experiments**, such as the study investigating coat coloration in mouse populations, are designed to demonstrate the effect of one variable by testing control groups and experimental groups that differ in only that one variable.

- A scientific **theory** is broad in scope, generates new hypotheses, and is supported by a large body of evidence.

? *What are the roles of gathering and interpreting data in the process of scientific inquiry?*

CONCEPT 1.4

Science benefits from a cooperative approach and diverse viewpoints (pp. 21–24)

- Science is a social activity. The work of each scientist builds on the work of others that have come before. Scientists must be able to repeat each other's results, so integrity is key. Biologists approach questions at different levels; their approaches complement each other.

- **Technology** consists of any method or device that applies scientific knowledge for some specific purpose that affects society. The ultimate impact of basic research is not always immediately obvious.

- Diversity among scientists promotes progress in science.

? *Explain why different approaches and diverse backgrounds among scientists are important.*

TEST YOUR UNDERSTANDING

LEVEL 1: KNOWLEDGE/COMPREHENSION

1. All the organisms on your campus make up
   a. an ecosystem.
   b. a community.
   c. a population.
   d. a taxonomic domain.

2. Which of the following is a correct sequence of levels in life's hierarchy, proceeding downward from an individual animal?
   a. organism, brain, organ system, nerve cell
   b. organ system, nervous tissue, brain, nerve cell
   c. organism, organ system, tissue, cell, organ
   d. nervous system, brain, nervous tissue, nerve cell

3. Which of the following is *not* an observation or inference on which Darwin's theory of natural selection is based?
   a. Poorly adapted individuals never produce offspring.
   b. There is heritable variation among individuals.
   c. Because of overproduction of offspring, there is competition for limited resources.
   d. A population can become adapted to its environment over time.

4. Systems biology is mainly an attempt to
   a. analyze genomes from different species.
   b. simplify complex problems by reducing the system into smaller, less complex units.
   c. understand the behavior of entire biological systems by studying interactions among its component parts.
   d. build high-throughput machines for the rapid acquisition of biological data.

5. Protists and bacteria are grouped into different domains because
   a. protists eat bacteria.
   b. bacteria are not made of cells.
   c. protists have a membrane-bounded nucleus.
   d. protists are photosynthetic.

6. Which of the following best demonstrates the unity among all organisms?
   a. emergent properties
   b. descent with modification
   c. the structure and function of DNA
   d. natural selection

7. A controlled experiment is one that
   a. proceeds slowly enough that a scientist can make careful records of the results.
   b. tests experimental and control groups in parallel.
   c. is repeated many times to make sure the results are accurate.
   d. keeps all variables constant.

8. Which of the following statements best distinguishes hypotheses from theories in science?
   a. Theories are hypotheses that have been proved.
   b. Hypotheses are guesses; theories are correct answers.
   c. Hypotheses usually are relatively narrow in scope; theories have broad explanatory power.
   d. Theories are proved true; hypotheses are often contradicted by experimental results.

LEVEL 2: APPLICATION/ANALYSIS

9. Which of the following is an example of qualitative data?
   a. The fish swam in a zigzag motion.
   b. The contents of the stomach are mixed every 20 seconds.
   c. The temperature decreased from 20°C to 15°C.
   d. The six pairs of robins hatched an average of three chicks each.

10. Which of the following best describes the logic of scientific inquiry?
    a. If I generate a testable hypothesis, tests and observations will support it.
    b. If my prediction is correct, it will lead to a testable hypothesis.
    c. If my observations are accurate, they will support my hypothesis.
    d. If my hypothesis is correct, I can expect certain test results.

11. **DRAW IT** With rough sketches, draw a biological hierarchy similar to the one in Figure 1.3 but using a coral reef as the ecosystem, a fish as the organism, its stomach as the organ, and DNA as the molecule. Include all levels in the hierarchy.

LEVEL 3: SYNTHESIS/EVALUATION

12. **EVOLUTION CONNECTION**
    A typical prokaryotic cell has about 3,000 genes in its DNA, while a human cell has almost 21,000 genes. About 1,000 of these genes are present in both types of cells. Based on your understanding of evolution, explain how such different organisms could have this same subset of 1,000 genes. What sorts of functions might these shared genes have?

13. **SCIENTIFIC INQUIRY**
    Based on the results of the mouse coloration case study, suggest another hypothesis researchers might use to further study the role of predators in the natural selection process.

14. **WRITE ABOUT A THEME: EVOLUTION**
    In a short essay (100–150 words), discuss Darwin's view of how natural selection resulted in both unity and diversity of life on Earth. Include in your discussion some of his evidence. (See a suggested grading rubric and tips for writing good essays in the Study Area of MasteringBiology under "Write About a Theme.")

15. **SYNTHESIZE YOUR KNOWLEDGE**

Can you pick out the mossy leaf-tailed gecko lying against the tree trunk in this photo? How is the appearance of the gecko a benefit in terms of survival? Given what you learned about evolution, natural selection, and genetic information in this chapter, describe how the gecko's coloration might have evolved.

For selected answers, see Appendix A.

MasteringBiology®

Students Go to **MasteringBiology** for assignments, the eText, and the Study Area with practice tests, animations, and activities.

Instructors Go to **MasteringBiology** for automatically graded tutorials and questions that you can assign to your students, plus Instructor Resources.

AN INTERVIEW WITH

Venki Ramakrishnan

Born in India, Venkatraman (Venki) Ramakrishnan received his B.Sc. from Baroda University and a Ph.D. in physics from Ohio University. Changing to biology, he then spent two years as a graduate student at the University of California, San Diego, followed by postdoctoral work at Yale University, where he began to study ribosomes. He spent 12 years at the Brookhaven National Laboratory and four more years at the University of Utah before moving to the MRC Laboratory of Molecular Biology in Cambridge, England in 1999. In 2009, he shared the Nobel Prize in Chemistry for research on ribosomal structure and function.

Tell us about your switch from physics to biology.

While at graduate school in physics, I found that my work did not engage me, and I became distracted. Among other things, I spent time reading *Scientific American*, and I was fascinated by the explosive growth of biology. Every month, there'd be some big new discovery! So I thought I'd go into biology, and I wrote to a few universities asking if I could join their graduate program in biology. The reason was I didn't know any biology. This led to my going to UC San Diego as a biology graduate student. But towards the end of my second year, I realized that I'd learned quite a bit of biology and didn't actually need a second Ph.D. So at that point I went to Yale, to work on ribosomes.

> " We could never understand how a ribosome functions if we didn't know its molecular structure. "

▶ Computer model of a ribosome.

What is a ribosome?

A ribosome (see below) is one of the most fundamental structures in all of biology. It is an assembly of many different proteins and large pieces of RNA, which make up two-thirds of its mass and actually play the key roles in its functioning. The ribosome takes the information in RNA transcribed from a gene and then stitches together a specific sequence of amino acids to make a protein. Everything made by the cell is made either by ribosomes or by proteins called enzymes, which are made by ribosomes.

The ribosome is the interface between genetic information and how things actually appear. It's at the crossroads of biology, in a way. So people worldwide have devoted decades to trying to understand how the ribosome works.

How do you study ribosome structure?

There are many ribosomes in every cell—many thousands in cells that make lots of protein, such as liver cells or actively growing bacteria. To date, nearly all the work we've done is on bacterial ribosomes. We grow bacteria in a large fermenter, break them open, and purify the ribosomes. To determine their structure, we crystallize them and then use a technique called X-ray crystallography. After crystallization, the scattering pattern produced when X-rays are passed through a crystal can be converted into a detailed image by computer analysis.

Why is the structure of a ribosome useful in understanding its function?

I can give you an analogy. Suppose some Martians come to visit Earth. They hover around, and they see all these machines going up and down the streets—cars. Now if they don't know the details of car structure, the only thing they can tell is that gasoline goes in and carbon dioxide and water come out (along with some pollutants). The thing moves as a result, but they wouldn't be able to tell how it worked. To tell how it worked, they would need to look at it in detail: They would need to open up the hood, look at the engine, see how all the parts are connected, and so on.

The ribosome can be thought of as a molecular machine. We could never understand how a ribosome functions if we didn't know its molecular structure. Knowing the structure in detail means we can do experiments to find out in detail how it works.

 For an extended interview and video clip, go to the Study Area in **MasteringBiology**.

2

The Chemical Context of Life

KEY CONCEPTS

2.1 Matter consists of chemical elements in pure form and in combinations called compounds

2.2 An element's properties depend on the structure of its atoms

2.3 The formation and function of molecules depend on chemical bonding between atoms

2.4 Chemical reactions make and break chemical bonds

▲ **Figure 2.1 What weapon are these wood ants shooting into the air?**

A Chemical Connection to Biology

Like other animals, ants have structures and mechanisms that defend them from attack. Wood ants live in colonies of hundreds or thousands, and the colony as a whole has a particularly effective mechanism for dealing with enemies. When threatened, the ants shoot volleys of formic acid into the air from their abdomens, and the acid rains down upon the potential invaders **(Figure 2.1)**. This substance is produced by many species of ants and in fact got its name from the Latin word for ant, *formica*. For quite a few ant species, the formic acid isn't shot out, but probably serves as a disinfectant that protects the ants against microbial parasites. Scientists have long known that chemicals play a major role in insect communication, the attraction of mates, and defense against predators.

Research on ants and other insects is a good example of how relevant chemistry is to the study of life. Unlike college courses, nature is not neatly packaged into individual sciences—biology, chemistry, physics, and so forth. Biologists specialize in the study of life, but organisms and their environments are natural systems to which the concepts of chemistry and physics apply. Biology is multidisciplinary.

This unit of chapters introduces some basic concepts of chemistry that apply to the study of life. Somewhere in the transition from molecules to cells, we will cross the blurry boundary between nonlife and life. This chapter focuses on the chemical components that make up all matter.

Matter consists of chemical elements in pure form and in combinations called compounds

Organisms are composed of **matter**, which is anything that takes up space and has mass.* Matter exists in many forms. Rocks, metals, oils, gases, and living organisms are a few examples of what seems to be an endless assortment of matter.

Elements and Compounds

Matter is made up of elements. An **element** is a substance that cannot be broken down to other substances by chemical reactions. Today, chemists recognize 92 elements occurring in nature; gold, copper, carbon, and oxygen are examples. Each element has a symbol, usually the first letter or two of its name. Some symbols are derived from Latin or German; for instance, the symbol for sodium is Na, from the Latin word *natrium*.

A **compound** is a substance consisting of two or more different elements combined in a fixed ratio. Table salt, for example, is sodium chloride (NaCl), a compound composed of the elements sodium (Na) and chlorine (Cl) in a 1:1 ratio. Pure sodium is a metal, and pure chlorine is a poisonous gas. When chemically combined, however, sodium and chlorine form an edible compound. Water (H_2O), another compound, consists of the elements hydrogen (H) and oxygen (O) in a 2:1 ratio. These are simple examples of organized matter having emergent properties: A compound has characteristics different from those of its elements **(Figure 2.2)**.

Sodium + **Chlorine** → **Sodium chloride**

▲ **Figure 2.2 The emergent properties of a compound.** The metal sodium combines with the poisonous gas chlorine, forming the edible compound sodium chloride, or table salt.

---

*In everyday language we tend to substitute the term weight for mass, although the two are not identical. Mass is the amount of matter in an object, whereas the weight of an object is how strongly that mass is pulled by gravity. The weight of an astronaut walking on the moon is approximately ⅙ the astronaut's weight on Earth, but his or her mass is the same. However, as long as we are earthbound, the weight of an object is a measure of its mass; in everyday language, therefore, we tend to use the terms interchangeably.

The Elements of Life

Of the 92 natural elements, about 20–25% are **essential elements** that an organism needs to live a healthy life and reproduce. The essential elements are similar among organisms, but there is some variation—for example, humans need 25 elements, but plants need only 17.

Just four elements—oxygen (O), carbon (C), hydrogen (H), and nitrogen (N)—make up 96% of living matter. Calcium (Ca), phosphorus (P), potassium (K), sulfur (S), and a few other elements account for most of the remaining 4% of an organism's mass. **Trace elements** are required by an organism in only minute quantities. Some trace elements, such as iron (Fe), are needed by all forms of life; others are required only by certain species. For example, in vertebrates (animals with backbones), the element iodine (I) is an essential ingredient of a hormone produced by the thyroid gland. A daily intake of only 0.15 milligram (mg) of iodine is adequate for normal activity of the human thyroid. An iodine deficiency in the diet causes the thyroid gland to grow to abnormal size, a condition called goiter. Where it is available, eating seafood or iodized salt reduces the incidence of goiter. All the elements needed by the human body are listed in **Table 2.1**.

Some naturally occurring elements are toxic to organisms. In humans, for instance, the element arsenic has been linked to numerous diseases and can be lethal. In some areas of the world, arsenic occurs naturally and can make its way into the groundwater. As a result of using water from drilled

Table 2.1 Elements in the Human Body

Element	Symbol	Percentage of Body Mass (including water)	
Oxygen	O	65.0%	
Carbon	C	18.5%	96.3%
Hydrogen	H	9.5%	
Nitrogen	N	3.3%	
Calcium	Ca	1.5%	
Phosphorus	P	1.0%	
Potassium	K	0.4%	
Sulfur	S	0.3%	3.7%
Sodium	Na	0.2%	
Chlorine	Cl	0.2%	
Magnesium	Mg	0.1%	

Trace elements (less than 0.01% of mass): Boron (B), chromium (Cr), cobalt (Co), copper (Cu), fluorine (F), iodine (I), iron (Fe), manganese (Mn), molybdenum (Mo), selenium (Se), silicon (Si), tin (Sn), vanadium (V), zinc (Zn)

INTERPRET THE DATA *Given what you know about the human body, what do you think could account for the high percentage of oxygen (65.0%)?*

▲ **Figure 2.3 Serpentine plant community.**
These plants are growing on serpentine soil, which contains elements that are usually toxic to plants. The insets show a close-up of serpentine rock and one of the plants, a Tiburon Mariposa lily.

wells in southern Asia, millions of people have been inadvertently exposed to arsenic-laden water. Efforts are under way to reduce arsenic levels in their water supply.

Case Study: Evolution of Tolerance to Toxic Elements

EVOLUTION Some species have become adapted to environments containing elements that are usually toxic; an example is serpentine plant communities. Serpentine is a jade-like mineral that contains elevated concentrations of elements such as chromium, nickel, and cobalt. Although most plants cannot survive in soil that forms from serpentine rock, a small number of plant species have adaptations that allow them to do so (Figure 2.3). Presumably, variants of ancestral, nonserpentine species arose that could survive in serpentine soils, and subsequent natural selection resulted in the distinctive array of species we see in these areas today. Researchers are studying whether serpentine-adapted plants could take up toxic heavy metals in contaminated areas, concentrating them for safer disposal.

CONCEPT CHECK 2.1

1. MAKE CONNECTIONS Explain how table salt has emergent properties. (See Concept 1.1.)

2. Is a trace element an essential element? Explain.

3. WHAT IF? In humans, iron is a trace element required for the proper functioning of hemoglobin, the molecule that carries oxygen in red blood cells. What might be the effects of an iron deficiency?

4. MAKE CONNECTIONS Explain how natural selection might have played a role in the evolution of species that are tolerant of serpentine soils. (Review Concept 1.2.)

For suggested answers, see Appendix A.

An element's properties depend on the structure of its atoms

Each element consists of a certain type of atom that is different from the atoms of any other element. An **atom** is the smallest unit of matter that still retains the properties of an element. Atoms are so small that it would take about a million of them to stretch across the period printed at the end of this sentence. We symbolize atoms with the same abbreviation used for the element that is made up of those atoms. For example, the symbol C stands for both the element carbon and a single carbon atom.

Subatomic Particles

Although the atom is the smallest unit having the properties of an element, these tiny bits of matter are composed of even smaller parts, called *subatomic particles*. Using high-energy collisions, physicists have produced more than a hundred types of particles from the atom, but only three kinds of particles are relevant here: **neutrons**, **protons**, and **electrons**. Protons and electrons are electrically charged. Each proton has one unit of positive charge, and each electron has one unit of negative charge. A neutron, as its name implies, is electrically neutral.

Protons and neutrons are packed together tightly in a dense core, or **atomic nucleus**, at the center of an atom; protons give the nucleus a positive charge. The rapidly moving electrons form a "cloud" of negative charge around the nucleus, and it is the attraction between opposite charges that keeps the electrons in the vicinity of the nucleus. Figure 2.4

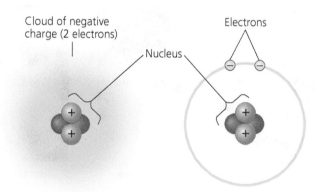

(a) This model represents the two electrons as a cloud of negative charge.

(b) In this more simplified model, the electrons are shown as two small yellow spheres on a circle around the nucleus.

▲ **Figure 2.4 Simplified models of a helium (He) atom.** The helium nucleus consists of 2 neutrons (brown) and 2 protons (pink). Two electrons (yellow) exist outside the nucleus. These models are not to scale; they greatly overestimate the size of the nucleus in relation to the electron cloud.

shows two commonly used models of the structure of the helium atom as an example.

The neutron and proton are almost identical in mass, each about 1.7×10^{-24} gram (g). Grams and other conventional units are not very useful for describing the mass of objects that are so minuscule. Thus, for atoms and subatomic particles (and for molecules, too), we use a unit of measurement called the **dalton**, in honor of John Dalton, the British scientist who helped develop atomic theory around 1800. (The dalton is the same as the *atomic mass unit*, or *amu*, a unit you may have encountered elsewhere.) Neutrons and protons have masses close to 1 dalton. Because the mass of an electron is only about 1/2,000 that of a neutron or proton, we can ignore electrons when computing the total mass of an atom.

Atomic Number and Atomic Mass

Atoms of the various elements differ in their number of subatomic particles. All atoms of a particular element have the same number of protons in their nuclei. This number of protons, which is unique to that element, is called the **atomic number** and is written as a subscript to the left of the symbol for the element. The abbreviation $_2$He, for example, tells us that an atom of the element helium has 2 protons in its nucleus. Unless otherwise indicated, an atom is neutral in electrical charge, which means that its protons must be balanced by an equal number of electrons. Therefore, the atomic number tells us the number of protons and also the number of electrons in an electrically neutral atom.

We can deduce the number of neutrons from a second quantity, the **mass number**, which is the sum of protons plus neutrons in the nucleus of an atom. The mass number is written as a superscript to the left of an element's symbol. For example, we can use this shorthand to write an atom of helium as $_2^4$He. Because the atomic number indicates how many protons there are, we can determine the number of neutrons by subtracting the atomic number from the mass number. Accordingly, the helium atom $_2^4$He has 2 neutrons. For sodium (Na):

Mass number = number of protons + neutrons
= 23 for sodium

$_{11}^{23}$Na

Atomic number = number of protons
= number of electrons in a neutral atom
= 11 for sodium

Number of neutrons = mass number − atomic number
= 23 − 11 = 12 for sodium

The simplest atom is hydrogen $_1^1$H, which has no neutrons; it consists of a single proton with a single electron.

Because the contribution of electrons to mass is negligible, almost all of an atom's mass is concentrated in its nucleus. And since neutrons and protons each have a mass very close to 1 dalton, the mass number is an approximation of the total mass of an atom, called its **atomic mass**. So we might say that the atomic mass of sodium ($_{11}^{23}$Na) is 23 daltons, although more precisely it is 22.9898 daltons.

Isotopes

All atoms of a given element have the same number of protons, but some atoms have more neutrons than other atoms of the same element and therefore have greater mass. These different atomic forms of the same element are called **isotopes** of the element. In nature, an element occurs as a mixture of its isotopes. As an explanatory example, let's consider the three naturally occurring isotopes of the element carbon, which has the atomic number 6. The most common isotope is carbon-12, $_6^{12}$C, which accounts for about 99% of the carbon in nature. The isotope $_6^{12}$C has 6 neutrons. Most of the remaining 1% of carbon consists of atoms of the isotope $_6^{13}$C, with 7 neutrons. A third, even rarer isotope, $_6^{14}$C, has 8 neutrons. Notice that all three isotopes of carbon have 6 protons; otherwise, they would not be carbon. Although the isotopes of an element have slightly different masses, they behave identically in chemical reactions. (The number usually given as the atomic mass of an element, such as 12.01 daltons for carbon, is actually an average of the atomic masses of all the element's naturally occurring isotopes, weighted according to the abundance of each.)

Both ^{12}C and ^{13}C are stable isotopes, meaning that their nuclei do not have a tendency to lose subatomic particles, a process called decay. The isotope ^{14}C, however, is unstable, or radioactive. A **radioactive isotope** is one in which the nucleus decays spontaneously, giving off particles and energy. When the radioactive decay leads to a change in the number of protons, it transforms the atom to an atom of a different element. For example, when an atom of carbon-14 (^{14}C) decays, it becomes an atom of nitrogen (^{14}N). Radioactive isotopes have many useful applications in biology.

Radioactive Tracers

Radioactive isotopes are often used as diagnostic tools in medicine. Cells can use radioactive atoms just as they would use nonradioactive isotopes of the same element. The radioactive isotopes are incorporated into biologically active molecules, which are then used as tracers to track atoms during metabolism, the chemical processes of an organism. For example, certain kidney disorders are diagnosed by injecting small doses of radioactively-labeled substances into the blood and then analyzing the tracer molecules excreted in the urine. Radioactive tracers are also used in combination with sophisticated imaging instruments, such as PET

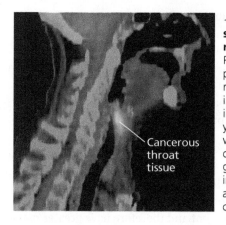

◀ **Figure 2.5 A PET scan, a medical use for radioactive isotopes.** PET, an acronym for positron-emission tomography, detects locations of intense chemical activity in the body. The bright yellow spot marks an area with an elevated level of radioactively labeled glucose, which in turn indicates high metabolic activity, a hallmark of cancerous tissue.

scanners that can monitor growth and metabolism of cancers in the body (**Figure 2.5**).

Although radioactive isotopes are very useful in biological research and medicine, radiation from decaying isotopes also poses a hazard to life by damaging cellular molecules. The severity of this damage depends on the type and amount of radiation an organism absorbs. One of the most serious environmental threats is radioactive fallout from nuclear accidents. The doses of most isotopes used in medical diagnosis, however, are relatively safe.

Radiometric Dating

EVOLUTION Researchers measure radioactive decay in fossils to date these relics of past life. Fossils provide a large body of evidence for evolution, documenting differences between organisms from the past and those living at present and giving us insight into species that have disappeared over time. While the layering of fossil beds establishes that deeper fossils are older than more shallow ones, the actual age (in years) of the fossils in each layer cannot be determined by position alone. This is where radioactive isotopes come in.

A "parent" isotope decays into its "daughter" isotope at a fixed rate, expressed as the **half-life** of the isotope—the time it takes for 50% of the parent isotope to decay. Each radioactive isotope has a characteristic half-life that is not affected by temperature, pressure, or any other environmental variable. Using a process called **radiometric dating**, scientists measure the ratio of different isotopes and calculate how many half-lives (in years) have passed since an organism was fossilized or a rock was formed. Half-life values range from very short for some isotopes, measured in seconds or days, to extremely long—uranium-238 has a half-life of 4.5 billion years! Each isotope can best "measure" a particular range of years: Uranium 238 was used to determine that moon rocks are approximately 4.5 billion years old, similar to the estimated age of Earth. In the Scientific Skills Exercise, you can work with data from an experiment that used carbon-14 to determine the age of an important fossil. (You'll learn more about radiometric dating of fossils in Chapter 25.)

The Energy Levels of Electrons

The simplified models of the atom in Figure 2.4 greatly exaggerate the size of the nucleus relative to that of the whole atom. If an atom of helium were the size of a typical football stadium, the nucleus would be the size of a pencil eraser in the center of the field. Moreover, the electrons would be like two tiny gnats buzzing around the stadium. Atoms are mostly empty space. When two atoms approach each other during a chemical reaction, their nuclei do not come close enough to interact. Of the three subatomic particles we have discussed, only electrons are directly involved in chemical reactions.

An atom's electrons vary in the amount of energy they possess. **Energy** is defined as the capacity to cause change—for instance, by doing work. **Potential energy** is the energy that matter possesses because of its location or structure. For example, water in a reservoir on a hill has potential energy because of its altitude. When the gates of the reservoir's dam are opened and the water runs downhill, the energy can be used to do work, such as moving the blades of turbines to generate electricity. Because energy has been expended, the water has less energy at the bottom of the hill than it did in the reservoir. Matter has a natural tendency to move toward the lowest possible state of potential energy; in our example, the water runs downhill. To restore the potential energy of a reservoir, work must be done to elevate the water against gravity.

The electrons of an atom have potential energy due to their distance from the nucleus (**Figure 2.6**). The negatively

(a) A ball bouncing down a flight of stairs provides an analogy for energy levels of electrons, because the ball can come to rest only on each step, not between steps.

Third shell (highest energy level in this model)

Second shell (next highest energy level)

First shell (lowest energy level)

Energy absorbed

Energy lost

Atomic nucleus

(b) An electron can move from one shell to another only if the energy it gains or loses is exactly equal to the difference in energy between the energy levels of the two shells. Arrows in this model indicate some of the stepwise changes in potential energy that are possible.

▲ **Figure 2.6 Energy levels of an atom's electrons.** Electrons exist only at fixed levels of potential energy called electron shells.

Calibrating a Standard Radioactive Isotope Decay Curve and Interpreting Data

When Did Neanderthals Become Extinct? Neanderthals (*Homo neanderthalensis*) were living in Europe by 350,000 years ago, perhaps coexisting with early *Homo sapiens* in parts of Eurasia for hundreds or thousands of years. Researchers sought to more accurately determine the extent of their overlap by pinning down when Neanderthals became extinct. They used carbon-14 dating to determine the age of a Neanderthal fossil from the most recent (uppermost) archeological layer containing Neanderthal bones. In this exercise you will calibrate a standard carbon-14 decay curve and use it to determine the age of this Neanderthal fossil. The age will help you approximate the last time the two species may have coexisted at the site where this fossil was collected.

How the Experiment Was Done Carbon-14 (^{14}C) is a radioactive isotope of carbon that decays to ^{14}N at a constant rate. ^{14}C is present in the atmosphere in small amounts at a constant ratio with both ^{13}C and ^{12}C, two other isotopes of carbon. When carbon is taken up from the atmosphere by a plant during photosynthesis, ^{12}C, ^{13}C, and ^{14}C isotopes are incorporated into the plant in the same proportions in which they were present in the atmosphere. These proportions remain the same in the tissues of an animal that eats the plant. While an organism is alive, the ^{14}C in its body constantly decays to ^{14}N but is constantly replaced by new carbon from the environment. Once an organism dies, it stops taking in new ^{14}C but the ^{14}C in its tissues continues to decay, while the ^{12}C in its tissues remains the same because it is not radioactive and does not decay. Thus, scientists can calculate how long the pool of original ^{14}C has been decaying in a fossil by measuring the ratio of ^{14}C to ^{12}C and comparing it to the ratio of ^{14}C to ^{12}C present originally in the atmosphere. The fraction of ^{14}C in a fossil compared to the original fraction of ^{14}C can be converted to years because we know that the half-life of ^{14}C is 5,730 years—in other words, half of the ^{14}C in a fossil decays every 5,730 years.

Data from the Experiment The researchers found that the Neanderthal fossil had approximately 0.0078 (or, in scientific notation, 7.8×10^{-3}) as much ^{14}C as the atmosphere. The questions will guide you through translating this fraction into the age of the fossil.

Interpret the Data

1. A standard graph of radioactive isotope decay is shown at the top of the right column. The graph line shows the fraction of the radioactive isotope over time (before present) in units of half-lives. Recall that a half-life is the amount of time it takes for half of the radioactive isotope to decay. Labeling each data point with the corresponding fractions will help orient you to this graph. Draw an arrow to the data point for half-life = 1 and write the fraction of ^{14}C that will remain after one half-life. Calculate the fraction of ^{14}C remaining at each half-life and write the fractions on the graph near arrows pointing to the data points. Convert each fraction to a decimal number and round off to a maximum of three significant digits (zeros at the

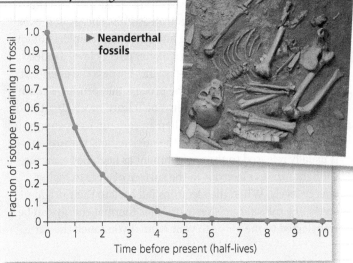

beginning of the number do not count as significant digits). Also write each decimal number in scientific notation.

2. Recall that ^{14}C has a half-life of 5,730 years. To calibrate the *x*-axis for ^{14}C decay, write the time before present in years below each half-life.

3. The researchers found that the Neanderthal fossil had approximately 0.0078 as much ^{14}C as found originally in the atmosphere. (a) Using the numbers on your graph, determine how many half-lives have passed since the Neanderthal died. (b) Using your ^{14}C calibration on the *x*-axis, what is the approximate age of the Neanderthal fossil in years (round off to the nearest thousand)? (c) Approximately when did Neanderthals become extinct according to this study? (d) The researchers cite evidence that modern humans (*H. sapiens*) became established in the same region as the last Neanderthals approximately 39,000–42,000 years ago. What does this suggest about the overlap of Neanderthals and modern humans?

4. Carbon-14 dating works for fossils up to about 75,000 years old; fossils older than that contain too little ^{14}C to be detected. Most dinosaurs went extinct 65.5 million years ago. (a) Can ^{14}C be used to date dinosaur bones? Explain. (b) Radioactive uranium-235 has a half-life of 704 million years. If it was incorporated into dinosaur bones, could it be used to date the dinosaur fossils? Explain.

(MB) A version of this Scientific Skills Exercise can be assigned in MasteringBiology.

Data from R. Pinhasi et al., Revised age of late Neanderthal occupation and the end of the Middle Paleolithic in the northern Caucasus, *Proceedings of the National Academy of Sciences USA* 147:8611–8616 (2011). doi 10.1073/pnas.1018938108

charged electrons are attracted to the positively charged nucleus. It takes work to move a given electron farther away from the nucleus, so the more distant an electron is from the nucleus, the greater its potential energy. Unlike the continuous flow of water downhill, changes in the potential energy of electrons can occur only in steps of fixed amounts. An electron having a certain amount of energy is something like a ball on a staircase **(Figure 2.6a)**. The ball can have different amounts of potential energy, depending on which step it is on, but it cannot spend much time between the steps.

Similarly, an electron's potential energy is determined by its energy level. An electron can exist only at certain energy levels, not between them.

An electron's energy level is correlated with its average distance from the nucleus. Electrons are found in different **electron shells**, each with a characteristic average distance and energy level. In diagrams, shells can be represented by concentric circles **(Figure 2.6b)**. The first shell is closest to the nucleus, and electrons in this shell have the lowest potential energy. Electrons in the second shell have more energy, and electrons in the third shell even more energy. An electron can move from one shell to another, but only by absorbing or losing an amount of energy equal to the difference in potential energy between its position in the old shell and that in the new shell. When an electron absorbs energy, it moves to a shell farther out from the nucleus. For example, light energy can excite an electron to a higher energy level. (Indeed, this is the first step taken when plants harness the energy of sunlight for photosynthesis, the process that produces food from carbon dioxide and water. You'll learn more about photosynthesis in Chapter 10.) When an electron loses energy, it "falls back" to a shell closer to the nucleus, and the lost energy is usually released to the environment as heat. For example, sunlight excites electrons in the surface of a car to higher energy levels. When the electrons fall back to their original levels, the car's surface heats up. This thermal energy can be transferred to the air or to your hand if you touch the car.

Electron Distribution and Chemical Properties

The chemical behavior of an atom is determined by the distribution of electrons in the atom's electron shells. Beginning with hydrogen, the simplest atom, we can imagine building the atoms of the other elements by adding 1 proton and 1 electron at a time (along with an appropriate number of neutrons). **Figure 2.7**, an abbreviated version of what is called the *periodic table of the elements*, shows this distribution of electrons for the first 18 elements, from hydrogen ($_1$H) to argon ($_{18}$Ar). The elements are arranged in three rows, or *periods*, corresponding to the number of electron shells in their atoms. The left-to-right sequence of elements in each row corresponds to the sequential addition of electrons and protons. (See Appendix B for the complete periodic table.)

Hydrogen's 1 electron and helium's 2 electrons are located in the first shell. Electrons, like all matter, tend to exist in the lowest available state of potential energy. In an atom, this state is in the first shell. However, the first shell can hold no more than 2 electrons; thus, hydrogen and helium are the only elements in the first row of the table. In an atom with more than 2 electrons, the additional electrons must occupy higher shells because the first shell is full. The next element, lithium, has 3 electrons. Two of these electrons fill the first shell, while the third electron occupies the second shell. The second shell holds a maximum of 8 electrons. Neon, at the

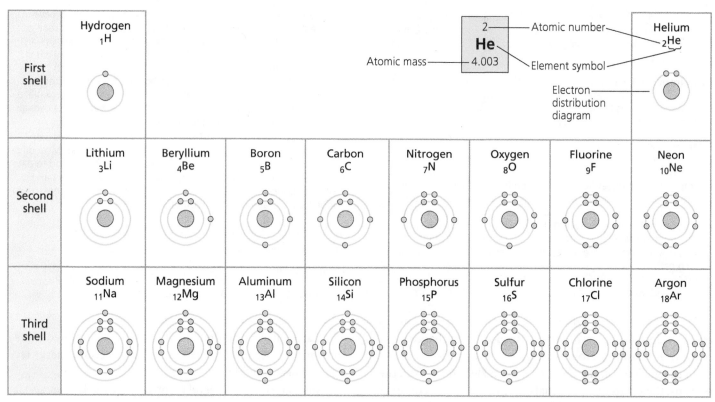

▲ **Figure 2.7 Electron distribution diagrams for the first 18 elements in the periodic table.** In a standard periodic table (see Appendix B), information for each element is presented as shown for helium in the inset. In the diagrams in this table, electrons are represented as yellow dots and electron shells as concentric circles. These diagrams are a convenient way to picture the distribution of an atom's electrons among its electron shells, but these simplified models do not accurately represent the shape of the atom or the location of its electrons. The elements are arranged in rows, each representing the filling of an electron shell. As electrons are added, they occupy the lowest available shell.

[?] *What is the atomic number of magnesium? How many protons and electrons does it have? How many electron shells? How many valence electrons?*

end of the second row, has 8 electrons in the second shell, giving it a total of 10 electrons.

The chemical behavior of an atom depends mostly on the number of electrons in its *outermost* shell. We call those outer electrons **valence electrons** and the outermost electron shell the **valence shell**. In the case of lithium, there is only 1 valence electron, and the second shell is the valence shell. Atoms with the same number of electrons in their valence shells exhibit similar chemical behavior. For example, fluorine (F) and chlorine (Cl) both have 7 valence electrons, and both form compounds when combined with the element sodium (Na): Sodium fluoride (NaF) is commonly added to toothpaste to prevent tooth decay, and, as described earlier, NaCl is table salt (see Figure 2.2). An atom with a completed valence shell is unreactive; that is, it will not interact readily with other atoms. At the far right of the periodic table are helium, neon, and argon, the only three elements shown in Figure 2.7 that have full valence shells. These elements are said to be *inert*, meaning chemically unreactive. All the other atoms in Figure 2.7 are chemically reactive because they have incomplete valence shells.

Electron Orbitals

In the early 1900s, the electron shells of an atom were visualized as concentric paths of electrons orbiting the nucleus, somewhat like planets orbiting the sun. It is still convenient to use two-dimensional concentric-circle diagrams, as in Figure 2.7, to symbolize three-dimensional electron shells. However, you need to remember that each concentric circle represents only the *average* distance between an electron in that shell and the nucleus. Accordingly, the concentric-circle diagrams do not give a real picture of an atom. In reality, we can never know the exact location of an electron. What we can do instead is describe the space in which an electron spends most of its time. The three-dimensional space where an electron is found 90% of the time is called an **orbital**.

Each electron shell contains electrons at a particular energy level, distributed among a specific number of orbitals of distinctive shapes and orientations. **Figure 2.8** shows the orbitals of neon as an example, with its electron distribution diagram for reference. You can think of an orbital as a component of an electron shell. The first electron shell has only one spherical *s* orbital (called 1*s*), but the second shell has four orbitals: one large spherical *s* orbital (called 2*s*) and three dumbbell-shaped *p* orbitals (called 2*p* orbitals). (The third shell and other higher electron shells also have *s* and *p* orbitals, as well as orbitals of more complex shapes.)

No more than 2 electrons can occupy a single orbital. The first electron shell can therefore accommodate up to 2 electrons in its *s* orbital. The lone electron of a hydrogen atom occupies the 1*s* orbital, as do the 2 electrons of a helium atom. The four orbitals of the second electron shell can hold

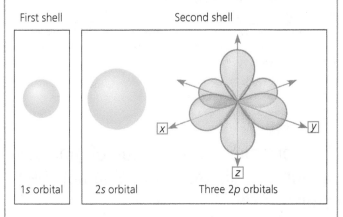

(a) Electron distribution diagram. An electron distribution diagram is shown here for a neon atom, which has a total of 10 electrons. Each concentric circle represents an electron shell, which can be subdivided into electron orbitals.

First shell   Second shell

1*s* orbital   2*s* orbital   Three 2*p* orbitals

(b) Separate electron orbitals. The three-dimensional shapes represent electron orbitals—the volumes of space where the electrons of an atom are most likely to be found. Each orbital holds a maximum of 2 electrons. The first electron shell, on the left, has one spherical (*s*) orbital, designated 1*s*. The second shell, on the right, has one larger *s* orbital (designated 2*s* for the second shell) plus three dumbbell-shaped orbitals called *p* orbitals (2*p* for the second shell). The three 2*p* orbitals lie at right angles to one another along imaginary *x*-, *y*-, and *z*-axes of the atom. Each 2*p* orbital is outlined here in a different color.

1*s*, 2*s*, and 2*p* orbitals

(c) Superimposed electron orbitals. To reveal the complete picture of the electron orbitals of neon, we superimpose the 1*s* orbital of the first shell and the 2*s* and three 2*p* orbitals of the second shell.

▲ **Figure 2.8 Electron orbitals.**

up to 8 electrons, 2 in each orbital. Electrons in each of the four orbitals have nearly the same energy, but they move in different volumes of space.

The reactivity of an atom arises from the presence of unpaired electrons in one or more orbitals of its valence shell. As you will see in the next section, atoms interact in a way that completes their valence shells. When they do so, it is the *unpaired* electrons that are involved.

1. A lithium atom has 3 protons and 4 neutrons. What is its mass number?

2. A nitrogen atom has 7 protons, and the most common isotope of nitrogen has 7 neutrons. A radioactive isotope of nitrogen has 8 neutrons. Write the atomic number and mass number of this radioactive nitrogen as a chemical symbol with a subscript and superscript.

3. How many electrons does fluorine have? How many electron shells? Name the orbitals that are occupied. How many electrons are needed to fill the valence shell?

4. **WHAT IF?** In Figure 2.7, if two or more elements are in the same row, what do they have in common? If two or more elements are in the same column, what do they have in common?

For suggested answers, see Appendix A.

CONCEPT 2.3

The formation and function of molecules depend on chemical bonding between atoms

Now that we have looked at the structure of atoms, we can move up the hierarchy of organization and see how atoms combine to form molecules and ionic compounds. Atoms with incomplete valence shells can interact with certain other atoms in such a way that each partner completes its valence shell: The atoms either share or transfer valence electrons. These interactions usually result in atoms staying close together, held by attractions called **chemical bonds**. The strongest kinds of chemical bonds are covalent bonds and ionic bonds (when in dry ionic compounds).

Covalent Bonds

A **covalent bond** is the sharing of a pair of valence electrons by two atoms. For example, let's consider what happens when two hydrogen atoms approach each other. Recall that hydrogen has 1 valence electron in the first shell, but the shell's capacity is 2 electrons. When the two hydrogen atoms come close enough for their 1s orbitals to overlap, they can share their electrons (**Figure 2.9**). Each hydrogen atom is now associated with 2 electrons in what amounts to a completed valence shell. Two or more atoms held together by covalent bonds constitute a **molecule**, in this case a hydrogen molecule.

Figure 2.10a shows several ways of representing a hydrogen molecule. Its *molecular formula*, H_2, simply indicates that the molecule consists of two atoms of hydrogen. Electron sharing can be depicted by an electron distribution diagram or by a *Lewis dot structure*, in which element symbols are surrounded by dots that represent the valence electrons (H:H). We can also use a *structural formula*, H—H, where

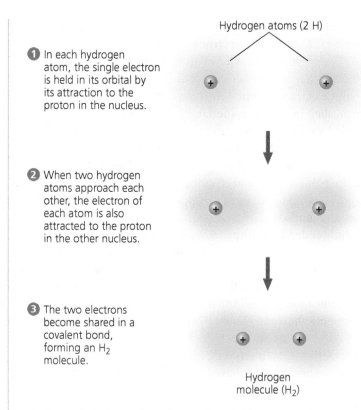

❶ In each hydrogen atom, the single electron is held in its orbital by its attraction to the proton in the nucleus.

❷ When two hydrogen atoms approach each other, the electron of each atom is also attracted to the proton in the other nucleus.

❸ The two electrons become shared in a covalent bond, forming an H_2 molecule.

Hydrogen atoms (2 H)

Hydrogen molecule (H_2)

▲ **Figure 2.9 Formation of a covalent bond.**

the line represents a **single bond**, a pair of shared electrons. A space-filling model comes closest to representing the actual shape of the molecule. You may also be familiar with ball-and-stick models, which are shown in Figure 2.15.

Oxygen has 6 electrons in its second electron shell and therefore needs 2 more electrons to complete its valence shell. Two oxygen atoms form a molecule by sharing *two* pairs of valence electrons (**Figure 2.10b**). The atoms are thus joined by what is called a **double bond** (O=O).

Each atom that can share valence electrons has a bonding capacity corresponding to the number of covalent bonds the atom can form. When the bonds form, they give the atom a full complement of electrons in the valence shell. The bonding capacity of oxygen, for example, is 2. This bonding capacity is called the atom's **valence** and usually equals the number of unpaired electrons required to complete the atom's outermost (valence) shell. See if you can determine the valences of hydrogen, oxygen, nitrogen, and carbon by studying the electron distribution diagrams in Figure 2.7. You can see that the valence of hydrogen is 1; oxygen, 2; nitrogen, 3; and carbon, 4. However, the situation is more complicated for elements in the third row of the periodic table. Phosphorus, for example, can have a valence of 3, as we would predict from the presence of 3 unpaired electrons in its valence shell. In some molecules that are biologically important, however, phosphorus can form three single bonds and one double bond. Therefore, it can also have a valence of 5.

Name and Molecular Formula	Electron Distribution Diagram	Lewis Dot Structure and Structural Formula	Space-Filling Model
(a) Hydrogen (H_2). Two hydrogen atoms share one pair of electrons, forming a single bond.		H : H H — H	
(b) Oxygen (O_2). Two oxygen atoms share two pairs of electrons, forming a double bond.		$\ddot{O}::\ddot{O}$ O = O	
(c) Water (H_2O). Two hydrogen atoms and one oxygen atom are joined by single bonds, forming a molecule of water.		$:\ddot{O}:$ H H O — H | H	
(d) Methane (CH_4). Four hydrogen atoms can satisfy the valence of one carbon atom, forming methane.		H H : $\ddot{C}$: H H H | H — C — H | H	

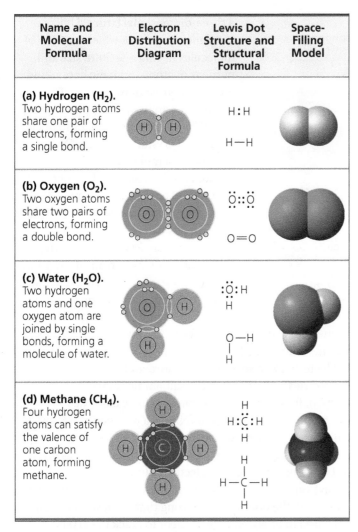

▲ **Figure 2.10 Covalent bonding in four molecules.** The number of electrons required to complete an atom's valence shell generally determines how many covalent bonds that atom will form. This figure shows several ways of indicating covalent bonds.

The molecules H_2 and O_2 are pure elements rather than compounds because a compound is a combination of two or more *different* elements. Water, with the molecular formula H_2O, is a compound. Two atoms of hydrogen are needed to satisfy the valence of one oxygen atom. **Figure 2.10c** shows the structure of a water molecule. (Water is so important to life that Chapter 3 is devoted entirely to its structure and behavior.)

Methane, the main component of natural gas, is a compound with the molecular formula CH_4. It takes four hydrogen atoms, each with a valence of 1, to complement one atom of carbon, with its valence of 4 **(Figure 2.10d)**. (We will look at many other compounds of carbon in Chapter 4.)

Atoms in a molecule attract shared bonding electrons to varying degrees, depending on the element. The attraction of a particular atom for the electrons of a covalent bond is called its **electronegativity**. The more electronegative an atom is, the more strongly it pulls shared electrons toward

Because oxygen (O) is more electronegative than hydrogen (H), shared electrons are pulled more toward oxygen.

This results in a partial negative charge on the oxygen and a partial positive charge on the hydrogens.

▲ **Figure 2.11 Polar covalent bonds in a water molecule.**

itself. In a covalent bond between two atoms of the same element, the electrons are shared equally because the two atoms have the same electronegativity—the tug-of-war is at a standoff. Such a bond is called a **nonpolar covalent bond**. For example, the single bond of H_2 is nonpolar, as is the double bond of O_2. However, when an atom is bonded to a more electronegative atom, the electrons of the bond are not shared equally. This type of bond is called a **polar covalent bond**. Such bonds vary in their polarity, depending on the relative electronegativity of the two atoms. For example, the bonds between the oxygen and hydrogen atoms of a water molecule are quite polar **(Figure 2.11)**.

Oxygen is one of the most electronegative elements, attracting shared electrons much more strongly than hydrogen does. In a covalent bond between oxygen and hydrogen, the electrons spend more time near the oxygen nucleus than they do near the hydrogen nucleus. Because electrons have a negative charge and are pulled toward oxygen in a water molecule, the oxygen atom has a partial negative charge (indicated by the Greek letter δ with a minus sign, δ−, or "delta minus"), and each hydrogen atom has a partial positive charge (δ+, or "delta plus"). In contrast, the individual bonds of methane (CH_4) are much less polar because the electronegativities of carbon and hydrogen are similar.

Ionic Bonds

In some cases, two atoms are so unequal in their attraction for valence electrons that the more electronegative atom strips an electron completely away from its partner. The two resulting oppositely charged atoms (or molecules) are called **ions**. A positively charged ion is called a **cation**, while a negatively charged ion is called an **anion**. Because of their opposite charges, cations and anions attract each other; this attraction is called an ionic bond. Note that the transfer of an electron is not, by itself, the formation of a bond; rather, it allows a bond to form because it results in two ions of opposite charge. Any two ions of opposite charge can form an **ionic bond**. The ions do not need to have acquired their charge by an electron transfer with each other.

❶ The lone valence electron of a sodium atom is transferred to join the 7 valence electrons of a chlorine atom.

❷ Each resulting ion has a completed valence shell. An ionic bond can form between the oppositely charged ions.

Na Sodium atom

Cl Chlorine atom

Na⁺ Sodium ion (a cation)

Cl⁻ Chloride ion (an anion)

Sodium chloride (NaCl)

▲ **Figure 2.12 Electron transfer and ionic bonding.** The attraction between oppositely charged atoms, or ions, is an ionic bond. An ionic bond can form between any two oppositely charged ions, even if they have not been formed by transfer of an electron from one to the other.

This is what happens when an atom of sodium ($_{11}$Na) encounters an atom of chlorine ($_{17}$Cl) **(Figure 2.12)**. A sodium atom has a total of 11 electrons, with its single valence electron in the third electron shell. A chlorine atom has a total of 17 electrons, with 7 electrons in its valence shell. When these two atoms meet, the lone valence electron of sodium is transferred to the chlorine atom, and both atoms end up with their valence shells complete. (Because sodium no longer has an electron in the third shell, the second shell is now the valence shell.) The electron transfer between the two atoms moves one unit of negative charge from sodium to chlorine. Sodium, now with 11 protons but only 10 electrons, has a net electrical charge of 1+; the sodium atom has become a cation. Conversely, the chlorine atom, having gained an extra electron, now has 17 protons and 18 electrons, giving it a net electrical charge of 1−; it has become a chloride ion—an anion.

Compounds formed by ionic bonds are called **ionic compounds**, or **salts**. We know the ionic compound sodium chloride (NaCl) as table salt **(Figure 2.13)**. Salts are often found in nature as crystals of various sizes and shapes. Each salt crystal is an aggregate of vast numbers of cations and anions bonded by their electrical attraction and arranged in

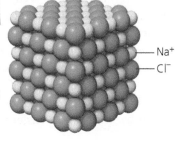

— Na⁺
— Cl⁻

▲ **Figure 2.13 A sodium chloride (NaCl) crystal.** The sodium ions (Na⁺) and chloride ions (Cl⁻) are held together by ionic bonds. The formula NaCl tells us that the ratio of Na⁺ to Cl⁻ is 1:1.

a three-dimensional lattice. Unlike a covalent compound, which consists of molecules having a definite size and number of atoms, an ionic compound does not consist of molecules. The formula for an ionic compound, such as NaCl, indicates only the ratio of elements in a crystal of the salt. "NaCl" by itself is not a molecule.

Not all salts have equal numbers of cations and anions. For example, the ionic compound magnesium chloride (MgCl$_2$) has two chloride ions for each magnesium ion. Magnesium ($_{12}$Mg) must lose 2 outer electrons if the atom is to have a complete valence shell, so it has a tendency to become a cation with a net charge of 2+ (Mg^{2+}). One magnesium cation can therefore form ionic bonds with two chloride anions (Cl⁻).

The term *ion* also applies to entire molecules that are electrically charged. In the salt ammonium chloride (NH$_4$Cl), for instance, the anion is a single chloride ion (Cl⁻), but the cation is ammonium (NH$_4^+$), a nitrogen atom covalently bonded to four hydrogen atoms. The whole ammonium ion has an electrical charge of 1+ because it has given up 1 electron and thus is 1 electron short.

Environment affects the strength of ionic bonds. In a dry salt crystal, the bonds are so strong that it takes a hammer and chisel to break enough of them to crack the crystal in two. If the same salt crystal is dissolved in water, however, the ionic bonds are much weaker because each ion is partially shielded by its interactions with water molecules. Most drugs are manufactured as salts because they are quite stable when dry but can dissociate (come apart) easily in water. (In the next chapter, you will learn how water dissolves salts.)

Weak Chemical Bonds

In organisms, most of the strongest chemical bonds are covalent bonds, which link atoms to form a cell's molecules. But weaker bonding within and between molecules is also indispensable, contributing greatly to the emergent properties of life. Many large biological molecules are held in their functional form by weak bonds. In addition, when two molecules in the cell make contact, they may adhere temporarily by weak bonds. The reversibility of weak bonding can be an advantage: Two molecules can come together, respond to one another in some way, and then separate.

Several types of weak chemical bonds are important in organisms. One is the ionic bond as it exists between ions dissociated in water, which we just discussed. Hydrogen bonds and van der Waals interactions are also crucial to life.

Water (H_2O)

δ^- δ^+

This hydrogen bond results from the attraction between the partial positive charge on the hydrogen atom of water and the partial negative charge on the nitrogen atom of ammonia.

δ^+

δ^-

Ammonia (NH_3)

δ^+ δ^+

δ^+

▲ **Figure 2.14**
A hydrogen bond.

DRAW IT *Draw five water molecules. (Use structural formulas; show partial charges.) Show how they make hydrogen bonds with each other.*

Hydrogen Bonds

Among weak chemical bonds, hydrogen bonds are so central to the chemistry of life that they deserve special attention. When a hydrogen atom is covalently bonded to an electronegative atom, the hydrogen atom has a partial positive charge that allows it to be attracted to a different electronegative atom nearby. This attraction between a hydrogen and an electronegative atom is called a **hydrogen bond**. In living cells, the electronegative partners are usually oxygen or nitrogen atoms. Refer to **Figure 2.14** to examine the simple case of hydrogen bonding between water (H_2O) and ammonia (NH_3).

Van der Waals Interactions

Even a molecule with nonpolar covalent bonds may have positively and negatively charged regions. Electrons are not always evenly distributed; at any instant, they may accumulate by chance in one part of a molecule or another. The results are ever-changing regions of positive and negative charge that enable all atoms and molecules to stick to one another. These **van der Waals interactions** are individually weak and occur only when atoms and molecules are very close together. When many such interactions occur simultaneously, however, they can be powerful: Van der Waals interactions allow a gecko lizard (below) to walk straight up a wall! The anatomy of the gecko's foot—including many minuscule hair-like projections from the toes and strong tendons underlying the skin—strikes a balance between maximum surface contact with the wall and necessary stiffness of the foot. The van der Waals interactions between the foot molecules and the molecules of the wall's surface are so numerous that despite their individual weakness, together they can support the

gecko's body weight. This discovery has inspired development of an artificial adhesive called Geckskin™: A patch the size of an index card can hold a 700 pound weight to a wall!

Van der Waals interactions, hydrogen bonds, ionic bonds in water, and other weak bonds may form not only between molecules but also between parts of a large molecule, such as a protein. The cumulative effect of weak bonds is to reinforce the three-dimensional shape of the molecule. (You will learn more about the very important biological roles of weak bonds in Chapter 5.)

Molecular Shape and Function

A molecule has a characteristic size and precise shape, which are crucial to its function in the living cell. A molecule consisting of two atoms, such as H_2 or O_2, is always linear, but most molecules with more than two atoms have more complicated shapes. These shapes are determined by the positions of the atoms' orbitals (**Figure 2.15**). When an

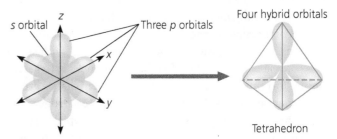

(a) Hybridization of orbitals. The single *s* and three *p* orbitals of a valence shell involved in covalent bonding combine to form four teardrop-shaped hybrid orbitals. These orbitals extend to the four corners of an imaginary tetrahedron (outlined in pink).

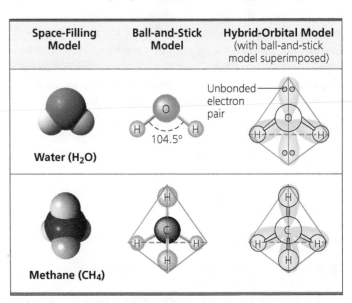

Space-Filling Model	Ball-and-Stick Model	Hybrid-Orbital Model (with ball-and-stick model superimposed)
Water (H_2O)	104.5°	Unbonded electron pair
Methane (CH_4)		

(b) Molecular-shape models. Three models representing molecular shape are shown for water and methane. The positions of the hybrid orbitals determine the shapes of the molecules.

▲ **Figure 2.15 Molecular shapes due to hybrid orbitals.**

atom forms covalent bonds, the orbitals in its valence shell undergo rearrangement. For atoms with valence electrons in both *s* and *p* orbitals (review Figure 2.8), the single *s* and three *p* orbitals form four new hybrid orbitals shaped like identical teardrops extending from the region of the atomic nucleus (Figure 2.15a). If we connect the larger ends of the teardrops with lines, we have the outline of a geometric shape called a tetrahedron, a pyramid with a triangular base.

For water molecules (H_2O), two of the hybrid orbitals in the oxygen's valence shell are shared with hydrogens (Figure 2.15b). The result is a molecule shaped roughly like a V, with its two covalent bonds at an angle of 104.5°.

The methane molecule (CH_4) has the shape of a completed tetrahedron because all four hybrid orbitals of the carbon atom are shared with hydrogen atoms (see Figure 2.15b). The carbon nucleus is at the center, with its four covalent bonds radiating to hydrogen nuclei at the corners of the tetrahedron. Larger molecules containing multiple carbon atoms, including many of the molecules that make up living matter, have more complex overall shapes. However, the tetrahedral shape of a carbon atom bonded to four other atoms is often a repeating motif within such molecules.

Molecular shape is crucial: It determines how biological molecules recognize and respond to one another with specificity. Biological molecules often bind temporarily to each other by forming weak bonds, but only if their shapes are complementary. Consider the effects of opiates, drugs such as morphine and heroin derived from opium. Opiates relieve pain and alter mood by weakly binding to specific receptor molecules on the surfaces of brain cells. Why would brain cells carry receptors for opiates, compounds that are not made by the body? In 1975, the discovery of endorphins answered this question. Endorphins are signaling molecules made by the pituitary gland that bind to the receptors, relieving pain and producing euphoria durisng times of stress, such as intense exercise. Opiates have shapes similar to endorphins and mimic them by binding to endorphin receptors in the brain. That is why opiates and endorphins have similar effects (Figure 2.16). The role of molecular shape in brain chemistry illustrates how biological organization leads to a match between structure and function, one of biology's unifying themes.

CONCEPT CHECK 2.3

1. Why does the structure H—C≡C—H fail to make sense chemically?

2. What holds the atoms together in a crystal of magnesium chloride ($MgCl_2$)?

3. **WHAT IF?** If you were a pharmaceutical researcher, why would you want to learn the three-dimensional shapes of naturally occurring signaling molecules?

For suggested answers, see Appendix A.

Key

■ Carbon   ■ Nitrogen
□ Hydrogen   ■ Sulfur
   ■ Oxygen

Natural endorphin

Morphine

(a) **Structures of endorphin and morphine.** The boxed portion of the endorphin molecule (left) binds to receptor molecules on target cells in the brain. The boxed portion of the morphine molecule (right) is a close match.

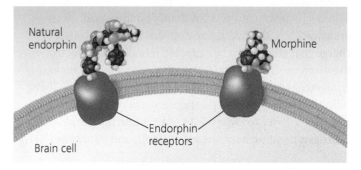

Natural endorphin

Morphine

Endorphin receptors

Brain cell

(b) **Binding to endorphin receptors.** Both endorphin and morphine can bind to endorphin receptors on the surface of a brain cell.

▲ Figure 2.16 **A molecular mimic.** Morphine affects pain perception and emotional state by mimicking the brain's natural endorphins.

CONCEPT 2.4

Chemical reactions make and break chemical bonds

The making and breaking of chemical bonds, leading to changes in the composition of matter, are called **chemical reactions**. An example is the reaction between hydrogen and oxygen molecules that forms water:

$$2 H_2 + O_2 \longrightarrow 2 H_2O$$

Reactants   **Reaction**   **Products**

This reaction breaks the covalent bonds of H_2 and O_2 and forms the new bonds of H_2O. When we write a chemical reaction, we use an arrow to indicate the conversion of the starting materials, called the **reactants**, to the **products**. The coefficients indicate the number of molecules involved; for example, the coefficient 2 in front of the H_2 means that the reaction starts with two molecules of hydrogen. Notice that all atoms of the reactants must be accounted for in the products. Matter is conserved in a chemical reaction: Reactions cannot create or destroy atoms but can only rearrange (redistribute) the electrons among them.

Photosynthesis, which takes place within the cells of green plant tissues, is an important biological example of how chemical reactions rearrange matter. Humans and other animals ultimately depend on photosynthesis for food and oxygen, and this process is at the foundation of almost all ecosystems. The following chemical shorthand summarizes the process of photosynthesis:

$$6\ CO_2 + 6\ H_2O \rightarrow C_6H_{12}O_6 + 6\ O_2$$

The raw materials of photosynthesis are carbon dioxide (CO_2), which is taken from the air, and water (H_2O), which is absorbed from the soil. Within the plant cells, sunlight powers the conversion of these ingredients to a sugar called glucose ($C_6H_{12}O_6$) and oxygen molecules (O_2), a by-product that the plant releases into the surroundings (**Figure 2.17**). Although photosynthesis is actually a sequence of many chemical reactions, we still end up with the same number and types of atoms that we had when we started. Matter has simply been rearranged, with an input of energy provided by sunlight.

All chemical reactions are reversible, with the products of the forward reaction becoming the reactants for the reverse reaction. For example, hydrogen and nitrogen molecules can combine to form ammonia, but ammonia can also decompose to regenerate hydrogen and nitrogen:

$$3\ H_2 + N_2 \rightleftharpoons 2\ NH_3$$

The two opposite-headed arrows indicate that the reaction is reversible.

One of the factors affecting the rate of a reaction is the concentration of reactants. The greater the concentration of reactant molecules, the more frequently they collide with one another and have an opportunity to react and form products. The same holds true for products. As products accumulate, collisions resulting in the reverse reaction become more frequent. Eventually, the forward and reverse reactions occur at the same rate, and the relative concentrations of products and reactants stop changing. The point at which the reactions offset one another exactly is called **chemical equilibrium**. This is a dynamic equilibrium; reactions are still going on, but with no net effect on the concentrations of reactants and products. Equilibrium does *not* mean that the

▲ **Figure 2.17 Photosynthesis: a solar-powered rearrangement of matter.** *Elodea*, a freshwater plant, produces sugar by rearranging the atoms of carbon dioxide and water in the chemical process known as photosynthesis, which is powered by sunlight. Much of the sugar is then converted to other food molecules. Oxygen gas (O_2) is a by-product of photosynthesis; notice the bubbles of O_2-containing gas escaping from the leaves submerged in water.

? *Explain how this photo relates to the reactants and products in the equation for photosynthesis given in the text. (You will learn more about photosynthesis in Chapter 10.)*

reactants and products are equal in concentration, but only that their concentrations have stabilized at a particular ratio. The reaction involving ammonia reaches equilibrium when ammonia decomposes as rapidly as it forms. In some chemical reactions, the equilibrium point may lie so far to the right that these reactions go essentially to completion; that is, virtually all the reactants are converted to products.

We will return to the subject of chemical reactions after more detailed study of the various types of molecules that are important to life. In the next chapter, we focus on water, the substance in which all the chemical processes of organisms occur.

CONCEPT CHECK 2.4

1. **MAKE CONNECTIONS** Consider the reaction between hydrogen and oxygen that forms water, shown with ball-and-stick models at the beginning of Concept 2.4. Study Figure 2.10 and draw the Lewis dot structures representing this reaction.

2. Which type of chemical reaction occurs faster at equilibrium, the formation of products from reactants or reactants from products?

3. Write an equation that uses the products of photosynthesis as reactants and the reactants of photosynthesis as products. Add energy as another product. This new equation describes a process that occurs in your cells. Describe this equation in words. How does this equation relate to breathing?

For suggested answers, see Appendix A.

SUMMARY OF KEY CONCEPTS

CONCEPT 2.1

Matter consists of chemical elements in pure form and in combinations called compounds (pp. 29–30)

- **Elements** cannot be broken down chemically to other substances. A **compound** contains two or more different elements in a fixed ratio. Oxygen, carbon, hydrogen, and nitrogen make up approximately 96% of living matter.

  ? *In what way does the need for iodine or iron in your diet differ from your need for calcium or phosphorus?*

CONCEPT 2.2

An element's properties depend on the structure of its atoms (pp. 30–36)

- An **atom**, the smallest unit of an element, has the following components:

- An electrically neutral atom has equal numbers of electrons and protons; the number of protons determines the **atomic number**. The **atomic mass** is measured in **daltons** and is roughly equal to the **mass number**, the sum of protons plus neutrons. **Isotopes** of an element differ from each other in neutron number and therefore mass. Unstable isotopes give off particles and energy as radioactivity.
- In an atom, electrons occupy specific **electron shells**; the electrons in a shell have a characteristic energy level. Electron distribution in shells determines the chemical behavior of an atom. An atom that has an incomplete outer shell, the **valence shell**, is reactive.
- Electrons exist in **orbitals**, three-dimensional spaces with specific shapes that are components of electron shells.

  DRAW IT *Draw the electron distribution diagrams for neon ($_{10}$Ne) and argon ($_{18}$Ar). Use these diagrams to explain why these elements are chemically unreactive.*

CONCEPT 2.3

The formation and function of molecules depend on chemical bonding between atoms (pp. 36–40)

- **Chemical bonds** form when atoms interact and complete their valence shells. **Covalent bonds** form when pairs of electrons are shared.

H· + H· ⟶ H:H
Single covalent bond

:Ö· + ·Ö: ⟶ Ö::Ö
Double covalent bond

- **Molecules** consist of two or more covalently bonded atoms. The attraction of an atom for the electrons of a covalent bond is its **electronegativity**. If both atoms are the same, they have the same electronegativity and share a **nonpolar covalent bond**. Electrons of a **polar covalent bond** are pulled closer to the more electronegative atom.
- An **ion** forms when an atom or molecule gains or loses an electron and becomes charged. An **ionic bond** is the attraction between two oppositely charged ions.

| Na Sodium atom | Cl Chlorine atom | Na⁺ Sodium ion (a cation) | Cl⁻ Chloride ion (an anion) |

- Weak bonds reinforce the shapes of large molecules and help molecules adhere to each other. A **hydrogen bond** is an attraction between a hydrogen atom carrying a partial positive charge ($\delta+$) and an electronegative atom ($\delta-$). **Van der Waals interactions** occur between transiently positive and negative regions of molecules.
- A molecule's shape is determined by the positions of its atoms' valence orbitals. Covalent bonds result in hybrid orbitals, which are responsible for the shapes of H_2O, CH_4, and many more complex biological molecules. Shape is usually the basis for the recognition of one biological molecule by another.

  ? *In terms of electron sharing between atoms, compare nonpolar covalent bonds, polar covalent bonds, and the formation of ions.*

CONCEPT 2.4

Chemical reactions make and break chemical bonds (pp. 40–41)

- **Chemical reactions** change **reactants** into **products** while conserving matter. All chemical reactions are theoretically reversible. **Chemical equilibrium** is reached when the forward and reverse reaction rates are equal.

  ? *What would happen to the concentration of products if more reactants were added to a reaction that was in chemical equilibrium? How would this addition affect the equilibrium?*

TEST YOUR UNDERSTANDING

LEVEL 1: KNOWLEDGE/COMPREHENSION

1. In the term *trace element*, the adjective *trace* means that
   a. the element is required in very small amounts.
   b. the element can be used as a label to trace atoms through an organism's metabolism.
   c. the element is very rare on Earth.
   d. the element enhances health but is not essential for the organism's long-term survival.

2. Compared with ^{31}P, the radioactive isotope ^{32}P has
   a. a different atomic number.
   b. one more proton.
   c. one more electron.
   d. one more neutron.

3. The reactivity of an atom arises from
   a. the average distance of the outermost electron shell from the nucleus.
   b. the existence of unpaired electrons in the valence shell.
   c. the sum of the potential energies of all the electron shells.
   d. the potential energy of the valence shell.

4. Which statement is true of all atoms that are anions?
   a. The atom has more electrons than protons.
   b. The atom has more protons than electrons.
   c. The atom has fewer protons than does a neutral atom of the same element.
   d. The atom has more neutrons than protons.

5. Which of the following statements correctly describes any chemical reaction that has reached equilibrium?
   a. The concentrations of products and reactants are equal.
   b. The reaction is now irreversible.
   c. Both forward and reverse reactions have halted.
   d. The rates of the forward and reverse reactions are equal.

LEVEL 2: APPLICATION/ANALYSIS

6. We can represent atoms by listing the number of protons, neutrons, and electrons—for example, $2p^+$, $2n^0$, $2e^-$ for helium. Which of the following represents the ^{18}O isotope of oxygen?
   a. $7p^+$, $2n^0$, $9e^-$
   b. $8p^+$, $10n^0$, $8e^-$
   c. $9p^+$, $9n^0$, $9e^-$
   d. $10p^+$, $8n^0$, $9e^-$

7. The atomic number of sulfur is 16. Sulfur combines with hydrogen by covalent bonding to form a compound, hydrogen sulfide. Based on the number of valence electrons in a sulfur atom, predict the molecular formula of the compound.
   a. HS
   b. HS_2
   c. H_2S
   d. H_4S

8. What coefficients must be placed in the following blanks so that all atoms are accounted for in the products?

   $$C_6H_{12}O_6 \rightarrow \underline{\quad} C_2H_6O + \underline{\quad} CO_2$$

   a. 2; 1
   b. 3; 1
   c. 1; 3
   d. 2; 2

9. **DRAW IT** Draw Lewis dot structures for each hypothetical molecule shown below, using the correct number of valence electrons for each atom. Determine which molecule makes sense because each atom has a complete valence shell and each bond has the correct number of electrons. Explain what makes the other molecules nonsensical, considering the number of bonds each type of atom can make.

$$H-O-C-C=O \quad\quad H-C-H-C=O$$

   (a)   (b)

LEVEL 3: SYNTHESIS/EVALUATION

10. **EVOLUTION CONNECTION**
    The percentages of naturally occurring elements making up the human body (see Table 2.1) are similar to the percentages of these elements found in other organisms. How could you account for this similarity among organisms?

11. **SCIENTIFIC INQUIRY**
    Female silkworm moths (*Bombyx mori*) attract males by emitting chemical signals that spread through the air. A male hundreds of meters away can detect these molecules and fly toward their source. The sensory organs responsible for this behavior are the comblike antennae visible in the photograph shown here. Each filament of an antenna is equipped with thousands of receptor cells that detect the sex attractant. Based on what you learned in this chapter, propose a hypothesis to account for the ability of the male moth to detect a specific molecule in the presence of many other molecules in the air. What predictions does your hypothesis make? Design an experiment to test one of these predictions.

12. **WRITE ABOUT A THEME: ORGANIZATION**
    While waiting at an airport, Neil Campbell once overheard this claim: "It's paranoid and ignorant to worry about industry or agriculture contaminating the environment with their chemical wastes. After all, this stuff is just made of the same atoms that were already present in our environment." Drawing on your knowledge of electron distribution, bonding, and emergent properties (see Concept 1.1), write a short essay (100–150 words) countering this argument.

13. **SYNTHESIZE YOUR KNOWLEDGE**

This bombardier beetle is spraying a boiling hot liquid that contains irritating chemicals, used as a defense mechanism against its enemies. The beetle stores two sets of chemicals separately in its glands. Using what you learned about chemistry in this chapter, propose a possible explanation for why the beetle is not harmed by the chemicals it stores and what causes the explosive discharge.

For selected answers, see Appendix A.

MasteringBiology®

Students Go to **MasteringBiology** for assignments, the eText, and the Study Area with practice tests, animations, and activities.

Instructors Go to **MasteringBiology** for automatically graded tutorials and questions that you can assign to your students, plus Instructor Resources.

3

Water and Life

▲ A young whooper swan paddles after its parent.

▲ **Figure 3.1 How does the habitat of a whooper swan depend on the chemistry of water?**

The Molecule That Supports All of Life

Life on Earth began in water and evolved there for 3 billion years before spreading onto land. Water is the substance that makes possible life as we know it here on Earth. All organisms familiar to us are made mostly of water and live in an environment dominated by water. Water is the biological medium here on Earth, and possibly on other planets as well.

Three-quarters of Earth's surface is covered by water. Although most of this water is in liquid form, water is also present on Earth as a solid (ice) and a gas (water vapor). Water is the only common substance to exist in the natural environment in all three physical states of matter. Furthermore, the solid state of water floats on the liquid, a rare property emerging from the chemistry of the water molecule. All three states of water can be seen in **Figure 3.1**, which shows water vapor rising from hot springs that feed into a partially frozen lake in Hokkaido, Japan. The lake is a migratory stop for the elegant whooper swan (*Cygnus cygnus*). The growing young require a watery habitat because their legs can't support their body weight on land for long periods of time.

In this chapter, you will learn how the structure of a water molecule allows it to interact with other molecules, including other water molecules. This ability leads to water's unique emergent properties that help make Earth suitable for life.

CONCEPT 3.1

Polar covalent bonds in water molecules result in hydrogen bonding

Water is so familiar to us that it is easy to overlook its many extraordinary qualities. Following the theme of emergent properties, we can trace water's unique behavior to the structure and interactions of its molecules.

Studied on its own, the water molecule is deceptively simple. It is shaped like a wide V, with its two hydrogen atoms joined to the oxygen atom by single covalent bonds. Oxygen is more electronegative than hydrogen, so the electrons of the covalent bonds spend more time closer to oxygen than to hydrogen; these are **polar covalent bonds** (see Figure 2.11). This unequal sharing of electrons and water's V-like shape make it a **polar molecule**, meaning that its overall charge is unevenly distributed. In water, the oxygen region of the molecule has a partial negative charge ($\delta-$), and each hydrogen has a partial positive charge ($\delta+$).

The properties of water arise from attractions between oppositely charged atoms of different water molecules: The slightly positive hydrogen of one molecule is attracted to the slightly negative oxygen of a nearby molecule. The two molecules are thus held together by a hydrogen bond **(Figure 3.2)**. When water is in its liquid form, its hydrogen bonds are very fragile, each only about 1/20 as strong as a covalent bond. The hydrogen bonds form, break, and re-form with great

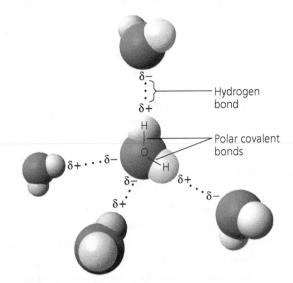

▲ **Figure 3.2 Hydrogen bonds between water molecules.** The charged regions in a water molecule are due to its polar covalent bonds. Oppositely charged regions of neighboring water molecules are attracted to each other, forming hydrogen bonds. Each molecule can hydrogen-bond to multiple partners, and these associations are constantly changing.

DRAW IT *Draw partial charges on the water molecule at the far left, and draw two more water molecules hydrogen-bonded to it.*

frequency. Each lasts only a few trillionths of a second, but the molecules are constantly forming new hydrogen bonds with a succession of partners. Therefore, at any instant, most of the water molecules are hydrogen-bonded to their neighbors. The extraordinary properties of water emerge from this hydrogen bonding, which organizes water molecules into a higher level of structural order.

CONCEPT CHECK 3.1

1. **MAKE CONNECTIONS** What is electronegativity, and how does it affect interactions between water molecules? (Review Figure 2.11.)

2. Why is it unlikely that two neighboring water molecules would be arranged like this?

$$O \overset{H \; H}{\diagdown} \quad \overset{H \; H}{\diagup} O$$

3. **WHAT IF?** What would be the effect on the properties of the water molecule if oxygen and hydrogen had equal electronegativity?

For suggested answers, see Appendix A.

CONCEPT 3.2

Four emergent properties of water contribute to Earth's suitability for life

We will examine four emergent properties of water that contribute to Earth's suitability as an environment for life: cohesive behavior, ability to moderate temperature, expansion upon freezing, and versatility as a solvent.

Cohesion of Water Molecules

Water molecules stay close to each other as a result of hydrogen bonding. Although the arrangement of molecules in a sample of liquid water is constantly changing, at any given moment many of the molecules are linked by multiple hydrogen bonds. These linkages make water more structured than most other liquids. Collectively, the hydrogen bonds hold the substance together, a phenomenon called **cohesion**.

Cohesion due to hydrogen bonding contributes to the transport of water and dissolved nutrients against gravity in plants. Water from the roots reaches the leaves through a network of water-conducting cells **(Figure 3.3)**. As water evaporates from a leaf, hydrogen bonds cause water molecules leaving the veins to tug on molecules farther down, and the upward pull is transmitted through the water-conducting cells all the way to the roots. **Adhesion**, the clinging of one substance to another, also plays a role. Adhesion of

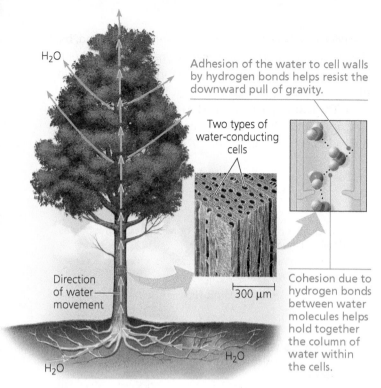

H₂O

Adhesion of the water to cell walls by hydrogen bonds helps resist the downward pull of gravity.

Two types of water-conducting cells

Direction of water movement

300 μm

Cohesion due to hydrogen bonds between water molecules helps hold together the column of water within the cells.

Direction of water movement

H₂O   H₂O

▲ **Figure 3.3 Water transport in plants.** Evaporation from leaves pulls water upward from the roots through water-conducting cells. Because of the properties of cohesion and adhesion, the tallest trees can transport water more than 100 m upward—approximately one-quarter the height of the Empire State Building in New York City.

ANIMATION ***BioFlix*** Visit the Study Area in **MasteringBiology** for the BioFlix ® 3-D Animation on Water Transport in Plants.

water by hydrogen bonds to the molecules of cell walls helps counter the downward pull of gravity (see Figure 3.3).

Related to cohesion is **surface tension**, a measure of how difficult it is to stretch or break the surface of a liquid. At the interface between water and air is an ordered arrangement of water molecules, hydrogen-bonded to one another and to the water below. This gives water an unusually high surface tension, making it behave as though it were coated with an invisible film. You can observe the surface tension of water by slightly overfilling a drinking glass; the water will stand above the rim. The spider in **Figure 3.4** takes advantage of the surface tension of water to walk across a pond without breaking the surface.

▼ **Figure 3.4 Walking on water.** The high surface tension of water, resulting from the collective strength of its hydrogen bonds, allows this raft spider to walk on the surface of a pond.

Moderation of Temperature by Water

Water moderates air temperature by absorbing heat from air that is warmer and releasing the stored heat to air that is cooler. Water is effective as a heat bank because it can absorb or release a relatively large amount of heat with only a slight change in its own temperature. To understand this capability of water, let's first look at temperature and heat.

Temperature and Heat

Anything that moves has **kinetic energy**, the energy of motion. Atoms and molecules have kinetic energy because they are always moving, although not necessarily in any particular direction. The faster a molecule moves, the greater its kinetic energy. The kinetic energy associated with the random movement of atoms or molecules is called **thermal energy**. Thermal energy is related to temperature, but they are not the same thing. **Temperature** is a measure of energy that represents the *average* kinetic energy of the molecules in a body of matter, regardless of volume, whereas the *total* thermal energy depends in part on the matter's volume. When water is heated in a coffeemaker, the average speed of the molecules increases, and the thermometer records this as a rise in temperature of the liquid. The total amount of thermal energy also increases in this case. Note, however, that although the pot of coffee has a much higher temperature than, say, the water in a swimming pool, the swimming pool contains more thermal energy because of its much greater volume.

Whenever two objects of different temperature are brought together, thermal energy passes from the warmer to the cooler object until the two are the same temperature. Molecules in the cooler object speed up at the expense of the thermal energy of the warmer object. An ice cube cools a drink not by adding coldness to the liquid, but by absorbing thermal energy from the liquid as the ice itself melts. Thermal energy in transfer from one body of matter to another is defined as **heat**.

One convenient unit of heat used in this book is the **calorie (cal)**. A calorie is the amount of heat it takes to raise the temperature of 1 g of water by 1°C. Conversely, a calorie is also the amount of heat that 1 g of water releases when it cools by 1°C. A **kilocalorie (kcal)**, 1,000 cal, is the quantity of heat required to raise the temperature of 1 kilogram (kg) of water by 1°C. (The "calories" on food packages are actually kilocalories.) Another energy unit used in this book is the **joule (J)**. One joule equals 0.239 cal; one calorie equals 4.184 J.

Water's High Specific Heat

The ability of water to stabilize temperature stems from its relatively high specific heat. The **specific heat** of a substance is defined as the amount of heat that must be absorbed or lost for 1 g of that substance to change its temperature by 1°C. We already know water's specific heat because we have defined a calorie as the amount of heat that causes 1 g of water to change its temperature by 1°C. Therefore, the specific heat of water is 1 calorie per gram and per degree Celsius, abbreviated as 1 cal/g · °C. Compared with most other substances, water has an unusually high specific heat. For example, ethyl alcohol, the type of alcohol in alcoholic beverages, has a specific heat of 0.6 cal/g · °C; that is, only 0.6 cal is required to raise the temperature of 1 g of ethyl alcohol by 1°C.

Because of the high specific heat of water relative to other materials, water will change its temperature less than other liquids when it absorbs or loses a given amount of heat. The reason you can burn your fingers by touching the side of an iron pot on the stove when the water in the pot is still lukewarm is that the specific heat of water is ten times greater than that of iron. In other words, the same amount of heat will raise the temperature of 1 g of the iron much faster than it will raise the temperature of 1 g of the water. Specific heat can be thought of as a measure of how well a substance resists changing its temperature when it absorbs or releases heat. Water resists changing its temperature; when it does change its temperature, it absorbs or loses a relatively large quantity of heat for each degree of change.

We can trace water's high specific heat, like many of its other properties, to hydrogen bonding. Heat must be absorbed in order to break hydrogen bonds; by the same token, heat is released when hydrogen bonds form. A calorie of heat causes a relatively small change in the temperature of water because much of the heat is used to disrupt hydrogen bonds before the water molecules can begin moving faster. And when the temperature of water drops slightly, many additional hydrogen bonds form, releasing a considerable amount of energy in the form of heat.

What is the relevance of water's high specific heat to life on Earth? A large body of water can absorb and store a huge amount of heat from the sun in the daytime and during summer while warming up only a few degrees. At night and during winter, the gradually cooling water can warm the air. This capability of water serves to moderate air temperatures in coastal areas (Figure 3.5). The high specific heat of water also

tends to stabilize ocean temperatures, creating a favorable environment for marine life. Thus, because of its high specific heat, the water that covers most of Earth keeps temperature fluctuations on land and in water within limits that permit life. Also, because organisms are made primarily of water, they are better able to resist changes in their own temperature than if they were made of a liquid with a lower specific heat.

Evaporative Cooling

Molecules of any liquid stay close together because they are attracted to one another. Molecules moving fast enough to overcome these attractions can depart the liquid and enter the air as a gas (vapor). This transformation from a liquid to a gas is called vaporization, or evaporation. Recall that the speed of molecular movement varies and that temperature is the *average* kinetic energy of molecules. Even at low temperatures, the speediest molecules can escape into the air. Some evaporation occurs at any temperature; a glass of water at room temperature, for example, will eventually evaporate completely. If a liquid is heated, the average kinetic energy of molecules increases and the liquid evaporates more rapidly.

Heat of vaporization is the quantity of heat a liquid must absorb for 1 g of it to be converted from the liquid to the gaseous state. For the same reason that water has a high specific heat, it also has a high heat of vaporization relative to most other liquids. To evaporate 1 g of water at 25°C, about 580 cal of heat is needed—nearly double the amount needed to vaporize a gram of alcohol or ammonia. Water's high heat of vaporization is another emergent property resulting from the strength of its hydrogen bonds, which must be broken before the molecules can exit from the liquid in the form of water vapor (see Figure 3.1).

The high amount of energy required to vaporize water has a wide range of effects. On a global scale, for example, it helps moderate Earth's climate. A considerable amount of solar heat absorbed by tropical seas is consumed during the evaporation of surface water. Then, as moist tropical air circulates poleward, it releases heat as it condenses and forms rain. On an organismal level, water's high heat of vaporization accounts for the severity of steam burns. These burns are caused by the heat energy released when steam condenses into liquid on the skin.

As a liquid evaporates, the surface of the liquid that remains behind cools down (its temperature decreases). This **evaporative cooling** occurs because the "hottest" molecules, those with the greatest kinetic energy, are the most likely to leave as gas. It is as if the hundred fastest runners at a college transferred to another school; the average speed of the remaining students would decline.

Evaporative cooling of water contributes to the stability of temperature in lakes and ponds and also provides a mechanism that prevents terrestrial organisms from overheating. For example, evaporation of water from the leaves of a plant

▲ Figure 3.5 **Temperatures for the Pacific Ocean and Southern California on an August day.**

INTERPRET THE DATA *Explain the pattern of temperatures shown in this diagram.*

helps keep the tissues in the leaves from becoming too warm in the sunlight. Evaporation of sweat from human skin dissipates body heat and helps prevent overheating on a hot day or when excess heat is generated by strenuous activity. High humidity on a hot day increases discomfort because the high concentration of water vapor in the air inhibits the evaporation of sweat from the body.

Floating of Ice on Liquid Water

Water is one of the few substances that are less dense as a solid than as a liquid. In other words, ice floats on liquid water. While other materials contract and become denser when they solidify, water expands. The cause of this exotic behavior is, once again, hydrogen bonding. At temperatures above 4°C, water behaves like other liquids, expanding as it warms and contracting as it cools. As the temperature falls from 4°C to 0°C, water begins to freeze because more and more of its molecules are moving too slowly to break hydrogen bonds. At 0°C, the molecules become locked into a crystalline lattice, each water molecule hydrogen-bonded to four partners (Figure 3.6). The hydrogen bonds keep the molecules at "arm's length," far enough apart to make ice about 10% less dense (10% fewer molecules for the same volume) than liquid water at 4°C. When ice absorbs enough heat for its temperature to rise above 0°C, hydrogen bonds between molecules are disrupted. As the crystal collapses, the ice melts, and molecules are free to slip closer together. Water reaches its greatest density at 4°C and then begins to expand as the molecules move faster. Even in liquid water, many of the molecules are connected by hydrogen bonds, though only transiently: The hydrogen bonds are constantly breaking and re-forming.

The ability of ice to float due to its lower density is an important factor in the suitability of the environment for life. If ice sank, then eventually all ponds, lakes, and even oceans would freeze solid, making life as we know it impossible on Earth. During summer, only the upper few inches of the ocean would thaw. Instead, when a deep body of water cools, the floating ice insulates the liquid water below, preventing it from freezing and allowing life to exist under the frozen surface, as shown in the photo in Figure 3.6. Besides insulating the water below, ice also provides a solid habitat for some animals, such as polar bears and seals.

Many scientists are worried that these bodies of ice are at risk of disappearing. Global warming, which is caused by carbon dioxide and other "greenhouse" gases in the atmosphere, is having a profound effect on icy environments around the globe. In the Arctic, the average air temperature has risen 1.4°C just since 1961. This temperature increase has affected the seasonal balance between Arctic sea ice and liquid water, causing ice to form later in the year, to melt earlier, and to cover a smaller area. The rate at which glaciers and Arctic sea ice are disappearing is posing an extreme challenge to animals that depend on ice for their survival.

Water: The Solvent of Life

A sugar cube placed in a glass of water will dissolve with a little stirring. The glass will then contain a uniform mixture of sugar and water; the concentration of dissolved sugar will be the same everywhere in the mixture. A liquid that is a completely homogeneous mixture of two or more substances is called a **solution**. The dissolving agent of a solution is the **solvent**, and the substance that is dissolved is the **solute**. In this case, water is the solvent and sugar is the solute. An **aqueous solution** is one in which the solute is dissolved in water; water is the solvent.

Water is a very versatile solvent, a quality we can trace to the polarity of the water molecule. Suppose, for example, that a spoonful of table salt, the ionic compound sodium chloride (NaCl), is placed in water (Figure 3.7). At the surface of each grain, or crystal, of salt, the sodium and chloride ions are exposed to the solvent. These ions and regions of the water molecules are attracted to each other due to their opposite

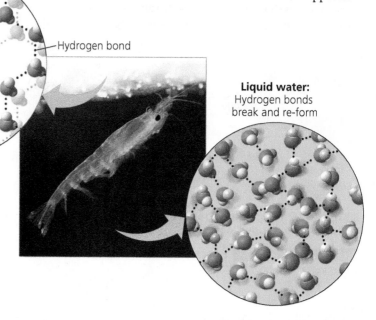

▶ Figure 3.6 **Ice: crystalline structure and floating barrier.** In ice, each molecule is hydrogen-bonded to four neighbors in a three-dimensional crystal. Because the crystal is spacious, ice has fewer molecules than an equal volume of liquid water. In other words, ice is less dense than liquid water. Floating ice becomes a barrier that insulates the liquid water below from the colder air. The marine organism shown here is a type of shrimp called krill; it was photographed beneath floating ice in the Southern Ocean near Antarctica.

WHAT IF? *If water did not form hydrogen bonds, what would happen to the shrimp's habitat, shown here?*

Ice:
Hydrogen bonds
are stable

Hydrogen bond

Liquid water:
Hydrogen bonds
break and re-form

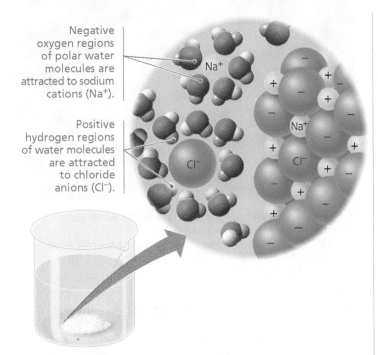

Negative oxygen regions of polar water molecules are attracted to sodium cations (Na⁺).

Positive hydrogen regions of water molecules are attracted to chloride anions (Cl⁻).

▲ **Figure 3.7 Table salt dissolving in water.** A sphere of water molecules, called a hydration shell, surrounds each solute ion.

WHAT IF? *What would happen if you heated this solution for a long time?*

charges. The oxygen regions of the water molecules are negatively charged and are attracted to sodium cations. The hydrogen regions are positively charged and are attracted to chloride anions. As a result, water molecules surround the individual sodium and chloride ions, separating and shielding them from one another. The sphere of water molecules around each dissolved ion is called a **hydration shell**. Working inward from the surface of each salt crystal, water eventually dissolves all the ions. The result is a solution of two solutes, sodium cations and chloride anions, homogeneously mixed with water, the solvent. Other ionic compounds also dissolve in water. Seawater, for instance, contains a great variety of dissolved ions, as do living cells.

A compound does not need to be ionic to dissolve in water; many compounds made up of nonionic polar molecules, such as the sugar in the sugar cube mentioned earlier, are also water-soluble. Such compounds dissolve when water molecules surround each of the solute molecules, forming hydrogen bonds with them. Even molecules as large as proteins can dissolve in water if they have ionic and polar regions on their surface **(Figure 3.8)**. Many different kinds of polar

compounds are dissolved (along with ions) in the water of such biological fluids as blood, the sap of plants, and the liquid within all cells. Water is the solvent of life.

Hydrophilic and Hydrophobic Substances

Any substance that has an affinity for water is said to be **hydrophilic** (from the Greek *hydro*, water, and *philos*, loving). In some cases, substances can be hydrophilic without actually dissolving. For example, some molecules in cells are so large that they do not dissolve. Another example of a hydrophilic substance that does not dissolve is cotton, a plant product. Cotton consists of giant molecules of cellulose, a compound with numerous regions of partial positive and partial negative charges that can form hydrogen bonds with water. Water adheres to the cellulose fibers. Thus, a cotton towel does a great job of drying the body, yet it does not dissolve in the washing machine. Cellulose is also present in the walls of water-conducting cells in a plant; you read earlier how the adhesion of water to these hydrophilic walls helps water move up the plant against gravity.

There are, of course, substances that do not have an affinity for water. Substances that are nonionic and nonpolar (or otherwise cannot form hydrogen bonds) actually seem to repel water; these substances are said to be **hydrophobic** (from the Greek *phobos*, fearing). An example from the kitchen is vegetable oil, which, as you know, does not mix stably with water-based substances such as vinegar. The hydrophobic behavior of the oil molecules results from a prevalence of relatively nonpolar covalent bonds, in this case bonds between carbon and hydrogen, which share electrons almost equally. Hydrophobic molecules related to oils are major ingredients of cell membranes. (Imagine what would happen to a cell if its membrane dissolved!)

▶ **Figure 3.8 A water-soluble protein.** Human lysozyme is a protein found in tears and saliva that has antibacterial action. This model shows the lysozyme molecule (purple) in an aqueous environment. Ionic and polar regions on the protein's surface attract water molecules.

This oxygen is attracted to a slight positive charge on the lysozyme molecule.

This hydrogen is attracted to a slight negative charge on the lysozyme molecule.

Solute Concentration in Aqueous Solutions

Most of the chemical reactions in organisms involve solutes dissolved in water. To understand such reactions, we must know how many atoms and molecules are involved and calculate the concentration of solutes in an aqueous solution (the number of solute molecules in a volume of solution).

When carrying out experiments, we use mass to calculate the number of molecules. We must first calculate the **molecular mass**, which is the sum of the masses of all the atoms in a molecule. As an example, let's calculate the molecular mass of table sugar (sucrose), $C_{12}H_{22}O_{11}$. In round numbers of daltons, the mass of a carbon atom is 12, the mass of a hydrogen atom is 1, and the mass of an oxygen atom is 16. Thus, sucrose has a molecular mass of $(12 \times 12) + (22 \times 1) + (11 \times 16) = 342$ daltons. Because we can't weigh out small numbers of molecules, we usually measure substances in units called moles. Just as a dozen always means 12 objects, a **mole (mol)** represents an exact number of objects: 6.02×10^{23}, which is called Avogadro's number. Because of the way in which Avogadro's number and the unit *dalton* were originally defined, there are 6.02×10^{23} daltons in 1 g. Once we determine the molecular mass of a molecule such as sucrose, we can use the same number (342), but with the unit *gram*, to represent the mass of 6.02×10^{23} molecules of sucrose, or 1 mol of sucrose (this is sometimes called the *molar mass*). To obtain 1 mol of sucrose in the lab, therefore, we weigh out 342 g.

The practical advantage of measuring a quantity of chemicals in moles is that a mole of one substance has exactly the same number of molecules as a mole of any other substance. If the molecular mass of substance A is 342 daltons and that of substance B is 10 daltons, then 342 g of A will have the same number of molecules as 10 g of B. A mole of ethyl alcohol (C_2H_6O) also contains 6.02×10^{23} molecules, but its mass is only 46 g because the mass of a molecule of ethyl alcohol is less than that of a molecule of sucrose. Measuring in moles makes it convenient for scientists working in the laboratory to combine substances in fixed ratios of molecules.

How would we make a liter (L) of solution consisting of 1 mol of sucrose dissolved in water? We would measure out 342 g of sucrose and then gradually add water, while stirring, until the sugar was completely dissolved. We would then add enough water to bring the total volume of the solution up to 1 L. At that point, we would have a 1-molar (1 M) solution of sucrose. **Molarity**—the number of moles of solute per liter of solution—is the unit of concentration most often used by biologists for aqueous solutions.

Water's capacity as a versatile solvent complements the other properties discussed in this chapter. Since these remarkable properties allow water to support life on Earth so well, scientists who seek life elsewhere in the universe look for water as a sign that a planet might sustain life.

▲ **Figure 3.9 Evidence for subsurface liquid water on Mars.** The dark streaks running down the lower portion of the photo are proposed to be streams of subsurface flowing water because they appear only during the warm season. The gullies in the middle of the photo could have been formed by flowing water.

Possible Evolution of Life on Other Planets

EVOLUTION Biologists who look for life elsewhere in the universe (known as *astrobiologists*) have concentrated their search on planets that might have water. More than 800 planets have been found outside our solar system, and there is evidence for the presence of water vapor on a few of them. In our own solar system, Mars has been a focus of study. Like Earth, Mars has an ice cap at both poles. Images from spacecraft sent to Mars show that ice is present just under the surface of Mars and enough water vapor exists in its atmosphere for frost to form. **Figure 3.9** shows streaks that form along steep slopes during the Mars spring and summer, features that vanish during the winter. Some scientists have proposed that these are seasonal streams of flowing water occurring when subsurface ice melts during the warm season, while others think they are the result of CO_2 rather than water. Drilling below the surface may be the next step in the search for signs of life on Mars. If any life-forms or fossils are found, their study will shed light on the process of evolution from an entirely new perspective.

CONCEPT CHECK **3.2**

1. Describe how properties of water contribute to the upward movement of water in a tree.
2. Explain the saying "It's not the heat; it's the humidity."
3. How can the freezing of water crack boulders?
4. **WHAT IF?** A water strider (which can walk on water) has legs that are coated with a hydrophobic substance. What might be the benefit? What would happen if the substance were hydrophilic?
5. **INTERPRET THE DATA** The concentration of the appetite-regulating hormone ghrelin is about 1.3×10^{-10} M in the blood of a fasting person. How many molecules of ghrelin are in 1 L of blood?

For suggested answers, see Appendix A.

Acidic and basic conditions affect living organisms

Occasionally, a hydrogen atom participating in a hydrogen bond between two water molecules shifts from one molecule to the other. When this happens, the hydrogen atom leaves its electron behind, and what is actually transferred is a **hydrogen ion** (H^+), a single proton with a charge of 1+. The water molecule that lost a proton is now a **hydroxide ion** (OH^-), which has a charge of 1−. The proton binds to the other water molecule, making that molecule a **hydronium ion** (H_3O^+). We can picture the chemical reaction as follows:

2 H_2O Hydronium ion (H_3O^+)   Hydroxide ion (OH^-)

By convention, H^+ (the hydrogen ion) is used to represent H_3O^+ (the hydronium ion), and we follow that practice in this book. Keep in mind, though, that H^+ does not exist on its own in an aqueous solution. It is always associated with a water molecule in the form of H_3O^+.

As indicated by the double arrows, this is a reversible reaction that reaches a state of dynamic equilibrium when water molecules dissociate at the same rate that they are being reformed from H^+ and OH^-. At this equilibrium point, the concentration of water molecules greatly exceeds the concentrations of H^+ and OH^-. In pure water, only one water molecule in every 554 million is dissociated; the concentration of each ion in pure water is 10^{-7} M (at 25°C). This means there is only one ten-millionth of a mole of hydrogen ions per liter of pure water and an equal number of hydroxide ions. (Even so, this is a huge number—over 60,000 *trillion*—of each ion.)

Although the dissociation of water is reversible and statistically rare, it is exceedingly important in the chemistry of life. H^+ and OH^- are very reactive. Changes in their concentrations can drastically affect a cell's proteins and other complex molecules. As we have seen, the concentrations of H^+ and OH^- are equal in pure water, but adding certain kinds of solutes, called acids and bases, disrupts this balance. Biologists use something called the pH scale to describe how acidic or basic (the opposite of acidic) a solution is. In the remainder of this chapter, you will learn about acids, bases, and pH and why changes in pH can adversely affect organisms.

Acids and Bases

What would cause an aqueous solution to have an imbalance in H^+ and OH^- concentrations? When acids dissolve in water, they donate additional H^+ to the solution. An **acid** is a substance that increases the hydrogen ion concentration of a solution. For example, when hydrochloric acid (HCl) is added to water, hydrogen ions dissociate from chloride ions:

$$HCl \rightarrow H^+ + Cl^-$$

This source of H^+ (dissociation of water is the other source) results in an acidic solution—one having more H^+ than OH^-.

A substance that reduces the hydrogen ion concentration of a solution is called a **base**. Some bases reduce the H^+ concentration directly by accepting hydrogen ions. Ammonia (NH_3), for instance, acts as a base when the unshared electron pair in nitrogen's valence shell attracts a hydrogen ion from the solution, resulting in an ammonium ion (NH_4^+):

$$NH_3 + H^+ \rightleftharpoons NH_4^+$$

Other bases reduce the H^+ concentration indirectly by dissociating to form hydroxide ions, which combine with hydrogen ions and form water. One such base is sodium hydroxide (NaOH), which in water dissociates into its ions:

$$NaOH \rightarrow Na^+ + OH^-$$

In either case, the base reduces the H^+ concentration. Solutions with a higher concentration of OH^- than H^+ are known as basic solutions. A solution in which the H^+ and OH^- concentrations are equal is said to be neutral.

Notice that single arrows were used in the reactions for HCl and NaOH. These compounds dissociate completely when mixed with water, so hydrochloric acid is called a strong acid and sodium hydroxide a strong base. In contrast, ammonia is a weak base. The double arrows in the reaction for ammonia indicate that the binding and release of hydrogen ions are reversible reactions, although at equilibrium there will be a fixed ratio of NH_4^+ to NH_3.

Weak acids are acids that reversibly release and accept back hydrogen ions. An example is carbonic acid:

$$H_2CO_3 \rightleftharpoons HCO_3^- + H^+$$
Carbonic acid   Bicarbonate ion   Hydrogen ion

Here the equilibrium so favors the reaction in the left direction that when carbonic acid is added to pure water, only 1% of the molecules are dissociated at any particular time. Still, that is enough to shift the balance of H^+ and OH^- from neutrality.

The pH Scale

In any aqueous solution at 25°C, the *product* of the H^+ and OH^- concentrations is constant at 10^{-14}. This can be written

$$[H^+][OH^-] = 10^{-14}$$

In such an equation, brackets indicate molar concentration. In a neutral solution at 25°C (close to room temperature), $[H^+] = 10^{-7}$ and $[OH^-] = 10^{-7}$, so in this case, 10^{-14} is the product of 10^{-7} and 10^{-7}. If enough acid is added to a solution to increase [H^+] to 10^{-5} M, then [OH^-] will decline by an equivalent factor to 10^{-9} M (note that $10^{-5} \times 10^{-9} = 10^{-14}$). This constant relationship expresses the behavior of acids and bases in an aqueous solution. An acid not only adds hydrogen ions to a solution, but also removes hydroxide ions because of the tendency for H^+ to combine with OH^-, forming water. A base has the opposite effect, increasing OH^- concentration but also reducing H^+ concentration by the formation of water. If enough of a base is added to raise the OH^- concentration to 10^{-4} M, it will cause the H^+ concentration to drop to 10^{-10} M. Whenever we know the concentration of either H^+ or OH^- in an aqueous solution, we can deduce the concentration of the other ion.

Because the H^+ and OH^- concentrations of solutions can vary by a factor of 100 trillion or more, scientists have developed a way to express this variation more conveniently than in moles per liter. The pH scale (**Figure 3.10**) compresses the range of H^+ and OH^- concentrations by employing logarithms. The **pH** of a solution is defined as the negative logarithm (base 10) of the hydrogen ion concentration:

$$pH = -\log [H^+]$$

For a neutral aqueous solution, [H^+] is 10^{-7} M, giving us

$$-\log 10^{-7} = -(-7) = 7$$

Notice that pH *declines* as H^+ concentration *increases*. Notice, too, that although the pH scale is based on H^+ concentration, it also implies OH^- concentration. A solution of pH 10 has a hydrogen ion concentration of 10^{-10} M and a hydroxide ion concentration of 10^{-4} M.

The pH of a neutral aqueous solution at 25°C is 7, the midpoint of the pH scale. A pH value less than 7 denotes an acidic solution; the lower the number, the more acidic the solution. The pH for basic solutions is above 7. Most biological fluids, such as blood and saliva, are within the range of pH 6–8. There are a few exceptions, however, including the strongly acidic digestive juice of the human stomach, which has a pH of about 2.

Remember that each pH unit represents a tenfold difference in H^+ and OH^- concentrations. It is this mathematical feature that makes the pH scale so compact. A solution of pH 3 is not twice as acidic as a solution of pH 6, but a thousand times ($10 \times 10 \times 10$) more acidic. When the pH of a solution changes slightly, the actual concentrations of H^+ and OH^- in the solution change substantially.

Buffers

The internal pH of most living cells is close to 7. Even a slight change in pH can be harmful, because the chemical processes of the cell are very sensitive to the concentrations of hydrogen and hydroxide ions. The pH of human blood is very close to 7.4, which is slightly basic. A person cannot survive for more than a few minutes if the blood pH drops to 7 or rises to 7.8, and a chemical system exists in the blood that maintains a stable pH. If 0.01 mol of a strong acid is added to a liter of pure water, the pH drops from 7.0 to 2.0. If the same amount of acid is added to a liter of blood, however, the pH decrease is only from 7.4 to 7.3. Why does the addition of acid have so much less of an effect on the pH of blood than it does on the pH of water?

The presence of substances called buffers allows biological fluids to maintain a relatively constant pH despite the addition of acids or bases. A **buffer** is a substance that minimizes changes in the concentrations of H^+ and OH^- in a solution. It does so by accepting hydrogen ions from the solution when they are in excess and donating hydrogen ions to the solution when they have been depleted. Most buffer solutions contain a weak acid and its corresponding base, which combine reversibly with hydrogen ions.

Several buffers contribute to pH stability in human blood and many other biological solutions. One of these is

pH Scale

- 0
- 1 — Battery acid
- 2 — Gastric juice, lemon juice
- 3 — Vinegar, wine, cola
- 4 — Tomato juice / Beer
- 5 — Black coffee
- Rainwater
- 6 — Urine
- Saliva
- 7 — **Pure water** / Human blood, tears
- 8 — Seawater / Inside of small intestine
- 9
- 10
- Milk of magnesia
- 11 — Household ammonia
- 12
- 13 — Household bleach
- Oven cleaner
- 14

Increasingly Acidic [H^+] > [OH^-]

Neutral [H^+] = [OH^-]

Increasingly Basic [H^+] < [OH^-]

Acidic solution

Neutral solution

Basic solution

▲ **Figure 3.10 The pH scale and pH values of some aqueous solutions.**

carbonic acid (H_2CO_3), which is formed when CO_2 reacts with water in blood plasma. As mentioned earlier, carbonic acid dissociates to yield a bicarbonate ion (HCO_3^-) and a hydrogen ion (H^+):

$$H_2CO_3 \underset{\text{Response to a drop in pH}}{\overset{\text{Response to a rise in pH}}{\rightleftharpoons}} HCO_3^- + H^+$$

H^+ donor (acid) H^+ acceptor (base)   Hydrogen ion

The chemical equilibrium between carbonic acid and bicarbonate acts as a pH regulator, the reaction shifting left or right as other processes in the solution add or remove hydrogen ions. If the H^+ concentration in blood begins to fall (that is, if pH rises), the reaction proceeds to the right and more carbonic acid dissociates, replenishing hydrogen ions. But when the H^+ concentration in blood begins to rise (when pH drops), the reaction proceeds to the left, with HCO_3^- (the base) removing the hydrogen ions from the solution and forming H_2CO_3. Thus, the carbonic acid–bicarbonate buffering system consists of an acid and a base in equilibrium with each other. Most other buffers are also acid-base pairs.

Acidification: A Threat to Water Quality

Among the many threats to water quality posed by human activities is the burning of fossil fuels, which releases gaseous compounds into the atmosphere. When certain of these compounds react with water, the water becomes more acidic, altering the delicate balance of conditions for life on Earth. Carbon dioxide is the main product of fossil fuel combustion. About 25% of human-generated CO_2 is absorbed by the oceans. In spite of the huge volume of water in the oceans, scientists worry that the absorption of so much CO_2 will harm marine ecosystems.

Recent data have shown that such fears are well founded. When CO_2 dissolves in seawater, it reacts with water to form carbonic acid, which lowers ocean pH, a process known as **ocean acidification**. Based on measurements of CO_2 levels in air bubbles trapped in ice over thousands of years, scientists calculate that the pH of the oceans is 0.1 pH unit lower now than at any time in the past 420,000 years. Recent studies predict that it will drop another 0.3–0.5 pH unit by the end of this century.

As seawater acidifies, the extra hydrogen ions combine with carbonate ions (CO_3^{2-}) to form bicarbonate ions (HCO_3^-), thereby reducing the carbonate ion concentration (Figure 3.11). Scientists predict that ocean acidification will cause the carbonate ion concentration to decrease by 40% by the year 2100. This is of great concern because carbonate ions are required for calcification, the production of calcium carbonate ($CaCO_3$) by many marine organisms, including reef-building corals and animals that build shells. The Scientific Skills Exercise allows you to work with data

Some carbon dioxide (CO_2) in the atmosphere dissolves in the ocean, where it reacts with water to form carbonic acid (H_2CO_3).

$$CO_2 + H_2O \rightarrow H_2CO_3$$

Carbonic acid dissociates into hydrogen ions (H^+) and bicarbonate ions (HCO_3^-).

$$H_2CO_3 \rightarrow H^+ + HCO_3^-$$

The added H^+ combines with carbonate ions (CO_3^{2-}), forming more HCO_3^-.

$$H^+ + CO_3^{2-} \rightarrow HCO_3^-$$

Less CO_3^{2-} is available for calcification—the formation of calcium carbonate ($CaCO_3$)—by marine organisms such as corals.

$$CO_3^{2-} + Ca^{2+} \rightarrow CaCO_3$$

▲ Figure 3.11 **Atmospheric CO_2 from human activities and its fate in the ocean.**

from an experiment examining the effect of carbonate ion concentration on coral reefs. Coral reefs are sensitive ecosystems that act as havens for a great diversity of marine life. The disappearance of coral reef ecosystems would be a tragic loss of biological diversity.

If there is any reason for optimism about the future quality of water resources on our planet, it is that we have made progress in learning about the delicate chemical balances in oceans, lakes, and rivers. Continued progress can come only from the actions of informed individuals, like yourselves, who are concerned about environmental quality. This requires understanding the crucial role that water plays in the suitability of the environment for continued life on Earth.

CONCEPT CHECK 3.3

1. Compared with a basic solution at pH 9, the same volume of an acidic solution at pH 4 has _____ times as many hydrogen ions (H^+).

2. HCl is a strong acid that dissociates in water: $HCl \rightarrow H^+ + Cl^-$. What is the pH of 0.01 M HCl?

3. Acetic acid (CH_3COOH) can be a buffer, similar to carbonic acid. Write the dissociation reaction, identifying the acid, base, H^+ acceptor, and H^+ donor.

4. **WHAT IF?** Given a liter of pure water and a liter solution of acetic acid, what would happen to the pH if you added 0.01 mol of a strong acid to each? Use the reaction equation from question 3 to explain the result.

For suggested answers, see Appendix A.

Interpreting a Scatter Plot with a Regression Line

How Does the Carbonate Ion Concentration of Seawater Affect the Calcification Rate of a Coral Reef? Scientists predict that acidification of the ocean due to higher levels of atmospheric CO_2 will lower the concentration of dissolved carbonate ions, which living corals use to build calcium carbonate reef structures. In this exercise, you will analyze data from a controlled experiment that examined the effect of carbonate ion concentration ($[CO_3^{2-}]$) on calcium carbonate deposition, a process called calcification.

How the Experiment Was Done The Biosphere 2 aquarium in Arizona contains a large coral reef system that behaves like a natural reef. For several years, a group of researchers measured the rate of calcification by the reef organisms and examined how the calcification rate changed with differing amounts of dissolved carbonate ions in the seawater.

Data from the Experiment The black data points in the graph form a scatter plot. The red line, known as a linear regression line, is the best-fitting straight line for these points.

Interpret the Data

1. When presented with a graph of experimental data, the first step in analysis is to determine what each axis represents. (a) In words, explain what is being shown on the *x*-axis. Be sure to include the units. (b) What is being shown on the *y*-axis (including units)? (c) Which variable is the independent variable—the variable that was *manipulated* by the researchers? (d) Which variable is the dependent variable—the variable that responded to or depended on the treatment, which was *measured* by the researchers? (For additional information about graphs, see the Scientific Skills Review in Appendix F and in the Study Area in MasteringBiology.)

2. Based on the data shown in the graph, describe in words the relationship between carbonate ion concentration and calcification rate.

3. (a) If the seawater carbonate ion concentration is 270 µmol/kg, what is the approximate rate of calcification, and approximately how many days would it take 1 square meter of reef to accumulate 30 mmol of

calcium carbonate ($CaCO_3$)? (b) If the seawater carbonate ion concentration is 250 µmol/kg, what is the approximate rate of calcification, and approximately how many days would it take 1 square meter of reef to accumulate 30 mmol of calcium carbonate? (c) If carbonate ion concentration decreases, how does the calcification rate change, and how does that affect the time it takes coral to grow?

4. (a) Referring to the equations in Figure 3.11, determine which step of the process is measured in this experiment. (b) Are the results of this experiment consistent with the hypothesis that increased atmospheric $[CO_2]$ will slow the growth of coral reefs? Why or why not?

(MB) A version of this Scientific Skills Exercise can be assigned in MasteringBiology.

Data from C. Langdon et al., Effect of calcium carbonate saturation state on the calcification rate of an experimental coral reef, *Global Biogeochemical Cycles* 14:639–654 (2000).

---

3 Chapter Review

SUMMARY OF KEY CONCEPTS

CONCEPT 3.1

Polar covalent bonds in water molecules result in hydrogen bonding (p. 45)

- Water is a **polar molecule**. A hydrogen bond forms when the slightly negatively charged oxygen of one water molecule is attracted to the slightly positively charged hydrogen of a nearby water molecule. Hydrogen bonding between water molecules is the basis for water's properties.

> **DRAW IT** *Label a hydrogen bond and a polar covalent bond in this figure. Is a hydrogen bond a covalent bond? Explain.*

CONCEPT 3.2

Four emergent properties of water contribute to Earth's suitability for life (pp. 45–50)

- Hydrogen bonding keeps water molecules close to each other, and this **cohesion** helps pull water upward in the microscopic water-conducting cells of plants. Hydrogen bonding is also responsible for water's **surface tension**.

- Water has a high **specific heat**: Heat is absorbed when hydrogen bonds break and is released when hydrogen bonds form. This helps keep temperatures relatively steady, within limits that permit life. **Evaporative cooling** is based on water's high **heat of vaporization**. The evaporative loss of the most energetic water molecules cools a surface.

- Ice floats because it is less dense than liquid water. This property allows life to exist under the frozen surfaces of lakes and polar seas.

- Water is an unusually versatile **solvent** because its polar molecules are attracted to ions and polar substances that can form hydrogen bonds. **Hydrophilic** substances have an affinity for water; **hydrophobic** substances do not. **Molarity**, the number of moles of **solute** per liter of **solution**, is used as a measure of solute concentration in solutions. A **mole** is a certain number of molecules of a substance. The mass of a mole of a substance in grams is the same as the **molecular mass** in daltons.

- The emergent properties of water support life on Earth and may contribute to the potential for life to have evolved on other planets.

> [?] *Describe how different types of solutes dissolve in water. Explain what a solution is.*

CONCEPT 3.3

Acidic and basic conditions affect living organisms (pp. 51–54)

- A water molecule can transfer an H^+ to another water molecule to form H_3O^+ (represented simply by H^+) and OH^-.

- The concentration of H^+ is expressed as **pH**; $pH = -\log[H^+]$. A **buffer** consists of an acid-base pair that combines reversibly with hydrogen ions, allowing it to resist pH changes.

Acidic [H^+] > [OH^-]

Acids donate H^+ in aqueous solutions.

Neutral [H^+] = [OH^-]

Bases donate OH^- or accept H^+ in aqueous solutions.

Basic [H^+] < [OH^-]

0
7
14

- The burning of fossil fuels increases the amount of CO_2 in the atmosphere. Some CO_2 dissolves in the oceans, causing **ocean acidification**, which has potentially grave consequences for coral reefs.

> [?] *Explain how increasing amounts of CO_2 dissolving in the ocean leads to ocean acidification. How does this change in pH affect carbonate ion concentration and the rate of calcification?*

TEST YOUR UNDERSTANDING

LEVEL 1: KNOWLEDGE/COMPREHENSION

1. Which of the following is a hydrophobic material?
   a. paper
   b. table salt
   c. wax
   d. sugar

2. We can be sure that a mole of table sugar and a mole of vitamin C are equal in their
   a. mass.
   b. volume.
   c. number of atoms.
   d. number of molecules.

3. Measurements show that the pH of a particular lake is 4.0. What is the hydrogen ion concentration of the lake?
   a. $4.0\ M$
   b. $10^{-10}\ M$
   c. $10^{-4}\ M$
   d. $10^4\ M$

4. What is the *hydroxide* ion concentration of the lake described in question 3?
   a. $10^{-10}\ M$
   b. $10^{-4}\ M$
   c. $10^{-7}\ M$
   d. $10.0\ M$

LEVEL 2: APPLICATION/ANALYSIS

5. A slice of pizza has 500 kcal. If we could burn the pizza and use all the heat to warm a 50-L container of cold water, what would be the approximate increase in the temperature of the water? (*Note:* A liter of cold water weighs about 1 kg.)
   a. 50°C
   b. 5°C
   c. 100°C
   d. 10°C

6. **DRAW IT** Draw the hydration shells that form around a potassium ion and a chloride ion when potassium chloride (KCl) dissolves in water. Label the positive, negative, and partial charges on the atoms.

LEVEL 3: SYNTHESIS/EVALUATION

7. In agricultural areas, farmers pay close attention to the weather forecast. Right before a predicted overnight freeze, farmers spray water on crops to protect the plants. Use the properties of water to explain how this method works. Be sure to mention why hydrogen bonds are responsible for this phenomenon.

8. **EVOLUTION CONNECTION**
   This chapter explains how the emergent properties of water contribute to the suitability of the environment for life. Until fairly recently, scientists assumed that other physical requirements for life included a moderate range of temperature, pH, atmospheric pressure, and salinity, as well as low levels of toxic chemicals. That view has changed with the discovery of organisms known as extremophiles, which have been found flourishing in hot, acidic sulfur springs, around hydrothermal vents deep in the ocean, and in soils with high levels of toxic metals. Why would astrobiologists be interested in studying extremophiles? What does the existence of life in such extreme environments say about the possibility of life on other planets?

9. **SCIENTIFIC INQUIRY**
   Design a controlled experiment to test the hypothesis that water acidification caused by acidic rain would inhibit the growth of *Elodea*, a freshwater plant (see Figure 2.17).

10. **WRITE ABOUT A THEME: ORGANIZATION**
    Several emergent properties of water contribute to the suitability of the environment for life. In a short essay (100–150 words), describe how the ability of water to function as a versatile solvent arises from the structure of water molecules.

11. **SYNTHESIZE YOUR KNOWLEDGE**

How do cats drink? While dogs form their tongues into spoons and scoop water into their mouths, scientists using high-speed video have shown that cats use a different technique to drink aqueous substances like water and milk. Four times a second, the cat touches the tip of its tongue to the water and draws a column of water up into its mouth (as you can see in the photo), which then shuts before gravity can pull the water back down. Describe how the properties of water allow cats to drink in this fashion, including how water's molecular structure contributes to the process.

For selected answers, see Appendix A.

MasteringBiology®

Students Go to **MasteringBiology** for assignments, the eText, and the Study Area with practice tests, animations, and activities.

Instructors Go to **MasteringBiology** for automatically graded tutorials and questions that you can assign to your students, plus Instructor Resources.

4

Carbon and the Molecular Diversity of Life

▲ **Figure 4.1 What properties make carbon the basis of all life?**

Carbon: The Backbone of Life

Living organisms, such as the plants and the Qinling golden snub-nosed monkeys shown in **Figure 4.1**, are made up of chemicals based mostly on the element carbon. Carbon enters the biosphere through the action of plants and other photosynthetic organisms. Plants use solar energy to transform atmospheric CO_2 into the molecules of life, which are then taken in by plant-eating animals.

Of all the chemical elements, carbon is unparalleled in its ability to form molecules that are large, complex, and varied, making possible the diversity of organisms that have evolved on Earth. Proteins, DNA, carbohydrates, and other molecules that distinguish living matter from inanimate material are all composed of carbon atoms bonded to one another and to atoms of other elements. Hydrogen (H), oxygen (O), nitrogen (N), sulfur (S), and phosphorus (P) are other common ingredients of these compounds, but it is the element carbon (C) that accounts for the enormous variety of biological molecules.

Large biological molecules, such as proteins, are the main focus of Chapter 5. In this chapter, we investigate the properties of smaller molecules. We will use these small molecules to illustrate concepts of molecular architecture that will help explain why carbon is so important to life, at the same time highlighting the theme that emergent properties arise from the organization of matter in living organisms.

▲ Carbon can bond to four other atoms or groups of atoms, making a large variety of molecules possible.

CONCEPT 4.1

Organic chemistry is the study of carbon compounds

For historical reasons, compounds containing carbon are said to be organic, and their study is called **organic chemistry**. By the early 1800s, chemists had learned to make simple compounds in the laboratory by combining elements under the right conditions. Artificial synthesis of the complex molecules extracted from living matter seemed impossible, however. Organic compounds were thought to arise only in living organisms, which were believed to contain a life force beyond the jurisdiction of physical and chemical laws.

Chemists began to chip away at this notion when they learned to synthesize organic compounds in the laboratory. In 1828, Friedrich Wöhler, a German chemist, tried to make an "inorganic" salt, ammonium cyanate, by mixing solutions of ammonium ions (NH_4^+) and cyanate ions (CNO^-). Wöhler was astonished to find that instead he had made urea, an organic compound present in the urine of animals.

The next few decades saw laboratory synthesis of increasingly complex organic compounds, supporting the view that physical and chemical laws govern the processes of life. Organic chemistry was redefined as the study of carbon compounds, regardless of origin. Organic compounds range from simple molecules, such as methane (CH_4), to colossal ones, such as proteins, with thousands of atoms.

Organic Molecules and the Origin of Life on Earth

EVOLUTION In 1953, Stanley Miller, a graduate student of Harold Urey's at the University of Chicago, helped bring the abiotic (nonliving) synthesis of organic compounds into the context of evolution. Study **Figure 4.2** to learn about his classic experiment. From his results, Miller concluded that complex organic molecules could arise spontaneously under conditions thought at that time to have existed on the early Earth. You can work with the data from a related experiment in the Scientific Skills Exercise. These experiments support the idea that abiotic synthesis of organic compounds, perhaps near volcanoes, could have been an early stage in the origin of life (see Chapter 25).

The overall percentages of the major elements of life—C, H, O, N, S, and P—are quite uniform from one organism to another, reflecting the common evolutionary origin of all life. Because of carbon's ability to form four bonds, however, this limited assortment of atomic building blocks can be used to build an inexhaustible variety of organic molecules. Different species of organisms, and different individuals within a species, are distinguished by variations in the types

▼ **Figure 4.2**   **Inquiry**

Can organic molecules form under conditions estimated to simulate those on the early Earth?

Experiment In 1953, Stanley Miller set up a closed system to mimic conditions thought at that time to have existed on the early Earth. A flask of water simulated the primeval sea. The water was heated so that some vaporized and moved into a second, higher flask containing the "atmosphere"—a mixture of gases. Sparks were discharged in the synthetic atmosphere to mimic lightning.

2 The "atmosphere" contained a mixture of hydrogen gas (H_2), methane (CH_4), ammonia (NH_3), and water vapor.

3 Sparks were discharged to mimic lightning.

1 The water mixture in the "sea" flask was heated; vapor entered the "atmosphere" flask.

"Atmosphere"
CH₄
Water vapor
Electrode
NH₃ H₂
Condenser
Cooled "rain" containing organic molecules
Cold water
H_2O "sea"
Sample for chemical analysis

5 As material cycled through the apparatus, Miller periodically collected samples for analysis.

4 A condenser cooled the atmosphere, raining water and dissolved molecules into the sea flask.

Results Miller identified a variety of organic molecules that are common in organisms. These included simple compounds, such as formaldehyde (CH_2O) and hydrogen cyanide (HCN), and more complex molecules, such as amino acids and long chains of carbon and hydrogen known as hydrocarbons.

Conclusion Organic molecules, a first step in the origin of life, may have been synthesized abiotically on the early Earth. Although new evidence indicates that the early Earth's atmosphere was different from the "atmosphere" used by Miller in this experiment, recent experiments using the revised list of chemicals also produced organic molecules. (We will explore this hypothesis in more detail in Chapter 25.)

Source: S. L. Miller, A production of amino acids under possible primitive Earth conditions, *Science* 117:528–529 (1953).

WHAT IF? *If Miller had increased the concentration of NH_3 in his experiment, how might the relative amounts of the products HCN and CH_2O have differed?*

Working with Moles and Molar Ratios

Could the First Biological Molecules Have Formed Near Volcanoes on Early Earth? In 2007, Jeffrey Bada, a former graduate student of Stanley Miller's, discovered some vials of samples that had never been analyzed from an experiment performed by Miller in 1958. In this experiment, Miller used hydrogen sulfide gas (H_2S) as one of the gases in the reactant mixture. Since H_2S is released by volcanoes, the H_2S experiment was designed to mimic conditions near volcanoes on early Earth. In 2011, Bada and colleagues published the results of their analysis of these "lost" samples. In this exercise, you will make calculations using the molar ratios of reactants and products from the H_2S experiment.

How the Experiment Was Done According to his laboratory notebook, Miller used the same apparatus as in his original experiment (see Figure 4.2), but the mixture of gaseous reactants included methane (CH_4), carbon dioxide (CO_2), hydrogen sulfide (H_2S), and ammonia (NH_3). After three days of simulated volcanic activity, he collected samples of the liquid, partially purified the chemicals, and sealed the samples in sterile vials. In 2011, Bada's research team used modern analytical methods to analyze the products in the vials for the presence of amino acids, the building blocks of proteins.

Data from the Experiment The table below shows 4 of the 23 amino acids detected in the samples from Miller's 1958 H_2S experiment.

Product Compound	Molecular Formula	Molar Ratio (Relative to Glycine)
Glycine	$C_2H_5NO_2$	1.0
Serine	$C_3H_7NO_3$	3.0×10^{-2}
Methionine	$C_5H_{11}NO_2S$	1.8×10^{-3}
Alanine	$C_3H_7NO_2$	1.1

Interpret the Data

1. A *mole* is the number of grams of a substance that equals its molecular (or atomic) mass in daltons. There are 6.02×10^{23} molecules (or atoms) in 1.0 mole (Avogadro's number; see Concept 3.2). The data table shows the "molar ratios" of some of the products from the Miller H_2S experiment. In a molar ratio, each unitless value is expressed relative to a standard for that experiment. Here, the standard is the number of moles of the amino acid glycine, which is set to a value of 1.0. For instance, serine has a molar ratio of 3.0×10^{-2}, meaning that for every mole of glycine, there is 3.0×10^{-2} mole of serine. (a) Give the molar ratio of methionine to glycine and explain what it means. (b) How many molecules of glycine are present in 1.0 mole? (c) For every 1.0 mole of glycine in the sample, how many molecules of methionine are present? (Recall that to multiply two

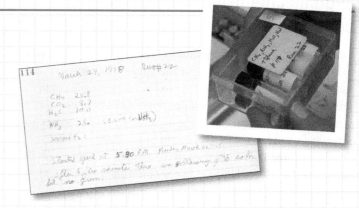

▲ Some of Stanley Miller's notes from his 1958 hydrogen sulfide (H_2S) experiment along with his original vials.

numbers with exponents, you add their exponents; to divide them, you subtract the exponent in the denominator from that in the numerator.)

2. (a) Which amino acid is present in higher amounts than glycine? (b) How many more molecules of that amino acid are present than the number of molecules in 1.0 mole of glycine?

3. The synthesis of products is limited by the amount of reactants. (a) If one mole each of CH_4, NH_3, H_2S, and CO_2 is added to 1 liter of water (= 55.5 moles of H_2O) in a flask, how many moles of hydrogen, carbon, oxygen, nitrogen, and sulfur are in the flask? (b) Looking at the molecular formula in the table, how many moles of each element would be needed to make 1.0 mole of glycine? (c) What is the maximum number of moles of glycine that could be made in that flask, with the specified ingredients, if no other molecules were made? Explain. (d) If serine or methionine were made individually, which element(s) would be used up first for each? How much of each product could be made?

4. The earlier published experiment carried out by Miller did not include H_2S in the reactants (see Figure 4.2). Which of the compounds shown in the data table can be made in the H_2S experiment but could not be made in the earlier experiment?

(MB) A version of this Scientific Skills Exercise can be assigned in MasteringBiology.

Data from E. T. Parker et al., Primordial synthesis of amines and amino acids in a 1958 Miller H_2S-rich spark discharge experiment, *Proceedings of the National Academy of Sciences USA* 108:5526-5531 (2011). www.pnas.org/cgi/doi/10.1073/pnas.1019191108.

of organic molecules they make. In a sense, the great diversity of living organisms we see on the planet (and in fossil remains) is made possible by the unique chemical versatility of the element carbon.

CONCEPT CHECK 4.1

1. Why was Wöhler astonished to find he had made urea?
2. **WHAT IF?** Miller carried out a control experiment without the electrical discharge and found no organic compounds. What might explain this result?

For suggested answers, see Appendix A.

CONCEPT 4.2

Carbon atoms can form diverse molecules by bonding to four other atoms

The key to an atom's chemical characteristics is its electron configuration. This configuration determines the kinds and number of bonds an atom will form with other atoms. Recall that it is the valence electrons, those in the outermost shell, that are available to form bonds with other atoms.

Molecule and Molecular Shape	Molecular Formula	Structural Formula	Ball-and-Stick Model (molecular shape in pink)	Space-Filling Model
(a) Methane. When a carbon atom has four single bonds to other atoms, the molecule is tetrahedral.	CH_4	H—C—H (with H above and below)		
(b) Ethane. A molecule may have more than one tetrahedral group of single-bonded atoms. (Ethane consists of two such groups.)	C_2H_6	H—C—C—H (with H above and below each C)		
(c) Ethene (ethylene). When two carbon atoms are joined by a double bond, all atoms attached to those carbons are in the same plane, and the molecule is flat.	C_2H_4	C=C (with H's attached)		

▲ **Figure 4.3 The shapes of three simple organic molecules.**

The Formation of Bonds with Carbon

Carbon has 6 electrons, with 2 in the first electron shell and 4 in the second shell; thus, it has 4 valence electrons in a shell that can hold up to 8 electrons. A carbon atom usually completes its valence shell by sharing its 4 electrons with other atoms so that 8 electrons are present. Each pair of shared electrons constitutes a covalent bond (see Figure 2.10d). In organic molecules, carbon usually forms single or double covalent bonds. Each carbon atom acts as an intersection point from which a molecule can branch off in as many as four directions. This enables carbon to form large, complex molecules.

When a carbon atom forms four single covalent bonds, the arrangement of its four hybrid orbitals causes the bonds to angle toward the corners of an imaginary tetrahedron. The bond angles in methane (CH_4) are 109.5° **(Figure 4.3a)**, and they are roughly the same in any group of atoms where carbon has four single bonds. For example, ethane (C_2H_6) is shaped like two overlapping tetrahedrons **(Figure 4.3b)**. In molecules with more carbons, every grouping of a carbon bonded to four other atoms has a tetrahedral shape. But when two carbon atoms are joined by a double bond, as in ethene (C_2H_4), the bonds from both carbons are all in the same plane, so the atoms joined to those carbons are in the same plane as well **(Figure 4.3c)**. We find it convenient to write molecules as structural formulas, as if the molecules being represented are two-dimensional, but keep in mind that molecules are three-dimensional and that the shape of a molecule is central to its function.

Hydrogen (valence = 1)	Oxygen (valence = 2)	Nitrogen (valence = 3)	Carbon (valence = 4)

▲ **Figure 4.4 Valences of the major elements of organic molecules.** Valence is the number of covalent bonds an atom can form. It is generally equal to the number of electrons required to complete the valence (outermost) shell (see Figure 2.7). All the electrons are shown for each atom in the electron distribution diagrams (top). Only the valence shell electrons are shown in the Lewis dot structures (bottom). Note that carbon can form four bonds.

MAKE CONNECTIONS *Draw the Lewis dot structures for sodium, phosphorus, sulfur, and chlorine. (Refer to Figure 2.7.)*

The electron configuration of carbon gives it covalent compatibility with many different elements. **Figure 4.4** shows the valences of carbon and its most frequent bonding partners—hydrogen, oxygen, and nitrogen. These are the four major atomic components of organic molecules. These valences are the basis for the rules of covalent bonding in organic chemistry—the building code for the architecture of organic molecules.

How do the rules of covalent bonding apply to carbon atoms with partners other than hydrogen? We'll look at two examples, the simple molecules carbon dioxide and urea.

In the carbon dioxide molecule (CO_2), a single carbon atom is joined to two atoms of oxygen by double covalent bonds. The structural formula for CO_2 is shown here:

$$O=C=O$$

Each line in a structural formula represents a pair of shared electrons. Thus, the two double bonds in CO_2 have the same number of shared electrons as four single bonds. The arrangement completes the valence shells of all atoms in the molecule. Because CO_2 is a very simple molecule and lacks hydrogen, it is often considered inorganic, even though it contains carbon. Whether we call CO_2 organic or inorganic, however, it is clearly important to the living world as the source of carbon for all organic molecules in organisms.

Urea, $CO(NH_2)_2$, is the organic compound found in urine that Wöhler synthesized in the early 1800s. Again, each atom has the required number of covalent bonds. In this case, one carbon atom participates in both single and double bonds.

Urea and carbon dioxide are molecules with only one carbon atom. But as Figure 4.3 shows, a carbon atom can also use one or more valence electrons to form covalent bonds to other carbon atoms, each of which can also form four bonds. Thus, the atoms can be linked into chains of seemingly infinite variety.

Molecular Diversity Arising from Variation in Carbon Skeletons

Carbon chains form the skeletons of most organic molecules. The skeletons vary in length and may be straight, branched, or arranged in closed rings (Figure 4.5). Some carbon skeletons have double bonds, which vary in number and location. Such variation in carbon skeletons is one important source of the molecular complexity and diversity that characterize living matter. In addition, atoms of other elements can be bonded to the skeletons at available sites.

Hydrocarbons

All of the molecules that are shown in Figures 4.3 and 4.5 are **hydrocarbons**, organic molecules consisting of only carbon and hydrogen. Atoms of hydrogen are attached to the carbon skeleton wherever electrons are available for covalent bonding. Hydrocarbons are the major components of petroleum, which is called a fossil fuel because it consists of the partially decomposed remains of organisms that lived millions of years ago.

Although hydrocarbons are not prevalent in most living organisms, many of a cell's organic molecules have regions consisting of only carbon and hydrogen. For example, the

▼ Figure 4.5 **Four ways that carbon skeletons can vary.**

(a) Length

Ethane   Propane

Carbon skeletons vary in length.

(b) Branching

Butane   2-Methylpropane
(commonly called isobutane)

Skeletons may be unbranched or branched.

(c) Double bond position

1-Butene   2-Butene

The skeleton may have double bonds, which can vary in location.

(d) Presence of rings

Cyclohexane   Benzene

Some carbon skeletons are arranged in rings. In the abbreviated structural formula for each compound (at the right), each corner represents a carbon and its attached hydrogens.

molecules known as fats have long hydrocarbon tails attached to a nonhydrocarbon component (Figure 4.6). Neither petroleum nor fat dissolves in water; both are hydrophobic compounds because the great majority of their bonds are relatively nonpolar carbon-to-hydrogen linkages. Another characteristic of hydrocarbons is that they can undergo reactions that release a relatively large amount of energy. The gasoline that fuels a car consists of hydrocarbons, and the hydrocarbon tails of fats serve as stored fuel for plant embryos (seeds) and animals.

Nucleus

Fat droplets

10 µm

(a) Part of a human adipose cell   (b) A fat molecule

▲ **Figure 4.6 The role of hydrocarbons in fats. (a)** Mammalian adipose cells stockpile fat molecules as a fuel reserve. This colorized micrograph shows part of a human adipose cell with many fat droplets, each containing a large number of fat molecules. **(b)** A fat molecule consists of a small, nonhydrocarbon component joined to three hydrocarbon tails that account for the hydrophobic behavior of fats. The tails can be broken down to provide energy. (Black = carbon; gray = hydrogen; red = oxygen.)

MAKE CONNECTIONS *How do the tails account for the hydrophobic nature of fats? (See Concept 3.2.)*

Isomers

Variation in the architecture of organic molecules can be seen in **isomers**, compounds that have the same numbers of atoms of the same elements but different structures and hence different properties. We will examine three types of isomers: structural isomers, *cis-trans* isomers, and enantiomers.

Structural isomers differ in the covalent arrangements of their atoms. Compare, for example, the two five-carbon compounds in **Figure 4.7a**. Both have the molecular formula C_5H_{12}, but they differ in the covalent arrangement of their carbon skeletons. The skeleton is straight in one compound but branched in the other. The number of possible isomers increases tremendously as carbon skeletons increase in size. There are only three forms of C_5H_{12} (two of which are shown in Figure 4.7a), but there are 18 variations of C_8H_{18} and 366,319 possible structural isomers of $C_{20}H_{42}$. Structural isomers may also differ in the location of double bonds.

In *cis-trans* **isomers** (formerly called *geometric isomers*), carbons have covalent bonds to the same atoms, but these atoms differ in their spatial arrangements due to the inflexibility of double bonds. Single bonds allow the atoms they join to rotate freely about the bond axis without changing the compound. In contrast, double bonds do not permit such rotation. If a double bond joins two carbon atoms, and each C also has two different atoms (or groups of atoms) attached to it, then two distinct *cis-trans* isomers are possible. Consider a simple molecule with two double-bonded carbons, each of which has an H and an X attached to it **(Figure 4.7b)**. The arrangement with both Xs on the same side of the double bond is called a *cis isomer*, and that with the Xs on opposite sides is

(a) Structural isomers

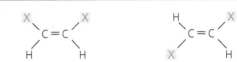

Pentane   2-methyl butane

Structural isomers differ in covalent partners, as shown in this example of two isomers of C_5H_{12}.

(b) *Cis-trans* isomers

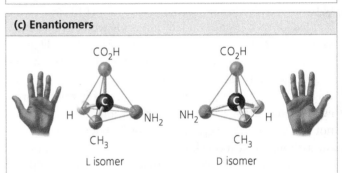

cis isomer: The two Xs are on the same side.   ***trans*** isomer: The two Xs are on opposite sides.

Cis-trans isomers differ in arrangement about a double bond. In these diagrams, X represents an atom or group of atoms attached to a double-bonded carbon.

(c) Enantiomers

CO_2H CO_2H

H   C NH_2 NH_2 C   H

CH_3 CH_3

L isomer   D isomer

Enantiomers differ in spatial arrangement around an asymmetric carbon, resulting in molecules that are mirror images, like left and right hands. The two isomers here are designated the L and D isomers from the Latin for "left" and "right" (*levo* and *dextro*). Enantiomers cannot be superimposed on each other.

DRAW IT *There are three structural isomers of C_5H_{12}; draw the one not shown in (a).*

called a *trans isomer*. The subtle difference in shape between such isomers can dramatically affect the biological activities of organic molecules. For example, the biochemistry of vision involves a light-induced change of retinal, a chemical compound in the eye, from the *cis* isomer to the *trans* isomer (see Figure 50.17). Another example involves *trans* fats, which are discussed in Chapter 5.

Enantiomers are isomers that are mirror images of each other and that differ in shape due to the presence of an *asymmetric carbon*, one that is attached to four different atoms or groups of atoms. (See the middle carbon in

Drug	Effects	Effective Enantiomer	Ineffective Enantiomer
Ibuprofen	Reduces inflammation and pain	S-Ibuprofen	R-Ibuprofen
Albuterol	Relaxes bronchial (airway) muscles, improving airflow in asthma patients	R-Albuterol	S-Albuterol

▲ **Figure 4.8 The pharmacological importance of enantiomers.** Ibuprofen and albuterol are drugs whose enantiomers have different effects. (*S* and *R* are used here to distinguish between enantiomers.) Ibuprofen is commonly sold as a mixture of the two enantiomers; the *S* enantiomer is 100 times more effective than the *R* form. Albuterol is synthesized and sold only as the *R* form of the drug; the *S* form counteracts the active *R* form.

the ball-and-stick models shown in **Figure 4.7c**.) The four groups can be arranged in space around the asymmetric carbon in two different ways that are mirror images. Enantiomers are, in a way, left-handed and right-handed versions of the molecule. Just as your right hand won't fit into a left-handed glove, a "right-handed" molecule won't fit into the same space as the "left-handed" version. Usually, only one isomer is biologically active because only that form can bind to specific molecules in an organism.

The concept of enantiomers is important in the pharmaceutical industry because the two enantiomers of a drug may not be equally effective, as is the case for both ibuprofen and the asthma medication albuterol (**Figure 4.8**). Methamphetamine also occurs in two enantiomers that have very different effects. One enantiomer is the highly addictive stimulant drug known as "crank," sold illegally in the street drug trade. The other has a much weaker effect and is the active ingredient in an over-the-counter vapor inhaler for treatment of nasal congestion. The differing effects of enantiomers in the body demonstrate that organisms are sensitive to even the most subtle variations in molecular architecture. Once again, we see that molecules have emergent properties that depend on the specific arrangement of their atoms.

CONCEPT CHECK 4.2

1. **DRAW IT** (a) Draw a structural formula for C_2H_4. (b) Draw the *trans* isomer of $C_2H_2Cl_2$.
2. Which molecules in Figure 4.5 are isomers? For each pair, identify the type of isomer.
3. How are gasoline and fat chemically similar?
4. Can propane (C_3H_8) form isomers? Explain.

For suggested answers, see Appendix A.

CONCEPT 4.3

A few chemical groups are key to molecular function

The properties of an organic molecule depend not only on the arrangement of its carbon skeleton but also on the chemical groups attached to that skeleton. We can think of hydrocarbons, the simplest organic molecules, as the underlying framework for more complex organic molecules. A number of chemical groups can replace one or more hydrogens of the hydrocarbon. These groups may participate in chemical reactions or may contribute to function indirectly by their effects on molecular shape; they help give each molecule its unique properties.

The Chemical Groups Most Important in the Processes of Life

Consider the differences between estradiol (a type of estrogen) and testosterone. These compounds are female and male sex hormones, respectively, in humans and other vertebrates. Both are steroids, organic molecules with a common carbon skeleton in the form of four fused rings. They differ only in the chemical groups attached to the rings (shown here in abbreviated form); the distinctions in molecular architecture are shaded in blue:

The different actions of these two molecules on many targets throughout the body are the basis of gender, producing the contrasting features of male and female vertebrates. In this case, the chemical groups are important because they affect molecular shape, contributing to function.

In other cases, chemical groups are directly involved in chemical reactions; such groups are known as **functional groups**. Each has certain properties, such as shape and charge, that cause it to participate in chemical reactions in a characteristic way.

The seven chemical groups most important in biological processes are the hydroxyl, carbonyl, carboxyl, amino, sulfhydryl, phosphate, and methyl groups. The first six groups can be chemically reactive; of these, all except the sulfhydryl group are also hydrophilic and thus increase the solubility of organic compounds in water. The methyl group is not reactive, but instead often serves as a recognizable tag on biological molecules. Study **Figure 4.9** to become familiar with these biologically important chemical groups.

Chemical Group	Group Properties and Compound Name	Examples
Hydroxyl group (—OH) (may be written HO—)	Is polar due to electronegative oxygen. Forms hydrogen bonds with water, helping dissolve compounds such as sugars. Compound name: Alcohol (specific name usually ends in -*ol*)	**Ethanol**, the alcohol present in alcoholic beverages
Carbonyl group ($\rangle$C=O)	Sugars with ketone groups are called ketoses; those with aldehydes are called aldoses. Compound name: Ketone (carbonyl group is within a carbon skeleton) or aldehyde (carbonyl group is at the end of a carbon skeleton)	**Acetone**, the simplest ketone **Propanal**, an aldehyde
Carboxyl group (—COOH)	Acts as an acid (can donate H⁺) because the covalent bond between oxygen and hydrogen is so polar. Compound name: Carboxylic acid, or organic acid	**Acetic acid**, which gives vinegar its sour taste $\rightleftharpoons$ + H⁺ Ionized form of —COOH (carboxylate ion), found in cells
Amino group (—NH₂)	Acts as a base; can pick up an H⁺ from the surrounding solution (water, in living organisms). Compound name: Amine	**Glycine**, an amino acid (note its carboxyl group) + H⁺ $\rightleftharpoons$ Ionized form of —NH₂, found in cells
Sulfhydryl group (—SH) (may be written HS —)	Two —SH groups can react, forming a "cross-link" that helps stabilize protein structure. Hair protein cross-links maintain the straightness or curliness of hair; in hair salons, permanent treatments break cross-links, then re-form them while the hair is in the desired shape. Compound name: Thiol	**Cysteine**, a sulfur-containing amino acid
Phosphate group (—OPO₃²⁻)	Contributes negative charge (1– when positioned inside a chain of phosphates; 2– when at the end). When attached, confers on a molecule the ability to react with water, releasing energy. Compound name: Organic phosphate	**Glycerol phosphate**, which takes part in many important chemical reactions in cells
Methyl group (—CH₃)	Affects the expression of genes when on DNA or on proteins bound to DNA. Affects the shape and function of male and female sex hormones. Compound name: Methylated compound	**5-Methyl cytosine**, a component of DNA that has been modified by addition of a methyl group

ATP: An Important Source of Energy for Cellular Processes

The "Phosphate group" row in Figure 4.9 shows a simple example of an organic phosphate molecule. A more complicated organic phosphate, **adenosine triphosphate**, or **ATP**, is worth mentioning here because its function in the cell is so important. ATP consists of an organic molecule called adenosine attached to a string of three phosphate groups:

Where three phosphates are present in series, as in ATP, one phosphate may be split off as a result of a reaction with water. This inorganic phosphate ion, $HOPO_3^{2-}$, is often abbreviated ℗$_i$ in this book, and a phosphate group in an organic molecule is often written as ℗. Having lost one phosphate, ATP becomes adenosine *di*phosphate, or ADP. Although ATP is sometimes said to store energy, it is more accurate to think of it as storing the potential to react with water. This reaction releases energy that can be used by the cell. You will learn about this in more detail in Chapter 8.

Reacts with H_2O

℗–℗–℗–Adenosine ⟶ ℗$_i$ + ℗–℗–Adenosine + Energy

ATP   Inorganic   ADP
           phosphate

CONCEPT CHECK 4.3

1. What does the term *amino acid* signify about the structure of such a molecule?
2. What chemical change occurs to ATP when it reacts with water and releases energy?
3. **WHAT IF?** Suppose you had an organic molecule such as cysteine (see Figure 4.9, sulfhydryl group example), and you chemically removed the —NH_2 group and replaced it with —COOH. Draw the structural formula for this molecule and speculate about its chemical properties. Is the central carbon asymmetric before the change? After?

For suggested answers, see Appendix A.

The Chemical Elements of Life: *A Review*

Living matter, as you have learned, consists mainly of carbon, oxygen, hydrogen, and nitrogen, with smaller amounts of sulfur and phosphorus. These elements all form strong covalent bonds, an essential characteristic in the architecture of complex organic molecules. Of all these elements, carbon is the virtuoso of the covalent bond. The versatility of carbon makes possible the great diversity of organic molecules, each with particular properties that emerge from the unique arrangement of its carbon skeleton and the chemical groups appended to that skeleton. This variation at the molecular level provides the foundation for the rich biological diversity found on our planet.

4 Chapter Review

SUMMARY OF KEY CONCEPTS

CONCEPT 4.1

Organic chemistry is the study of carbon compounds (pp. 57–58)

- Organic compounds, once thought to arise only within living organisms, were finally synthesized in the laboratory.
- Living matter is made mostly of carbon, oxygen, hydrogen, and nitrogen. Biological diversity results from carbon's ability to form a huge number of molecules with particular shapes and properties.

? *How did Stanley Miller's experiments support the idea that, even at life's origins, physical and chemical laws govern the processes of life?*

CONCEPT 4.2

Carbon atoms can form diverse molecules by bonding to four other atoms (pp. 58–62)

- Carbon, with a valence of 4, can bond to various other atoms, including O, H, and N. Carbon can also bond to other carbon atoms, forming the carbon skeletons of organic compounds. These skeletons vary in length and shape and have bonding sites for atoms of other elements.
- **Hydrocarbons** consist of carbon and hydrogen.
- **Isomers** are compounds that have the same molecular formula but different structures and therefore different properties. Three types of isomers are **structural isomers**, *cis-trans* isomers, and **enantiomers**.

? *Refer back to Figure 4.9. What type of isomers are acetone and propanal? How many asymmetric carbons are present in acetic acid, glycine, and glycerol phosphate? Can these three molecules exist as forms that are enantiomers?*

CONCEPT 4.3

A few chemical groups are key to molecular function (pp. 62–64)

- Chemical groups attached to the carbon skeletons of organic molecules participate in chemical reactions (**functional groups**) or contribute to function by affecting molecular shape (see Figure 4.9).
- **ATP (adenosine triphosphate)** consists of adenosine attached to three phosphate groups. ATP can react with water, forming

inorganic phosphate and ADP (adenosine diphosphate). This reaction releases energy that can be used by the cell.

Reacts
with H₂O

Ⓟ–Ⓟ–Ⓟ–[Adenosine] ⟶ Ⓟᵢ + Ⓟ–Ⓟ–[Adenosine] + Energy

ATP   Inorganic   ADP
             phosphate

? *In what ways does a methyl group differ chemically from the other six important chemical groups shown in Figure 4.9?*

TEST YOUR UNDERSTANDING

LEVEL 1: KNOWLEDGE/COMPREHENSION

1. Organic chemistry is currently defined as
   a. the study of compounds made only by living cells.
   b. the study of carbon compounds.
   c. the study of natural (as opposed to synthetic) compounds.
   d. the study of hydrocarbons.

2. Which functional group is *not* present in this molecule?
   a. carboxyl
   b. sulfhydryl
   c. hydroxyl
   d. amino

3. **MAKE CONNECTIONS** Which chemical group is most likely to be responsible for an organic molecule behaving as a base (see Concept 3.3)?
   a. hydroxyl
   b. carbonyl
   c. amino
   d. phosphate

LEVEL 2: APPLICATION/ANALYSIS

4. Which of the following hydrocarbons has a double bond in its carbon skeleton?
   a. C_3H_8 c. C_2H_4
   b. C_2H_6 d. C_2H_2

5. Choose the term that correctly describes the relationship between these two sugar molecules:
   a. structural isomers
   b. *cis-trans* isomers
   c. enantiomers
   d. isotopes

6. Identify the asymmetric carbon in this molecule:

7. Which action could produce a carbonyl group?
   a. the replacement of the —OH of a carboxyl group with hydrogen
   b. the addition of a thiol to a hydroxyl
   c. the addition of a hydroxyl to a phosphate
   d. the replacement of the nitrogen of an amine with oxygen

8. Which of the molecules shown in question 5 has an asymmetric carbon? Which carbon is asymmetric?

LEVEL 3: SYNTHESIS/EVALUATION

9. **EVOLUTION CONNECTION**
   DRAW IT Some scientists think that life elsewhere in the universe might be based on the element silicon, rather than on carbon, as on Earth. Look at the electron distribution diagram for silicon in Figure 2.7 and draw the Lewis dot structure for silicon. What properties does silicon share with carbon that would make silicon-based life more likely than, say, neon-based life or aluminum-based life?

10. **SCIENTIFIC INQUIRY**
    50 years ago, pregnant women who were prescribed thalidomide for morning sickness gave birth to children with birth defects. Thalidomide is a mixture of two enantiomers; one reduces morning sickness, but the other causes severe birth defects. Today, the FDA has approved this drug for non-pregnant individuals with Hansen's disease (leprosy) or newly diagnosed multiple myeloma, a blood and bone marrow cancer. The beneficial enantiomer can be synthesized and given to patients, but over time, both the beneficial *and* the harmful enantiomer can be detected in the body. Propose a possible explanation for the presence of the harmful enantiomer.

11. **WRITE ABOUT A THEME: ORGANIZATION**
    In 1918, an epidemic of sleeping sickness caused an unusual rigid paralysis in some survivors, similar to symptoms of advanced Parkinson's disease. Years later, L-dopa (below, left), a chemical used to treat Parkinson's disease, was given to some of these patients. L-dopa was remarkably effective at eliminating the paralysis, at least temporarily. However, its enantiomer, D-dopa (right), was subsequently shown to have no effect at all, as is the case for Parkinson's disease. In a short essay (100–150 words), discuss how the effectiveness of one enantiomer and not the other illustrates the theme of structure and function.

L-dopa   **D-dopa**

12. **SYNTHESIZE YOUR KNOWLEDGE**

Explain how the chemical structure of the carbon atom accounts for the differences between the male and female lions seen in the photo.

For selected answers, see Appendix A.

MasteringBiology®

Students Go to **MasteringBiology** for assignments, the eText, and the Study Area with practice tests, animations, and activities.

Instructors Go to **MasteringBiology** for automatically graded tutorials and questions that you can assign to your students, plus Instructor Resources.

5

The Structure and Function of Large Biological Molecules

▲ Figure 5.1 **Why is the structure of a protein important for its function?**

The Molecules of Life

Given the rich complexity of life on Earth, it might surprise you that the most important large molecules found in all living things—from bacteria to elephants—can be sorted into just four main classes: carbohydrates, lipids, proteins, and nucleic acids. On the molecular scale, members of three of these classes—carbohydrates, proteins, and nucleic acids—are huge and are therefore called **macromolecules**. For example, a protein may consist of thousands of atoms that form a molecular colossus with a mass well over 100,000 daltons. Considering the size and complexity of macromolecules, it is noteworthy that biochemists have determined the detailed structure of so many of them. The image in **Figure 5.1** is a molecular model of a protein called alcohol dehydrogenase, which breaks down alcohol in the body.

The architecture of a large biological molecule plays an essential role in its function. Like water and simple organic molecules, large biological molecules exhibit unique emergent properties arising from the orderly arrangement of their atoms. In this chapter, we'll first consider how macromolecules are built. Then we'll examine the structure and function of all four classes of large biological molecules: carbohydrates, lipids, proteins, and nucleic acids.

66

CONCEPT 5.1

Macromolecules are polymers, built from monomers

The macromolecules in three of the four classes of life's organic compounds—carbohydrates, proteins, and nucleic acids, all except lipids—are chain-like molecules called polymers (from the Greek *polys*, many, and *meros*, part). A **polymer** is a long molecule consisting of many similar or identical building blocks linked by covalent bonds, much as a train consists of a chain of cars. The repeating units that serve as the building blocks of a polymer are smaller molecules called **monomers** (from the Greek *monos*, single). Some monomers also have other functions of their own.

The Synthesis and Breakdown of Polymers

Although each class of polymer is made up of a different type of monomer, the chemical mechanisms by which cells make and break down polymers are basically the same in all cases. In cells, these processes are facilitated by **enzymes**, specialized macromolecules that speed up chemical reactions. Monomers are connected by a reaction in which two molecules are covalently bonded to each other, with the loss of a water molecule; this is known as a **dehydration reaction (Figure 5.2a)**. When a bond forms between two monomers, each monomer contributes part of the water molecule that is released during the reaction: One monomer provides a hydroxyl group (—OH), while the other provides a hydrogen (—H). This reaction is repeated as monomers are added to the chain one by one, making a polymer.

Polymers are disassembled to monomers by **hydrolysis**, a process that is essentially the reverse of the dehydration reaction **(Figure 5.2b)**. Hydrolysis means water breakage (from the Greek *hydro*, water, and *lysis*, break). The bond between monomers is broken by the addition of a water molecule, with a hydrogen from water attaching to one monomer and the hydroxyl group attaching to the other. An example of hydrolysis within our bodies is the process of digestion. The bulk of the organic material in our food is in the form of polymers that are much too large to enter our cells. Within the digestive tract, various enzymes attack the polymers, speeding up hydrolysis. Released monomers are then absorbed into the bloodstream for distribution to all body cells. Those cells can then use dehydration reactions to assemble the monomers into new, different polymers that can perform specific functions required by the cell.

The Diversity of Polymers

A cell has thousands of different macromolecules; the collection varies from one type of cell to another. The inherited

▼ **Figure 5.2 The synthesis and breakdown of polymers.**

(a) Dehydration reaction: synthesizing a polymer

Short polymer / Unlinked monomer

Dehydration removes a water molecule, forming a new bond.

H_2O

Longer polymer

(b) Hydrolysis: breaking down a polymer

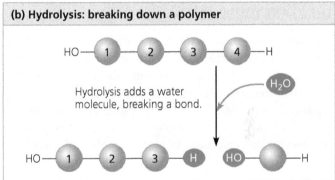

Hydrolysis adds a water molecule, breaking a bond.

H_2O

differences between close relatives such as human siblings reflect small variations in polymers, particularly DNA and proteins. Molecular differences between unrelated individuals are more extensive, and those between species greater still. The diversity of macromolecules in the living world is vast, and the possible variety is effectively limitless.

What is the basis for such diversity in life's polymers? These molecules are constructed from only 40 to 50 common monomers and some others that occur rarely. Building a huge variety of polymers from such a limited number of monomers is analogous to constructing hundreds of thousands of words from only 26 letters of the alphabet. The key is arrangement—the particular linear sequence that the units follow. However, this analogy falls far short of describing the great diversity of macromolecules because most biological polymers have many more monomers than the number of letters a word, even the longest ones. Proteins, for example, are built from 20 kinds of amino acids arranged in chains that are typically hundreds of amino acids long. The molecular logic of life is simple but elegant: Small molecules common to all organisms are ordered into unique macromolecules.

Despite this immense diversity, molecular structure and function can still be grouped roughly by class. Let's examine each of the four major classes of large biological molecules. For each class, the large molecules have emergent properties not found in their individual building blocks.

1. What are the four main classes of large biological molecules? Which class does not consist of polymers?

2. How many molecules of water are needed to completely hydrolyze a polymer that is ten monomers long?

3. **WHAT IF?** If you eat a piece of fish, what reactions must occur for the amino acid monomers in the protein of the fish to be converted to new proteins in your body?

For suggested answers, see Appendix A.

CONCEPT 5.2

Carbohydrates serve as fuel and building material

Carbohydrates include sugars and polymers of sugars. The simplest carbohydrates are the monosaccharides, or simple sugars; these are the monomers from which more complex carbohydrates are built. Disaccharides are double sugars, consisting of two monosaccharides joined by a covalent bond. Carbohydrate macromolecules are polymers called polysaccharides, composed of many sugar building blocks.

Sugars

Monosaccharides (from the Greek *monos*, single, and *sacchar*, sugar) generally have molecular formulas that are some multiple of the unit CH_2O. Glucose ($C_6H_{12}O_6$), the most common monosaccharide, is of central importance in the chemistry of life. In the structure of glucose, we can see the trademarks of a sugar: The molecule has a carbonyl group (CO) and multiple hydroxyl groups (—OH) **(Figure 5.3)**. Depending on the location of the carbonyl group, a sugar is either an aldose (aldehyde sugar) or a ketose (ketone sugar). Glucose, for example, is an aldose; fructose, an isomer of glucose, is a ketose. (Most names for sugars end in *-ose*.) Another criterion for classifying sugars is the size of the carbon skeleton, which ranges from three to seven carbons long. Glucose, fructose, and other sugars that have six carbons are called hexoses. Trioses (three-carbon sugars) and pentoses (five-carbon sugars) are also common.

Still another source of diversity for simple sugars is in the spatial arrangement of their parts around asymmetric carbons. (Recall that an asymmetric carbon is a carbon attached to four different atoms or groups of atoms.) Glucose and galactose, for example, differ only in the placement of parts around one asymmetric carbon (see the purple boxes in Figure 5.3). What seems like a small difference is significant enough to give the two sugars distinctive shapes and binding activities, thus different behaviors.

Although it is convenient to draw glucose with a linear carbon skeleton, this representation is not completely accurate.

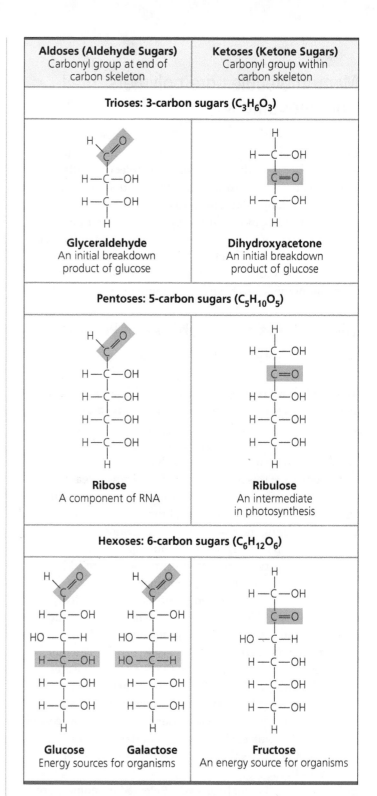

▲ **Figure 5.3 The structure and classification of some monosaccharides.** Sugars vary in the location of their carbonyl groups (orange), the length of their carbon skeletons, and the spatial arrangement around asymmetric carbons (compare, for example, the purple portions of glucose and galactose).

MAKE CONNECTIONS *In the 1970s, a process was developed that converts the glucose in corn syrup to its sweeter-tasting isomer, fructose. High-fructose corn syrup, a common ingredient in soft drinks and processed food, is a mixture of glucose and fructose. What type of isomers are glucose and fructose? (See Figure 4.7.)*

(a) **Linear and ring forms.** Chemical equilibrium between the linear and ring structures greatly favors the formation of rings. The carbons of the sugar are numbered 1 to 6, as shown. To form the glucose ring, carbon 1 (magenta) bonds to the oxygen (blue) attached to carbon 5.

(b) **Abbreviated ring structure.** Each unlabeled corner represents a carbon. The ring's thicker edge indicates that you are looking at the ring edge-on; the components attached to the ring lie above or below the plane of the ring.

▲ **Figure 5.4   Linear and ring forms of glucose.**

DRAW IT *Start with the linear form of fructose (see Figure 5.3) and draw the formation of the fructose ring in two steps. First, number the carbons starting at the top of the linear structure. Then draw the molecule in the same orientation as the glucose in the middle of (a) above, attaching carbon 5 via its oxygen to carbon 2. Compare the number of carbons in the fructose and glucose rings.*

In aqueous solutions, glucose molecules, as well as most other five- and six-carbon sugars, form rings (**Figure 5.4**).

Monosaccharides, particularly glucose, are major nutrients for cells. In the process known as cellular respiration, cells extract energy from glucose molecules by breaking them down in a series of reactions. Not only are simple-sugar molecules a major fuel for cellular work, but their carbon skeletons also serve as raw material for the synthesis of other types of small organic molecules, such as amino acids and fatty acids. Sugar molecules that are not immediately used in these ways are generally incorporated as monomers into disaccharides or polysaccharides.

A **disaccharide** consists of two monosaccharides joined by a **glycosidic linkage**, a covalent bond formed between two monosaccharides by a dehydration reaction. For example, maltose is a disaccharide formed by the linking of two molecules of glucose (**Figure 5.5a**). Also known as malt sugar, maltose is an ingredient used in brewing beer. The most prevalent disaccharide is sucrose, which is table sugar. Its two monomers are glucose and fructose (**Figure 5.5b**). Plants generally transport carbohydrates from leaves to roots and other nonphotosynthetic organs in the form of sucrose. Lactose, the sugar present in milk, is another disaccharide, in this case a glucose molecule joined to a galactose molecule.

(a) **Dehydration reaction in the synthesis of maltose.** The bonding of two glucose units forms maltose. The 1–4 glycosidic linkage joins the number 1 carbon of one glucose to the number 4 carbon of the second glucose. Joining the glucose monomers in a different way would result in a different disaccharide.

Glucose   Glucose   Maltose

(b) **Dehydration reaction in the synthesis of sucrose.** Sucrose is a disaccharide formed from glucose and fructose. Notice that fructose forms a five-sided ring, though it is a hexose like glucose.

Glucose   Fructose   Sucrose

▲ **Figure 5.5   Examples of disaccharide synthesis.**

DRAW IT *Referring to Figures 5.3 and 5.4, number the carbons in each sugar in this figure. Insert arrows linking the carbons to show how the numbering is consistent with the name of each glycosidic linkage.*

Polysaccharides

Polysaccharides are macromolecules, polymers with a few hundred to a few thousand monosaccharides joined by glycosidic linkages. Some polysaccharides serve as storage material, hydrolyzed as needed to provide sugar for cells. Other polysaccharides serve as building material for structures that protect the cell or the whole organism. The architecture and function of a polysaccharide are determined by its sugar monomers and by the positions of its glycosidic linkages.

Storage Polysaccharides

Both plants and animals store sugars for later use in the form of storage polysaccharides (**Figure 5.6**). Plants store **starch**, a polymer of glucose monomers, as granules within cellular structures known as plastids, which include chloroplasts. Synthesizing starch enables the plant to stockpile surplus glucose. Because glucose is a major cellular fuel, starch represents stored energy. The sugar can later be withdrawn from this carbohydrate "bank" by hydrolysis, which breaks the bonds between the glucose monomers. Most animals, including humans, also have enzymes that can hydrolyze plant starch, making glucose available as a nutrient for cells. Potato tubers and grains are the major sources of starch in the human diet.

Most of the glucose monomers in starch are joined by 1–4 linkages (number 1 carbon to number 4 carbon), like the glucose units in maltose (see Figure 5.5a). The simplest form of starch, amylose, is unbranched. Amylopectin, a more complex starch, is a branched polymer with 1–6 linkages at the branch points. Both of these starches are shown in **Figure 5.6a**.

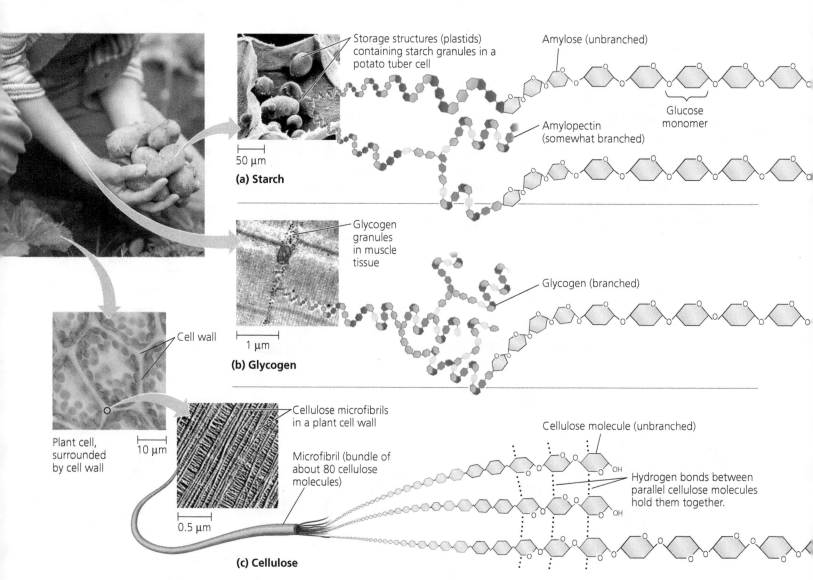

▲ Figure 5.6 Polysaccharides of plants and animals. (a) Starch stored in plant cells, **(b)** glycogen stored in muscle cells, and **(c)** structural cellulose fibers in plant cell walls are all polysaccharides composed entirely of glucose monomers (green hexagons). In starch and glycogen, the polymer chains tend to form helices in unbranched regions because of the angle of the linkages between glucose molecules. There are two kinds of starch: amylose and amylopectin. Cellulose, with a different kind of glucose linkage, is always unbranched.

Animals store a polysaccharide called **glycogen**, a polymer of glucose that is like amylopectin but more extensively branched **(Figure 5.6b)**. Vertebrates store glycogen mainly in liver and muscle cells. Hydrolysis of glycogen in these cells releases glucose when the demand for sugar increases. This stored fuel cannot sustain an animal for long, however. In humans, for example, glycogen stores are depleted in about a day unless they are replenished by consumption of food. This is an issue of concern in low-carbohydrate diets, which can result in weakness and fatigue.

Structural Polysaccharides

Organisms build strong materials from structural polysaccharides. For example, the polysaccharide called **cellulose** is a major component of the tough walls that enclose plant cells **(Figure 5.6c)**. On a global scale, plants produce almost 10^{14} kg (100 billion tons) of cellulose per year; it is the most abundant organic compound on Earth.

Like starch, cellulose is a polymer of glucose, but the glycosidic linkages in these two polymers differ. The difference is based on the fact that there are actually two slightly different ring structures for glucose **(Figure 5.7a)**. When glucose forms a ring, the hydroxyl group attached to the number 1 carbon is positioned either below or above the plane of the ring. These two ring forms for glucose are called alpha (α) and beta (β), respectively. (Greek letters are often used as a "numbering" system for different versions of biological structures, much as we use the letters a, b, c, and so on for the parts of a question or a figure.) In starch, all the glucose monomers are in the α configuration **(Figure 5.7b)**, the

arrangement we saw in Figures 5.4 and 5.5. In contrast, the glucose monomers of cellulose are all in the β configuration, making every glucose monomer "upside down" with respect to its neighbors **(Figure 5.7c; see also Figure 5.6c)**.

The differing glycosidic linkages in starch and cellulose give the two molecules distinct three-dimensional shapes. Whereas certain starch molecules are largely helical, a cellulose molecule is straight. Cellulose is never branched, and some hydroxyl groups on its glucose monomers are free to hydrogen-bond with the hydroxyls of other cellulose molecules lying parallel to it. In plant cell walls, parallel cellulose molecules held together in this way are grouped into units called microfibrils (see Figure 5.6c). These cable-like microfibrils are a strong building material for plants and an important substance for humans because cellulose is the major constituent of paper and the only component of cotton.

Enzymes that digest starch by hydrolyzing its α linkages are unable to hydrolyze the β linkages of cellulose due to the different shapes of these two molecules. In fact, few organisms possess enzymes that can digest cellulose. Almost all animals, including humans, do not; the cellulose in our food passes through the digestive tract and is eliminated with the feces. Along the way, the cellulose abrades the wall of the digestive tract and stimulates the lining to secrete mucus, which aids in the smooth passage of food through the tract. Thus, although cellulose is not a nutrient for humans, it is an important part of a healthful diet. Most fruits, vegetables, and whole grains are rich in cellulose. On food packages, "insoluble fiber" refers mainly to cellulose.

Some microorganisms can digest cellulose, breaking it down into glucose monomers. A cow harbors

(a) α and β glucose ring structures. These two interconvertible forms of glucose differ in the placement of the hydroxyl group (highlighted in blue) attached to the number 1 carbon.

α Glucose

β Glucose

(b) Starch: 1–4 linkage of α glucose monomers. All monomers are in the same orientation. Compare the positions of the —OH groups highlighted in yellow with those in cellulose (c).

(c) Cellulose: 1–4 linkage of β glucose monomers. In cellulose, every β glucose monomer is upside down with respect to its neighbors. (See the highlighted —OH groups.)

▲ **Figure 5.7 Starch and cellulose structures.**

CH₂OH structure...

◄ The structure of the chitin monomer

◄ Chitin, embedded in proteins, forms the exoskeleton of arthropods. This cicada is molting—shedding its old exoskeleton and emerging in adult form.

► Chitin is used to make a strong and flexible surgical thread that decomposes after the wound or incision heals.

▲ **Figure 5.8 Chitin, a structural polysaccharide.**

cellulose-digesting prokaryotes and protists in its gut. These microbes hydrolyze the cellulose of hay and grass and convert the glucose to other compounds that nourish the cow. Similarly, a termite, which is unable to digest cellulose by itself, has prokaryotes or protists living in its gut that can make a meal of wood. Some fungi can also digest cellulose in soil and elsewhere, thereby helping recycle chemical elements within Earth's ecosystems.

Another important structural polysaccharide is **chitin**, the carbohydrate used by arthropods (insects, spiders, crustaceans, and related animals) to build their exoskeletons **(Figure 5.8)**. An exoskeleton is a hard case that surrounds the soft parts of an animal. Made up of chitin embedded in a layer of proteins, the case is leathery and flexible at first, but becomes hardened when the proteins are chemically linked to each other (as in insects) or encrusted with calcium carbonate (as in crabs). Chitin is also found in fungi, which use this polysaccharide rather than cellulose as the building material for their cell walls. Chitin is similar to cellulose, with β linkages, except that the glucose monomer of chitin has a nitrogen-containing appendage (see Figure 5.8, top right).

CONCEPT CHECK 5.2

1. Write the formula for a monosaccharide that has three carbons.
2. A dehydration reaction joins two glucose molecules to form maltose. The formula for glucose is $C_6H_{12}O_6$. What is the formula for maltose?
3. **WHAT IF?** After a cow is given antibiotics to treat an infection, a vet gives the animal a drink of "gut culture" containing various prokaryotes. Why is this necessary?

For suggested answers, see Appendix A.

CONCEPT 5.3

Lipids are a diverse group of hydrophobic molecules

Lipids are the one class of large biological molecules that does not include true polymers, and they are generally not big enough to be considered macromolecules. The compounds called **lipids** are grouped with each other because they share one important trait: They mix poorly, if at all, with water. The hydrophobic behavior of lipids is based on their molecular structure. Although they may have some polar bonds associated with oxygen, lipids consist mostly of hydrocarbon regions. Lipids are varied in form and function. They include waxes and certain pigments, but we will focus on the types of lipids that are most biologically important: fats, phospholipids, and steroids.

Fats

Although fats are not polymers, they are large molecules assembled from smaller molecules by dehydration reactions. A **fat** is constructed from two kinds of smaller molecules: glycerol and fatty acids **(Figure 5.9a)**. Glycerol is an alcohol; each of its three carbons bears a hydroxyl group. A **fatty acid** has a long carbon skeleton, usually 16 or 18 carbon atoms in length. The carbon at one end of the skeleton is part of a carboxyl group, the functional group that gives these molecules the name fatty *acid*. The rest of the skeleton consists of a hydrocarbon chain. The relatively nonpolar C—H bonds in the hydrocarbon chains of fatty acids are the reason fats are hydrophobic. Fats separate from water because the water molecules hydrogen-bond to one another and exclude the fats. This is the reason that vegetable oil (a liquid fat) separates from the aqueous vinegar solution in a bottle of salad dressing.

In making a fat, three fatty acid molecules are each joined to glycerol by an ester linkage, a bond formed by a dehydration reaction between a hydroxyl group and a carboxyl group. The resulting fat, also called a **triacylglycerol**, thus consists of three fatty acids linked to one glycerol molecule.

(a) One of three dehydration reactions in the synthesis of a fat

Glycerol

Fatty acid
(in this case, palmitic acid)

Ester linkage

(b) Fat molecule (triacylglycerol)

▲ **Figure 5.9 The synthesis and structure of a fat, or triacyl-glycerol.** The molecular building blocks of a fat are one molecule of glycerol and three molecules of fatty acids. **(a)** One water molecule is removed for each fatty acid joined to the glycerol. **(b)** A fat molecule with three fatty acid units, two of them identical. The carbons of the fatty acids are arranged zigzag to suggest the actual orientations of the four single bonds extending from each carbon (see Figure 4.3a).

(Still another name for a fat is *triglyceride*, a word often found in the list of ingredients on packaged foods.) The fatty acids in a fat can all be the same, or they can be of two or three different kinds, as in **Figure 5.9b**.

The terms *saturated* fats and *unsaturated* fats are commonly used in the context of nutrition (**Figure 5.10**). These terms refer to the structure of the hydrocarbon chains of the fatty acids. If there are no double bonds between carbon atoms composing a chain, then as many hydrogen atoms as possible are bonded to the carbon skeleton. Such a structure is said to be *saturated* with hydrogen, and the resulting fatty acid is therefore called a **saturated fatty acid** (**Figure 5.10a**). An **unsaturated fatty acid** has one or more double bonds, with one fewer hydrogen atom on each double-bonded carbon. Nearly all double bonds in naturally occurring fatty acids are *cis* double bonds, which cause a kink in the hydrocarbon chain wherever they occur (**Figure 5.10b**). (See Figure 4.7b to remind yourself about *cis* and *trans* double bonds.)

A fat made from saturated fatty acids is called a saturated fat. Most animal fats are saturated: The hydrocarbon chains of their fatty acids—the "tails" of the fat molecules—lack double bonds, and their flexibility allows the fat molecules to pack together tightly. Saturated animal fats—such as lard

▼ **Figure 5.10 Saturated and unsaturated fats and fatty acids.**

(a) Saturated fat

At room temperature, the molecules of a saturated fat, such as the fat in butter, are packed closely together, forming a solid.

Structural formula of a saturated fat molecule (Each hydrocarbon chain is represented as a zigzag line, where each bend represents a carbon atom and hydrogens are not shown.)

Space-filling model of stearic acid, a saturated fatty acid (red = oxygen, black = carbon, gray = hydrogen)

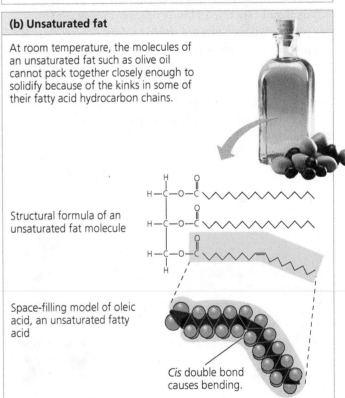

(b) Unsaturated fat

At room temperature, the molecules of an unsaturated fat such as olive oil cannot pack together closely enough to solidify because of the kinks in some of their fatty acid hydrocarbon chains.

Structural formula of an unsaturated fat molecule

Space-filling model of oleic acid, an unsaturated fatty acid

Cis double bond causes bending.

and butter—are solid at room temperature. In contrast, the fats of plants and fishes are generally unsaturated, meaning that they are built of one or more types of unsaturated fatty acids. Usually liquid at room temperature, plant and fish fats are referred to as oils—olive oil and cod liver oil are examples. The kinks where the *cis* double bonds are located prevent the molecules from packing together closely enough to solidify at room temperature. The phrase "hydrogenated vegetable oils" on food labels means that unsaturated fats have been synthetically converted to saturated fats by adding hydrogen. Peanut butter, margarine, and many other products are hydrogenated to prevent lipids from separating out in liquid (oil) form.

A diet rich in saturated fats is one of several factors that may contribute to the cardiovascular disease known as atherosclerosis. In this condition, deposits called plaques develop within the walls of blood vessels, causing inward bulges that impede blood flow and reduce the resilience of the vessels. Recent studies have shown that the process of hydrogenating vegetable oils produces not only saturated fats but also unsaturated fats with *trans* double bonds. These **trans fats** may contribute more than saturated fats to atherosclerosis (see Chapter 42) and other problems. Because trans fats are especially common in baked goods and processed foods, the U.S. Department of Agriculture requires nutritional labels to include information on trans fat content. Some U.S. cities and at least two countries—Denmark and Switzerland—have even banned the use of trans fats in restaurants.

The major function of fats is energy storage. The hydrocarbon chains of fats are similar to gasoline molecules and just as rich in energy. A gram of fat stores more than twice as much energy as a gram of a polysaccharide, such as starch. Because plants are relatively immobile, they can function with bulky energy storage in the form of starch. (Vegetable oils are generally obtained from seeds, where more compact storage is an asset to the plant.) Animals, however, must carry their energy stores with them, so there is an advantage to having a more compact reservoir

of fuel—fat. Humans and other mammals stock their long-term food reserves in adipose cells (see Figure 4.6a), which swell and shrink as fat is deposited and withdrawn from storage. In addition to storing energy, adipose tissue also cushions such vital organs as the kidneys, and a layer of fat beneath the skin insulates the body. This subcutaneous layer is especially thick in whales, seals, and most other marine mammals, protecting them from cold ocean water.

Phospholipids

Cells as we know them could not exist without another type of lipid—phospholipids. Phospholipids are essential for cells because they are major constituents of cell membranes. Their structure provides a classic example of how form fits function at the molecular level. As shown in **Figure 5.11**, a **phospholipid** is similar to a fat molecule but has only two fatty acids attached to glycerol rather than three. The third hydroxyl group of glycerol is joined to a phosphate group, which has a negative electrical charge in the cell. Typically, an additional small charged or polar molecule is also linked to the phosphate group. Choline is one such molecule (see Figure 5.11), but there are many others as well, allowing formation of a variety of phospholipids that differ from each other.

The two ends of phospholipids show different behavior toward water. The hydrocarbon tails are hydrophobic and are excluded from water. However, the phosphate group and its attachments form a hydrophilic head that has an affinity for water. When phospholipids are added to water, they self-assemble into double-layered structures called

◀ **Figure 5.11 The structure of a phospholipid.** A phospholipid has a hydrophilic (polar) head and two hydrophobic (nonpolar) tails. This particular phospholipid, called a phosphatidylcholine, has a choline attached to a phosphate group. Shown here are **(a)** the structural formula, **(b)** the space-filling model (yellow = phosphorus, blue = nitrogen), **(c)** the symbol for a phospholipid that will appear throughout this book, and **(d)** the bilayer structure formed by self-assembly of phospholipids in an aqueous environment.

DRAW IT *Draw an oval around the hydrophilic head of the space-filling model.*

© Pearson Education, Inc.

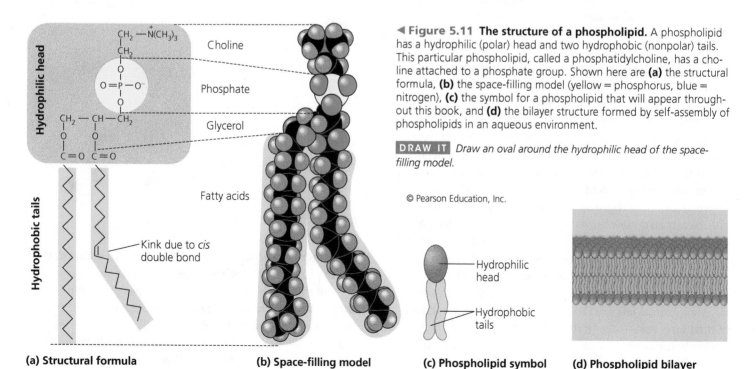

(a) Structural formula   (b) Space-filling model   (c) Phospholipid symbol   (d) Phospholipid bilayer "bilayers," shielding their hydrophobic portions from water (Figure 5.11d).

At the surface of a cell, phospholipids are arranged in a similar bilayer. The hydrophilic heads of the molecules are on the outside of the bilayer, in contact with the aqueous solutions inside and outside of the cell. The hydrophobic tails point toward the interior of the bilayer, away from the water. The phospholipid bilayer forms a boundary between the cell and its external environment; in fact, the existence of cells depends on the properties of phospholipids.

Steroids

Steroids are lipids characterized by a carbon skeleton consisting of four fused rings. Different steroids are distinguished by the particular chemical groups attached to this ensemble of rings. **Cholesterol**, a type of steroid, is a crucial molecule in animals (**Figure 5.12**). It is a common component of animal cell membranes and is also the precursor from which other steroids, such as the vertebrate sex hormones, are synthesized. In vertebrates, cholesterol is synthesized in the liver and is also obtained from the diet. A high level of cholesterol in the blood may contribute to atherosclerosis. In fact, both saturated fats and trans fats exert their negative impact on health by affecting cholesterol levels.

▲ **Figure 5.12 Cholesterol, a steroid.** Cholesterol is the molecule from which other steroids, including the sex hormones, are synthesized. Steroids vary in the chemical groups attached to their four interconnected rings (shown in gold).

MAKE CONNECTIONS *Compare cholesterol with the sex hormones shown in the figure at the beginning of Concept 4.3. Circle the chemical groups that cholesterol has in common with estradiol; put a square around the chemical groups that cholesterol has in common with testosterone.*

CONCEPT CHECK 5.3

1. Compare the structure of a fat (triglyceride) with that of a phospholipid.
2. Why are human sex hormones considered lipids?
3. **WHAT IF?** Suppose a membrane surrounded an oil droplet, as it does in the cells of plant seeds and in some animal cells. Describe and explain the form it might take.

For suggested answers, see Appendix A.

Proteins include a diversity of structures, resulting in a wide range of functions

Nearly every dynamic function of a living being depends on proteins. In fact, the importance of proteins is underscored by their name, which comes from the Greek word *proteios*, meaning "first," or "primary." Proteins account for more than 50% of the dry mass of most cells, and they are instrumental in almost everything organisms do. Some proteins speed up chemical reactions, while others play a role in defense, storage, transport, cellular communication, movement, or structural support. **Figure 5.13** shows examples of proteins with these functions, which you'll learn more about in later chapters.

Life would not be possible without enzymes, most of which are proteins. Enzymatic proteins regulate metabolism by acting as **catalysts**, chemical agents that selectively speed up chemical reactions without being consumed by the reaction. Because an enzyme can perform its function over and over again, these molecules can be thought of as workhorses that keep cells running by carrying out the processes of life.

A human has tens of thousands of different proteins, each with a specific structure and function; proteins, in fact, are the most structurally sophisticated molecules known. Consistent with their diverse functions, they vary extensively in structure, each type of protein having a unique three-dimensional shape.

Diverse as proteins are, they are all constructed from the same set of 20 amino acids, linked in unbranched polymers. The bond between amino acids is called a peptide bond, so a polymer of amino acids is called a **polypeptide**. A **protein** is a biologically functional molecule made up of one or more polypeptides, each folded and coiled into a specific three-dimensional structure.

Amino Acid Monomers

All amino acids share a common structure. An **amino acid** is an organic molecule with both an amino group and a carboxyl group (see Figure 4.9). The figure at the right shows the general formula for an amino acid. At the center of the amino acid is an asymmetric carbon atom called the *alpha* (α) *carbon.* Its four different partners are an amino group, a carboxyl group, a hydrogen atom, and a variable group symbolized by R. The R group, also called the side chain, differs with each amino acid.

Side chain (R group)

R

α carbon

Amino group

Carboxyl group

▼ Figure 5.13 An overview of protein functions.

Enzymatic proteins

Function: Selective acceleration of chemical reactions
Example: Digestive enzymes catalyze the hydrolysis of bonds in food molecules.

Defensive proteins

Function: Protection against disease
Example: Antibodies inactivate and help destroy viruses and bacteria.

Storage proteins

Function: Storage of amino acids
Examples: Casein, the protein of milk, is the major source of amino acids for baby mammals. Plants have storage proteins in their seeds. Ovalbumin is the protein of egg white, used as an amino acid source for the developing embryo.

Transport proteins

Function: Transport of substances
Examples: Hemoglobin, the iron-containing protein of vertebrate blood, transports oxygen from the lungs to other parts of the body. Other proteins transport molecules across membranes, as shown here.

Hormonal proteins

Function: Coordination of an organism's activities
Example: Insulin, a hormone secreted by the pancreas, causes other tissues to take up glucose, thus regulating blood sugar concentration.

Receptor proteins

Function: Response of cell to chemical stimuli
Example: Receptors built into the membrane of a nerve cell detect signaling molecules released by other nerve cells.

Contractile and motor proteins

Function: Movement
Examples: Motor proteins are responsible for the undulations of cilia and flagella. Actin and myosin proteins are responsible for the contraction of muscles.

Structural proteins

Function: Support
Examples: Keratin is the protein of hair, horns, feathers, and other skin appendages. Insects and spiders use silk fibers to make their cocoons and webs, respectively. Collagen and elastin proteins provide a fibrous framework in animal connective tissues.

Figure 5.14 shows the 20 amino acids that cells use to build their thousands of proteins. Here the amino groups and carboxyl groups are all depicted in ionized form, the way they usually exist at the pH found in a cell.

The physical and chemical properties of the side chain determine the unique characteristics of a particular amino acid, thus affecting its functional role in a polypeptide. In Figure 5.14, the amino acids are grouped according to the properties of their side chains. One group consists of amino acids with nonpolar side chains, which are hydrophobic.

Another group consists of amino acids with polar side chains, which are hydrophilic. Acidic amino acids are those with side chains that are generally negative in charge due to the presence of a carboxyl group, which is usually dissociated (ionized) at cellular pH. Basic amino acids have amino groups in their side chains that are generally positive in charge. (Notice that *all* amino acids have carboxyl groups and amino groups; the terms *acidic* and *basic* in this context refer only to groups in the side chains.) Because they are charged, acidic and basic side chains are also hydrophilic.

▼ **Figure 5.14 The 20 amino acids of proteins.** The amino acids are grouped here according to the properties of their side chains (R groups) and shown in their prevailing ionic forms at pH 7.2, the pH within a cell. The three-letter and one-letter abbreviations for the amino acids are in parentheses. All of the amino acids used in proteins are L enantiomers (see Figure 4.7c).

Nonpolar side chains; hydrophobic

Polar side chains; hydrophilic

Electrically charged side chains; hydrophilic

Polypeptides (Amino Acid Polymers)

Now that we have examined amino acids, let's see how they are linked to form polymers **(Figure 5.15)**. When two amino acids are positioned so that the carboxyl group of one is adjacent to the amino group of the other, they can become joined by a dehydration reaction, with the removal of a water molecule. The resulting covalent bond is called a **peptide bond**. Repeated over and over, this process yields a polypeptide, a polymer of many amino acids linked by peptide bonds.

The repeating sequence of atoms highlighted in purple in Figure 5.15 is called the *polypeptide backbone*. Extending from this backbone are the different side chains (R groups) of the amino acids. Polypeptides range in length from a few amino acids to a thousand or more. Each specific polypeptide has a unique linear sequence of amino acids. Note that one end of the polypeptide chain has a free amino group, while

the opposite end has a free carboxyl group. Thus, a polypeptide of any length has a single amino end (N-terminus) and a single carboxyl end (C-terminus). In a polypeptide of any significant size, the side chains far outnumber the terminal groups, so the chemical nature of the molecule as a whole is determined by the kind and sequence of the side chains. The immense variety of polypeptides in nature illustrates an important concept introduced earlier—that cells can make many different polymers by linking a limited set of monomers into diverse sequences.

Protein Structure and Function

The specific activities of proteins result from their intricate three-dimensional architecture, the simplest level of which is the sequence of their amino acids. The pioneer in determining the amino acid sequence of proteins was Frederick Sanger, who, with his colleagues at Cambridge University in England, worked on the hormone insulin in the late 1940s and early 1950s. He used agents that break polypeptides at specific places, followed by chemical methods to determine the amino acid sequence in these small fragments. Sanger and his co-workers were able, after years of effort, to reconstruct the complete amino acid sequence of insulin. Since then, the steps involved in sequencing a polypeptide have been automated.

Once we have learned the amino acid sequence of a polypeptide, what can it tell us about the three-dimensional structure (commonly referred to simply as the "structure") of the protein and its function? The term *polypeptide* is not synonymous with the term *protein*. Even for a protein consisting of a single polypeptide, the relationship is somewhat analogous to that between a long strand of yarn and a sweater of particular size and shape that can be knit from the yarn. A functional protein is not *just* a polypeptide chain, but one or more polypeptides precisely twisted, folded, and coiled into a molecule of unique shape, which can be shown in several different types of models **(Figure 5.16)**. And it is the amino acid sequence of each polypeptide that determines what three-dimensional structure the protein will have under normal cellular conditions.

When a cell synthesizes a polypeptide, the chain may fold spontaneously, assuming the functional structure for that protein. This folding is driven and reinforced by the formation of various bonds between parts of the chain, which in turn depends on the sequence of amino acids. Many proteins are roughly spherical (*globular proteins*), while others are shaped like long fibers (*fibrous proteins*). Even within these broad categories, countless variations exist.

A protein's specific structure determines how it works. In almost every case, the function of a protein depends on its ability to recognize and bind to some other molecule. In an especially striking example of the marriage of form and

▲ **Figure 5.15 Making a polypeptide chain.** Peptide bonds are formed by dehydration reactions, which link the carboxyl group of one amino acid to the amino group of the next. The peptide bonds are formed one at a time, starting with the amino acid at the amino end (N-terminus). The polypeptide has a repetitive backbone (purple) to which the amino acid side chains (yellow and green) are attached.

DRAW IT *Label the three amino acids in the upper part of the figure using three-letter and one-letter codes. Circle and label the carboxyl and amino groups that will form the new peptide bond.*

Groove

Groove

Target molecule

(a) A **ribbon model** shows how the single polypeptide chain folds and coils to form the functional protein. (The yellow lines represent disulfide bridges that stabilize the protein's shape.)

(b) A **space-filling model** shows more clearly the globular shape seen in many proteins, as well as the specific three-dimensional structure unique to lysozyme.

(c) In this view, a ribbon model is superimposed on a **wireframe model**, which shows the backbone with the side chains extending from it. The yellow structure is the target molecule.

▲ **Figure 5.16 Structure of a protein, the enzyme lysozyme.** Present in our sweat, tears, and saliva, lysozyme is an enzyme that helps prevent infection by binding to and catalyzing the destruction of specific molecules on the surface of many kinds of bacteria. The groove is the part of the protein that recognizes and binds to the target molecules on bacterial walls.

function, **Figure 5.17** shows the exact match of shape between an antibody (a protein in the body) and the particular foreign substance on a flu virus that the antibody binds to and marks for destruction. In Chapter 43, you'll learn more about how the immune system generates antibodies that match the shapes of specific foreign molecules so well. Also, you may recall from Chapter 2 that natural signaling molecules called endorphins bind to specific receptor proteins on the surface of brain cells in humans, producing euphoria and relieving pain. Morphine, heroin, and other opiate drugs are able to mimic endorphins because they all share a similar shape with endorphins and can thus fit into and bind to endorphin receptors in the brain. This fit is very specific, something like a lock and key (see Figure 2.16). Thus, the function of a protein—for instance, the ability of a receptor protein to bind to a particular pain-relieving signaling molecule—is an emergent property resulting from exquisite molecular order.

Four Levels of Protein Structure

With the goal of understanding the function of a protein, learning about its structure is often productive. In spite of their great diversity, all proteins share three superimposed levels of structure, known as primary, secondary, and tertiary structure. A fourth level, quaternary structure, arises

Antibody protein   Protein from flu virus

▲ **Figure 5.17 An antibody binding to a protein from a flu virus.** A technique called X-ray crystallography was used to generate a computer model of an antibody protein (blue and orange, left) bound to a flu virus protein (green and yellow, right). Computer software was then used to back the images away from each other, revealing the exact complementarity of shape between the two protein surfaces.

when a protein consists of two or more polypeptide chains. **Figure 5.18** describes these four levels of protein structure. Be sure to study this figure thoroughly before going on to the next section.

Exploring Levels of Protein Structure

Primary Structure

Linear chain of amino acids

Amino acids

Primary structure of transthyretin

+H₃N— Gly Pro Thr Gly Thr Gly Glu Ser Lys Cys
Amino end

Carboxyl end

Secondary Structure

Regions stabilized by hydrogen bonds between atoms of the polypeptide backbone

α helix

Hydrogen bond

β pleated sheet

β strand, often shown as a flat arrow pointing toward the carboxyl end (here, shown folded)

Hydrogen bond

The **primary structure** of a protein is its sequence of amino acids. As an example, let's consider transthyretin, a globular blood protein that transports vitamin A and one of the thyroid hormones throughout the body. Transthyretin is made up of four identical polypeptide chains, each composed of 127 amino acids. Shown here is one of these chains unraveled for a closer look at its primary structure. Each of the 127 positions along the chain is occupied by one of the 20 amino acids, indicated here by its three-letter abbreviation.

The primary structure is like the order of letters in a very long word. If left to chance, there would be 20^{127} different ways of making a polypeptide chain 127 amino acids long. However, the precise primary structure of a protein is determined not by the random linking of amino acids, but by inherited genetic information. The primary structure in turn dictates secondary and tertiary structure, due to the chemical nature of the backbone and the side chains (R groups) of the amino acids along the polypeptide.

Most proteins have segments of their polypeptide chains repeatedly coiled or folded in patterns that contribute to the protein's overall shape. These coils and folds, collectively referred to as **secondary structure**, are the result of hydrogen bonds between the repeating constituents of the polypeptide backbone (not the amino acid side chains). Within the backbone, the oxygen atoms have a partial negative charge, and the hydrogen atoms attached to the nitrogens have a partial positive charge (see Figure 2.14); therefore, hydrogen bonds can form between these atoms. Individually, these hydrogen bonds are weak, but because there are so many of them over a relatively long region of the polypeptide chain, they can support a particular shape for that part of the protein.

One such secondary structure is the **α helix**, a delicate coil held together by hydrogen bonding between every fourth amino acid, as shown above. Although each transthyretin polypeptide has only one α helix region (see tertiary structure), other globular proteins have multiple stretches of α helix separated by nonhelical regions (see hemoglobin on the next page). Some fibrous proteins, such as α-keratin, the structural protein of hair, have the α helix structure over most of their length.

The other main type of secondary structure is the **β pleated sheet**. As shown above, in this structure two or more segments of the polypeptide chain lying side by side (called β strands) are connected by hydrogen bonds between parts of the two parallel segments of the polypeptide backbone. β pleated sheets make up the core of many globular proteins, as is the case for transthyretin (see tertiary structure), and dominate some fibrous proteins, including the silk protein of a spider's web. The teamwork of so many hydrogen bonds makes each spider silk fiber stronger than a steel strand of the same weight.

▼ Spiders secrete silk fibers made of a structural protein containing β pleated sheets, which allow the spider web to stretch and recoil.

Tertiary Structure

Three-dimensional shape stabilized by interactions between side chains

Quaternary Structure

Association of two or more polypeptides (some proteins only)

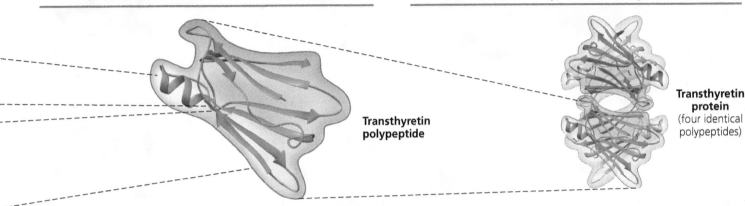

Transsthyretin polypeptide

Transthyretin protein
(four identical polypeptides)

Superimposed on the patterns of secondary structure is a protein's tertiary structure, shown above in a ribbon model of the transthyretin polypeptide. While secondary structure involves interactions between backbone constituents, **tertiary structure** is the overall shape of a polypeptide resulting from interactions between the side chains (R groups) of the various amino acids. One type of interaction that contributes to tertiary structure is called—somewhat misleadingly— a **hydrophobic interaction**. As a polypeptide folds into its functional shape, amino acids with hydrophobic (nonpolar) side chains usually end up in clusters at the core of the protein, out of contact with water. Thus, a "hydrophobic interaction" is actually caused by the exclusion of nonpolar substances by water molecules. Once nonpolar amino acid side chains are close together, van der Waals interactions help hold them together. Meanwhile, hydrogen bonds between polar side chains and ionic bonds between positively and negatively charged side chains also help stabilize tertiary structure. These are all weak interactions in the aqueous cellular environment, but their cumulative effect helps give the protein a unique shape.

Covalent bonds called **disulfide bridges** may further reinforce the shape of a protein. Disulfide bridges form where two cysteine monomers, which have sulfhydryl groups (—SH) on their side chains (see Figure 4.9), are brought close together by the folding of the protein. The sulfur of one cysteine bonds to the sulfur of the second, and the disulfide bridge (—S—S—) rivets parts of the protein together (see the yellow lines in Figure 5.16a). All of these different kinds of interactions can contribute to the tertiary structure of a protein, as shown here in a small part of a hypothetical protein:

Some proteins consist of two or more polypeptide chains aggregated into one functional macromolecule. **Quaternary structure** is the overall protein structure that results from the aggregation of these polypeptide subunits. For example, shown above is the complete globular transthyretin protein, made up of its four polypeptides.

Another example is collagen, shown below, which is a fibrous protein that has three identical helical polypeptides intertwined into a larger triple helix, giving the long fibers great strength. This suits collagen fibers to their function as the girders of connective tissue in skin, bone, tendons, ligaments, and other body parts. (Collagen accounts for 40% of the protein in a human body.)

Collagen

Hemoglobin, the oxygen-binding protein of red blood cells shown below, is another example of a globular protein with quaternary structure. It consists of four polypeptide subunits, two of one kind (α) and two of another kind (β). Both α and β subunits consist primarily of α-helical secondary structure. Each subunit has a nonpolypeptide component, called heme, with an iron atom that binds oxygen.

Heme
Iron
β subunit
α subunit
α subunit
β subunit

Hydrogen bond
Hydrophobic interactions and van der Waals interactions
Disulfide bridge
Ionic bond
Polypeptide backbone

Hemoglobin

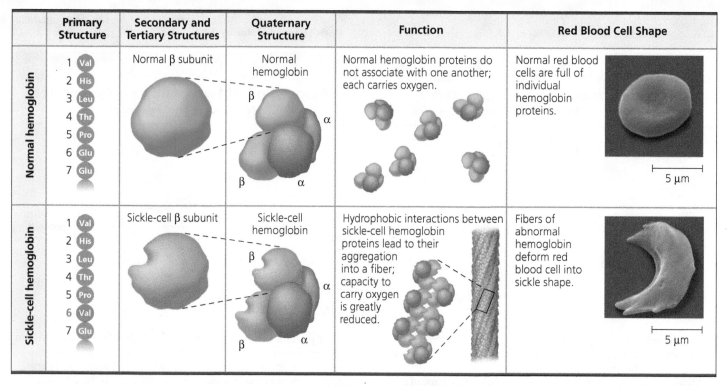

	Primary Structure	Secondary and Tertiary Structures	Quaternary Structure	Function	Red Blood Cell Shape
Normal hemoglobin	1 Val 2 His 3 Leu 4 Thr 5 Pro 6 Glu 7 Glu	Normal β subunit	Normal hemoglobin β α β α	Normal hemoglobin proteins do not associate with one another; each carries oxygen.	Normal red blood cells are full of individual hemoglobin proteins. 5 μm
Sickle-cell hemoglobin	1 Val 2 His 3 Leu 4 Thr 5 Pro 6 Val 7 Glu	Sickle-cell β subunit	Sickle-cell hemoglobin β α β α	Hydrophobic interactions between sickle-cell hemoglobin proteins lead to their aggregation into a fiber; capacity to carry oxygen is greatly reduced.	Fibers of abnormal hemoglobin deform red blood cell into sickle shape. 5 μm

▲ **Figure 5.19 A single amino acid substitution in a protein causes sickle-cell disease.**

MAKE CONNECTIONS *Considering the chemical characteristics of the amino acids valine and glutamic acid (see Figure 5.14), propose a possible explanation for the dramatic effect on protein function that occurs when valine is substituted for glutamic acid.*

Sickle-Cell Disease: A Change in Primary Structure

Even a slight change in primary structure can affect a protein's shape and ability to function. For instance, **sickle-cell disease**, an inherited blood disorder, is caused by the substitution of one amino acid (valine) for the normal one (glutamic acid) at a particular position in the primary structure of hemoglobin, the protein that carries oxygen in red blood cells. Normal red blood cells are disk-shaped, but in sickle-cell disease, the abnormal hemoglobin molecules tend to aggregate into chains, deforming some of the cells into a sickle shape **(Figure 5.19)**. A person with the disease has periodic "sickle-cell crises" when the angular cells clog tiny blood vessels, impeding blood flow. The toll taken on such patients is a dramatic example of how a simple change in protein structure can have devastating effects on protein function.

What Determines Protein Structure?

You've learned that a unique shape endows each protein with a specific function. But what are the key factors determining protein structure? You already know most of the answer: A polypeptide chain of a given amino acid sequence can be arranged into a three-dimensional shape determined by the interactions responsible for secondary and tertiary structure. This folding normally occurs as the protein is being synthesized in the crowded environment within a cell, aided by other proteins. However, protein structure also depends on the physical and chemical conditions of the protein's environment. If the pH, salt concentration, temperature, or other aspects of its environment are altered, the weak chemical bonds and interactions within a protein may be destroyed, causing the protein to unravel and lose its native shape, a change called **denaturation** **(Figure 5.20)**. Because it is misshapen, the denatured protein is biologically inactive.

Most proteins become denatured if they are transferred from an aqueous environment to a nonpolar solvent, such as ether or chloroform; the polypeptide chain refolds so that its hydrophobic regions face outward toward the solvent. Other denaturation agents include chemicals that disrupt

Normal protein   Denatured protein

▲ **Figure 5.20 Denaturation and renaturation of a protein.** High temperatures or various chemical treatments will denature a protein, causing it to lose its shape and hence its ability to function. If the denatured protein remains dissolved, it may renature when the chemical and physical aspects of its environment are restored to normal.

the hydrogen bonds, ionic bonds, and disulfide bridges that maintain a protein's shape. Denaturation can also result from excessive heat, which agitates the polypeptide chain enough to overpower the weak interactions that stabilize the structure. The white of an egg becomes opaque during cooking because the denatured proteins are insoluble and solidify. This also explains why excessively high fevers can be fatal: Proteins in the blood tend to denature at very high body temperatures.

When a protein in a test-tube solution has been denatured by heat or chemicals, it can sometimes return to its functional shape when the denaturing agent is removed. (Sometimes this is not possible: For example, a fried egg will not become liquefied when placed back into the refrigerator!) We can conclude that the information for building specific shape is intrinsic to the protein's primary structure. The sequence of amino acids determines the protein's shape—where an α helix can form, where β pleated sheets can exist, where disulfide bridges are located, where ionic bonds can form, and so on. But how does protein folding occur in the cell?

Protein Folding in the Cell

Biochemists now know the amino acid sequence for more than 24 million proteins, with about 1 million added each month, and the three-dimensional shape for more than 25,000. Researchers have tried to correlate the primary structure of many proteins with their three-dimensional structure to discover the rules of protein folding. Unfortunately, however, the protein-folding process is not that simple. Most proteins probably go through several intermediate structures on their way to a stable shape, and looking at the mature structure does not reveal the stages of folding required to achieve that form. However, biochemists have developed methods for tracking a protein through such stages.

Crucial to the folding process are **chaperonins** (also called chaperone proteins), protein molecules that assist in the proper folding of other proteins **(Figure 5.21)**. Chaperonins do not specify the final structure of a polypeptide.

Instead, they keep the new polypeptide segregated from disruptive chemical conditions in the cytoplasmic environment while it folds spontaneously. The chaperonin shown in Figure 5.21, from the bacterium *E. coli*, is a giant multiprotein complex shaped like a hollow cylinder. The cavity provides a shelter for folding polypeptides, and recent research suggests that minute amounts of water are present, ensuring a hydrophilic environment that aids the folding process. Molecular systems have been identified that interact with chaperonins and check whether proper folding has occurred. Such systems either refold the misfolded proteins correctly or mark them for destruction.

Misfolding of polypeptides is a serious problem in cells that has come under increasing scrutiny by medical researchers. Many diseases—such as cystic fibrosis, Alzheimer's, Parkinson's, and mad cow disease—are associated with an accumulation of misfolded proteins. In fact, misfolded versions of the transthyretin protein featured in Figure 5.18 have been implicated in several diseases, including one form of senile dementia.

Even when scientists have a correctly folded protein in hand, determining its exact three-dimensional structure is not simple, for a single protein molecule has thousands of atoms. The first 3-D structures were worked out in the late 1950s for hemoglobin and a related protein called myoglobin. The method that made these feats possible was **X-ray crystallography**, which has since been used to determine the 3-D structure of many other proteins. In a recent example, Roger Kornberg and his colleagues at Stanford University used this method to elucidate the structure of RNA polymerase, an enzyme that plays a crucial role in the expression of genes **(Figure 5.22)**. Another method for analyzing protein structure is nuclear magnetic resonance (NMR) spectroscopy, which does not require protein crystallization. A still newer approach employs bioinformatics (see Concept 5.6) to predict the 3-D structure of polypeptides from their amino acid sequence. X-ray crystallography, NMR spectroscopy, and bioinformatics are complementary approaches to understanding protein structure and function.

▶ **Figure 5.21 A chaperonin in action.** The computer graphic (left) shows a large chaperonin protein complex from the bacterium *E. coli*. It has an interior space that provides a shelter for the proper folding of newly made polypeptides. The complex consists of two proteins: One is a hollow cylinder; the other is a cap that can fit on either end. The steps of chaperonin activity are shown at the right.

Cap

Hollow cylinder

Chaperonin (fully assembled)

Polypeptide

❶ An unfolded polypeptide enters the cylinder from one end.

❷ Cap attachment causes the cylinder to change shape, creating a hydrophilic environment for polypeptide folding.

Correctly folded protein

❸ The cap comes off, and the properly folded protein is released.

▼ Figure 5.22 Inquiry

What can the 3-D shape of the enzyme RNA polymerase II tell us about its function?

Experiment In 2006, Roger Kornberg was awarded the Nobel Prize in Chemistry for using X-ray crystallography to determine the 3-D shape of RNA polymerase II, which binds to the DNA double helix and synthesizes RNA. After crystallizing a complex of all three components, Kornberg and his colleagues aimed an X-ray beam through the crystal. The atoms of the crystal diffracted (bent) the X-rays into an orderly array that a digital detector recorded as a pattern of spots called an X-ray diffraction pattern.

Results Using data from X-ray diffraction patterns, as well as the amino acid sequence determined by chemical methods, the researchers built a 3-D model of the complex with the help of computer software.

Conclusion Analysis of the model led to a hypothesis about the functions of different regions of RNA polymerase II. For example, the region above the DNA may act as a clamp that holds the nucleic acids in place. (You'll learn more about this enzyme in Chapter 17.)

Source: A. L. Gnatt et al., Structural basis of transcription: an RNA polymerase II elongation complex at 3.3Å, *Science* 292:1876–1882 (2001). Computer graphic copyright © 2001 by AAAS. Reprinted with permission.

WHAT IF? *Looking at the model, can you identify any elements of secondary structure?*

CONCEPT CHECK 5.4

1. What parts of a polypeptide participate in the bonds that hold together secondary structure? Tertiary structure?

2. Thus far in the chapter, the Greek letters α and β have been used to specify at least three different pairs of structures. Name and briefly describe them.

3. **WHAT IF?** Where would you expect a polypeptide region rich in the amino acids valine, leucine, and isoleucine to be located in a folded polypeptide? Explain.

For suggested answers, see Appendix A.

CONCEPT 5.5

Nucleic acids store, transmit, and help express hereditary information

If the primary structure of polypeptides determines a protein's shape, what determines primary structure? The amino acid sequence of a polypeptide is programmed by a discrete unit of inheritance known as a **gene**. Genes consist of DNA, which belongs to the class of compounds called nucleic acids. **Nucleic acids** are polymers made of monomers called nucleotides.

The Roles of Nucleic Acids

The two types of nucleic acids, **deoxyribonucleic acid (DNA)** and **ribonucleic acid (RNA)**, enable living organisms to reproduce their complex components from one generation to the next. Unique among molecules, DNA provides directions for its own replication. DNA also directs RNA synthesis and, through RNA, controls protein synthesis; this entire process is called **gene expression (Figure 5.23)**.

DNA is the genetic material that organisms inherit from their parents. Each chromosome contains one long DNA molecule, usually carrying several hundred or more genes. When a cell reproduces itself by dividing, its DNA molecules are copied and passed along from one generation of

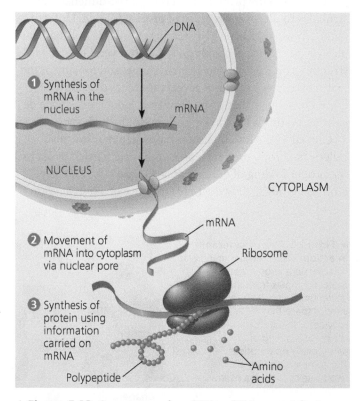

▲ **Figure 5.23 Gene expression: DNA → RNA → protein.** In a eukaryotic cell, DNA in the nucleus programs protein production in the cytoplasm by dictating synthesis of messenger RNA (mRNA).

cells to the next. Encoded in the structure of DNA is the information that programs all the cell's activities. The DNA, however, is not directly involved in running the operations of the cell, any more than computer software by itself can read the bar code on a box of cereal. Just as a scanner is needed to read a bar code, proteins are required to implement genetic programs. The molecular hardware of the cell—the tools for biological functions—consists mostly of proteins. For example, the oxygen carrier in red blood cells is the protein hemoglobin that you saw earlier (see Figure 5.17), not the DNA that specifies its structure.

How does RNA, the other type of nucleic acid, fit into gene expression, the flow of genetic information from DNA to proteins? Each gene along a DNA molecule directs synthesis of a type of RNA called *messenger RNA* (*mRNA*). The mRNA molecule interacts with the cell's protein-synthesizing machinery to direct production of a polypeptide, which folds into all or part of a protein. We can summarize the flow of genetic information as DNA → RNA → protein (see Figure 5.23). The sites of protein synthesis are cellular structures called ribosomes. (In the Unit 1 interview before Chapter 2, Venki Ramakrishnan describes how the structure of ribosomes was determined by X-ray crystallography.) In a eukaryotic cell, ribosomes are in the region between the nucleus and the plasma membrane (the cytoplasm), but DNA resides in the nucleus. Messenger RNA conveys genetic instructions for building proteins from the nucleus to the cytoplasm. Prokaryotic cells lack nuclei but still use mRNA to convey a message from the DNA to ribosomes and other cellular equipment that translate the coded information into amino acid sequences. In Chapter 18, you'll read about other functions of some recently discovered RNA molecules.

The Components of Nucleic Acids

Nucleic acids are macromolecules that exist as polymers called **polynucleotides** (Figure 5.24a). As indicated by the name, each polynucleotide consists of monomers called **nucleotides**. A nucleotide, in general, is composed of three parts: a five-carbon sugar (a pentose), a nitrogen-containing (nitrogenous) base, and one or more phosphate groups (Figure 5.24b). In a polynucleotide, each monomer has only one phosphate group. The portion of a nucleotide without any phosphate groups is called a *nucleoside*.

To build a nucleotide, let's first consider the nitrogenous bases (Figure 5.24c). Each nitrogenous base has one or two rings that include nitrogen atoms. (They are called nitrogenous *bases* because the nitrogen atoms tend to take up

▼ Figure 5.24 **Components of nucleic acids. (a)** A polynucleotide has a sugar-phosphate backbone with variable appendages, the nitrogenous bases. **(b)** A nucleotide monomer includes a nitrogenous base, a sugar, and a phosphate group. Note that carbon numbers in the sugar include primes ('). **(c)** A nucleoside includes a nitrogenous base (purine or pyrimidine) and a five-carbon sugar (deoxyribose or ribose).

(a) Polynucleotide, or nucleic acid

(b) Nucleotide

(c) Nucleoside components

H^+ from solution, thus acting as bases.) There are two families of nitrogenous bases: pyrimidines and purines. A **pyrimidine** has one six-membered ring of carbon and nitrogen atoms. The members of the pyrimidine family are cytosine (C), thymine (T), and uracil (U). **Purines** are larger, with a six-membered ring fused to a five-membered ring. The purines are adenine (A) and guanine (G). The specific pyrimidines and purines differ in the chemical groups attached to the rings. Adenine, guanine, and cytosine are found in both DNA and RNA; thymine is found only in DNA and uracil only in RNA.

Now let's add the sugar to which the nitrogenous base is attached. In DNA the sugar is **deoxyribose**; in RNA it is **ribose** (see Figure 5.24c). The only difference between these two sugars is that deoxyribose lacks an oxygen atom on the second carbon in the ring; hence the name *deoxy*ribose.

So far, we have built a nucleoside (nitrogenous base plus sugar). To complete the construction of a nucleotide, we attach a phosphate group to the 5′ carbon of the sugar (see Figure 5.24b). The molecule is now a nucleoside monophosphate, more often called a nucleotide.

Nucleotide Polymers

The linkage of nucleotides into a polynucleotide involves a dehydration reaction. (You will learn the details in Chapter 16). In the polynucleotide, adjacent nucleotides are joined by a phosphodiester linkage, which consists of a phosphate group that links the sugars of two nucleotides. This bonding results in a repeating pattern of sugar-phosphate units called the *sugar-phosphate backbone* (see Figure 5.24a). (Note that the nitrogenous bases are not part of the backbone.) The two free ends of the polymer are distinctly different from each other. One end has a phosphate attached to a 5′ carbon, and the other end has a hydroxyl group on a 3′ carbon; we refer to these as the *5′ end* and the *3′ end*, respectively. We can say that a polynucleotide has a built-in directionality along its sugar-phosphate backbone, from 5′ to 3′, somewhat like a one-way street. All along this sugar-phosphate backbone are appendages consisting of the nitrogenous bases.

The sequence of bases along a DNA (or mRNA) polymer is unique for each gene and provides very specific information to the cell. Because genes are hundreds to thousands of nucleotides long, the number of possible base sequences is effectively limitless. A gene's meaning to the cell is encoded in its specific sequence of the four DNA bases. For example, the sequence 5′-AGGTAACTT-3′ means one thing, whereas the sequence 5′-CGCTTTAAC-3′ has a different meaning. (Entire genes, of course, are much longer.) The linear order of bases in a gene specifies the amino acid sequence—the primary structure—of a protein, which in turn specifies that protein's three-dimensional structure and its function in the cell.

The Structures of DNA and RNA Molecules

DNA molecules have two polynucleotides, or "strands," that wind around an imaginary axis, forming a **double helix** (Figure 5.25a). The two sugar-phosphate backbones run in opposite 5′ → 3′ directions from each other; this arrangement is referred to as **antiparallel**, somewhat like a divided highway. The sugar-phosphate backbones are on the outside of the helix, and the nitrogenous bases are paired in the interior of the helix. The two strands are held together by hydrogen bonds between the paired bases (see Figure 5.25a). Most DNA molecules are very long, with thousands or even millions of base pairs. For example, the one long DNA double helix in a eukaryotic chromosome includes many genes, each one a particular segment of the molecule.

In base pairing, only certain bases in the double helix are compatible with each other. Adenine (A) in one strand always pairs with thymine (T) in the other, and guanine (G) always pairs with cytosine (C). Reading the sequence of bases along one strand of the double helix would tell us the sequence of bases along the other strand. If a stretch of one strand has the base sequence 5′-AGGTCCG-3′, then the base-pairing rules tell us that the same stretch of the other strand must have the sequence 3′-TCCAGGC-5′. The two strands of the double helix are *complementary*, each the predictable counterpart of the other. It is this feature of DNA that makes it possible to generate two identical copies of each DNA molecule in a cell that is preparing to divide. When the cell divides, the copies are distributed to the daughter cells, making them genetically identical to the parent cell. Thus, the structure of DNA accounts for its function of transmitting genetic information whenever a cell reproduces.

RNA molecules, by contrast, exist as single strands. Complementary base pairing can occur, however, between regions of two RNA molecules or even between two stretches of nucleotides in the *same* RNA molecule. In fact, base pairing within an RNA molecule allows it to take on the particular three-dimensional shape necessary for its function. Consider, for example, the type of RNA called *transfer RNA (tRNA)*, which brings amino acids to the ribosome during the synthesis of a polypeptide. A tRNA molecule is about 80 nucleotides in length. Its functional shape results from base pairing between nucleotides where complementary stretches of the molecule can run antiparallel to each other (Figure 5.25b).

Note that in RNA, adenine (A) pairs with uracil (U); thymine (T) is not present in RNA. Another difference between RNA and DNA is that DNA almost always exists as a double helix, whereas RNA molecules are more variable in shape. RNAs are very versatile molecules, and many biologists believe RNA may have preceded DNA as the carrier of genetic information in early forms of life (see Concept 25.1).

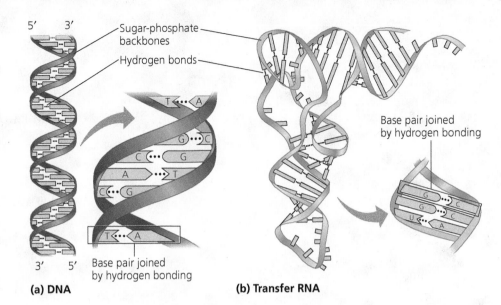

▶ **Figure 5.25 The structures of DNA and tRNA molecules. (a)** The DNA molecule is usually a double helix, with the sugar-phosphate backbones of the antiparallel polynucleotide strands (symbolized here by blue ribbons) on the outside of the helix. Hydrogen bonds between pairs of nitrogenous bases hold the two strands together. As illustrated here with symbolic shapes for the bases, adenine (A) can pair only with thymine (T), and guanine (G) can pair only with cytosine (C). Each DNA strand in this figure is the structural equivalent of the polynucleotide diagrammed in Figure 5.24a. **(b)** A tRNA molecule has a roughly L-shaped structure, with complementary base pairing of antiparallel stretches of RNA. In RNA, A pairs with U.

(a) DNA

(b) Transfer RNA

CONCEPT CHECK 5.5

1. **DRAW IT** Go to Figure 5.24a and, for the top three nucleotides, number all the carbons in the sugars, circle the nitrogenous bases, and star the phosphates.

2. **DRAW IT** In a DNA double helix, a region along one DNA strand has this sequence of nitrogenous bases: 5'-TAGGCCT-3'. Copy this sequence, and write down its complementary strand, clearly indicating the 5' and 3' ends of the complementary strand.

For suggested answers, see Appendix A.

CONCEPT 5.6

Genomics and proteomics have transformed biological inquiry and applications

Experimental work in the first half of the 20th century established the role of DNA as the bearer of genetic information, passed from generation to generation, that specified the functioning of living cells and organisms. Once the structure of the DNA molecule was described in 1953, and the linear sequence of nucleotide bases was understood to specify the amino acid sequence of proteins, biologists sought to "decode" genes by learning their base sequences.

The first chemical techniques for *DNA sequencing*, or determining the sequence of nucleotides along a DNA strand, one by one, were developed in the 1970s. Researchers began to study gene sequences, gene by gene, and the more they learned, the more questions they had: How was expression of genes regulated? Genes and their protein products clearly interacted with each other, but how? What was the function, if any, of the DNA that is not part of genes? To fully understand the genetic functioning of a living organism, the entire sequence of the full complement of DNA, the organism's

genome, would be most enlightening. In spite of the apparent impracticality of this idea, in the late 1980s several prominent biologists put forth an audacious proposal to launch a project that would sequence the entire human genome—all 3 billion bases of it! This endeavor began in 1990 and was effectively completed in the early 2000s.

An unplanned but profound side benefit of this project—the Human Genome Project—was the rapid development of faster and less expensive methods of sequencing. This trend has continued apace: The cost for sequencing 1 million bases in 2001, well over $5,000, has decreased to less than $0.10 in 2012. And a human genome, the first of which took over 10 years to sequence, could be completed at today's pace in just a few days. The number of genomes that have been fully sequenced has burgeoned, generating reams of data and prompting development of *bioinformatics*, the use of computer software and other computational tools that can handle and analyze these large data sets.

The reverberations of these developments have transformed the study of biology and related fields. Biologists often look at problems by analyzing large sets of genes or even comparing whole genomes of different species, an approach called **genomics**. A similar analysis of large sets of proteins, including their sequences, is called **proteomics**. (Protein sequences can be determined either by using biochemical techniques or by translating the DNA sequences that code for them.) These approaches permeate all fields of biology, some examples of which are shown in **Figure 5.26**.

Perhaps the most significant impact of genomics and proteomics on the field of biology as a whole has been their contributions to our understanding of evolution. In addition to confirming evidence for evolution from the study of fossils and characteristics of currently existing species, genomics has helped us tease out relationships among different groups of organisms that had not been resolved by previous types of evidence, and thus infer evolutionary history.

Contributions of Genomics and Proteomics to Biology

Nucleotide sequencing and the analysis of large sets of genes and proteins can be done rapidly and inexpensively due to advances in technology and information processing. Taken together, genomics and proteomics have advanced our understanding of biology across many different fields.

Paleontology

New DNA sequencing techniques have allowed decoding of minute quantities of DNA found in ancient tissues from our extinct relatives, the Neanderthals (*Homo neanderthalensis*). Sequencing the Neanderthal genome has informed our understanding of their physical appearance as well as their relationship with modern humans. *See Figure 34.49.*

Medical Science

Identifying the genetic basis for human diseases like cancer helps researchers focus their search for potential future treatments. Currently, sequencing the sets of genes expressed in an individual's tumor can allow a more targeted approach to treating the cancer, a type of "personalized medicine." *See Figures 12.20 and 18.27.*

Evolution

A major aim of evolutionary biology is to understand the relationships among species, both living and extinct. For example, genome sequence comparisons have identified the hippopotamus as the land mammal sharing the most recent common ancestor with whales. *See Figure 22.20.*

Hippopotamus

Short-finned pilot whale

Conservation Biology

The tools of molecular genetics and genomics are increasingly used by ecologists to identify which species of animals and plants are killed illegally. In one case, genomic sequences of DNA from illegal shipments of elephant tusks were used to track down poachers and pinpoint the territory where they were operating. *See Figure 56.9.*

Species Interactions

Over 90% of all plant species exist in a mutually beneficial partnership with fungi that are associated with the plants' roots. Genome sequencing and analysis of gene expression in several plant-fungal pairs promise major advances in our understanding of such interactions and may have implications for agricultural practices. *(See the Scientific Skills Exercise in Chapter 31.)*

MAKE CONNECTIONS *Considering the examples provided here, describe how the approaches of genomics and proteomics*

DNA and Proteins as Tape Measures of Evolution

EVOLUTION We are accustomed to thinking of shared traits, such as hair and milk production in mammals, as evidence of shared ancestry. Because DNA carries heritable information in the form of genes, sequences of genes and their protein products document the hereditary background of an organism. The linear sequences of nucleotides in DNA molecules are passed from parents to offspring; these sequences determine the amino acid sequences of proteins. As a result, siblings have greater similarity in their DNA and proteins than do unrelated individuals of the same species.

Given our evolutionary view of life, we can extend this concept of "molecular genealogy" to relationships between species: We would expect two species that appear to be closely related based on anatomical evidence (and possibly fossil evidence) to also share a greater proportion of their DNA and protein sequences than do less closely related species. In fact, that is the case. An example is the comparison of the β polypeptide chain of human hemoglobin with the corresponding hemoglobin polypeptide in other vertebrates. In this chain of 146 amino acids, humans and gorillas differ in just 1 amino acid, while humans and frogs, more distantly related, differ in 67 amino acids. In the Scientific Skills Exercise, you can apply this sort of reasoning to additional species. And this conclusion holds true as well when comparing whole genomes: The human genome is 95–98% identical to that of the chimpanzee, but only roughly 85% identical to that of the mouse, a more distant evolutionary relative. Molecular biology has added a new tape measure to the toolkit biologists use to assess evolutionary kinship.

CONCEPT CHECK 5.6

1. How would sequencing the entire genome of an organism help scientists to understand how that organism functioned?

2. Given the function of DNA, why would you expect two species with very similar traits to also have very similar genomes?

For suggested answers, see Appendix A.

SCIENTIFIC SKILLS EXERCISE

Analyzing Polypeptide Sequence Data

 ▶ Human   ▶ Rhesus monkey   ▶ Gibbon

Are Rhesus Monkeys or Gibbons More Closely Related to Humans? DNA and polypeptide sequences from closely related species are more similar to each other than are sequences from more distantly related species. In this exercise, you will look at amino acid sequence data for the β polypeptide chain of hemoglobin, often called β-globin. You will then interpret the data to hypothesize whether the monkey or the gibbon is more closely related to humans.

How Such Experiments Are Done Researchers can isolate the polypeptide of interest from an organism and then determine the amino acid sequence. More frequently, the DNA of the relevant gene is sequenced, and the amino acid sequence of the polypeptide is deduced from the DNA sequence of its gene.

Data from the Experiments In the data below, the letters give the sequence of the 146 amino acids in β-globin from humans, rhesus monkeys, and gibbons. Because a complete sequence would not fit on one line here, the sequences are broken into three segments. The sequences for the three different species are aligned so that you can compare them easily. For example, you can see that for all three species, the first amino acid is V (valine) and the 146th amino acid is H (histidine).

Interpret the Data

1. Scan the monkey and gibbon sequences, letter by letter, circling any amino acids that do not match the human sequence. (a) How many amino acids differ between the monkey and the human sequences? (b) Between the gibbon and human?

2. For each nonhuman species, what percent of its amino acids are identical to the human sequence of β-globin?

3. Based on these data alone, state a hypothesis for which of these two species is more closely related to humans. What is your reasoning?

4. What other evidence could you use to support your hypothesis?

(MB) A version of this Scientific Skills Exercise can be assigned in MasteringBiology.

Data from Human: http://www.ncbi.nlm.nih.gov/protein/AAA21113.1; rhesus monkey: http://www.ncbi.nlm.nih.gov/protein/122634; gibbon: http://www.ncbi.nlm.nih.gov/protein/122616

Species	Alignment of Amino Acid Sequences of β-globin
Human	1 VHLTPEEKSA VTALWGKVNV DEVGGEALGR LLVVYPWTQR FFESFGDLST
Monkey	1 VHLTPEEKNA VTTLWGKVNV DEVGGEALGR LLLVYPWTQR FFESFGDLSS
Gibbon	1 VHLTPEEKSA VTALWGKVNV DEVGGEALGR LLVVYPWTQR FFESFGDLST
Human	51 PDAVMGNPKV KAHGKKVLGA FSDGLAHLDN LKGTFATLSE LHCDKLHVDP
Monkey	51 PDAVMGNPKV KAHGKKVLGA FSDGLNHLDN LKGTFAQLSE LHCDKLHVDP
Gibbon	51 PDAVMGNPKV KAHGKKVLGA FSDGLAHLDN LKGTFAQLSE LHCDKLHVDP
Human	101 ENFRLLGNVL VCVLAHHFGK EFTPPVQAAY QKVVAGVANA LAHKYH
Monkey	101 ENFKLLGNVL VCVLAHHFGK EFTPQVQAAY QKVVAGVANA LAHKYH
Gibbon	101 ENFRLLGNVL VCVLAHHFGK EFTPQVQAAY QKVVAGVANA LAHKYH

CONCEPT 5.1

Macromolecules are polymers, built from monomers (pp. 67–68)

- Large carbohydrates (polysaccharides), proteins, and nucleic acids are **polymers**, which are chains of **monomers**. The

components of lipids vary. Monomers form larger molecules by **dehydration reactions**, in which water molecules are released. Polymers can disassemble by the reverse process, **hydrolysis**. An immense variety of polymers can be built from a small set of monomers.

? *What is the fundamental basis for the differences between large carbohydrates, proteins, and nucleic acids?*

Large Biological Molecules	Components	Examples	Functions
CONCEPT 5.2 **Carbohydrates serve as fuel and building material (pp. 68–72)** ? *Compare the composition, structure, and function of starch and cellulose. What role do starch and cellulose play in the human body?*	 Monosaccharide monomer	**Monosaccharides:** glucose, fructose	Fuel; carbon sources that can be converted to other molecules or combined into polymers
		Disaccharides: lactose, sucrose	
		Polysaccharides: • Cellulose (plants) • Starch (plants) • Glycogen (animals) • Chitin (animals and fungi)	• Strengthens plant cell walls • Stores glucose for energy • Stores glucose for energy • Strengthens exoskeletons and fungal cell walls
CONCEPT 5.3 **Lipids are a diverse group of hydrophobic molecules (pp. 72–75)** ? *Why are lipids not considered to be polymers or macromolecules?*	 Glycerol, 3 fatty acids	**Triacylglycerols** (fats or oils): glycerol + 3 fatty acids	Important energy source
	 Head with P, 2 fatty acids	**Phospholipids:** glycerol + phosphate group + 2 fatty acids	Lipid bilayers of membranes
	 Steroid backbone	**Steroids:** four fused rings with attached chemical groups	• Component of cell membranes (cholesterol) • Signaling molecules that travel through the body (hormones)
CONCEPT 5.4 **Proteins include a diversity of structures, resulting in a wide range of functions (pp. 75–84)** ? *Explain the basis for the great diversity of proteins.*	 Amino acid monomer (20 types)	• Enzymes • Structural proteins • Hormones • Receptor proteins • Motor proteins • Defensive proteins	• Catalyze chemical reactions • Provide structural support • Coordinate organismal responses • Receive signals from outside cell • Function in cell movement • Protect against disease
CONCEPT 5.5 **Nucleic acids store, transmit, and help express hereditary information (pp. 84–87)** ? *What role does complementary base pairing play in the functions of nucleic acids?*	 Nucleotide monomer	**DNA:** • Sugar = deoxyribose • Nitrogenous bases = C, G, A, T • Usually double-stranded	Stores hereditary information
		RNA: • Sugar = ribose • Nitrogenous bases = C, G, A, U • Usually single-stranded	Various functions in gene expression, including carrying instructions from DNA to ribosomes

CONCEPT 5.6

Genomics and proteomics have transformed biological inquiry and applications (pp. 87–89)

- Recent technological advances in DNA sequencing have given rise to **genomics**, an approach that analyzes large sets of genes or whole genomes, and **proteomics**, a similar approach for large sets of proteins. Bioinformatics is the use of computational tools and computer software to analyze these large data sets.
- The more closely two species are related evolutionarily, the more similar their DNA sequences are. DNA sequence data confirms models of evolution based on fossils and anatomical evidence.

? *Given the sequences of a particular gene in fruit flies, fish, mice, and humans, predict the relative similarity of the human sequence to that of each of the other species.*

TEST YOUR UNDERSTANDING

LEVEL 1: KNOWLEDGE/COMPREHENSION

1. Which of the following categories includes all others in the list?
   a. monosaccharide
   b. polysaccharide
   c. starch
   d. carbohydrate

2. The enzyme amylase can break glycosidic linkages between glucose monomers only if the monomers are in the α form. Which of the following could amylase break down?
   a. glycogen, starch, and amylopectin
   b. glycogen and cellulose
   c. cellulose and chitin
   d. starch, chitin, and cellulose

3. Which of the following is true of *unsaturated* fats?
   a. They are more common in animals than in plants.
   b. They have double bonds in the carbon chains of their fatty acids.
   c. They generally solidify at room temperature.
   d. They contain more hydrogen than do saturated fats having the same number of carbon atoms.

4. The structural level of a protein *least* affected by a disruption in hydrogen bonding is the
   a. primary level.
   b. secondary level.
   c. tertiary level.
   d. quaternary level.

5. Enzymes that break down DNA catalyze the hydrolysis of the covalent bonds that join nucleotides together. What would happen to DNA molecules treated with these enzymes?
   a. The two strands of the double helix would separate.
   b. The phosphodiester linkages of the polynucleotide backbone would be broken.
   c. The pyrimidines would be separated from the deoxyribose sugars.
   d. All bases would be separated from the deoxyribose sugars.

LEVEL 2: APPLICATION/ANALYSIS

6. The molecular formula for glucose is $C_6H_{12}O_6$. What would be the molecular formula for a polymer made by linking ten glucose molecules together by dehydration reactions?
   a. $C_{60}H_{120}O_{60}$
   b. $C_{60}H_{102}O_{51}$
   c. $C_{60}H_{100}O_{50}$
   d. $C_{60}H_{111}O_{51}$

7. Which of the following pairs of base sequences could form a short stretch of a normal double helix of DNA?
   a. 5'-AGCT-3' with 5'-TCGA-3'
   b. 5'-GCGC-3' with 5'-TATA-3'
   c. 5'-ATGC-3' with 5'-GCAT-3'
   d. All of these pairs are correct.

8. Construct a table that organizes the following terms, and label the columns and rows.

Monosaccharides	Polypeptides	Phosphodiester linkages
Fatty acids	Triacylglycerols	Peptide bonds
Amino acids	Polynucleotides	Glycosidic linkages
Nucleotides	Polysaccharides	Ester linkages

9. **DRAW IT** Copy the polynucleotide strand in Figure 5.24a and label the bases G, T, C, and T, starting from the 5' end. Assuming this is a DNA polynucleotide, now draw the complementary strand, using the same symbols for phosphates (circles), sugars (pentagons), and bases. Label the bases. Draw arrows showing the 5' → 3' direction of each strand. Use the arrows to make sure the second strand is antiparallel to the first. *Hint:* After you draw the first strand vertically, turn the paper upside down; it is easier to draw the second strand from the 5' toward the 3' direction as you go from top to bottom.

LEVEL 3: SYNTHESIS/EVALUATION

10. **EVOLUTION CONNECTION**
    Comparisons of amino acid sequences can shed light on the evolutionary divergence of related species. If you were comparing two living species, would you expect all proteins to show the same degree of divergence? Why or why not?

11. **SCIENTIFIC INQUIRY**
    Suppose you are a research assistant in a lab studying DNA-binding proteins. You have been given the amino acid sequences of all the proteins encoded by the genome of a certain species and have been asked to find candidate proteins that could bind DNA. What type of amino acids would you expect to see in the DNA-binding regions of such proteins? Why?

12. **WRITE ABOUT A THEME: ORGANIZATION**
    Proteins, which have diverse functions in a cell, are all polymers of the same kinds of monomers—amino acids. Write a short essay (100–150 words) that discusses how the structure of amino acids allows this one type of polymer to perform so many functions.

13. **SYNTHESIZE YOUR KNOWLEDGE**

Given that the function of egg yolk is to nourish and support the developing chick, explain why egg yolks are so high in fat, protein, and cholesterol.

For selected answers, see Appendix A.

MasteringBiology®

Students Go to **MasteringBiology** for assignments, the eText, and the Study Area with practice tests, animations, and activities.

Instructors Go to **MasteringBiology** for automatically graded tutorials and questions that you can assign to your students, plus Instructor Resources.

AN INTERVIEW WITH

Haifan Lin

Born in China, Haifan Lin majored in biochemistry at Fudan University in Shanghai. He then earned a Ph.D. in genetics and development from Cornell University and was a postdoctoral fellow at the Carnegie Institution of Washington (now the Carnegie Institution for Science). There, he started using the fruit fly (*Drosophila melanogaster*) as a model to explore fundamental questions in stem cells. Dr. Lin then spent 12 years as a faculty member at Duke University, broadening his study of stem cells by working on mammalian models and clinical applications. He is one of the discoverers of Piwi-interacting RNAs, a finding that was heralded by *Science* magazine as a Discovery of the Year in 2006. That same year, Dr. Lin moved to Yale University, where he founded and now directs the Yale Stem Cell Center.

"If we hadn't started by working on basic cell biology in *Drosophila*, I don't think we could have found this connection to cancer so quickly."

How did you get interested in science?

As a child I liked to build things, so I imagined myself a ship builder or an architect, something like that. I didn't get attracted to biology until high school. Genetic engineering had become a very fashionable term in China, and I thought, "That's cool. That's the engineering of life." I was more attracted by the word "engineering" than "genetics." However, people told me it was important to have a solid biochemistry foundation in order to become a genetic engineer, so I became a biochemistry major in college. And the more I learned about biology, the more I loved it.

◀ Cross section of a tubule in the testis of a mouse, showing the Piwi protein (red-orange in this fluorescence micrograph).

What did you study in graduate school and as a postdoc?

At Cornell, I thought about the very first cell division of the embryo. To me, it's literally the first step of life—the division of a fertilized egg. Working on a cell division process with developmental significance was really intellectually rewarding. For my postdoc, I felt that I should continue to study cell division with developmental consequences but expand to a different cell type, so I turned to stem cells.

What is a stem cell?

Stem cells are really the mother of all cells. Embryonic stem cells lead to the development of all tissues—the entire adult body. Tissue stem cells are responsible for the generation and/or maintenance of a specific tissue. All stem cells share a unique property—they can self-renew (reproduce) as well as give rise to more specialized cells. In theory, stem cells are immortal; they are like a fountain of youth that goes on and on.

How do you study stem cells?

To study stem cells, you have to identify the cell unambiguously, so cell biology is the first step. Cell biology defines a problem, describes the phenomenon, and provides the biological context for further mechanistic studies. It's crucially important. Then we move on to genetics, and, in my style of research, biochemistry usually comes as a third component.

What is the most interesting thing you have discovered about stem cells?

Using the genetic approach, we found a fruit fly (*Drosophila*) gene that encodes a protein called Piwi. The Piwi protein is also required in mammalian stem cells that make the testis (see micrograph). Piwi proteins bind to a kind of small RNA we and others independently discovered and called Piwi-interacting RNAs (or piRNAs). One of the wonderful things about working with fruit flies is that as soon as you identify new genes in flies and confirm that they function in stem cells, you can immediately look in humans to see whether these same genes become overactivated in cancer. It turns out the human Piwi gene is expressed at least sixfold more in a common kind of testicular cancer. We published the Piwi gene family in 1998, and amazingly, in 2002, we already had the results on this human cancer. If we hadn't started by working on basic cell biology in *Drosophila*, I don't think we could have found this connection to cancer so quickly.

(MB) For an extended interview and video clip, go to the Study Area in **MasteringBiology**.

6

A Tour of the Cell

▲ Figure 6.1 **How do your cells help you learn about biology?**

The Fundamental Units of Life

Cells are as fundamental to the living systems of biology as the atom is to chemistry. Many different types of cells are working for you right now. The contraction of muscle cells moves your eyes as you read this sentence. **Figure 6.1** shows extensions from a nerve cell (orange) making contact with muscle cells (red). The words on the page are translated into signals that nerve cells carry to your brain, where they are passed on to other nerve cells. As you study, you are making cell connections like these that solidify memories and permit learning to occur.

All organisms are made of cells. In the hierarchy of biological organization, the cell is the simplest collection of matter that can be alive. Indeed, many forms of life exist as single-celled organisms. Larger, more complex organisms, including plants and animals, are multicellular; their bodies are cooperatives of many kinds of specialized cells that could not survive for long on their own. Even when cells are arranged into higher levels of organization, such as tissues and organs, the cell remains the organism's basic unit of structure and function.

All cells are related by their descent from earlier cells. During the long evolutionary history of life on Earth, cells have been modified in many different ways. But although cells can differ substantially from one another, they share common features. In this chapter, we'll first examine the tools and techniques that allow us to understand cells, then tour the cell and become acquainted with its components.

93

CONCEPT 6.1

Biologists use microscopes and the tools of biochemistry to study cells

Dr. Haifan Lin, featured in the interview before this chapter, points out that studying the inner workings of cells is often the first step in making exciting biological discoveries. But how do we study cells, usually too small to be seen by the unaided eye?

Microscopy

The development of instruments that extend the human senses allowed the discovery and early study of cells. Microscopes were invented in 1590 and further refined during the 1600s. Cell walls were first seen by Robert Hooke in 1665 as he looked through a microscope at dead cells from the bark of an oak tree. But it took the wonderfully crafted lenses of Antoni van Leeuwenhoek to visualize living cells. Imagine Hooke's awe when he visited van Leeuwenhoek in 1674 and the world of microorganisms—what his host called "very little animalcules"—was revealed to him.

The microscopes first used by Renaissance scientists, as well as the microscopes you are likely to use in the laboratory, are all light microscopes. In a **light microscope (LM)**, visible light is passed through the specimen and then through glass lenses. The lenses refract (bend) the light in such a way that the image of the specimen is magnified as it is projected into the eye or into a camera (see Appendix D).

Three important parameters in microscopy are magnification, resolution, and contrast. *Magnification* is the ratio of an object's image size to its real size. Light microscopes can magnify effectively to about 1,000 times the actual size of the specimen; at greater magnifications, additional details cannot be seen clearly. *Resolution* is a measure of the clarity of the image; it is the minimum distance two points can be separated and still be distinguished as separate points. For example, what appears to the unaided eye as one star in the sky may be resolved as twin stars with a telescope, which has a higher resolving ability than the eye. Similarly, using standard techniques, the light microscope cannot resolve detail finer than about 0.2 micrometer (µm), or 200 nanometers (nm), regardless of the magnification (**Figure 6.2**). The third parameter, *contrast*, is the difference in brightness between the light and dark areas of an image. Methods for enhancing contrast include staining or labeling cell components to stand out visually. **Figure 6.3** shows some different types of microscopy; study this figure as you read this section.

Until recently, the resolution barrier prevented cell biologists from using standard light microscopy when studying **organelles**, the membrane-enclosed structures within eukaryotic cells. To see these structures in any detail required the development of a new instrument. In the 1950s, the electron microscope was introduced to biology. Rather than

▲ **Figure 6.2 The size range of cells.** Most cells are between 1 and 100 µm in diameter (yellow region of chart) and their components are even smaller, as are viruses. Notice that the scale along the left side is logarithmic, to accommodate the range of sizes shown. Starting at the top of the scale with 10 m and going down, each reference measurement marks a tenfold decrease in diameter or length. For a complete table of the metric system, see Appendix C.

1 centimeter (cm) = 10^{-2} meter (m) = 0.4 inch
1 millimeter (mm) = 10^{-3} m
1 micrometer (µm) = 10^{-3} mm = 10^{-6} m
1 nanometer (nm) = 10^{-3} µm = 10^{-9} m

focusing light, the **electron microscope (EM)** focuses a beam of electrons through the specimen or onto its surface (see Appendix D). Resolution is inversely related to the wavelength of the light (or electrons) a microscope uses for imaging, and electron beams have much shorter wavelengths than visible light. Modern electron microscopes can theoretically achieve a resolution of about 0.002 nm, though in practice they usually cannot resolve structures smaller than about 2 nm across. Still, this is a 100-fold improvement over the standard light microscope.

The **scanning electron microscope (SEM)** is especially useful for detailed study of the topography of a specimen

Exploring Microscopy

Light Microscopy (LM)

Brightfield (unstained specimen).
Light passes directly through the specimen. Unless the cell is naturally pigmented or artificially stained, the image has little contrast. (The first four light micrographs show human cheek epithelial cells; the scale bar pertains to all four micrographs.)

Brightfield (stained specimen).
Staining with various dyes enhances contrast. Most staining procedures require that cells be fixed (preserved), thereby killing them.

Phase-contrast. Variations in density within the specimen are amplified to enhance contrast in unstained cells; this is especially useful for examining living, unpigmented cells.

Differential-interference-contrast (Nomarski). As in phase-contrast microscopy, optical modifications are used to exaggerate differences in density; the image appears almost 3-D.

Fluorescence. The locations of specific molecules in the cell can be revealed by labeling the molecules with fluorescent dyes or antibodies; some cells have molecules that fluoresce on their own. Fluorescent substances absorb ultraviolet radiation and emit visible light. In this fluorescently labeled uterine cell, nuclear material is blue, organelles called mitochondria are orange, and the cell's "skeleton" is green.

50 μm

10 μm

Confocal. The top image is a standard fluorescence micrograph of fluorescently labeled nervous tissue (nerve cells are green, support cells are orange, and regions of overlap are yellow); below it is a confocal image of the same tissue. Using a laser, this "optical sectioning" technique eliminates out-of-focus light from a thick sample, creating a single plane of fluorescence in the image. By capturing sharp images at many different planes, a 3-D reconstruction can be created. The standard image is blurry because out-of-focus light is not excluded.

Deconvolution. The top of this split image is a compilation of standard fluorescence micrographs through the depth of a white blood cell. Below is an image of the same cell reconstructed from many blurry images at different planes, each of which was processed using deconvolution software. This process digitally removes out-of-focus light and reassigns it to its source, creating a much sharper 3-D image.

Super-resolution. On the top is a confocal image of part of a nerve cell, using a fluorescent label that binds to a molecule clustered in small sacs in the cell (vesicles) that are 40 nm in diameter. The greenish-yellow spots are blurry because 40 nm is below the 200-nm limit of resolution for standard light microscopy. Below is an image of the same part of the cell, seen using a new super-resolution technique. Sophisticated equipment is used to light up individual fluorescent molecules and record their position. Combining information from many molecules in different places "breaks" the limit of resolution, resulting in the sharp greenish-yellow dots seen here. (Each dot is a 40-nm vesicle.)

50 μm

10 μm

1 μm

Electron Microscopy (EM)

Scanning electron microscopy (SEM). Micrographs taken with a scanning electron microscope show a 3-D image of the surface of a specimen. This SEM shows the surface of a cell from a trachea (windpipe) covered with cilia. Beating of the cilia helps move inhaled debris upward toward the throat. Electron micrographs are black and white, but are often artificially colorized to highlight particular structures, as has been done with both micrographs (SEM and TEM) shown here.

Abbreviations used in figure legends in this book:
LM = Light Micrograph
SEM = Scanning Electron Micrograph
TEM = Transmission Electron Micrograph

Longitudinal section of cilium   Cross section of cilium

Cilia

2 μm

2 μm

Transmission electron microscopy (TEM).
A transmission electron microscope profiles a thin section of a specimen. Here we see a section through a tracheal cell, revealing its internal structure. In preparing the specimen, some cilia were cut along their lengths, creating longitudinal sections, while other cilia were cut straight across, creating cross sections.

(see Figure 6.3). The electron beam scans the surface of the sample, usually coated with a thin film of gold. The beam excites electrons on the surface, and these secondary electrons are detected by a device that translates the pattern of electrons into an electronic signal sent to a video screen. The result is an image of the specimen's surface that appears three-dimensional.

The **transmission electron microscope (TEM)** is used to study the internal structure of cells (see Figure 6.3). The TEM aims an electron beam through a very thin section of the specimen, much as a light microscope aims light through a sample on a slide. For the TEM, the specimen has been stained with atoms of heavy metals, which attach to certain cellular structures, thus enhancing the electron density of some parts of the cell more than others. The electrons passing through the specimen are scattered more in the denser regions, so fewer are transmitted. The image displays the pattern of transmitted electrons. Instead of using glass lenses, both the SEM and TEM use electromagnets as lenses to bend the paths of the electrons, ultimately focusing the image onto a monitor for viewing.

Electron microscopes have revealed many subcellular structures that were impossible to resolve with the light microscope. But the light microscope offers advantages, especially in studying living cells. A disadvantage of electron microscopy is that the methods used to prepare the specimen kill the cells. Specimen preparation for any type of microscopy can introduce artifacts, structural features seen in micrographs that do not exist in the living cell.

In the past several decades, light microscopy has been revitalized by major technical advances (see Figure 6.3). Labeling individual cellular molecules or structures with fluorescent markers has made it possible to see such structures with increasing detail. In addition, both confocal and deconvolution microscopy have produced sharper images of three-dimensional tissues and cells. Finally, a group of new techniques and labeling molecules developed in recent years have allowed researchers to "break" the resolution barrier and distinguish subcellular structures as small as 10–20 nm across. As this *super-resolution microscopy* becomes more widespread, the images we see of living cells are proving as awe-inspiring to us as van Leeuwenhoek's were to Robert Hooke 350 years ago.

Microscopes are the most important tools of *cytology*, the study of cell structure. Understanding the function of each structure, however, required the integration of cytology and *biochemistry*, the study of the chemical processes (metabolism) of cells.

Cell Fractionation

A useful technique for studying cell structure and function is **cell fractionation** (Figure 6.4), which takes cells apart

▼ Figure 6.4   Research Method

Cell Fractionation

Application Cell fractionation is used to isolate (fractionate) cell components based on size and density.

Technique Cells are homogenized in a blender to break them up. The resulting mixture (homogenate) is centrifuged. The supernatant (liquid) is poured into another tube and centrifuged at a higher speed for a longer period. This process is repeated several times. This "differential centrifugation" results in a series of pellets, each containing different cell components.

Results In early experiments, researchers used microscopy to identify the organelles in each pellet and biochemical methods to determine their metabolic functions. These identifications established a baseline for this method, enabling today's researchers to know which cell fraction they should collect in order to isolate and study particular organelles.

and separates major organelles and other subcellular structures from one another. The piece of equipment that is used for this task is the centrifuge, which spins test tubes holding mixtures of disrupted cells at a series of increasing speeds. At each speed, the resulting force causes a subset of the cell components to settle to the bottom of the tube, forming a pellet. At lower speeds, the pellet consists of larger components, and higher speeds result in a pellet with smaller components.

Cell fractionation enables researchers to prepare specific cell components in bulk and identify their functions, a task not usually possible with intact cells. For example, on one of the cell fractions, biochemical tests showed the presence of enzymes involved in cellular respiration, while electron microscopy revealed large numbers of the organelles called mitochondria. Together, these data helped biologists determine that mitochondria are the sites of cellular respiration. Biochemistry and cytology thus complement each other in correlating cell function with structure.

CONCEPT CHECK 6.1

1. How do stains used for light microscopy compare with those used for electron microscopy?
2. **WHAT IF?** Which type of microscope would you use to study (a) the changes in shape of a living white blood cell and (b) the details of surface texture of a hair?

For suggested answers, see Appendix A.

Eukaryotic cells have internal membranes that compartmentalize their functions

Cells—the basic structural and functional units of every organism—are of two distinct types: prokaryotic and eukaryotic. Organisms of the domains Bacteria and Archaea consist of prokaryotic cells. Protists, fungi, animals, and plants all consist of eukaryotic cells. ("Protist" is an informal term referring to a group of mostly unicellular eukaryotes.)

Comparing Prokaryotic and Eukaryotic Cells

All cells share certain basic features: They are all bounded by a selective barrier, called the *plasma membrane*. Inside all cells is a semifluid, jellylike substance called **cytosol**, in which subcellular components are suspended. All cells contain *chromosomes*, which carry genes in the form of DNA. And all cells have *ribosomes*, tiny complexes that make proteins according to instructions from the genes.

A major difference between prokaryotic and eukaryotic cells is the location of their DNA. In a **eukaryotic cell**, most of the DNA is in an organelle called the *nucleus*, which is bounded by a double membrane (see Figure 6.8). In a **prokaryotic cell**, the DNA is concentrated in a region that is not membrane-enclosed, called the **nucleoid** (Figure 6.5).

Fimbriae: attachment structures on the surface of some prokaryotes

Nucleoid: region where the cell's DNA is located (not enclosed by a membrane)

Ribosomes: complexes that synthesize proteins

Plasma membrane: membrane enclosing the cytoplasm

Cell wall: rigid structure outside the plasma membrane

Capsule: jellylike outer coating of many prokaryotes

Bacterial chromosome

Flagella: locomotion organelles of some bacteria

(a) A typical rod-shaped bacterium

0.5 μm

(b) A thin section through the bacterium *Bacillus coagulans* (TEM)

▲ **Figure 6.5 A prokaryotic cell.** Lacking a true nucleus and the other membrane-enclosed organelles of the eukaryotic cell, the prokaryotic cell appears much simpler in internal structure. Prokaryotes include bacteria and archaea; the general cell structure of the two domains is quite similar.

Eukaryotic means "true nucleus" (from the Greek *eu*, true, and *karyon*, kernel, referring to the nucleus), and *prokaryotic* means "before nucleus" (from the Greek *pro*, before), reflecting the earlier evolution of prokaryotic cells.

The interior of either type of cell is called the **cytoplasm**; in eukaryotic cells, this term refers only to the region between the nucleus and the plasma membrane. Within the cytoplasm of a eukaryotic cell, suspended in cytosol, are a variety of organelles of specialized form and function. These membrane-bounded structures are absent in prokaryotic cells, another distinction between prokaryotic and eukaryotic cells. However, in spite of the absence of organelles, the prokaryotic cytoplasm is not a formless soup of cytoplasm, but appears to be organized into different regions.

Eukaryotic cells are generally much larger than prokaryotic cells (see Figure 6.2). Size is a general feature of cell structure that relates to function. The logistics of carrying out cellular metabolism sets limits on cell size. At the lower limit, the smallest cells known are bacteria called mycoplasmas, which have diameters between 0.1 and 1.0 µm. These are perhaps the smallest packages with enough DNA to program metabolism and enough enzymes and other cellular equipment to carry out the activities necessary for a cell to sustain itself and reproduce. Typical bacteria are 1–5 µm in diameter, about ten times the size of mycoplasmas. Eukaryotic cells are typically 10–100 µm in diameter.

Metabolic requirements also impose theoretical upper limits on the size that is practical for a single cell. At the boundary of every cell, the **plasma membrane** functions as a selective barrier that allows passage of enough oxygen, nutrients, and wastes to service the entire cell (**Figure 6.6**). For each square micrometer of membrane, only a limited amount of a particular substance can cross per second, so the ratio of surface area to volume is critical. As a cell (or any other object) increases in size, its surface area grows proportionately less than its volume. (Area is proportional to a linear dimension squared, whereas volume is proportional to the linear dimension cubed.) Thus, a smaller object has a greater ratio of surface area to volume (**Figure 6.7**). The Scientific Skills Exercise gives you a chance to calculate the volumes and surface areas of two actual cells—a mature yeast cell and a cell budding from it.

The need for a surface area sufficiently large to accommodate the volume helps explain the microscopic size of most cells and the narrow, elongated shapes of others, such as nerve cells. Larger organisms do not generally have *larger* cells than smaller organisms—they simply have *more* cells (see Figure 6.7). A sufficiently high ratio of surface area to volume is especially important in cells that exchange a lot of material with their surroundings, such as intestinal cells. Such cells may have many long, thin projections from their surface called *microvilli*, which increase surface area without an appreciable increase in volume.

(a) TEM of a plasma membrane. The plasma membrane, here in a red blood cell, appears as a pair of dark bands separated by a light band.

Outside of cell

Inside of cell |— 0.1 µm —|

Carbohydrate side chains

Hydrophilic region

Hydrophobic region

Hydrophilic region

Phospholipid

Proteins

(b) Structure of the plasma membrane

© Pearson Education, Inc.

▲ **Figure 6.6 The plasma membrane.** The plasma membrane and the membranes of organelles consist of a double layer (bilayer) of phospholipids with various proteins attached to or embedded in it. The hydrophobic parts of phospholipids and membrane proteins are found in the interior of the membrane, while the hydrophilic parts are in contact with aqueous solutions on either side. Carbohydrate side chains may be attached to proteins or lipids on the outer surface of the plasma membrane.

MAKE CONNECTIONS *Review Figure 5.11 and describe the characteristics of phospholipids that allow them to function as the major components of the plasma membrane.*

Surface area increases while total volume remains constant

Total surface area [sum of the surface areas (height × width) of all box sides × number of boxes]	6	150	750
Total volume [height × width × length × number of boxes]	1	125	125
Surface-to-volume (S-to-V) ratio [surface area ÷ volume]	6	1.2	6

▲ **Figure 6.7 Geometric relationships between surface area and volume.** In this diagram, cells are represented as boxes. Using arbitrary units of length, we can calculate the cell's surface area (in square units, or units²), volume (in cubic units, or units³), and ratio of surface area to volume. A high surface-to-volume ratio facilitates the exchange of materials between a cell and its environment.

Using a Scale Bar to Calculate Volume and Surface Area of a Cell

How Much New Cytoplasm and Plasma Membrane Are Made by a Growing Yeast Cell? The unicellular yeast *Saccharomyces cerevisiae* divides by budding off a small new cell that then grows to full size (see the yeast cells at the bottom of Figure 6.8). During its growth, the new cell synthesizes new cytoplasm, which increases its volume, and new plasma membrane, which increases its surface area. In this exercise, you will use a scale bar to determine the sizes of a mature parent yeast cell and a cell budding from it. You will then calculate the volume and surface area of each cell. You will use your calculations to determine how much cytoplasm and plasma membrane the new cell needs to synthesize to grow to full size.

How the Experiment Was Done Yeast cells were grown under conditions that promoted division by budding. The cells were then viewed with a differential interference contrast light microscope and photographed.

Data from the Experiment This light micrograph shows a budding yeast cell about to be released from the mature parent cell:

Mature parent cell

Budding cell

1 μm

Interpret the Data

1. Examine the micrograph of the yeast cells. The scale bar under the photo is labeled 1 μm. The scale bar works in the same way as a scale on a map, where, for example, 1 inch equals 1 mile. In this case the bar represents one thousandth of a millimeter. Using the scale bar as a basic unit, determine the diameter of the mature parent cell and the

new cell. Start by measuring the scale bar and then the diameter of each cell. The units you use are irrelevant, but working in millimeters is convenient. Divide each diameter by the length of the scale bar and then multiply by the scale bar's length value to give you the diameter in micrometers.

2. The shape of a yeast cell can be approximated by a sphere. (a) Calculate the volume of each cell using the formula for the volume of a sphere:

$$V = \frac{4}{3}\pi r^3$$

Note that π (the Greek letter pi) is a constant with an approximate value of 3.14, d stands for diameter, and r stands for radius, which is half the diameter. (b) How much new cytoplasm will the new cell have to synthesize as it matures? To determine this, calculate the difference between the volume of the full-sized cell and the volume of the new cell.

3. As the new cell grows, its plasma membrane needs to expand to contain the increased volume of the cell. (a) Calculate the surface area of each cell using the formula for the surface area of a sphere: $A = 4\pi r^2$. (b) How much area of new plasma membrane will the new cell have to synthesize as it matures?

4. When the new cell matures, it will be approximately how many times greater in volume and how many times greater in surface area than its current size?

Micrograph from Kelly Tatchell, using yeast cells grown for experiments described in L. Kozubowski et al., Role of the septin ring in the asymmetric localization of proteins at the mother-bud neck in *Saccharomyces cerevisiae*, *Molecular Biology of the Cell* 16:3455–3466 (2005).

(MB) A version of this Scientific Skills Exercise can be assigned in MasteringBiology.

The evolutionary relationships between prokaryotic and eukaryotic cells will be discussed later in this chapter, and prokaryotic cells will be described in detail in Chapter 27. Most of the discussion of cell structure that follows in this chapter applies to eukaryotic cells.

A Panoramic View of the Eukaryotic Cell

In addition to the plasma membrane at its outer surface, a eukaryotic cell has extensive, elaborately arranged internal membranes that divide the cell into compartments—the organelles mentioned earlier. The cell's compartments provide different local environments that support specific metabolic functions, so incompatible processes can occur simultaneously in a single cell. The plasma membrane and organelle membranes also participate directly in the cell's metabolism, because many enzymes are built right into the membranes.

The basic fabric of most biological membranes is a double layer of phospholipids and other lipids. Embedded in this lipid bilayer or attached to its surfaces are diverse proteins (see Figure 6.6). However, each type of membrane has a unique composition of lipids and proteins suited to that membrane's specific functions. For example, enzymes embedded in the membranes of the organelles called mitochondria function in cellular respiration. Because membranes are so fundamental to the organization of the cell, Chapter 7 will discuss them in detail.

Before continuing with this chapter, examine the eukaryotic cells in **Figure 6.8**, on the next two pages. The generalized diagrams of an animal cell and a plant cell introduce the various organelles and show the key differences between animal and plant cells. The micrographs at the bottom of the figure give you a glimpse of cells from different types of eukaryotic organisms.

Exploring Eukaryotic Cells

Animal Cell (cutaway view of generalized cell)

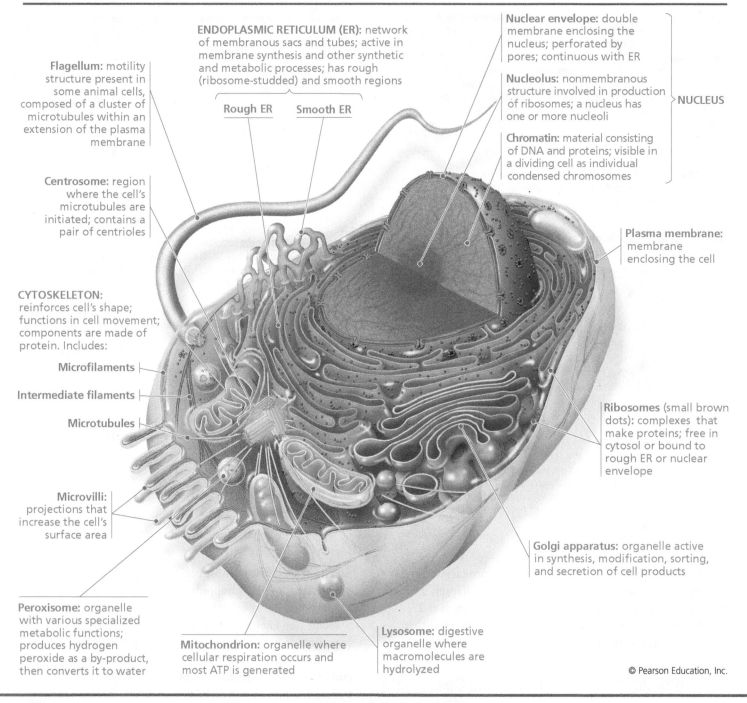

Flagellum: motility structure present in some animal cells, composed of a cluster of microtubules within an extension of the plasma membrane

ENDOPLASMIC RETICULUM (ER): network of membranous sacs and tubes; active in membrane synthesis and other synthetic and metabolic processes; has rough (ribosome-studded) and smooth regions

Rough ER | Smooth ER

Nuclear envelope: double membrane enclosing the nucleus; perforated by pores; continuous with ER

Nucleolus: nonmembranous structure involved in production of ribosomes; a nucleus has one or more nucleoli

Chromatin: material consisting of DNA and proteins; visible in a dividing cell as individual condensed chromosomes

NUCLEUS

Centrosome: region where the cell's microtubules are initiated; contains a pair of centrioles

Plasma membrane: membrane enclosing the cell

CYTOSKELETON: reinforces cell's shape; functions in cell movement; components are made of protein. Includes:

Microfilaments

Intermediate filaments

Microtubules

Ribosomes (small brown dots): complexes that make proteins; free in cytosol or bound to rough ER or nuclear envelope

Microvilli: projections that increase the cell's surface area

Golgi apparatus: organelle active in synthesis, modification, sorting, and secretion of cell products

Peroxisome: organelle with various specialized metabolic functions; produces hydrogen peroxide as a by-product, then converts it to water

Mitochondrion: organelle where cellular respiration occurs and most ATP is generated

Lysosome: digestive organelle where macromolecules are hydrolyzed

© Pearson Education, Inc.

Animal Cells

10 μm

Cell

Nucleus

Nucleolus

Human cells from lining of uterus (colorized TEM)

Fungal Cells

Parent cell

Buds

5 μm

Yeast cells: reproducing by budding (above, colorized SEM) and a single cell (right, colorized TEM)

1 μm

Cell wall

Vacuole

Nucleus

Mitochondrion

Plant Cell (cutaway view of generalized cell)

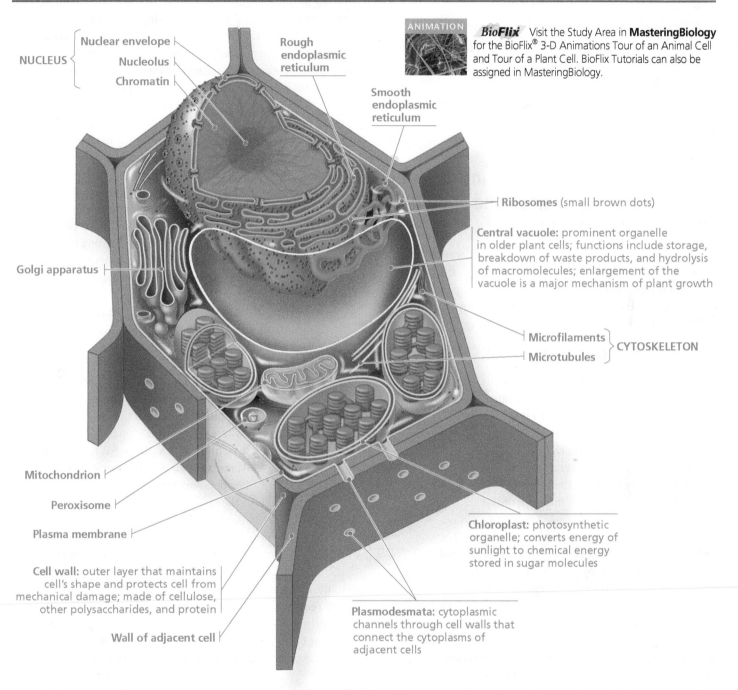

NUCLEUS {
Nuclear envelope
Nucleolus
Chromatin
}

Rough endoplasmic reticulum

Smooth endoplasmic reticulum

ANIMATION *BioFlix* Visit the Study Area in **MasteringBiology** for the BioFlix® 3-D Animations Tour of an Animal Cell and Tour of a Plant Cell. BioFlix Tutorials can also be assigned in MasteringBiology.

Ribosomes (small brown dots)

Central vacuole: prominent organelle in older plant cells; functions include storage, breakdown of waste products, and hydrolysis of macromolecules; enlargement of the vacuole is a major mechanism of plant growth

Golgi apparatus

Microfilaments
Microtubules
} **CYTOSKELETON**

Mitochondrion

Peroxisome

Plasma membrane

Chloroplast: photosynthetic organelle; converts energy of sunlight to chemical energy stored in sugar molecules

Cell wall: outer layer that maintains cell's shape and protects cell from mechanical damage; made of cellulose, other polysaccharides, and protein

Wall of adjacent cell

Plasmodesmata: cytoplasmic channels through cell walls that connect the cytoplasms of adjacent cells

Plant Cells

5 μm

Cell
Cell wall
Chloroplast
Mitochondrion
Nucleus
Nucleolus

Cells from duckweed (*Spirodela oligorrhiza*), a floating plant (colorized TEM)

Unicellular Eukaryotes

8 μm

Unicellular green alga *Chlamydomonas* (above, colorized SEM; right, colorized TEM)

1 μm

Flagella
Nucleus
Nucleolus
Vacuole
Chloroplast
Cell wall

1. Briefly describe the structure and function of the nucleus, the mitochondrion, the chloroplast, and the endoplasmic reticulum.

2. **WHAT IF?** Imagine an elongated cell (such as a nerve cell) that measures 125 × 1 × 1 arbitrary units. Predict how its surface-to-volume ratio would compare with those in Figure 6.7. Then calculate the ratio and check your prediction.

For suggested answers, see Appendix A.

CONCEPT 6.3

The eukaryotic cell's genetic instructions are housed in the nucleus and carried out by the ribosomes

On the first stop of our detailed tour of the eukaryotic cell, let's look at two cellular components involved in the genetic control of the cell: the nucleus, which houses most of the cell's DNA, and the ribosomes, which use information from the DNA to make proteins.

The Nucleus: Information Central

The **nucleus** contains most of the genes in the eukaryotic cell. (Some genes are located in mitochondria and chloroplasts.) It is generally the most conspicuous organelle (see blue structure in cell on right), averaging about 5 μm in diameter. The **nuclear envelope** encloses the nucleus (**Figure 6.9**), separating its contents from the cytoplasm.

The nuclear envelope is a *double* membrane. The two membranes, each a lipid bilayer with associated proteins, are separated by a space of 20–40 nm. The envelope is perforated by pore structures that are about 100 nm in diameter. At the lip of each pore, the inner and outer membranes of the nuclear envelope are continuous. An intricate protein structure called a *pore complex* lines each pore and plays an important role in the cell by regulating the entry and exit of proteins and RNAs, as well as large complexes of macromolecules. Except at the pores, the nuclear side of the envelope is lined by the **nuclear lamina**, a netlike array of protein filaments that maintains the shape of the nucleus by mechanically supporting the nuclear envelope. There is also much evidence for a *nuclear matrix*, a framework of protein fibers extending throughout the nuclear interior. The nuclear lamina and matrix may help organize the genetic material so it functions efficiently.

Within the nucleus, the DNA is organized into discrete units called **chromosomes**, structures that carry the genetic

Nucleus

5 μm

information. Each chromosome contains one long DNA molecule associated with many proteins. Some of the proteins help coil the DNA molecule of each chromosome, reducing its length and allowing it to fit into the nucleus. The complex of DNA and proteins making up chromosomes is called **chromatin**. When a cell is not dividing, stained chromatin appears as a diffuse mass in micrographs, and the chromosomes cannot be distinguished from one another, even though discrete chromosomes are present. As a cell prepares to divide, however, the chromosomes coil (condense) further, becoming thick enough to be distinguished under a microscope as separate structures. Each eukaryotic species has a characteristic number of chromosomes. For example, a typical human cell has 46 chromosomes in its nucleus; the exceptions are the sex cells (eggs and sperm), which have only 23 chromosomes in humans. A fruit fly cell has 8 chromosomes in most cells and 4 in the sex cells.

A prominent structure within the nondividing nucleus is the **nucleolus** (plural, *nucleoli*), which appears through the electron microscope as a mass of densely stained granules and fibers adjoining part of the chromatin. Here a type of RNA called *ribosomal RNA* (rRNA) is synthesized from instructions in the DNA. Also in the nucleolus, proteins imported from the cytoplasm are assembled with rRNA into large and small subunits of ribosomes. These subunits then exit the nucleus through the nuclear pores to the cytoplasm, where a large and a small subunit can assemble into a ribosome. Sometimes there are two or more nucleoli; the number depends on the species and the stage in the cell's reproductive cycle.

As we saw in Figure 5.23, the nucleus directs protein synthesis by synthesizing messenger RNA (mRNA) according to instructions provided by the DNA. The mRNA is then transported to the cytoplasm via the nuclear pores. Once an mRNA molecule reaches the cytoplasm, ribosomes translate the mRNA's genetic message into the primary structure of a specific polypeptide. (This process of transcribing and translating genetic information is described in detail in Chapter 17.)

Ribosomes: Protein Factories

Ribosomes, which are complexes made of ribosomal RNA and protein, are the cellular components that carry out protein synthesis (**Figure 6.10**). (Note that ribosomes are not membrane bounded and thus are not considered organelles.) Cells that have high rates of protein synthesis have particularly large numbers of ribosomes. For example, a human pancreas cell, which makes many digestive enzymes, has a few million ribosomes. Not surprisingly, cells active in protein synthesis also have prominent nucleoli.

▲ **Surface of nuclear envelope (TEM).** This specimen was prepared by a technique known as freeze-fracture.

Nucleus

Nucleolus

Chromatin

Nuclear envelope:
Inner membrane
Outer membrane

Nuclear pore

Nucleus

Rough ER

Pore complex

Ribosome

◀ **Close-up of nuclear envelope**

▲ **Pore complexes (TEM).** Each pore is ringed by protein particles.

▲ **Chromatin.** This segment of a chromosome from a non-dividing cell shows two states of coiling of the DNA (blue) and protein (purple) complex. The thicker form is sometimes also organized into long loops.

◀ **Nuclear lamina (TEM).** The netlike lamina lines the inner surface of the nuclear envelope.

© Pearson Education, Inc.

▲ **Figure 6.9 The nucleus and its envelope.** Within the nucleus are the chromosomes, which appear as a mass of chromatin (DNA and associated proteins) and one or more nucleoli (singular, *nucleolus*), which function in ribosome synthesis. The nuclear envelope, which consists of two membranes separated by a narrow space, is perforated with pores and lined by the nuclear lamina.

MAKE CONNECTIONS *Since the chromosomes contain the genetic material and reside in the nucleus, how does the rest of the cell get access to the information they carry? (See Figure 5.23.)*

Ribosomes

ER

Free ribosomes in cytosol

Endoplasmic reticulum (ER)

Ribosomes bound to ER

Large subunit

Small subunit

TEM showing ER and ribosomes

Diagram of a ribosome

Computer model of a ribosome

▲ **Figure 6.10 Ribosomes.** This electron micrograph of a pancreas cell shows both free and bound ribosomes. The simplified diagram and computer model show the two subunits of a ribosome.

Ribosomes build proteins in two cytoplasmic locales. At any given time, *free ribosomes* are suspended in the cytosol, while *bound ribosomes* are attached to the outside of the endoplasmic reticulum or nuclear envelope (see Figure 6.10). Bound and free ribosomes are structurally identical, and ribosomes can alternate between the two roles. Most of the proteins made on free ribosomes function within the cytosol; examples are enzymes that catalyze the first steps of sugar breakdown. Bound ribosomes generally make proteins that are destined for insertion into membranes, for packaging within certain organelles such as lysosomes (see Figure 6.8), or for export from the cell (secretion). Cells that specialize in protein secretion—for instance, the cells of the pancreas that secrete digestive enzymes—frequently have a high proportion of bound ribosomes. (You will learn more about ribosome structure and function in Chapter 17.)

CONCEPT CHECK 6.3

1. What role do ribosomes play in carrying out genetic instructions?
2. Describe the molecular composition of nucleoli and explain their function.
3. **WHAT IF?** As a cell begins the process of dividing, its chromosomes become shorter, thicker, and individually visible in an LM. Explain what is happening at the molecular level.

For suggested answers, see Appendix A.

CONCEPT 6.4

The endomembrane system regulates protein traffic and performs metabolic functions in the cell

Many of the different membranes of the eukaryotic cell are part of the **endomembrane system**, which includes the nuclear envelope, the endoplasmic reticulum, the Golgi apparatus, lysosomes, various kinds of vesicles and vacuoles, and the plasma membrane. This system carries out a variety of tasks in the cell, including synthesis of proteins, transport of proteins into membranes and organelles or out of the cell, metabolism and movement of lipids, and detoxification of poisons. The membranes of this system are related either through direct physical continuity or by the transfer of membrane segments as tiny **vesicles** (sacs made of membrane). Despite these relationships, the various membranes are not identical in structure and function. Moreover, the thickness, molecular composition, and types of chemical reactions carried out in a given membrane are not fixed, but may be modified several times during the membrane's life. Having already discussed the nuclear envelope, we will now

focus on the endoplasmic reticulum and the other endomembranes to which the endoplasmic reticulum gives rise.

The Endoplasmic Reticulum: Biosynthetic Factory

The **endoplasmic reticulum (ER)** is such an extensive network of membranes that it accounts for more than half the total membrane in many eukaryotic cells. (The word *endoplasmic* means "within the cytoplasm," and *reticulum* is Latin for "little net.") The ER consists of a network of membranous tubules and sacs called cisternae (from the Latin *cisterna*, a reservoir for a liquid). The ER membrane separates the internal compartment of the ER, called the *ER lumen* (cavity) or cisternal space, from the cytosol. And because the ER membrane is continuous with the nuclear envelope, the space between the two membranes of the envelope is continuous with the lumen of the ER **(Figure 6.11)**.

There are two distinct, though connected, regions of the ER that differ in structure and function: smooth ER and rough ER. **Smooth ER** is so named because its outer surface lacks ribosomes. **Rough ER** is studded with ribosomes on the outer surface of the membrane and thus appears rough through the electron microscope. As already mentioned, ribosomes are also attached to the cytoplasmic side of the nuclear envelope's outer membrane, which is continuous with rough ER.

Functions of Smooth ER

The smooth ER functions in diverse metabolic processes, which vary with cell type. These processes include synthesis of lipids, metabolism of carbohydrates, detoxification of drugs and poisons, and storage of calcium ions.

Enzymes of the smooth ER are important in the synthesis of lipids, including oils, steroids, and new membrane phospholipids. Among the steroids produced by the smooth ER in animal cells are the sex hormones of vertebrates and the various steroid hormones secreted by the adrenal glands. The cells that synthesize and secrete these hormones—in the testes and ovaries, for example—are rich in smooth ER, a structural feature that fits the function of these cells.

Other enzymes of the smooth ER help detoxify drugs and poisons, especially in liver cells. Detoxification usually involves adding hydroxyl groups to drug molecules, making them more soluble and easier to flush from the body. The sedative phenobarbital and other barbiturates are examples of drugs metabolized in this manner by smooth ER in liver cells. In fact, barbiturates, alcohol, and many other drugs induce the proliferation of smooth ER and its associated detoxification enzymes, thus increasing the rate of detoxification. This, in turn, increases tolerance to the drugs, meaning that higher doses are required to achieve a particular effect, such as sedation. Also, because some of the detoxification enzymes have relatively broad action, the proliferation of smooth ER in response to one drug can increase the need for higher dosages of other drugs as well. Barbiturate abuse, for example, can decrease the effectiveness of certain antibiotics and other useful drugs.

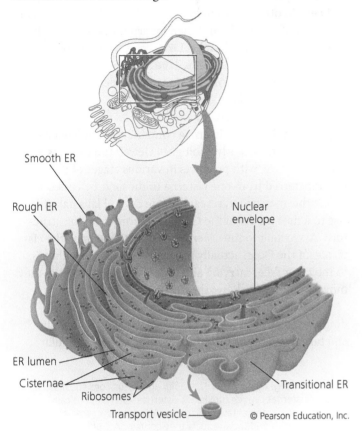

Smooth ER

Rough ER

Nuclear envelope

ER lumen

Cisternae

Ribosomes

Transitional ER

Transport vesicle

© Pearson Education, Inc.

Smooth ER

Rough ER

0.20 μm

▲ **Figure 6.11 Endoplasmic reticulum (ER).** A membranous system of interconnected tubules and flattened sacs called cisternae, the ER is also continuous with the nuclear envelope, as shown in the cutaway diagram at the top. The membrane of the ER encloses a continuous compartment called the ER lumen (or cisternal space). Rough ER, which is studded on its outer surface with ribosomes, can be distinguished from smooth ER in the electron micrograph (TEM). Transport vesicles bud off from a region of the rough ER called transitional ER and travel to the Golgi apparatus and other destinations.

The smooth ER also stores calcium ions. In muscle cells, for example, the smooth ER membrane pumps calcium ions from the cytosol into the ER lumen. When a muscle cell is stimulated by a nerve impulse, calcium ions rush back across the ER membrane into the cytosol and trigger contraction of the muscle cell. In other cell types, calcium ion release from the smooth ER triggers different responses, such as secretion of vesicles carrying newly synthesized proteins.

Functions of Rough ER

Many cells secrete proteins that are produced by ribosomes attached to rough ER. For example, certain pancreatic cells synthesize the protein insulin in the ER and secrete this hormone into the bloodstream. As a polypeptide chain grows from a bound ribosome, the chain is threaded into the ER lumen through a pore formed by a protein complex in the ER membrane. The new polypeptide folds into its functional shape as it enters the ER lumen. Most secretory proteins are **glycoproteins**, proteins with carbohydrates covalently bonded to them. The carbohydrates are attached to the proteins in the ER lumen by enzymes built into the ER membrane.

After secretory proteins are formed, the ER membrane keeps them separate from proteins that are produced by free ribosomes and that will remain in the cytosol. Secretory proteins depart from the ER wrapped in the membranes of vesicles that bud like bubbles from a specialized region called transitional ER (see Figure 6.11). Vesicles in transit from one part of the cell to another are called **transport vesicles**; we will discuss their fate shortly.

In addition to making secretory proteins, rough ER is a membrane factory for the cell; it grows in place by adding membrane proteins and phospholipids to its own membrane. As polypeptides destined to be membrane proteins grow from the ribosomes, they are inserted into the ER membrane itself and anchored there by their hydrophobic portions. Like the smooth ER, the rough ER also makes membrane phospholipids; enzymes built into the ER membrane assemble phospholipids from precursors in the cytosol. The ER membrane expands, and portions of it are transferred in the form of transport vesicles to other components of the endomembrane system.

The Golgi Apparatus: Shipping and Receiving Center

After leaving the ER, many transport vesicles travel to the **Golgi apparatus**. We can think of the Golgi as a warehouse for receiving, sorting, shipping, and even some manufacturing. Here, products of the ER, such as proteins, are modified and stored and then sent to other destinations. Not surprisingly, the Golgi apparatus is especially extensive in cells specialized for secretion.

The Golgi apparatus consists of flattened membranous sacs—cisternae—looking like a stack of pita bread (Figure 6.12). A cell may have many, even hundreds, of these stacks. The membrane of each cisterna in a stack separates its internal space from the cytosol. Vesicles concentrated in the vicinity of the Golgi apparatus are engaged in the transfer of material between parts of the Golgi and other structures.

A Golgi stack has a distinct structural directionality, with the membranes of cisternae on opposite sides of the stack differing in thickness and molecular composition. The two sides of a Golgi stack are referred to as the *cis* face and the *trans* face; these act, respectively, as the receiving and shipping departments of the Golgi apparatus. The term *cis* means "on the same side," and the *cis* face is usually located near the ER. Transport vesicles move material from the ER to the Golgi apparatus. A vesicle that buds from the ER can add its membrane and the contents of its lumen to the *cis* face by fusing with a Golgi membrane. The *trans* face ("on the opposite side") gives rise to vesicles that pinch off and travel to other sites.

Products of the endoplasmic reticulum are usually modified during their transit from the *cis* region to the *trans* region of the Golgi apparatus. For example, glycoproteins formed in the ER have their carbohydrates modified, first in the ER itself, then as they pass through the Golgi. The Golgi removes some sugar monomers and substitutes others, producing a large variety of carbohydrates. Membrane phospholipids may also be altered in the Golgi.

In addition to its finishing work, the Golgi apparatus also manufactures some macromolecules. Many polysaccharides secreted by cells are Golgi products. For example, pectins and certain other noncellulose polysaccharides are made in the Golgi of plant cells and then incorporated along with cellulose into their cell walls. Like secretory proteins, nonprotein Golgi products that will be secreted depart from the *trans* face of the Golgi inside transport vesicles that eventually fuse with the plasma membrane.

The Golgi manufactures and refines its products in stages, with different cisternae containing unique teams of enzymes. Until recently, biologists viewed the Golgi as a static structure, with products in various stages of processing transferred from one cisterna to the next by vesicles. While this may occur, research from several labs has given rise to a new model of the Golgi as a more dynamic structure. According to the *cisternal maturation model*, the cisternae of the Golgi actually progress forward from the *cis* to the *trans* face, carrying and modifying their cargo as they move. Figure 6.12 shows the details of this model.

Before a Golgi stack dispatches its products by budding vesicles from the *trans* face, it sorts these products and targets them for various parts of the cell. Molecular

▼ **Figure 6.12 The Golgi apparatus.** The Golgi apparatus consists of stacks of flattened sacs, or cisternae, which (unlike ER cisternae) are not physically connected, as you can see in the cutaway diagram. A Golgi stack receives and dispatches transport vesicles and the products they contain. A Golgi stack has a structural and functional directionality, with a *cis* face that receives vesicles containing ER products and a *trans* face that dispatches vesicles. The cisternal maturation model proposes that the Golgi cisternae themselves "mature," moving from the *cis* to the *trans* face while carrying some proteins along. In addition, some vesicles recycle enzymes that had been carried forward in moving cisternae, transporting them "backward" to a less mature region where their functions are needed.

Golgi apparatus

cis face ("receiving" side of Golgi apparatus)

❶ Vesicles move from ER to Golgi.

❷ Vesicles coalesce to form new *cis* Golgi cisternae.

❻ Vesicles also transport certain proteins back to ER, their site of function.

Cisternae

❸ Cisternal maturation: Golgi cisternae move in a *cis*-to-*trans* direction.

❹ Vesicles form and leave Golgi, carrying specific products to other locations or to the plasma membrane for secretion.

❺ Vesicles transport some proteins backward to less mature Golgi cisternae, where they function.

trans face ("shipping" side of Golgi apparatus)

0.1 μm

TEM of Golgi apparatus

© Pearson Education, Inc.

identification tags, such as phosphate groups added to the Golgi products, aid in sorting by acting like zip codes on mailing labels. Finally, transport vesicles budded from the Golgi may have external molecules on their membranes that recognize "docking sites" on the surface of specific organelles or on the plasma membrane, thus targeting the vesicles appropriately.

Lysosomes: Digestive Compartments

A **lysosome** is a membranous sac of hydrolytic enzymes that many eukaryotic cells use to digest (hydrolyze) macromolecules. Lysosomal enzymes work best in the acidic environment found in lysosomes. If a lysosome breaks open or leaks its contents, the released enzymes are not very active because the cytosol has a near-neutral pH. However, excessive leakage from a large number of lysosomes can destroy a cell by self-digestion.

Hydrolytic enzymes and lysosomal membrane are made by rough ER and then transferred to the Golgi apparatus for further processing. At least some lysosomes probably arise by budding from the *trans* face of the Golgi apparatus (see Figure 6.12). How are the proteins of the inner surface of the lysosomal membrane and the digestive enzymes themselves spared from destruction? Apparently, the three-dimensional shapes of these proteins protect vulnerable bonds from enzymatic attack.

Lysosomes carry out intracellular digestion in a variety of circumstances. Amoebas and many other unicellular eukaryotes eat by engulfing smaller organisms or food particles, a process called **phagocytosis** (from the Greek *phagein*, to eat, and *kytos*, vessel, referring here to the cell). The *food vacuole* formed in this way then fuses with a lysosome, whose enzymes digest the food (**Figure 6.13a**, bottom). Digestion products, including simple sugars, amino acids, and other monomers, pass into the cytosol and become nutrients for the cell. Some human cells also carry out phagocytosis. Among them are macrophages, a type of white blood cell that helps defend the body by engulfing and destroying bacteria and other invaders (see Figure 6.13a, top, and Figure 6.31).

(a) Phagocytosis: lysosome digesting food

(b) Autophagy: lysosome breaking down damaged organelles

▲ **Figure 6.13 Lysosomes.** Lysosomes digest (hydrolyze) materials taken into the cell and recycle intracellular materials. **(a)** *Top*: In this macrophage (a type of white blood cell) from a rat, the lysosomes are very dark because of a stain that reacts with one of the products of digestion inside the lysosome (TEM).

Macrophages ingest bacteria and viruses and destroy them using lysosomes. *Bottom*: This diagram shows a lysosome fusing with a food vacuole during the process of phagocytosis by a unicellular eukaryote. **(b)** *Top*: In the cytoplasm of this rat liver cell is a vesicle containing two disabled organelles (TEM). The vesicle will fuse

with a lysosome in the process of autophagy. *Bottom*: This diagram shows fusion of such a vesicle with a lysosome. This type of vesicle has a double membrane of unknown origin. The outer membrane fuses with the lysosome, and the inner membrane is degraded along with the damaged organelles.

Lysosomes also use their hydrolytic enzymes to recycle the cell's own organic material, a process called *autophagy*. During autophagy, a damaged organelle or small amount of cytosol becomes surrounded by a double membrane (of unknown origin), and a lysosome fuses with the outer membrane of this vesicle (Figure 6.13b). The lysosomal enzymes dismantle the enclosed material, and the resulting small organic compounds are released to the cytosol for reuse. With the help of lysosomes, the cell continually renews itself. A human liver cell, for example, recycles half of its macromolecules each week.

The cells of people with inherited lysosomal storage diseases lack a functioning hydrolytic enzyme normally present in lysosomes. The lysosomes become engorged with indigestible material, which begins to interfere with other cellular activities. In Tay-Sachs disease, for example, a lipid-digesting enzyme is missing or inactive, and the brain becomes impaired by an accumulation of lipids in the cells. Fortunately, lysosomal storage diseases are rare in the general population.

Vacuoles: Diverse Maintenance Compartments

Vacuoles are large vesicles derived from the endoplasmic reticulum and Golgi apparatus. Thus, vacuoles are an integral part of a cell's endomembrane system. Like all cellular membranes, the vacuolar membrane is selective in transporting solutes; as a result, the solution inside a vacuole differs in composition from the cytosol.

Vacuoles perform a variety of functions in different kinds of cells. **Food vacuoles**, formed by phagocytosis, have already been mentioned (see Figure 6.13a). Many unicellular eukaryotes living in fresh water have **contractile vacuoles** that pump excess water out of the cell, thereby maintaining a suitable concentration of ions and molecules inside the cell (see Figure 7.13). In plants and fungi, certain vacuoles carry out enzymatic hydrolysis, a function shared by lysosomes in animal cells. (In fact, some biologists consider these hydrolytic vacuoles to be a type of lysosome.) In plants, small vacuoles can hold reserves of important organic compounds, such as the proteins stockpiled in the storage cells in seeds. Vacuoles may also help protect the plant against herbivores by storing compounds that are poisonous or unpalatable to animals. Some plant vacuoles contain pigments, such as the red and blue pigments of petals that help attract pollinating insects to flowers.

Mature plant cells generally contain a large **central vacuole (Figure 6.14)**, which develops by the coalescence of smaller vacuoles. The solution inside the central vacuole, called cell sap, is the plant cell's main repository of inorganic ions, including potassium and chloride. The central vacuole plays a major role in the growth of plant cells, which enlarge

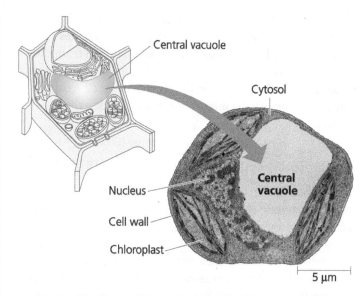

▲ Figure 6.14 **The plant cell vacuole.** The central vacuole is usually the largest compartment in a plant cell; the rest of the cytoplasm is often confined to a narrow zone between the vacuolar membrane and the plasma membrane (TEM).

as the vacuole absorbs water, enabling the cell to become larger with a minimal investment in new cytoplasm. The cytosol often occupies only a thin layer between the central vacuole and the plasma membrane, so the ratio of plasma membrane surface to cytosolic volume is sufficient, even for a large plant cell.

The Endomembrane System: *A Review*

Figure 6.15 reviews the endomembrane system, showing the flow of membrane lipids and proteins through the various organelles. As the membrane moves from the ER to the Golgi and then elsewhere, its molecular composition and metabolic functions are modified, along with those of its contents. The endomembrane system is a complex and dynamic player in the cell's compartmental organization.

We'll continue our tour of the cell with some organelles that are not closely related to the endomembrane system but play crucial roles in the energy transformations carried out by cells.

CONCEPT CHECK 6.4

1. Describe the structural and functional distinctions between rough and smooth ER.

2. Describe how transport vesicles integrate the endomembrane system.

3. **WHAT IF?** Imagine a protein that functions in the ER but requires modification in the Golgi apparatus before it can achieve that function. Describe the protein's path through the cell, starting with the mRNA molecule that specifies the protein.

For suggested answers, see Appendix A.

① Nuclear envelope is connected to rough ER, which is also continuous with smooth ER.

Nucleus

Rough ER

Smooth ER

② Membranes and proteins produced by the ER flow in the form of transport vesicles to the Golgi.

cis Golgi

③ Golgi pinches off transport vesicles and other vesicles that give rise to lysosomes, other types of specialized vesicles, and vacuoles.

Plasma membrane

trans Golgi

④ Lysosome is available for fusion with another vesicle for digestion.

⑤ Transport vesicle carries proteins to plasma membrane for secretion.

⑥ Plasma membrane expands by fusion of vesicles; proteins are secreted from cell.

© Pearson Education, Inc.

▲ **Figure 6.15 Review: relationships among organelles of the endomembrane system.**
The red arrows show some of the migration pathways for membranes and the materials they enclose.

CONCEPT 6.5

Mitochondria and chloroplasts change energy from one form to another

Organisms transform the energy they acquire from their surroundings. In eukaryotic cells, mitochondria and chloroplasts are the organelles that convert energy to forms that cells can use for work. **Mitochondria** (singular, *mitochondrion*) are the sites of cellular respiration, the metabolic process that uses oxygen to drive the generation of ATP by extracting energy from sugars, fats, and other fuels. **Chloroplasts**, found in plants and algae, are the sites of photosynthesis. This process in chloroplasts converts solar energy to chemical energy by absorbing sunlight and using it to drive the synthesis of organic compounds such as sugars from carbon dioxide and water.

In addition to having related functions, mitochondria and chloroplasts share similar evolutionary origins, which we'll discuss briefly before describing their structures. In this section, we will also consider the peroxisome, an oxidative organelle. The evolutionary origin of the peroxisome, as well as its relation to other organelles, is still a matter of some debate.

The Evolutionary Origins of Mitochondria and Chloroplasts

EVOLUTION Mitochondria and chloroplasts display similarities with bacteria that led to the **endosymbiont theory**, illustrated in **Figure 6.16.** This theory states that an early ancestor of eukaryotic cells engulfed an oxygen-using nonphotosynthetic prokaryotic cell. Eventually, the engulfed cell formed a relationship with the host cell in which it was enclosed, becoming an *endosymbiont* (a cell living within another cell). Indeed, over the course of evolution, the host cell and its endosymbiont merged into a single organism, a eukaryotic cell with a mitochondrion. At least one of these cells may have then taken up a photosynthetic prokaryote, becoming the ancestor of eukaryotic cells that contain chloroplasts.

This is a widely accepted theory, which we will discuss in more detail in Chapter 25. This theory is consistent with many structural features of mitochondria and chloroplasts. First, rather than being bounded by a single membrane like organelles of the endomembrane system, mitochondria and typical chloroplasts have two membranes surrounding them. (Chloroplasts also have an internal system of membranous sacs.) There is evidence that the ancestral engulfed

Endoplasmic reticulum

Nucleus

Nuclear envelope

Ancestor of eukaryotic cells (host cell)

Engulfing of oxygen-using nonphotosynthetic prokaryote, which, over many generations of cells, becomes a mitochondrion

Mitochondrion

Engulfing of photosynthetic prokaryote

Chloroplast

Mitochondrion

At least one cell

Nonphotosynthetic eukaryote

Photosynthetic eukaryote

▲ **Figure 6.16 The endosymbiont theory of the origins of mitochondria and chloroplasts in eukaryotic cells.** According to this theory, the proposed ancestors of mitochondria were oxygen-using nonphotosynthetic prokaryotes, while the proposed ancestors of chloroplasts were photosynthetic prokaryotes. The large arrows represent change over evolutionary time; the small arrows inside the cells show the process of the endosymbiont becoming an organelle, also over long periods of time.

prokaryotes had two outer membranes, which became the double membranes of mitochondria and chloroplasts. Second, like prokaryotes, mitochondria and chloroplasts contain ribosomes, as well as multiple circular DNA molecules associated with their inner membranes. The DNA in these organelles programs the synthesis of some organelle proteins on ribosomes that have been synthesized and assembled there as well. Third, also consistent with their probable evolutionary origins as cells, mitochondria and chloroplasts are autonomous (somewhat independent) organelles that grow and reproduce within the cell.

Next, we focus on the structures of mitochondria and chloroplasts, while providing an overview of their structures and functions. (In Chapters 9 and 10, we will examine their roles as energy transformers.)

Mitochondria: Chemical Energy Conversion

Mitochondria are found in nearly all eukaryotic cells, including those of plants, animals, fungi, and most unicellular eukaryotes. Some cells have a single large mitochondrion,

but more often a cell has hundreds or even thousands of mitochondria; the number correlates with the cell's level of metabolic activity. For example, cells that move or contract have proportionally more mitochondria per volume than less active cells.

Each of the two membranes enclosing the mitochondrion is a phospholipid bilayer with a unique collection of embedded proteins **(Figure 6.17)**. The outer membrane is smooth, but the inner membrane is convoluted, with infoldings called **cristae**. The inner membrane divides the mitochondrion into two internal compartments. The first is the intermembrane space, the narrow region between the inner and outer membranes. The second compartment, the **mitochondrial matrix**, is enclosed by the inner membrane. The matrix contains many different enzymes as well as the mitochondrial DNA and ribosomes. Enzymes in the matrix catalyze some of the steps of cellular respiration. Other proteins that function in respiration, including the enzyme that makes ATP, are built into the inner membrane. As highly folded surfaces, the cristae give the inner mitochondrial membrane a large surface area, thus enhancing the productivity of cellular respiration. This is another example of structure fitting function.

Mitochondria are generally in the range of 1–10 µm long. Time-lapse films of living cells reveal mitochondria moving around, changing their shapes, and fusing or dividing in two, unlike the static structures seen in electron micrographs of dead cells. These observations helped cell biologists understand that mitochondria in a living cell form a branched tubular network, seen in a whole cell in Figure 6.17b, that is in a dynamic state of flux.

Chloroplasts: Capture of Light Energy

Chloroplasts contain the green pigment chlorophyll, along with enzymes and other molecules that function in the photosynthetic production of sugar. These lens-shaped organelles, about 3–6 µm in length, are found in leaves and other green organs of plants and in algae **(Figure 6.18;** see also Figure 6.26c).

The contents of a chloroplast are partitioned from the cytosol by an envelope consisting of two membranes separated by a very narrow intermembrane space. Inside the chloroplast is another membranous system in the form of flattened, interconnected sacs called **thylakoids**. In some regions, thylakoids are stacked like poker chips; each stack is called a **granum** (plural, *grana*). The fluid outside the thylakoids is the **stroma**, which contains the chloroplast DNA and ribosomes as well as many enzymes. The membranes of the chloroplast divide the chloroplast space into three compartments: the intermembrane space, the stroma, and the thylakoid space. This compartmental organization enables the chloroplast to convert light energy to chemical energy

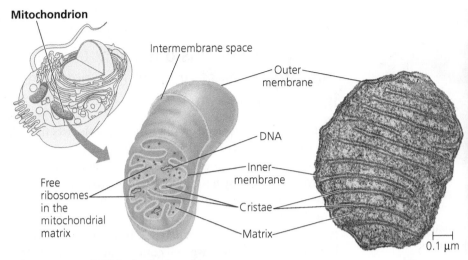

Mitochondrion

Intermembrane space

Outer membrane

DNA

Inner membrane

Cristae

Matrix

Free ribosomes in the mitochondrial matrix

0.1 μm

(a) Diagram and TEM of mitochondrion

10 μm

Mitochondria

Mitochondrial DNA

Nuclear DNA

(b) Network of mitochondria in *Euglena* (LM)

▲ **Figure 6.17 The mitochondrion, site of cellular respiration. (a)** The inner and outer membranes of the mitochondrion are evident in the drawing and electron micrograph (TEM). The cristae are infoldings of the inner membrane, which increase its surface area. The cutaway drawing shows the two compartments bounded by the membranes: the intermembrane space and the mitochondrial matrix. Many respiratory enzymes are found in the inner membrane and the matrix. Free ribosomes are also present in the matrix. The DNA molecules are usually circular and they are associated with the inner mitochondrial membrane.

(b) The light micrograph shows an entire unicellular eukaryote (*Euglena gracilis*) at a much lower magnification than the TEM. The mitochondrial matrix has been stained green. The mitochondria form a branched tubular network. The nuclear DNA is stained red; molecules of mitochondrial DNA appear as bright yellow spots.

during photosynthesis. (You will learn more about photosynthesis in Chapter 10.)

As with mitochondria, the static and rigid appearance of chloroplasts in micrographs or schematic diagrams is not true to their dynamic behavior in the living cell. Their shape is changeable, and they grow and occasionally pinch in two, reproducing themselves. They are mobile and, with mitochondria and other organelles, move around the cell along tracks of the cytoskeleton, a structural network we will consider later in this chapter.

The chloroplast is a specialized member of a family of closely related plant organelles called **plastids**. One type of plastid, the *amyloplast*, is a colorless organelle that stores starch (amylose), particularly in roots and tubers. Another is the *chromoplast*, which has pigments that give fruits and flowers their orange and yellow hues.

Chloroplast

Ribosomes

Stroma

Inner and outer membranes

Granum

DNA

Thylakoid

Intermembrane space

(a) Diagram and TEM of chloroplast

1 μm

50 μm

Chloroplasts (red)

(b) Chloroplasts in an algal cell

▼ **Figure 6.18 The chloroplast, site of photosynthesis. (a)** Many plants have lens-shaped chloroplasts, as shown here. A typical chloroplast has three compartments: the intermembrane space, the stroma, and the thylakoid space. Free ribosomes are present in the stroma, as are copies of chloroplast DNA molecules. **(b)** This fluorescence micrograph shows a whole cell of the green alga *Spirogyra crassa*, which is named for its spiral chloroplasts. Under natural light the chloroplasts appear green, but under ultraviolet light they naturally fluoresce red, as shown here.

▶ **Figure 6.19**
A peroxisome. Peroxisomes are roughly spherical and often have a granular or crystalline core that is thought to be a dense collection of enzyme molecules. Chloroplasts and mitochondria cooperate with peroxisomes in certain metabolic functions (TEM).

Peroxisome
Mitochon-
drion

Chloroplasts

1 μm

Peroxisomes: Oxidation

The **peroxisome** is a specialized metabolic compartment bounded by a single membrane **(Figure 6.19)**. Peroxisomes contain enzymes that remove hydrogen atoms from various substrates and transfer them to oxygen (O_2), producing hydrogen peroxide (H_2O_2) as a by-product (from which the organelle derives its name). These reactions have many different functions. Some peroxisomes use oxygen to break fatty acids down into smaller molecules that are transported to mitochondria and used as fuel for cellular respiration. Peroxisomes in the liver detoxify alcohol and other harmful compounds by transferring hydrogen from the poisons to oxygen. The H_2O_2 formed by peroxisomes is itself toxic, but the organelle also contains an enzyme that converts H_2O_2 to water. This is an excellent example of how the cell's compartmental structure is crucial to its functions: The enzymes that produce H_2O_2 and those that dispose of this toxic compound are sequestered away from other cellular components that could be damaged.

Specialized peroxisomes called *glyoxysomes* are found in the fat-storing tissues of plant seeds. These organelles contain enzymes that initiate the conversion of fatty acids to sugar, which the emerging seedling uses as a source of energy and carbon until it can produce its own sugar by photosynthesis.

How peroxisomes are related to other organelles is still an open question. They grow larger by incorporating proteins made in the cytosol and ER, as well as lipids made in the ER and within the peroxisome itself. Peroxisomes may increase in number by splitting in two when they reach a certain size, sparking the suggestion of an endosymbiotic evolutionary origin, but others argue against this scenario. Discussion of this issue is ongoing.

CONCEPT CHECK 6.5

1. Describe two common characteristics of chloroplasts and mitochondria. Consider both function and membrane structure.

2. Do plant cells have mitochondria? Explain.

3. **WHAT IF?** A classmate proposes that mitochondria and chloroplasts should be classified in the endomembrane system. Argue against the proposal.

For suggested answers, see Appendix A.

The cytoskeleton is a network of fibers that organizes structures and activities in the cell

In the early days of electron microscopy, biologists thought that the organelles of a eukaryotic cell floated freely in the cytosol. But improvements in both light microscopy and electron microscopy have revealed the **cytoskeleton**, a network of fibers extending throughout the cytoplasm **(Figure 6.20)**. Bacterial cells also have fibers that form a type of cytoskeleton, constructed of proteins similar to eukaryotic ones, but here we will concentrate on eukaryotes. The eukaryotic cytoskeleton, which plays a major role in organizing the structures and activities of the cell, is composed of three types of molecular structures: microtubules, microfilaments, and intermediate filaments.

Roles of the Cytoskeleton: Support and Motility

The most obvious function of the cytoskeleton is to give mechanical support to the cell and maintain its shape. This is especially important for animal cells, which lack walls. The remarkable strength and resilience of the cytoskeleton as a whole are based on its architecture. Like a dome tent, the cytoskeleton is stabilized by a balance between opposing forces exerted by its elements. And just as the skeleton of an animal helps fix the positions of other body parts, the cytoskeleton provides anchorage for many organelles and even cytosolic enzyme molecules. The cytoskeleton is more dynamic than an animal skeleton, however. It can be quickly dismantled in one part of the cell and reassembled in a new location, changing the shape of the cell.

10 μm

▲ **Figure 6.20 The cytoskeleton.** As shown in this fluorescence micrograph, the cytoskeleton extends throughout the cell. The cytoskeletal elements have been tagged with different fluorescent molecules: green for microtubules and reddish orange for microfilaments. A third component of the cytoskeleton, intermediate filaments, is not evident here. (The blue color tags the DNA in the nucleus.)

Some types of cell motility (movement) also involve the cytoskeleton. The term *cell motility* includes both changes in cell location and movements of cell parts. Cell motility generally requires interaction of the cytoskeleton with **motor proteins**. There are many such examples: Cytoskeletal elements and motor proteins work together with plasma membrane molecules to allow whole cells to move along fibers outside the cell. Inside the cell, vesicles and other organelles often use motor protein "feet" to "walk" to their destinations along a track provided by the cytoskeleton. For example, this is how vesicles containing neurotransmitter molecules migrate to the tips of axons, the long extensions of nerve cells that release these molecules as chemical signals to adjacent nerve cells (Figure 6.21). The cytoskeleton also manipulates the plasma membrane, bending it inward to form food vacuoles or other phagocytic vesicles.

Components of the Cytoskeleton

Now let's look more closely at the three main types of fibers that make up the cytoskeleton: *Microtubules* are the thickest of the three types; *microfilaments* (also called actin filaments) are the thinnest; and *intermediate filaments* are fibers with diameters in a middle range (Table 6.1).

(a) Motor proteins that attach to receptors on vesicles can "walk" the vesicles along microtubules or, in some cases, along microfilaments.

(b) In this SEM of a squid giant axon (a nerve cell extension), two vesicles containing neurotransmitters move toward the axon's tip.

▲ Figure 6.21 **Motor proteins and the cytoskeleton.**

Table 6.1 The Structure and Function of the Cytoskeleton			
Property	**Microtubules (Tubulin Polymers)**	**Microfilaments (Actin Filaments)**	**Intermediate Filaments**
Structure	Hollow tubes	Two intertwined strands of actin	Fibrous proteins coiled into cables
Diameter	25 nm with 15-nm lumen	7 nm	8–12 nm
Protein subunits	Tubulin, a dimer consisting of α-tubulin and β-tubulin	Actin	One of several different proteins (such as keratins)
Main functions	Maintenance of cell shape (compression-resisting "girders"); cell motility (as in cilia or flagella); chromosome movements in cell division; organelle movements	Maintenance of cell shape (tension-bearing elements); changes in cell shape; muscle contraction; cytoplasmic streaming in plant cells; cell motility (as in amoeboid movement); division of animal cells	Maintenance of cell shape (tension-bearing elements); anchorage of nucleus and certain other organelles; formation of nuclear lamina
Fluorescence micrographs of fibroblasts. Fibroblasts are a favorite cell type for cell biology studies. In each, the structure of interest has been tagged with fluorescent molecules. The DNA in the nucleus has also been tagged in the first micrograph (blue) and third micrograph (orange).	10 µm — Column of tubulin dimers — 25 nm — α β Tubulin dimer	10 µm — Actin subunit — 7 nm	5 µm — Keratin proteins — Fibrous subunit (keratins coiled together) — 8–12 nm

Microtubules

All eukaryotic cells have **microtubules**, hollow rods constructed from a globular protein called tubulin. Each tubulin protein is a *dimer*, a molecule made up of two subunits. A tubulin dimer consists of two slightly different polypeptides, α-tubulin and β-tubulin. Microtubules grow in length by adding tubulin dimers; they can also be disassembled and their tubulin used to build microtubules elsewhere in the cell. Because of the orientation of tubulin dimers, the two ends of a microtubule are slightly different. One end can accumulate or release tubulin dimers at a much higher rate than the other, thus growing and shrinking significantly during cellular activities. (This is called the "plus end," not because it can only add tubulin proteins but because it's the end where both "on" and "off" rates are much higher.)

Microtubules shape and support the cell and also serve as tracks along which organelles equipped with motor proteins can move. In addition to the example in Figure 6.21, microtubules guide vesicles from the ER to the Golgi apparatus and from the Golgi to the plasma membrane. Microtubules are also involved in the separation of chromosomes during cell division, which will be discussed in Chapter 12.

Centrosomes and Centrioles In animal cells, microtubules grow out from a **centrosome**, a region that is often located near the nucleus. These microtubules function as compression-resisting girders of the cytoskeleton. Within the centrosome is a pair of **centrioles**, each composed of nine sets of triplet microtubules arranged in a ring **(Figure 6.22).** Although centrosomes with centrioles may help organize microtubule assembly in animal cells, many other eukaryotic cells lack centrosomes with centrioles and instead organize microtubules by other means.

Cilia and Flagella In eukaryotes, a specialized arrangement of microtubules is responsible for the beating of **flagella** (singular, *flagellum*) and **cilia** (singular, *cilium*), microtubule-containing extensions that project from some cells. (The bacterial flagellum, shown in Figure 6.5, has a completely different structure.) Many unicellular eukaryotes are propelled through water by cilia or flagella that act as locomotor appendages, and the sperm of animals, algae, and some plants have flagella. When cilia or flagella extend from cells that are held in place as part of a tissue layer, they can move fluid over the surface of the tissue. For example, the ciliated lining of the trachea (windpipe) sweeps mucus containing trapped debris out of the lungs (see the EMs in Figure 6.3). In a woman's reproductive tract, the cilia lining the oviducts help move an egg toward the uterus.

Motile cilia usually occur in large numbers on the cell surface. Flagella are usually limited to just one or a few per cell, and they are longer than cilia. Flagella and cilia differ in their beating patterns **(Figure 6.23).** A flagellum has an

Centrosome

Microtubule

Centrioles

0.25 µm

Longitudinal section of one centriole   Microtubules   Cross section of the other centriole

▲ **Figure 6.22 Centrosome containing a pair of centrioles.** Most animal cells have a centrosome, a region near the nucleus where the cell's microtubules are initiated. Within the centrosome is a pair of centrioles, each about 250 nm (0.25 µm) in diameter. The two centrioles are at right angles to each other, and each is made up of nine sets of three microtubules. The blue portions of the drawing represent nontubulin proteins that connect the microtubule triplets.

? *How many microtubules are in a centrosome? In the drawing, circle and label one microtubule and describe its structure. Circle and label a triplet.*

undulating motion like the tail of a fish. In contrast, cilia work more like oars, with alternating power and recovery strokes, much like the oars of a racing crew boat.

A cilium may also act as a signal-receiving "antenna" for the cell. Cilia that have this function are generally nonmotile, and there is only one per cell. (In fact, in vertebrate animals, it appears that almost all cells have such a cilium, which is called a *primary cilium.*) Membrane proteins on this kind of cilium transmit molecular signals from the cell's environment to its interior, triggering signaling pathways that may lead to changes in the cell's activities. Cilium-based

(a) **Motion of flagella.** A flagellum usually undulates, its snakelike motion driving a cell in the same direction as the axis of the flagellum. Propulsion of a human sperm cell is an example of flagellate locomotion (LM).

Direction of swimming

5 µm

(b) **Motion of cilia.** Cilia have a back-and-forth motion. The rapid power stroke moves the cell in a direction perpendicular to the axis of the cilium. Then, during the slower recovery stroke, the cilium bends and sweeps sideways, closer to the cell surface. A dense nap of cilia, beating at a rate of about 40 to 60 strokes a second, covers this *Colpidium*, a freshwater protist (colorized SEM).

Direction of organism's movement

Power stroke   Recovery stroke

15 µm

▲ **Figure 6.23 A comparison of the beating of flagella and motile cilia.**

signaling appears to be crucial to brain function and to embryonic development.

Though different in length, number per cell, and beating pattern, motile cilia and flagella share a common structure. Each motile cilium or flagellum has a group of microtubules sheathed in an extension of the plasma membrane **(Figure 6.24a)**. Nine doublets of microtubules are arranged in a ring, with two single microtubules in its center **(Figure 6.24b)**. This arrangement, referred to as the "9 + 2" pattern, is found in nearly all eukaryotic flagella and motile cilia. (Nonmotile primary cilia have a "9 + 0" pattern, lacking the central pair of microtubules.) The microtubule assembly of a cilium or flagellum is anchored in the cell by a **basal body**, which is structurally very similar to a centriole, with microtubule triplets in a "9 + 0" pattern **(Figure 6.24c)**. In fact, in many animals (including humans), the basal body of the fertilizing sperm's flagellum enters the egg and becomes a centriole.

How does the microtubule assembly produce the bending movements of flagella and motile cilia? Bending involves large motor proteins called **dyneins** (red in the diagram in Figure 6.24) that are attached along each outer microtubule doublet. A typical dynein protein has two "feet" that "walk" along the microtubule of the adjacent doublet, using ATP

for energy. One foot maintains contact, while the other releases and reattaches one step farther along the microtubule (see Figure 6.21). The outer doublets and two central microtubules are held together by flexible cross-linking proteins (blue in the diagram in Figure 6.24), and the walking movement is coordinated so that it happens on one side of the circle at a time. If the doublets were not held in place, the walking action would make them slide past each other. Instead, the movements of the dynein feet cause the microtubules—and the organelle as a whole—to bend.

Microfilaments (Actin Filaments)

Microfilaments are thin solid rods. They are also called actin filaments because they are built from molecules of **actin**, a globular protein. A microfilament is a twisted double chain of actin subunits (see Table 6.1). Besides occurring as linear filaments, microfilaments can form structural networks when certain proteins bind along the side of such a filament and allow a new filament to extend as a branch. Like microtubules, microfilaments seem to be present in all eukaryotic cells.

In contrast to the compression-resisting role of microtubules, the structural role of microfilaments in the cytoskeleton is to bear tension (pulling forces). A three-dimensional

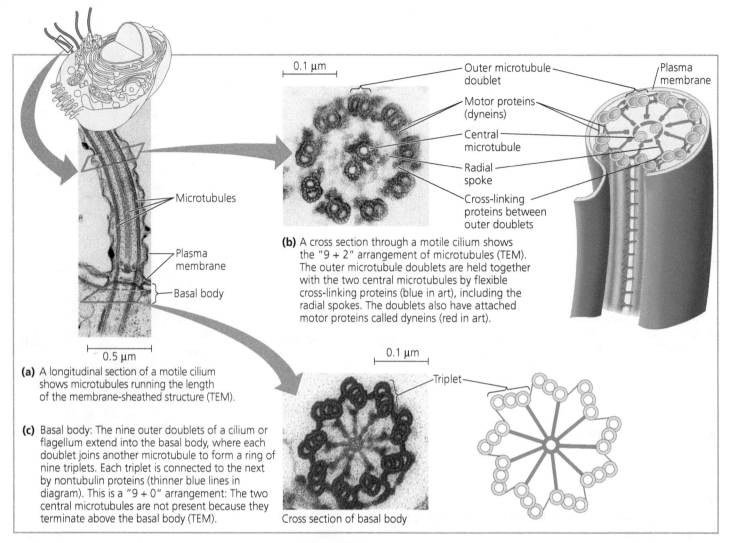

0.1 µm

Outer microtubule doublet
Motor proteins (dyneins)
Central microtubule
Radial spoke
Cross-linking proteins between outer doublets

Plasma membrane

Microtubules

Plasma membrane

Basal body

0.5 µm

(b) A cross section through a motile cilium shows the "9 + 2" arrangement of microtubules (TEM). The outer microtubule doublets are held together with the two central microtubules by flexible cross-linking proteins (blue in art), including the radial spokes. The doublets also have attached motor proteins called dyneins (red in art).

(a) A longitudinal section of a motile cilium shows microtubules running the length of the membrane-sheathed structure (TEM).

(c) Basal body: The nine outer doublets of a cilium or flagellum extend into the basal body, where each doublet joins another microtubule to form a ring of nine triplets. Each triplet is connected to the next by nontubulin proteins (thinner blue lines in diagram). This is a "9 + 0" arrangement: The two central microtubules are not present because they terminate above the basal body (TEM).

0.1 µm

Triplet

Cross section of basal body

▲ **Figure 6.24 Structure of a flagellum or motile cilium.**

DRAW IT *In (a) and (b), circle the central pair of microtubules. In (a), show where they terminate, and explain why they aren't seen in the cross section of the basal body in (c).*

network formed by microfilaments just inside the plasma membrane (*cortical microfilaments*) helps support the cell's shape (see Figure 6.8). This network gives the outer cytoplasmic layer of a cell, called the **cortex**, the semisolid consistency of a gel, in contrast with the more fluid state of the interior cytoplasm. In some kinds of animal cells, such as nutrient-absorbing intestinal cells, bundles of microfilaments make up the core of microvilli, delicate projections that increase the cell's surface area **(Figure 6.25).**

Microfilaments are well known for their role in cell motility. Thousands of actin filaments and thicker filaments made of a protein called **myosin** interact to cause

Microvillus

0.25 µm

Plasma membrane

Microfilaments (actin filaments)

Intermediate filaments

▶ **Figure 6.25 A structural role of microfilaments.** The surface area of this nutrient-absorbing intestinal cell is increased by its many microvilli (singular, *microvillus*), cellular extensions reinforced by bundles of microfilaments. These actin filaments are anchored to a network of intermediate filaments (TEM).

contraction of muscle cells (**Figure 6.26a**); muscle contraction is described in detail in Chapter 50. In the unicellular eukaryote *Amoeba* and some of our white blood cells, localized contractions brought about by actin and myosin are involved in the amoeboid (crawling) movement of the cells (**Figure 6.26b**). The cell crawls along a surface by extending cellular extensions called **pseudopodia** (from the Greek *pseudes*, false, and *pod*, foot) and moving toward them. In plant cells, both actin-myosin interactions contribute to **cytoplasmic streaming**, a circular flow of cytoplasm within cells (**Figure 6.26c**). This movement, which is especially common in large plant cells, speeds the distribution of materials within the cell.

Intermediate Filaments

Intermediate filaments are named for their diameter, which is larger than the diameter of microfilaments but smaller than that of microtubules (see Table 6.1). Unlike microtubules and microfilaments, which are found in all eukaryotic cells, intermediate filaments are only found in the cells of some animals, including vertebrates. Specialized for bearing tension (like microfilaments), intermediate filaments are a diverse class of cytoskeletal elements. Each type is constructed from a particular molecular subunit belonging to a family of proteins whose members include the keratins. Microtubules and microfilaments, in contrast, are consistent in diameter and composition in all eukaryotic cells.

Intermediate filaments are more permanent fixtures of cells than are microfilaments and microtubules, which are often disassembled and reassembled in various parts of a cell. Even after cells die, intermediate filament networks often persist; for example, the outer layer of our skin consists of dead skin cells full of keratin filaments. Chemical treatments that remove microfilaments and microtubules from the cytoplasm of living cells leave a web of intermediate filaments that retains its original shape. Such experiments suggest that intermediate filaments are especially sturdy and that they play an important role in reinforcing the shape of a cell and fixing the position of certain organelles. For instance, the nucleus typically sits within a cage made of intermediate filaments, fixed in location by branches of the filaments that extend into the cytoplasm. Other intermediate filaments make up the nuclear lamina, which lines the interior of the nuclear envelope (see Figure 6.9). By supporting a cell's shape, intermediate filaments help the cell carry out its specific function. For example, the network of intermediate filaments shown in Figure 6.25 anchor the microfilaments supporting the intestinal microvilli. Thus, the various kinds of intermediate filaments may function together as the permanent framework of the entire cell.

(a) Myosin motors in muscle cell contraction. The "walking" of myosin projections (the so-called heads) drives the parallel myosin and actin filaments past each other so that the actin filaments approach each other in the middle (red arrows). This shortens the muscle cell. Muscle contraction involves the shortening of many muscle cells at the same time (TEM).

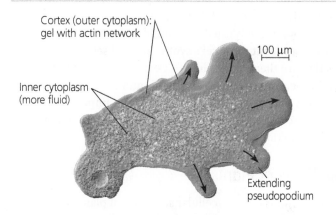

(b) Amoeboid movement. Interaction of actin filaments with myosin causes contraction of the cell, pulling the cell's trailing end (at left) forward (to the right) (LM).

(c) Cytoplasmic streaming in plant cells. A layer of cytoplasm cycles around the cell, moving over a carpet of parallel actin filaments. Myosin motors attached to organelles in the fluid cytosol may drive the streaming by interacting with the actin (LM).

▲ **Figure 6.26 Microfilaments and motility.** In these three examples, interactions between actin filaments and motor proteins bring about cell movement.

1. Describe shared features of microtubule-based motion of flagella and microfilament-based muscle contraction.
2. **WHAT IF?** Males afflicted with Kartagener's syndrome are sterile because of immotile sperm, and they tend to suffer from lung infections. This disorder has a genetic basis. Suggest what the underlying defect might be.

For suggested answers, see Appendix A.

CONCEPT 6.7

Extracellular components and connections between cells help coordinate cellular activities

Having crisscrossed the cell to explore its interior components, we complete our tour of the cell by returning to the surface of this microscopic world, where there are additional structures with important functions. The plasma membrane is usually regarded as the boundary of the living cell, but most cells synthesize and secrete materials that are then extracellular, or external to the plasma membrane. Although these materials and the structures they form are outside the cell, their study is important to cell biology because they are involved in a great many important cellular functions.

Cell Walls of Plants

The **cell wall** is an extracellular structure of plant cells that distinguishes them from animal cells (see Figure 6.8). The wall protects the plant cell, maintains its shape, and prevents excessive uptake of water. On the level of the whole plant, the strong walls of specialized cells hold the plant up against the force of gravity. Prokaryotes, fungi, and some unicellular eukaryotes also have cell walls, as you saw in Figures 6.5 and 6.8, but we will postpone discussion of them until Unit Five.

Plant cell walls are much thicker than the plasma membrane, ranging from 0.1 μm to several micrometers. The exact chemical composition of the wall varies from species to species and even from one cell type to another in the same plant, but the basic design of the wall is consistent. Microfibrils made of the polysaccharide cellulose (see Figure 5.6) are synthesized by an enzyme called cellulose synthase and secreted to the extracellular space, where they become embedded in a matrix of other polysaccharides and proteins. This combination of materials, strong fibers in a "ground substance" (matrix), is the same basic architectural design found in steel-reinforced concrete and in fiberglass.

A young plant cell first secretes a relatively thin and flexible wall called the **primary cell wall** (Figure 6.27). Between primary walls of adjacent cells is the **middle lamella**, a thin layer rich in sticky polysaccharides called pectins. The

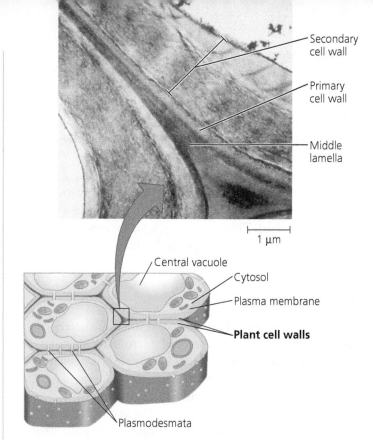

▲ **Figure 6.27 Plant cell walls.** The drawing shows several cells, each with a large vacuole, a nucleus, and several chloroplasts and mitochondria. The transmission electron micrograph shows the cell walls where two cells come together. The multilayered partition between plant cells consists of adjoining walls individually secreted by the cells.

middle lamella glues adjacent cells together. (Pectin is used in cooking as a thickening agent in jams and jellies.) When the cell matures and stops growing, it strengthens its wall. Some plant cells do this simply by secreting hardening substances into the primary wall. Other cells add a **secondary cell wall** between the plasma membrane and the primary wall. The secondary wall, often deposited in several laminated layers, has a strong and durable matrix that affords the cell protection and support. Wood, for example, consists mainly of secondary walls. Plant cell walls are usually perforated by channels between adjacent cells called plasmodesmata (see Figure 6.27), which will be discussed shortly.

The Extracellular Matrix (ECM) of Animal Cells

Although animal cells lack walls akin to those of plant cells, they do have an elaborate **extracellular matrix (ECM)**. The main ingredients of the ECM are glycoproteins and other carbohydrate-containing molecules secreted by the cells. (Recall that glycoproteins are proteins with covalently bonded carbohydrates, usually short chains of sugars.) The most abundant glycoprotein in the ECM of most animal cells is **collagen**, which forms strong fibers outside the cells (see Figure 5.18). In fact, collagen accounts for about 40% of the total protein in the human body. The collagen fibers are embedded in a network woven out of **proteoglycans**

▲ Figure 6.28 Extracellular matrix (ECM) of an animal cell. The molecular composition and structure of the ECM vary from one cell type to another. In this example, three different types of ECM molecules are present: proteoglycans, collagen, and fibronectin.

In the figure:

Collagen fibers are embedded in a web of proteoglycan complexes.

Fibronectin attaches the ECM to integrins embedded in the plasma membrane.

Plasma membrane

EXTRACELLULAR FLUID

A **proteoglycan complex** consists of hundreds of proteoglycan molecules attached noncovalently to a single long polysaccharide molecule.

Integrins, membrane proteins with two subunits, bind to the ECM on the outside and to associated proteins attached to microfilaments on the inside. This linkage can transmit signals between the cell's external environment and its interior and can result in changes in cell behavior.

Micro-filaments

CYTOPLASM

Polysaccharide molecule

Carbohydrates

Core protein

Proteoglycan molecule

Proteoglycan complex

secreted by cells (**Figure 6.28**). A proteoglycan molecule consists of a small core protein with many carbohydrate chains covalently attached, so that it may be up to 95% carbohydrate. Large proteoglycan complexes can form when hundreds of proteoglycan molecules become noncovalently attached to a single long polysaccharide molecule, as shown in Figure 6.28. Some cells are attached to the ECM by ECM glycoproteins such as **fibronectin**. Fibronectin and other ECM proteins bind to cell-surface receptor proteins called **integrins** that are built into the plasma membrane. Integrins span the membrane and bind on their cytoplasmic side to associated proteins attached to microfilaments of the cytoskeleton. The name *integrin* is based on the word *integrate*: Integrins are in a position to transmit signals between the ECM and the cytoskeleton and thus to integrate changes occurring outside and inside the cell.

Current research on fibronectin, other ECM molecules, and integrins is revealing the influential role of the ECM in the lives of cells. By communicating with a cell through integrins, the ECM can regulate a cell's behavior. For example, some cells in a developing embryo migrate along specific pathways by matching the orientation of their microfilaments to the "grain" of fibers in the extracellular matrix. Researchers have also learned that the extracellular matrix around a cell can influence the activity of genes in the nucleus. Information about the ECM probably reaches the nucleus by a combination of mechanical and chemical signaling pathways. Mechanical signaling involves fibronectin, integrins, and microfilaments of the cytoskeleton. Changes in the cytoskeleton may in turn trigger chemical signaling pathways inside the cell, leading to changes in the

set of proteins being made by the cell and therefore changes in the cell's function. In this way, the extracellular matrix of a particular tissue may help coordinate the behavior of all the cells of that tissue. Direct connections between cells also function in this coordination, as we discuss next.

Cell Junctions

Cells in an animal or plant are organized into tissues, organs, and organ systems. Neighboring cells often adhere, interact, and communicate via sites of direct physical contact.

Plasmodesmata in Plant Cells

It might seem that the nonliving cell walls of plants would isolate plant cells from one another. But in fact, as shown in **Figure 6.29**, cell walls are perforated with **plasmodesmata** (singular, *plasmodesma*; from the Greek *desma*, bond), channels that connect cells. Cytosol passing

Interior of cell

Interior of cell

Cell walls

0.5 μm

Plasmodesmata   Plasma membranes

▲ Figure 6.29 Plasmodesmata between plant cells. The cytoplasm of one plant cell is continuous with the cytoplasm of its neighbors via plasmodesmata, cytoplasmic channels through the cell walls (TEM).

through the plasmodesmata joins the internal chemical environments of adjacent cells. These connections unify most of the plant into one living continuum. The plasma membranes of adjacent cells line the channel of each plasmodesma and thus are continuous. Water and small solutes can pass freely from cell to cell, and several experiments have shown that in some circumstances, certain proteins and RNA molecules can do this as well (see Concept 36.6). The macromolecules transported to neighboring cells appear to reach the plasmodesmata by moving along fibers of the cytoskeleton.

Tight Junctions, Desmosomes, and Gap Junctions in Animal Cells

In animals, there are three main types of cell junctions: *tight junctions*, *desmosomes*, and *gap junctions*. (Gap junctions are most like the plasmodesmata of plants, although gap junction pores are not lined with membrane.) All three types of cell junctions are especially common in epithelial tissue, which lines the external and internal surfaces of the body. **Figure 6.30** uses epithelial cells of the intestinal lining to illustrate these junctions.

▼ Figure 6.30

Exploring Cell Junctions in Animal Tissues

Tight junctions prevent fluid from moving across a layer of cells.

Tight junction

TEM — 0.5 µm

Tight junction

Intermediate filaments

Desmosome

Gap junction

Ions or small molecules

Plasma membranes of adjacent cells

Space between cells

Extracellular matrix

TEM — 1 µm

TEM — 0.1 µm

Tight Junctions

At **tight junctions**, the plasma membranes of neighboring cells are very tightly pressed against each other, bound together by specific proteins (purple). Forming continuous seals around the cells, tight junctions establish a barrier that prevents leakage of extracellular fluid across a layer of epithelial cells (see red dashed arrow). For example, tight junctions between skin cells make us watertight.

Desmosomes

Desmosomes (also called *anchoring junctions*) function like rivets, fastening cells together into strong sheets. Intermediate filaments made of sturdy keratin proteins anchor desmosomes in the cytoplasm. Desmosomes attach muscle cells to each other in a muscle. Some "muscle tears" involve the rupture of desmosomes.

Gap Junctions

Gap junctions (also called *communicating junctions*) provide cytoplasmic channels from one cell to an adjacent cell and in this way are similar in their function to the plasmodesmata in plants. Gap junctions consist of membrane proteins that surround a pore through which ions, sugars, amino acids, and other small molecules may pass. Gap junctions are necessary for communication between cells in many types of tissues, such as heart muscle, and in animal embryos.

1. In what way are the cells of plants and animals structurally different from single-celled eukaryotes?
2. **WHAT IF?** If the plant cell wall or the animal extracellular matrix were impermeable, what effect would this have on cell function?
3. **MAKE CONNECTIONS** The polypeptide chain that makes up a tight junction weaves back and forth through the membrane four times, with two extracellular loops, and one loop plus short C-terminal and N-terminal tails in the cytoplasm. Looking at Figure 5.14, what would you predict about the amino acid sequence of the tight-junction protein?

For suggested answers, see Appendix A.

▲ **Figure 6.31 The emergence of cellular functions.** The ability of this macrophage (brown) to recognize, apprehend, and destroy bacteria (yellow) is a coordinated activity of the whole cell. Its cytoskeleton, lysosomes, and plasma membrane are among the components that function in phagocytosis (colorized SEM).

The Cell: A Living Unit Greater Than the Sum of Its Parts

From our panoramic view of the cell's compartmental organization to our close-up inspection of each organelle's architecture, this tour of the cell has provided many opportunities to correlate structure with function. (This would be a good time to review cell structure by returning to Figure 6.8.) But even as we dissect the cell, remember that none of its components works alone. As an example of cellular integration, consider the microscopic scene in **Figure 6.31**. The large cell is a macrophage (see Figure 6.13a). It helps defend the mammalian body against infections by ingesting bacteria (the smaller cells) into phagocytic vesicles. The macrophage crawls along a surface and reaches out to the bacteria with thin pseudopodia

(specifically, filopodia). Actin filaments interact with other elements of the cytoskeleton in these movements. After the macrophage engulfs the bacteria, they are destroyed by lysosomes. The elaborate endomembrane system produces the lysosomes. The digestive enzymes of the lysosomes and the proteins of the cytoskeleton are all made by ribosomes. And the synthesis of these proteins is programmed by genetic messages dispatched from the DNA in the nucleus. All these processes require energy, which mitochondria supply in the form of ATP. Cellular functions arise from cellular order: The cell is a living unit greater than the sum of its parts.

6 Chapter Review

SUMMARY OF KEY CONCEPTS

CONCEPT 6.1

Biologists use microscopes and the tools of biochemistry to study cells (pp. 94–97)

- Improvements in microscopy that affect the parameters of magnification, resolution, and contrast have catalyzed progress in the study of cell structure. **Light microscopy** (LM) and **electron microscopy** (EM), as well as other types, remain important tools.
- Cell biologists can obtain pellets enriched in particular cellular components by centrifuging disrupted cells at sequential speeds, a process known as **cell fractionation**. Larger cellular components are in the pellet after lower-speed centrifugation, and smaller components are in the pellet after higher-speed centrifugation.

? *How do microscopy and biochemistry complement each other to reveal cell structure and function?*

CONCEPT 6.2

Eukaryotic cells have internal membranes that compartmentalize their functions (pp. 97–102)

- All cells are bounded by a **plasma membrane**.
- **Prokaryotic cells** lack nuclei and other membrane-enclosed **organelles**, while **eukaryotic cells** have internal membranes that compartmentalize cellular functions.
- The surface-to-volume ratio is an important parameter affecting cell size and shape.
- Plant and animal cells have most of the same organelles: a nucleus, endoplasmic reticulum, Golgi apparatus, and mitochondria. Chloroplasts are present only in cells of photosynthetic eukaryotes.

? *Explain how the compartmental organization of a eukaryotic cell contributes to its biochemical functioning.*

	Cell Component	Structure	Function
CONCEPT 6.3 The eukaryotic cell's genetic instructions are housed in the nucleus and carried out by the ribosomes (pp. 102–104) [?] *Describe the relationship between the nucleus and ribosomes.*	Nucleus (ER)	Surrounded by nuclear envelope (double membrane) perforated by nuclear pores; nuclear envelope continuous with endoplasmic reticulum (ER)	Houses chromosomes, which are made of chromatin (DNA and proteins); contains nucleoli, where ribosomal subunits are made; pores regulate entry and exit of materials
	Ribosome	Two subunits made of ribosomal RNA and proteins; can be free in cytosol or bound to ER	Protein synthesis
CONCEPT 6.4 The endomembrane system regulates protein traffic and performs metabolic functions in the cell (pp. 104–109) [?] *Describe the key role played by transport vesicles in the endomembrane system.*	Endoplasmic reticulum (Nuclear envelope)	Extensive network of membrane-bounded tubules and sacs; membrane separates lumen from cytosol; continuous with nuclear envelope	Smooth ER: synthesis of lipids, metabolism of carbohydrates, Ca^{2+} storage, detoxification of drugs and poisons Rough ER: aids in synthesis of secretory and other proteins from bound ribosomes; adds carbohydrates to proteins to make glycoproteins; produces new membrane
	Golgi apparatus	Stacks of flattened membranous sacs; has polarity (*cis* and *trans* faces)	Modification of proteins, carbohydrates on proteins, and phospholipids; synthesis of many polysaccharides; sorting of Golgi products, which are then released in vesicles
	Lysosome	Membranous sac of hydrolytic enzymes (in animal cells)	Breakdown of ingested substances, cell macromolecules, and damaged organelles for recycling
	Vacuole	Large membrane-bounded vesicle	Digestion, storage, waste disposal, water balance, cell growth, and protection
CONCEPT 6.5 Mitochondria and chloroplasts change energy from one form to another (pp. 109–112) [?] *What is the endosymbiont theory?*	Mitochondrion	Bounded by double membrane; inner membrane has infoldings (cristae)	Cellular respiration
	Chloroplast	Typically two membranes around fluid stroma, which contains thylakoids stacked into grana (in cells of photosynthetic eukaryotes, including plants)	Photosynthesis
	Peroxisome	Specialized metabolic compartment bounded by a single membrane	Contains enzymes that transfer hydrogen atoms from substrates to oxygen, producing hydrogen peroxide (H_2O_2) as a by-product; H_2O_2 is converted to water by another enzyme

CONCEPT 6.6

The cytoskeleton is a network of fibers that organizes structures and activities in the cell (pp. 112–118)

- The **cytoskeleton** functions in structural support for the cell and in motility and signal transmission.
- **Microtubules** shape the cell, guide organelle movement, and separate chromosomes in dividing cells. **Cilia** and **flagella** are motile appendages containing microtubules. Primary cilia also play sensory and signaling roles. **Microfilaments** are thin rods that function in muscle contraction, amoeboid movement, **cytoplasmic streaming**, and support of microvilli. **Intermediate filaments** support cell shape and fix organelles in place.

? *Describe the role of motor proteins inside the eukaryotic cell and in whole-cell movement.*

CONCEPT 6.7

Extracellular components and connections between cells help coordinate cellular activities (pp. 118–121)

- Plant **cell walls** are made of cellulose fibers embedded in other polysaccharides and proteins.
- Animal cells secrete glycoproteins and proteoglycans that form the **extracellular matrix (ECM)**, which functions in support, adhesion, movement, and regulation.
- Cell junctions connect neighboring cells. Plants have **plasmodesmata** that pass through adjoining cell walls. Animal cells have **tight junctions**, **desmosomes**, and **gap junctions**.

? *Compare the structure and functions of a plant cell wall and the extracellular matrix of an animal cell.*

TEST YOUR UNDERSTANDING

LEVEL 1: KNOWLEDGE/COMPREHENSION

1. Which structure is *not* part of the endomembrane system?
   a. nuclear envelope
   b. chloroplast
   c. Golgi apparatus
   d. plasma membrane

2. Which structure is common to plant *and* animal cells?
   a. chloroplast
   b. central vacuole
   c. mitochondrion
   d. centriole

3. Which of the following is present in a prokaryotic cell?
   a. mitochondrion
   b. ribosome
   c. nuclear envelope
   d. chloroplast

4. Which structure-function pair is *mismatched*?
   a. microtubule; muscle contraction
   b. ribosome; protein synthesis
   c. Golgi; protein trafficking
   d. nucleolus; production of ribosomal subunits

LEVEL 2: APPLICATION/ANALYSIS

5. Cyanide binds to at least one molecule involved in producing ATP. If a cell is exposed to cyanide, most of the cyanide will be found within the
   a. mitochondria.
   b. ribosomes.
   c. peroxisomes.
   d. lysosomes.

6. What is the most likely pathway taken by a newly synthesized protein that will be secreted by a cell?
   a. Golgi → ER → lysosome
   b. nucleus → ER → Golgi
   c. ER → Golgi → vesicles that fuse with plasma membrane
   d. ER → lysosomes → vesicles that fuse with plasma membrane

7. Which cell would be best for studying lysosomes?
   a. muscle cell
   b. nerve cell
   c. phagocytic white blood cell
   d. bacterial cell

8. **DRAW IT** From memory, draw two eukaryotic cells, labeling the structures listed here and showing any physical connections between the internal structures of each cell: nucleus, rough ER, smooth ER, mitochondrion, centrosome, chloroplast, vacuole, lysosome, microtubule, cell wall, ECM, microfilament, Golgi apparatus, intermediate filament, plasma membrane, peroxisome, ribosome, nucleolus, nuclear pore, vesicle, flagellum, microvilli, plasmodesma.

LEVEL 3: SYNTHESIS/EVALUATION

9. **EVOLUTION CONNECTION**
   Which aspects of cell structure best reveal evolutionary unity? What are some examples of specialized modifications?

10. **SCIENTIFIC INQUIRY**
    Imagine protein X, destined to span the plasma membrane. Assume that the mRNA carrying the genetic message for protein X has already been translated by ribosomes in a cell culture. If you fractionate the cells (see Figure 6.4), in which fraction would you find protein X? Explain by describing its transit through the cell.

11. **WRITE ABOUT A THEME: ORGANIZATION**
    Considering some of the characteristics that define life and drawing on your knowledge of cellular structures and functions, write a short essay (100–150 words) that discusses this statement: Life is an emergent property that appears at the level of the cell. (See Concept 1.1.)

12. **SYNTHESIZE YOUR KNOWLEDGE**

Epithelial cell

The cells in the SEM are epithelial cells from the small intestine. Discuss how aspects of their structure contribute to their specialized functions of nutrient absorption and as a barrier between the intestinal contents and the blood supply on the other side of the sheet of epithelial cells.

For selected answers, see Appendix A.

MasteringBiology®

7

Membrane Structure and Function

▲ Figure 7.1 **How do cell membrane proteins help regulate chemical traffic?**

Life at the Edge

The plasma membrane is the edge of life, the boundary that separates the living cell from its surroundings and controls traffic into and out of the cell it surrounds. Like all biological membranes, the plasma membrane exhibits **selective permeability**; that is, it allows some substances to cross it more easily than others. The ability of the cell to discriminate in its chemical exchanges with its environment is fundamental to life, and it is the plasma membrane and its component molecules that make this selectivity possible.

In this chapter, you will learn how cellular membranes control the passage of substances. The image in **Figure 7.1** shows a computer model of water molecules (red and gray) passing through a short section of membrane. The blue ribbons within the lipid bilayer (green) represent helical regions of a membrane protein called an aquaporin. One molecule of this protein enables billions of water molecules to pass through the membrane every second, many more than could cross on their own. Found in many cells, aquaporins are but one example of how the plasma membrane and its proteins enable cells to survive and function. To understand how membranes work, we'll begin by examining their structure. Then, in the rest of the chapter, we'll describe in some detail how plasma membranes control transport into and out of cells, sometimes through proteins like the ion channel to the left.

CONCEPT 7.1

Cellular membranes are fluid mosaics of lipids and proteins

Lipids and proteins are the staple ingredients of membranes, although carbohydrates are also important. The most abundant lipids in most membranes are phospholipids. The ability of phospholipids to form membranes is inherent in their molecular structure. A phospholipid is an **amphipathic** molecule, meaning it has both a hydrophilic region and a hydrophobic region (see Figure 5.11). Other types of membrane lipids are also amphipathic. A phospholipid bilayer can exist as a stable boundary between two aqueous compartments because the molecular arrangement shelters the hydrophobic tails of the phospholipids from water while exposing the hydrophilic heads to water (Figure 7.2).

Like membrane lipids, most membrane proteins are amphipathic. Such proteins can reside in the phospholipid bilayer with their hydrophilic regions protruding. This molecular orientation maximizes contact of hydrophilic regions of proteins with water in the cytosol and extracellular fluid, while providing their hydrophobic

▼ **Figure 7.2 Phospholipid bilayer (cross section).**

WATER

Hydrophilic head

Hydrophobic tail

WATER

MAKE CONNECTIONS *Consulting Figure 5.11, circle the hydrophilic and hydrophobic portions of the enlarged phospholipids on the right. Explain what each portion contacts when the phospholipids are in the plasma membrane.*

parts with a nonaqueous environment. **Figure 7.3** shows the currently accepted model of the arrangement of molecules in the plasma membrane. In this **fluid mosaic model**, the membrane is a mosaic of protein molecules bobbing in a fluid bilayer of phospholipids.

Fibers of extra-cellular matrix (ECM)

Glyco-protein

Carbohydrate

Glycolipid

EXTRACELLULAR SIDE OF MEMBRANE

Cholesterol

Microfilaments of cytoskeleton

Peripheral proteins

Integral protein

CYTOPLASMIC SIDE OF MEMBRANE

▲ **Figure 7.3 Updated model of an animal cell's plasma membrane (cutaway view).**

The proteins are not randomly distributed in the membrane, however. Groups of proteins are often associated in long-lasting, specialized patches, where they carry out common functions. The lipids themselves appear to form defined regions as well. Also, in some regions the membrane may be much more packed with proteins than shown in Figure 7.3. Like all models, the fluid mosaic model is continually being refined as new research reveals more about membrane structure.

The Fluidity of Membranes

Membranes are not static sheets of molecules locked rigidly in place. A membrane is held together primarily by hydrophobic interactions, which are much weaker than covalent bonds (see Figure 5.18). Most of the lipids and some of the proteins can shift about laterally—that is, in the plane of the membrane, like partygoers elbowing their way through a crowded room. Very rarely, also, a lipid may flip-flop across the membrane, switching from one phospholipid layer to the other.

The lateral movement of phospholipids within the membrane is rapid. Adjacent phospholipids switch positions about 10^7 times per second, which means that a phospholipid can travel about 2 μm—the length of many bacterial cells—in 1 second. Proteins are much larger than lipids and move more slowly, but some membrane proteins do drift, as shown in a classic experiment described in **Figure 7.4**. Some membrane proteins seem to move in a highly directed manner, perhaps driven along cytoskeletal fibers in the cell by motor proteins connected to the membrane proteins' cytoplasmic regions. However, many other membrane proteins seem to be held immobile by their attachment to the cytoskeleton or to the extracellular matrix (see Figure 7.3).

A membrane remains fluid as temperature decreases until the phospholipids settle into a closely packed arrangement and the membrane solidifies, much as bacon grease forms lard when it cools. The temperature at which a membrane solidifies depends on the types of lipids it is made of. The membrane remains fluid to a lower temperature if it is rich in phospholipids with unsaturated hydrocarbon tails (see Figures 5.10 and 5.11). Because of kinks in the tails where double bonds are located, unsaturated hydrocarbon tails cannot pack together as closely as saturated hydrocarbon tails, making the membrane more fluid **(Figure 7.5a)**.

The steroid cholesterol, which is wedged between phospholipid molecules in the plasma membranes of animal cells, has different effects on membrane fluidity at different temperatures **(Figure 7.5b)**. At relatively high temperatures—at 37°C, the body temperature of humans, for example—cholesterol makes the membrane less fluid by restraining phospholipid movement. However, because cholesterol also hinders the close packing of phospholipids, it lowers the temperature required for the membrane to solidify. Thus, cholesterol can be thought of as a "fluidity buffer" for the membrane, resisting changes in membrane fluidity that can be caused by changes in temperature.

▼ **Figure 7.4**   Inquiry

Do membrane proteins move?

Experiment Larry Frye and Michael Edidin, at Johns Hopkins University, labeled the plasma membrane proteins of a mouse cell and a human cell with two different markers and fused the cells. Using a microscope, they observed the markers on the hybrid cell.

Results

Conclusion The mixing of the mouse and human membrane proteins indicates that at least some membrane proteins move sideways within the plane of the plasma membrane.

Source: L. D. Frye and M. Edidin, The rapid intermixing of cell surface antigens after formation of mouse-human heterokaryons, *Journal of Cell Science* 7:319 (1970).

WHAT IF? *Suppose the proteins did not mix in the hybrid cell, even many hours after fusion. Would you be able to conclude that proteins don't move within the membrane? What other explanation could there be?*

▼ **Figure 7.5 Factors that affect membrane fluidity.**

(a) Unsaturated versus saturated hydrocarbon tails.

(b) Cholesterol within the animal cell membrane.

Cholesterol reduces membrane fluidity at moderate temperatures by reducing phospholipid movement, but at low temperatures it hinders solidification by disrupting the regular packing of phospholipids.

Membranes must be fluid to work properly; the fluidity of a membrane affects both its permeability and the ability of membrane proteins to move to where their function is needed. Usually, membranes are about as fluid as salad oil. When a membrane solidifies, its permeability changes, and enzymatic proteins in the membrane may become inactive if their activity requires movement within the membrane. However, membranes that are too fluid cannot support protein function either. Therefore, extreme environments pose a challenge for life, resulting in evolutionary adaptations that include differences in membrane lipid composition.

Evolution of Differences in Membrane Lipid Composition

EVOLUTION Variations in the cell membrane lipid compositions of many species appear to be evolutionary adaptations that maintain the appropriate membrane fluidity under specific environmental conditions. For instance, fishes that live in extreme cold have membranes with a high proportion of unsaturated hydrocarbon tails, enabling their membranes to remain fluid (see Figure 7.5a). At the other extreme, some bacteria and archaea thrive at temperatures greater than 90°C (194°F) in thermal hot springs and geysers. Their membranes include unusual lipids that may prevent excessive fluidity at such high temperatures.

The ability to change the lipid composition of cell membranes in response to changing temperatures has evolved in organisms that live where temperatures vary. In many plants that tolerate extreme cold, such as winter wheat, the percentage of unsaturated phospholipids increases in autumn, an adjustment that keeps the membranes from solidifying during winter. Certain bacteria and archaea can also change the proportion of unsaturated phospholipids in their cell membranes, depending on the temperature at which they are growing. Overall, natural selection has apparently favored organisms whose mix of membrane lipids ensures an appropriate level of membrane fluidity for their environment.

Membrane Proteins and Their Functions

Now we come to the *mosaic* aspect of the fluid mosaic model. Somewhat like a tile mosaic, a membrane is a collage of different proteins, often clustered together in groups, embedded in the fluid matrix of the lipid bilayer (see Figure 7.3). In the plasma membrane of red blood cells alone, for example, more than 50 kinds of proteins have been found so far. Phospholipids form the main fabric of the membrane, but proteins determine most of the membrane's functions. Different types of cells contain different sets of membrane proteins, and the various membranes within a cell each have a unique collection of proteins.

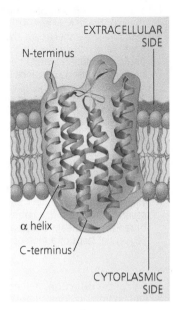

▶ **Figure 7.6 The structure of a transmembrane protein.** Bacteriorhodopsin (a bacterial transport protein) has a distinct orientation in the membrane, with its N-terminus outside the cell and its C-terminus inside. This ribbon model highlights the α-helical secondary structure of the hydrophobic parts, which lie mostly within the hydrophobic interior of the membrane. The protein includes seven transmembrane helices. The nonhelical hydrophilic segments are in contact with the aqueous solutions on the extracellular and cytoplasmic sides of the membrane. Although shown as simple purple shapes in many figures in this book, each protein has its own unique structure.

Notice in Figure 7.3 that there are two major populations of membrane proteins: integral proteins and peripheral proteins. **Integral proteins** penetrate the hydrophobic interior of the lipid bilayer. The majority are *transmembrane proteins*, which span the membrane; other integral proteins extend only partway into the hydrophobic interior. The hydrophobic regions of an integral protein consist of one or more stretches of nonpolar amino acids (see Figure 5.14), usually coiled into α helices (**Figure 7.6**). The hydrophilic parts of the molecule are exposed to the aqueous solutions on either side of the membrane. Some proteins also have one or more hydrophilic channels that allow passage through the membrane of hydrophilic substances (even of water itself; see Figure 7.1). **Peripheral proteins** are not embedded in the lipid bilayer at all; they are appendages loosely bound to the surface of the membrane, often to exposed parts of integral proteins (see Figure 7.3).

On the cytoplasmic side of the plasma membrane, some membrane proteins are held in place by attachment to the cytoskeleton. And on the extracellular side, certain membrane proteins are attached to fibers of the extracellular matrix (see Figure 6.28; *integrins* are one type of integral, transmembrane protein). These attachments combine to give animal cells a stronger framework than the plasma membrane alone could provide.

A single cell may have cell surface membrane proteins that carry out several different functions, such as transport through the cell membrane, enzymatic activity, or attaching a cell to either a neighboring cell or the extracellular matrix. Furthermore, a single membrane protein may itself carry out multiple functions. Thus, the membrane is not only a structural mosaic, but also a functional mosaic. **Figure 7.7** illustrates six major functions performed by proteins of the plasma membrane.

(a) Transport. *Left:* A protein that spans the membrane may provide a hydrophilic channel across the membrane that is selective for a particular solute. *Right:* Other transport proteins shuttle a substance from one side to the other by changing shape (see Figure 7.14b). Some of these proteins hydrolyze ATP as an energy source to actively pump substances across the membrane.

(b) Enzymatic activity. A protein built into the membrane may be an enzyme with its active site exposed to substances in the adjacent solution. In some cases, several enzymes in a membrane are organized as a team that carries out sequential steps of a metabolic pathway.

(c) Signal transduction. A membrane protein (receptor) may have a binding site with a specific shape that fits the shape of a chemical messenger, such as a hormone. The external messenger (signaling molecule) may cause the protein to change shape, allowing it to relay the message to the inside of the cell, usually by binding to a cytoplasmic protein (see Figure 11.6).

(d) Cell-cell recognition. Some glycoproteins serve as identification tags that are specifically recognized by membrane proteins of other cells. This type of cell-cell binding is usually short-lived compared to that shown in (e).

(e) Intercellular joining. Membrane proteins of adjacent cells may hook together in various kinds of junctions, such as gap junctions or tight junctions (see Figure 6.30). This type of binding is more long-lasting than that shown in (d).

(f) Attachment to the cytoskeleton and extracellular matrix (ECM). Microfilaments or other elements of the cytoskeleton may be noncovalently bound to membrane proteins, a function that helps maintain cell shape and stabilizes the location of certain membrane proteins. Proteins that can bind to ECM molecules can coordinate extracellular and intracellular changes (see Figure 6.28).

▲ **Figure 7.7 Some functions of membrane proteins.** In many cases, a single protein performs multiple tasks.

? *Some transmembrane proteins can bind to a particular ECM molecule and, when bound, transmit a signal into the cell. Use the proteins shown in (c) and (f) to explain how this might occur.*

Proteins on a cell's surface are important in the medical field. For example, a protein called CD4 on the surface of immune cells helps the human immunodeficiency virus (HIV) infect these cells, leading to acquired immune deficiency syndrome (AIDS). Despite multiple exposures to HIV, however, a small number of people do not develop AIDS and show no evidence of HIV-infected cells. Comparing their genes with the genes of infected individuals, researchers learned that resistant people have an unusual form of a gene that codes for an immune cell-surface protein called CCR5. Further work showed although CD4 is the main HIV receptor, HIV must also bind to CCR5 as a "co-receptor" to infect most cells **(Figure 7.8a)**. An absence of CCR5 on the cells of resistant individuals, due to the gene alteration, prevents the virus from entering the cells **(Figure 7.8b)**.

This information has been key to developing a treatment for HIV infection. Interfering with CD4 could cause dangerous side effects because it performs many important functions in cells. Discovery of the CCR5 co-receptor provided a safer target for development of drugs that mask this protein and block HIV entry. One such drug, maraviroc (brand name Selzentry), was approved for treatment of HIV in 2007 and is still being used today. A clinical trial began in 2012 to test whether this drug might also work to prevent HIV infection in uninfected, at-risk patients.

The Role of Membrane Carbohydrates in Cell-Cell Recognition

Cell-cell recognition, a cell's ability to distinguish one type of neighboring cell from another, is crucial to the functioning of an organism. It is important, for example, in the sorting of cells into tissues and organs in an animal embryo. It is also the basis for the rejection of foreign cells by the immune

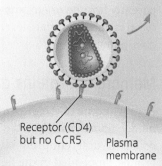

(a) .... **(b)**

▲ **Figure 7.8 The genetic basis for HIV resistance. (a)** HIV can infect a cell with CCR5 on its surface, as in most people. **(b)** HIV cannot infect a cell lacking CCR5 on its surface, as in resistant individuals.

MAKE CONNECTIONS *Study Figures 2.16 and 5.17, both of which show pairs of molecules binding to each other. What would you predict about CCR5 that would allow HIV to bind to it? How could a drug molecule interfere with this binding?*

system, an important line of defense in vertebrate animals (see Chapter 43). Cells recognize other cells by binding to molecules, often containing carbohydrates, on the extracellular surface of the plasma membrane (see Figure 7.7d).

Membrane carbohydrates are usually short, branched chains of fewer than 15 sugar units. Some are covalently bonded to lipids, forming molecules called **glycolipids**. (Recall that *glyco* refers to the presence of carbohydrate.) However, most are covalently bonded to proteins, which are thereby **glycoproteins** (see Figure 7.3).

The carbohydrates on the extracellular side of the plasma membrane vary from species to species, among individuals of the same species, and even from one cell type to another in a single individual. The diversity of the molecules and their location on the cell's surface enable membrane carbohydrates to function as markers that distinguish one cell from another. For example, the four human blood types designated A, B, AB, and O reflect variation in the carbohydrate part of glycoproteins on the surface of red blood cells.

Synthesis and Sidedness of Membranes

Membranes have distinct inside and outside faces. The two lipid layers may differ in lipid composition, and each protein has directional orientation in the membrane (see Figure 7.6). **Figure 7.9** shows how membrane sidedness arises: The asymmetrical arrangement of proteins, lipids, and their

associated carbohydrates in the plasma membrane is determined as the membrane is being built by the endoplasmic reticulum (ER) and Golgi apparatus, components of the endomembrane system (see Figure 6.15).

CONCEPT CHECK 7.1

1. Plasma membrane proteins have carbohydrates attached to them in the ER and Golgi apparatus, then are transported in vesicles to the cell surface. On which side of the vesicle membrane are the carbohydrates?

2. **WHAT IF?** How would the membrane lipid composition of a native grass found in very warm soil around hot springs compare with that of a native grass found in cooler soil? Explain.

For suggested answers, see Appendix A.

CONCEPT 7.2

Membrane structure results in selective permeability

The biological membrane is an exquisite example of a supramolecular structure—many molecules ordered into a higher level of organization—with emergent properties beyond those of the individual molecules. The remainder of this chapter focuses on one of those properties: the ability to regulate transport across cellular boundaries, a function

▼ Figure 7.9 **Synthesis of membrane components and their orientation in the membrane.** The cytoplasmic (orange) face of the plasma membrane differs from the extracellular (aqua) face. The latter arises from the inside face of ER, Golgi, and vesicle membranes.

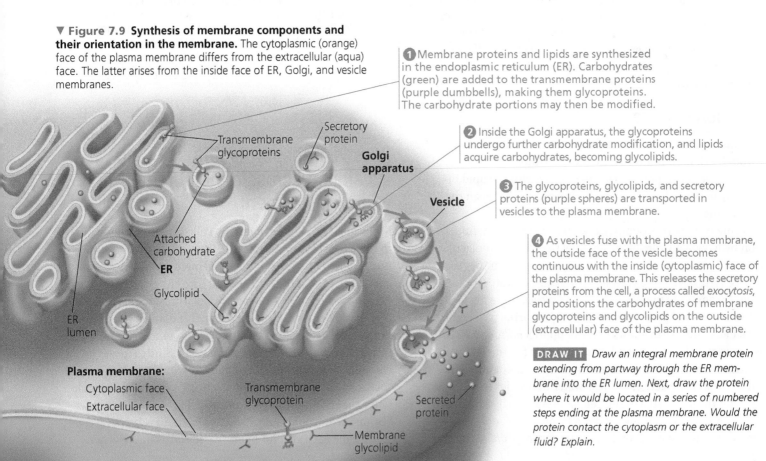

❶ Membrane proteins and lipids are synthesized in the endoplasmic reticulum (ER). Carbohydrates (green) are added to the transmembrane proteins (purple dumbbells), making them glycoproteins. The carbohydrate portions may then be modified.

❷ Inside the Golgi apparatus, the glycoproteins undergo further carbohydrate modification, and lipids acquire carbohydrates, becoming glycolipids.

❸ The glycoproteins, glycolipids, and secretory proteins (purple spheres) are transported in vesicles to the plasma membrane.

❹ As vesicles fuse with the plasma membrane, the outside face of the vesicle becomes continuous with the inside (cytoplasmic) face of the plasma membrane. This releases the secretory proteins from the cell, a process called *exocytosis*, and positions the carbohydrates of membrane glycoproteins and glycolipids on the outside (extracellular) face of the plasma membrane.

DRAW IT *Draw an integral membrane protein extending from partway through the ER membrane into the ER lumen. Next, draw the protein where it would be located in a series of numbered steps ending at the plasma membrane. Would the protein contact the cytoplasm or the extracellular fluid? Explain.*

Transmembrane glycoproteins
Secretory protein
Golgi apparatus
Vesicle
Attached carbohydrate
ER
Glycolipid
ER lumen
Plasma membrane:
Cytoplasmic face
Extracellular face
Transmembrane glycoprotein
Secreted protein
Membrane glycolipid

essential to the cell's existence. We will see once again that form fits function: The fluid mosaic model helps explain how membranes regulate the cell's molecular traffic.

A steady traffic of small molecules and ions moves across the plasma membrane in both directions. Consider the chemical exchanges between a muscle cell and the extracellular fluid that bathes it. Sugars, amino acids, and other nutrients enter the cell, and metabolic waste products leave it. The cell takes in O_2 for use in cellular respiration and expels CO_2. Also, the cell regulates its concentrations of inorganic ions, such as Na^+, K^+, Ca^{2+}, and Cl^-, by shuttling them one way or the other across the plasma membrane. Although the heavy traffic through them may seem to suggest otherwise, cell membranes are selectively permeable, and substances do not cross the barrier indiscriminately. The cell is able to take up some small molecules and ions and exclude others.

The Permeability of the Lipid Bilayer

Nonpolar molecules, such as hydrocarbons, CO_2, and O_2, are hydrophobic. They can therefore dissolve in the lipid bilayer of the membrane and cross it easily, without the aid of membrane proteins. However, the hydrophobic interior of the membrane impedes direct passage through the membrane of ions and polar molecules, which are hydrophilic. Polar molecules such as glucose and other sugars pass only slowly through a lipid bilayer, and even water, a very small polar molecule, does not cross rapidly. A charged atom or molecule and its surrounding shell of water (see Figure 3.7) are even less likely to penetrate the hydrophobic interior of the membrane. Furthermore, the lipid bilayer is only one aspect of the gatekeeper system responsible for a cell's selective permeability. Proteins built into the membrane play key roles in regulating transport.

Transport Proteins

Specific ions and a variety of polar molecules can't move through cell membranes on their own. However, these hydrophilic substances can avoid contact with the lipid bilayer by passing through **transport proteins** that span the membrane.

Some transport proteins, called *channel proteins*, function by having a hydrophilic channel that certain molecules or atomic ions use as a tunnel through the membrane (see Figure 7.7a, left). For example, the passage of water molecules through the membrane in certain cells is greatly facilitated by channel proteins known as **aquaporins** (see Figure 7.1). Each aquaporin allows entry of up to *3 billion* (3×10^9) water molecules per second, passing single file through its central channel, which fits ten at a time. Without aquaporins, only a tiny fraction of these water molecules would pass through the same area of the cell membrane in a second, so the channel protein brings about a tremendous increase in rate. Other transport proteins, called *carrier proteins*, hold

onto their passengers and change shape in a way that shuttles them across the membrane (see Figure 7.7a, right).

A transport protein is specific for the substance it translocates (moves), allowing only a certain substance (or a small group of related substances) to cross the membrane. For example, a specific carrier protein in the plasma membrane of red blood cells transports glucose across the membrane 50,000 times faster than glucose can pass through on its own. This "glucose transporter" is so selective that it even rejects fructose, a structural isomer of glucose.

Thus, the selective permeability of a membrane depends on both the discriminating barrier of the lipid bilayer and the specific transport proteins built into the membrane. But what establishes the *direction* of traffic across a membrane? At a given time, what determines whether a particular substance will enter the cell or leave the cell? And what mechanisms actually drive molecules across membranes? We will address these questions next as we explore two modes of membrane traffic: passive transport and active transport.

CONCEPT CHECK 7.2

1. What property allows O_2 and CO_2 to cross a lipid bilayer without the help of membrane proteins?

2. Why is a transport protein needed to move many water molecules rapidly across a membrane?

3. MAKE CONNECTIONS Aquaporins exclude passage of hydronium ions (H_3O^+), but some aquaporins allow passage of glycerol, a three-carbon alcohol (see Figure 5.9), as well as H_2O. Since H_3O^+ is closer in size to water than glycerol is, yet cannot pass through, what might be the basis of this selectivity?

For suggested answers, see Appendix A.

CONCEPT 7.3

Passive transport is diffusion of a substance across a membrane with no energy investment

Molecules have a type of energy called thermal energy, due to their constant motion (see Concept 3.2). One result of this motion is **diffusion**, the movement of particles of any substance so that they spread out into the available space. Each molecule moves randomly, yet diffusion of a *population* of molecules may be directional. To understand this process, let's imagine a synthetic membrane separating pure water from a solution of a dye in water. Study **Figure 7.10a** carefully to appreciate how diffusion would result in both solutions having equal concentrations of the dye molecules. Once that point is reached, there will be a dynamic equilibrium, with roughly as many dye molecules crossing the membrane each second in one direction as in the other.

Molecules of dye — Membrane (cross section)

WATER

Net diffusion   Net diffusion   Equilibrium

(a) Diffusion of one solute. The membrane has pores large enough for molecules of dye to pass through. Random movement of dye molecules will cause some to pass through the pores; this will happen more often on the side with more dye molecules. The dye diffuses from where it is more concentrated to where it is less concentrated (called diffusing down a concentration gradient). This leads to a dynamic equilibrium: The solute molecules continue to cross the membrane, but at roughly equal rates in both directions.

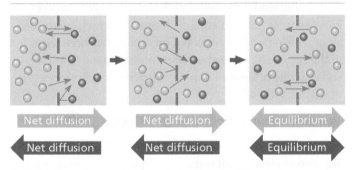

Net diffusion   Net diffusion   Equilibrium

Net diffusion   Net diffusion   Equilibrium

(b) Diffusion of two solutes. Solutions of two different dyes are separated by a membrane that is permeable to both. Each dye diffuses down its own concentration gradient. There will be a net diffusion of the purple dye toward the left, even though the *total* solute concentration was initially greater on the left side.

▲ **Figure 7.10 The diffusion of solutes across a synthetic membrane.** Each of the large arrows under the diagrams shows the net diffusion of the dye molecules of that color.

We can now state a simple rule of diffusion: In the absence of other forces, a substance will diffuse from where it is more concentrated to where it is less concentrated. Put another way, any substance will diffuse down its **concentration gradient**, the region along which the density of a chemical substance increases or decreases (in this case, decreases). No work must be done to make this happen; diffusion is a spontaneous process, needing no input of energy. Note that each substance diffuses down its *own* concentration gradient, unaffected by the concentration gradients of other substances **(Figure 7.10b)**.

Much of the traffic across cell membranes occurs by diffusion. When a substance is more concentrated on one side of a membrane than on the other, there is a tendency for the substance to diffuse across the membrane down its concentration gradient (assuming that the membrane is permeable to that substance). One important example is the uptake of oxygen by a cell performing cellular respiration. Dissolved oxygen diffuses into the cell across the plasma membrane. As long as cellular respiration consumes the O_2 as it enters, diffusion into the cell will continue because the concentration gradient favors movement in that direction.

The diffusion of a substance across a biological membrane is called **passive transport** because the cell does not have to expend energy to make it happen. The concentration gradient itself represents potential energy (see Concept 2.2 and Figure 8.5b) and drives diffusion. Remember, however, that membranes are selectively permeable and therefore have different effects on the rates of diffusion of various molecules. In the case of water, aquaporins allow water to diffuse very rapidly across the membranes of certain cells. As we'll see next, the movement of water across the plasma membrane has important consequences for cells.

Effects of Osmosis on Water Balance

To see how two solutions with different solute concentrations interact, picture a U-shaped glass tube with a selectively permeable artificial membrane separating two sugar solutions **(Figure 7.11)**. Pores in this synthetic membrane

Lower concentration of solute (sugar)   Higher concentration of solute   More similar concentrations of solute

Sugar molecule

H_2O

Selectively permeable membrane

Water molecules can pass through pores, but sugar molecules cannot.   Water molecules cluster around sugar molecules.

This side has fewer solute molecules, more free water molecules.   This side has more solute molecules, fewer free water molecules.

Osmosis

Water moves from an area of higher to lower free water concentration (lower to higher solute concentration).

▲ **Figure 7.11 Osmosis.** Two sugar solutions of different concentrations are separated by a membrane that the solvent (water) can pass through but the solute (sugar) cannot. Water molecules move randomly and may cross in either direction, but overall, water diffuses from the solution with less concentrated solute to that with more concentrated solute. This passive transport of water, or osmosis, makes the sugar concentrations on both sides more nearly equal. (The concentrations are prevented from being exactly equal due to the effect of water pressure on the higher side, which is not discussed here for simplicity.)

WHAT IF? *If an orange dye capable of passing through the membrane was added to the left side of the tube above, how would it be distributed at the end of the experiment? (See Figure 7.10.) Would the final solution levels in the tube be affected?*

are too small for sugar molecules to pass through but large enough for water molecules. However, tight clustering of water molecules around the hydrophilic solute molecules makes some of the water unavailable to cross the membrane. As a result, the solution with a higher solute concentration has a lower *free* water concentration. Water diffuses across the membrane from the region of higher free water concentration (lower solute concentration) to that of lower free water concentration (higher solute concentration) until the solute concentrations on both sides of the membrane are more nearly equal. The diffusion of free water across a selectively permeable membrane, whether artificial or cellular, is called **osmosis**. The movement of water across cell membranes and the balance of water between the cell and its environment are crucial to organisms. Let's now apply what we've learned in this system to living cells.

Water Balance of Cells Without Cell Walls

To explain the behavior of a cell in a solution, we must consider both solute concentration and membrane permeability. Both factors are taken into account in the concept of **tonicity**, the ability of a surrounding solution to cause a cell to gain or lose water. The tonicity of a solution depends in part on its concentration of solutes that cannot cross the membrane (nonpenetrating solutes) relative to that inside the cell. If there is a higher concentration of nonpenetrating solutes in the surrounding solution, water will tend to leave the cell, and vice versa.

If a cell without a cell wall, such as an animal cell, is immersed in an environment that is **isotonic** to the cell (*iso* means "same"), there will be no *net* movement of water across the plasma membrane. Water diffuses across the membrane, but at the same rate in both directions. In an isotonic environment, the volume of an animal cell is stable **(Figure 7.12a)**.

Let's transfer the cell to a solution that is **hypertonic** to the cell (*hyper* means "more," in this case referring to nonpenetrating solutes). The cell will lose water, shrivel, and probably die. This is why an increase in the salinity (saltiness) of a lake can kill the animals there; if the lake water becomes hypertonic to the animals' cells, they might shrivel and die. However, taking up too much water can be just as hazardous as losing water. If we place the cell in a solution that is **hypotonic** to the cell (*hypo* means "less"), water will enter the cell faster than it leaves, and the cell will swell and lyse (burst) like an overfilled water balloon.

A cell without rigid cell walls can tolerate neither excessive uptake nor excessive loss of water. This problem of water balance is automatically solved if such a cell lives in isotonic surroundings. Seawater is isotonic to many marine invertebrates. The cells of most terrestrial (land-dwelling) animals are bathed in an extracellular fluid that is isotonic to the cells. In hypertonic or hypotonic environments, however, organisms that lack rigid cell walls must have other adaptations for **osmoregulation**, the control of solute concentrations and water balance. For example, the unicellular protist *Paramecium caudatum* lives in pond water, which is hypotonic to the cell. *P. caudatum* has a plasma membrane that is much less permeable to water than the membranes of most other cells, but this only slows the uptake of water, which continually enters the cell. The *P. caudatum* cell doesn't burst because it is also equipped with a contractile vacuole, an organelle that functions as a bilge pump to force water out of the cell as fast as it enters by osmosis **(Figure 7.13)**. We will examine other evolutionary adaptations for osmoregulation in Chapter 44.

Water Balance of Cells with Cell Walls

The cells of plants, prokaryotes, fungi, and some protists are surrounded by cell walls (see Figure 6.27). When such a cell is immersed in a hypotonic solution—bathed in rainwater, for example—the cell wall helps maintain the cell's water balance. Consider a plant cell. Like an animal cell, the plant cell swells as water enters by osmosis **(Figure 7.12b)**. However, the relatively inelastic cell wall will expand only so much before it exerts a back pressure on the cell, called *turgor pressure*, that opposes further water uptake. At this

(a) Animal cell. An animal cell fares best in an isotonic environment unless it has special adaptations that offset the osmotic uptake or loss of water.

(b) Plant cell. Plant cells are turgid (firm) and generally healthiest in a hypotonic environment, where the uptake of water is eventually balanced by the wall pushing back on the cell.

Hypotonic solution	Isotonic solution	Hypertonic solution
Lysed	Normal	Shriveled
Turgid (normal)	Flaccid	Plasmolyzed

▲ **Figure 7.12 The water balance of living cells.** How living cells react to changes in the solute concentration of their environment depends on whether or not they have cell walls. **(a)** Animal cells, such as this red blood cell, do not have cell walls. **(b)** Plant cells do. (Arrows indicate net water movement after the cells were first placed in these solutions.)

Contractile vacuole

50 μm

▲ **Figure 7.13 The contractile vacuole of *Paramecium caudatum*.** The vacuole collects fluid from a system of canals in the cytoplasm. When full, the vacuole and canals contract, expelling fluid from the cell (LM).

point, the cell is **turgid** (very firm), which is the healthy state for most plant cells. Plants that are not woody, such as most houseplants, depend for mechanical support on cells kept turgid by a surrounding hypotonic solution. If a plant's cells and their surroundings are isotonic, there is no net tendency for water to enter, and the cells become **flaccid** (limp).

However, a cell wall is of no advantage if the cell is immersed in a hypertonic environment. In this case, a plant cell, like an animal cell, will lose water to its surroundings and shrink. As the plant cell shrivels, its plasma membrane pulls away from the cell wall at multiple places. This phenomenon, called **plasmolysis**, causes the plant to wilt and can lead to plant death. The walled cells of bacteria and fungi also plasmolyze in hypertonic environments.

Facilitated Diffusion: Passive Transport Aided by Proteins

Let's look more closely at how water and certain hydrophilic solutes cross a membrane. As mentioned earlier, many polar molecules and ions impeded by the lipid bilayer of the membrane diffuse passively with the help of transport proteins that span the membrane. This phenomenon is called **facilitated diffusion**. Cell biologists are still trying to learn exactly how various transport proteins facilitate diffusion. Most transport proteins are very specific: They transport some substances but not others.

As mentioned earlier, the two types of transport proteins are channel proteins and carrier proteins. Channel proteins simply provide corridors that allow specific molecules or ions to cross the membrane **(Figure 7.14a)**. The hydrophilic passageways provided by these proteins can allow water molecules or small ions to diffuse very quickly from one side of the membrane to the other. Aquaporins, the water channel proteins, facilitate the massive amounts of diffusion that occur in plant cells and in animal cells such as red blood cells (see Figure 7.12). Certain kidney cells also have a high number of aquaporins, allowing them to reclaim water from

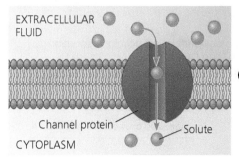

EXTRACELLULAR FLUID

Channel protein

CYTOPLASM

Solute

(a) A channel protein (purple) has a channel through which water molecules or a specific solute can pass.

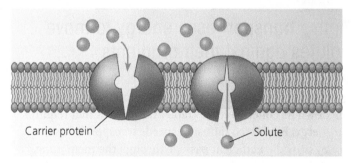

Carrier protein

Solute

(b) A carrier protein alternates between two shapes, moving a solute across the membrane during the shape change.

▲ **Figure 7.14 Two types of transport proteins that carry out facilitated diffusion.** In both cases, the protein can transport the solute in either direction, but the net movement is down the concentration gradient of the solute.

urine before it is excreted. If the kidneys did not perform this function, you would excrete about 180 L of urine per day—and have to drink an equal volume of water!

Channel proteins that transport ions are called **ion channels**. Many ion channels function as **gated channels**, which open or close in response to a stimulus. For some gated channels, the stimulus is electrical. In a nerve cell, for example, an ion channel opens in response to an electrical stimulus, allowing a stream of potassium ions to leave the cell. (See the orange ion in the center of the ion channel shown at the bottom left of the chapter-opening page.) This restores the cell's ability to fire again. Other gated channels open or close when a specific substance other than the one to be transported binds to the channel. These are also important in the functioning of the nervous system, as you'll learn in Chapter 48.

Carrier proteins, such as the glucose transporter mentioned earlier, seem to undergo a subtle change in shape that somehow translocates the solute-binding site across the membrane **(Figure 7.14b)**. Such a change in shape may be triggered by the binding and release of the transported molecule. Like ion channels, carrier proteins involved in facilitated diffusion result in the net movement of a substance down its concentration gradient. No energy input is thus required: This is passive transport. The Scientific Skills Exercise gives you an opportunity to work with data from an experiment related to glucose transport.

CONCEPT CHECK 7.3

1. How do you think a cell performing cellular respiration rids itself of the resulting CO_2?
2. **WHAT IF?** If a *Paramecium caudatum* swims from a hypotonic to an isotonic environment, will its contractile vacuole become more active or less? Why?

For suggested answers, see Appendix A.

CONCEPT 7.4

Active transport uses energy to move solutes against their gradients

Despite the help of transport proteins, facilitated diffusion is considered passive transport because the solute is moving down its concentration gradient, a process that requires no energy. Facilitated diffusion speeds transport of a solute by providing efficient passage through the membrane, but it does not alter the direction of transport. Some other transport proteins, however, can move solutes against their concentration gradients, across the plasma membrane from the side where they are less concentrated (whether inside or outside) to the side where they are more concentrated.

The Need for Energy in Active Transport

To pump a solute across a membrane against its gradient requires work; the cell must expend energy. Therefore, this type of membrane traffic is called **active transport**. The transport proteins that move solutes against their concentration gradients are all carrier proteins rather than channel proteins. This makes sense because when channel proteins are open, they merely allow solutes to diffuse down their concentration gradients rather than picking them up and transporting them against their gradients.

Active transport enables a cell to maintain internal concentrations of small solutes that differ from concentrations in its environment. For example, compared with its surroundings, an animal cell has a much higher concentration of potassium ions (K^+) and a much lower concentration of sodium ions (Na^+). The plasma membrane helps maintain these steep gradients by pumping Na^+ out of the cell and K^+ into the cell.

As in other types of cellular work, ATP supplies the energy for most active transport. One way ATP can power active transport is by transferring its terminal phosphate group directly to the transport protein. This can induce the protein to change its shape in a manner that translocates a solute

---

SCIENTIFIC SKILLS EXERCISE

Interpreting a Scatter Plot with Two Sets of Data

Is Glucose Uptake into Cells Affected by Age? Glucose, an important energy source for animals, is transported into cells by facilitated diffusion using protein carriers. In this exercise, you will interpret a graph with two sets of data from an experiment that examined glucose uptake over time in red blood cells from guinea pigs of different ages. You will determine if the age of the guinea pigs affected their cells' rate of glucose uptake.

How the Experiment Was Done Researchers incubated guinea pig red blood cells in a 300 m*M* (millimolar) radioactive glucose solution at pH 7.4 at 25°C. Every 10 or 15 minutes, they removed a sample of cells and measured the concentration of radioactive glucose inside those cells. The cells came from either a 15-day-old or 1-month-old guinea pig.

Data from the Experiment When you have multiple sets of data, it can be useful to plot them on the same graph for comparison. In the graph here, each set of dots (of the same color) forms a *scatter plot*, in which every data point represents two numerical values, one for each variable. For each data set, a curve that best fits the points has been drawn to make it easier to see the trends. (For additional information about graphs, see the Scientific Skills Review in Appendix F and in the Study Area in MasteringBiology.)

Interpret the Data

1. First make sure you understand the parts of the graph. (a) Which variable is the independent variable—the variable controlled by the researchers? (b) Which variable is the dependent variable—the variable that depended on the treatment and was measured by the researchers? (c) What do the red dots represent? (d) the blue dots?
2. From the data points on the graph, construct a table of the data. Put "Incubation Time (min)" in the left column of the table.

Glucose Uptake Over Time in Guinea Pig Red Blood Cells

3. What does the graph show? Compare and contrast glucose uptake in red blood cells from 15-day-old and 1-month-old guinea pigs.
4. Develop a hypothesis to explain the difference between glucose uptake in red blood cells from 15-day-old and 1-month-old guinea pigs. (Think about how glucose gets into cells.)
5. Design an experiment to test your hypothesis.

(MB) A version of this Scientific Skills Exercise can be assigned in MasteringBiology.

Data from T. Kondo and E. Beutler, Developmental changes in glucose transport of guinea pig erythrocytes, *Journal of Clinical Investigation* 65:1–4 (1980).

► **Figure 7.15 The sodium-potassium pump: a specific case of active transport.** This transport system pumps ions against steep concentration gradients: Sodium ion concentration ([Na⁺]) is high outside the cell and low inside, while potassium ion concentration ([K⁺]) is low outside the cell and high inside. The pump oscillates between two shapes in a cycle that moves 3 Na⁺ out of the cell for every 2 K⁺ pumped into the cell. The two shapes have different affinities for Na⁺ and K⁺. ATP powers the shape change by transferring a phosphate group to the transport protein (phosphorylating the protein).

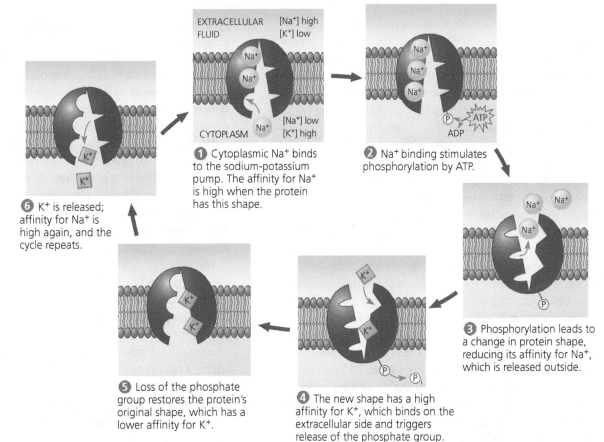

EXTRACELLULAR FLUID   [Na⁺] high   [K⁺] low

CYTOPLASM   [Na⁺] low   [K⁺] high

❶ Cytoplasmic Na⁺ binds to the sodium-potassium pump. The affinity for Na⁺ is high when the protein has this shape.

❷ Na⁺ binding stimulates phosphorylation by ATP.

❸ Phosphorylation leads to a change in protein shape, reducing its affinity for Na⁺, which is released outside.

❹ The new shape has a high affinity for K⁺, which binds on the extracellular side and triggers release of the phosphate group.

❺ Loss of the phosphate group restores the protein's original shape, which has a lower affinity for K⁺.

❻ K⁺ is released; affinity for Na⁺ is high again, and the cycle repeats.

bound to the protein across the membrane. One transport system that works this way is the **sodium-potassium pump**, which exchanges Na⁺ for K⁺ across the plasma membrane of animal cells **(Figure 7.15)**. The distinction between passive transport and active transport is reviewed in **Figure 7.16**.

How Ion Pumps Maintain Membrane Potential

All cells have voltages across their plasma membranes. Voltage is electrical potential energy—a separation of opposite charges. The cytoplasmic side of the membrane is negative in charge relative to the extracellular side because of an unequal distribution of anions and cations on the two sides. The voltage across a membrane, called a **membrane potential**, ranges from about −50 to −200 millivolts (mV). (The minus sign indicates that the inside of the cell is negative relative to the outside.)

The membrane potential acts like a battery, an energy source that affects the traffic of all charged substances across the membrane. Because the inside of the cell is negative compared with the outside, the membrane potential favors the passive transport of cations into the cell and anions out of the cell. Thus, *two* forces drive the diffusion of ions across a membrane: a chemical force (the ion's concentration gradient) and an electrical force (the effect of the membrane potential on the ion's movement). This combination of forces acting on an ion is called the **electrochemical gradient**.

▼ **Figure 7.16 Review: passive and active transport.**

Passive transport. Substances diffuse spontaneously down their concentration gradients, crossing a membrane with no expenditure of energy by the cell. The rate of diffusion can be greatly increased by transport proteins in the membrane.

Diffusion. Hydrophobic molecules and (at a slow rate) very small uncharged polar molecules can diffuse through the lipid bilayer.

Facilitated diffusion. Many hydrophilic substances diffuse through membranes with the assistance of transport proteins, either channel proteins (left) or carrier proteins (right).

Active transport. Some transport proteins act as pumps, moving substances across a membrane against their concentration (or electrochemical) gradients. Energy for this work is usually supplied by ATP.

?   *For each solute in the right panel, describe its direction of movement, and state whether it is going with or against its concentration gradient.*

In the case of ions, then, we must refine our concept of passive transport: An ion diffuses not simply down its *concentration* gradient but, more exactly, down its *electrochemical* gradient. For example, the concentration of Na$^+$ inside a resting nerve cell is much lower than outside it. When the cell is stimulated, gated channels open that facilitate Na$^+$ diffusion. Sodium ions then "fall" down their electrochemical gradient, driven by the concentration gradient of Na$^+$ and by the attraction of these cations to the negative side (inside) of the membrane. In this example, both electrical and chemical contributions to the electrochemical gradient act in the same direction across the membrane, but this is not always so. In cases where electrical forces due to the membrane potential oppose the simple diffusion of an ion down its concentration gradient, active transport may be necessary. In Chapter 48, you'll learn about the importance of electrochemical gradients and membrane potentials in the transmission of nerve impulses.

Some membrane proteins that actively transport ions contribute to the membrane potential. An example is the sodium-potassium pump. Notice in Figure 7.15 that the pump does not translocate Na$^+$ and K$^+$ one for one, but pumps three sodium ions out of the cell for every two potassium ions it pumps into the cell. With each "crank" of the pump, there is a net transfer of one positive charge from the cytoplasm to the extracellular fluid, a process that stores energy as voltage. A transport protein that generates voltage across a membrane is called an **electrogenic pump**. The sodium-potassium pump appears to be the major electrogenic pump of animal cells. The main electrogenic pump of plants, fungi, and bacteria is a **proton pump**, which actively transports protons (hydrogen ions, H$^+$) out of the cell. The pumping of H$^+$ transfers positive charge from the cytoplasm to the extracellular solution (**Figure 7.17**). By generating voltage across membranes, electrogenic pumps help store energy that can be tapped for cellular work. One important use of proton gradients in the cell is for ATP synthesis during cellular respiration, as you will see in Chapter 9. Another is a type of membrane traffic called cotransport.

Cotransport: Coupled Transport by a Membrane Protein

A solute that exists in different concentrations across a membrane can do work as it moves across that membrane by diffusion down its concentration gradient. This is analogous to water that has been pumped uphill and performs work as it flows back down. In a mechanism called **cotransport**, a transport protein (a cotransporter) can couple the "downhill" diffusion of the solute to the "uphill" transport of a second substance against its own concentration gradient. For instance, a plant cell uses the gradient of H$^+$ generated by its ATP-powered proton pumps to drive the active transport of amino acids, sugars, and several other nutrients into the cell. In the example shown in **Figure 7.18,** a cotransporter couples the return of H$^+$ to the transport of sucrose into the cell. This protein can translocate sucrose into the cell against its concentration gradient, but only if the sucrose molecule travels in the company of an H$^+$. The H$^+$ uses the transport protein as an avenue to diffuse down its own electrochemical gradient, which is maintained by the proton pump. Plants use sucrose-H$^+$ cotransport to load sucrose produced by photosynthesis into cells in the veins of leaves. The vascular tissue of the plant can then distribute the sugar to nonphotosynthetic organs, such as roots.

What we know about cotransport proteins in animal cells has helped us find more effective treatments for diarrhea, a serious problem in developing countries. Normally, sodium in waste is reabsorbed in the colon, maintaining constant levels in the body, but diarrhea expels waste so rapidly that

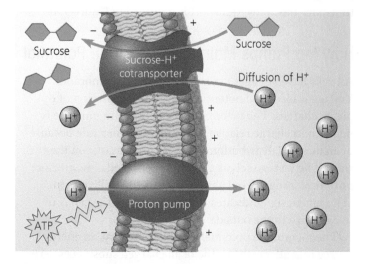

▲ Figure 7.18 **Cotransport: active transport driven by a concentration gradient.** A carrier protein, such as this sucrose-H$^+$ cotransporter in a plant cell (top), is able to use the diffusion of H$^+$ down its electrochemical gradient into the cell to drive the uptake of sucrose. (The cell wall is not shown.) Although not technically part of the cotransport process, an ATP-driven proton pump is shown here (bottom), which concentrates H$^+$ outside the cell. The resulting H$^+$ gradient represents potential energy that can be used for active transport—of sucrose, in this case. Thus, ATP indirectly provides the energy necessary for cotransport.

▲ Figure 7.17 **A proton pump.** Proton pumps are electrogenic pumps that store energy by generating voltage (charge separation) across membranes. A proton pump translocates positive charge in the form of hydrogen ions. The voltage and H$^+$ concentration gradient represent a dual energy source that can drive other processes, such as the uptake of nutrients. Most proton pumps are powered by ATP.

reabsorption is not possible, and sodium levels fall precipitously. To treat this life-threatening condition, patients are given a solution to drink containing high concentrations of salt (NaCl) and glucose. The solutes are taken up by sodium-glucose cotransporters on the surface of intestinal cells and passed through the cells into the blood. This simple treatment has lowered infant mortality worldwide.

CONCEPT CHECK 7.4

1. Sodium-potassium pumps help nerve cells establish a voltage across their plasma membranes. Do these pumps use ATP or produce ATP? Explain.
2. Explain why the sodium-potassium pump in Figure 7.15 would not be considered a cotransporter.
3. MAKE CONNECTIONS Review the characteristics of the lysosome in Concept 6.4. Given the internal environment of a lysosome, what transport protein might you expect to see in its membrane?

For suggested answers, see Appendix A.

CONCEPT 7.5

Bulk transport across the plasma membrane occurs by exocytosis and endocytosis

Water and small solutes enter and leave the cell by diffusing through the lipid bilayer of the plasma membrane or by being pumped or moved across the membrane by transport proteins. However, large molecules—such as proteins and polysaccharides, as well as larger particles—generally cross the membrane in bulk, packaged in vesicles. Like active transport, these processes require energy.

Exocytosis

As seen in Chapter 6, the cell secretes certain molecules by the fusion of vesicles with the plasma membrane; this process is called **exocytosis**. A transport vesicle that has budded from the Golgi apparatus moves along microtubules of the cytoskeleton to the plasma membrane. When the vesicle membrane and plasma membrane come into contact, specific proteins rearrange the lipid molecules of the two bilayers so that the two membranes fuse. The contents of the vesicle spill out of the cell, and the vesicle membrane becomes part of the plasma membrane (see Figure 7.9, step 4).

Many secretory cells use exocytosis to export products. For example, cells in the pancreas that make insulin secrete it into the extracellular fluid by exocytosis. In another example, nerve cells use exocytosis to release neurotransmitters that signal other neurons or muscle cells. When plant cells are making cell walls, exocytosis delivers proteins and carbohydrates from Golgi vesicles to the outside of the cell.

Endocytosis

In **endocytosis**, the cell takes in molecules and particulate matter by forming new vesicles from the plasma membrane. Although the proteins involved in the processes are different, the events of endocytosis look like the reverse of exocytosis. First, a small area of the plasma membrane sinks inward to form a pocket. Then, as the pocket deepens, it pinches in, forming a vesicle containing material that had been outside the cell. Study **Figure 7.19** carefully to understand the three types of endocytosis: phagocytosis ("cellular eating"), pinocytosis ("cellular drinking"), and receptor-mediated endocytosis (which is considered a form of pinocytosis).

Human cells use receptor-mediated endocytosis to take in cholesterol for membrane synthesis and the synthesis of other steroids. Cholesterol travels in the blood in particles called low-density lipoproteins (LDLs), each a complex of lipids and a protein. LDLs bind to LDL receptors on plasma membranes and then enter the cells by endocytosis. (LDLs thus act as **ligands**, a term for any molecule that binds specifically to a receptor site on another molecule.) In the inherited disease familial hypercholesterolemia, characterized by a very high level of cholesterol in the blood, LDLs cannot enter cells because the LDL receptor proteins are defective or missing. Consequently, cholesterol accumulates in the blood, where it contributes to early atherosclerosis, the buildup of lipid deposits within the walls of blood vessels. This buildup narrows the space in the vessels and impedes blood flow, and can result in heart damage and stroke.

Vesicles not only transport substances to be released from the cell but also provide a mechanism for rejuvenating or remodeling the plasma membrane. Endocytosis and exocytosis occur continually in most eukaryotic cells, yet the amount of plasma membrane in a nongrowing cell remains fairly constant. The addition of membrane by one process appears to offset the loss of membrane by the other.

Energy and cellular work have figured prominently in our study of membranes. We have seen, for example, that active transport is powered by ATP. In the next three chapters, you will learn more about how cells acquire chemical energy to do the work of life.

CONCEPT CHECK 7.5

1. As a cell grows, its plasma membrane expands. Does this involve endocytosis or exocytosis? Explain.
2. DRAW IT Return to Figure 7.9, and circle a patch of plasma membrane that is coming from a vesicle involved in exocytosis.
3. MAKE CONNECTIONS In Concept 6.7, you learned that animal cells make an extracellular matrix (ECM). Describe the cellular pathway of synthesis and deposition of an ECM glycoprotein.

For suggested answers, see Appendix A.

Exploring Endocytosis in Animal Cells

Phagocytosis

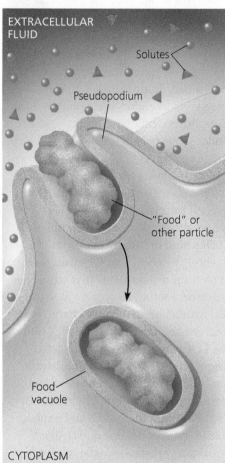

EXTRACELLULAR FLUID

Solutes

Pseudopodium

"Food" or other particle

Food vacuole

CYTOPLASM

In **phagocytosis**, a cell engulfs a particle by extending pseudopodia (singular, *pseudopodium*) around it and packaging it within a membranous sac called a food vacuole. The particle will be digested after the food vacuole fuses with a lysosome (see Figure 6.13a).

Pseudopodium of amoeba

Bacterium

Food vacuole

1 μm

An amoeba engulfing a bacterium via phago-cytosis (TEM).

ANIMATION **BioFlix** Visit the Study Area in **MasteringBiology** for the BioFlix® 3-D Animation on Membrane Transport. BioFlix Tutorials can also be assigned in MasteringBiology.

Pinocytosis

Plasma membrane

Coat protein

Coated pit

Coated vesicle

In **pinocytosis**, a cell continually "gulps" droplets of extracellular fluid into tiny vesicles, formed by infoldings of the plasma membrane. In this way, the cell obtains molecules dissolved in the droplets. Because any and all solutes are taken into the cell, pinocytosis as shown here is nonspecific for the substances it transports. In many cases, as above, the parts of the plasma membrane that form vesicles are lined on their cytoplasmic side by a fuzzy layer of coat protein; the "pits" and resulting vesicles are said to be "coated."

0.25 μm

Pinocytotic vesicles forming (TEMs).

Receptor-Mediated Endocytosis

Receptor

Receptor-mediated endocytosis is a specialized type of pinocytosis that enables the cell to acquire bulk quantities of specific substances, even though those substances may not be very concentrated in the extracellular fluid. Embedded in the plasma membrane are proteins with receptor sites exposed to the extracellular fluid. Specific solutes bind to the sites. The receptor proteins then cluster in coated pits, and each coated pit forms a vesicle containing the bound molecules. Notice that there are relatively more bound molecules (purple triangles) inside the vesicle, but other molecules (green balls) are also present. After the ingested material is liberated from the vesicle, the emptied receptors are recycled to the plasma membrane by the same vesicle (not shown).

Plasma membrane

Coat protein

0.25 μm

Top: A coated pit. *Bottom*: A coated vesicle forming during receptor-mediated endocytosis (TEMs).

SUMMARY OF KEY CONCEPTS

CONCEPT 7.1

Cellular membranes are fluid mosaics of lipids and proteins (pp. 125–129)

- In the **fluid mosaic model**, **amphipathic** proteins are embedded in the phospholipid bilayer. Proteins with related functions often cluster in patches.
- Phospholipids and some proteins move laterally within the membrane. The unsaturated hydrocarbon tails of some phospholipids keep membranes fluid at lower temperatures, while cholesterol helps membranes resist changes in fluidity caused by temperature changes. Differences in membrane lipid composition, as well as the ability to change lipid composition, are evolutionary adaptations that ensure membrane fluidity.
- **Integral proteins** are embedded in the lipid bilayer; **peripheral proteins** are attached to the membrane surface. The functions of membrane proteins include transport, enzymatic activity, signal transduction, cell-cell recognition, intercellular joining, and attachment to the cytoskeleton and extracellular matrix. Short chains of sugars linked to proteins (in **glycoproteins**) and lipids (in **glycolipids**) on the exterior side of the plasma membrane interact with surface molecules of other cells.
- Membrane proteins and lipids are synthesized in the ER and modified in the ER and Golgi apparatus. The inside and outside faces of membranes differ in molecular composition.

> **?** *In what ways are membranes crucial to life?*

CONCEPT 7.2

Membrane structure results in selective permeability (pp. 129–130)

- A cell must exchange molecules and ions with its surroundings, a process controlled by the **selective permeability** of the plasma membrane. Hydrophobic substances are soluble in lipids and pass through membranes rapidly, whereas polar molecules and ions generally require specific **transport proteins** to cross the membrane.

> **?** *How do **aquaporins** affect the permeability of a membrane?*

CONCEPT 7.3

Passive transport is diffusion of a substance across a membrane with no energy investment (pp. 130–134)

- **Diffusion** is the spontaneous movement of a substance down its **concentration gradient**. Water diffuses out through the permeable membrane of a cell (**osmosis**) if the solution outside has a higher solute concentration (**hypertonic**) than the cytosol; water enters the cell if the solution has a lower solute concentration (**hypotonic**). If the concentrations are equal (**isotonic**), no net osmosis occurs. Cell survival depends on balancing water uptake and loss. Cells lacking cell walls (as in animals and some protists) are isotonic with their environments or have adaptations for **osmoregulation**. Plants, prokaryotes, fungi, and some protists have relatively inelastic cell walls, so the cells don't burst in a hypotonic environment.

- In a type of **passive transport** called **facilitated diffusion**, a transport protein speeds the movement of water or a solute across a membrane down its concentration gradient. **Ion channels**, some of which are **gated channels**, facilitate the diffusion of ions across a membrane. Carrier proteins can undergo changes in shape that translocate bound solutes across the membrane.

Passive transport: Facilitated diffusion

Channel protein

Carrier protein

> **?** *What happens to a cell placed in a hypertonic solution? Describe the free water concentration inside and out.*

CONCEPT 7.4

Active transport uses energy to move solutes against their gradients (pp. 134–137)

- Specific membrane proteins use energy, usually in the form of ATP, to do the work of **active transport**. One example of such a protein is the **sodium-potassium pump**.
- Ions can have both a concentration (chemical) gradient and an electrical gradient (voltage). These gradients combine in the **electrochemical gradient**, which determines the net direction of ionic diffusion. **Electrogenic pumps**, such as the sodium-potassium pump and **proton pumps**, are transport proteins that contribute to electrochemical gradients.
- **Cotransport** of two solutes occurs when a membrane protein enables the "downhill" diffusion of one solute to drive the "uphill" transport of the other.

Active transport

> **?** *ATP is not directly involved in the functioning of a cotransporter. Why, then, is cotransport considered active transport?*

CONCEPT 7.5

Bulk transport across the plasma membrane occurs by exocytosis and endocytosis (pp. 137–138)

- In **exocytosis**, transport vesicles migrate to the plasma membrane, fuse with it, and release their contents. In **endocytosis**, molecules enter cells within vesicles that pinch inward from the plasma membrane. The three types of endocytosis are **phagocytosis**, **pinocytosis**, and **receptor-mediated endocytosis**.

> **?** *Which type of endocytosis involves ligands? What does this type of transport enable a cell to do?*

LEVEL 1: KNOWLEDGE/COMPREHENSION

1. In what way do the membranes of a eukaryotic cell vary?
   a. Phospholipids are found only in certain membranes.
   b. Certain proteins are unique to each membrane.
   c. Only certain membranes of the cell are selectively permeable.
   d. Only certain membranes are constructed from amphipathic molecules.

2. According to the fluid mosaic model of membrane structure, proteins of the membrane are mostly
   a. spread in a continuous layer over the inner and outer surfaces of the membrane.
   b. confined to the hydrophobic interior of the membrane.
   c. embedded in a lipid bilayer.
   d. randomly oriented in the membrane, with no fixed inside-outside polarity.

3. Which of the following factors would tend to increase membrane fluidity?
   a. a greater proportion of unsaturated phospholipids
   b. a greater proportion of saturated phospholipids
   c. a lower temperature
   d. a relatively high protein content in the membrane

LEVEL 2: APPLICATION/ANALYSIS

4. Which of the following processes includes all the others?
   a. osmosis
   b. diffusion of a solute across a membrane
   c. passive transport
   d. transport of an ion down its electrochemical gradient

5. Based on Figure 7.18, which of these experimental treatments would increase the rate of sucrose transport into a plant cell?
   a. decreasing extracellular sucrose concentration
   b. decreasing extracellular pH
   c. decreasing cytoplasmic pH
   d. adding a substance that makes the membrane more permeable to hydrogen ions

6. **DRAW IT** An artificial "cell" consisting of an aqueous solution enclosed in a selectively permeable membrane is immersed in a beaker containing a different solution, the "environment," as shown below. The membrane is permeable to water and to the simple sugars glucose and fructose but impermeable to the disaccharide sucrose.
   a. Draw solid arrows to indicate the net movement of solutes into and/or out of the cell.
   b. Is the solution outside the cell isotonic, hypotonic, or hypertonic?
   c. Draw a dashed arrow to show the net osmosis, if any.
   d. Will the artificial cell become more flaccid, more turgid, or stay the same?
   e. Eventually, will the two solutions have the same or different solute concentrations?

"Cell"
0.03 *M* sucrose
0.02 *M* glucose

"Environment"
0.01 *M* sucrose
0.01 *M* glucose
0.01 *M* fructose

LEVEL 3: SYNTHESIS/EVALUATION

7. **EVOLUTION CONNECTION**
   Paramecium and other protists that live in hypotonic environments have cell membranes that limit water uptake, while those living in isotonic environments have membranes that are more permeable to water. What adaptations might have evolved in protists in hypertonic habitats such as the Great Salt Lake? In habitats with changing salt concentration?

8. **SCIENTIFIC INQUIRY**
   An experiment is designed to study the mechanism of sucrose uptake by plant cells. Cells are immersed in a sucrose solution, and the pH of the solution is monitored. Samples of the cells are taken at intervals, and their sucrose concentration is measured. After a decrease in the pH of the solution to a steady, slightly acidic level, sucrose uptake begins. Propose a hypothesis for these results. What do you think would happen if an inhibitor of ATP regeneration by the cell were added to the beaker once the pH was at a steady level? Explain.

9. **SCIENCE, TECHNOLOGY, AND SOCIETY**
   Extensive irrigation in arid regions causes salts to accumulate in the soil. (When water evaporates, salts that were dissolved in the water are left behind in the soil.) Based on what you learned about water balance in plant cells, explain why increased soil salinity (saltiness) might be harmful to crops.

10. **WRITE ABOUT A THEME: INTERACTIONS**
    A human pancreatic cell obtains O_2, and necessary molecules such as glucose, amino acids, and cholesterol, from its environment, and it releases CO_2 as a waste product. In response to hormonal signals, the cell secretes digestive enzymes. It also regulates its ion concentrations by exchange with its environment. Based on what you have just learned about the structure and function of cellular membranes, write a short essay (100–150 words) that describes how such a cell accomplishes these interactions with its environment.

11. **SYNTHESIZE YOUR KNOWLEDGE**

In the supermarket, lettuce and other produce is often sprayed with water. Explain why this makes vegetables crisp.

For selected answers, see Appendix A.

MasteringBiology®

Students Go to **MasteringBiology** for assignments, the eText, and the Study Area with practice tests, animations, and activities.

Instructors Go to **MasteringBiology** for automatically graded tutorials and questions that you can assign to your students, plus Instructor Resources.

8

An Introduction to Metabolism

▲ Figure 8.1 **What causes these breaking waves to glow?**

The Energy of Life

The living cell is a chemical factory in miniature, where thousands of reactions occur within a microscopic space. Sugars can be converted to amino acids that are linked together into proteins when needed. Conversely, when food is digested, proteins are dismantled into amino acids that can be converted to sugars. In multicellular organisms, many cells export chemical products that are used in other parts of the organism. The process called cellular respiration drives this cellular economy by extracting the energy stored in sugars and other fuels. Cells apply this energy to perform various types of work, such as the transport of solutes across the plasma membrane, which we discussed in Chapter 7.

In a more exotic example, the ocean waves shown in **Figure 8.1** are brightly illuminated from within by free-floating, single-celled marine organisms called dinoflagellates. These dinoflagellates convert the energy stored in certain organic molecules to light, a process called bioluminescence. Most bioluminescent organisms are found in the oceans, but some exist on land, such as the bioluminescent fungus seen at the lower left. Bioluminescence and other metabolic activities carried out by a cell are precisely coordinated and controlled. In its complexity, its efficiency, and its responsiveness to subtle changes, the cell is peerless as a chemical factory. The concepts of metabolism that you learn in this chapter will help you understand how matter and energy flow during life's processes and how that flow is regulated.

141

An organism's metabolism transforms matter and energy, subject to the laws of thermodynamics

The totality of an organism's chemical reactions is called **metabolism** (from the Greek *metabole*, change). Metabolism is an emergent property of life that arises from orderly interactions between molecules.

Organization of the Chemistry of Life into Metabolic Pathways

We can picture a cell's metabolism as an elaborate road map of the thousands of chemical reactions that occur in a cell, arranged as intersecting metabolic pathways. A **metabolic pathway** begins with a specific molecule, which is then altered in a series of defined steps, resulting in a certain product. Each step of the pathway is catalyzed by a specific enzyme:

Analogous to the red, yellow, and green stoplights that control the flow of automobile traffic, mechanisms that regulate enzymes balance metabolic supply and demand.

Metabolism as a whole manages the material and energy resources of the cell. Some metabolic pathways release energy by breaking down complex molecules to simpler compounds. These degradative processes are called **catabolic pathways**, or breakdown pathways. A major pathway of catabolism is cellular respiration, in which the sugar glucose and other organic fuels are broken down in the presence of oxygen to carbon dioxide and water. (Pathways can have more than one starting molecule and/or product.) Energy that was stored in the organic molecules becomes available to do the work of the cell, such as ciliary beating or membrane transport. **Anabolic pathways**, in contrast, consume energy to build complicated molecules from simpler ones; they are sometimes called biosynthetic pathways. Examples of anabolism are the synthesis of an amino acid from simpler molecules and the synthesis of a protein from amino acids. Catabolic and anabolic pathways are the "downhill" and "uphill" avenues of the metabolic landscape. Energy released from the downhill reactions of catabolic pathways can be stored and then used to drive the uphill reactions of anabolic pathways.

In this chapter, we will focus on mechanisms common to metabolic pathways. Because energy is fundamental to all metabolic processes, a basic knowledge of energy is necessary to understand how the living cell works. Although we will use some nonliving examples to study energy, the concepts demonstrated by these examples also apply to **bioenergetics**, the study of how energy flows through living organisms.

Forms of Energy

Energy is the capacity to cause change. In everyday life, energy is important because some forms of energy can be used to do work—that is, to move matter against opposing forces, such as gravity and friction. Put another way, energy is the ability to rearrange a collection of matter. For example, you expend energy to turn the pages of this book, and your cells expend energy in transporting certain substances across membranes. Energy exists in various forms, and the work of life depends on the ability of cells to transform energy from one form to another.

Energy can be associated with the relative motion of objects; this energy is called **kinetic energy**. Moving objects can perform work by imparting motion to other matter: A pool player uses the motion of the cue stick to push the cue ball, which in turn moves the other balls; water gushing through a dam turns turbines; and the contraction of leg muscles pushes bicycle pedals. **Thermal energy** is kinetic energy associated with the random movement of atoms or molecules; thermal energy in transfer from one object to another is called **heat**. Light is also a type of energy that can be harnessed to perform work, such as powering photosynthesis in green plants.

An object not presently moving may still possess energy. Energy that is not kinetic is called **potential energy**; it is energy that matter possesses because of its location or structure. Water behind a dam, for instance, possesses energy because of its altitude above sea level. Molecules possess energy because of the arrangement of electrons in the bonds between their atoms. **Chemical energy** is a term used by biologists to refer to the potential energy available for release in a chemical reaction. Recall that catabolic pathways release energy by breaking down complex molecules. Biologists say that these complex molecules, such as glucose, are high in chemical energy. During a catabolic reaction, some bonds are broken and others formed, releasing energy and resulting in lower-energy breakdown products. This transformation also occurs in the engine of a car when the hydrocarbons of gasoline react explosively with oxygen, releasing the energy that pushes the pistons and producing exhaust. Although less explosive, a similar reaction of food molecules with oxygen provides chemical energy in biological systems, producing carbon dioxide and water as waste products. Biochemical pathways, carried out in the context of cellular structures, enable cells to release chemical energy from food molecules and use the energy to power life processes.

A diver has more potential energy on the platform than in the water.

Diving converts potential energy to kinetic energy.

Climbing up converts the kinetic energy of muscle movement to potential energy.

A diver has less potential energy in the water than on the platform.

▲ **Figure 8.2 Transformations between potential and kinetic energy.**

How is energy converted from one form to another? Consider **Figure 8.2**. The young woman climbing the ladder to the diving platform is releasing chemical energy from the food she ate for lunch and using some of that energy to perform the work of climbing. The kinetic energy of muscle movement is thus being transformed into potential energy due to her increasing height above the water. The young man diving is converting his potential energy to kinetic energy, which is then transferred to the water as he enters it. A small amount of energy is lost as heat due to friction.

Now let's consider the original source of the organic food molecules that provided the necessary chemical energy for the diver to climb the steps. This chemical energy was itself derived from light energy by plants during photosynthesis. Organisms are energy transformers.

The Laws of Energy Transformation

The study of the energy transformations that occur in a collection of matter is called **thermodynamics**. Scientists use the word *system* to denote the matter under study; they refer to the rest of the universe—everything outside the system—as the *surroundings*. An *isolated system*, such as that approximated by liquid in a thermos bottle, is unable to exchange either energy or matter with its surroundings outside the thermos. In an *open system*, energy and matter can be transferred between the system and its surroundings. Organisms are open systems. They absorb energy—for instance, light energy or chemical energy in the form of organic molecules—and release heat and metabolic waste products, such as carbon dioxide, to the surroundings. Two laws of thermodynamics govern energy transformations in organisms and all other collections of matter.

The First Law of Thermodynamics

According to the **first law of thermodynamics**, the energy of the universe is constant: *Energy can be transferred and transformed, but it cannot be created or destroyed.* The first law is also known as the *principle of conservation of energy*. The electric company does not make energy, but merely converts it to a form that is convenient for us to use. By converting sunlight to chemical energy, a plant acts as an energy transformer, not an energy producer.

The brown bear in **Figure 8.3a** will convert the chemical energy of the organic molecules in its food to kinetic and other forms of energy as it carries out biological processes.

Chemical energy

Heat

CO_2
+
H_2O

(a) First law of thermodynamics: Energy can be transferred or transformed but neither created nor destroyed. For example, chemical reactions in this brown bear will convert the chemical (potential) energy in the fish into the kinetic energy of running.

(b) Second law of thermodynamics: Every energy transfer or transformation increases the disorder (entropy) of the universe. For example, as it runs, disorder is increased around the bear by the release of heat and small molecules that are the by-products of metabolism. A brown bear can run at speeds up to 35 miles per hour (56 km/hr)—as fast as a racehorse.

▲ **Figure 8.3 The two laws of thermodynamics.**

What happens to this energy after it has performed work? The second law of thermodynamics helps to answer this question.

The Second Law of Thermodynamics

If energy cannot be destroyed, why can't organisms simply recycle their energy over and over again? It turns out that during every energy transfer or transformation, some energy becomes unavailable to do work. In most energy transformations, more usable forms of energy are at least partly converted to thermal energy and released as heat. Only a small fraction of the chemical energy from the food in Figure 8.3a is transformed into the motion of the brown bear shown in **Figure 8.3b**; most is lost as heat, which dissipates rapidly through the surroundings.

In the process of carrying out chemical reactions that perform various kinds of work, living cells unavoidably convert other forms of energy to heat. A system can put this energy to work only when there is a temperature difference that results in thermal energy flowing as heat from a warmer location to a cooler one. If temperature is uniform, as it is in a living cell, then the heat generated during a chemical reaction will simply warm a body of matter, such as the organism. (This can make a room crowded with people uncomfortably warm, as each person is carrying out a multitude of chemical reactions!)

A logical consequence of the loss of usable energy as heat to the surroundings is that each energy transfer or transformation makes the universe more disordered. Scientists use a quantity called **entropy** as a measure of disorder, or randomness. The more randomly arranged a collection of matter is, the greater its entropy. We can now state the **second law of thermodynamics**: *Every energy transfer or transformation increases the entropy of the universe.* Although order can increase locally, there is an unstoppable trend toward randomization of the universe as a whole.

In many cases, increased entropy is evident in the physical disintegration of a system's organized structure. For example, you can observe increasing entropy in the gradual decay of an unmaintained building. Much of the increasing entropy of the universe is less obvious, however, because it takes the form of increasing amounts of heat and less ordered forms of matter. As the bear in Figure 8.3b converts chemical energy to kinetic energy, it is also increasing the disorder of its surroundings by producing heat and small molecules, such as the CO_2 it exhales, that are the breakdown products of food.

The concept of entropy helps us understand why certain processes are energetically favorable and occur on their own. It turns out that if a given process, by itself, leads to an increase in entropy, that process can proceed without requiring an input of energy. Such a process is called a **spontaneous process**. Note that as we're using it here, the word *spontaneous* does not imply that the process would occur quickly; rather, the word signifies that it is energetically favorable. (In fact, it may be helpful for you to think of the phrase "energetically favorable" when you read the formal term "spontaneous.") Some spontaneous processes, such as an explosion, may be virtually instantaneous, while others, such as the rusting of an old car over time, are much slower.

A process that, considered on its own, leads to a decrease in entropy is said to be nonspontaneous: It will happen only if energy is supplied. We know from experience that certain events occur spontaneously and others do not. For instance, we know that water flows downhill spontaneously but moves uphill only with an input of energy, such as when a machine pumps the water against gravity. Some energy is inevitably lost as heat, increasing entropy in the surroundings, so usage of energy ensures that a nonspontaneous process also leads to an increase in the entropy of the universe as a whole.

Biological Order and Disorder

Living systems increase the entropy of their surroundings, as predicted by thermodynamic law. It is true that cells create ordered structures from less organized starting materials. For example, simpler molecules are ordered into the more complex structure of an amino acid, and amino acids are ordered into polypeptide chains. At the organismal level as well, complex and beautifully ordered structures result from biological processes that use simpler starting materials **(Figure 8.4)**. However, an organism also takes in organized forms of matter and energy from the surroundings and replaces them with less ordered forms. For example, an animal obtains starch, proteins, and other complex molecules from the food it eats. As catabolic pathways break these molecules down, the animal releases carbon

▲ **Figure 8.4 Order as a characteristic of life.** Order is evident in the detailed structures of the sea urchin skeleton and the succulent plant shown here. As open systems, organisms can increase their order as long as the order of their surroundings decreases.

dioxide and water—small molecules that possess less chemical energy than the food did (see Figure 8.3b). The depletion of chemical energy is accounted for by heat generated during metabolism. On a larger scale, energy flows into most ecosystems in the form of light and exits in the form of heat (see Figure 1.10).

During the early history of life, complex organisms evolved from simpler ancestors. For instance, we can trace the ancestry of the plant kingdom from much simpler organisms called green algae to more complex flowering plants. However, this increase in organization over time in no way violates the second law. The entropy of a particular system, such as an organism, may actually decrease as long as the total entropy of the *universe*—the system plus its surroundings—increases. Thus, organisms are islands of low entropy in an increasingly random universe. The evolution of biological order is perfectly consistent with the laws of thermodynamics.

CONCEPT 8.2

The free-energy change of a reaction tells us whether or not the reaction occurs spontaneously

The laws of thermodynamics that we've just discussed apply to the universe as a whole. As biologists, we want to understand the chemical reactions of life—for example, which reactions occur spontaneously and which ones require some input of energy from outside. But how can we know this without assessing the energy and entropy changes in the entire universe for each separate reaction?

Free-Energy Change, ΔG

Recall that the universe is really equivalent to "the system" plus "the surroundings." In 1878, J. Willard Gibbs, a professor at Yale, defined a very useful function called the Gibbs free energy of a system (without considering its surroundings), symbolized by the letter *G*. We'll refer to the Gibbs free energy simply as free energy. **Free energy** is the portion of a system's energy that can perform work when temperature and pressure are uniform throughout the system, as in a living cell. Let's consider how we determine the free-energy change that occurs when a system changes—for example, during a chemical reaction.

The change in free energy, ΔG, can be calculated for a chemical reaction by applying the following equation:

$$\Delta G = \Delta H - T\Delta S$$

This equation uses only properties of the system (the reaction) itself: ΔH symbolizes the change in the system's *enthalpy* (in biological systems, equivalent to total energy); ΔS is the change in the system's entropy; and T is the absolute temperature in Kelvin (K) units (K = °C + 273; see Appendix C).

Once we know the value of ΔG for a process, we can use it to predict whether the process will be spontaneous (that is, whether it is energetically favorable and will occur without an input of energy). More than a century of experiments has shown that only processes with a negative ΔG are spontaneous. For ΔG to be negative, ΔH must be negative (the system gives up enthalpy and H decreases) or $T\Delta S$ must be positive (the system gives up order and S increases), or both: When ΔH and $T\Delta S$ are tallied, ΔG has a negative value ($\Delta G < 0$) for all spontaneous processes. In other words, every spontaneous process decreases the system's free energy, and processes that have a positive or zero ΔG are never spontaneous.

This information is immensely interesting to biologists, for it gives us the power to predict which kinds of change can happen without an input of energy. Such spontaneous changes can be harnessed to perform work. This principle is very important in the study of metabolism, where a major goal is to determine which reactions can supply energy for cellular work.

Free Energy, Stability, and Equilibrium

As we saw in the previous section, when a process occurs spontaneously in a system, we can be sure that ΔG is negative. Another way to think of ΔG is to realize that it represents the difference between the free energy of the final state and the free energy of the initial state:

$$\Delta G = G_{\text{final state}} - G_{\text{initial state}}$$

Thus, ΔG can be negative only when the process involves a loss of free energy during the change from initial state to final state. Because it has less free energy, the system in its final state is less likely to change and is therefore more stable than it was previously.

We can think of free energy as a measure of a system's instability—its tendency to change to a more stable state. Unstable systems (higher G) tend to change in such a way that they become more stable (lower G). For example, a diver on top of a platform is less stable (more likely to fall) than when floating in the water; a drop of concentrated dye is less stable (more likely to disperse) than when the dye is spread randomly through the liquid; and a glucose molecule is less stable (more likely to break down) than the simpler molecules into which it can be split **(Figure 8.5)**. Unless something prevents it, each of these systems will move toward greater stability: The diver falls, the solution becomes uniformly colored, and the glucose molecule is broken down into smaller molecules.

Another term that describes a state of maximum stability is *equilibrium*, which you learned about in Chapter 2 in connection with chemical reactions. There is an important relationship between free energy and equilibrium, including chemical equilibrium. Recall that most chemical reactions are reversible and proceed to a point at which the forward and backward reactions occur at the same rate. The reaction is then said to be at chemical equilibrium, and there is no further net change in the relative concentration of products and reactants.

As a reaction proceeds toward equilibrium, the free energy of the mixture of reactants and products decreases. Free energy increases when a reaction is somehow pushed away from equilibrium, perhaps by removing some of the products (and thus changing their concentration relative to that of the reactants). For a system at equilibrium, G is at its lowest possible value in that system. We can think of the equilibrium state as a free-energy valley. Any change from the equilibrium position will have a positive ΔG and will not be spontaneous. For this reason, systems never spontaneously move away from equilibrium. Because a system at equilibrium cannot spontaneously change, it can do no work. *A process is spontaneous and can perform work only when it is moving toward equilibrium.*

Free Energy and Metabolism

We can now apply the free-energy concept more specifically to the chemistry of life's processes.

Exergonic and Endergonic Reactions in Metabolism

Based on their free-energy changes, chemical reactions can be classified as either exergonic ("energy outward") or endergonic ("energy inward"). An **exergonic reaction** proceeds

• More free energy (higher G)
• Less stable
• Greater work capacity

In a **spontaneous change**
• The free energy of the system decreases ($\Delta G < 0$)
• The system becomes more stable
• The released free energy can be harnessed to do work

• Less free energy (lower G)
• More stable
• Less work capacity

(a) Gravitational motion. Objects move spontaneously from a higher altitude to a lower one.

(b) Diffusion. Molecules in a drop of dye diffuse until they are randomly dispersed.

(c) Chemical reaction. In a cell, a glucose molecule is broken down into simpler molecules.

▲ **Figure 8.5 The relationship of free energy to stability, work capacity, and spontaneous change.** Unstable systems (top) are rich in free energy, G. They have a tendency to change spontaneously to a more stable state (bottom), and it is possible to harness this "downhill" change to perform work.

MAKE CONNECTIONS *Compare the redistribution of molecules shown in (b) to the transport of hydrogen ions (H^+) across a membrane by a proton pump, creating a concentration gradient, as shown in Figure 7.17. Which process(es) result(s) in higher free energy? Which system(s) can do work?*

▼ Figure 8.6 Free energy changes (ΔG) in exergonic and endergonic reactions.

(a) Exergonic reaction: energy released, spontaneous

(b) Endergonic reaction: energy required, nonspontaneous

reactant and product, 25°C, pH 7), 686 kcal (2,870 kJ) of energy are made available for work. Because energy must be conserved, the chemical products of respiration store 686 kcal less free energy per mole than the reactants. The products are, in a sense, the spent exhaust of a process that tapped the free energy stored in the bonds of the sugar molecules.

It is important to realize that the breaking of bonds does not release energy; on the contrary, as you will soon see, it requires energy. The phrase "energy stored in bonds" is shorthand for the potential energy that can be released when new bonds are formed after the original bonds break, as long as the products are of lower free energy than the reactants.

An **endergonic reaction** is one that absorbs free energy from its surroundings (**Figure 8.6b**). Because this kind of reaction essentially *stores* free energy in molecules (G increases), ΔG is positive. Such reactions are nonspontaneous, and the magnitude of ΔG is the quantity of energy required to drive the reaction. If a chemical process is exergonic (downhill), releasing energy in one direction, then the reverse process must be endergonic (uphill), using energy. A reversible process cannot be downhill in both directions. If $\Delta G = -686$ kcal/mol for respiration, which converts glucose and oxygen to carbon dioxide and water, then the reverse process—the conversion of carbon dioxide and water to glucose and oxygen—must be strongly endergonic, with $\Delta G = +686$ kcal/mol. Such a reaction would never happen by itself.

How, then, do plants make the sugar that organisms use for energy? Plants get the required energy—686 kcal to make a mole of glucose—from the environment by capturing light and converting its energy to chemical energy. Next, in a long series of exergonic steps, they gradually spend that chemical energy to assemble glucose molecules.

Equilibrium and Metabolism

Reactions in an isolated system eventually reach equilibrium and can then do no work, as illustrated by the isolated hydroelectric system in **Figure 8.7**. The chemical reactions of metabolism are reversible, and they, too, would reach

▲ **Figure 8.7 Equilibrium and work in an isolated hydroelectric system.** Water flowing downhill turns a turbine that drives a generator providing electricity to a lightbulb, but only until the system reaches equilibrium.

with a net release of free energy (**Figure 8.6a**). Because the chemical mixture loses free energy (G decreases), ΔG is negative for an exergonic reaction. Using ΔG as a standard for spontaneity, exergonic reactions are those that occur spontaneously. (Remember, the word *spontaneous* implies that it is energetically favorable, not that it will occur rapidly.) The magnitude of ΔG for an exergonic reaction represents the maximum amount of work the reaction can perform.* The greater the decrease in free energy, the greater the amount of work that can be done.

We can use the overall reaction for cellular respiration as an example:

$$C_6H_{12}O_6 + 6\ O_2 \rightarrow 6\ CO_2 + 6\ H_2O$$
$$\Delta G = -686\ \text{kcal/mol}\ (-2{,}870\ \text{kJ/mol})$$

For each mole (180 g) of glucose broken down by respiration under what are called "standard conditions" (1 *M* of each

---

*The word *maximum* qualifies this statement, because some of the free energy is released as heat and cannot do work. Therefore, ΔG represents a theoretical upper limit of available energy.

equilibrium if they occurred in the isolation of a test tube. Because systems at equilibrium are at a minimum of *G* and can do no work, a cell that has reached metabolic equilibrium is dead! The fact that metabolism as a whole is never at equilibrium is one of the defining features of life.

Like most systems, a living cell is not in equilibrium. The constant flow of materials in and out of the cell keeps the metabolic pathways from ever reaching equilibrium, and the cell continues to do work throughout its life. This principle is illustrated by the open (and more realistic) hydroelectric system in **Figure 8.8a**. However, unlike this simple system in which water flowing downhill turns a single turbine, a catabolic pathway in a cell releases free energy in a series of reactions. An example is cellular respiration, illustrated by analogy in **Figure 8.8b**. Some of the reversible reactions of respiration are constantly "pulled" in one direction—that is, they are kept out of equilibrium. The key to maintaining this lack of equilibrium is that the product of a reaction does not accumulate but instead becomes a reactant in the next step; finally, waste products are expelled from the cell. The overall sequence of reactions is kept going by the huge free-energy difference between glucose and oxygen at the top of the energy "hill" and carbon dioxide and water at the "downhill" end. As long as our cells have a steady supply of glucose or other fuels and oxygen and are able to expel waste products to the surroundings,

their metabolic pathways never reach equilibrium and can continue to do the work of life.

Stepping back to look at the big picture, we can see once again how important it is to think of organisms as open systems. Sunlight provides a daily source of free energy for an ecosystem's plants and other photosynthetic organisms. Animals and other nonphotosynthetic organisms in an ecosystem must have a source of free energy in the form of the organic products of photosynthesis. Now that we have applied the free-energy concept to metabolism, we are ready to see how a cell actually performs the work of life.

CONCEPT 8.3

ATP powers cellular work by coupling exergonic reactions to endergonic reactions

A cell does three main kinds of work:

- *Chemical work*, the pushing of endergonic reactions that would not occur spontaneously, such as the synthesis of polymers from monomers (chemical work will be discussed further here and in Chapters 9 and 10)
- *Transport work*, the pumping of substances across membranes against the direction of spontaneous movement (see Chapter 7)
- *Mechanical work*, such as the beating of cilia (see Chapter 6), the contraction of muscle cells, and the movement of chromosomes during cellular reproduction

A key feature in the way cells manage their energy resources to do this work is **energy coupling**, the use of an exergonic process to drive an endergonic one. ATP is responsible for mediating most energy coupling in cells, and in most cases it acts as the immediate source of energy that powers cellular work.

(a) An open hydroelectric system. Water flowing through a turbine keeps driving the generator because intake and outflow of water keep the system from reaching equilibrium.

$\Delta G < 0$

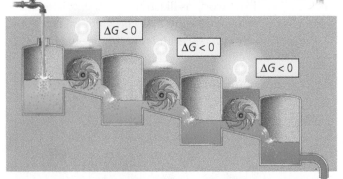

$\Delta G < 0$ $\Delta G < 0$ $\Delta G < 0$

(b) A multistep open hydroelectric system. Cellular respiration is analogous to this system: Glucose is broken down in a series of exergonic reactions that power the work of the cell. The product of each reaction is used as the reactant for the next, so no reaction reaches equilibrium.

▲ **Figure 8.8 Equilibrium and work in open systems.**

The Structure and Hydrolysis of ATP

ATP (adenosine triphosphate) was introduced when we discussed the phosphate group as a functional group (see Concept 4.3). ATP contains the sugar ribose, with the nitrogenous base adenine and a chain of three phosphate groups (the triphosphate group) bonded to it **(Figure 8.9a)**. In addition to its role in energy coupling, ATP is also one of the nucleoside triphosphates used to make RNA (see Figure 5.24).

The bonds between the phosphate groups of ATP can be broken by hydrolysis. When the terminal phosphate bond is broken by addition of a water molecule, a molecule of inorganic phosphate ($HOPO_3^{2-}$, abbreviated Ⓟ$_i$ throughout this book) leaves the ATP, which becomes adenosine diphosphate, or ADP **(Figure 8.9b)**. The reaction is exergonic and releases 7.3 kcal of energy per mole of ATP hydrolyzed:

$$ATP + H_2O \rightarrow ADP + Ⓟ_i$$
$$\Delta G = -7.3 \text{ kcal/mol } (-30.5 \text{ kJ/mol})$$

This is the free-energy change measured under standard conditions. In the cell, conditions do not conform to standard conditions, primarily because reactant and product concentrations differ from 1 *M*. For example, when ATP hydrolysis occurs under cellular conditions, the actual ΔG is about -13 kcal/mol, 78% greater than the energy released by ATP hydrolysis under standard conditions.

Because their hydrolysis releases energy, the phosphate bonds of ATP are sometimes referred to as high-energy phosphate bonds, but the term is misleading. The phosphate bonds of ATP are not unusually strong bonds, as "high-energy" may imply; rather, the reactants (ATP and water) themselves have high energy relative to the energy of the products (ADP and Ⓟ$_i$). The release of energy during the hydrolysis of ATP comes from the chemical change of the system to a state of lower free energy, not from the phosphate bonds themselves.

ATP is useful to the cell because the energy it releases on losing a phosphate group is somewhat greater than the energy most other molecules could deliver. But why does this hydrolysis release so much energy? If we reexamine the ATP molecule in Figure 8.9a, we can see that all three phosphate groups are negatively charged. These like charges are crowded together, and their mutual repulsion contributes to the instability of this region of the ATP molecule. The triphosphate tail of ATP is the chemical equivalent of a compressed spring.

How the Hydrolysis of ATP Performs Work

When ATP is hydrolyzed in a test tube, the release of free energy merely heats the surrounding water. In an organism, this same generation of heat can sometimes be beneficial. For instance, the process of shivering uses ATP hydrolysis during muscle contraction to warm the body. In most cases

(a) The structure of ATP. In the cell, most hydroxyl groups of phosphates are ionized (—O⁻).

(b) The hydrolysis of ATP. The reaction of ATP and water yields inorganic phosphate ((Ⓟ)$_i$) and ADP and releases energy.

▲ **Figure 8.9 The structure and hydrolysis of adenosine triphosphate (ATP).** Throughout this book, the chemical structure of the triphosphate group seen in (a) will be represented by the three joined yellow circles shown in (b).

in the cell, however, the generation of heat alone would be an inefficient (and potentially dangerous) use of a valuable energy resource. Instead, the cell's proteins harness the energy released during ATP hydrolysis in several ways to perform the three types of cellular work—chemical, transport, and mechanical.

For example, with the help of specific enzymes, the cell is able to use the energy released by ATP hydrolysis directly to drive chemical reactions that, by themselves, are endergonic. If the ΔG of an endergonic reaction is less than the amount of energy released by ATP hydrolysis, then the two reactions can be coupled so that, overall, the coupled reactions are exergonic. This usually involves phosphorylation, the transfer of a phosphate group from ATP to some other molecule, such as the reactant. The recipient molecule with the phosphate group covalently bonded to it is then called a **phosphorylated intermediate**. The key to coupling exergonic and endergonic reactions is the formation of this phosphorylated intermediate, which is more reactive

(a) Glutamic acid conversion to glutamine.
Glutamine synthesis from glutamic acid
(Glu) by itself is endergonic (ΔG is positive),
so it is not spontaneous.

$\Delta G_{Glu} = +3.4$ kcal/mol

Glutamic acid   Ammonia   Glutamine

(b) Conversion reaction coupled with ATP hydrolysis. In the cell, glutamine synthesis occurs in two steps, coupled by a phosphorylated intermediate. **1** ATP phosphorylates glutamic acid, making it less stable. **2** Ammonia displaces the phosphate group, forming glutamine.

Glutamic acid   Phosphorylated intermediate   Glutamine

(c) Free-energy change for coupled reaction. ΔG for the glutamic acid conversion to glutamine (+3.4 kcal/mol) plus ΔG for ATP hydrolysis (–7.3 kcal/mol) gives the free-energy change for the overall reaction (–3.9 kcal/mol). Because the overall process is exergonic (net ΔG is negative), it occurs spontaneously.

$\Delta G_{Glu} = +3.4$ kcal/mol

$\Delta G_{ATP} = -7.3$ kcal/mol

$\Delta G_{Glu} = +3.4$ kcal/mol
$+ \Delta G_{ATP} = -7.3$ kcal/mol
_____
Net $\Delta G = -3.9$ kcal/mol

▲ **Figure 8.10 How ATP drives chemical work: Energy coupling using ATP hydrolysis.**
In this example, the exergonic process of ATP hydrolysis is used to drive an endergonic process—
the cellular synthesis of the amino acid glutamine from glutamic acid and ammonia.

MAKE CONNECTIONS *Referring to Figure 5.14, explain why glutamine (Gln) is diagrammed as a glutamic acid (Glu) with an amino group attached.*

(less stable) than the original unphosphorylated molecule (**Figure 8.10**).

Transport and mechanical work in the cell are also nearly always powered by the hydrolysis of ATP. In these cases, ATP hydrolysis leads to a change in a protein's shape and often its ability to bind another molecule. Sometimes this occurs via a phosphorylated intermediate, as seen for the transport protein in **Figure 8.11a**. In most instances of mechanical work involving motor proteins "walking" along cytoskeletal elements (**Figure 8.11b**), a cycle occurs in which ATP is first bound noncovalently to the motor protein. Next, ATP is hydrolyzed, releasing ADP and P_i. Another ATP molecule can then bind. At each stage, the motor protein changes its shape and ability to bind the cytoskeleton, resulting in movement of the protein along the cytoskeletal track. Phosphorylation and dephosphorylation promote crucial protein shape changes during many other important cellular processes as well.

(a) Transport work: ATP phosphorylates transport proteins.

(b) Mechanical work: ATP binds noncovalently to motor proteins and then is hydrolyzed.

▲ **Figure 8.11 How ATP drives transport and mechanical work.** ATP hydrolysis causes changes in the shapes and binding affinities of proteins. This can occur either **(a)** directly, by phosphorylation, as shown for a membrane protein carrying out active transport of a solute (see also Figure 7.15), or **(b)** indirectly, via noncovalent binding of ATP and its hydrolytic products, as is the case for motor proteins that move vesicles (and other organelles) along cytoskeletal "tracks" in the cell (see also Figure 6.21).

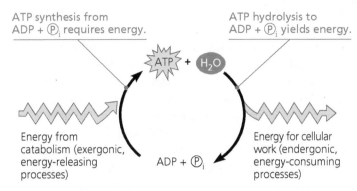

ATP synthesis from ADP + P_i requires energy.

ATP hydrolysis to ADP + P_i yields energy.

Energy from catabolism (exergonic, energy-releasing processes)

Energy for cellular work (endergonic, energy-consuming processes)

ADP + P_i

▲ **Figure 8.12 The ATP cycle.** Energy released by breakdown reactions (catabolism) in the cell is used to phosphorylate ADP, regenerating ATP. Chemical potential energy stored in ATP drives most cellular work.

The Regeneration of ATP

An organism at work uses ATP continuously, but ATP is a renewable resource that can be regenerated by the addition of phosphate to ADP **(Figure 8.12)**. The free energy required to phosphorylate ADP comes from exergonic breakdown reactions (catabolism) in the cell. This shuttling of inorganic phosphate and energy is called the ATP cycle, and it couples the cell's energy-yielding (exergonic) processes to the energy-consuming (endergonic) ones. The ATP cycle proceeds at an astonishing pace. For example, a working muscle cell recycles its entire pool of ATP in less than a minute. That turnover represents 10 million molecules of ATP consumed and regenerated per second per cell. If ATP could not be regenerated by the phosphorylation of ADP, humans would use up nearly their body weight in ATP each day.

Because both directions of a reversible process cannot be downhill, the regeneration of ATP is necessarily endergonic:

$$\text{ADP} + \text{P}_i \rightarrow \text{ATP} + \text{H}_2\text{O}$$
$$\Delta G = +7.3 \text{ kcal/mol } (+30.5 \text{ kJ/mol}) \text{ (standard conditions)}$$

Since ATP formation from ADP and P_i is not spontaneous, free energy must be spent to make it occur. Catabolic (exergonic) pathways, especially cellular respiration, provide the energy for the endergonic process of making ATP. Plants also use light energy to produce ATP. Thus, the ATP cycle is a revolving door through which energy passes during its transfer from catabolic to anabolic pathways.

CONCEPT CHECK 8.3

1. How does ATP typically transfer energy from exergonic to endergonic reactions in the cell?

2. Which of the following has more free energy: glutamic acid + ammonia + ATP OR glutamine + ADP + P_i? Explain your answer.

3. **MAKE CONNECTIONS** Does Figure 8.11a show passive or active transport? Explain. (See Concepts 7.3 and 7.4.)

For suggested answers, see Appendix A.

Enzymes speed up metabolic reactions by lowering energy barriers

The laws of thermodynamics tell us what will and will not happen under given conditions but say nothing about the rate of these processes. A spontaneous chemical reaction occurs without any requirement for outside energy, but it may occur so slowly that it is imperceptible. For example, even though the hydrolysis of sucrose (table sugar) to glucose and fructose is exergonic, occurring spontaneously with a release of free energy ($\Delta G = -7$ kcal/mol), a solution of sucrose dissolved in sterile water will sit for years at room temperature with no appreciable hydrolysis. However, if we add a small amount of the enzyme sucrase to the solution, then all the sucrose may be hydrolyzed within seconds, as shown below:

Sucrase

H_2O

Sucrose ($\text{C}_{12}\text{H}_{22}\text{O}_{11}$)

Glucose ($\text{C}_6\text{H}_{12}\text{O}_6$)

Fructose ($\text{C}_6\text{H}_{12}\text{O}_6$)

How does the enzyme do this?

An **enzyme** is a macromolecule that acts as a **catalyst**, a chemical agent that speeds up a reaction without being consumed by the reaction. In this chapter, we are focusing on enzymes that are proteins. (Some RNA molecules, called ribozymes, can function as enzymes; these will be discussed in Chapters 17 and 25.) Without regulation by enzymes, chemical traffic through the pathways of metabolism would become terribly congested because many chemical reactions would take such a long time. In the next two sections, we will see why spontaneous reactions can be slow and how an enzyme changes the situation.

The Activation Energy Barrier

Every chemical reaction between molecules involves both bond breaking and bond forming. For example, the hydrolysis of sucrose involves breaking the bond between glucose and fructose and one of the bonds of a water molecule and then forming two new bonds, as shown above. Changing one molecule into another generally involves contorting the starting molecule into a highly unstable state before the reaction can proceed. This contortion can be compared to the bending of a metal key ring when you pry it open to add a new key. The key ring is highly unstable in its opened form but returns to a stable state once the key is threaded all the way onto the ring. To reach the contorted state where bonds can change, reactant molecules must absorb energy from their surroundings. When the new bonds of the product molecules form, energy is released as heat, and the molecules return to stable shapes with lower energy than the contorted state.

The initial investment of energy for starting a reaction—the energy required to contort the reactant molecules so the bonds can break—is known as the *free energy of activation*, or **activation energy**, abbreviated E_A in this book. We can think of activation energy as the amount of energy needed to push the reactants to the top of an energy barrier, or uphill, so that the "downhill" part of the reaction can begin. Activation energy is often supplied by heat in the form of thermal energy that the reactant molecules absorb from the surroundings. The absorption of thermal energy accelerates the reactant molecules, so they collide more often and more forcefully. It also agitates the atoms within the molecules, making the breakage of bonds more likely. When the molecules have absorbed enough energy for the bonds to break, the reactants are in an unstable condition known as the *transition state*.

Figure 8.13 graphs the energy changes for a hypothetical exergonic reaction that swaps portions of two reactant molecules:

$$AB + CD \rightarrow AC + BD$$
Reactants   Products

The reactants AB and CD must absorb enough energy from the surroundings to reach the unstable transition state, where bonds can break.

After bonds have broken, new bonds form, releasing energy to the surroundings.

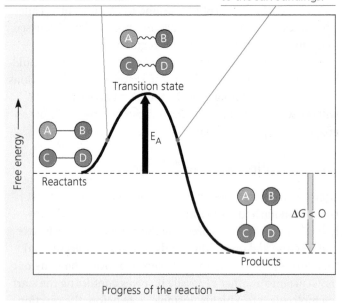

▲ **Figure 8.13 Energy profile of an exergonic reaction.** The "molecules" are hypothetical, with A, B, C, and D representing portions of the molecules. Thermodynamically, this is an exergonic reaction, with a negative ΔG, and the reaction occurs spontaneously. However, the activation energy (E_A) provides a barrier that determines the rate of the reaction.

DRAW IT *Graph the progress of an endergonic reaction in which EF and GH form products EG and FH, assuming that the reactants must pass through a transition state.*

The activation of the reactants is represented by the uphill portion of the graph, in which the free-energy content of the reactant molecules is increasing. At the summit, when energy equivalent to E_A has been absorbed, the reactants are in the transition state: They are activated, and their bonds can be broken. As the atoms then settle into their new, more stable bonding arrangements, energy is released to the surroundings. This corresponds to the downhill part of the curve, which shows the loss of free energy by the molecules. The overall decrease in free energy means that E_A is repaid with dividends, as the formation of new bonds releases more energy than was invested in the breaking of old bonds.

The reaction shown in Figure 8.13 is exergonic and occurs spontaneously ($\Delta G < 0$). However, the activation energy provides a barrier that determines the rate of the reaction. The reactants must absorb enough energy to reach the top of the activation energy barrier before the reaction can occur. For some reactions, E_A is modest enough that even at room temperature there is sufficient thermal energy for many of the reactant molecules to reach the transition state in a short time. In most cases, however, E_A is so high and the transition state is reached so rarely that the reaction will hardly proceed at all. In these cases, the reaction will occur at a noticeable rate only if energy is provided, usually by heat. For example, the reaction of gasoline and oxygen is exergonic and will occur spontaneously, but energy is required for the molecules to reach the transition state and react. Only when the spark plugs fire in an automobile engine can there be the explosive release of energy that pushes the pistons. Without a spark, a mixture of gasoline hydrocarbons and oxygen will not react because the E_A barrier is too high.

How Enzymes Speed Up Reactions

Proteins, DNA, and other complex cellular molecules are rich in free energy and have the potential to decompose spontaneously; that is, the laws of thermodynamics favor their breakdown. These molecules persist only because at temperatures typical for cells, few molecules can make it over the hump of activation energy. The barriers for selected reactions must occasionally be surmounted, however, for cells to carry out the processes needed for life. Heat can increase the rate of a reaction by allowing reactants to attain the transition state more often, but this would not work well in biological systems. First, high temperature denatures proteins and kills cells. Second, heat would speed up *all* reactions, not just those that are needed. Instead of heat, organisms use catalysis to speed up reactions.

An enzyme catalyzes a reaction by lowering the E_A barrier **(Figure 8.14)**, enabling the reactant molecules to absorb enough energy to reach the transition state even at moderate temperatures, as we'll discuss shortly. An enzyme cannot change the ΔG for a reaction; it cannot make an endergonic

▲ Figure 8.14 The effect of an enzyme on activation energy. Without affecting the free-energy change (ΔG) for a reaction, an enzyme speeds the reaction by reducing its activation energy (E_A).

reaction exergonic. Enzymes can only hasten reactions that would eventually occur anyway, but this enables the cell to have a dynamic metabolism, routing chemicals smoothly through metabolic pathways. Also, enzymes are very specific for the reactions they catalyze, so they determine which chemical processes will be going on in the cell at any given time.

Substrate Specificity of Enzymes

The reactant an enzyme acts on is referred to as the enzyme's **substrate**. The enzyme binds to its substrate (or substrates, when there are two or more reactants), forming an **enzyme-substrate complex**. While enzyme and substrate are joined, the catalytic action of the enzyme converts the

substrate to the product (or products) of the reaction. The overall process can be summarized as follows:

$$\text{Enzyme} + \text{Substrate(s)} \rightleftharpoons \begin{array}{c}\text{Enzyme-}\\\text{substrate}\\\text{complex}\end{array} \rightleftharpoons \begin{array}{c}\text{Enzyme} +\\\text{Product(s)}\end{array}$$

For example, the enzyme sucrase (most enzyme names end in *-ase*) catalyzes the hydrolysis of the disaccharide sucrose into its two monosaccharides, glucose and fructose (see p. 151):

$$\begin{array}{c}\text{Sucrase} +\\\text{Sucrose} +\\\text{H}_2\text{O}\end{array} \rightleftharpoons \begin{array}{c}\text{Sucrase-}\\\text{sucrose-H}_2\text{O}\\\text{complex}\end{array} \rightleftharpoons \begin{array}{c}\text{Sucrase} +\\\text{Glucose} +\\\text{Fructose}\end{array}$$

The reaction catalyzed by each enzyme is very specific; an enzyme can recognize its specific substrate even among closely related compounds. For instance, sucrase will act only on sucrose and will not bind to other disaccharides, such as maltose. What accounts for this molecular recognition? Recall that most enzymes are proteins, and proteins are macromolecules with unique three-dimensional configurations. The specificity of an enzyme results from its shape, which is a consequence of its amino acid sequence.

Only a restricted region of the enzyme molecule actually binds to the substrate. This region, called the **active site**, is typically a pocket or groove on the surface of the enzyme where catalysis occurs (**Figure 8.15a**). Usually, the active site is formed by only a few of the enzyme's amino acids, with the rest of the protein molecule providing a framework that determines the shape of the active site. The specificity of an enzyme is attributed to a complementary fit between the shape of its active site and the shape of the substrate.

An enzyme is not a stiff structure locked into a given shape. In fact, recent work by biochemists has shown clearly that enzymes (and other proteins as well) seem to "dance" between subtly different shapes in a dynamic equilibrium, with slight differences in free energy for each "pose." The shape that best fits the substrate isn't necessarily the one with the lowest energy, but during the very short time the enzyme takes on this shape, its active site can bind to the substrate. It has been known for more than 50 years that the active site itself is also not a rigid receptacle for the substrate. As the substrate enters the active site, the enzyme changes shape slightly due to interactions between the substrate's chemical groups and chemical groups on the side chains of the amino acids that form the active site. This shape change makes the active site fit even more snugly around the substrate (**Figure 8.15b**). The process is like

Substrate

Active site

Enzyme

Enzyme-substrate complex

(a) In this space-filling model of the enzyme hexokinase (blue), the active site forms a groove on the surface. The enzyme's substrate is glucose (red).

(b) When the substrate enters the active site, it forms weak bonds with the enzyme, inducing a change in the shape of the protein. This change allows additional weak bonds to form, causing the active site to enfold the substrate and hold it in place.

▲ Figure 8.15 Induced fit between an enzyme and its substrate.

a clasping handshake, with binding between enzyme and substrate becoming tighter after the initial contact. This so-called **induced fit** brings chemical groups of the active site into positions that enhance their ability to catalyze the chemical reaction.

Catalysis in the Enzyme's Active Site

In most enzymatic reactions, the substrate is held in the active site by so-called weak interactions, such as hydrogen bonds and ionic bonds. R groups of a few of the amino acids that make up the active site catalyze the conversion of substrate to product, and the product departs from the active site. The enzyme is then free to take another substrate molecule into its active site. The entire cycle happens so fast that a single enzyme molecule typically acts on about a thousand substrate molecules per second, and some enzymes are even faster. Enzymes, like other catalysts, emerge from the reaction in their original form. Therefore, very small amounts of enzyme can have a huge metabolic impact by functioning over and over again in catalytic cycles. **Figure 8.16** shows a catalytic cycle involving two substrates and two products.

Most metabolic reactions are reversible, and an enzyme can catalyze either the forward or the reverse reaction, depending on which direction has a negative ΔG. This in turn depends mainly on the relative concentrations of reactants and products. The net effect is always in the direction of equilibrium.

Enzymes use a variety of mechanisms that lower activation energy and speed up a reaction (see Figure 8.16, step ❸):

- When there are two or more reactants, the active site provides a template on which the substrates can come together in the proper orientation for a reaction to occur between them.

- As the active site of an enzyme clutches the bound substrates, the enzyme may stretch the substrate molecules toward their transition-state form, stressing and bending critical chemical bonds that must be broken during the reaction. Because E_A is proportional to the difficulty of breaking the bonds, distorting the substrate helps it approach the transition state and thus reduces the amount of free energy that must be absorbed to achieve that state.

- The active site may also provide a microenvironment that is more conducive to a particular type of reaction than the solution itself would be without the enzyme. For example, if the active site has amino acids with acidic R groups, the active site may be a pocket of low pH in an otherwise neutral cell. In such cases, an acidic amino acid may facilitate H^+ transfer to the substrate as a key step in catalyzing the reaction.

- Amino acids in the active site directly participate in the chemical reaction. Sometimes this process even involves

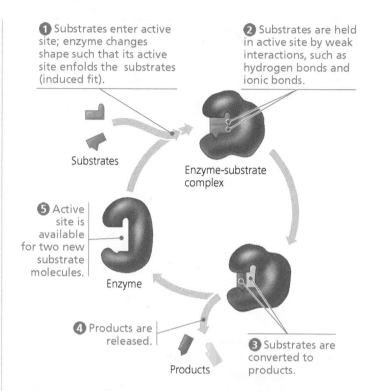

❶ Substrates enter active site; enzyme changes shape such that its active site enfolds the substrates (induced fit).

❷ Substrates are held in active site by weak interactions, such as hydrogen bonds and ionic bonds.

Substrates

Enzyme-substrate complex

❺ Active site is available for two new substrate molecules.

Enzyme

❹ Products are released.

Products

❸ Substrates are converted to products.

▲ **Figure 8.16 The active site and catalytic cycle of an enzyme.** An enzyme can convert one or more reactant molecules to one or more product molecules. The enzyme shown here converts two substrate molecules to two product molecules.

DRAW IT *The enzyme-substrate complex passes through a transition state (see Figure 8.13). Label the part of the cycle where the transition state occurs.*

brief covalent bonding between the substrate and the side chain of an amino acid of the enzyme. Subsequent steps of the reaction restore the side chains to their original states, so that the active site is the same after the reaction as it was before.

The rate at which a particular amount of enzyme converts substrate to product is partly a function of the initial concentration of the substrate: The more substrate molecules that are available, the more frequently they access the active sites of the enzyme molecules. However, there is a limit to how fast the reaction can be pushed by adding more substrate to a fixed concentration of enzyme. At some point, the concentration of substrate will be high enough that all enzyme molecules have their active sites engaged. As soon as the product exits an active site, another substrate molecule enters. At this substrate concentration, the enzyme is said to be *saturated*, and the rate of the reaction is determined by the speed at which the active site converts substrate to product. When an enzyme population is saturated, the only way to increase the rate of product formation is to add more enzyme. Cells often increase the rate of a reaction by producing more enzyme molecules. You can graph the overall progress of an enzymatic reaction in the Scientific Skills Exercise.

Making a Line Graph and Calculating a Slope

Does the Rate of Glucose 6-Phosphatase Activity Change over Time in Isolated Liver Cells? Glucose 6-phosphatase, which is found in mammalian liver cells, is a key enzyme in control of blood glucose levels. The enzyme catalyzes the breakdown of glucose 6-phosphate into glucose and inorganic phosphate (Ⓟ$_i$). These products are transported out of liver cells into the blood, increasing blood glucose levels. In this exercise, you will graph data from a time-course experiment that measured Ⓟ$_i$ concentration in the buffer outside isolated liver cells, thus indirectly measuring glucose 6-phosphatase activity inside the cells.

How the Experiment Was Done Isolated rat liver cells were placed in a dish with buffer at physiological conditions (pH 7.4, 37°C). Glucose 6-phosphate (the substrate) was added to the dish, where it was taken up by the cells. Then a sample of buffer was removed every 5 minutes and the concentration of Ⓟ$_i$ determined.

Data from the Experiment

Time (min)	Concentration of Ⓟ$_i$ (μmol/mL)
0	0
5	10
10	90
15	180
20	270
25	330
30	355
35	355
40	355

Interpret the Data

1. To see patterns in the data from a time-course experiment like this, it is helpful to graph the data. First, determine which set of data goes on each axis. (a) What did the researchers intentionally vary in the experiment? This is the independent variable, which goes on the *x*-axis. (b) What are the units (abbreviated) for the independent variable? Explain in words what the abbreviation stands for. (c) What was measured by the researchers? This is the dependent variable, which goes on the *y*-axis. (d) What does the units abbreviation stand for? Label each axis, including the units.

2. Next, you'll want to mark off the axes with just enough evenly spaced tick marks to accommodate the full set of data. Determine the range of data values for each axis. (a) What is the largest value to go on the *x*-axis? What is a reasonable spacing for the tick marks, and what should be the highest one? (b) What is the largest value to go on the *y*-axis? What is a reasonable spacing for the tick marks, and what should be the highest one?

3. Plot the data points on your graph. Match each *x*-value with its partner *y*-value and place a point on the graph at that coordinate. Draw a line that connects the points. (For additional information about graphs, see the Scientific Skills Review in Appendix F and in the Study Area in MasteringBiology.)

4. Examine your graph and look for patterns in the data. (a) Does the concentration of Ⓟ$_i$ increase evenly through the course of the experiment? To answer this question, describe the pattern you see in the graph. (b) What part of the graph shows the highest rate of enzyme activity? Consider that the rate of enzyme activity is related to the slope of the line, $\Delta y/\Delta x$ (the "rise" over the "run"), in μmol/mL · min, with the steepest slope indicating the highest rate of enzyme activity. Calculate the rate of enzyme activity (slope) where the graph is steepest. (c) Can you think of a biological explanation for the pattern you see?

5. If your blood sugar level is low from skipping lunch, what reaction (discussed in this exercise) will occur in your liver cells? Write out the reaction and put the name of the enzyme over the reaction arrow. How will this reaction affect your blood sugar level?

ⓂⒷ A version of this Scientific Skills Exercise can be assigned in MasteringBiology.

Data from S. R. Commerford et al., Diets enriched in sucrose or fat increase gluconeogenesis and G-6-Pase but not basal glucose production in rats, *American Journal of Physiology—Endocrinology and Metabolism* 283:E545–E555 (2002).

Effects of Local Conditions on Enzyme Activity

The activity of an enzyme—how efficiently the enzyme functions—is affected by general environmental factors, such as temperature and pH. It can also be affected by chemicals that specifically influence that enzyme. In fact, researchers have learned much about enzyme function by employing such chemicals.

Effects of Temperature and pH

Recall from Chapter 5 that the three-dimensional structures of proteins are sensitive to their environment. As a consequence, each enzyme works better under some conditions than under other conditions, because these *optimal conditions* favor the most active shape for the enzyme.

Temperature and pH are environmental factors important in the activity of an enzyme. Up to a point, the rate of an enzymatic reaction increases with increasing temperature, partly because substrates collide with active sites more frequently when the molecules move rapidly. Above that temperature, however, the speed of the enzymatic reaction drops sharply. The thermal agitation of the enzyme molecule disrupts the hydrogen bonds, ionic bonds, and other weak interactions that stabilize the active shape of the enzyme, and the protein molecule eventually denatures. Each enzyme has an optimal temperature at which its reaction rate is greatest. Without denaturing the enzyme, this temperature allows the greatest number of molecular collisions and the fastest conversion of the reactants to product molecules. Most human enzymes have optimal temperatures of about 35–40°C (close to human body temperature). The thermophilic bacteria that live in hot springs contain enzymes with optimal temperatures of 70°C or higher **(Figure 8.17a)**.

(a) Optimal temperature for two enzymes

(b) Optimal pH for two enzymes

▲ **Figure 8.17 Environmental factors affecting enzyme activity.** Each enzyme has an optimal **(a)** temperature and **(b)** pH that favor the most active shape of the protein molecule.

DRAW IT *Given that a mature lysosome has an internal pH of around 4.5, draw a curve in (b) showing what you would predict for a lysosomal enzyme, labeling its optimal pH.*

Just as each enzyme has an optimal temperature, it also has a pH at which it is most active. The optimal pH values for most enzymes fall in the range of pH 6–8, but there are exceptions. For example, pepsin, a digestive enzyme in the human stomach, works best at pH 2. Such an acidic environment denatures most enzymes, but pepsin is adapted to maintain its functional three-dimensional structure in the acidic environment of the stomach. In contrast, trypsin, a digestive enzyme residing in the alkaline environment of the human intestine, has an optimal pH of 8 and would be denatured in the stomach **(Figure 8.17b)**.

Cofactors

Many enzymes require nonprotein helpers for catalytic activity. These adjuncts, called **cofactors**, may be bound tightly to the enzyme as permanent residents, or they may bind loosely and reversibly along with the substrate. The cofactors of some enzymes are inorganic, such as the metal atoms zinc, iron, and copper in ionic form. If the cofactor is an organic molecule, it is referred to, more specifically, as a **coenzyme**. Most vitamins are important in nutrition because they act as coenzymes or raw materials from which coenzymes are made.

Enzyme Inhibitors

Certain chemicals selectively inhibit the action of specific enzymes. Sometimes, the inhibitor attaches to the enzyme by covalent bonds, in which case the inhibition is usually irreversible. Many enzyme inhibitors, however, bind to the enzyme by weak interactions, and when this occurs the inhibition is reversible. Some reversible inhibitors resemble the normal substrate molecule and compete for admission into the active site **(Figure 8.18a** and **b)**. These mimics, called **competitive inhibitors**, reduce the productivity of enzymes by blocking substrates from entering active sites. This kind of inhibition can be overcome by increasing the concentration of substrate so that as active sites become available, more substrate molecules than inhibitor molecules are around to gain entry to the sites.

In contrast, **noncompetitive inhibitors** do not directly compete with the substrate to bind to the enzyme at the active site **(Figure 8.18c)**. Instead, they impede enzymatic reactions by binding to another part of the enzyme. This interaction causes the enzyme molecule to change its shape

▼ **Figure 8.18 Inhibition of enzyme activity.**

(a) Normal binding

A substrate can bind normally to the active site of an enzyme.

Substrate
Active site
Enzyme

(b) Competitive inhibition

A competitive inhibitor mimics the substrate, competing for the active site.

Competitive inhibitor

(c) Noncompetitive inhibition

A noncompetitive inhibitor binds to the enzyme away from the active site, altering the shape of the enzyme so that even if the substrate can bind, the active site functions less effectively, if it all.

Noncompetitive inhibitor

in such a way that the active site becomes less effective at catalyzing the conversion of substrate to product.

Toxins and poisons are often irreversible enzyme inhibitors. An example is sarin, a nerve gas. Sarin was released by terrorists in the Tokyo subway in 1995, causing the death of several people and injury to many others. This small molecule binds covalently to the R group on the amino acid serine, which is found in the active site of acetylcholinesterase, an enzyme important in the nervous system. Other examples include the pesticides DDT and parathion, inhibitors of key enzymes in the nervous system. Finally, many antibiotics are inhibitors of specific enzymes in bacteria. For instance, penicillin blocks the active site of an enzyme that many bacteria use to make their cell walls.

The Evolution of Enzymes

EVOLUTION Thus far, biochemists have discovered and named more than 4,000 different enzymes in various species, most likely a very small fraction of all enzymes. How did this grand profusion of enzymes arise? Recall that most enzymes are proteins, and proteins are encoded by genes. A permanent change in a gene, known as a *mutation*, can result in a protein with one or more changed amino acids. In the case of an enzyme, if the changed amino acids are in the active site or some other crucial region, the altered enzyme might have a novel activity or might bind to a different substrate. Under environmental conditions where the new function benefits the organism, natural selection would tend to favor the mutated form of the gene, causing it to persist in the population. This simplified model is generally accepted as the main way in which the multitude of different enzymes arose over the past few billion years of life's history.

Data supporting this model have been collected by researchers using a lab procedure that mimics evolution in natural populations. One group tested whether the function of an enzyme called β-galactosidase could change over time in populations of the bacterium *Escherichia coli* (*E. coli*). β-galactosidase breaks down the disaccharide lactose into the simple sugars glucose and galactose. Using molecular techniques, the researchers introduced random mutations into *E. coli* genes and then tested the bacteria for their ability to break down a slightly different disaccharide (one that has the sugar fucose in place of galactose). At the end of the experiment, the "evolved" enzyme bound the new substrate several hundred times more strongly, and broke it down 10 to 20 times more quickly, than did the original enzyme.

The researchers found that six amino acids had changed in the enzyme altered in this experiment. Two of these changed amino acids were in the active site, two were nearby, and two were on the surface of the protein (**Figure 8.19**). This experiment and others like it strengthen the notion that a few changes can indeed alter enzyme function.

Two changed amino acids were found near the active site.

Active site

Two changed amino acids were found in the active site.

Two changed amino acids were found on the surface.

▲ **Figure 8.19 Mimicking evolution of an enzyme with a new function.** After seven rounds of mutation and selection in a lab, the enzyme β-galactosidase evolved into an enzyme specialized for breaking down a sugar different from lactose. This ribbon model shows one subunit of the altered enzyme; six amino acids were different.

CONCEPT CHECK 8.4

1. Many spontaneous reactions occur very slowly. Why don't all spontaneous reactions occur instantly?

2. Why do enzymes act only on very specific substrates?

3. **WHAT IF?** Malonate is an inhibitor of the enzyme succinate dehydrogenase. How would you determine whether malonate is a competitive or noncompetitive inhibitor?

4. **MAKE CONNECTIONS** In nature, what conditions could lead to natural selection favoring bacteria with enzymes that could break down the fucose-containing disaccharide discussed above? See the discussion of natural selection in Concept 1.2.

For suggested answers, see Appendix A.

CONCEPT 8.5

Regulation of enzyme activity helps control metabolism

Chemical chaos would result if all of a cell's metabolic pathways were operating simultaneously. Intrinsic to life's processes is a cell's ability to tightly regulate its metabolic pathways by controlling when and where its various enzymes are active. It does this either by switching on and off the genes that encode specific enzymes (as we will discuss in Unit Three) or, as we discuss here, by regulating the activity of enzymes once they are made.

Allosteric Regulation of Enzymes

In many cases, the molecules that naturally regulate enzyme activity in a cell behave something like reversible noncompetitive inhibitors (see Figure 8.18c): These regulatory molecules change an enzyme's shape and the functioning of its active site by binding to a site elsewhere on the molecule, via noncovalent interactions. **Allosteric regulation** is the term used to describe any case in which a protein's function at one site is affected by the binding of a regulatory molecule to a separate site. It may result in either inhibition or stimulation of an enzyme's activity.

Allosteric Activation and Inhibition

Most enzymes known to be allosterically regulated are constructed from two or more subunits, each composed of a polypeptide chain with its own active site. The entire complex oscillates between two different shapes, one catalytically active and the other inactive **(Figure 8.20a)**. In the simplest kind of allosteric regulation, an activating or inhibiting regulatory molecule binds to a regulatory site (sometimes called an allosteric site), often located where subunits join. The binding of an *activator* to a regulatory site stabilizes the shape that has functional active sites, whereas the binding of an *inhibitor* stabilizes the inactive form of the enzyme. The subunits of an allosteric enzyme fit together in such a way that a shape change in one subunit is transmitted to all others. Through this interaction of subunits, a single activator or inhibitor molecule that binds to one regulatory site will affect the active sites of all subunits.

Fluctuating concentrations of regulators can cause a sophisticated pattern of response in the activity of cellular enzymes. The products of ATP hydrolysis (ADP and P_i), for example, play a complex role in balancing the flow of traffic between anabolic and catabolic pathways by their effects on key enzymes. ATP binds to several catabolic enzymes allosterically, lowering their affinity for substrate and thus inhibiting their activity. ADP, however, functions as an activator of the same enzymes. This is logical because catabolism functions in regenerating ATP. If ATP production lags behind its use, ADP accumulates and activates the enzymes that speed up catabolism, producing more ATP. If the supply of ATP exceeds demand, then catabolism slows down as ATP molecules accumulate and bind to the same enzymes, inhibiting them. (You'll see specific examples of this type of regulation when you learn about cellular respiration in the next chapter.) ATP, ADP, and other related molecules also affect key enzymes in anabolic pathways. In this way, allosteric enzymes control the rates of important reactions in both sorts of metabolic pathways.

In another kind of allosteric activation, a *substrate* molecule binding to one active site in a multisubunit enzyme triggers a shape change in all the subunits, thereby increasing catalytic activity at the other active sites **(Figure 8.20b)**. Called **cooperativity**, this mechanism amplifies the response of enzymes to substrates: One substrate molecule primes an enzyme to act on additional substrate molecules more readily. Cooperativity is considered "allosteric" regulation

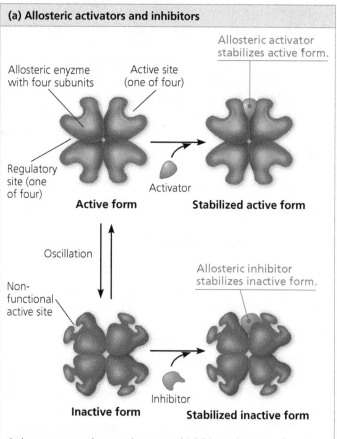

(a) Allosteric activators and inhibitors

Allosteric enzyme with four subunits

Active site (one of four)

Regulatory site (one of four)

Activator

Allosteric activator stabilizes active form.

Active form　　**Stabilized active form**

Oscillation

Non-functional active site

Allosteric inhibitor stabilizes inactive form.

Inhibitor

Inactive form　　**Stabilized inactive form**

At low concentrations, activators and inhibitors dissociate from the enzyme. The enzyme can then oscillate again.

(b) Cooperativity: another type of allosteric activation

Binding of one substrate molecule to active site of one subunit locks all subunits in active conformation.

Substrate

Inactive form　　**Stabilized active form**

The inactive form shown on the left oscillates with the active form when the active form is not stabilized by substrate.

because binding of the substrate to one active site affects catalysis in another active site.

Although hemoglobin is not an enzyme (it carries O_2), classic studies on hemoglobin have elucidated the principle of cooperativity. Hemoglobin is made up of four subunits, each with an oxygen-binding site (see Figure 5.18). The binding of an oxygen molecule to one binding site increases the affinity for oxygen of the remaining binding sites. Thus, where oxygen is at high levels, such as in the lungs or gills, hemoglobin's affinity for oxygen increases as more binding sites are filled. In oxygen-deprived tissues, however, the release of each oxygen molecule decreases the oxygen affinity of the other binding sites, resulting in the release of oxygen where it is most needed. Cooperativity works similarly in multisubunit enzymes that have been studied.

Feedback Inhibition

When ATP allosterically inhibits an enzyme in an ATP-generating pathway, the result is feedback inhibition, a common mode of metabolic control. In **feedback inhibition**, a metabolic pathway is halted by the inhibitory binding of its end product to an enzyme that acts early in the pathway. **Figure 8.21** shows an example of feedback inhibition operating on an anabolic pathway. Some cells use this five-step pathway to synthesize the amino acid isoleucine from threonine, another amino acid. As isoleucine accumulates, it slows down its own synthesis by allosterically inhibiting the enzyme for the first step of the pathway. Feedback inhibition thereby prevents the cell from making more isoleucine than is necessary and thus wasting chemical resources.

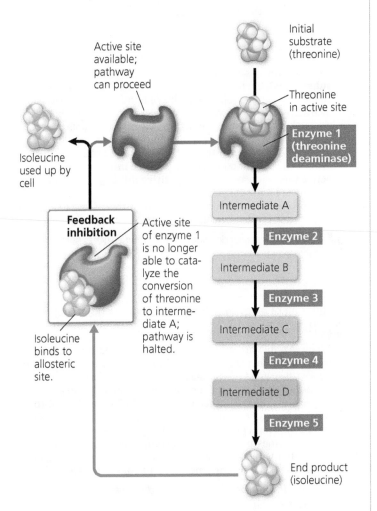

▲ **Figure 8.21 Feedback inhibition in isoleucine synthesis.**

▲ **Figure 8.22 Organelles and structural order in metabolism.** Organelles such as the mitochondrion (TEM) contain enzymes that carry out specific functions, in this case cellular respiration.

Localization of Enzymes Within the Cell

The cell is not just a bag of chemicals with thousands of different kinds of enzymes and substrates in a random mix. The cell is compartmentalized, and cellular structures help bring order to metabolic pathways. In some cases, a team of enzymes for several steps of a metabolic pathway are assembled into a multienzyme complex. The arrangement facilitates the sequence of reactions, with the product from the first enzyme becoming the substrate for an adjacent enzyme in the complex, and so on, until the end product is released. Some enzymes and enzyme complexes have fixed locations within the cell and act as structural components of particular membranes. Others are in solution within particular membrane-enclosed eukaryotic organelles, each with its own internal chemical environment. For example, in eukaryotic cells, the enzymes for cellular respiration reside in specific locations within mitochondria **(Figure 8.22)**.

In this chapter, you have learned that metabolism, the intersecting set of chemical pathways characteristic of life, is a choreographed interplay of thousands of different kinds of cellular molecules. In the next chapter, we will explore cellular respiration, the major catabolic pathway that breaks down organic molecules, releasing energy that can be used for the crucial processes of life.

CONCEPT CHECK 8.5

1. How do an activator and an inhibitor have different effects on an allosterically regulated enzyme?
2. Regulation of isoleucine synthesis is an example of feedback inhibition of an anabolic pathway. With that in mind, explain how ATP might be involved in feedback inhibition of a catabolic pathway.

For suggested answers, see Appendix A.

SUMMARY OF KEY CONCEPTS

CONCEPT 8.1

An organism's metabolism transforms matter and energy, subject to the laws of thermodynamics (pp. 142–145)

- **Metabolism** is the collection of chemical reactions that occur in an organism. Enzymes catalyze reactions in intersecting **metabolic pathways**, which may be **catabolic** (breaking down molecules, releasing energy) or **anabolic** (building molecules, consuming energy).
- **Energy** is the capacity to cause change; some forms of energy do work by moving matter. **Kinetic energy** is associated with motion and includes **thermal energy** associated with random motion of atoms or molecules. **Heat** is thermal energy in transfer from one object to another. **Potential energy** is related to the location or structure of matter and includes **chemical energy** possessed by a molecule due to its structure.
- **The first law of thermodynamics**, conservation of energy, states that energy cannot be created or destroyed, only transferred or transformed. The **second law of thermodynamics** states that **spontaneous processes**, those requiring no outside input of energy, increase the **entropy** (disorder) of the universe.

? *Explain how the highly ordered structure of a cell does not conflict with the second law of thermodynamics.*

CONCEPT 8.2

The free-energy change of a reaction tells us whether or not the reaction occurs spontaneously (pp. 145–148)

- A living system's **free energy** is energy that can do work under cellular conditions. The change in free energy (ΔG) during a biological process is related directly to enthalpy change (ΔH) and to the change in entropy (ΔS): $\Delta G = \Delta H - T\Delta S$. Organisms live at the expense of free energy. A spontaneous process occurs with no energy input; during such a process, free energy decreases and the stability of a system increases. At maximum stability, the system is at equilibrium and can do no work.
- In an **exergonic** (spontaneous) chemical reaction, the products have less free energy than the reactants ($-\Delta G$). **Endergonic** (nonspontaneous) reactions require an input of energy ($+\Delta G$). The addition of starting materials and the removal of end products prevent metabolism from reaching equilibrium.

? *Explain the meaning of each component in the equation for the change in free energy of a spontaneous chemical reaction. Why are spontaneous reactions important in the metabolism of a cell?*

CONCEPT 8.3

ATP powers cellular work by coupling exergonic reactions to endergonic reactions (pp. 148–151)

- **ATP** is the cell's energy shuttle. Hydrolysis of its terminal phosphate yields ADP and P_i and releases free energy.
- Through **energy coupling**, the exergonic process of ATP hydrolysis drives endergonic reactions by transfer of a phosphate group to specific reactants, forming a **phosphorylated intermediate** that is more reactive. ATP hydrolysis (sometimes with protein phosphorylation) also causes changes in the shape and binding affinities of transport and motor proteins.
- Catabolic pathways drive regeneration of ATP from ADP + P_i.

? *Describe the ATP cycle: How is ATP used and regenerated in a cell?*

CONCEPT 8.4

Enzymes speed up metabolic reactions by lowering energy barriers (pp. 151–157)

- In a chemical reaction, the energy necessary to break the bonds of the reactants is the **activation energy**, E_A.
- **Enzymes** lower the E_A barrier:

- Each enzyme has a unique **active site** that binds one or more **substrate(s)**, the reactants on which it acts. It then changes shape, binding the substrate(s) more tightly (**induced fit**).
- The active site can lower an E_A barrier by orienting substrates correctly, straining their bonds, providing a favorable microenvironment, or even covalently bonding with the substrate.
- Each enzyme has an optimal temperature and pH. Inhibitors reduce enzyme function. A **competitive inhibitor** binds to the active site, whereas a **noncompetitive inhibitor** binds to a different site on the enzyme.
- Natural selection, acting on organisms with variant enzymes, is responsible for the diversity of enzymes found in organisms.

? *How do both activation energy barriers and enzymes help maintain the structural and metabolic order of life?*

CONCEPT 8.5

Regulation of enzyme activity helps control metabolism (pp. 157–159)

- Many enzymes are subject to **allosteric regulation**: Regulatory molecules, either activators or inhibitors, bind to specific regulatory sites, affecting the shape and function of the enzyme. In **cooperativity**, binding of one substrate molecule can stimulate binding or activity at other active sites. In **feedback inhibition**, the end product of a metabolic pathway allosterically inhibits the enzyme for a previous step in the pathway.
- Some enzymes are grouped into complexes, some are incorporated into membranes, and some are contained inside organelles, increasing the efficiency of metabolic processes.

? *What roles do allosteric regulation and feedback inhibition play in the metabolism of a cell?*

TEST YOUR UNDERSTANDING

LEVEL 1: KNOWLEDGE/COMPREHENSION

1. Choose the pair of terms that correctly completes this sentence: Catabolism is to anabolism as _____ is to _____.
    a. exergonic; spontaneous
    b. exergonic; endergonic
    c. free energy; entropy
    d. work; energy

2. Most cells cannot harness heat to perform work because
    a. heat does not involve a transfer of energy.
    b. cells do not have much thermal energy; they are relatively cool.
    c. temperature is usually uniform throughout a cell.
    d. heat can never be used to do work.

3. Which of the following metabolic processes can occur without a net influx of energy from some other process?
    a. $ADP + ⓟ_i \rightarrow ATP + H_2O$
    b. $C_6H_{12}O_6 + 6\,O_2 \rightarrow 6\,CO_2 + 6\,H_2O$
    c. $6\,CO_2 + 6\,H_2O \rightarrow C_6H_{12}O_6 + 6\,O_2$
    d. Amino acids $\rightarrow$ Protein

4. If an enzyme in solution is saturated with substrate, the most effective way to obtain a faster yield of products is to
    a. add more of the enzyme.
    b. heat the solution to 90°C.
    c. add more substrate.
    d. add a noncompetitive inhibitor.

5. Some bacteria are metabolically active in hot springs because
    a. they are able to maintain a lower internal temperature.
    b. high temperatures make catalysis unnecessary.
    c. their enzymes have high optimal temperatures.
    d. their enzymes are completely insensitive to temperature.

LEVEL 2: APPLICATION/ANALYSIS

6. If an enzyme is added to a solution where its substrate and product are in equilibrium, what will occur?
    a. Additional substrate will be formed.
    b. The reaction will change from endergonic to exergonic.
    c. The free energy of the system will change.
    d. Nothing; the reaction will stay at equilibrium.

LEVEL 3: SYNTHESIS/EVALUATION

7. **DRAW IT** Using a series of arrows, draw the branched metabolic reaction pathway described by the following statements, and then answer the question at the end. Use red arrows and minus signs to indicate inhibition.

    L can form either M or N.

    M can form O.

    O can form either P or R.

    P can form Q.

    R can form S.

    O inhibits the reaction of L to form M.

    Q inhibits the reaction of O to form P.

    S inhibits the reaction of O to form R.

    Which reaction would prevail if both Q and S were present in the cell in high concentrations?
    a. L → M
    b. M → O
    c. L → N
    d. O → P

8. **EVOLUTION CONNECTION** A recent revival of the antievolutionary "intelligent design" argument holds that biochemical pathways are too complex to have evolved, because all intermediate steps in a given pathway must be present to produce the final product. Critique this argument. How could you use the diversity of metabolic pathways that produce the same or similar products to support your case?

9. **SCIENTIFIC INQUIRY**
     DRAW IT A researcher has developed an assay to measure the activity of an important enzyme present in liver cells growing in culture. She adds the enzyme's substrate to a dish of cells and then measures the appearance of reaction products. The results are graphed as the amount of product on the *y*-axis versus time on the *x*-axis. The researcher notes four sections of the graph. For a short period of time, no products appear (section A). Then (section B) the reaction rate is quite high (the slope of the line is steep). Next, the reaction gradually slows down (section C). Finally, the graph line becomes flat (section D). Draw and label the graph, and propose a model to explain the molecular events occurring at each stage of this reaction profile.

10. **WRITE ABOUT A THEME: ENERGY AND MATTER** Life requires energy. In a short essay (100–150 words), describe the basic principles of bioenergetics in an animal cell. How is the flow and transformation of energy different in a photosynthesizing cell? Include the role of ATP and enzymes in your discussion.

11. **SYNTHESIZE YOUR KNOWLEDGE**

Explain what is happening in this photo in terms of kinetic energy and potential energy. Include the energy conversions that occur when the penguins eat fish and climb back up on the glacier. Describe the role of ATP and enzymes in the underlying molecular processes, including what happens to the free energy of some of the molecules involved.

For selected answers, see Appendix A.

MasteringBiology®

Students Go to **MasteringBiology** for assignments, the eText, and the Study Area with practice tests, animations, and activities.

Instructors Go to **MasteringBiology** for automatically graded tutorials and questions that you can assign to your students, plus Instructor Resources.

9

Cellular Respiration and Fermentation

▲ Figure 9.1 How do these leaves power the work of life for this giraffe?

Life Is Work

Living cells require transfusions of energy from outside sources to perform their many tasks—for example, assembling polymers, pumping substances across membranes, moving, and reproducing. The giraffe in **Figure 9.1** is obtaining energy for its cells by eating the leaves of plants; some other animals obtain energy by feeding on other organisms that eat plants.

The energy stored in the organic molecules of food ultimately comes from the sun. Energy flows into an ecosystem as sunlight and exits as heat; in contrast, the chemical elements essential to life are recycled **(Figure 9.2)**. Photosynthesis generates oxygen and organic molecules that are used by the mitochondria of eukaryotes (including plants and algae) as fuel for cellular respiration. Respiration breaks this fuel down, generating ATP. The waste products of this type of respiration, carbon dioxide and water, are the raw materials for photosynthesis.

In this chapter, we consider how cells harvest the chemical energy stored in organic molecules and use it to generate ATP, the molecule that drives most cellular work. After presenting some basics about respiration, we'll focus on three key pathways of respiration: glycolysis, the citric acid cycle, and oxidative phosphorylation. We'll also consider fermentation, a somewhat simpler pathway coupled to glycolysis that has deep evolutionary roots.

▲ Figure 9.2 Energy flow and chemical recycling in ecosystems. Energy flows into an ecosystem as sunlight and ultimately leaves as heat, while the chemical elements essential to life are recycled.

CONCEPT 9.1

Catabolic pathways yield energy by oxidizing organic fuels

Metabolic pathways that release stored energy by breaking down complex molecules are called catabolic pathways (see Chapter 8). Electron transfer plays a major role in these pathways. In this section, we consider these processes, which are central to cellular respiration.

Catabolic Pathways and Production of ATP

Organic compounds possess potential energy as a result of the arrangement of electrons in the bonds between their atoms. Compounds that can participate in exergonic reactions can act as fuels. Through the activity of enzymes, a cell systematically degrades complex organic molecules that are rich in potential energy to simpler waste products that have less energy. Some of the energy taken out of chemical storage can be used to do work; the rest is dissipated as heat.

One catabolic process, **fermentation**, is a partial degradation of sugars or other organic fuel that occurs without the use of oxygen. However, the most efficient catabolic pathway is **aerobic respiration**, in which oxygen is consumed as a reactant along with the organic fuel (*aerobic* is from the Greek *aer*, air, and *bios*, life). The cells of most eukaryotic and many prokaryotic organisms can carry out aerobic respiration. Some prokaryotes use substances other than oxygen as reactants in a similar process that harvests chemical energy without oxygen; this process is called *anaerobic respiration* (the prefix *an-* means "without"). Technically, the term **cellular respiration** includes both aerobic and anaerobic processes. However, it originated as a synonym for aerobic respiration because of the relationship of that process to organismal respiration, in which an animal breathes in oxygen. Thus, *cellular respiration* is often used to refer to the aerobic process, a practice we follow in most of this chapter.

Although very different in mechanism, aerobic respiration is in principle similar to the combustion of gasoline in an automobile engine after oxygen is mixed with the fuel (hydrocarbons). Food provides the fuel for respiration, and the exhaust is carbon dioxide and water. The overall process can be summarized as follows:

$$\text{Organic compounds} + \text{Oxygen} \rightarrow \text{Carbon dioxide} + \text{Water} + \text{Energy}$$

Carbohydrates, fats, and protein molecules from food can all be processed and consumed as fuel, as we will discuss later in the chapter. In animal diets, a major source of carbohydrates is starch, a storage polysaccharide that can be broken down into glucose ($C_6H_{12}O_6$) subunits. Here, we will learn the steps of cellular respiration by tracking the degradation of the sugar glucose:

$$C_6H_{12}O_6 + 6\ O_2 \rightarrow 6\ CO_2 + 6\ H_2O + \text{Energy (ATP + heat)}$$

This breakdown of glucose is exergonic, having a free-energy change of −686 kcal (2,870 kJ) per mole of glucose decomposed ($\Delta G = -686$ kcal/mol). Recall that a negative ΔG indicates that the products of the chemical process store less energy than the reactants and that the reaction can happen spontaneously—in other words, without an input of energy.

Catabolic pathways do not directly move flagella, pump solutes across membranes, polymerize monomers, or perform other cellular work. Catabolism is linked to work by a chemical drive shaft—ATP (see Chapter 8). To keep working, the cell must regenerate its supply of ATP from ADP and P_i (see Figure 8.12). To understand how cellular respiration accomplishes this, let's examine the fundamental chemical processes known as oxidation and reduction.

Redox Reactions: Oxidation and Reduction

How do the catabolic pathways that decompose glucose and other organic fuels yield energy? The answer is based on the transfer of electrons during the chemical reactions. The relocation of electrons releases energy stored in organic molecules, and this energy ultimately is used to synthesize ATP.

The Principle of Redox

In many chemical reactions, there is a transfer of one or more electrons (e^-) from one reactant to another. These electron transfers are called oxidation-reduction reactions, or **redox reactions** for short. In a redox reaction, the loss of electrons from one substance is called **oxidation**, and the addition of electrons to another substance is known as **reduction**. (Note that *adding* electrons is called *reduction*; adding negatively charged electrons to an atom *reduces* the amount of positive charge of that atom.) To take a simple, nonbiological example, consider the reaction between the elements sodium (Na) and chlorine (Cl) that forms table salt:

$$\overbrace{\underbrace{Na \; + \; Cl \; \longrightarrow \; Na^+ \; + \; Cl^-}}$$

becomes oxidized (loses electron)

becomes reduced (gains electron)

We could generalize a redox reaction this way:

becomes oxidized

$$Xe^- \; + \; Y \; \longrightarrow \; X \; + \; Ye^-$$

becomes reduced

In the generalized reaction, substance Xe^-, the electron donor, is called the **reducing agent**; it reduces Y, which accepts the donated electron. Substance Y, the electron acceptor, is the **oxidizing agent**; it oxidizes Xe^- by removing its electron. Because an electron transfer requires both an electron donor and an acceptor, oxidation and reduction always go hand in hand.

Not all redox reactions involve the complete transfer of electrons from one substance to another; some change the degree of electron sharing in covalent bonds. Methane combustion, shown in **Figure 9.3**, is an example. The covalent electrons in methane are shared nearly equally between the bonded atoms because carbon and hydrogen have about the same affinity for valence electrons; they are about equally electronegative (see Chapter 2). But when methane reacts with oxygen, forming carbon dioxide, electrons end up shared less equally between the carbon atom and its new covalent partners, the oxygen atoms, which are very electronegative. In effect, the carbon atom has partially "lost" its shared electrons; thus, methane has been oxidized.

Now let's examine the fate of the reactant O_2. The two atoms of the oxygen molecule (O_2) share their electrons equally. But when oxygen reacts with the hydrogen from methane, forming water, the electrons of the covalent bonds spend more time near the oxygen (see Figure 9.3). In effect, each oxygen atom has partially "gained" electrons, so the oxygen molecule has been reduced. Because oxygen is so electronegative, it is one of the most potent of all oxidizing agents.

Energy must be added to pull an electron away from an atom, just as energy is required to push a ball uphill. The more electronegative the atom (the stronger its pull on electrons), the more energy is required to take an electron away from it. An electron loses potential energy when it shifts from a less electronegative atom toward a more electronegative one, just as a ball loses potential energy when it rolls

▲ **Figure 9.3 Methane combustion as an energy-yielding redox reaction.** The reaction releases energy to the surroundings because the electrons lose potential energy when they end up being shared unequally, spending more time near electronegative atoms such as oxygen.

downhill. A redox reaction that moves electrons closer to oxygen, such as the burning (oxidation) of methane, therefore releases chemical energy that can be put to work.

Oxidation of Organic Fuel Molecules During Cellular Respiration

The oxidation of methane by oxygen is the main combustion reaction that occurs at the burner of a gas stove. The combustion of gasoline in an automobile engine is also a redox reaction; the energy released pushes the pistons. But the energy-yielding redox process of greatest interest to biologists is respiration: the oxidation of glucose and other molecules in food. Examine again the summary equation for cellular respiration, but this time think of it as a redox process:

becomes oxidized

$$C_6H_{12}O_6 \; + \; 6\,O_2 \; \longrightarrow \; 6\,CO_2 \; + \; 6\,H_2O \; + \; \text{Energy}$$

becomes reduced

As in the combustion of methane or gasoline, the fuel (glucose) is oxidized and oxygen is reduced. The electrons lose potential energy along the way, and energy is released.

In general, organic molecules that have an abundance of hydrogen are excellent fuels because their bonds are a source of "hilltop" electrons, whose energy may be released as these electrons "fall" down an energy gradient when they are transferred to oxygen. The summary equation for respiration indicates that hydrogen is transferred from glucose to oxygen. But the important point, not visible in the summary equation, is that the energy state of the electron changes as hydrogen (with its electron) is transferred to oxygen. In respiration, the oxidation of glucose transfers electrons to a lower energy state, liberating energy that becomes available for ATP synthesis.

The main energy-yielding foods—carbohydrates and fats—are reservoirs of electrons associated with hydrogen.

Only the barrier of activation energy holds back the flood of electrons to a lower energy state (see Figure 8.13). Without this barrier, a food substance like glucose would combine almost instantaneously with O_2. If we supply the activation energy by igniting glucose, it burns in air, releasing 686 kcal (2,870 kJ) of heat per mole of glucose (about 180 g). Body temperature is not high enough to initiate burning, of course. Instead, if you swallow some glucose, enzymes in your cells will lower the barrier of activation energy, allowing the sugar to be oxidized in a series of steps.

Stepwise Energy Harvest via NAD+ and the Electron Transport Chain

If energy is released from a fuel all at once, it cannot be harnessed efficiently for constructive work. For example, if a gasoline tank explodes, it cannot drive a car very far. Cellular respiration does not oxidize glucose (or any other organic fuel) in a single explosive step either. Rather, glucose is broken down in a series of steps, each one catalyzed by an enzyme. At key steps, electrons are stripped from the glucose. As is often the case in oxidation reactions, each electron travels with a proton—thus, as a hydrogen atom. The hydrogen atoms are not transferred directly to oxygen, but instead are usually passed first to an electron carrier, a coenzyme called **NAD+** (nicotinamide adenine dinucleotide, a derivative of the vitamin niacin). NAD+ is well suited as an electron carrier because it can cycle easily between oxidized (NAD+) and reduced (NADH) states. As an electron acceptor, NAD+ functions as an oxidizing agent during respiration.

How does NAD+ trap electrons from glucose and the other organic molecules in food? Enzymes called dehydrogenases remove a pair of hydrogen atoms (2 electrons and 2 protons) from the substrate (glucose, in the above example),

thereby oxidizing it. The enzyme delivers the 2 electrons along with 1 proton to its coenzyme, NAD+ **(Figure 9.4)**. The other proton is released as a hydrogen ion (H^+) into the surrounding solution:

$$H-\overset{|}{\underset{|}{C}}-OH + NAD^+ \xrightarrow{\text{Dehydrogenase}} \overset{|}{C}=O + NADH + H^+$$

By receiving 2 negatively charged electrons but only 1 positively charged proton, the nicotinamide portion of NAD+ has its charge neutralized when NAD+ is reduced to NADH. The name NADH shows the hydrogen that has been received in the reaction. NAD+ is the most versatile electron acceptor in cellular respiration and functions in several of the redox steps during the breakdown of glucose.

Electrons lose very little of their potential energy when they are transferred from glucose to NAD+. Each NADH molecule formed during respiration represents stored energy. This energy can be tapped to make ATP when the electrons complete their "fall" in a series of steps down an energy gradient from NADH to oxygen.

How do electrons that are extracted from glucose and stored as potential energy in NADH finally reach oxygen? It will help to compare the redox chemistry of cellular respiration to a much simpler reaction: the reaction between hydrogen and oxygen to form water **(Figure 9.5a)**. Mix H_2 and O_2, provide a spark for activation energy, and the gases combine explosively. In fact, combustion of liquid H_2 and O_2 was harnessed to help power the main engines of the Space Shuttle, boosting it into orbit. The explosion represents a release of energy as the electrons of hydrogen "fall" closer to the electronegative oxygen atoms. Cellular respiration also brings hydrogen and oxygen together to form water, but there are two important differences. First, in cellular respiration, the hydrogen that reacts with oxygen is derived from

▲ **Figure 9.4 NAD+ as an electron shuttle.** The full name for NAD+, nicotinamide adenine dinucleotide, describes its structure—the molecule consists of two nucleotides joined together at their phosphate groups (shown in yellow). (Nicotinamide is a nitrogenous base, although not one that is present in DNA or RNA; see Figure 5.24.) The enzymatic transfer of 2 electrons and 1 proton (H^+) from an organic molecule in food to NAD+ reduces the NAD+ to NADH: Most of the electrons removed from food are transferred initially to NAD+, forming NADH.

? *Describe the structural differences between the oxidized form and the reduced form of nicotinamide.*

organic molecules rather than H_2. Second, instead of occurring in one explosive reaction, respiration uses an electron transport chain to break the fall of electrons to oxygen into several energy-releasing steps (**Figure 9.5b**). An **electron transport chain** consists of a number of molecules, mostly proteins, built into the inner membrane of the mitochondria of eukaryotic cells (and the plasma membrane of respiring prokaryotes). Electrons removed from glucose are shuttled by NADH to the "top," higher-energy end of the chain. At the "bottom," lower-energy end, O_2 captures these electrons along with hydrogen nuclei (H^+), forming water. (Anaerobically respiring prokaryotes have an electron acceptor at the end of the chain that is different from O_2.)

Electron transfer from NADH to oxygen is an exergonic reaction with a free-energy change of −53 kcal/mol (−222 kJ/mol). Instead of this energy being released and wasted in a single explosive step, electrons cascade down the chain from one carrier molecule to the next in a series of redox reactions, losing a small amount of energy with each step until they finally reach oxygen, the terminal electron acceptor, which has a very great affinity for electrons. Each "downhill" carrier is more electronegative than, and thus capable of oxidizing, its "uphill" neighbor, with oxygen at the bottom of the chain. Therefore, the electrons transferred from glucose to NAD^+, which is thus reduced to NADH, fall down an energy gradient in the electron transport chain to a far more stable location in the electronegative oxygen atom. Put another way, oxygen pulls electrons down the chain in

an energy-yielding tumble analogous to gravity pulling objects downhill.

In summary, during cellular respiration, most electrons travel the following "downhill" route: glucose → NADH → electron transport chain → oxygen. Later in this chapter, you will learn more about how the cell uses the energy released from this exergonic electron fall to regenerate its supply of ATP. For now, having covered the basic redox mechanisms of cellular respiration, let's look at the entire process by which energy is harvested from organic fuels.

The Stages of Cellular Respiration: *A Preview*

The harvesting of energy from glucose by cellular respiration is a cumulative function of three metabolic stages. We list them here along with a color-coding scheme we will use throughout the chapter to help you keep track of the big picture:

1. GLYCOLYSIS (color-coded blue throughout the chapter)
2. PYRUVATE OXIDATION and the CITRIC ACID CYCLE (color-coded orange)
3. OXIDATIVE PHOSPHORYLATION: Electron transport and chemiosmosis (color-coded purple)

Biochemists usually reserve the term *cellular respiration* for stages 2 and 3 together. In this text, however, we include glycolysis as a part of cellular respiration because most respiring cells deriving energy from glucose use glycolysis to produce the starting material for the citric acid cycle.

As diagrammed in **Figure 9.6**, glycolysis and pyruvate oxidation followed by the citric acid cycle are the catabolic pathways that break down glucose and other organic fuels. **Glycolysis**, which occurs in the cytosol, begins the degradation process by breaking glucose into two molecules of a compound called pyruvate. In eukaryotes, pyruvate enters the mitochondrion and is oxidized to a compound called acetyl CoA, which enters the **citric acid cycle**. There, the breakdown of glucose to carbon dioxide is completed. (In prokaryotes, these processes take place in the cytosol.) Thus, the carbon dioxide produced by respiration represents fragments of oxidized organic molecules.

Some of the steps of glycolysis and the citric acid cycle are redox reactions in which dehydrogenases transfer electrons from substrates to NAD^+, forming NADH. In the third stage of respiration, the electron transport chain accepts electrons (most often via

▲ Figure 9.5 An introduction to electron transport chains. (a) The one-step exergonic reaction of hydrogen with oxygen to form water releases a large amount of energy in the form of heat and light: an explosion. **(b)** In cellular respiration, the same reaction occurs in stages: An electron transport chain breaks the "fall" of electrons in this reaction into a series of smaller steps and stores some of the released energy in a form that can be used to make ATP. (The rest of the energy is released as heat.)

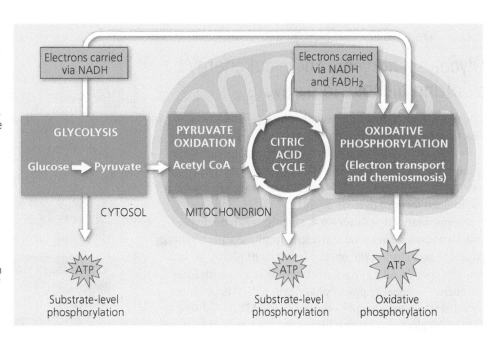

▶ **Figure 9.6 An overview of cellular respiration.** During glycolysis, each glucose molecule is broken down into two molecules of the compound pyruvate. In eukaryotic cells, as shown here, the pyruvate enters the mitochondrion. There it is oxidized to acetyl CoA, which is further oxidized to CO_2 in the citric acid cycle. NADH and a similar electron carrier, a coenzyme called $FADH_2$, transfer electrons derived from glucose to electron transport chains, which are built into the inner mitochondrial membrane. (In prokaryotes, the electron transport chains are located in the plasma membrane.) During oxidative phosphorylation, electron transport chains convert the chemical energy to a form used for ATP synthesis in the process called chemiosmosis.

BioFlix Visit the Study Area in **MasteringBiology** for the BioFlix® 3-D Animation on Cellular Respiration. BioFlix Tutorials can also be assigned in MasteringBiology.

NADH) from the breakdown products of the first two stages and passes these electrons from one molecule to another. At the end of the chain, the electrons are combined with molecular oxygen and hydrogen ions (H^+), forming water (see Figure 9.5b). The energy released at each step of the chain is stored in a form the mitochondrion (or prokaryotic cell) can use to make ATP from ADP. This mode of ATP synthesis is called **oxidative phosphorylation** because it is powered by the redox reactions of the electron transport chain.

In eukaryotic cells, the inner membrane of the mitochondrion is the site of electron transport and chemiosmosis, the processes that together constitute oxidative phosphorylation. (In prokaryotes, these processes take place in the plasma membrane.) Oxidative phosphorylation accounts for almost 90% of the ATP generated by respiration. A smaller amount of ATP is formed directly in a few reactions of glycolysis and the citric acid cycle by a mechanism called **substrate-level phosphorylation (Figure 9.7)**. This

mode of ATP synthesis occurs when an enzyme transfers a phosphate group from a substrate molecule to ADP, rather than adding an inorganic phosphate to ADP as in oxidative phosphorylation. "Substrate molecule" here refers to an organic molecule generated as an intermediate during the catabolism of glucose. You'll see examples of substrate-level phosphorylation later in the chapter, in both glycolysis and the citric acid cycle.

When you withdraw a relatively large sum of money from an ATM machine, it is not delivered to you in a single bill of larger denomination. Instead, a number of smaller denomination bills are dispensed that you can spend more easily. This is analogous to ATP production during cellular respiration. For each molecule of glucose degraded to carbon dioxide and water by respiration, the cell makes up to about 32 molecules of ATP, each with 7.3 kcal/mol of free energy. Respiration cashes in the large denomination of energy banked in a single molecule of glucose (686 kcal/mol) for the small change of many molecules of ATP, which is more practical for the cell to spend on its work.

This preview has introduced you to how glycolysis, the citric acid cycle, and oxidative phosphorylation fit into the process of cellular respiration. We are now ready to take a closer look at each of these three stages of respiration.

▲ **Figure 9.7 Substrate-level phosphorylation.** Some ATP is made by direct transfer of a phosphate group from an organic substrate to ADP by an enzyme. (For examples in glycolysis, see Figure 9.9, steps 7 and 10.)

MAKE CONNECTIONS *Review Figure 8.9. Do you think the potential energy is higher for the reactants or the products in the reaction shown above? Explain.*

CONCEPT CHECK 9.1

1. Compare and contrast aerobic and anaerobic respiration.

2. **WHAT IF?** If the following redox reaction occurred, which compound would be oxidized? Reduced?

$$C_4H_6O_5 + NAD^+ \rightarrow C_4H_4O_5 + NADH + H^+$$

For suggested answers, see Appendix A.

CONCEPT 9.2

Glycolysis harvests chemical energy by oxidizing glucose to pyruvate

The word *glycolysis* means "sugar splitting," and that is exactly what happens during this pathway. Glucose, a six-carbon sugar, is split into two three-carbon sugars. These smaller sugars are then oxidized and their remaining atoms rearranged to form two molecules of pyruvate. (Pyruvate is the ionized form of pyruvic acid.)

As summarized in **Figure 9.8**, glycolysis can be divided into two phases: the energy investment phase and the energy payoff phase. During the energy investment phase, the cell actually spends ATP. This investment is repaid with interest during the energy payoff phase, when ATP is produced by substrate-level phosphorylation and NAD^+ is reduced to NADH by electrons released from the oxidation of glucose. The net energy yield from glycolysis, per glucose molecule, is 2 ATP plus 2 NADH. The ten steps of the glycolytic pathway are shown in **Figure 9.9**.

All of the carbon originally present in glucose is accounted for in the two molecules of pyruvate; no carbon is released as CO_2 during glycolysis. Glycolysis occurs whether or not O_2 is present. However, if O_2 *is* present, the chemical energy stored in pyruvate and NADH can be extracted by pyruvate oxidation, the citric acid cycle, and oxidative phosphorylation.

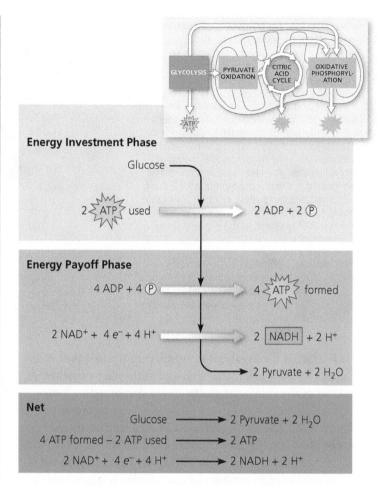

Energy Investment Phase

Glucose

$2 \, ATP$ used $\longrightarrow$ $2 \, ADP + 2 \, \textcircled{P}$

Energy Payoff Phase

$4 \, ADP + 4 \, \textcircled{P}$ $\longrightarrow$ $4 \, ATP$ formed

$2 \, NAD^+ + 4 \, e^- + 4 \, H^+$ $\longrightarrow$ $2 \, \boxed{NADH} + 2 \, H^+$

$\longrightarrow$ 2 Pyruvate + 2 H_2O

Net

Glucose $\longrightarrow$ 2 Pyruvate + 2 H_2O

4 ATP formed – 2 ATP used $\longrightarrow$ 2 ATP

$2 \, NAD^+ + 4 \, e^- + 4 \, H^+$ $\longrightarrow$ 2 NADH + 2 H^+

▲ **Figure 9.8 The energy input and output of glycolysis.**

▼ **Figure 9.9 A closer look at glycolysis.** Note that glycolysis is a source of ATP and NADH.

GLYCOLYSIS: Energy Investment Phase

WHAT IF? *What would happen if you removed the dihydroxyacetone phosphate generated in step 4 as fast as it was produced?*

Glucose

ATP

ADP

Hexokinase

①

Hexokinase transfers a phosphate group from ATP to glucose, making it more chemically reactive. The charge on the phosphate also traps the sugar in the cell.

Glucose 6-phosphate

Phosphogluco-isomerase

②

Glucose 6-phosphate is converted to fructose 6-phosphate.

Fructose 6-phosphate

ATP

ADP

Phospho-fructokinase

③

Phosphofructokinase transfers a phosphate group from ATP to the opposite end of the sugar, investing a second molecule of ATP. This is a key step for regulation of glycolysis.

Fructose 1,6-bisphosphate

Aldolase

④

Aldolase cleaves the sugar molecule into two different three-carbon sugars.

Glyceraldehyde 3-phosphate (G3P)

Isomerase

⑤

Dihydroxyacetone phosphate (DHAP)

Conversion between DHAP and G3P: This reaction never reaches equilibrium; G3P is used in the next step as fast as it forms.

1. During the redox reaction in glycolysis (step 6 in Figure 9.9), which molecule acts as the oxidizing agent? The reducing agent?

For suggested answers, see Appendix A.

CONCEPT 9.3

After pyruvate is oxidized, the citric acid cycle completes the energy-yielding oxidation of organic molecules

Glycolysis releases less than a quarter of the chemical energy in glucose that can be harvested by cells; most of the energy remains stockpiled in the two molecules of pyruvate. When O_2 is present, the pyruvate in eukaryotic cells enters a mitochondrion, where the oxidation of glucose is completed. In aerobically respiring prokaryotic cells, this process occurs in the cytosol. (Later in the chapter, we'll discuss what happens to pyruvate when O_2 is unavailable or in a prokaryote that is unable to use O_2.)

Oxidation of Pyruvate to Acetyl CoA

Upon entering the mitochondrion via active transport, pyruvate is first converted to a compound called acetyl coenzyme A, or **acetyl CoA (Figure 9.10)**. This step, linking glycolysis and the citric acid cycle, is carried out by a multienzyme

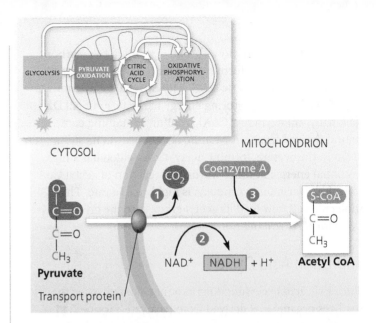

▲ **Figure 9.10 Oxidation of pyruvate to acetyl CoA, the step before the citric acid cycle.** Pyruvate is a charged molecule, so in eukaryotic cells it must enter the mitochondrion via active transport, with the help of a transport protein. Next, a complex of several enzymes (the pyruvate dehydrogenase complex) catalyzes the three numbered steps, which are described in the text. The acetyl group of acetyl CoA will enter the citric acid cycle. The CO_2 molecule will diffuse out of the cell. By convention, coenzyme A is abbreviated S-CoA when it is attached to a molecule, emphasizing the sulfur atom (S).

complex that catalyzes three reactions: ❶ Pyruvate's carboxyl group (—COO⁻), which is already fully oxidized and thus has little chemical energy, is removed and given off as a molecule of CO_2. This is the first step in which CO_2 is

The energy payoff phase occurs after glucose is split into two three-carbon sugars. Thus, the coefficient 2 precedes all molecules in this phase.

GLYCOLYSIS: Energy Payoff Phase

Triose phosphate dehydrogenase ❻

1,3-Bisphospho-glycerate

Phosphoglycerokinase ❼

3-Phospho-glycerate

Phosphoglyceromutase ❽

2-Phospho-glycerate

Enolase ❾

Phosphoenol-pyruvate (PEP)

Pyruvate kinase ❿

Pyruvate

Two sequential reactions: (1) The sugar is oxidized by the transfer of electrons to NAD⁺, forming NADH. (2) Using energy from this exergonic redox reaction, a phosphate group is attached to the oxidized substrate, making a high-energy product.

The phosphate group is transferred to ADP (substrate-level phosphorylation) in an exergonic reaction. The carbonyl group of G3P has been oxidized to the carboxyl group (—COO⁻) of an organic acid (3-phosphoglycerate).

This enzyme relocates the remaining phosphate group.

Enolase causes a double bond to form in the substrate by extracting a water molecule, yielding phosphoenolpyruvate (PEP), a compound with a very high potential energy.

The phosphate group is transferred from PEP to ADP (a second example of substrate-level phosphorylation), forming pyruvate.

© Pearson Education, Inc.

released during respiration. ❷ The remaining two-carbon fragment is oxidized, forming acetate (CH_3COO^-, which is the ionized form of acetic acid). The extracted electrons are transferred to NAD^+, storing energy in the form of NADH. ❸ Finally, coenzyme A (CoA), a sulfur-containing compound derived from a B vitamin, is attached via its sulfur atom to the acetate, forming acetyl CoA, which has a high potential energy; in other words, the reaction of acetyl CoA to yield lower-energy products is highly exergonic. This molecule will now feed its acetyl group into the citric acid cycle for further oxidation.

The Citric Acid Cycle

The citric acid cycle functions as a metabolic furnace that oxidizes organic fuel derived from pyruvate. **Figure 9.11** summarizes the inputs and outputs as pyruvate is broken

▲ **Figure 9.11 An overview of pyruvate oxidation and the citric acid cycle.** The inputs and outputs per pyruvate molecule are shown. To calculate on a per-glucose basis, multiply by 2, because each glucose molecule is split during glycolysis into two pyruvate molecules.

down to three CO_2 molecules, including the molecule of CO_2 released during the conversion of pyruvate to acetyl CoA. The cycle generates 1 ATP per turn by substrate-level phosphorylation, but most of the chemical energy is transferred to NAD^+ and a related electron carrier, the coenzyme FAD (flavin adenine dinucleotide, derived from riboflavin, a B vitamin), during the redox reactions. The reduced coenzymes, NADH and $FADH_2$, shuttle their cargo of high-energy electrons into the electron transport chain. The citric acid cycle is also called the tricarboxylic acid cycle or the Krebs cycle, the latter honoring Hans Krebs, the German-British scientist who was largely responsible for working out the pathway in the 1930s.

Now let's look at the citric acid cycle in more detail. The cycle has eight steps, each catalyzed by a specific enzyme. You can see in **Figure 9.12** that for each turn of the citric acid cycle, two carbons (red) enter in the relatively reduced form of an acetyl group (step ❶), and two different carbons (blue) leave in the completely oxidized form of CO_2 molecules (steps ❸ and ❹). The acetyl group of acetyl CoA joins the cycle by combining with the compound oxaloacetate, forming citrate (step ❶). Citrate is the ionized form of citric acid, for which the cycle is named. The next seven steps decompose the citrate back to oxaloacetate. It is this regeneration of oxaloacetate that makes the process a *cycle*.

We can refer to Figure 9.12 in order to tally the energy-rich molecules produced by the citric acid cycle. For each acetyl group entering the cycle, 3 NAD^+ are reduced to NADH (steps ❸, ❹, and ❽). In step ❻, electrons are transferred not to NAD^+, but to FAD, which accepts 2 electrons and 2 protons to become $FADH_2$. In many animal tissue cells, the reaction in step ❺ produces a guanosine triphosphate (GTP) molecule by substrate-level phosphorylation. GTP is a molecule similar to ATP in its structure and cellular function. This GTP may be used to make an ATP molecule (as shown) or directly power work in the cell. In the cells of plants, bacteria, and some animal tissues, step ❺ forms an ATP molecule directly by substrate-level phosphorylation. The output from step ❺ represents the only ATP generated during the citric acid cycle. Recall that each glucose gives rise to two acetyl CoAs that enter the cycle. Because the numbers noted earlier are obtained from a single acetyl group entering the pathway, the total yield per glucose from the citric acid cycle turns out to be 6 NADHs, 2 $FADH_2$s, and the equivalent of 2 ATPs.

Most of the ATP produced by respiration results from oxidative phosphorylation, when the NADH and $FADH_2$ produced by the citric acid cycle relay the electrons extracted from food to the electron transport chain. In the process, they supply the necessary energy for the phosphorylation of ADP to ATP. We will explore this process in the next section.

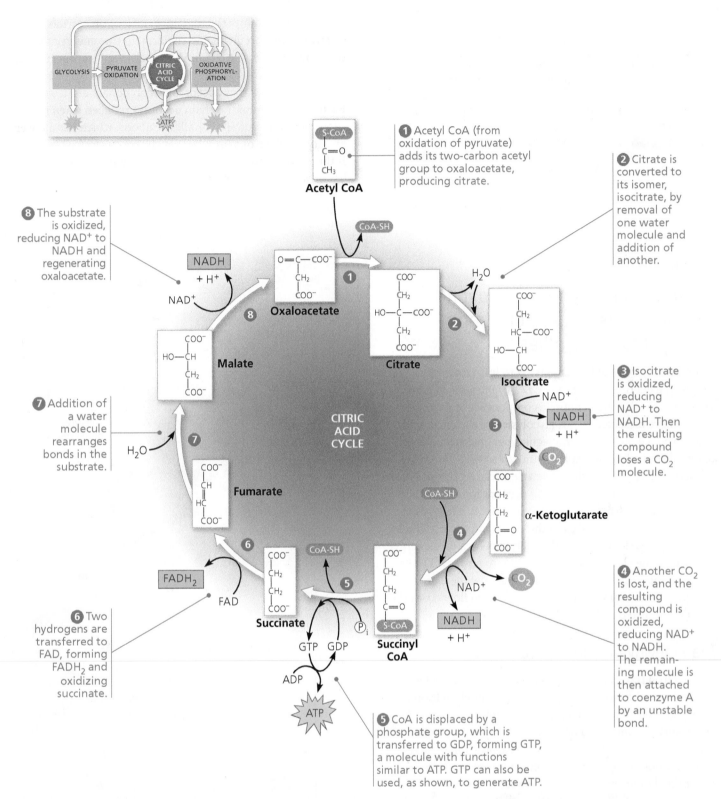

1 Acetyl CoA (from oxidation of pyruvate) adds its two-carbon acetyl group to oxaloacetate, producing citrate.

2 Citrate is converted to its isomer, isocitrate, by removal of one water molecule and addition of another.

8 The substrate is oxidized, reducing NAD+ to NADH and regenerating oxaloacetate.

3 Isocitrate is oxidized, reducing NAD+ to NADH. Then the resulting compound loses a CO_2 molecule.

7 Addition of a water molecule rearranges bonds in the substrate.

4 Another CO_2 is lost, and the resulting compound is oxidized, reducing NAD+ to NADH. The remaining molecule is then attached to coenzyme A by an unstable bond.

6 Two hydrogens are transferred to FAD, forming $FADH_2$ and oxidizing succinate.

5 CoA is displaced by a phosphate group, which is transferred to GDP, forming GTP, a molecule with functions similar to ATP. GTP can also be used, as shown, to generate ATP.

CITRIC ACID CYCLE

Acetyl CoA

Oxaloacetate

Citrate

Isocitrate

α-Ketoglutarate

Succinyl CoA

Succinate

Fumarate

Malate

▲ **Figure 9.12 A closer look at the citric acid cycle.** In the chemical structures, red type traces the fate of the two carbon atoms that enter the cycle via acetyl CoA (step 1), and blue type indicates the two carbons that exit the cycle as CO_2 in steps 3 and 4. (The red type goes only through step 5 because the succinate molecule is symmetrical; the two ends cannot be distinguished from each other.) Notice that the carbon atoms that enter the cycle from acetyl CoA do not leave the cycle in the same turn. They remain in the cycle, occupying a different location in the molecules on their next turn, after another acetyl group is added. Therefore, the oxaloacetate regenerated at step 8 is made up of different carbon atoms each time around. In eukaryotic cells, all the citric acid cycle enzymes are located in the mitochondrial matrix except for the enzyme that catalyzes step 6, which resides in the inner mitochondrial membrane. Carboxylic acids are represented in their ionized forms, as —COO⁻, because the ionized forms prevail at the pH within the mitochondrion.

1. Name the molecules that conserve most of the energy from the redox reactions of the citric acid cycle (see Figure 9.12). How is this energy converted to a form that can be used to make ATP?

2. What processes in your cells produce the CO_2 that you exhale?

3. **WHAT IF?** The conversions shown in Figure 9.10 and step 4 of Figure 9.12 are each catalyzed by a large multi-enzyme complex. What similarities are there in the reactions that occur in these two cases?

For suggested answers, see Appendix A.

CONCEPT 9.4

During oxidative phosphorylation, chemiosmosis couples electron transport to ATP synthesis

Our main objective in this chapter is to learn how cells harvest the energy of glucose and other nutrients in food to make ATP. But the metabolic components of respiration we have dissected so far, glycolysis and the citric acid cycle, produce only 4 ATP molecules per glucose molecule, all by substrate-level phosphorylation: 2 net ATP from glycolysis and 2 ATP from the citric acid cycle. At this point, molecules of NADH (and $FADH_2$) account for most of the energy extracted from each glucose molecule. These electron escorts link glycolysis and the citric acid cycle to the machinery of oxidative phosphorylation, which uses energy released by the electron transport chain to power ATP synthesis. In this section, you will learn first how the electron transport chain works and then how electron flow down the chain is coupled to ATP synthesis.

The Pathway of Electron Transport

The electron transport chain is a collection of molecules embedded in the inner membrane of the mitochondrion in eukaryotic cells. (In prokaryotes, these molecules reside in the plasma membrane.) The folding of the inner membrane to form cristae increases its surface area, providing space for thousands of copies of the electron transport chain in each mitochondrion. Once again, we see that structure fits function—the infolded membrane with its placement of electron carrier molecules in a row, one after the other, is well-suited for the series of sequential redox reactions that take place along the electron transport chain. Most components of the chain are proteins, which exist in multiprotein complexes numbered I through IV. Tightly bound to these proteins are *prosthetic groups*, nonprotein components essential for the catalytic functions of certain enzymes.

Figure 9.13 shows the sequence of electron carriers in the electron transport chain and the drop in free energy as electrons travel down the chain. During electron transport along the chain, electron carriers alternate between reduced and oxidized states as they accept and then donate electrons. Each component of the chain becomes reduced when it accepts electrons from its "uphill" neighbor, which has a lower affinity for electrons (in other words, is less electronegative). It then returns to its oxidized form as it passes electrons to its "downhill," more electronegative neighbor.

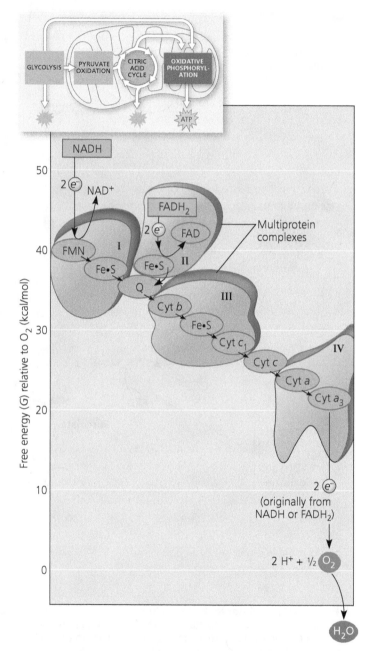

▲ **Figure 9.13 Free-energy change during electron transport.** The overall energy drop (ΔG) for electrons traveling from NADH to oxygen is 53 kcal/mol, but this "fall" is broken up into a series of smaller steps by the electron transport chain. (An oxygen atom is represented here as $\frac{1}{2} O_2$ to emphasize that the electron transport chain reduces molecular oxygen, O_2, not individual oxygen atoms.)

Now let's take a closer look at the electron transport chain in Figure 9.13. We'll first describe the passage of electrons through complex I in some detail, as an illustration of the general principles involved in electron transport. Electrons acquired from glucose by NAD^+ during glycolysis and the citric acid cycle are transferred from NADH to the first molecule of the electron transport chain in complex I. This molecule is a flavoprotein, so named because it has a prosthetic group called flavin mononucleotide (FMN). In the next redox reaction, the flavoprotein returns to its oxidized form as it passes electrons to an iron-sulfur protein (Fe·S in complex I), one of a family of proteins with both iron and sulfur tightly bound. The iron-sulfur protein then passes the electrons to a compound called ubiquinone (Q in Figure 9.13). This electron carrier is a small hydrophobic molecule, the only member of the electron transport chain that is not a protein. Ubiquinone is individually mobile within the membrane rather than residing in a particular complex. (Another name for ubiquinone is coenzyme Q, or CoQ; you may have seen it sold as a nutritional supplement in health food stores.)

Most of the remaining electron carriers between ubiquinone and oxygen are proteins called **cytochromes**. Their prosthetic group, called a heme group, has an iron atom that accepts and donates electrons. (The heme group in the cytochromes is similar to the heme group in hemoglobin, the protein of red blood cells, except that the iron in hemoglobin carries oxygen, not electrons.) The electron transport chain has several types of cytochromes, each a different protein with a slightly different electron-carrying heme group. The last cytochrome of the chain, Cyt a_3, passes its electrons to oxygen, which is *very* electronegative. Each oxygen atom also picks up a pair of hydrogen ions (protons) from the aqueous solution, neutralizing the −2 charge of the added electrons and forming water.

Another source of electrons for the transport chain is $FADH_2$, the other reduced product of the citric acid cycle. Notice in Figure 9.13 that $FADH_2$ adds its electrons to the electron transport chain from within complex II, at a lower energy level than NADH does. Consequently, although NADH and $FADH_2$ each donate an equivalent number of electrons (2) for oxygen reduction, the electron transport chain provides about one-third less energy for ATP synthesis when the electron donor is $FADH_2$ rather than NADH. We'll see why in the next section.

The electron transport chain makes no ATP directly. Instead, it eases the fall of electrons from food to oxygen, breaking a large free-energy drop into a series of smaller steps that release energy in manageable amounts, step by step. How does the mitochondrion (or the plasma membrane, in the case of prokaryotes) couple this electron transport and energy release to ATP synthesis? The answer is a mechanism called chemiosmosis.

INTERMEMBRANE SPACE

1 H^+ ions flowing down their gradient enter a channel in a **stator**, which is anchored in the membrane.

2 H^+ ions enter binding sites within a **rotor**, changing the shape of each subunit so that the rotor spins within the membrane.

3 Each H^+ ion makes one complete turn before leaving the rotor and passing through a second channel in the stator into the mitochondrial matrix.

4 Spinning of the rotor causes an internal **rod** to spin as well. This rod extends like a stalk into the **knob** below it, which is held stationary by part of the stator.

5 Turning of the rod activates catalytic sites in the knob that produce ATP from ADP and $\textcircled{P}_i$.

H^+ Stator
Rotor
Internal rod
Catalytic knob
ADP + $\textcircled{P}_i$
ATP
MITOCHONDRIAL MATRIX

▲ **Figure 9.14 ATP synthase, a molecular mill.** The ATP synthase protein complex functions as a mill, powered by the flow of hydrogen ions. Multiple ATP synthases reside in eukaryotic mitochondrial and chloroplast membranes and in prokaryotic plasma membranes. Each part of the complex consists of a number of polypeptide subunits. ATP synthase is the smallest molecular rotary motor known in nature.

Chemiosmosis: The Energy-Coupling Mechanism

Populating the inner membrane of the mitochondrion or the prokaryotic plasma membrane are many copies of a protein complex called **ATP synthase**, the enzyme that makes ATP from ADP and inorganic phosphate **(Figure 9.14)**. ATP synthase works like an ion pump running in reverse. Ion pumps usually use ATP as an energy source to transport ions against their gradients. Enzymes can catalyze a reaction in either direction, depending on the ΔG for the reaction, which is affected by the local concentrations of reactants and products (see Chapter 8). Rather than hydrolyzing ATP to pump protons against their concentration gradient, under the conditions of cellular respiration ATP synthase uses the energy of an existing ion gradient to power ATP synthesis. The power source for ATP synthase is a difference in the concentration of H^+ on opposite sides of the inner mitochondrial membrane.

Inner mitochondrial membrane

Intermembrane space

Inner mitochondrial membrane

Mitochondrial matrix

Protein complex of electron carriers

Cyt c

ATP synthase

I

Q

II
FADH₂ → FAD

III

IV

$2 H^+ + \frac{1}{2} O_2$

H_2O

NADH (carrying electrons from food) → NAD⁺

$ADP + Ⓟ_i$

ATP

1 **Electron transport chain**
Electron transport and pumping of protons (H⁺), which create an H⁺ gradient across the membrane

2 **Chemiosmosis**
ATP synthesis powered by the flow of H⁺ back across the membrane

Oxidative phosphorylation

▲ **Figure 9.15 Chemiosmosis couples the electron transport chain to ATP synthesis.**
1 NADH and FADH₂ shuttle high-energy electrons extracted from food during glycolysis and the citric acid cycle into an electron transport chain built into the inner mitochondrial membrane. The gold arrows trace the transport of electrons, which are finally passed to a terminal acceptor (O_2, in the case of aerobic respiration) at the "downhill" end of the chain, forming water. Most of the electron carriers of the chain are grouped into four complexes (I–IV). Two mobile carriers, ubiquinone (Q) and cytochrome c (Cyt c), move rapidly, ferrying electrons between the large complexes. As the complexes shuttle electrons, they pump protons from the mitochondrial matrix into the intermembrane space. FADH₂ deposits its electrons via complex II—at a lower energy level than complex I, where NADH deposits its electrons—and so results in fewer protons being pumped into the intermembrane space than occurs with NADH. Chemical energy that was originally harvested from food is transformed into a proton-motive force, a gradient of H⁺ across the membrane.
2 During chemiosmosis, the protons flow back down their gradient via ATP synthase, which is built into the membrane nearby. The ATP synthase harnesses the proton-motive force to phosphorylate ADP, forming ATP. Together, electron transport and chemiosmosis make up oxidative phosphorylation.

WHAT IF? *If complex IV were nonfunctional, could chemiosmosis produce any ATP, and if so, how would the rate of synthesis differ?*

This process, in which energy stored in the form of a hydrogen ion gradient across a membrane is used to drive cellular work such as the synthesis of ATP, is called **chemiosmosis** (from the Greek *osmos*, push). We have previously used the word *osmosis* in discussing water transport, but here it refers to the flow of H⁺ across a membrane.

From studying the structure of ATP synthase, scientists have learned how the flow of H⁺ through this large enzyme powers ATP generation. ATP synthase is a multisubunit complex with four main parts, each made up of multiple polypeptides. Protons move one by one into binding sites on one of the parts (the rotor), causing it to spin in a way that catalyzes ATP production from ADP and inorganic phosphate. The flow of protons thus behaves somewhat like a rushing stream that turns a waterwheel.

How does the inner mitochondrial membrane or the prokaryotic plasma membrane generate and maintain the H⁺ gradient that drives ATP synthesis by the ATP synthase protein complex? Establishing the H⁺ gradient is a major function of the electron transport chain, which is shown in its mitochondrial location in **Figure 9.15**. The chain is an energy converter that uses the exergonic flow of electrons from NADH and FADH₂ to pump H⁺ across the membrane, from the mitochondrial matrix into the intermembrane space. The H⁺ has a tendency to move back across the membrane, diffusing down its gradient. And the ATP synthases are the only sites that provide a route through the membrane for H⁺. As we described previously, the passage of H⁺ through ATP synthase uses the exergonic flow of H⁺ to drive the phosphorylation of ADP. Thus, the energy stored in an

H^+ gradient across a membrane couples the redox reactions of the electron transport chain to ATP.

At this point, you may be wondering how the electron transport chain pumps hydrogen ions. Researchers have found that certain members of the electron transport chain accept and release protons (H^+) along with electrons. (The aqueous solutions inside and surrounding the cell are a ready source of H^+.) At certain steps along the chain, electron transfers cause H^+ to be taken up and released into the surrounding solution. In eukaryotic cells, the electron carriers are spatially arranged in the inner mitochondrial membrane in such a way that H^+ is accepted from the mitochondrial matrix and deposited in the intermembrane space (see Figure 9.15). The H^+ gradient that results is referred to as a **proton-motive force**, emphasizing the capacity of the gradient to perform work. The force drives H^+ back across the membrane through the H^+ channels provided by ATP synthases.

In general terms, *chemiosmosis is an energy-coupling mechanism that uses energy stored in the form of an H^+ gradient across a membrane to drive cellular work.* In mitochondria, the energy for gradient formation comes from exergonic redox reactions, and ATP synthesis is the work performed. But chemiosmosis also occurs elsewhere and in other variations. Chloroplasts use chemiosmosis to generate ATP during photosynthesis; in these organelles, light (rather than chemical energy) drives both electron flow down an electron transport chain and the resulting H^+ gradient

formation. Prokaryotes, as already mentioned, generate H^+ gradients across their plasma membranes. They then tap the proton-motive force not only to make ATP inside the cell but also to rotate their flagella and to pump nutrients and waste products across the membrane. Because of its central importance to energy conversions in prokaryotes and eukaryotes, chemiosmosis has helped unify the study of bioenergetics. Peter Mitchell was awarded the Nobel Prize in 1978 for originally proposing the chemiosmotic model.

An Accounting of ATP Production by Cellular Respiration

In the last few sections, we have looked rather closely at the key processes of cellular respiration. Now let's take a step back and remind ourselves of its overall function: harvesting the energy of glucose for ATP synthesis.

During respiration, most energy flows in this sequence: glucose → NADH → electron transport chain → proton-motive force → ATP. We can do some bookkeeping to calculate the ATP profit when cellular respiration oxidizes a molecule of glucose to six molecules of carbon dioxide. The three main departments of this metabolic enterprise are glycolysis, pyruvate oxidation and the citric acid cycle, and the electron transport chain, which drives oxidative phosphorylation. **Figure 9.16** gives a detailed accounting of the ATP yield for each glucose molecule that is oxidized. The tally adds the

▲ **Figure 9.16 ATP yield per molecule of glucose at each stage of cellular respiration.**

? *Explain exactly how the total of 26 or 28 ATP (see the yellow bar in the figure) was calculated.*

4 ATP produced directly by substrate-level phosphorylation during glycolysis and the citric acid cycle to the many more molecules of ATP generated by oxidative phosphorylation. Each NADH that transfers a pair of electrons from glucose to the electron transport chain contributes enough to the proton-motive force to generate a maximum of about 3 ATP.

Why are the numbers in Figure 9.16 inexact? There are three reasons we cannot state an exact number of ATP molecules generated by the breakdown of one molecule of glucose. First, phosphorylation and the redox reactions are not directly coupled to each other, so the ratio of the number of NADH molecules to the number of ATP molecules is not a whole number. We know that 1 NADH results in 10 H^+ being transported out across the inner mitochondrial membrane, but the exact number of H^+ that must reenter the mitochondrial matrix via ATP synthase to generate 1 ATP has long been debated. Based on experimental data, however, most biochemists now agree that the most accurate number is 4 H^+. Therefore, a single molecule of NADH generates enough proton-motive force for the synthesis of 2.5 ATP. The citric acid cycle also supplies electrons to the electron transport chain via $FADH_2$, but since its electrons enter later in the chain, each molecule of this electron carrier is responsible for transport of only enough H^+ for the synthesis of 1.5 ATP. These numbers also take into account the slight energetic cost of moving the ATP formed in the mitochondrion out into the cytosol, where it will be used.

Second, the ATP yield varies slightly depending on the type of shuttle used to transport electrons from the cytosol into the mitochondrion. The mitochondrial inner membrane is impermeable to NADH, so NADH in the cytosol is segregated from the machinery of oxidative phosphorylation. The 2 electrons of NADH captured in glycolysis must be conveyed into the mitochondrion by one of several electron shuttle systems. Depending on the kind of shuttle in a particular cell type, the electrons are passed either to NAD^+ or to FAD in the mitochondrial matrix (see Figure 9.16). If the electrons are passed to FAD, as in brain cells, only about 1.5 ATP can result from each NADH that was originally generated in the cytosol. If the electrons are passed to mitochondrial NAD^+, as in liver cells and heart cells, the yield is about 2.5 ATP per NADH.

A third variable that reduces the yield of ATP is the use of the proton-motive force generated by the redox reactions of respiration to drive other kinds of work. For example, the proton-motive force powers the mitochondrion's uptake of pyruvate from the cytosol. However, if *all* the proton-motive force generated by the electron transport chain were used to drive ATP synthesis, one glucose molecule could generate a maximum of 28 ATP produced by oxidative phosphorylation plus 4 ATP (net) from substrate-level phosphorylation to give a total yield of about 32 ATP (or only about 30 ATP if the less efficient shuttle were functioning).

We can now roughly estimate the efficiency of respiration—that is, the percentage of chemical energy in glucose that has been transferred to ATP. Recall that the complete oxidation of a mole of glucose releases 686 kcal of energy under standard conditions ($\Delta G = -686$ kcal/mol). Phosphorylation of ADP to form ATP stores at least 7.3 kcal per mole of ATP. Therefore, the efficiency of respiration is 7.3 kcal per mole of ATP times 32 moles of ATP per mole of glucose divided by 686 kcal per mole of glucose, which equals 0.34. Thus, about 34% of the potential chemical energy in glucose has been transferred to ATP; the actual percentage is bound to vary as ΔG varies under different cellular conditions. Cellular respiration is remarkably efficient in its energy conversion. By comparison, even the most efficient automobile converts only about 25% of the energy stored in gasoline to energy that moves the car.

The rest of the energy stored in glucose is lost as heat. We humans use some of this heat to maintain our relatively high body temperature (37°C), and we dissipate the rest through sweating and other cooling mechanisms.

Surprisingly, perhaps, it may be beneficial under certain conditions to reduce the efficiency of cellular respiration. A remarkable adaptation is shown by hibernating mammals, which overwinter in a state of inactivity and lowered metabolism. Although their internal body temperature is lower than normal, it still must be kept significantly higher than the external air temperature. One type of tissue, called brown fat, is made up of cells packed full of mitochondria. The inner mitochondrial membrane contains a channel protein called the uncoupling protein that allows protons to flow back down their concentration gradient without generating ATP. Activation of these proteins in hibernating mammals results in ongoing oxidation of stored fuel stores (fats), generating heat without any ATP production. In the absence of such an adaptation, the buildup of ATP would eventually cause cellular respiration to be shut down by regulatory mechanisms that will be discussed later. In the Scientific Skills Exercise, you can work with data in a related but different case where a decrease in metabolic efficiency in cells is used to generate heat.

CONCEPT CHECK 9.4

1. What effect would an absence of O_2 have on the process shown in Figure 9.15?

2. **WHAT IF?** In the absence of O_2, as in question 1, what do you think would happen if you decreased the pH of the intermembrane space of the mitochondrion? Explain your answer.

3. **MAKE CONNECTIONS** Membranes must be fluid to function properly (as you learned in Concept 7.1). How does the operation of the electron transport chain support that assertion?

For suggested answers, see Appendix A.

Making a Bar Graph and Evaluating a Hypothesis

Does Thyroid Hormone Level Affect Oxygen Consumption in Cells? Some animals, such as mammals and birds, maintain a relatively constant body temperature, above that of their environment, by using heat produced as a by-product of metabolism. When the core temperature of these animals drops below an internal set point, their cells are triggered to reduce the efficiency of ATP production by the electron transport chains in mitochondria. At lower efficiency, extra fuel must be consumed to produce the same number of ATPs, generating additional heat. Because this response is moderated by the endocrine system, researchers hypothesized that thyroid hormone might trigger this cellular response. In this exercise, you will use a bar graph to visualize data from an experiment that compared the metabolic rate (by measuring oxygen consumption) in mitochondria of cells from animals with different levels of thyroid hormone.

How the Experiment Was Done Liver cells were isolated from sibling rats that had low, normal, or elevated thyroid hormone levels. The oxygen consumption rate due to activity of the mitochondrial electron transport chains of each type of cell was measured under controlled conditions.

Data from the Experiment

Thyroid Hormone Level	Oxygen Consumption Rate (nmol O_2/min · mg cells)
Low	4.3
Normal	4.8
Elevated	8.7

Interpret the Data

1. To visualize any differences in oxygen consumption between cell types, it will be useful to graph the data in a bar graph. First, set up the axes. (a) What is the independent variable (intentionally varied by the researchers), which goes on the *x*-axis? List the categories along the *x*-axis; because they are discrete rather than continuous, you can list them in any order. (b) What is the dependent variable (measured by the researchers), which goes on the *y*-axis? (c) What units (abbreviated) should go on the *y*-axis? Label the *y*-axis, including the units specified in the data table. Determine the range of values of the data that will need to go on the *y*-axis. What is the largest value? Draw evenly spaced tick marks and label them, starting with 0 at the bottom.

2. Graph the data for each sample. Match each *x*-value with its *y*-value and place a mark on the graph at that coordinate, then draw a bar from the *x*-axis up to the correct height for each sample. Why is a bar graph more appropriate than a scatter plot or line graph? (For additional information about graphs, see the Scientific Skills Review in Appendix F and in the Study Area in MasteringBiology.)

3. Examine your graph and look for a pattern in the data. (a) Which cell type had the highest rate of oxygen consumption, and which had the lowest? (b) Does this support the researchers' hypothesis? Explain. (c) Based on what you know about mitochondrial electron transport and heat production, predict which rats had the highest, and which had the lowest, body temperature.

(MB) A version of this Scientific Skills Exercise can be assigned in MasteringBiology.

Data from M. E. Harper and M. D. Brand, The quantitative contributions of mitochondrial proton leak and ATP turnover reactions to the changed respiration rates of hepatocytes from rats of different thyroid status, *Journal of Biological Chemistry* 268:14850–14860 (1993).

CONCEPT 9.5

Fermentation and anaerobic respiration enable cells to produce ATP without the use of oxygen

Because most of the ATP generated by cellular respiration is due to the work of oxidative phosphorylation, our estimate of ATP yield from aerobic respiration is contingent on an adequate supply of oxygen to the cell. Without the electronegative oxygen to pull electrons down the transport chain, oxidative phosphorylation eventually ceases. However, there are two general mechanisms by which certain cells can oxidize organic fuel and generate ATP *without* the use of oxygen: anaerobic respiration and fermentation. The distinction between these two is that an electron transport chain is used in anaerobic respiration but not in fermentation. (The electron transport chain is also called the respiratory chain because of its role in both types of cellular respiration.)

We have already mentioned anaerobic respiration, which takes place in certain prokaryotic organisms that live in environments without oxygen. These organisms have an electron transport chain but do not use oxygen as a final electron acceptor at the end of the chain. Oxygen performs this function very well because it is extremely electronegative, but other, less electronegative substances can also serve as final electron acceptors. Some "sulfate-reducing" marine bacteria, for instance, use the sulfate ion (SO_4^{2-}) at the end of their respiratory chain. Operation of the chain builds up a proton-motive force used to produce ATP, but H_2S (hydrogen sulfide) is made as a by-product rather than water. The rotten-egg odor you may have smelled while walking through a salt marsh or a mudflat signals the presence of sulfate-reducing bacteria.

Fermentation is a way of harvesting chemical energy without using either oxygen or any electron transport chain—in other words, without cellular respiration. How can food be oxidized without cellular respiration? Remember, oxidation simply refers to the loss of electrons to an electron acceptor, so it does not need to involve oxygen. Glycolysis oxidizes glucose to two molecules of pyruvate. The oxidizing agent of glycolysis is NAD^+, and neither oxygen nor any electron transfer chain is involved. Overall, glycolysis is exergonic, and some of the energy made available is used to produce 2 ATP (net) by substrate-level phosphorylation. If oxygen *is* present, then additional ATP is made by oxidative phosphorylation when NADH passes electrons removed from glucose to the electron transport chain. But glycolysis generates 2 ATP whether oxygen is present or not—that is, whether conditions are aerobic or anaerobic.

As an alternative to respiratory oxidation of organic nutrients, fermentation is an extension of glycolysis that allows continuous generation of ATP by the substrate-level phosphorylation of glycolysis. For this to occur, there must be a sufficient supply of NAD^+ to accept electrons during the oxidation step of glycolysis. Without some mechanism to recycle NAD^+ from NADH, glycolysis would soon deplete the cell's pool of NAD^+ by reducing it all to NADH and would shut itself down for lack of an oxidizing agent. Under aerobic conditions, NAD^+ is recycled from NADH by the transfer of electrons to the electron transport chain. An anaerobic alternative is to transfer electrons from NADH to pyruvate, the end product of glycolysis.

Types of Fermentation

Fermentation consists of glycolysis plus reactions that regenerate NAD^+ by transferring electrons from NADH to pyruvate or derivatives of pyruvate. The NAD^+ can then be reused to oxidize sugar by glycolysis, which nets two molecules of ATP by substrate-level phosphorylation. There are many types of fermentation, differing in the end products formed from pyruvate. Two types commonly harnessed by humans for food and industrial production are alcohol fermentation and lactic acid fermentation.

In **alcohol fermentation** (Figure 9.17a), pyruvate is converted to ethanol (ethyl alcohol) in two steps. The first step releases carbon dioxide from the pyruvate, which is

▲ **Figure 9.17 Fermentation.** In the absence of oxygen, many cells use fermentation to produce ATP by substrate-level phosphorylation. Pyruvate, the end product of glycolysis, serves as an electron acceptor for oxidizing NADH back to NAD^+, which can then be reused in glycolysis. Two of the common end products formed from fermentation are **(a)** ethanol and **(b)** lactate, the ionized form of lactic acid.

converted to the two-carbon compound acetaldehyde. In the second step, acetaldehyde is reduced by NADH to ethanol. This regenerates the supply of NAD^+ needed for the continuation of glycolysis. Many bacteria carry out alcohol fermentation under anaerobic conditions. Yeast (a fungus) also carries out alcohol fermentation. For thousands of years, humans have used yeast in brewing, winemaking, and baking. The CO_2 bubbles generated by baker's yeast during alcohol fermentation allow bread to rise.

During **lactic acid fermentation** (Figure 9.17b), pyruvate is reduced directly by NADH to form lactate as an end product, with no release of CO_2. (Lactate is the ionized form of lactic acid.) Lactic acid fermentation by certain fungi and bacteria is used in the dairy industry to make cheese and yogurt.

Human muscle cells make ATP by lactic acid fermentation when oxygen is scarce. This occurs during strenuous exercise, when sugar catabolism for ATP production outpaces the muscle's supply of oxygen from the blood. Under these conditions, the cells switch from aerobic respiration to fermentation. The lactate that accumulates was previously thought to cause muscle fatigue and pain, but recent research suggests instead that increased levels of potassium ions (K^+) may be to blame, while lactate appears to enhance muscle performance. In any case, the excess lactate is gradually carried away by the blood to the liver, where it is converted back to pyruvate by liver cells. Because oxygen is available, this pyruvate can then enter the mitochondria in liver cells and complete cellular respiration.

Comparing Fermentation with Anaerobic and Aerobic Respiration

Fermentation, anaerobic respiration, and aerobic respiration are three alternative cellular pathways for producing ATP by harvesting the chemical energy of food. All three use glycolysis to oxidize glucose and other organic fuels to pyruvate, with a net production of 2 ATP by substrate-level phosphorylation. And in all three pathways, NAD^+ is the oxidizing agent that accepts electrons from food during glycolysis.

A key difference is the contrasting mechanisms for oxidizing NADH back to NAD^+, which is required to sustain glycolysis. In fermentation, the final electron acceptor is an organic molecule such as pyruvate (lactic acid fermentation) or acetaldehyde (alcohol fermentation). In cellular respiration, by contrast, electrons carried by NADH are transferred to an electron transport chain, which regenerates the NAD^+ required for glycolysis.

Another major difference is the amount of ATP produced. Fermentation yields 2 molecules of ATP, produced by substrate-level phosphorylation. In the absence of an electron transport chain, the energy stored in pyruvate is unavailable. In cellular respiration, however, pyruvate is completely oxidized in the mitochondrion. Most of the chemical energy from this process is shuttled by NADH and $FADH_2$ in the form of electrons to the electron transport chain. There, the electrons move stepwise down a series of redox reactions to a final electron acceptor. (In aerobic respiration, the final electron acceptor is oxygen; in anaerobic respiration, the final acceptor is another molecule that is electronegative, although less so than oxygen.) Stepwise electron transport drives oxidative phosphorylation, yielding ATPs. Thus, cellular respiration harvests much more energy from each sugar molecule than fermentation can. In fact, aerobic respiration yields up to 32 molecules of ATP per glucose molecule—up to 16 times as much as does fermentation.

Some organisms, called **obligate anaerobes**, carry out only fermentation or anaerobic respiration. In fact, these

▲ **Figure 9.18 Pyruvate as a key juncture in catabolism.** Glycolysis is common to fermentation and cellular respiration. The end product of glycolysis, pyruvate, represents a fork in the catabolic pathways of glucose oxidation. In a facultative anaerobe or a muscle cell, which are capable of both aerobic cellular respiration and fermentation, pyruvate is committed to one of those two pathways, usually depending on whether or not oxygen is present.

organisms cannot survive in the presence of oxygen, some forms of which can actually be toxic if protective systems are not present in the cell. A few cell types, such as cells of the vertebrate brain, can carry out only aerobic oxidation of pyruvate, not fermentation. Other organisms, including yeasts and many bacteria, can make enough ATP to survive using either fermentation or respiration. Such species are called **facultative anaerobes**. On the cellular level, our muscle cells behave as facultative anaerobes. In such cells, pyruvate is a fork in the metabolic road that leads to two alternative catabolic routes (**Figure 9.18**). Under aerobic conditions, pyruvate can be converted to acetyl CoA, and oxidation continues in the citric acid cycle via aerobic respiration. Under anaerobic conditions, lactic acid fermentation occurs: Pyruvate is diverted from the citric acid cycle, serving instead as an electron acceptor to recycle NAD^+. To make the same amount of ATP, a facultative anaerobe has to consume sugar at a much faster rate when fermenting than when respiring.

The Evolutionary Significance of Glycolysis

EVOLUTION The role of glycolysis in both fermentation and respiration has an evolutionary basis. Ancient prokaryotes are thought to have used glycolysis to make ATP long before oxygen was present in Earth's atmosphere. The oldest known fossils of bacteria date back 3.5 billion years, but appreciable quantities of oxygen probably did not begin to accumulate in the atmosphere until about 2.7 billion years ago. Cyanobacteria produced this O_2 as a by-product of photosynthesis. Therefore, early prokaryotes may have generated ATP exclusively from glycolysis. The fact that glycolysis is today the most widespread metabolic pathway among Earth's organisms suggests that it evolved very early in the history of life. The cytosolic location of glycolysis also implies great antiquity; the pathway does not require any of the membrane-enclosed organelles of the eukaryotic cell, which evolved approximately 1 billion years after the first prokaryotic cell. Glycolysis is a metabolic heirloom from early cells that continues to function in fermentation and as the first stage in the breakdown of organic molecules by respiration.

CONCEPT CHECK 9.5

1. Consider the NADH formed during glycolysis. What is the final acceptor for its electrons during fermentation? What is the final acceptor for its electrons during aerobic respiration?

2. **WHAT IF?** A glucose-fed yeast cell is moved from an aerobic environment to an anaerobic one. How would its rate of glucose consumption change if ATP were to be generated at the same rate?

For suggested answers, see Appendix A.

CONCEPT 9.6

Glycolysis and the citric acid cycle connect to many other metabolic pathways

So far, we have treated the oxidative breakdown of glucose in isolation from the cell's overall metabolic economy. In this section, you will learn that glycolysis and the citric acid cycle are major intersections of the cell's catabolic (breakdown) and anabolic (biosynthetic) pathways.

The Versatility of Catabolism

Throughout this chapter, we have used glucose as an example of a fuel for cellular respiration. But free glucose molecules are not common in the diets of humans and other animals. We obtain most of our calories in the form of fats, proteins, sucrose and other disaccharides, and starch, a polysaccharide. All these organic molecules in food can be used by cellular respiration to make ATP (Figure 9.19).

Glycolysis can accept a wide range of carbohydrates for catabolism. In the digestive tract, starch is hydrolyzed to glucose, which can then be broken down in the cells by glycolysis and the citric acid cycle. Similarly, glycogen, the polysaccharide that humans and many other animals store

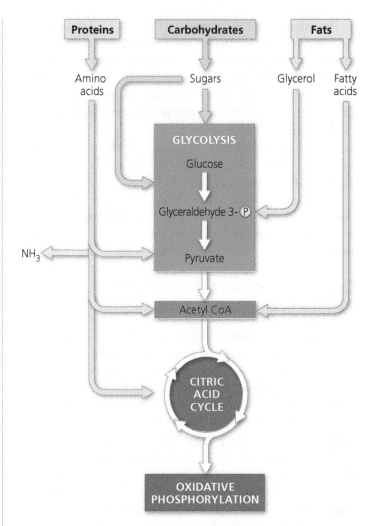

▲ Figure 9.19 **The catabolism of various molecules from food.** Carbohydrates, fats, and proteins can all be used as fuel for cellular respiration. Monomers of these molecules enter glycolysis or the citric acid cycle at various points. Glycolysis and the citric acid cycle are catabolic funnels through which electrons from all kinds of organic molecules flow on their exergonic fall to oxygen.

in their liver and muscle cells, can be hydrolyzed to glucose between meals as fuel for respiration. The digestion of disaccharides, including sucrose, provides glucose and other monosaccharides as fuel for respiration.

Proteins can also be used for fuel, but first they must be digested to their constituent amino acids. Many of the amino acids are used by the organism to build new proteins. Amino acids present in excess are converted by enzymes to intermediates of glycolysis and the citric acid cycle. Before amino acids can feed into glycolysis or the citric acid cycle, their amino groups must be removed, a process called *deamination*. The nitrogenous refuse is excreted from the animal in the form of ammonia (NH_3), urea, or other waste products.

Catabolism can also harvest energy stored in fats obtained either from food or from storage cells in the body. After fats are digested to glycerol and fatty acids, the glycerol is converted to glyceraldehyde 3-phosphate, an intermediate of glycolysis. Most of the energy of a fat is stored in the fatty acids. A metabolic sequence called **beta oxidation** breaks the fatty acids down to two-carbon fragments, which enter the citric acid cycle as acetyl CoA. NADH and $FADH_2$ are also generated during beta oxidation; they can enter the electron transport chain, leading to further ATP production. Fats make excellent fuels, in large part due to their chemical structure and the high energy level of their electrons (equally shared between carbon and hydrogen) compared to those of carbohydrates. A gram of fat oxidized by respiration produces more than twice as much ATP as a gram of carbohydrate. Unfortunately, this also means that a person trying to lose weight must work hard to use up fat stored in the body because so many calories are stockpiled in each gram of fat.

Biosynthesis (Anabolic Pathways)

Cells need substance as well as energy. Not all the organic molecules of food are destined to be oxidized as fuel to make ATP. In addition to calories, food must also provide the carbon skeletons that cells require to make their own molecules. Some organic monomers obtained from digestion can be used directly. For example, as previously mentioned, amino acids from the hydrolysis of proteins in food can be incorporated into the organism's own proteins. Often, however, the body needs specific molecules that are not present as such in food. Compounds formed as intermediates of glycolysis and the citric acid cycle can be diverted into anabolic pathways as precursors from which the cell can synthesize the molecules it requires. For example, humans can make about half of the 20 amino acids in proteins by modifying compounds siphoned away from the citric acid cycle; the rest are "essential amino acids" that must be obtained in the diet. Also, glucose can be made from pyruvate, and fatty acids can be synthesized from acetyl CoA. Of course, these anabolic, or biosynthetic, pathways do not generate ATP, but instead consume it.

In addition, glycolysis and the citric acid cycle function as metabolic interchanges that enable our cells to convert some kinds of molecules to others as we need them. For example, an intermediate compound generated during glycolysis, dihydroxyacetone phosphate (see Figure 9.9, step 5), can be converted to one of the major precursors of fats. If we eat more food than we need, we store fat even if our diet is fat-free. Metabolism is remarkably versatile and adaptable.

Regulation of Cellular Respiration via Feedback Mechanisms

Basic principles of supply and demand regulate the metabolic economy. The cell does not waste energy making more of a particular substance than it needs. If there is a glut of a

certain amino acid, for example, the anabolic pathway that synthesizes that amino acid from an intermediate of the citric acid cycle is switched off. The most common mechanism for this control is feedback inhibition: The end product of the anabolic pathway inhibits the enzyme that catalyzes an early step of the pathway (see Figure 8.21). This prevents the needless diversion of key metabolic intermediates from uses that are more urgent.

The cell also controls its catabolism. If the cell is working hard and its ATP concentration begins to drop, respiration speeds up. When there is plenty of ATP to meet demand, respiration slows down, sparing valuable organic molecules for other functions. Again, control is based mainly on regulating the activity of enzymes at strategic points in the catabolic pathway. As shown in **Figure 9.20**, one important

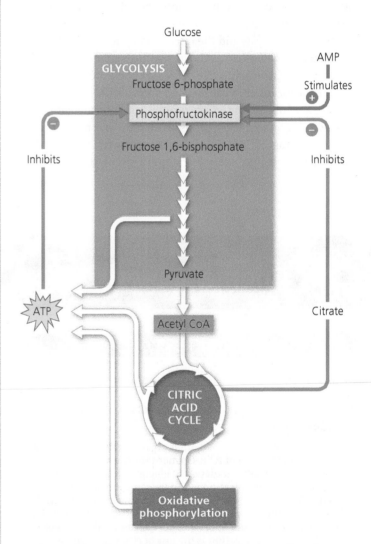

▲ **Figure 9.20 The control of cellular respiration.** Allosteric enzymes at certain points in the respiratory pathway respond to inhibitors and activators that help set the pace of glycolysis and the citric acid cycle. Phosphofructokinase, which catalyzes an early step in glycolysis (see Figure 9.9, step 3), is one such enzyme. It is stimulated by AMP (derived from ADP) but is inhibited by ATP and by citrate. This feedback regulation adjusts the rate of respiration as the cell's catabolic and anabolic demands change.

switch is phosphofructokinase, the enzyme that catalyzes step 3 of glycolysis (see Figure 9.9). That is the first step that commits the substrate irreversibly to the glycolytic pathway. By controlling the rate of this step, the cell can speed up or slow down the entire catabolic process. Phosphofructokinase can thus be considered the pacemaker of respiration.

Phosphofructokinase is an allosteric enzyme with receptor sites for specific inhibitors and activators. It is inhibited by ATP and stimulated by AMP (adenosine monophosphate), which the cell derives from ADP. As ATP accumulates, inhibition of the enzyme slows down glycolysis. The enzyme becomes active again as cellular work converts ATP to ADP (and AMP) faster than ATP is being regenerated. Phosphofructokinase is also sensitive to citrate, the first product of the citric acid cycle. If citrate accumulates in mitochondria, some of it passes into the cytosol and inhibits phosphofructokinase. This mechanism helps synchronize the rates of glycolysis and the citric acid cycle. As citrate accumulates, glycolysis slows down, and the supply of acetyl groups to the citric acid cycle decreases. If citrate consumption increases, either because of a demand for more ATP or because anabolic pathways are draining off intermediates of the citric acid cycle, glycolysis accelerates and meets the demand. Metabolic balance is augmented by the control of enzymes that catalyze other key steps of glycolysis and the citric acid cycle. Cells are thrifty, expedient, and responsive in their metabolism.

Cellular respiration and metabolic pathways play a role of central importance in organisms. Examine Figure 9.2 again to put cellular respiration into the broader context of energy flow and chemical cycling in ecosystems. The energy that keeps us alive is *released*, not *produced*, by cellular respiration. We are tapping energy that was stored in food by photosynthesis. In the next chapter, you will learn how photosynthesis captures light and converts it to chemical energy.

CONCEPT CHECK 9.6

1. **MAKE CONNECTIONS** Compare the structure of a fat (see Figure 5.9) with that of a carbohydrate (see Figure 5.3). What features of their structures make fat a much better fuel?

2. Under what circumstances might your body synthesize fat molecules?

3. **WHAT IF?** What will happen in a muscle cell that has used up its supply of oxygen and ATP? (Review Figures 9.18 and 9.20.)

4. **WHAT IF?** During intense exercise, can a muscle cell use fat as a concentrated source of chemical energy? Explain. (Review Figures 9.18 and 9.19.)

For suggested answers, see Appendix A.

9 Chapter Review

SUMMARY OF KEY CONCEPTS

CONCEPT 9.1

Catabolic pathways yield energy by oxidizing organic fuels (pp. 163–167)

- Cells break down glucose and other organic fuels to yield chemical energy in the form of ATP. **Fermentation** is a process that results in the partial degradation of glucose without the use of oxygen. **Cellular respiration** is a more complete breakdown of glucose; in **aerobic respiration**, oxygen is used as a reactant. The cell taps the energy stored in food molecules through **redox reactions**, in which one substance partially or totally shifts electrons to another. **Oxidation** is the loss of electrons from one substance, while **reduction** is the addition of electrons to the other.

- During aerobic respiration, glucose ($C_6H_{12}O_6$) is oxidized to CO_2, and O_2 is reduced to H_2O. Electrons lose potential energy during their transfer from glucose or other organic compounds to oxygen. Electrons are usually passed first to **NAD$^+$**, reducing it to NADH, and then from NADH to an **electron transport chain**, which conducts them to O_2 in energy-releasing steps. The energy is used to make ATP.

- Aerobic respiration occurs in three stages: (1) **glycolysis**, (2) pyruvate oxidation and the **citric acid cycle**, and (3) **oxidative phosphorylation** (electron transport and chemiosmosis).

? *Describe the difference between the two processes in cellular respiration that produce ATP: oxidative phosphorylation and substrate-level phosphorylation.*

CONCEPT 9.2

Glycolysis harvests chemical energy by oxidizing glucose to pyruvate (pp. 168–169)

- Glycolysis ("splitting of sugar") is a series of reactions that break down glucose into two pyruvate molecules, which may go on to enter the citric acid cycle, and nets 2 ATP and 2 NADH per glucose molecule.

Inputs		Outputs
Glucose	GLYCOLYSIS →	2 Pyruvate + 2 ATP + 2 NADH

? *Which reactions in glycolysis are the source of energy for the formation of ATP and NADH?*

After pyruvate is oxidized, the citric acid cycle completes the energy-yielding oxidation of organic molecules (pp. 169–172)

- In eukaryotic cells, pyruvate enters the mitochondrion and is oxidized to **acetyl CoA**, which is further oxidized in the citric acid cycle.

? *What molecular products indicate the complete oxidation of glucose during cellular respiration?*

During oxidative phosphorylation, chemiosmosis couples electron transport to ATP synthesis (pp. 172–177)

- NADH and $FADH_2$ transfer electrons to the electron transport chain. Electrons move down the chain, losing energy in several energy-releasing steps. Finally, electrons are passed to O_2, reducing it to H_2O.

- At certain steps along the electron transport chain, electron transfer causes protein complexes to move H^+ from the mitochondrial matrix (in eukaryotes) to the intermembrane space, storing energy as a **proton-motive force** (H^+ gradient). As H^+ diffuses back into the matrix through **ATP synthase**, its passage drives the phosphorylation of ADP to form ATP, a process called **chemiosmosis**.

- About 34% of the energy stored in a glucose molecule is transferred to ATP during cellular respiration, producing a maximum of about 32 ATP.

? *Briefly explain the mechanism by which ATP synthase produces ATP. List three locations in which ATP synthases are found.*

Fermentation and anaerobic respiration enable cells to produce ATP without the use of oxygen (pp. 177–180)

- Glycolysis nets 2 ATP by substrate-level phosphorylation, whether oxygen is present or not. Under anaerobic conditions, either anaerobic respiration or fermentation can take place. In anaerobic respiration, an electron transport chain is present with a final electron acceptor other than oxygen. In fermentation, the electrons from NADH are passed to pyruvate or a derivative of pyruvate, regenerating the NAD^+ required to oxidize more glucose. Two common types of fermentation are **alcohol fermentation** and **lactic acid fermentation**.
- Fermentation and anaerobic or aerobic respiration all use glycolysis to oxidize glucose, but they differ in their final electron acceptor and whether an electron transport chain is used (respiration) or not (fermentation). Respiration yields more ATP; aerobic respiration, with O_2 as the final electron acceptor, yields about 16 times as much ATP as does fermentation.
- Glycolysis occurs in nearly all organisms and is thought to have evolved in ancient prokaryotes before there was O_2 in the atmosphere.

? *Which process yields more ATP, fermentation or anaerobic respiration? Explain.*

Glycolysis and the citric acid cycle connect to many other metabolic pathways (pp. 180–182)

- Catabolic pathways funnel electrons from many kinds of organic molecules into cellular respiration. Many carbohydrates can enter glycolysis, most often after conversion to glucose. Amino acids of proteins must be deaminated before being oxidized. The fatty acids of fats undergo **beta oxidation** to two-carbon fragments and then enter the citric acid cycle as acetyl CoA. Anabolic pathways can use small molecules from food directly or build other substances using intermediates of glycolysis or the citric acid cycle.
- Cellular respiration is controlled by allosteric enzymes at key points in glycolysis and the citric acid cycle.

? *Describe how the catabolic pathways of glycolysis and the citric acid cycle intersect with anabolic pathways in the metabolism of a cell.*

TEST YOUR UNDERSTANDING

LEVEL 1: KNOWLEDGE/COMPREHENSION

1. The *immediate* energy source that drives ATP synthesis by ATP synthase during oxidative phosphorylation is the
   a. oxidation of glucose and other organic compounds.
   b. flow of electrons down the electron transport chain.
   c. H^+ concentration gradient across the membrane holding ATP synthase.
   d. transfer of phosphate to ADP.

2. Which metabolic pathway is common to both fermentation and cellular respiration of a glucose molecule?
   a. the citric acid cycle
   b. the electron transport chain
   c. glycolysis
   d. reduction of pyruvate to lactate

3. The final electron acceptor of the electron transport chain that functions in aerobic oxidative phosphorylation is
   a. oxygen. b. water. c. NAD^+. d. pyruvate.

4. In mitochondria, exergonic redox reactions
   a. are the source of energy driving prokaryotic ATP synthesis.
   b. provide the energy that establishes the proton gradient.
   c. reduce carbon atoms to carbon dioxide.
   d. are coupled via phosphorylated intermediates to endergonic processes.

LEVEL 2: APPLICATION/ANALYSIS

5. What is the oxidizing agent in the following reaction?

   $$\text{Pyruvate} + \text{NADH} + \text{H}^+ \rightarrow \text{Lactate} + \text{NAD}^+$$

   a. oxygen
   b. NADH
   c. lactate
   d. pyruvate

6. When electrons flow along the electron transport chains of mitochondria, which of the following changes occurs?
   a. The pH of the matrix increases.
   b. ATP synthase pumps protons by active transport.
   c. The electrons gain free energy.
   d. NAD^+ is oxidized.

7. Most CO_2 from catabolism is released during
   a. glycolysis.
   b. the citric acid cycle.
   c. lactate fermentation.
   d. electron transport.

8. **MAKE CONNECTIONS** Step 3 in Figure 9.9 is a major point of regulation of glycolysis. The enzyme phosphofructokinase is allosterically regulated by ATP and related molecules (see Concept 8.5). Considering the overall result of glycolysis, would you expect ATP to inhibit or stimulate activity of this enzyme? Explain. (*Hint:* Make sure you consider the role of ATP as an allosteric regulator, not as a substrate of the enzyme.)

9. **MAKE CONNECTIONS** The proton pump shown in Figure 7.17 is depicted as a simplified oval purple shape, but it is, in fact, an ATP synthase (see Figure 9.14). Compare the processes shown in the two figures, and say whether they are involved in active or passive transport (see Concepts 7.3 and 7.4).

LEVEL 3: SYNTHESIS/EVALUATION

10. **INTERPRET THE DATA**

    Phosphofructokinase is an enzyme that acts on fructose 6-phosphate at an early step in glucose breakdown. Regulation of this enzyme controls whether the sugar will continue on in the glycolytic pathway. Considering this graph, under which condition is phosphofructokinase more active? Given what you know about glycolysis and regulation of metabolism by this enzyme, explain the mechanism by which phosphofructokinase activity differs depending on ATP concentration.

11. **DRAW IT** The graph here shows the pH difference across the inner mitochondrial membrane over time in an actively respiring cell. At the time indicated by the vertical arrow, a metabolic poison is added that specifically and completely inhibits all function of mitochondrial ATP synthase. Draw what you would expect to see for the rest of the graphed line, and explain your reasoning for drawing the line as you did.

12. **EVOLUTION CONNECTION**
    ATP synthases are found in the prokaryotic plasma membrane and in mitochondria and chloroplasts. What does this suggest about the evolutionary relationship of these eukaryotic organelles to prokaryotes? How might the amino acid sequences of the ATP synthases from the different sources support or refute your hypothesis?

13. **SCIENTIFIC INQUIRY**
    In the 1930s, some physicians prescribed low doses of a compound called dinitrophenol (DNP) to help patients lose weight. This unsafe method was abandoned after some patients died. DNP uncouples the chemiosmotic machinery by making the lipid bilayer of the inner mitochondrial membrane leaky to H^+. Explain how this could cause weight loss and death.

14. **WRITE ABOUT A THEME: ORGANIZATION**
    In a short essay (100–150 words), explain how oxidative phosphorylation—production of ATP using energy from the redox reactions of a spatially organized electron transport chain followed by chemiosmosis—is an example of how new properties emerge at each level of the biological hierarchy.

15. **SYNTHESIZE YOUR KNOWLEDGE**

Coenzyme Q (CoQ) is sold as a nutritional supplement. One company uses this marketing slogan for CoQ: "Give your heart the fuel it craves most." Considering the role of coenzyme Q, how do you think this product might function as a nutritional supplement to benefit the heart? Is CoQ used as a "fuel" during cellular respiration?

For selected answers, see Appendix A.

MasteringBiology®

Students Go to **MasteringBiology** for assignments, the eText, and the Study Area with practice tests, animations, and activities.

Instructors Go to **MasteringBiology** for automatically graded tutorials and questions that you can assign to your students, plus Instructor Resources.

10

Photosynthesis

▲ Other organisms also benefit from photosynthesis.

▲ Figure 10.1 How does sunlight help build the trunk, branches, and leaves of this broadleaf tree?

The Process That Feeds the Biosphere

Life on Earth is solar powered. The chloroplasts in plants and other photosynthetic organisms capture light energy that has traveled 150 million kilometers from the sun and convert it to chemical energy that is stored in sugar and other organic molecules. This conversion process is called **photosynthesis**. Let's begin by placing photosynthesis in its ecological context.

Photosynthesis nourishes almost the entire living world directly or indirectly. An organism acquires the organic compounds it uses for energy and carbon skeletons by one of two major modes: autotrophic nutrition or heterotrophic nutrition. **Autotrophs** are "self-feeders" (*auto-* means "self," and *trophos* means "feeder"); they sustain themselves without eating anything derived from other living beings. Autotrophs produce their organic molecules from CO_2 and other inorganic raw materials obtained from the environment. They are the ultimate sources of organic compounds for all nonautotrophic organisms, and for this reason, biologists refer to autotrophs as the *producers* of the biosphere.

Almost all plants are autotrophs; the only nutrients they require are water and minerals from the soil and carbon dioxide from the air. Specifically, plants are *photo*autotrophs, organisms that use light as a source of energy to synthesize organic substances (Figure 10.1). Photosynthesis also occurs in algae, certain other unicellular eukaryotes, and some prokaryotes (Figure 10.2). In this chapter, we will touch on these other groups in passing, but our emphasis will be on plants. Variations in autotrophic nutrition that occur in prokaryotes and algae will be described in Chapters 27 and 28.

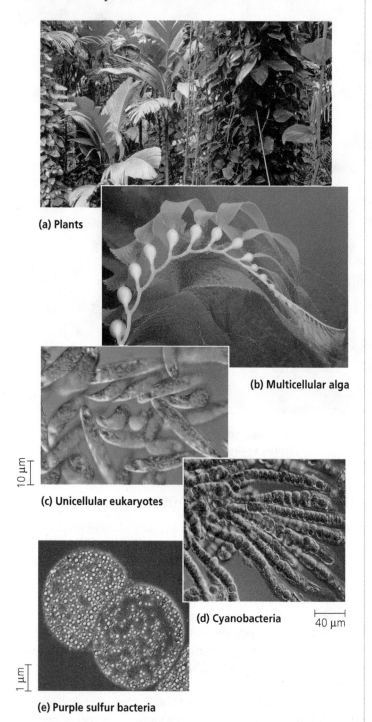

(a) Plants

(b) Multicellular alga

(c) Unicellular eukaryotes

(d) Cyanobacteria

40 μm

10 μm

1 μm

(e) Purple sulfur bacteria

▲ **Figure 10.2 Photoautotrophs.** These organisms use light energy to drive the synthesis of organic molecules from carbon dioxide and (in most cases) water. They feed themselves and the entire living world. **(a)** On land, plants are the predominant producers of food. In aquatic environments, photoautotrophs include unicellular and **(b)** multicellular algae, such as this kelp; **(c)** some non-algal unicellular eukaryotes, such as *Euglena*; **(d)** the prokaryotes called cyanobacteria; and **(e)** other photosynthetic prokaryotes, such as these purple sulfur bacteria, which produce sulfur (the yellow globules within the cells) (c–e, LMs).

Heterotrophs obtain organic material by the second major mode of nutrition. Unable to make their own food, they live on compounds produced by other organisms (*hetero-* means "other"). Heterotrophs are the biosphere's *consumers*. The most obvious "other-feeding" occurs when an animal eats plants or other animals. But heterotrophic nutrition may be more subtle. Some heterotrophs consume the remains of dead organisms by decomposing and feeding on organic litter such as carcasses, feces, and fallen leaves; these types of organisms are known as decomposers. Most fungi and many types of prokaryotes get their nourishment this way. Almost all heterotrophs, including humans, are completely dependent, either directly or indirectly, on photoautotrophs for food—and also for oxygen, a by-product of photosynthesis.

The Earth's supply of fossil fuels was formed from remains of organisms that died hundreds of millions of years ago. In a sense, then, fossil fuels represent stores of the sun's energy from the distant past. Because these resources are being used at a much higher rate than they are replenished, researchers are exploring methods of capitalizing on the photosynthetic process to provide alternative fuels (Figure 10.3).

In this chapter, you'll learn how photosynthesis works. After discussing general principles of photosynthesis, we'll consider the two stages of photosynthesis: the light reactions, which capture solar energy and transform it into chemical energy; and the Calvin cycle, which uses that chemical energy to make the organic molecules of food. Finally, we will consider some aspects of photosynthesis from an evolutionary perspective.

▲ **Figure 10.3 Alternative fuels from algae.** The power of sunlight can be tapped to generate a sustainable alternative to fossil fuels. Species of unicellular algae that are prolific producers of plant oils can be cultured in long, transparent tanks called photobioreactors, such as the one shown here at Arizona State University. A simple chemical process can yield "biodiesel," which can be mixed with gasoline or used alone to power vehicles.

WHAT IF? *The main product of fossil fuel combustion is CO_2, and this is the source of the increase in atmospheric CO_2 concentration. Scientists have proposed strategically situating containers of these algae near industrial plants or near highly congested city streets. Considering the process of photosynthesis, how does this arrangement make sense?*

Photosynthesis converts light energy to the chemical energy of food

The remarkable ability of an organism to harness light energy and use it to drive the synthesis of organic compounds emerges from structural organization in the cell: Photosynthetic enzymes and other molecules are grouped together in a biological membrane, enabling the necessary series of chemical reactions to be carried out efficiently. The process of photosynthesis most likely originated in a group of bacteria that had infolded regions of the plasma membrane containing clusters of such molecules. In existing photosynthetic bacteria, infolded photosynthetic membranes function similarly to the internal membranes of the chloroplast, a eukaryotic organelle. According to what has come to be known as the endosymbiont theory, the original chloroplast was a photosynthetic prokaryote that lived inside an ancestor of eukaryotic cells. (You learned about this theory in Chapter 6, and it will be described more fully in Chapter 25.) Chloroplasts are present in a variety of photosynthesizing organisms (see some examples in Figure 10.2), but here we focus on chloroplasts in plants.

Chloroplasts: The Sites of Photosynthesis in Plants

All green parts of a plant, including green stems and unripened fruit, have chloroplasts, but the leaves are the major sites of photosynthesis in most plants (**Figure 10.4**). There are about half a million chloroplasts in a chunk of leaf with a top surface area of 1 mm^2. Chloroplasts are found mainly in the cells of the **mesophyll**, the tissue in the interior of the leaf. Carbon dioxide enters the leaf, and oxygen exits, by way of microscopic pores called **stomata** (singular, *stoma*; from the Greek, meaning "mouth"). Water absorbed by the roots is delivered to the leaves in veins. Leaves also use veins to export sugar to roots and other nonphotosynthetic parts of the plant.

A typical mesophyll cell has about 30–40 chloroplasts, each measuring about 2–4 μm by 4–7 μm. A chloroplast has an envelope of two membranes surrounding a dense fluid called the **stroma**. Suspended within the stroma is a third membrane system, made up of sacs called **thylakoids**, which segregates the stroma from the *thylakoid space* inside these sacs. In some places, thylakoid sacs are stacked in columns called *grana* (singular, *granum*). **Chlorophyll**, the green pigment that gives leaves their color, resides in the thylakoid membranes of the chloroplast. (The internal photosynthetic membranes of some prokaryotes are also called thylakoid

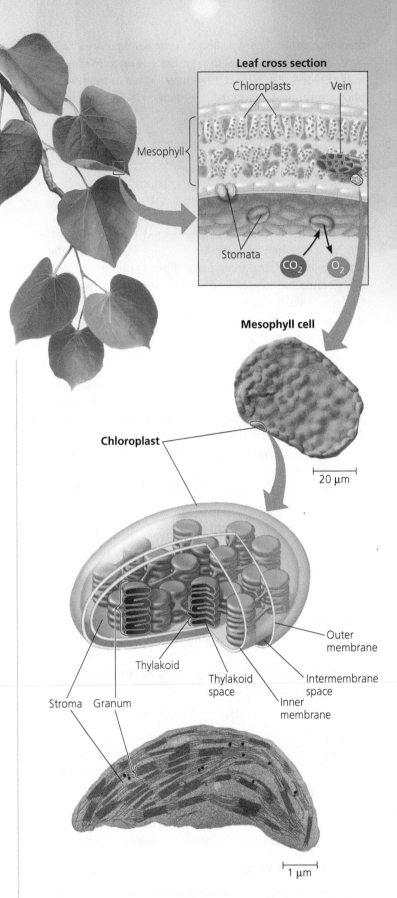

Leaf cross section

Chloroplasts   Vein

Mesophyll

Stomata

CO_2 O_2

Mesophyll cell

Chloroplast

20 μm

Outer membrane

Thylakoid

Thylakoid space

Intermembrane space

Stroma   Granum

Inner membrane

1 μm

▲ **Figure 10.4 Zooming in on the location of photosynthesis in a plant.** Leaves are the major organs of photosynthesis in plants. These pictures take you into a leaf, then into a cell, and finally into a chloroplast, the organelle where photosynthesis occurs (middle, LM; bottom, TEM).

membranes; see Figure 27.8b.) It is the light energy absorbed by chlorophyll that drives the synthesis of organic molecules in the chloroplast. Now that we have looked at the sites of photosynthesis in plants, we are ready to look more closely at the process of photosynthesis.

Tracking Atoms Through Photosynthesis: *Scientific Inquiry*

Scientists have tried for centuries to piece together the process by which plants make food. Although some of the steps are still not completely understood, the overall photosynthetic equation has been known since the 1800s: In the presence of light, the green parts of plants produce organic compounds and oxygen from carbon dioxide and water. Using molecular formulas, we can summarize the complex series of chemical reactions in photosynthesis with this chemical equation:

$$6 CO_2 + 12 H_2O + Light\ energy \rightarrow C_6H_{12}O_6 + 6 O_2 + 6 H_2O$$

We use glucose ($C_6H_{12}O_6$) here to simplify the relationship between photosynthesis and respiration, but the direct product of photosynthesis is actually a three-carbon sugar that can be used to make glucose. Water appears on both sides of the equation because 12 molecules are consumed and 6 molecules are newly formed during photosynthesis. We can simplify the equation by indicating only the net consumption of water:

$$6 CO_2 + 6 H_2O + Light\ energy \rightarrow C_6H_{12}O_6 + 6 O_2$$

Writing the equation in this form, we can see that the overall chemical change during photosynthesis is the reverse of the one that occurs during cellular respiration (see Concept 9.1). Both of these metabolic processes occur in plant cells. However, as you will soon learn, chloroplasts do not synthesize sugars by simply reversing the steps of respiration.

Now let's divide the photosynthetic equation by 6 to put it in its simplest possible form:

$$CO_2 + H_2O \rightarrow [CH_2O] + O_2$$

Here, the brackets indicate that CH_2O is not an actual sugar but represents the general formula for a carbohydrate (see Concept 5.2). In other words, we are imagining the synthesis of a sugar molecule one carbon at a time. Six repetitions would theoretically produce a glucose molecule ($C_6H_{12}O_6$). Let's now see how researchers tracked the elements C, H, and O from the reactants of photosynthesis to the products.

The Splitting of Water

One of the first clues to the mechanism of photosynthesis came from the discovery that the O_2 given off by plants is derived from H_2O and not from CO_2. The chloroplast splits water into hydrogen and oxygen. Before this discovery, the prevailing hypothesis was that photosynthesis split carbon dioxide ($CO_2 \rightarrow C + O_2$) and then added water to the carbon ($C + H_2O \rightarrow [CH_2O]$). This hypothesis predicted that the O_2 released during photosynthesis came from CO_2. This idea was challenged in the 1930s by C. B. van Niel, of Stanford University. Van Niel was investigating photosynthesis in bacteria that make their carbohydrate from CO_2 but do not release O_2. He concluded that, at least in these bacteria, CO_2 is not split into carbon and oxygen. One group of bacteria used hydrogen sulfide (H_2S) rather than water for photosynthesis, forming yellow globules of sulfur as a waste product (these globules are visible in Figure 10.2e). Here is the chemical equation for photosynthesis in these sulfur bacteria:

$$CO_2 + 2 H_2S \rightarrow [CH_2O] + H_2O + 2 S$$

Van Niel reasoned that the bacteria split H_2S and used the hydrogen atoms to make sugar. He then generalized that idea, proposing that all photosynthetic organisms require a hydrogen source but that the source varies:

Sulfur bacteria: $CO_2 + 2 H_2S \rightarrow [CH_2O] + H_2O + 2 S$
Plants: $CO_2 + 2 H_2O \rightarrow [CH_2O] + H_2O + O_2$
General: $CO_2 + 2 H_2X \rightarrow [CH_2O] + H_2O + 2 X$

Thus, van Niel hypothesized that plants split H_2O as a source of electrons from hydrogen atoms, releasing O_2 as a by-product.

Nearly 20 years later, scientists confirmed van Niel's hypothesis by using oxygen-18 (^{18}O), a heavy isotope, as a tracer to follow the fate of oxygen atoms during photosynthesis. The experiments showed that the O_2 from plants was labeled with ^{18}O *only* if water was the source of the tracer (experiment 1). If the ^{18}O was introduced to the plant in the form of CO_2, the label did not turn up in the released O_2 (experiment 2). In the following summary, red denotes labeled atoms of oxygen (^{18}O):

Experiment 1: $CO_2 + 2 H_2O \rightarrow [CH_2O] + H_2O + O_2$
Experiment 2: $CO_2 + 2 H_2O \rightarrow [CH_2O] + H_2O + O_2$

A significant result of the shuffling of atoms during photosynthesis is the extraction of hydrogen from water and its incorporation into sugar. The waste product of photosynthesis, O_2, is released to the atmosphere. **Figure 10.5** shows the fates of all atoms in photosynthesis.

▲ **Figure 10.5 Tracking atoms through photosynthesis.** The atoms from CO_2 are shown in magenta, and the atoms from H_2O are shown in blue.

Photosynthesis as a Redox Process

Let's briefly compare photosynthesis with cellular respiration. Both processes involve redox reactions. During cellular respiration, energy is released from sugar when electrons associated with hydrogen are transported by carriers to oxygen, forming water as a by-product. The electrons lose potential energy as they "fall" down the electron transport chain toward electronegative oxygen, and the mitochondrion harnesses that energy to synthesize ATP (see Figure 9.15). Photosynthesis reverses the direction of electron flow. Water is split, and electrons are transferred along with hydrogen ions from the water to carbon dioxide, reducing it to sugar.

$$\text{Energy} \ + \ 6\,CO_2 \ + \ 6\,H_2O \ \longrightarrow \ C_6H_{12}O_6 \ + \ 6\,O_2$$

becomes reduced

becomes oxidized

Because the electrons increase in potential energy as they move from water to sugar, this process requires energy—in other words is endergonic. This energy boost that occurs during photosynthesis is provided by light.

The Two Stages of Photosynthesis: *A Preview*

The equation for photosynthesis is a deceptively simple summary of a very complex process. Actually, photosynthesis is not a single process, but two processes, each with multiple steps. These two stages of photosynthesis are known as the **light reactions** (the *photo* part of photosynthesis) and the **Calvin cycle** (the *synthesis* part) **(Figure 10.6)**.

The light reactions are the steps of photosynthesis that convert solar energy to chemical energy. Water is split, providing a source of electrons and protons (hydrogen ions, H^+) and giving off O_2 as a by-product. Light absorbed by chlorophyll drives a transfer of the electrons and hydrogen ions from water to an acceptor called **NADP$^+$** (nicotinamide adenine dinucleotide phosphate), where they are temporarily stored. The electron acceptor NADP$^+$ is first cousin to NAD$^+$, which functions as an electron carrier in cellular respiration; the two molecules differ only by the presence of an extra phosphate group in the NADP$^+$ molecule. The light reactions use solar energy to reduce NADP$^+$ to NADPH by adding a pair of electrons along with an H^+. The light reactions also generate ATP, using chemiosmosis to power the addition of a phosphate group to ADP, a process called **photophosphorylation**. Thus, light energy is initially converted to chemical energy in the form of two compounds: NADPH and ATP. NADPH, a source of electrons, acts as "reducing power" that can be passed along to an electron acceptor, reducing it, while ATP is the versatile energy currency of cells. Notice that the light reactions produce no sugar; that happens in the second stage of photosynthesis, the Calvin cycle.

The Calvin cycle is named for Melvin Calvin, who, along with his colleagues James Bassham and Andrew Benson, began to elucidate its steps in the late 1940s. The cycle begins by incorporating CO_2 from the air into organic molecules already present in the chloroplast. This initial incorporation of carbon into organic compounds is known as **carbon fixation**. The Calvin cycle then reduces the fixed carbon

▶ **Figure 10.6 An overview of photosynthesis: cooperation of the light reactions and the Calvin cycle.** In the chloroplast, the thylakoid membranes (green) are the sites of the light reactions, whereas the Calvin cycle occurs in the stroma (gray). The light reactions use solar energy to make ATP and NADPH, which supply chemical energy and reducing power, respectively, to the Calvin cycle. The Calvin cycle incorporates CO_2 into organic molecules, which are converted to sugar. (Recall that most simple sugars have formulas that are some multiple of CH_2O.)

BioFlix Visit the Study Area in **MasteringBiology** for the BioFlix® 3-D Animation on Photosynthesis. BioFlix Tutorials can also be assigned in MasteringBiology.

to carbohydrate by the addition of electrons. The reducing power is provided by NADPH, which acquired its cargo of electrons in the light reactions. To convert CO_2 to carbohydrate, the Calvin cycle also requires chemical energy in the form of ATP, which is also generated by the light reactions. Thus, it is the Calvin cycle that makes sugar, but it can do so only with the help of the NADPH and ATP produced by the light reactions. The metabolic steps of the Calvin cycle are sometimes referred to as the dark reactions, or light-independent reactions, because none of the steps requires light *directly*. Nevertheless, the Calvin cycle in most plants occurs during daylight, for only then can the light reactions provide the NADPH and ATP that the Calvin cycle requires. In essence, the chloroplast uses light energy to make sugar by coordinating the two stages of photosynthesis.

As Figure 10.6 indicates, the thylakoids of the chloroplast are the sites of the light reactions, while the Calvin cycle occurs in the stroma. On the outside of the thylakoids, molecules of $NADP^+$ and ADP pick up electrons and phosphate, respectively, and NADPH and ATP are then released to the stroma, where they play crucial roles in the Calvin cycle. The two stages of photosynthesis are treated in this figure as metabolic modules that take in ingredients and crank out products. In the next two sections, we'll look more closely at how the two stages work, beginning with the light reactions.

CONCEPT CHECK 10.1

1. How do the reactant molecules of photosynthesis reach the chloroplasts in leaves?
2. How did the use of an oxygen isotope help elucidate the chemistry of photosynthesis?
3. **WHAT IF?** The Calvin cycle requires ATP and NADPH, products of the light reactions. If a classmate asserted that the light reactions don't depend on the Calvin cycle and, with continual light, could just keep on producing ATP and NADPH, how would you respond?

For suggested answers, see Appendix A.

CONCEPT 10.2

The light reactions convert solar energy to the chemical energy of ATP and NADPH

Chloroplasts are chemical factories powered by the sun. Their thylakoids transform light energy into the chemical energy of ATP and NADPH, which will be used to synthesize glucose and other molecules that can be used as energy sources. To better understand the conversion of light to chemical energy, we need to know about some important properties of light.

The Nature of Sunlight

Light is a form of energy known as electromagnetic energy, also called electromagnetic radiation. Electromagnetic energy travels in rhythmic waves analogous to those created by dropping a pebble into a pond. Electromagnetic waves, however, are disturbances of electric and magnetic fields rather than disturbances of a material medium such as water.

The distance between the crests of electromagnetic waves is called the **wavelength**. Wavelengths range from less than a nanometer (for gamma rays) to more than a kilometer (for radio waves). This entire range of radiation is known as the **electromagnetic spectrum** **(Figure 10.7)**. The segment most important to life is the narrow band from about 380 nm to 750 nm in wavelength. This radiation is known as **visible light** because it can be detected as various colors by the human eye.

The model of light as waves explains many of light's properties, but in certain respects light behaves as though it consists of discrete particles, called **photons**. Photons are not tangible objects, but they act like objects in that each of them has a fixed quantity of energy. The amount of energy is inversely related to the wavelength of the light: the shorter the wavelength, the greater the energy of each photon of that light. Thus, a photon of violet light packs nearly twice as much energy as a photon of red light (see Figure 10.7).

Although the sun radiates the full spectrum of electromagnetic energy, the atmosphere acts like a selective window, allowing visible light to pass through while screening out a substantial fraction of other radiation. The part of the spectrum we can see—visible light—is also the radiation that drives photosynthesis.

▲ **Figure 10.7 The electromagnetic spectrum.** White light is a mixture of all wavelengths of visible light. A prism can sort white light into its component colors by bending light of different wavelengths at different angles. (Droplets of water in the atmosphere can act as prisms, causing a rainbow to form.) Visible light drives photosynthesis.

Photosynthetic Pigments: The Light Receptors

When light meets matter, it may be reflected, transmitted, or absorbed. Substances that absorb visible light are known as *pigments*. Different pigments absorb light of different wavelengths, and the wavelengths that are absorbed disappear. If a pigment is illuminated with white light, the color we see is the color most reflected or transmitted by the pigment. (If a pigment absorbs all wavelengths, it appears black.) We see green when we look at a leaf because chlorophyll absorbs violet-blue and red light while transmitting and reflecting green light **(Figure 10.8)**. The ability of a pigment to absorb various wavelengths of light can be measured with an instrument called a **spectrophotometer**. This machine directs beams of light of different wavelengths through a solution of the pigment and measures the fraction of the light transmitted at each wavelength. A graph plotting a pigment's light absorption versus wavelength is called an **absorption spectrum (Figure 10.9)**.

The absorption spectra of chloroplast pigments provide clues to the relative effectiveness of different wavelengths for driving photosynthesis, since light can perform work in chloroplasts only if it is absorbed. **Figure 10.10a** shows the absorption spectra of three types of pigments in chloroplasts: **chlorophyll *a***, the key light-capturing pigment that participates directly in the light reactions; the accessory pigment **chlorophyll *b***; and a separate group of accessory pigments called carotenoids. The spectrum of chlorophyll

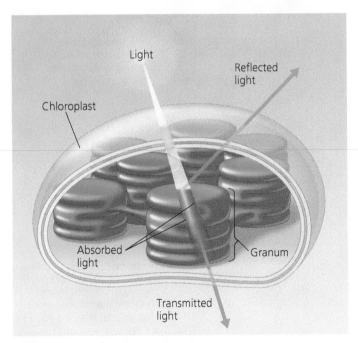

▲ **Figure 10.8 Why leaves are green: interaction of light with chloroplasts.** The chlorophyll molecules of chloroplasts absorb violet-blue and red light (the colors most effective in driving photosynthesis) and reflect or transmit green light. This is why leaves appear green.

▼ **Figure 10.9** **Research Method**

Determining an Absorption Spectrum

Application An absorption spectrum is a visual representation of how well a particular pigment absorbs different wavelengths of visible light. Absorption spectra of various chloroplast pigments help scientists decipher the role of each pigment in a plant.

Technique A spectrophotometer measures the relative amounts of light of different wavelengths absorbed and transmitted by a pigment solution.

1 White light is separated into colors (wavelengths) by a prism.

2 One by one, the different colors of light are passed through the sample (chlorophyll in this example). Green light and blue light are shown here.

3 The transmitted light strikes a photoelectric tube, which converts the light energy to electricity.

4 The electric current is measured by a galvanometer. The meter indicates the fraction of light transmitted through the sample, from which we can determine the amount of light absorbed.

Results See Figure 10.10a for absorption spectra of three types of chloroplast pigments.

a suggests that violet-blue and red light work best for photosynthesis, since they are absorbed, while green is the least effective color. This is confirmed by an **action spectrum** for photosynthesis **(Figure 10.10b)**, which profiles the relative effectiveness of different wavelengths of radiation in driving the process. An action spectrum is prepared by illuminating chloroplasts with light of different colors and then plotting wavelength against some measure of photosynthetic rate,

Which wavelengths of light are most effective in driving photosynthesis?

Experiment Absorption and action spectra, along with a classic experiment by Theodor W. Engelmann, reveal which wavelengths of light are photosynthetically important.

Results

(a) Absorption spectra. The three curves show the wavelengths of light best absorbed by three types of chloroplast pigments.

(b) Action spectrum. This graph plots the rate of photosynthesis versus wavelength. The resulting action spectrum resembles the absorption spectrum for chlorophyll *a* but does not match exactly (see part a). This is partly due to the absorption of light by accessory pigments such as chlorophyll *b* and carotenoids.

(c) Engelmann's experiment. In 1883, Theodor W. Engelmann illuminated a filamentous alga with light that had been passed through a prism, exposing different segments of the alga to different wavelengths. He used aerobic bacteria, which concentrate near an oxygen source, to determine which segments of the alga were releasing the most O_2 and thus photosynthesizing most. Bacteria congregated in greatest numbers around the parts of the alga illuminated with violet-blue or red light.

Conclusion Light in the violet-blue and red portions of the spectrum is most effective in driving photosynthesis.

Source: T. W. Engelmann, *Bacterium photometricum*. Ein Beitrag zur vergleichenden Physiologie des Licht-und Farbensinnes, *Archiv. für Physiologie* 30:95–124 (1883).

(MB) An Experimental Inquiry Tutorial can be assigned in MasteringBiology.

INTERPRET THE DATA *What wavelengths of light drive the highest rates of photosynthesis?*

such as CO_2 consumption or O_2 release. The action spectrum for photosynthesis was first demonstrated by Theodor W. Engelmann, a German botanist, in 1883. Before equipment for measuring O_2 levels had even been invented, Engelmann performed a clever experiment in which he used bacteria to measure rates of photosynthesis in filamentous algae **(Figure 10.10c)**. His results are a striking match to the modern action spectrum shown in Figure 10.10b.

Notice by comparing Figures 10.10a and 10.10b that the action spectrum for photosynthesis is much broader than the absorption spectrum of chlorophyll *a*. The absorption spectrum of chlorophyll *a* alone underestimates the effectiveness of certain wavelengths in driving photosynthesis. This is partly because accessory pigments with different absorption spectra also present in chloroplasts—including chlorophyll *b* and carotenoids—broaden the spectrum of colors that can be used for photosynthesis. **Figure 10.11** shows the structure of chlorophyll *a* compared with that of chlorophyll *b*. A slight structural difference between them is enough to cause the two pigments to absorb at slightly different wavelengths in the red and blue parts of the spectrum (see Figure 10.10a). As a result, chlorophyll *a* appears blue green and chlorophyll *b* olive green under visible light.

▲ **Figure 10.11 Structure of chlorophyll molecules in chloroplasts of plants.** Chlorophyll *a* and chlorophyll *b* differ only in one of the functional groups bonded to the porphyrin ring. (Also see the space-filling model of chlorophyll in Figure 1.3.)

Other accessory pigments include **carotenoids**, hydrocarbons that are various shades of yellow and orange because they absorb violet and blue-green light (see Figure 10.10a). Carotenoids may broaden the spectrum of colors that can drive photosynthesis. However, a more important function of at least some carotenoids seems to be *photoprotection*: These compounds absorb and dissipate excessive light energy that would otherwise damage chlorophyll or interact with oxygen, forming reactive oxidative molecules that are dangerous to the cell. Interestingly, carotenoids similar to the photoprotective ones in chloroplasts have a photoprotective role in the human eye. (Remember being told to eat your carrots for improved night vision?) These and related molecules are, of course, found naturally in many vegetables and fruits. They are also often advertised in health food products as "phytochemicals" (from the Greek *phyton*, plant), some of which have antioxidant properties. Plants can synthesize all the antioxidants they require, but humans and other animals must obtain some of them from their diets.

Excitation of Chlorophyll by Light

What exactly happens when chlorophyll and other pigments absorb light? The colors corresponding to the absorbed wavelengths disappear from the spectrum of the transmitted and reflected light, but energy cannot disappear. When a molecule absorbs a photon of light, one of the molecule's electrons is elevated to an orbital where it has more potential energy (see Figure 2.6b). When the electron is in its normal orbital, the pigment molecule is said to be in its ground state. Absorption of a photon boosts an electron to an orbital of higher energy, and the pigment molecule is then said to be in an excited state. The only photons absorbed are those whose energy is exactly equal to the energy difference between the ground state and an excited state, and this energy difference varies from one kind of molecule to another. Thus, a particular compound absorbs only photons corresponding to specific wavelengths, which is why each pigment has a unique absorption spectrum.

Once absorption of a photon raises an electron to an excited state, the electron cannot stay there long. The excited state, like all high-energy states, is unstable. Generally, when isolated pigment molecules absorb light, their excited electrons drop back down to the ground-state orbital in a billionth of a second, releasing their excess energy as heat. This conversion of light energy to heat is what makes the top of an automobile so hot on a sunny day. (White cars are coolest because their paint reflects all wavelengths of visible light.) In isolation, some pigments, including chlorophyll, emit light as well as heat after absorbing photons. As excited electrons fall back to the ground state, photons are given off, an afterglow called fluorescence. An illuminated solution of chlorophyll isolated from chloroplasts will fluoresce in the red part of the spectrum and also give off heat **(Figure 10.12)**. This is best seen by illuminating with ultraviolet light, which chlorophyll can also absorb (see Figures 10.7 and 10.10a). Viewed under visible light, the fluorescence would be harder to see against the green of the solution.

A Photosystem: A Reaction-Center Complex Associated with Light-Harvesting Complexes

Chlorophyll molecules excited by the absorption of light energy produce very different results in an intact chloroplast than they do in isolation (see Figure 10.12). In their native environment of the thylakoid membrane, chlorophyll molecules are organized along with other small organic molecules and proteins into complexes called photosystems.

▶ **Figure 10.12 Excitation of isolated chlorophyll by light. (a)** Absorption of a photon causes a transition of the chlorophyll molecule from its ground state to its excited state. The photon boosts an electron to an orbital where it has more potential energy. If the illuminated molecule exists in isolation, its excited electron immediately drops back down to the ground-state orbital, and its excess energy is given off as heat and fluorescence (light). **(b)** A chlorophyll solution excited with ultraviolet light fluoresces with a red-orange glow.

WHAT IF? *If a leaf containing a similar concentration of chlorophyll as the solution was exposed to the same ultraviolet light, no fluorescence would be seen. Propose an explanation for the difference in fluorescence emission between the solution and the leaf.*

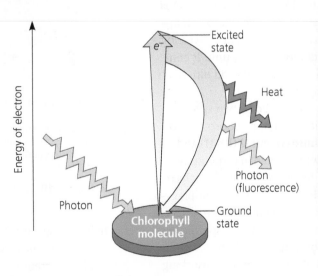

(a) Excitation of isolated chlorophyll molecule

(b) Fluorescence

A **photosystem** is composed of a **reaction-center complex** surrounded by several light-harvesting complexes (**Figure 10.13**). The reaction-center complex is an organized association of proteins holding a special pair of chlorophyll *a* molecules. Each **light-harvesting complex** consists of various pigment molecules (which may include chlorophyll *a*, chlorophyll *b*, and multiple carotenoids) bound to proteins. The number and variety of pigment molecules enable a photosystem to harvest light over a larger surface area and a larger portion of the spectrum than could any single pigment molecule alone. Together, these light-harvesting complexes act as an antenna for the reaction-center complex. When a pigment molecule absorbs a photon, the energy is transferred from pigment molecule to pigment molecule within a light-harvesting complex, somewhat like a human "wave" at a sports arena, until it is passed into the reaction-center complex. The reaction-center complex also contains a molecule capable of accepting electrons and becoming reduced; this is called the **primary electron acceptor**. The pair of chlorophyll *a* molecules in the reaction-center complex are special because their molecular environment—their location and the other molecules with which they are associated—enables them to use the energy from light not only to boost one of their electrons to a higher energy level, but also to transfer it to a different molecule—the primary electron acceptor.

The solar-powered transfer of an electron from the reaction-center chlorophyll *a* pair to the primary electron acceptor is the first step of the light reactions. As soon as the chlorophyll electron is excited to a higher energy level, the primary electron acceptor captures it; this is a redox reaction. In the flask shown in Figure 10.12b, isolated chlorophyll fluoresces because there is no electron acceptor, so electrons of photoexcited chlorophyll drop right back to the ground state. In the structured environment of a chloroplast, however, an electron acceptor is readily available, and the potential energy represented by the excited electron is not dissipated as light and heat. Thus, each photosystem—a reaction-center complex surrounded by light-harvesting complexes—functions in the chloroplast as a unit. It converts light energy to chemical energy, which will ultimately be used for the synthesis of sugar.

The thylakoid membrane is populated by two types of photosystems that cooperate in the light reactions of photosynthesis. They are called **photosystem II (PS II)** and **photosystem I (PS I)**. (They were named in order of their discovery, but photosystem II functions first in the light reactions.) Each has a characteristic reaction-center complex—a particular kind of primary electron acceptor next to a special pair of chlorophyll *a* molecules associated with specific proteins. The reaction-center chlorophyll *a* of photosystem II is known as P680 because this pigment is best at absorbing

(a) **How a photosystem harvests light.** When a photon strikes a pigment molecule in a light-harvesting complex, the energy is passed from molecule to molecule until it reaches the reaction-center complex. Here, an excited electron from the special pair of chlorophyll *a* molecules is transferred to the primary electron acceptor.

(b) **Structure of a photosystem.** This computer model, based on X-ray crystallography, shows two photosystem complexes side by side, oriented opposite to each other. Chlorophyll molecules (small green ball-and-stick models) are interspersed with protein subunits (cylinders and ribbons). For simplicity, this photosystem will be shown as a single complex in the rest of the chapter.

▲ **Figure 10.13 The structure and function of a photosystem.**

light having a wavelength of 680 nm (in the red part of the spectrum). The chlorophyll *a* at the reaction-center complex of photosystem I is called P700 because it most effectively absorbs light of wavelength 700 nm (in the far-red part of the spectrum). These two pigments, P680 and P700, are nearly identical chlorophyll *a* molecules. However, their association with different proteins in the thylakoid membrane affects the electron distribution in the two pigments and accounts for the slight differences in their light-absorbing properties. Now let's see how the two photosystems work together in using light energy to generate ATP and NADPH, the two main products of the light reactions.

Linear Electron Flow

Light drives the synthesis of ATP and NADPH by energizing the two photosystems embedded in the thylakoid membranes of chloroplasts. The key to this energy transformation is a flow of electrons through the photosystems and other molecular components built into the thylakoid membrane. This is called **linear electron flow**, and it occurs during the light reactions of photosynthesis, as shown in **Figure 10.14**. The numbered steps in the text correspond to the numbered steps in the figure.

❶ A photon of light strikes one of the pigment molecules in a light-harvesting complex of PS II, boosting one of its electrons to a higher energy level. As this electron falls back to its ground state, an electron in a nearby pigment molecule is simultaneously raised to an excited state. The process continues, with the energy being relayed to other pigment molecules until it reaches the P680 pair of chlorophyll *a* molecules in the PS II reaction-center complex. It excites an electron in this pair of chlorophylls to a higher energy state.

❷ This electron is transferred from the excited P680 to the primary electron acceptor. We can refer to the resulting form of P680, missing an electron, as P680$^+$.

❸ An enzyme catalyzes the splitting of a water molecule into two electrons, two hydrogen ions (H$^+$), and an oxygen atom. The electrons are supplied one by one to the P680$^+$ pair, each electron replacing one transferred to the primary electron acceptor. (P680$^+$ is the strongest biological oxidizing agent known; its electron "hole" must be filled. This greatly facilitates the transfer of electrons from the split water molecule.) The H$^+$ are released into

▼ **Figure 10.14 How linear electron flow during the light reactions generates ATP and NADPH.** The gold arrows trace the flow of light-driven electrons from water to NADPH. The black arrows trace the transfer of energy from pigment molecule to pigment molecule.

the thylakoid space. The oxygen atom immediately combines with an oxygen atom generated by the splitting of another water molecule, forming O_2.

4. Each photoexcited electron passes from the primary electron acceptor of PS II to PS I via an electron transport chain, the components of which are similar to those of the electron transport chain that functions in cellular respiration. The electron transport chain between PS II and PS I is made up of the electron carrier plastoquinone (Pq), a cytochrome complex, and a protein called plastocyanin (Pc).

5. The exergonic "fall" of electrons to a lower energy level provides energy for the synthesis of ATP. As electrons pass through the cytochrome complex, H^+ are pumped into the thylakoid space, contributing to the proton gradient that is subsequently used in chemiosmosis.

6. Meanwhile, light energy has been transferred via light-harvesting complex pigments to the PS I reaction-center complex, exciting an electron of the P700 pair of chlorophyll *a* molecules located there. The photoexcited electron is then transferred to PS I's primary electron acceptor, creating an electron "hole" in the P700—which we now can call P700$^+$. In other words, P700$^+$ can now act as an electron acceptor, accepting an electron that reaches the bottom of the electron transport chain from PS II.

7. Photoexcited electrons are passed in a series of redox reactions from the primary electron acceptor of PS I down a second electron transport chain through the protein ferredoxin (Fd). (This chain does not create a proton gradient and thus does not produce ATP.)

8. The enzyme NADP$^+$ reductase catalyzes the transfer of electrons from Fd to NADP$^+$. Two electrons are required for its reduction to NADPH. This molecule is at a higher energy level than water, so its electrons are more readily available for the reactions of the Calvin cycle. This process also removes an H^+ from the stroma.

▲ Figure 10.15 **A mechanical analogy for linear electron flow during the light reactions.**

The energy changes of electrons during their linear flow through the light reactions are shown in a mechanical analogy in **Figure 10.15.** Although the scheme shown in Figures 10.14 and 10.15 may seem complicated, do not lose track of the big picture: The light reactions use solar power to generate ATP and NADPH, which provide chemical energy and reducing power, respectively, to the carbohydrate-synthesizing reactions of the Calvin cycle.

Cyclic Electron Flow

In certain cases, photoexcited electrons can take an alternative path called **cyclic electron flow**, which uses photosystem I but not photosystem II. You can see in **Figure 10.16** that cyclic flow is a short circuit: The electrons cycle back from ferredoxin (Fd) to the cytochrome complex and from there continue on to a P700 chlorophyll in the PS I reaction-center

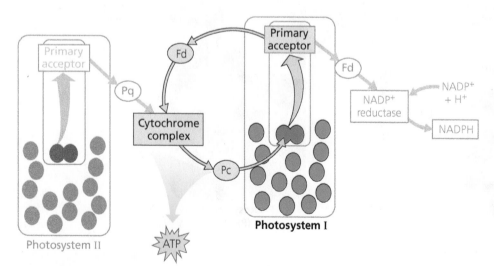

Photosystem II — Pq — Cytochrome complex — Pc — Photosystem I — ATP

Primary acceptor — Fd — Fd — NADP$^+$ reductase — NADP$^+$ + H$^+$ — NADPH

◀ Figure 10.16 **Cyclic electron flow.** Photoexcited electrons from PS I are occasionally shunted back from ferredoxin (Fd) to chlorophyll via the cytochrome complex and plastocyanin (Pc). This electron shunt supplements the supply of ATP (via chemiosmosis) but produces no NADPH. The "shadow" of linear electron flow is included in the diagram for comparison with the cyclic route. The two Fd molecules in this diagram are actually one and the same—the final electron carrier in the electron transport chain of PS I—although it is depicted twice to clearly show its role in two parts of the process.

? *Look at Figure 10.15, and explain how you would alter it to show a mechanical analogy for cyclic electron flow.*

complex. There is no production of NADPH and no release of oxygen that results from this process. On the other hand, cyclic flow does generate ATP.

Rather than having both PSII and PSI, several of the currently existing groups of photosynthetic bacteria are known to have a single photosystem related to either PSII or PSI. For these species, which include the purple sulfur bacteria (see Figure 10.2e) and the green sulfur bacteria, cyclic electron flow is the one and only means of generating ATP during the process of photosynthesis. Evolutionary biologists hypothesize that these bacterial groups are descendants of ancestral bacteria in which photosynthesis first evolved, in a form similar to cyclic electron flow.

Cyclic electron flow can also occur in photosynthetic species that possess both photosystems; this includes some prokaryotes, such as the cyanobacteria shown in Figure 10.2d, as well as the eukaryotic photosynthetic species that have been tested thus far. Although the process is probably in part an "evolutionary leftover," research suggests it plays at least one beneficial role for these organisms. Mutant plants that are not able to carry out cyclic electron flow are capable of growing well in low light, but do not grow well where light is intense. This is evidence for the idea that cyclic electron flow may be photoprotective. Later you'll learn more about cyclic electron flow as it relates to a particular adaptation of photosynthesis (C₄ plants; see Concept 10.4).

Whether ATP synthesis is driven by linear or cyclic electron flow, the actual mechanism is the same. Before we move on to consider the Calvin cycle, let's review chemiosmosis, the process that uses membranes to couple redox reactions to ATP production.

A Comparison of Chemiosmosis in Chloroplasts and Mitochondria

Chloroplasts and mitochondria generate ATP by the same basic mechanism: chemiosmosis. An electron transport chain pumps protons (H^+) across a membrane as electrons are passed through a series of carriers that are progressively more electronegative. Thus, electron transport chains transform redox energy to a proton-motive force, potential energy stored in the form of an H^+ gradient across a membrane. An ATP synthase complex in the same membrane couples the diffusion of hydrogen ions down their gradient to the phosphorylation of ADP, forming ATP.

Some of the electron carriers, including the iron-containing proteins called cytochromes, are very similar in chloroplasts and mitochondria. The ATP synthase complexes of the two organelles are also quite similar. But there are noteworthy differences between photophosphorylation in chloroplasts and oxidative phosphorylation in mitochondria. In chloroplasts, the high-energy electrons dropped down the transport chain come from water, while in mitochondria, they are extracted from organic molecules (which are thus oxidized). Chloroplasts do not need molecules from food to make ATP; their photosystems capture light energy and use it to drive the electrons from water to the top of the transport chain. In other words, mitochondria use chemiosmosis to transfer chemical energy from food molecules to ATP, whereas chloroplasts transform light energy into chemical energy in ATP.

Although the spatial organization of chemiosmosis differs slightly between chloroplasts and mitochondria, it is easy to see similarities in the two **(Figure 10.17)**. The inner

▶ **Figure 10.17 Comparison of chemiosmosis in mitochondria and chloroplasts.** In both kinds of organelles, electron transport chains pump protons (H^+) across a membrane from a region of low H^+ concentration (light gray in this diagram) to one of high H^+ concentration (dark gray). The protons then diffuse back across the membrane through ATP synthase, driving the synthesis of ATP.

membrane of the mitochondrion pumps protons from the mitochondrial matrix out to the intermembrane space, which then serves as a reservoir of hydrogen ions. The thylakoid membrane of the chloroplast pumps protons from the stroma into the thylakoid space (interior of the thylakoid), which functions as the H^+ reservoir. If you imagine the cristae of mitochondria pinching off from the inner membrane, this may help you see how the thylakoid space and the intermembrane space are comparable spaces in the two organelles, while the mitochondrial matrix is analogous to the stroma of the chloroplast.

In the mitochondrion, protons diffuse down their concentration gradient from the intermembrane space through ATP synthase to the matrix, driving ATP synthesis. In the chloroplast, ATP is synthesized as the hydrogen ions diffuse from the thylakoid space back to the stroma through ATP synthase complexes, whose catalytic knobs are on the stroma side of the membrane (**Figure 10.18**). Thus, ATP forms in the stroma, where it is used to help drive sugar synthesis during the Calvin cycle.

The proton (H^+) gradient, or pH gradient, across the thylakoid membrane is substantial. When chloroplasts in an

▲ **Figure 10.18 The light reactions and chemiosmosis: Current model of the organization of the thylakoid membrane.** The gold arrows track the linear electron flow outlined in Figure 10.14. At least three steps in the light reactions contribute to the H^+ gradient by increasing H^+ concentration in the thylakoid space: ❶ Water is split by photosystem II on the side of the membrane facing the thylakoid space; ❷ as plastoquinone (Pq) transfers electrons to the cytochrome complex, four protons are translocated across the membrane into the thylakoid space; and ❸ a hydrogen ion is removed from the stroma when it is taken up by $NADP^+$. Notice that in step 2, hydrogen ions are being pumped from the stroma into the thylakoid space, as in Figure 10.17. The diffusion of H^+ from the thylakoid space back to the stroma (along the H^+ concentration gradient) powers the ATP synthase. These light-driven reactions store chemical energy in NADPH and ATP, which shuttle the energy to the carbohydrate-producing Calvin cycle.

experimental setting are illuminated, the pH in the thylakoid space drops to about 5 (the H^+ concentration increases), and the pH in the stroma increases to about 8 (the H^+ concentration decreases). This gradient of three pH units corresponds to a thousandfold difference in H^+ concentration. If the lights are then turned off, the pH gradient is abolished, but it can quickly be restored by turning the lights back on. Experiments such as this provided strong evidence in support of the chemiosmotic model.

The currently-accepted model for the organization of the light-reaction "machinery" within the thylakoid membrane is based on several research studies. Each of the molecules and molecular complexes in the figure is present in numerous copies in each thylakoid. Notice that NADPH, like ATP, is produced on the side of the membrane facing the stroma, where the Calvin cycle reactions take place.

Let's summarize the light reactions. Electron flow pushes electrons from water, where they are at a low state of potential energy, ultimately to NADPH, where they are stored at a high state of potential energy. The light-driven electron flow also generates ATP. Thus, the equipment of the thylakoid membrane converts light energy to chemical energy stored in ATP and NADPH. (Oxygen is a by-product.) Let's now see how the Calvin cycle uses the products of the light reactions to synthesize sugar from CO_2.

CONCEPT CHECK 10.2

1. What color of light is *least* effective in driving photosynthesis? Explain.

2. In the light reactions, what is the initial electron donor? Where do the electrons finally end up?

3. WHAT IF? In an experiment, isolated chloroplasts placed in an illuminated solution with the appropriate chemicals can carry out ATP synthesis. Predict what would happen to the rate of synthesis if a compound is added to the solution that makes membranes freely permeable to hydrogen ions.

For suggested answers, see Appendix A.

CONCEPT 10.3

The Calvin cycle uses the chemical energy of ATP and NADPH to reduce CO_2 to sugar

The Calvin cycle is similar to the citric acid cycle in that a starting material is regenerated after some molecules enter the cycle and others exit the cycle. However, the citric acid cycle is catabolic, oxidizing acetyl CoA and using the energy to synthesize ATP. In contrast, the Calvin cycle is anabolic, building carbohydrates from smaller molecules and consuming energy. Carbon enters the Calvin cycle in the form of CO_2 and leaves in the form of sugar. The cycle spends ATP as an energy source and consumes NADPH as reducing power for adding high-energy electrons to make the sugar.

As we mentioned previously (in Concept 10.1), the carbohydrate produced directly from the Calvin cycle is actually not glucose, but a three-carbon sugar; the name of this sugar is **glyceraldehyde 3-phosphate (G3P)**. For the net synthesis of *one* molecule of G3P, the cycle must take place three times, fixing *three* molecules of CO_2—one per turn of the cycle. (Recall that the term carbon fixation refers to the initial incorporation of CO_2 into organic material.) As we trace the steps of the cycle, it's important to keep in mind that we are following three molecules of CO_2 through the reactions. **Figure 10.19** divides the Calvin cycle into three phases: carbon fixation, reduction, and regeneration of the CO_2 acceptor.

Phase 1: Carbon fixation. The Calvin cycle incorporates each CO_2 molecule, one at a time, by attaching it to a five-carbon sugar named ribulose bisphosphate (abbreviated RuBP). The enzyme that catalyzes this first step is RuBP carboxylase-oxygenase, or **rubisco**. (This is the most abundant protein in chloroplasts and is also thought to be the most abundant protein on Earth.) The product of the reaction is a six-carbon intermediate that is short-lived because it is so energetically unstable that it immediately splits in half, forming two molecules of 3-phosphoglycerate (for each CO_2 fixed).

Phase 2: Reduction. Each molecule of 3-phosphoglycerate receives an additional phosphate group from ATP, becoming 1,3-bisphosphoglycerate. Next, a pair of electrons donated from NADPH reduces 1,3-bisphosphoglycerate, which also loses a phosphate group in the process, becoming glyceraldehyde 3-phosphate (G3P). Specifically, the electrons from NADPH reduce a carboxyl group on 1,3-bisphosphoglycerate to the aldehyde group of G3P, which stores more potential energy. G3P is a sugar—the same three-carbon sugar formed in glycolysis by the splitting of glucose (see Figure 9.9). Notice in Figure 10.19 that for every *three* molecules of CO_2 that enter the cycle, there are *six* molecules of G3P formed. But only one molecule of this three-carbon sugar can be counted as a net gain of carbohydrate because the rest are required to complete the cycle. The cycle began with 15 carbons' worth of carbohydrate in the form of three molecules of the five-carbon sugar RuBP. Now there are 18 carbons' worth of carbohydrate in the form of six molecules of G3P. One molecule exits the cycle to be used by the plant cell, but the other five molecules must be recycled to regenerate the three molecules of RuBP.

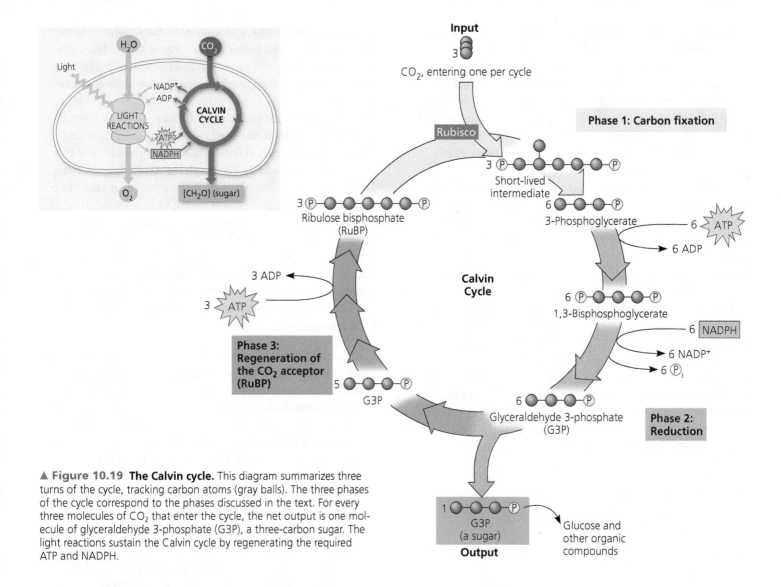

▲ **Figure 10.19** **The Calvin cycle.** This diagram summarizes three turns of the cycle, tracking carbon atoms (gray balls). The three phases of the cycle correspond to the phases discussed in the text. For every three molecules of CO_2 that enter the cycle, the net output is one molecule of glyceraldehyde 3-phosphate (G3P), a three-carbon sugar. The light reactions sustain the Calvin cycle by regenerating the required ATP and NADPH.

Phase 3: Regeneration of the CO_2 acceptor (RuBP). In a complex series of reactions, the carbon skeletons of five molecules of G3P are rearranged by the last steps of the Calvin cycle into three molecules of RuBP. To accomplish this, the cycle spends three more molecules of ATP. The RuBP is now prepared to receive CO_2 again, and the cycle continues.

For the net synthesis of one G3P molecule, the Calvin cycle consumes a total of nine molecules of ATP and six molecules of NADPH. The light reactions regenerate the ATP and NADPH. The G3P spun off from the Calvin cycle becomes the starting material for metabolic pathways that synthesize other organic compounds, including glucose (formed by combining two molecules of G3P), the disaccharide sucrose, and other carbohydrates. Neither the light reactions nor the Calvin cycle alone can make sugar from CO_2. Photosynthesis is an emergent property of the intact chloroplast, which integrates the two stages of photosynthesis.

CONCEPT CHECK 10.3

1. To synthesize one glucose molecule, the Calvin cycle uses _____ molecules of CO_2, _____ molecules of ATP, and _____ molecules of NADPH.

2. How are the large numbers of ATP and NADPH molecules used during the Calvin cycle consistent with the high value of glucose as an energy source?

3. **WHAT IF?** Explain why a poison that inhibits an enzyme of the Calvin cycle will also inhibit the light reactions.

4. **DRAW IT** Redraw the cycle in Figure 10.19 using numerals to indicate the numbers of carbons instead of gray balls, multiplying at each step to ensure that you have accounted for all carbons. In what forms do the carbon atoms enter and leave the cycle?

5. **MAKE CONNECTIONS** Review Figures 9.9 and 10.19. Discuss the roles of intermediate and product played by glyceraldehyde 3-phosphate (G3P) in the two processes shown in these figures.

For suggested answers, see Appendix A.

CONCEPT 10.4

Alternative mechanisms of carbon fixation have evolved in hot, arid climates

EVOLUTION   Ever since plants first moved onto land about 475 million years ago, they have been adapting to the problems of terrestrial life, particularly the problem of dehydration. In Chapters 29 and 36, we will consider anatomical adaptations that help plants conserve water, while in this chapter we are concerned with metabolic adaptations. The solutions often involve trade-offs. An important example is the compromise between photosynthesis and the prevention of excessive water loss from the plant. The CO_2 required for photosynthesis enters a leaf (and the resulting O_2 exits) via stomata, the pores on the leaf surface (see Figure 10.4). However, stomata are also the main avenues of transpiration, the evaporative loss of water from leaves. On a hot, dry day, most plants close their stomata, a response that conserves water. This response also reduces photosynthetic yield by limiting access to CO_2. With stomata even partially closed, CO_2 concentrations begin to decrease in the air spaces within the leaf, and the concentration of O_2 released from the light reactions begins to increase. These conditions within the leaf favor an apparently wasteful process called photorespiration.

Photorespiration: An Evolutionary Relic?

In most plants, initial fixation of carbon occurs via rubisco, the Calvin cycle enzyme that adds CO_2 to ribulose bisphosphate. Such plants are called C_3 **plants** because the first organic product of carbon fixation is a three-carbon compound, 3-phosphoglycerate (see Figure 10.19). Rice, wheat, and soybeans are C_3 plants that are important in agriculture. When their stomata partially close on hot, dry days, C_3 plants produce less sugar because the declining level of CO_2 in the leaf starves the Calvin cycle. In addition, rubisco is capable of binding O_2 in place of CO_2. As CO_2 becomes scarce within the air spaces of the leaf and O_2 builds up, rubisco adds O_2 to the Calvin cycle instead of CO_2. The product splits, and a two-carbon compound leaves the chloroplast. Peroxisomes and mitochondria within the plant cell rearrange and split this compound, releasing CO_2. The process is called **photorespiration** because it occurs in the light (*photo*) and consumes O_2 while producing CO_2 (*respiration*). However, unlike normal cellular respiration, photorespiration uses ATP rather than generating it. And unlike photosynthesis, photorespiration produces no sugar. In fact, photorespiration *decreases* photosynthetic output by siphoning organic material from the Calvin cycle and

releasing CO_2 that would otherwise be fixed. This CO_2 can eventually be fixed if it is still in the leaf once the CO_2 concentration is high enough. In the meantime, though, the process is energetically costly, much like a hamster running on its wheel.

How can we explain the existence of a metabolic process that seems to be counterproductive for the plant? According to one hypothesis, photorespiration is evolutionary baggage—a metabolic relic from a much earlier time when the atmosphere had less O_2 and more CO_2 than it does today. In the ancient atmosphere that prevailed when rubisco first evolved, the inability of the enzyme's active site to exclude O_2 would have made little difference. The hypothesis suggests that modern rubisco retains some of its chance affinity for O_2, which is now so concentrated in the atmosphere that a certain amount of photorespiration is inevitable.

We now know that, at least in some cases, photorespiration plays a protective role in plants. Plants that are impaired in their ability to carry out photorespiration (due to defective genes) are more susceptible to damage induced by excess light. Researchers consider this clear evidence that photorespiration acts to neutralize the otherwise damaging products of the light reactions, which build up when a low CO_2 concentration limits the progress of the Calvin cycle. Whether there are other benefits of photorespiration is still unknown. In many types of plants—including a significant number of crop plants—photorespiration drains away as much as 50% of the carbon fixed by the Calvin cycle. As heterotrophs that depend on carbon fixation in chloroplasts for our food, we naturally view photorespiration as wasteful. Indeed, if photorespiration could be reduced in certain plant species without otherwise affecting photosynthetic productivity, crop yields and food supplies might increase.

In some plant species, alternate modes of carbon fixation have evolved that minimize photorespiration and optimize the Calvin cycle—even in hot, arid climates. The two most important of these photosynthetic adaptations are C_4 photosynthesis and crassulacean acid metabolism (CAM).

C_4 Plants

The C_4 **plants** are so named because they preface the Calvin cycle with an alternate mode of carbon fixation that forms a four-carbon compound as its first product. The C_4 pathway is believed to have evolved independently at least 45 separate times and is used by several thousand species in at least 19 plant families. Among the C_4 plants important to agriculture are sugarcane and corn, members of the grass family.

The anatomy of a C_4 leaf is correlated with the mechanism of C_4 photosynthesis. In C_4 plants, there are two distinct types of photosynthetic cells: bundle-sheath cells and mesophyll cells. **Bundle-sheath cells** are arranged into tightly

▲ Figure 10.20 C₄ leaf anatomy and the C₄ pathway. The structure and biochemical functions of the leaves of C₄ plants are an evolutionary adaptation to hot, dry climates. This adaptation maintains a CO_2 concentration in the bundle sheath that favors photosynthesis over photorespiration.

packed sheaths around the veins of the leaf (**Figure 10.20**). Between the bundle sheath and the leaf surface are the more loosely arranged mesophyll cells, which, in C₄ leaves, are closely associated and never more than two to three cells away from the bundle-sheath cells. The Calvin cycle is confined to the chloroplasts of the bundle-sheath cells. However, the Calvin cycle is preceded by incorporation of CO_2 into organic compounds in the mesophyll cells. See the numbered steps in Figure 10.20, which are also described here:

❶ The first step is carried out by an enzyme present only in mesophyll cells called **PEP carboxylase**. This enzyme adds CO_2 to phosphoenolpyruvate (PEP), forming the four-carbon product oxaloacetate. PEP carboxylase has a much higher affinity for CO_2 than does rubisco and no affinity for O_2. Therefore, PEP carboxylase can fix carbon efficiently when rubisco cannot—that is, when it is hot and dry and stomata are partially closed, causing CO_2 concentration in the leaf to be lower and O_2 concentration to be relatively higher.

❷ After the C₄ plant fixes carbon from CO_2, the mesophyll cells export their four-carbon products (malate in the example shown in Figure 10.20) to bundle-sheath cells through plasmodesmata (see Figure 6.29).

❸ Within the bundle-sheath cells, the four-carbon compounds release CO_2, which is reassimilated into organic material by rubisco and the Calvin cycle. The same reaction regenerates pyruvate, which is transported to mesophyll cells. There, ATP is used to convert pyruvate to PEP, allowing the reaction cycle to continue.

This ATP can be thought of, in a sense, as the "price" of concentrating CO_2 in the bundle-sheath cells. To generate this extra ATP, bundle-sheath cells carry out cyclic electron flow, the process described earlier in this chapter (see Figure 10.16). In fact, these cells contain PS I but no PS II, so cyclic electron flow is their only photosynthetic mode of generating ATP.

In effect, the mesophyll cells of a C₄ plant pump CO_2 into the bundle sheath, keeping the CO_2 concentration in the bundle-sheath cells high enough for rubisco to bind CO_2 rather than O_2. The cyclic series of reactions involving PEP carboxylase and the regeneration of PEP can be thought of as a CO_2-concentrating pump that is powered by ATP. In this way, C₄ photosynthesis spends ATP energy to minimize photorespiration and enhance sugar production. This adaptation is especially advantageous in hot regions with intense sunlight, where stomata partially close during the day, and it is in such environments that C₄ plants evolved and thrive today.

The concentration of CO_2 in the atmosphere has drastically increased since the Industrial Revolution began in the 1800s, and it continues to rise today due to human activities such as the burning of fossil fuels. The resulting global climate change, including an increase in average temperatures around the planet, may have far-reaching effects on plant species. Scientists are concerned that increasing CO_2 concentration and temperature may affect C₃ and C₄ plants differently, thus changing the relative abundance of these species in a given plant community.

Which type of plant would stand to gain more from increasing CO_2 levels? Recall that in C_3 plants, the binding of O_2 rather than CO_2 by rubisco leads to photorespiration, lowering the efficiency of photosynthesis. C_4 plants overcome this problem by concentrating CO_2 in the bundle-sheath cells at the cost of ATP. Rising CO_2 levels should benefit C_3 plants by lowering the amount of photorespiration that occurs. At the same time, rising temperatures have the opposite effect, increasing photorespiration. (Other factors such as water availability may also come into play.) In contrast, many C_4 plants could be largely unaffected by increasing CO_2 levels or temperature. Researchers have investigated aspects of this question in several studies; you can work with

data from one such experiment in the Scientific Skills Exercise. In different regions, the particular combination of CO_2 concentration and temperature is likely to alter the balance of C_3 and C_4 plants in varying ways. The effects of such a widespread and variable change in community structure are unpredictable and thus a cause of legitimate concern.

CAM Plants

A second photosynthetic adaptation to arid conditions has evolved in many succulent (water-storing) plants, numerous cacti, pineapples, and representatives of several other plant families. These plants open their stomata during the night

---

and close them during the day, just the reverse of how other plants behave. Closing stomata during the day helps desert plants conserve water, but it also prevents CO_2 from entering the leaves. During the night, when their stomata are open, these plants take up CO_2 and incorporate it into a variety of organic acids. This mode of carbon fixation is called **crassulacean acid metabolism**, or **CAM**, after the plant family Crassulaceae, the succulents in which the process was first discovered. The mesophyll cells of **CAM plants** store the organic acids they make during the night in their vacuoles until morning, when the stomata close. During the day, when the light reactions can supply ATP and NADPH for the Calvin cycle, CO_2 is released from the organic acids made the night before to become incorporated into sugar in the chloroplasts.

Notice in **Figure 10.21** that the CAM pathway is similar to the C_4 pathway in that carbon dioxide is first incorporated into organic intermediates before it enters the Calvin

cycle. The difference is that in C_4 plants, the initial steps of carbon fixation are separated structurally from the Calvin cycle, whereas in CAM plants, the two steps occur at separate times but within the same cell. (Keep in mind that CAM, C_4, and C_3 plants all eventually use the Calvin cycle to make sugar from carbon dioxide.)

CONCEPT CHECK 10.4

1. Describe how photorespiration lowers photosynthetic output for plants.
2. The presence of only PS I, not PS II, in the bundle-sheath cells of C_4 plants has an effect on O_2 concentration. What is that effect, and how might that benefit the plant?
3. **MAKE CONNECTIONS** Refer to the discussion of ocean acidification in Concept 3.3. Ocean acidification and changes in the distribution of C_3 and C_4 plants may seem to be two very different problems, but what do they have in common? Explain.
4. **WHAT IF?** How would you expect the relative abundance of C_3 versus C_4 and CAM species to change in a geographic region whose climate becomes much hotter and drier, with no change in CO_2 concentration?

For suggested answers, see Appendix A.

The Importance of Photosynthesis: *A Review*

In this chapter, we have followed photosynthesis from photons to food. The light reactions capture solar energy and use it to make ATP and transfer electrons from water to $NADP^+$, forming NADPH. The Calvin cycle uses the ATP and NADPH to produce sugar from carbon dioxide. The energy that enters the chloroplasts as sunlight becomes stored as chemical energy in organic compounds. The entire process is reviewed visually in **Figure 10.22**, where photosynthesis is also put in its natural context.

As for the fates of photosynthetic products, enzymes in the chloroplast and cytosol convert the G3P made in the Calvin cycle to many other organic compounds. In fact, the sugar made in the chloroplasts supplies the entire plant with chemical energy and carbon skeletons for the synthesis of all the major organic molecules of plant cells. About 50% of the organic material made by photosynthesis is consumed as fuel for cellular respiration in plant cell mitochondria.

Technically, green cells are the only autotrophic parts of the plant. The rest of the plant depends on organic molecules exported from leaves via veins (see Figure 10.22, top). In most plants, carbohydrate is transported out of the leaves to the rest of the plant in the form of sucrose, a disaccharide. After arriving at nonphotosynthetic cells, the sucrose provides raw material for cellular respiration and a multitude of anabolic pathways that synthesize proteins, lipids, and other products. A considerable amount of sugar in the form of glucose is linked together to make the polysaccharide cellulose (see Figure 5.6c), especially in plant cells that are still

Sugarcane

Pineapple

C_4

CAM

(a) Spatial separation of steps. In C_4 plants, carbon fixation and the Calvin cycle occur in different types of cells.

(b) Temporal separation of steps. In CAM plants, carbon fixation and the Calvin cycle occur in the same cell at different times.

▲ **Figure 10.21 C_4 and CAM photosynthesis compared.** Both adaptations are characterized by ❶ preliminary incorporation of CO_2 into organic acids, followed by ❷ transfer of CO_2 to the Calvin cycle. The C_4 and CAM pathways are two evolutionary solutions to the problem of maintaining photosynthesis with stomata partially or completely closed on hot, dry days.

growing and maturing. Cellulose, the main ingredient of cell walls, is the most abundant organic molecule in the plant—and probably on the surface of the planet.

Most plants and other photosynthesizers make more organic material each day than they need to use as respiratory fuel and precursors for biosynthesis. They stockpile the extra sugar by synthesizing starch, storing some in the chloroplasts themselves and some in storage cells of roots, tubers, seeds, and fruits. In accounting for the consumption of the food molecules produced by photosynthesis, let's not forget that most plants lose leaves, roots, stems, fruits, and sometimes their entire bodies to heterotrophs, including humans.

On a global scale, photosynthesis is the process responsible for the presence of oxygen in our atmosphere.

Furthermore, while each chloroplast is minuscule, their collective productivity in terms of food production is prodigious: Photosynthesis makes an estimated 150 billion metric tons of carbohydrate per year (a metric ton is 1,000 kg, about 1.1 tons). That's organic matter equivalent in mass to a stack of about 60 trillion biology textbooks—17 stacks of books reaching from Earth to the sun! No chemical process is more important than photosynthesis to the welfare of life on Earth.

In Chapters 5 through 10, you have learned about many activities of cells. **Figure 10.23** integrates these processes in the context of a working plant cell. As you study the figure, reflect on how each process fits into the big picture: As the most basic unit of living organisms, a cell performs all functions characteristic of life.

▼ **Figure 10.22 A review of photosynthesis.** This diagram shows the main reactants and products of photosynthesis as they move through the tissues of a tree (left) and a chloroplast (right).

MAKE CONNECTIONS *Can plants use the sugar they produce during photosynthesis to directly power the work of the cell? Explain. (See Figures 8.10, 8.11, and 9.6.)*

MAKE CONNECTIONS

The Working Cell

This figure illustrates how a generalized plant cell functions, integrating the cellular activities you learned about in Chapters 5–10.

Flow of Genetic Information in the Cell:
DNA → RNA → Protein (Chapters 5–7)

1 In the nucleus, DNA serves as a template for the synthesis of mRNA, which moves to the cytoplasm. *See Figures 5.23 and 6.9.*

2 mRNA attaches to a ribosome, which remains free in the cytosol or binds to the rough ER. Proteins are synthesized. *See Figures 5.23 and 6.10.*

3 Proteins and membrane produced by the rough ER flow in vesicles to the Golgi apparatus, where they are processed. *See Figures 6.15 and 7.9.*

4 Transport vesicles carrying proteins pinch off from the Golgi apparatus. *See Figure 6.15.*

5 Some vesicles merge with the plasma membrane, releasing proteins by exocytosis. *See Figure 7.9.*

6 Proteins synthesized on free ribosomes stay in the cell and perform specific functions; examples include the enzymes that catalyze the reactions of cellular respiration and photosynthesis. *See Figures 9.7, 9.9, and 10.19.*

Labels in figure: DNA, Nucleus, mRNA, Nuclear pore, Protein in vesicle, Rough endoplasmic reticulum (ER), Protein, Ribosome, mRNA, Golgi apparatus, Vesicle forming, Protein, Plasma membrane, Cell wall

Energy Transformations in the Cell: Photosynthesis and Cellular Respiration (Chapters 8–10)

7 In chloroplasts, the process of photosynthesis uses the energy of light to convert CO_2 and H_2O to organic molecules, with O_2 as a by-product. *See Figure 10.22.*

8 In mitochondria, organic molecules are broken down by cellular respiration, capturing energy in molecules of ATP, which are used to power the work of the cell, such as protein synthesis and active transport. CO_2 and H_2O are by-products. *See Figures 8.9–8.11, 9.2, and 9.16.*

Movement Across Cell Membranes (Chapter 7)

9 Water diffuses into and out of the cell directly through the plasma membrane and by facilitated diffusion through aquaporins. *See Figure 7.1.*

10 By passive transport, the CO_2 used in photosynthesis diffuses into the cell and the O_2 formed as a by-product of photosynthesis diffuses out of the cell. Both solutes move down their concentration gradients. *See Figures 7.10 and 10.22.*

11 In active transport, energy (usually supplied by ATP) is used to transport a solute against its concentration gradient. *See Figure 7.16.*

Exocytosis (shown in step 5) and endocytosis move larger materials out of and into the cell. *See Figures 7.9 and 7.19.*

Vacuole

7 Photosynthesis in chloroplast

CO_2

H_2O

Organic molecules

O_2

ATP

ATP

ATP

ATP

8 Cellular respiration in mitochondrion

Transport pump

11

10

9

O_2

CO_2

H_2O

MAKE CONNECTIONS *The first enzyme that functions in glycolysis is hexokinase. In this plant cell, describe the entire process by which this enzyme is produced and where it functions, specifying the locations for each step. (See Figures 5.18, 5.23, and 9.9.)*

ANIMATION *BioFlix* Visit the Study Area in **MasteringBiology** for BioFlix® 3-D Animations in Chapters 6, 7, 9, and 10. BioFlix Tutorials can also be assigned in MasteringBiology.

SUMMARY OF KEY CONCEPTS

CONCEPT 10.1

Photosynthesis converts light energy to the chemical energy of food (pp. 187–190)

- In **autotrophic** eukaryotes, photosynthesis occurs in chloroplasts, organelles containing **thylakoids**. Stacks of thylakoids form grana. **Photosynthesis** is summarized as

$$6 \, CO_2 + 12 \, H_2O + \text{Light energy} \rightarrow C_6H_{12}O_6 + 6 \, O_2 + 6 \, H_2O.$$

Chloroplasts split water into hydrogen and oxygen, incorporating the electrons of hydrogen into sugar molecules. Photosynthesis is a redox process: H_2O is oxidized, and CO_2 is reduced. The **light reactions** in the thylakoid membranes split water, releasing O_2, producing ATP, and forming **NADPH**. The **Calvin cycle** in the **stroma** forms sugar from CO_2, using ATP for energy and NADPH for reducing power.

> **?** *Compare the roles of CO_2 and H_2O in respiration and photosynthesis.*

CONCEPT 10.2

The light reactions convert solar energy to the chemical energy of ATP and NADPH (pp. 190–199)

- Light is a form of electromagnetic energy. The colors we see as **visible light** include those **wavelengths** that drive photosynthesis. A pigment absorbs light of specific wavelengths; **chlorophyll *a*** is the main photosynthetic pigment in plants. Other accessory pigments absorb different wavelengths of light and pass the energy on to chlorophyll *a*.
- A pigment goes from a ground state to an excited state when a **photon** of light boosts one of the pigment's electrons to a higher-energy orbital. This excited state is unstable. Electrons from isolated pigments tend to fall back to the ground state, giving off heat and/or light.
- A **photosystem** is composed of a **reaction-center complex** surrounded by **light-harvesting complexes** that funnel the energy of photons to the reaction-center complex. When a special pair of reaction-center chlorophyll *a* molecules absorbs energy, one of its electrons is boosted to a higher energy level and transferred to the **primary electron acceptor**. **Photosystem II** contains P680 chlorophyll *a* molecules in the reaction-center complex; **photosystem I** contains P700 molecules.
- **Linear electron flow** during the light reactions uses both photosystems and produces NADPH, ATP, and oxygen:

- **Cyclic electron flow** employs only one photosystem, producing ATP but no NADPH or O_2.
- During chemiosmosis in both mitochondria and chloroplasts, electron transport chains generate an H^+ gradient across a membrane. ATP synthase uses this proton-motive force to make ATP.

> **?** *The absorption spectrum of chlorophyll a differs from the action spectrum of photosynthesis. Explain this observation.*

CONCEPT 10.3

The Calvin cycle uses the chemical energy of ATP and NADPH to reduce CO_2 to sugar (pp. 199–200)

- The Calvin cycle occurs in the stroma, using electrons from NADPH and energy from ATP. One molecule of **G3P** exits the cycle per three CO_2 molecules fixed and is converted to glucose and other organic molecules.

> **DRAW IT** *On the diagram above, draw where ATP and NADPH are used and where rubisco functions. Describe these steps.*

CONCEPT 10.4

Alternative mechanisms of carbon fixation have evolved in hot, arid climates (pp. 201–207)

- On dry, hot days, **C_3 plants** close their stomata, conserving water. Oxygen from the light reactions builds up. In **photorespiration**, O_2 substitutes for CO_2 in the active site of rubisco. This process consumes organic fuel and releases CO_2 without producing ATP or carbohydrate. Photorespiration may be an evolutionary relic, and it may play a photoprotective role.
- **C_4 plants** minimize the cost of photorespiration by incorporating CO_2 into four-carbon compounds in mesophyll cells. These compounds are exported to **bundle-sheath cells**, where they release carbon dioxide for use in the Calvin cycle.
- **CAM plants** open their stomata at night, incorporating CO_2 into organic acids, which are stored in mesophyll cells. During the day, the stomata close, and the CO_2 is released from the organic acids for use in the Calvin cycle.
- Organic compounds produced by photosynthesis provide the energy and building material for Earth's ecosystems.

> **?** *Why are C_4 and CAM photosynthesis more energetically expensive than C_3 photosynthesis? What climate conditions would favor C_4 and CAM plants?*

TEST YOUR UNDERSTANDING

LEVEL 1: KNOWLEDGE/COMPREHENSION

1. The light reactions of photosynthesis supply the Calvin cycle with
   a. light energy.
   b. CO_2 and ATP.
   c. H_2O and NADPH.
   d. ATP and NADPH.

2. Which of the following sequences correctly represents the flow of electrons during photosynthesis?
   a. NADPH $\rightarrow O_2 \rightarrow CO_2$
   b. $H_2O \rightarrow$ NADPH $\rightarrow$ Calvin cycle
   c. $H_2O \rightarrow$ photosystem I $\rightarrow$ photosystem II
   d. NADPH $\rightarrow$ electron transport chain $\rightarrow O_2$

3. How is photosynthesis similar in C_4 plants and CAM plants?
   a. In both cases, only photosystem I is used.
   b. Both types of plants make sugar without the Calvin cycle.
   c. In both cases, rubisco is not used to fix carbon initially.
   d. Both types of plants make most of their sugar in the dark.

4. Which of the following statements is a correct distinction between autotrophs and heterotrophs?
   a. Autotrophs, but not heterotrophs, can nourish themselves beginning with CO_2 and other nutrients that are inorganic.
   b. Only heterotrophs require chemical compounds from the environment.
   c. Cellular respiration is unique to heterotrophs.
   d. Only heterotrophs have mitochondria.

5. Which of the following does *not* occur during the Calvin cycle?
   a. carbon fixation
   b. oxidation of NADPH
   c. release of oxygen
   d. regeneration of the CO_2 acceptor

LEVEL 2: APPLICATION/ANALYSIS

6. In mechanism, photophosphorylation is most similar to
   a. substrate-level phosphorylation in glycolysis.
   b. oxidative phosphorylation in cellular respiration.
   c. carbon fixation.
   d. reduction of $NADP^+$.

7. Which process is most directly driven by light energy?
   a. creation of a pH gradient by pumping protons across the thylakoid membrane
   b. reduction of $NADP^+$ molecules
   c. removal of electrons from chlorophyll molecules
   d. ATP synthesis

LEVEL 3: SYNTHESIS/EVALUATION

8. **SCIENCE, TECHNOLOGY, AND SOCIETY**
   Scientific evidence indicates that the CO_2 added to the air by the burning of wood and fossil fuels is contributing to global warming, a rise in global temperature. Tropical rain forests are estimated to be responsible for approximately 20% of global photosynthesis, yet the consumption of large amounts of CO_2 by living trees is thought to make little or no *net* contribution to reduction of global warming. Why might this be? (*Hint:* What processes in both living and dead trees produce CO_2?)

9. **EVOLUTION CONNECTION**
   Photorespiration can decrease soybeans' photosynthetic output by about 50%. Would you expect this figure to be higher or lower in wild relatives of soybeans? Why?

10. **SCIENTIFIC INQUIRY**
    MAKE CONNECTIONS The following diagram represents an experiment with isolated thylakoids. The thylakoids were first made acidic by soaking them in a solution at pH 4. After the thylakoid space reached pH 4, the thylakoids were transferred to a basic solution at pH 8. The thylakoids then made ATP in the dark. (See Concept 3.3 to review pH.)

    Draw an enlargement of part of the thylakoid membrane in the beaker with the solution at pH 8. Draw ATP synthase. Label the areas of high H^+ concentration and low H^+ concentration. Show the direction protons flow through the enzyme, and show the reaction where ATP is synthesized. Would ATP end up in the thylakoid or outside of it? Explain why the thylakoids in the experiment were able to make ATP in the dark.

11. **WRITE ABOUT A THEME: ENERGY AND MATTER**
    Life is solar powered. Almost all the producers of the biosphere depend on energy from the sun to produce the organic molecules that supply the energy and carbon skeletons needed for life. In a short essay (100–150 words), describe how the process of photosynthesis in the chloroplasts of plants transforms the energy of sunlight into the chemical energy of sugar molecules.

12. **SYNTHESIZE YOUR KNOWLEDGE**

    The photo shows "watermelon snow" in Antarctica, caused by a species of photosynthetic green algae that thrives in subzero temperatures (*Chlamydomonas nivalis*). These algae are also found in high altitude year-round snowfields. In both locations, UV light levels tend to be high. Based on what you learned in this chapter, propose an explanation for why this photosynthetic alga appears reddish-pink.

    For selected answers, see Appendix A.

MasteringBiology®

Students Go to **MasteringBiology** for assignments, the eText, and the Study Area with practice tests, animations, and activities.

Instructors Go to **MasteringBiology** for automatically graded tutorials and questions that you can assign to your students, plus Instructor Resources.

11

Cell Communication

▶ Epinephrine

▲ Figure 11.1 How does cell signaling trigger the desperate flight of this impala?

Cellular Messaging

The impala in **Figure 11.1** flees for its life, racing to escape the predatory cheetah nipping at its heels. The impala is breathing rapidly, its heart pounding and its legs pumping furiously. These physiological functions are all part of the impala's "fight-or-flight" response, driven by hormones released from its adrenal glands at times of stress—in this case, upon sensing the cheetah. What systems of cell-to-cell communication allow the trillions of cells in the impala to "talk" to each other, coordinating their activities?

Cells can signal to each other and interpret the signals they receive from other cells and the environment. The signals may include light and touch, but are most often chemicals. The flight response shown here is triggered by a signaling molecule called epinephrine (also called adrenaline; see the model to the left). Studying cell communication, biologists have discovered ample evidence for the evolutionary relatedness of all life. The same small set of cell-signaling mechanisms shows up again and again in diverse species, in processes ranging from bacterial signaling to embryonic development to cancer. In this chapter, we focus on the main mechanisms by which cells receive, process, and respond to chemical signals sent from other cells. We will also consider *apoptosis*, a type of programmed cell death that integrates input from multiple signaling pathways.

External signals are converted to responses within the cell

What does a "talking" cell say to a "listening" cell, and how does the latter cell respond to the message? Let's approach these questions by first looking at communication among microorganisms.

Evolution of Cell Signaling

EVOLUTION One topic of cell "conversation" is sex. Cells of the yeast *Saccharomyces cerevisiae*—which are used to make bread, wine, and beer—identify their mates by chemical signaling. There are two sexes, or mating types, called **a** and **α** (Figure 11.2). Each type secretes a specific factor that binds to receptors only on the other type of cell. When exposed to each other's mating factors, a pair of cells of opposite type change shape, grow toward each other, and fuse (mate). The new **a**/**α** cell contains all the genes of both original cells, a combination of genetic resources that provides advantages to the cell's descendants, which arise by subsequent cell divisions.

Once received by the yeast cell surface receptor, a mating signal is changed, or *transduced*, into a form that brings

about the cellular response of mating. This occurs in a series of steps called a *signal transduction pathway*. Many such pathways exist in both yeast and animal cells. In fact, the molecular details of signal transduction in yeasts and mammals are strikingly similar, even though their last common ancestor lived over a billion years ago. This suggests that early versions of cell-signaling mechanisms evolved well before the first multicellular creatures appeared on Earth.

Scientists think that signaling mechanisms first evolved in ancient prokaryotes and single-celled eukaryotes and then were adopted for new uses by their multicellular descendants. Cell signaling is critical in the microbial world (Figure 11.3). Bacterial cells secrete molecules that can be detected by other bacterial cells. Sensing the concentration of such signaling molecules allows bacteria to monitor the local density of cells, a phenomenon called *quorum sensing*. Quorum sensing allows bacterial populations to coordinate their behaviors in activities that require a given number

1 Exchange of mating factors. Each cell type secretes a mating factor that binds to receptors on the other cell type.

Receptor

α factor

a

α

Yeast cell, mating type **a**

a factor

Yeast cell, mating type α

2 Mating. Binding of the factors to receptors induces changes in the cells that lead to their fusion.

a

α

3 New a/α cell. The nucleus of the fused cell includes all the genes from the **a** and α cells.

a/α

▲ **Figure 11.2 Communication between mating yeast cells.** *Saccharomyces cerevisiae* cells use chemical signaling to identify cells of opposite mating type and initiate the mating process. The two mating types and their corresponding chemical signaling molecules, or mating factors, are called **a** and *α*.

1 Individual rod-shaped cells

0.5 mm

2 Aggregation in progress

2.5 mm

3 Spore-forming structure (fruiting body)

Fruiting bodies

▲ **Figure 11.3 Communication among bacteria.** Soil-dwelling bacteria called myxobacteria ("slime bacteria") use chemical signals to share information about nutrient availability. When food is scarce, starving cells secrete a molecule that stimulates neighboring cells to aggregate. The cells form a structure, called a fruiting body, that produces thick-walled spores capable of surviving until the environment improves. The bacteria shown here are *Myxococcus xanthus* (steps 1–3, SEMs; lower photo, LM).

of cells acting synchronously. One example is formation of a *biofilm*, an aggregation of bacterial cells adhered to a surface. The cells in the biofilm generally derive nutrition from the surface they are on. You have probably encountered biofilms many times, perhaps without realizing it. The slimy coating on a fallen log or on leaves lying on a forest path, and even the film on your teeth each morning, are examples of bacterial biofilms. (In fact, tooth-brushing disrupts biofilms that would otherwise cause cavities.) The formation of biofilms requires a sophisticated communication system, the basis of which is cell signaling.

Local and Long-Distance Signaling

Like bacteria or yeast cells, cells in a multicellular organism usually communicate via signaling molecules targeted for cells that may or may not be immediately adjacent. As we saw in Chapters 6 and 7, eukaryotic cells may communicate by direct contact, one type of local signaling (Figure 11.4). Both animals and plants have cell junctions that, where present, directly connect the cytoplasms of adjacent cells (Figure 11.4a). In these cases, signaling substances dissolved in the cytosol can pass freely between adjacent cells. Moreover, animal cells may communicate via direct contact between membrane-bound cell-surface molecules in a process called cell-cell recognition (Figure 11.4b). This sort of local signaling is especially important in embryonic development and the immune response.

In many other cases of local signaling, messenger molecules are secreted by the signaling cell. Some of these travel only short distances; such local regulators influence cells in the vicinity. One class of local regulators in animals, *growth factors*, are compounds that stimulate nearby target cells to grow and divide. Numerous cells can simultaneously receive and respond to the molecules of growth factor produced by a single cell in their vicinity. This type of local signaling in animals is called *paracrine signaling* (Figure 11.5a).

Another, more specialized type of local signaling called *synaptic signaling* occurs in the animal nervous system (Figure 11.5b). An electrical signal along a nerve cell triggers the secretion of neurotransmitter molecules. These molecules act as chemical signals, diffusing across the synapse—the narrow space between the nerve cell and its target cell—triggering a response in the target cell.

Beyond communication through plasmodesmata (plant cell junctions), local signaling in plants is not as well understood. Because of their cell walls, plants use mechanisms different from those operating locally in animals.

Both animals and plants use chemicals called **hormones** for long-distance signaling. In hormonal signaling in animals, also known as *endocrine signaling*, specialized cells release hormone molecules, which travel via the circulatory system to other parts of the body, where they reach target cells that can recognize and respond to the hormones (Figure 11.5c). Plant hormones (often called *plant growth regulators*) sometimes travel in vessels but more often reach their targets by moving through cells or by diffusing through the air as a gas (see Concept 39.2). Hormones vary widely in size and type, as do local regulators. For instance, the plant hormone ethylene, a gas that promotes fruit ripening and helps regulate growth, is a hydrocarbon of only six atoms (C_2H_4), small enough to pass through cell walls. In contrast, the mammalian hormone insulin, which regulates sugar levels in the blood, is a protein with thousands of atoms.

What happens when a cell encounters a secreted signaling molecule? The ability of a cell to respond is determined by whether it has a specific receptor molecule that can bind to the signaling molecule. The information conveyed by this binding, the signal, must then be changed into another form—transduced—inside the cell before the cell can respond. The remainder of the chapter discusses this process, primarily as it occurs in animal cells.

The Three Stages of Cell Signaling: *A Preview*

Our current understanding of how chemical messengers act via signal transduction pathways had its origins in the pioneering work of Earl W. Sutherland, whose research led to a Nobel Prize in 1971. Sutherland and his colleagues at Vanderbilt University were investigating how the animal hormone epinephrine (adrenaline) stimulates the breakdown of the storage polysaccharide glycogen within liver cells and skeletal muscle cells. Glycogen breakdown releases the sugar glucose 1-phosphate, which the cell converts

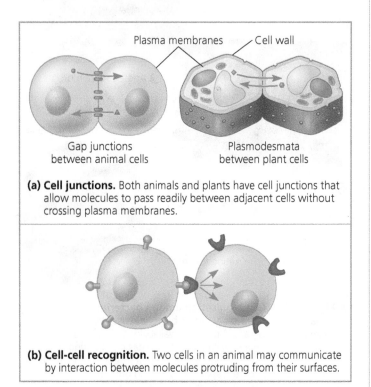

Plasma membranes — Cell wall

Gap junctions between animal cells

Plasmodesmata between plant cells

(a) Cell junctions. Both animals and plants have cell junctions that allow molecules to pass readily between adjacent cells without crossing plasma membranes.

(b) Cell-cell recognition. Two cells in an animal may communicate by interaction between molecules protruding from their surfaces.

▲ **Figure 11.4 Communication by direct contact between cells.**

Local signaling

Long-distance signaling

Target cells

Secreting cell

Secretory vesicles

Local regulator

Electrical signal triggers release of neurotransmitter.

Neurotransmitter diffuses across synapse.

Target cell

Endocrine cell

Target cell specifically binds hormone.

Hormone travels in bloodstream.

Blood vessel

(a) Paracrine signaling. A secreting cell acts on nearby target cells by secreting molecules of a local regulator (a growth factor, for example).

(b) Synaptic signaling. A nerve cell releases neurotransmitter molecules into a synapse, stimulating the target cell, such as a muscle or nerve cell.

(c) Endocrine (hormonal) signaling. Specialized endocrine cells secrete hormones into body fluids, often blood. Hormones reach virtually all body cells, but are bound only by some cells.

▲ **Figure 11.5 Local and long-distance cell signaling by secreted molecules in animals.** In both local and long-distance signaling, only specific target cells that can recognize a given signaling molecule will respond to it.

to glucose 6-phosphate. The liver or muscle cell can then use this compound, an early intermediate in glycolysis, for energy production. Alternatively, the compound can be stripped of phosphate and released from the cell into the blood as glucose, which can fuel cells throughout the body. Thus, one effect of epinephrine is the mobilization of fuel reserves, which can be used by the animal to either defend itself (fight) or escape whatever elicited a scare (flight). (The impala in Figure 11.1 is obviously engaged in the latter.)

Sutherland's research team discovered that epinephrine stimulates glycogen breakdown by somehow activating a cytosolic enzyme, glycogen phosphorylase. However, when epinephrine was added to a test-tube mixture containing the enzyme and its substrate, glycogen, no breakdown occurred. Glycogen phosphorylase could be activated by epinephrine only when the hormone was added to *intact* cells

in a solution. This result told Sutherland two things. First, epinephrine does not interact directly with the enzyme responsible for glycogen breakdown; an intermediate step or series of steps must be occurring inside the cell. Second, the plasma membrane itself is necessary for transmission of the signal to take place.

Sutherland's early work suggested that the process going on at the receiving end of a cellular conversation can be dissected into three stages: reception, transduction, and response **(Figure 11.6):**

❶ **Reception.** Reception is the target cell's detection of a signaling molecule coming from outside the cell. A chemical signal is "detected" when the signaling molecule binds to a receptor protein located at the cell's surface (or inside the cell, to be discussed later).

▶ **Figure 11.6 Overview of cell signaling.** From the perspective of the cell receiving the message, cell signaling can be divided into three stages: signal reception, signal transduction, and cellular response. When reception occurs at the plasma membrane, as shown here, the transduction stage is usually a pathway of several steps, with each specific relay molecule in the pathway bringing about a change in the next molecule. The final molecule in the pathway triggers the cell's response.

? *How does the epinephrine in Sutherland's experiment fit into this diagram of cell signaling?*

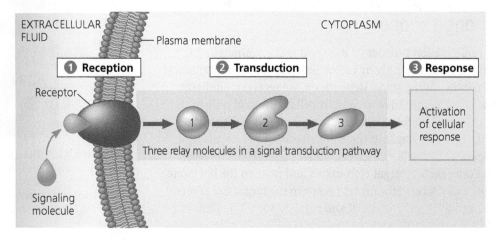

EXTRACELLULAR FLUID

CYTOPLASM

Plasma membrane

❶ **Reception**

❷ **Transduction**

❸ **Response**

Receptor

1 → 2 → 3

Three relay molecules in a signal transduction pathway

Activation of cellular response

Signaling molecule

Transduction. The binding of the signaling molecule changes the receptor protein in some way, initiating the process of transduction. The transduction stage converts the signal to a form that can bring about a specific cellular response. In Sutherland's system, the binding of epinephrine to a receptor protein in a liver cell's plasma membrane leads to activation of glycogen phosphorylase. Transduction sometimes occurs in a single step but more often requires a sequence of changes in a series of different molecules—a **signal transduction pathway**. The molecules in the pathway are often called relay molecules.

Response. In the third stage of cell signaling, the transduced signal finally triggers a specific cellular response. The response may be almost any imaginable cellular activity—such as catalysis by an enzyme (for example, glycogen phosphorylase), rearrangement of the cytoskeleton, or activation of specific genes in the nucleus. The cell-signaling process helps ensure that crucial activities like these occur in the right cells, at the right time, and in proper coordination with the activities of other cells of the organism. We'll now explore the mechanisms of cell signaling in more detail, including a discussion of regulation and termination of the process.

CONCEPT CHECK 11.1

1. Explain how signaling is involved in ensuring that yeast cells fuse only with cells of the opposite mating type.
2. In liver cells, glycogen phosphorylase acts in which of the three stages of the signaling pathway associated with an epinephrine-initiated signal?
3. **WHAT IF?** When epinephrine is mixed with glycogen phosphorylase and glycogen in a test tube, is glucose 1-phosphate generated? Why or why not?

For suggested answers, see Appendix A.

CONCEPT 11.2

Reception: A signaling molecule binds to a receptor protein, causing it to change shape

A radio station broadcasts its signal indiscriminately, but it can be picked up only by radios tuned to the right frequency: Reception of the signal depends on the receiver. Similarly, the signals emitted by an **a** yeast cell are "heard" only by its prospective mates, **α** cells. In the case of the epinephrine circulating throughout the bloodstream of the impala in Figure 11.1, the hormone encounters many types of cells, but only certain target cells detect and react to the hormone molecule. A receptor protein on or in the target cell allows the cell to "hear" the signal and respond to it. The signaling

molecule is complementary in shape to a specific site on the receptor and attaches there, like a key in a lock. The signaling molecule acts as a **ligand**, the term for a molecule that specifically binds to another molecule, often a larger one. Ligand binding generally causes a receptor protein to undergo a change in shape. For many receptors, this shape change directly activates the receptor, enabling it to interact with other cellular molecules. For other kinds of receptors, the immediate effect of ligand binding is to cause the aggregation of two or more receptor molecules, which leads to further molecular events inside the cell. Most signal receptors are plasma membrane proteins, but others are located inside the cell. We discuss both of these types next.

Receptors in the Plasma Membrane

Cell-surface receptor proteins play crucial roles in the biological systems of animals. The largest family of human cell surface receptors are the nearly 1,000 G protein-coupled receptors (GPCRs); an example is shown in **(Figure 11.7)**.

Most water-soluble signaling molecules bind to specific sites on transmembrane receptor proteins that transmit information from the extracellular environment to the inside of the cell. We can see how cell-surface transmembrane receptors work by looking at three major types: G protein-coupled receptors (GPCRs), receptor tyrosine kinases, and ion channel receptors. These receptors are discussed and illustrated in **Figure 11.8**; study this figure before going on.

Given the many important functions of cell-surface receptors, it is not surprising that their malfunctions are associated with many human diseases, including cancer, heart disease, and asthma. To better understand and treat these conditions, a major focus of both university research teams and the pharmaceutical industry has been to analyze the structure of these receptors.

▲ Figure 11.7 **The structure of a G protein-coupled receptor (GPCR).** Shown here is a model of the human β₂-adrenergic receptor in the presence of a molecule mimicking the natural ligand (green in the model) and cholesterol (orange). Two receptor molecules (blue) are shown as ribbon models in a side view within the plasma membrane.

G Protein-Coupled Receptors

Signaling molecule binding site

Segment that interacts with G proteins

G protein-coupled receptor

A **G protein-coupled receptor** (GPCR) is a cell-surface transmembrane receptor that works with the help of a **G protein**, a protein that binds the energy-rich molecule GTP. Many different signaling molecules—including yeast mating factors, epinephrine (adrenaline) and many other hormones, as well as neurotransmitters—use GPCRs. These receptors vary in the binding sites for their signaling molecules (often referred to as their ligands) and also for different types of G proteins inside the cell. Nevertheless, GPCR proteins are all remarkably similar in structure. In fact, they make up a large family of eukaryotic receptor proteins with a secondary structure in which the single polypeptide, represented here in a ribbon model, has seven transmembrane α helices, outlined with cylinders and depicted in a row for clarity. Specific loops between the helices (here, the loops on the right) form binding sites for signaling molecules (outside the cell) and G proteins (on the cytoplasmic side).

GPCR-based signaling systems are extremely widespread and diverse in their functions, including roles in embryonic development and sensory reception. In humans, for example, vision, smell, and taste depend on GPCRs. Similarities in structure in G proteins and GPCRs in diverse organisms suggest that G proteins and their associated receptors evolved very early among eukaryotes.

Malfunctions of the associated G proteins themselves are involved in many human diseases, including bacterial infections. The bacteria that cause cholera, pertussis (whooping cough), and botulism, among others, make their victims ill by producing toxins that interfere with G protein function. Pharmacologists now realize that up to 60% of all medicines used today exert their effects by influencing G protein pathways.

1 Loosely attached to the cytoplasmic side of the membrane, the G protein functions as a molecular switch that is either on or off, depending on which of two guanine nucleotides is attached, GDP or GTP—hence the term *G protein*. (GTP, or guanosine triphosphate, is similar to ATP.) When GDP is bound to the G protein, as shown above, the G protein is inactive. The receptor and G protein work together with another protein, usually an enzyme.

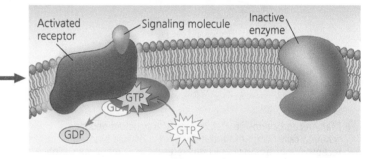

2 When the appropriate signaling molecule binds to the extracellular side of the receptor, the receptor is activated and changes shape. Its cytoplasmic side then binds an inactive G protein, causing a GTP to displace the GDP. This activates the G protein.

3 The activated G protein dissociates from the receptor, diffuses along the membrane, and then binds to an enzyme, altering the enzyme's shape and activity. Once activated, the enzyme can trigger the next step leading to a cellular response. Binding of signaling molecules is reversible: Like other ligands, they bind and dissociate many times. The ligand concentration outside the cell determines how often a ligand is bound and causes signaling.

4 The changes in the enzyme and G protein are only temporary because the G protein also functions as a GTPase enzyme—in other words, it then hydrolyzes its bound GTP to GDP and P_i. Now inactive again, the G protein leaves the enzyme, which returns to its original state. The G protein is now available for reuse. The GTPase function of the G protein allows the pathway to shut down rapidly when the signaling molecule is no longer present.

Continued on next page

Exploring Cell-Surface Transmembrane Receptors

Receptor Tyrosine Kinases

Receptor tyrosine kinases (RTKs) belong to a major class of plasma membrane receptors characterized by having enzymatic activity. A kinase is any enzyme that catalyzes the transfer of phosphate groups. The part of the receptor protein extending into the cytoplasm functions more specifically as a tyrosine kinase, an enzyme that catalyzes the transfer of a phosphate group from ATP to the amino acid tyrosine on a substrate protein. Thus, RTKs are membrane receptors that attach phosphates to tyrosines.

One RTK may activate ten or more different transduction pathways and cellular responses. Often, more than one signal transduction pathway can be triggered at once, helping the cell regulate and coordinate many aspects of cell growth and cell reproduction. The ability of a single ligand-binding event to trigger so many pathways is a key difference between RTKs and GPCRs, which activate a single transduction pathway. Abnormal RTKs that function even in the absence of signaling molecules are associated with many kinds of cancer.

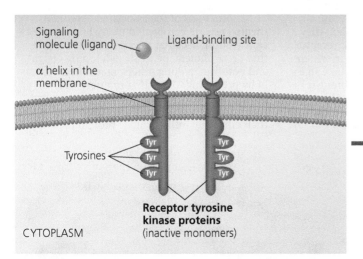

1 Many receptor tyrosine kinases have the structure depicted schematically here. Before the signaling molecule binds, the receptors exist as individual units referred to as monomers. Notice that each has an extracellular ligand-binding site, an α helix spanning the membrane, and an intracellular tail containing multiple tyrosines.

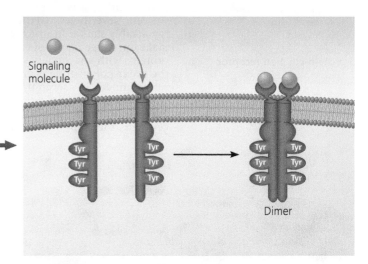

2 The binding of a signaling molecule (such as a growth factor) causes two receptor monomers to associate closely with each other, forming a complex known as a dimer in a process called dimerization. (In some cases, larger clusters form. The details of monomer association are a focus of current research.)

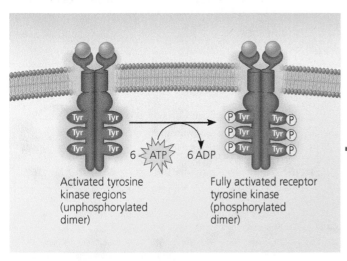

3 Dimerization activates the tyrosine kinase region of each monomer; each tyrosine kinase adds a phosphate from an ATP molecule to a tyrosine on the tail of the other monomer.

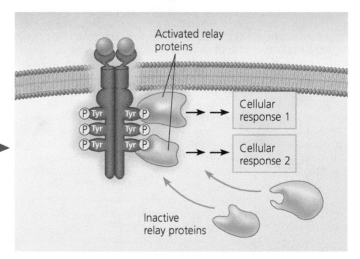

4 Now that the receptor is fully activated, it is recognized by specific relay proteins inside the cell. Each such protein binds to a specific phosphorylated tyrosine, undergoing a resulting structural change that activates the bound protein. Each activated protein triggers a transduction pathway, leading to a cellular response.

Ion Channel Receptors

A **ligand-gated ion channel** is a type of membrane receptor containing a region that can act as a "gate" when the receptor changes shape. When a signaling molecule binds as a ligand to the receptor protein, the gate opens or closes, allowing or blocking the flow of specific ions, such as Na^+ or Ca^{2+}, through a channel in the receptor. Like the other receptors we have discussed, these proteins bind the ligand at a specific site on their extracellular sides.

1 Here we show a ligand-gated ion channel receptor in which the gate remains closed until a ligand binds to the receptor.

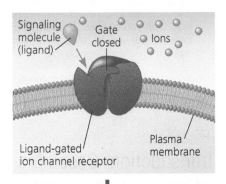

2 When the ligand binds to the receptor and the gate opens, specific ions can flow through the channel and rapidly change the concentration of that particular ion inside the cell. This change may directly affect the activity of the cell in some way.

3 When the ligand dissociates from this receptor, the gate closes and ions no longer enter the cell.

Ligand-gated ion channels are very important in the nervous system. For example, the neurotransmitter molecules released at a synapse between two nerve cells (see Figure 11.5b) bind as ligands to ion channels on the receiving cell, causing the channels to open. Ions flow in (or, in some cases, out), triggering an electrical signal that propagates down the length of the receiving cell. Some gated ion channels are controlled by electrical signals instead of ligands; these voltage-gated ion channels are also crucial to the functioning of the nervous system, as we will discuss in Chapter 48. Some ion channels are present on membranes of organelles, such as the ER.

MAKE CONNECTIONS *Is the flow of ions through a ligand-gated channel an example of active or passive transport? (Review Concepts 7.3 and 7.4.)*

Although cell-surface receptors represent 30% of all human proteins, determining their structures has proved challenging: They make up only 1% of the proteins whose structures have been determined by X-ray crystallography (see Figure 5.22). For one thing, cell-surface receptors tend to be flexible and inherently unstable, thus difficult to crystallize. It took years of persistent efforts for researchers to determine the first few of these structures, such as the GPCR shown in Figure 11.7. In that case, the β-adrenergic receptor was stable enough to be crystallized while it was among membrane molecules, in the presence of its ligand.

Abnormal functioning of receptor tyrosine kinases (RTKs) is associated with many types of cancers. For example, breast cancer patients have a poor prognosis if their tumor cells harbor excessive levels of a receptor tyrosine kinase called HER2 (see Concept 12.3 and Figure 18.27). Using molecular biological techniques, researchers have developed a protein called Herceptin that binds to HER2 on cells and inhibits cell division, thus thwarting further tumor development. In some clinical studies, treatment with Herceptin improved patient survival rates by more than one-third. One goal of ongoing research into these cell-surface receptors and other cell-signaling proteins is development of additional successful treatments.

Intracellular Receptors

Intracellular receptor proteins are found in either the cytoplasm or nucleus of target cells. To reach such a receptor, a signaling molecule passes through the target cell's plasma membrane. A number of important signaling molecules can do this because they are either hydrophobic enough or small enough to cross the hydrophobic interior of the membrane. These hydrophobic chemical messengers include the steroid hormones and thyroid hormones of animals. Another chemical signaling molecule with an intracellular receptor is nitric oxide (NO), a gas; its very small molecules readily pass between the membrane phospholipids.

Once a hormone has entered a cell, it may bind to an intracellular receptor in the cytoplasm or the nucleus. The binding changes the receptor into a hormone-receptor complex that is able to cause a response—in many cases, the turning on or off of particular genes.

The behavior of aldosterone is a representative example of how steroid hormones work. This hormone is secreted by cells of the adrenal gland, a gland that sits above the kidney. Aldosterone then travels through the blood and enters cells all over the body. However, a response occurs only in kidney cells, which contain receptor molecules for this hormone. In these cells, the hormone binds to the receptor protein, activating it. With aldosterone attached, the active form of the receptor protein then enters the nucleus and turns on specific genes that control water and sodium flow in kidney cells, ultimately affecting blood volume (**Figure 11.9**).

How does the activated hormone-receptor complex turn on genes? Recall that the genes in a cell's DNA function by being transcribed and processed into messenger RNA (mRNA), which leaves the nucleus and is translated into a specific protein by ribosomes in the cytoplasm (see Figure 5.23). Special proteins called *transcription factors* control which genes are turned on—that is, which genes are transcribed into mRNA—in a particular cell at a particular time. When the aldosterone receptor is activated, it acts as a transcription factor that turns on specific genes. (You'll learn more about transcription factors in Chapters 17 and 18.)

By acting as a transcription factor, the aldosterone receptor itself carries out the transduction part of the signaling pathway. Most other intracellular receptors function in the same way, although many of them, such as the thyroid hormone receptor, are already in the nucleus before the signaling molecule reaches them. Interestingly, many of these intracellular receptor proteins are structurally similar, suggesting an evolutionary kinship.

▲ **Figure 11.9 Steroid hormone interacting with an intracellular receptor.**

1 The steroid hormone aldosterone passes through the plasma membrane.

2 Aldosterone binds to a receptor protein in the cytoplasm, activating it.

3 The hormone-receptor complex enters the nucleus and binds to specific genes.

4 The bound protein acts as a transcription factor, stimulating the transcription of the gene into mRNA.

5 The mRNA is translated into a specific protein.

? *Why is a cell-surface receptor protein not required for this steroid hormone to enter the cell?*

CONCEPT 11.3

Transduction: Cascades of molecular interactions relay signals from receptors to target molecules in the cell

When receptors for signaling molecules are plasma membrane proteins, like most of those we have discussed, the transduction stage of cell signaling is usually a multistep pathway involving many molecules. Steps often include activation of proteins by addition or removal of phosphate groups or release of other small molecules or ions that act as messengers. One benefit of multiple steps is the possibility of greatly amplifying a signal. If each molecule in a pathway transmits the signal to numerous molecules at the next step in the series, the result is a geometric increase in the number of activated molecules by the end of the pathway. Moreover, multistep pathways provide more opportunities for coordination and control than do simpler systems. This allows regulation of the response, as we'll discuss later in the chapter.

Signal Transduction Pathways

The binding of a specific signaling molecule to a receptor in the plasma membrane triggers the first step in the chain of molecular interactions—the signal transduction pathway—that leads to a particular response within the cell. Like falling dominoes, the signal-activated receptor activates another molecule, which activates yet another molecule, and so on, until the protein that produces the final cellular response is activated. The molecules that relay a signal from receptor to response, which we call relay molecules in this book, are often proteins. The interaction of proteins is a major theme of cell signaling. Indeed, protein interaction is a unifying theme of all cellular activities.

Keep in mind that the original signaling molecule is not physically passed along a signaling pathway; in most cases, it never even enters the cell. When we say that the signal is relayed along a pathway, we mean that certain information is passed on. At each step, the signal is transduced into a different form, commonly a shape change in the next protein. Very often, the shape change is brought about by phosphorylation.

Protein Phosphorylation and Dephosphorylation

Previous chapters introduced the concept of activating a protein by adding one or more phosphate groups to it (see Figure 8.11a). In Figure 11.8, you have already seen how phosphorylation is involved in the activation of receptor tyrosine kinases. In fact, the phosphorylation and dephosphorylation of proteins is a widespread cellular mechanism

for regulating protein activity. An enzyme that transfers phosphate groups from ATP to a protein is generally known as a **protein kinase**. Recall that a receptor tyrosine kinase is a specific kind of protein kinase that phosphorylates tyrosines on the other receptor tyrosine kinase in a dimer. Most cytoplasmic protein kinases, however, act on proteins different from themselves. Another distinction is that most cytoplasmic protein kinases phosphorylate either of two other amino acids, serine or threonine, rather than tyrosine. Serine/threonine kinases are widely involved in signaling pathways in animals, plants, and fungi.

Many of the relay molecules in signal transduction pathways are protein kinases, and they often act on other protein kinases in the pathway. **Figure 11.10** depicts a hypothetical pathway containing three different protein kinases that create a **phosphorylation cascade**. The sequence of steps

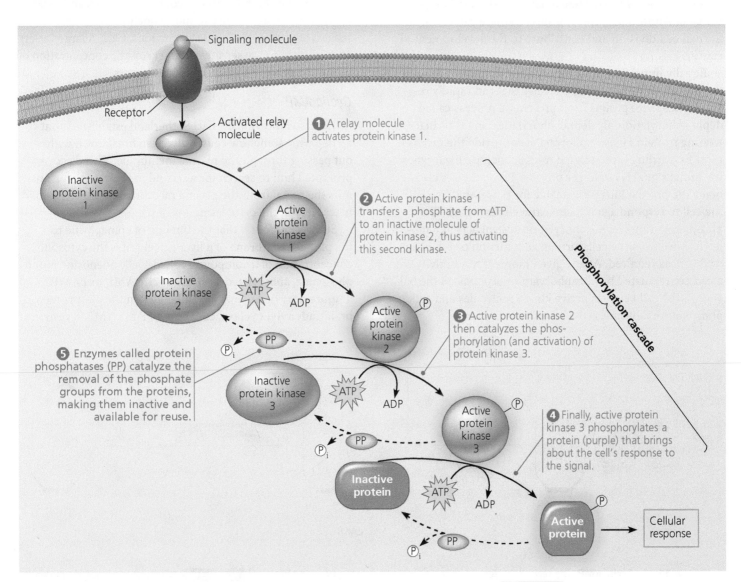

▲ **Figure 11.10 A phosphorylation cascade.** In a phosphorylation cascade, a series of different proteins in a pathway are phosphorylated in turn, each protein adding a phosphate group to the next one in line. Here, phosphorylation activates each protein, and dephosphorylation returns it to its inactive form. The active and inactive forms of each protein are represented by different shapes to remind you that activation is usually associated with a change in molecular shape.

WHAT IF? *What would happen if a mutation in protein kinase 3 made it incapable of being phosphorylated?*

shown in the figure is similar to many known pathways, including those triggered in yeast by mating factors and in animal cells by many growth factors. The signal is transmitted by a cascade of protein phosphorylations, each causing a shape change because of the interaction of the newly added phosphate groups with charged or polar amino acids on the protein being phosphorylated (see Figure 5.14). The change in shape alters the function of the protein, most often activating it. In some cases, though, phosphorylation *decreases* the activity of the protein.

The importance of protein kinases can hardly be overstated. About 2% of our own genes are thought to code for protein kinases. A single cell may have hundreds of different kinds, each specific for a different substrate protein. Together, they probably regulate the activity of a large proportion of the thousands of proteins in a cell. Among these are most of the proteins that, in turn, regulate cell division. Abnormal activity of such a kinase can cause abnormal cell division and contribute to the development of cancer.

Equally important in the phosphorylation cascade are the **protein phosphatases**, enzymes that can rapidly remove phosphate groups from proteins, a process called dephosphorylation. By dephosphorylating and thus inactivating protein kinases, phosphatases provide the mechanism for turning off the signal transduction pathway when the initial signal is no longer present. Phosphatases also make the protein kinases available for reuse, enabling the cell to respond again to an extracellular signal. The phosphorylation-dephosphorylation system acts as a molecular switch in the cell, turning activities on or off, or up or down, as required. At any given moment, the activity of a protein regulated by phosphorylation depends on the balance in the cell between active kinase molecules and active phosphatase molecules.

Small Molecules and Ions as Second Messengers

Not all components of signal transduction pathways are proteins. Many signaling pathways also involve small, nonprotein, water-soluble molecules or ions called **second messengers**. (This term is used because the pathway's "first messenger" is considered to be the extracellular signaling molecule—the ligand—that binds to the membrane receptor.) Because second messengers are small and also water-soluble, they can readily spread throughout the cell by diffusion. For example, as we'll see shortly, a second messenger called cyclic AMP carries the signal initiated by epinephrine from the plasma membrane of a liver or muscle cell into the cell's interior, where the signal eventually brings about glycogen breakdown. Second messengers participate in pathways that are initiated by both G protein-coupled receptors and receptor tyrosine kinases. The two most widely used second messengers are cyclic AMP and calcium ions, Ca^{2+}. A large variety of relay proteins are sensitive to the cytosolic concentration of one or the other of these second messengers.

Cyclic AMP

As discussed previously, Earl Sutherland established that epinephrine somehow causes glycogen breakdown without passing through the plasma membrane. This discovery prompted him to search for a second messenger that transmits the signal from the plasma membrane to the metabolic machinery in the cytoplasm.

Sutherland found that the binding of epinephrine to the plasma membrane of a liver cell elevates the cytosolic concentration of a compound called cyclic adenosine monophosphate, abbreviated as either **cyclic AMP** or **cAMP** (Figure 11.11). An enzyme embedded in the plasma membrane, **adenylyl cyclase**, converts ATP to cAMP in response

▲ **Figure 11.11 Cyclic AMP.** The second messenger cyclic AMP (cAMP) is made from ATP by adenylyl cyclase, an enzyme embedded in the plasma membrane. Note that the phosphate group in cAMP is attached to both the 5′ and the 3′ carbons; this cyclic arrangement is the basis for the molecule's name. Cyclic AMP is inactivated by phosphodiesterase, an enzyme that converts it to AMP.

WHAT IF? *What would happen if a molecule that inactivated phosphodiesterase were introduced into the cell?*

to an extracellular signal—in this case, provided by epinephrine. But epinephrine doesn't stimulate adenylyl cyclase directly. When epinephrine outside the cell binds to a specific receptor protein, the protein activates adenylyl cyclase, which in turn can catalyze the synthesis of many molecules of cAMP. In this way, the normal cellular concentration of cAMP can be boosted 20-fold in a matter of seconds. The cAMP broadcasts the signal to the cytoplasm. It does not persist for long in the absence of the hormone because another enzyme, called phosphodiesterase, converts cAMP to AMP. Another surge of epinephrine is needed to boost the cytosolic concentration of cAMP again.

Subsequent research has revealed that epinephrine is only one of many hormones and other signaling molecules that trigger the formation of cAMP. It has also brought to light the other components of cAMP pathways, including G proteins, G protein-coupled receptors, and protein kinases (**Figure 11.12**). The immediate effect of an elevation in cAMP levels is usually the activation of a serine/threonine kinase called *protein kinase A*. The activated protein kinase A then phosphorylates various other proteins, depending on the cell type. (The complete pathway for epinephrine's stimulation of glycogen breakdown is shown later, in Figure 11.16.)

Further regulation of cell metabolism is provided by other G protein systems that *inhibit* adenylyl cyclase. In these systems, a different signaling molecule activates a different receptor, which in turn activates an *inhibitory* G protein that blocks activation of adenylyl cyclase.

Now that we know about the role of cAMP in G protein signaling pathways, we can explain in molecular detail how certain microbes cause disease. Consider cholera, a disease that is frequently epidemic in places where the water supply is contaminated with human feces. People acquire the cholera bacterium, *Vibrio cholerae*, by drinking contaminated water. The bacteria form a biofilm on the lining of the small intestine and produce a toxin. The cholera toxin is an enzyme that chemically modifies a G protein involved in regulating salt and water secretion. Because the modified G protein is unable to hydrolyze GTP to GDP, it remains stuck in its active form, continuously stimulating adenylyl cyclase to make cAMP. The resulting high concentration of cAMP causes the intestinal cells to secrete large amounts of salts into the intestines, with water following by osmosis. An infected person quickly develops profuse diarrhea and if left untreated can soon die from the loss of water and salts.

Our understanding of signaling pathways involving cyclic AMP or related messengers has allowed us to develop treatments for certain conditions in humans. In one pathway, *cyclic GMP*, or *cGMP*, acts as a signaling molecule whose effects include relaxation of smooth muscle cells in artery walls. A compound that inhibits the hydrolysis of cGMP to GMP, thus prolonging the signal, was originally prescribed for chest pains because it increased blood flow to the heart muscle. Under the trade name Viagra, this compound is now widely used as a treatment for erectile dysfunction in human males. Because Viagra leads to dilation of blood vessels, it also allows increased blood flow to the penis, optimizing physiological conditions for penile erections.

Calcium Ions and Inositol Trisphosphate (IP₃)

Many of the signaling molecules that function in animals—including neurotransmitters, growth factors, and some hormones—induce responses in their target cells via signal transduction pathways that increase the cytosolic concentration of calcium ions (Ca^{2+}). Calcium is even more widely used than cAMP as a second messenger. Increasing the cytosolic concentration of Ca^{2+} causes many responses in animal cells, including muscle cell contraction, secretion of certain substances, and cell division. In plant cells, a wide range of hormonal and environmental stimuli can cause brief increases in cytosolic Ca^{2+} concentration, triggering various signaling pathways, such as the pathway for greening in response to light (see Figure 39.4). Cells use Ca^{2+} as a second messenger in pathways triggered by both G protein-coupled receptors and receptor tyrosine kinases.

Although cells always contain some Ca^{2+}, this ion can function as a second messenger because its concentration in the cytosol is normally much lower than the concentration

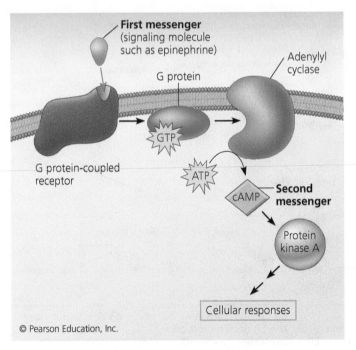

▲ **Figure 11.12 cAMP as a second messenger in a G protein signaling pathway.** The first messenger activates a G protein coupled receptor, which activates a specific G protein. In turn, the G protein activates adenylyl cyclase, which catalyzes the conversion of ATP to cAMP. The cAMP then acts as a second messenger and activates another protein, usually protein kinase A, leading to cellular responses.

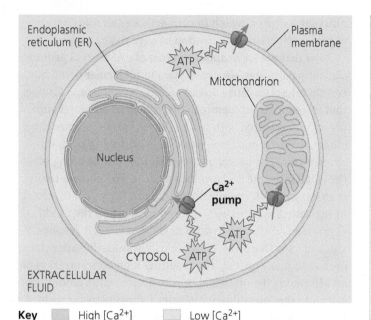

Endoplasmic reticulum (ER)

Plasma membrane

ATP

Mitochondrion

Nucleus

Ca²⁺ pump

ATP

ATP

CYTOSOL

ATP

EXTRACELLULAR FLUID

Key ☐ High [Ca²⁺] ☐ Low [Ca²⁺]

▲ **Figure 11.13 The maintenance of calcium ion concentrations in an animal cell.** The Ca²⁺ concentration in the cytosol is usually much lower (beige) than in the extracellular fluid and ER (blue). Protein pumps in the plasma membrane and the ER membrane, driven by ATP, move Ca²⁺ from the cytosol into the extracellular fluid and into the lumen of the ER. Mitochondrial pumps, driven by chemiosmosis (see Concept 9.4), move Ca²⁺ into mitochondria when the calcium level in the cytosol rises significantly.

messengers are produced by cleavage of a certain kind of phospholipid in the plasma membrane. **Figure 11.14** shows the complete picture of how a signal causes IP_3 to stimulate the release of calcium from the ER. Because IP_3 acts before calcium in these pathways, calcium could be considered a "*third* messenger." However, scientists use the term *second messenger* for all small, nonprotein components of signal transduction pathways.

CONCEPT CHECK 11.3

1. What is a protein kinase, and what is its role in a signal transduction pathway?

2. When a signal transduction pathway involves a phosphorylation cascade, how does the cell's response get turned off?

3. What is the actual "signal" that is being transduced in any signal transduction pathway, such as those shown in Figures 11.6 and 11.10? In what way is this information being passed from the exterior to the interior of the cell?

4. **WHAT IF?** Upon activation of phospholipase C by the binding of a ligand to a receptor, what effect does the IP_3-gated calcium channel have on Ca²⁺ concentration in the cytosol?

For suggested answers, see Appendix A.

outside the cell **(Figure 11.13).** In fact, the level of Ca²⁺ in the blood and extracellular fluid of an animal is often more than 10,000 times higher than that in the cytosol. Calcium ions are actively transported out of the cell and are actively imported from the cytosol into the endoplasmic reticulum (and, under some conditions, into mitochondria and chloroplasts) by various protein pumps. As a result, the calcium concentration in the ER is usually much higher than that in the cytosol. Because the cytosolic calcium level is low, a small change in absolute numbers of ions represents a relatively large percentage change in calcium concentration.

In response to a signal relayed by a signal transduction pathway, the cytosolic calcium level may rise, usually by a mechanism that releases Ca²⁺ from the cell's ER. The pathways leading to calcium release involve two other second messengers, **inositol trisphosphate (IP₃)** and **diacylglycerol (DAG).** These two

❶ A signaling molecule binds to a receptor, leading to activation of phospholipase C.

❷ Phospholipase C cleaves a plasma membrane phospholipid called PIP₂ into DAG and IP₃.

❸ DAG functions as a second messenger in other pathways.

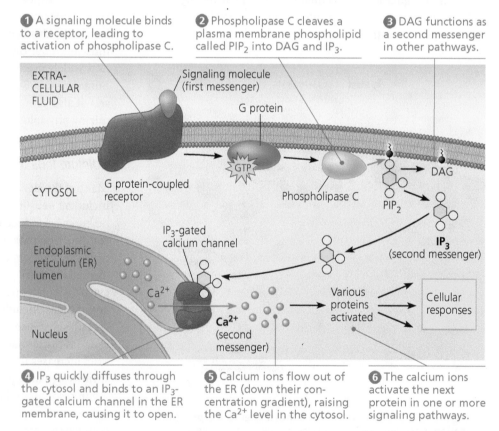

Signaling molecule (first messenger)

G protein

EXTRACELLULAR FLUID

G protein-coupled receptor

GTP

Phospholipase C

PIP₂

DAG

CYTOSOL

IP₃-gated calcium channel

Endoplasmic reticulum (ER) lumen

Ca²⁺

IP₃ (second messenger)

Various proteins activated

Cellular responses

Nucleus

Ca²⁺ (second messenger)

❹ IP₃ quickly diffuses through the cytosol and binds to an IP₃-gated calcium channel in the ER membrane, causing it to open.

❺ Calcium ions flow out of the ER (down their concentration gradient), raising the Ca²⁺ level in the cytosol.

❻ The calcium ions activate the next protein in one or more signaling pathways.

▲ **Figure 11.14 Calcium and IP₃ in signaling pathways.** Calcium ions (Ca²⁺) and inositol trisphosphate (IP₃) function as second messengers in many signal transduction pathways. In this figure, the process is initiated by the binding of a signaling molecule to a G protein-coupled receptor. A receptor tyrosine kinase could also initiate this pathway by activating phospholipase C.

Response: Cell signaling leads to regulation of transcription or cytoplasmic activities

We now take a closer look at the cell's subsequent response to an extracellular signal—what some researchers call the "output response." What is the nature of the final step in a signaling pathway?

Nuclear and Cytoplasmic Responses

Ultimately, a signal transduction pathway leads to the regulation of one or more cellular activities. The response at the end of the pathway may occur in the nucleus of the cell or in the cytoplasm.

Many signaling pathways ultimately regulate protein synthesis, usually by turning specific genes on or off in the nucleus. Like an activated steroid receptor (see Figure 11.9), the final activated molecule in a signaling pathway may function as a transcription factor. **Figure 11.15** shows an example in which a signaling pathway activates a transcription factor that turns a gene on: The response to this growth factor signal is transcription, the synthesis of one or more specific mRNAs, which will be translated in the cytoplasm into specific proteins. In other cases, the transcription factor might regulate a gene by turning it off. Often a transcription factor regulates several different genes.

Sometimes a signaling pathway may regulate the *activity* of proteins rather than causing their *synthesis* by activating gene expression. This directly affects proteins that function outside the nucleus. For example, a signal may cause the opening or closing of an ion channel in the plasma membrane or a change in cell metabolism. As we have seen, the response of liver cells to the hormone epinephrine helps regulate cellular energy metabolism by affecting the activity of an enzyme. The final step in the signaling pathway that begins with epinephrine binding activates the enzyme that catalyzes the breakdown of glycogen. **Figure 11.16** shows the complete pathway leading to the release of glucose 1-phosphate molecules from glycogen. Notice that as each molecule is activated, the response is amplified, a subject we'll return to shortly.

Signal receptors, relay molecules, and second messengers participate in a variety of pathways, leading to both nuclear and cytoplasmic responses. Some of these pathways lead to cell division. The molecular messengers that initiate cell division pathways include growth factors and certain plant and animal hormones. Malfunctioning of growth factor pathways like the one in Figure 11.15 can contribute to the development of cancer, as we'll see in Chapter 18.

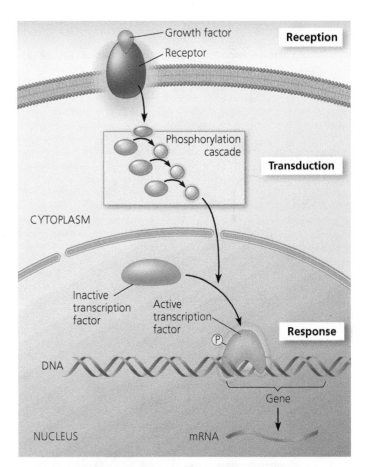

▲ **Figure 11.15 Nuclear responses to a signal: the activation of a specific gene by a growth factor.** This diagram is a simplified representation of a typical signaling pathway that leads to regulation of gene activity in the cell nucleus. The initial signaling molecule, a growth factor, triggers a phosphorylation cascade, as in Figure 11.10. (The ATP molecules and phosphate groups are not shown here.) Once phosphorylated, the last kinase in the sequence enters the nucleus and activates a gene-regulating protein, a transcription factor. This protein stimulates transcription of a specific gene (or genes). The resulting mRNAs then direct the synthesis of a particular protein in the cytoplasm.

Regulation of the Response

Whether the response occurs in the nucleus or in the cytoplasm, it is not simply turned "on" or "off." Rather, the extent and specificity of the response are regulated in multiple ways. Here we'll consider four aspects of this regulation. First, as mentioned earlier, signaling pathways generally amplify the cell's response to a single signaling event. The degree of amplification depends on the function of the specific molecules in the pathway. Second, the many steps in a multistep pathway provide control points at which the cell's response can be further regulated, contributing to the specificity of the response and allowing coordination with other signaling pathways. Third, the overall efficiency of the response is enhanced by the presence of proteins known as scaffolding proteins. Finally, a crucial point in regulating the response is the termination of the signal.

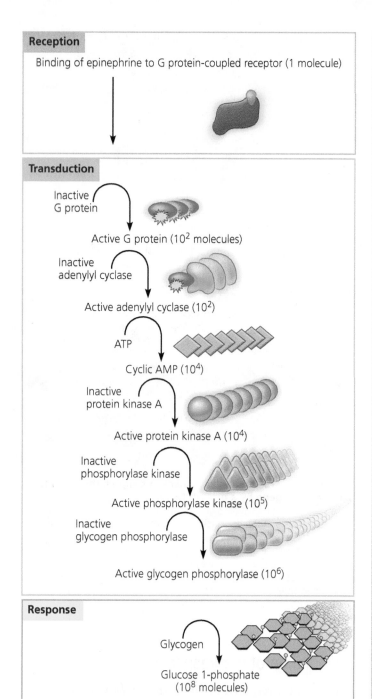

Reception

Binding of epinephrine to G protein-coupled receptor (1 molecule)

Transduction

Inactive G protein

Active G protein (10^2 molecules)

Inactive adenylyl cyclase

Active adenylyl cyclase (10^2)

ATP

Cyclic AMP (10^4)

Inactive protein kinase A

Active protein kinase A (10^4)

Inactive phosphorylase kinase

Active phosphorylase kinase (10^5)

Inactive glycogen phosphorylase

Active glycogen phosphorylase (10^6)

Response

Glycogen

Glucose 1-phosphate (10^8 molecules)

▲ **Figure 11.16 Cytoplasmic response to a signal: the stimulation of glycogen breakdown by epinephrine (adrenaline).** In this signaling system, the hormone epinephrine acts through a G protein-coupled receptor to activate a succession of relay molecules, including cAMP and two protein kinases (see also Figure 11.12). The final protein activated is the enzyme glycogen phosphorylase, which uses inorganic phosphate to release glucose monomers from glycogen in the form of glucose 1-phosphate molecules. This pathway amplifies the hormonal signal: One receptor protein can activate approximately 100 molecules of G protein, and each enzyme in the pathway, once activated, can act on many molecules of its substrate, the next molecule in the cascade. The number of activated molecules given for each step is approximate.

? *In the figure, how many glucose molecules are released in response to one signaling molecule? Calculate the factor by which the response is amplified in going from each step to the next.*

Signal Amplification

Elaborate enzyme cascades amplify the cell's response to a signal. At each catalytic step in the cascade, the number of activated products can be much greater than in the preceding step. For example, in the epinephrine-triggered pathway in Figure 11.16, each adenylyl cyclase molecule catalyzes the formation of 100 or so cAMP molecules, each molecule of protein kinase A phosphorylates about 10 molecules of the next kinase in the pathway, and so on. The amplification effect stems from the fact that these proteins persist in the active form long enough to process multiple molecules of substrate before they become inactive again. As a result of the signal's amplification, a small number of epinephrine molecules binding to receptors on the surface of a liver cell or muscle cell can lead to the release of hundreds of millions of glucose molecules from glycogen.

The Specificity of Cell Signaling and Coordination of the Response

Consider two different cells in your body—a liver cell and a heart muscle cell, for example. Both are in contact with your bloodstream and are therefore constantly exposed to many different hormone molecules, as well as to local regulators secreted by nearby cells. Yet the liver cell responds to some signals but ignores others, and the same is true for the heart cell. And some kinds of signals trigger responses in both cells—but different responses. For instance, epinephrine stimulates the liver cell to break down glycogen, but the main response of the heart cell to epinephrine is contraction, leading to a more rapid heartbeat. How do we account for this difference?

The explanation for the specificity exhibited in cellular responses to signals is the same as the basic explanation for virtually all differences between cells: Because different kinds of cells turn on different sets of genes, *different kinds of cells have different collections of proteins* (**Figure 11.17**). The response of a particular cell to a signal depends on its particular collection of signal receptor proteins, relay proteins, and proteins needed to carry out the response. A liver cell, for example, is poised to respond appropriately to epinephrine by having the proteins listed in Figure 11.16 as well as those needed to manufacture glycogen.

Thus, two cells that respond differently to the same signal differ in one or more of the proteins that handle and respond to the signal. Notice in Figure 11.17 that different pathways may have some molecules in common. For example, cells A, B, and C all use the same receptor protein for the red signaling molecule; differences in other proteins account for their differing responses. In cell D, a different receptor protein is used for the same signaling molecule, leading to yet another response. In cell B, a pathway that is triggered by a single kind of signal diverges to produce two

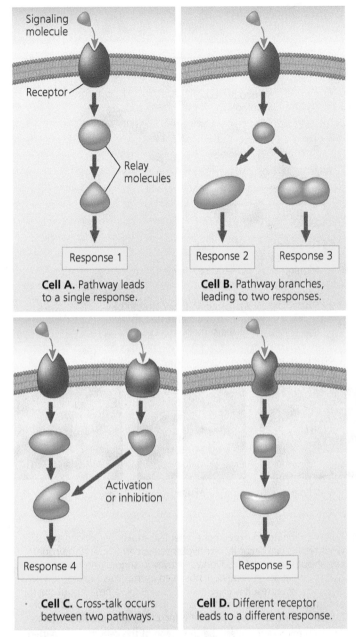

Response 1

Cell A. Pathway leads to a single response.

Response 2   Response 3

Cell B. Pathway branches, leading to two responses.

Activation or inhibition

Response 4

Cell C. Cross-talk occurs between two pathways.

Response 5

Cell D. Different receptor leads to a different response.

▲ **Figure 11.17 The specificity of cell signaling.** The particular proteins a cell possesses determine what signaling molecules it responds to and the nature of the response. The four cells in these diagrams respond to the same signaling molecule (red) in different ways because each has a different set of proteins (purple and teal). Note, however, that the same kinds of molecules can participate in more than one pathway.

MAKE CONNECTIONS *Study the signaling pathway shown in Figure 11.14, and explain how the situation pictured for cell B above could apply to that pathway.*

responses; such branched pathways often involve receptor tyrosine kinases (which can activate multiple relay proteins) or second messengers (which can regulate numerous proteins). In cell C, two pathways triggered by separate signals converge to modulate a single response. Branching of pathways and "cross-talk" (interaction) between pathways are

important in regulating and coordinating a cell's responses to information coming in from different sources in the body. (You'll learn more about this coordination in Concept 11.5.) Moreover, the use of some of the same proteins in more than one pathway allows the cell to economize on the number of different proteins it must make.

An example of a signal that leads to a complex, coordinated cellular response can be found in the processes leading to the mating of yeast cells described earlier (see Figure 11.2). In the Scientific Skills Exercise, you can work with data from experiments investigating the cellular response of a yeast cell to the signal initiated by a mating factor from a cell of the opposite mating type.

Signaling Efficiency: Scaffolding Proteins and Signaling Complexes

The illustrations of signaling pathways in Figure 11.17 (as well as diagrams of other pathways in this chapter) are greatly simplified. The diagrams show only a few relay molecules and, for clarity's sake, display these molecules spread out in the cytosol. If this were true in the cell, signaling pathways would operate very inefficiently because most relay molecules are proteins, and proteins are too large to diffuse quickly through the viscous cytosol. How does a particular protein kinase, for instance, find its substrate?

In many cases, the efficiency of signal transduction is apparently increased by the presence of **scaffolding proteins**, large relay proteins to which several other relay proteins are simultaneously attached. For example, one scaffolding protein isolated from mouse brain cells holds three protein kinases and carries these kinases with it when it binds to an appropriately activated membrane receptor; it thus facilitates a specific phosphorylation cascade **(Figure 11.18)**. Researchers have found scaffolding proteins in brain cells that *permanently* hold together networks of signaling pathway proteins at synapses. This hardwiring enhances the speed and accuracy of signal transfer between cells, because the

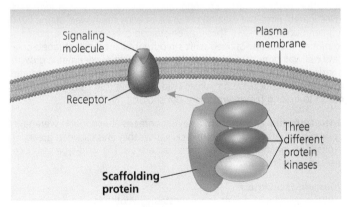

▲ **Figure 11.18 A scaffolding protein.** The scaffolding protein shown here simultaneously binds to a specific activated membrane receptor and three different protein kinases. This physical arrangement facilitates signal transduction by these molecules.

Using Experiments to Test a Model

1. Mating factor activates receptor.

Mating factor

G protein-coupled receptor

2. G protein binds GTP and becomes activated.

GDP

GTP

Phosphoryl-ation cascade

Fus3

Fus3

3. Phosphorylation cascade activates Fus3, which moves to plasma membrane.

Fus3

4. Fus3 phos-phorylates formin, activating it.

Formin

Formin

Shmoo projection forming

Formin

Actin subunit

Microfilament

5. Formin initiates growth of microfilaments that form the shmoo projections.

Are Both Fus3 Kinase and Formin Required for Directional Cell Growth During Mating in Yeast? When a yeast cell binds mating factor molecules from a cell of the opposite mating type, a signaling pathway causes it to grow a projection toward the potential mate. The cell with the projection is called a "shmoo" (because it resembles a 1950s cartoon character by that name). Researchers sought to determine how mating factor signaling leads to growth of this cell projection on one side of the cell—in other words, to asymmetric cell growth. Previous work had shown that activation of Fus3, one of the kinases in the signaling cascade, caused it to move to the membrane near where the mating factor bound its receptor. The researchers' first experiment identified one of the phosphorylation targets of Fus3 kinase as formin, a protein directing microfilament construction. Based on this information, the researchers developed the working model shown here for the signaling pathway that leads to the formation of shmoo projections in yeast cells.

How the Experiment Was Done To determine if Fus3 and formin were required for shmoo formation, the researchers generated two mutant yeast strains: one that lacked the gene for making Fus3 kinase (a strain called ΔFus3) and one that lacked the gene for making formin (Δformin). To observe the effects of these mutations on schmoo formation after cells' exposure to mating factor, the symmetry of growth was investigated. First, the existing cell walls of each strain were stained with a green fluorescent dye. These green-stained cells were then exposed to mating factor and stained with a red fluorescent dye that labels only new cell wall growth. Growth of the cell on all sides (symmetric growth) is indicated by a uniform yellow color, resulting from merged green and red stains. (This occurs normally in wild-type cells that have not been exposed to mating factor, which are not shown.)

Data from the Experiment The micrographs above, right, were taken of wild-type, ΔFus3, and Δformin cells after they were stained green, exposed to mating factor, and then stained red. The wild-type cells expressed both Fus3 and formin.

Interpret the Data

1. A model helps scientists form a testable hypothesis. The diagram shows the working model of shmoo formation developed by the researchers. (a) What hypothesis from the model was being tested with the ΔFus3 strain? (b) With the Δformin strain? (c) What is the purpose of including wild-type yeast cells in the experiment?

Wild type   ΔFus3   Δformin

2. When designing an experiment, scientists make predictions about what results will occur if their hypothesis is correct. (a) If the hypothesis about the role of Fus3 kinase activity in shmoo production is correct, what result should be observed in the ΔFus3 strain? If it is incorrect, what result is expected? (b) If the hypothesis about the role of formin in shmoo production is correct, what result should be observed in the Δformin strain? If it is incorrect, what result is expected?

3. For each micrograph, describe the shape of the cells and the pattern of cell wall staining. Explain the significance of your observations. Which strain(s) of yeast cells formed shmoos?

4. (a) Do the data support the hypothesis about the role of Fus3 kinase in shmoo production? (b) Do the data support the hypothesis about the role of formin in shmoo production? (c) Do the data support the working model (the working hypothesis) in the diagram?

5. Fus3 kinase and formin proteins are generally distributed evenly throughout a yeast cell. Based on the model in the diagram, explain why the projection would emerge on the same side of the cell that bound the mating factor.

6. What do you predict would happen if the yeast had a mutation that prevented the G protein from binding GTP?

MB A version of this Scientific Skills Exercise can be assigned in MasteringBiology.

Data from D. Matheos et al., Pheromone-induced polarization is dependent on the Fus3p MAPK acting through the formin Bni1p, *Journal of Cell Biology* 165:99–109 (2004).

rate of protein-protein interaction is not limited by diffusion. Furthermore, in some cases the scaffolding proteins themselves may directly activate relay proteins.

When signaling pathways were first discovered, they were thought to be linear, independent pathways. Our understanding of cellular communication has benefited from the realization that signaling pathway components interact with each other in various ways. As seen in Figure 11.17, some proteins may participate in more than one pathway, either in different cell types or in the same cell at different times or under different conditions. These observations underscore the importance of transient—or, in some cases, permanent—protein complexes in the process of cell signaling.

The importance of the relay proteins that serve as points of branching or intersection in signaling pathways is highlighted by the problems arising when these proteins are defective or missing. For instance, in an inherited disorder called Wiskott-Aldrich syndrome (WAS), the absence of a single relay protein leads to such diverse effects as abnormal bleeding, eczema, and a predisposition to infections and leukemia. These symptoms are thought to arise primarily from the absence of the protein in cells of the immune system. By studying normal cells, scientists found that the WAS protein is located just beneath the immune cell surface. The protein interacts both with microfilaments of the cytoskeleton and with several different components of signaling pathways that relay information from the cell surface, including pathways regulating immune cell proliferation. This multifunctional relay protein is thus both a branch point and an important intersection point in a complex signal transduction network that controls immune cell behavior. When the WAS protein is absent, the cytoskeleton is not properly organized and signaling pathways are disrupted, leading to the WAS symptoms.

Termination of the Signal

To keep Figure 11.17 simple, we did not indicate the *inactivation* mechanisms that are an essential aspect of any cell-signaling pathway. For a cell of a multicellular organism to remain capable of responding to incoming signals, each molecular change in its signaling pathways must last only a short time. As we saw in the cholera example, if a signaling pathway component becomes locked into one state, whether active or inactive, consequences for the organism can be dire.

The ability of a cell to receive new signals depends on reversibility of the changes produced by prior signals. The binding of signaling molecules to receptors is reversible. As the external concentration of signaling molecules falls, fewer receptors are bound at any given moment, and the unbound receptors revert to their inactive form. The cellular response occurs only when the concentration of receptors with bound signaling molecules is above a certain threshold. When the number of active receptors falls below that threshold, the cellular response ceases. Then, by a variety of means, the relay molecules return to their inactive forms: The GTPase activity intrinsic to a G protein hydrolyzes its bound GTP; the enzyme phosphodiesterase converts cAMP to AMP; protein phosphatases inactivate phosphorylated kinases and other proteins; and so forth. As a result, the cell is soon ready to respond to a fresh signal.

In this section, we explored the complexity of signaling initiation and termination in a single pathway, and we saw the potential for pathways to intersect with each other. In the next section, we'll consider one especially important network of interacting pathways in the cell.

CONCEPT CHECK 11.4

1. How can a target cell's response to a single hormone molecule result in a response that affects a million other molecules?

2. WHAT IF? If two cells have different scaffolding proteins, explain how they might behave differently in response to the same signaling molecule.

3. MAKE CONNECTIONS Some human diseases are associated with malfunctioning protein phosphatases. How would such proteins affect signaling pathways? (Review the discussion of protein phosphatases in Concept 11.3, and see Figure 11.10.)

For suggested answers, see Appendix A.

CONCEPT 11.5

Apoptosis integrates multiple cell-signaling pathways

To be or not to be? One of the most elaborate networks of signaling pathways in the cell seems to ask and answer this question, originally posed by Hamlet. Cells that are infected, are damaged, or have reached the end of their functional life span often undergo "programmed cell death" (Figure 11.19).

▲ **Figure 11.19 Apoptosis of a human white blood cell.** On the left is a normal white blood cell, while on the right is a white blood cell undergoing apoptosis. The apoptotic cell is shrinking and forming lobes ("blebs"), which eventually are shed as membrane-bounded cell fragments (colorized SEMs).

2 μm

The best-understood type of this controlled cell suicide is **apoptosis** (from the Greek, meaning "falling off," and used in a classic Greek poem to refer to leaves falling from a tree). During this process, cellular agents chop up the DNA and fragment the organelles and other cytoplasmic components. The cell shrinks and becomes lobed (a change called "blebbing"), and the cell's parts are packaged up in vesicles that are engulfed and digested by specialized scavenger cells, leaving no trace. Apoptosis protects neighboring cells from damage that they would otherwise suffer if a dying cell merely leaked out all its contents, including its many digestive enzymes.

The signal that triggers apoptosis can come from either outside or inside the cell. Outside the cell, signaling molecules released from other cells can initiate a signal transduction pathway that activates the genes and proteins responsible for carrying out cell death. Within a cell whose DNA has been irretrievably damaged, a series of protein-protein interactions can pass along a signal that similarly triggers cell death. Considering some examples of apoptosis can help us to see how signaling pathways are integrated in cells.

Apoptosis in the Soil Worm *Caenorhabditis elegans*

The molecular mechanisms of apoptosis were worked out by researchers studying embryonic development of a small soil worm, a nematode called *Caenorhabditis elegans*. Because the adult worm has only about 1,000 cells, the researchers were able to work out the entire ancestry of each cell. The timely suicide of cells occurs exactly 131 times during normal development of *C. elegans*, at precisely the same points in the cell lineage of each worm. In worms and other species, apoptosis is triggered by signals that activate a cascade of "suicide" proteins in the cells destined to die.

Genetic research on *C. elegans* initially revealed two key apoptosis genes, called *ced-3* and *ced-4* (*ced* stands for "cell death"), which encode proteins essential for apoptosis. The proteins are called Ced-3 and Ced-4, respectively. These and most other proteins involved in apoptosis are continually present in cells, but in inactive form; thus, regulation in this case occurs at the level of protein activity rather than through gene activity and protein synthesis. In *C. elegans*, a protein in the outer mitochondrial membrane, called Ced-9 (the product of the *ced-9* gene), serves as a master regulator of apoptosis, acting as a brake in the absence of a signal promoting apoptosis (**Figure 11.20**). When a death signal is received by the cell, signal transduction involves a change in Ced-9 that disables the brake, and the apoptotic pathway activates proteases and nucleases, enzymes that cut up the proteins and DNA of the cell. The main proteases of apoptosis are called *caspases*; in the nematode, the chief caspase is the Ced-3 protein.

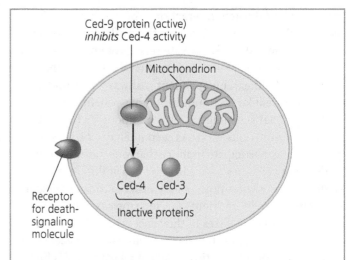

(a) No death signal. As long as Ced-9, located in the outer mitochondrial membrane, is active, apoptosis is inhibited, and the cell remains alive.

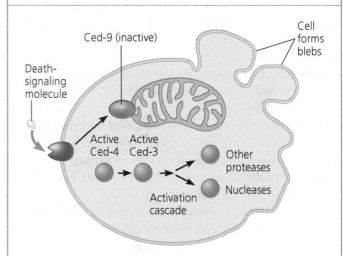

(b) Death signal. When a cell receives a death signal, Ced-9 is inactivated, relieving its inhibition of Ced-3 and Ced-4. Active Ced-3, a protease, triggers a cascade of reactions leading to activation of nucleases and other proteases. The action of these enzymes causes the changes seen in apoptotic cells and eventual cell death.

▲ **Figure 11.20 Molecular basis of apoptosis in *C. elegans*.** Three proteins, Ced-3, Ced-4, and Ced-9, are critical to apoptosis and its regulation in the nematode. Apoptosis is more complicated in mammals but involves proteins similar to those in the nematode.

Apoptotic Pathways and the Signals That Trigger Them

In humans and other mammals, several different pathways, involving about 15 different caspases, can carry out apoptosis. The pathway that is used depends on the type of cell and on the particular signal that initiates apoptosis. One major pathway involves certain mitochondrial proteins that are triggered to form molecular pores in the mitochondrial outer membrane, causing it to leak and release other proteins that promote apoptosis. Perhaps surprisingly, these latter include cytochrome *c*, which functions in mitochondrial electron transport in healthy cells (see Figure 9.15) but acts as a cell death factor when released from mitochondria. The process of mitochondrial apoptosis in mammals uses proteins similar to the nematode proteins Ced-3, Ced-4, and Ced-9. These can be thought of as relay proteins capable of transducing the apoptotic signal.

At key gateways into the apoptotic program, relay proteins integrate signals from several different sources and can send a cell down an apoptotic pathway. Often, the signal originates outside the cell, like the death-signaling molecule depicted in Figure 11.20b, which presumably was released by a neighboring cell. When a death-signaling ligand occupies a cell-surface receptor, this binding leads to activation of caspases and other enzymes that carry out apoptosis, without involving the mitochondrial pathway. This process of signal reception, transduction, and response is similar to what we have discussed throughout this chapter. In a twist on the classic scenario, two other types of alarm signals that can lead to apoptosis originate from *inside* the cell rather than from a cell-surface receptor. One signal comes from the nucleus, generated when the DNA has suffered irreparable damage, and a second comes from the endoplasmic reticulum when excessive protein misfolding occurs. Mammalian cells make life-or-death "decisions" by somehow integrating the death signals and life signals they receive from these external and internal sources.

A built-in cell suicide mechanism is essential to development and maintenance in all animals. The similarities between apoptosis genes in nematodes and those in mammals, as well as the observation that apoptosis occurs in multicellular fungi and even in single-celled yeasts, indicate that the basic mechanism evolved early in the evolution of eukaryotes. In vertebrates, apoptosis is essential for normal development of the nervous system, for normal operation of the immune system, and for normal morphogenesis of hands and feet in humans and paws in other mammals (Figure 11.21). The level of apoptosis between the developing digits is lower in the webbed feet of ducks and other water birds than in the nonwebbed feet of land birds, such as chickens. In the case of humans, the failure of appropriate apoptosis can result in webbed fingers and toes.

Significant evidence points to the involvement of apoptosis in certain degenerative diseases of the nervous system, such as Parkinson's disease and Alzheimer's disease. In Alzheimer's disease, an accumulation of aggregated proteins in neuronal cells activates an enzyme that triggers apoptosis, resulting in the loss of brain function seen in these patients. Furthermore, cancer can result from a failure of cell suicide; some cases of human melanoma, for example, have been linked to faulty forms of the human version of the *C. elegans* Ced-4 protein. It is not surprising, therefore, that the signaling pathways feeding into apoptosis are quite elaborate. After all, the life-or-death question is the most fundamental one imaginable for a cell.

This chapter has introduced you to many of the general mechanisms of cell communication, such as ligand binding, protein-protein interactions and shape changes, cascades of interactions, and protein phosphorylation. Throughout your study of biology, you will encounter numerous examples of cell signaling.

CONCEPT CHECK 11.5

1. Give an example of apoptosis during embryonic development, and explain its function in the developing embryo.

2. **WHAT IF?** What types of protein defects could result in apoptosis occurring when it should not? What types could result in apoptosis not occurring when it should?

For suggested answers, see Appendix A.

▲ Figure 11.21 Effect of apoptosis during paw development in the mouse. In mice, humans, other mammals, and land birds, the embryonic region that develops into feet or hands initially has a solid, platelike structure.

Apoptosis eliminates the cells in the interdigital regions, thus forming the digits. The embryonic mouse paws shown in these fluorescence light micrographs are stained so that cells undergoing apoptosis appear a bright yellowish green.

Apoptosis of cells begins at the margin of each interdigital region (left), peaks as the tissue in these regions is reduced (middle), and is no longer visible when the interdigital tissue has been eliminated (right).

SUMMARY OF KEY CONCEPTS

CONCEPT 11.1

External signals are converted to responses within the cell (pp. 211–214)

- **Signal transduction pathways** are crucial for many processes. Signaling during yeast cell mating has much in common with processes in multicellular organisms, suggesting an early evolutionary origin of signaling mechanisms. Bacterial cells can sense the local density of bacterial cells (quorum sensing).
- Local signaling by animal cells involves direct contact or the secretion of local regulators. For long-distance signaling, animal and plant cells use **hormones**; animals also pass signals electrically.
- Like other hormones that bind to membrane receptors, epinephrine triggers a three-stage cell-signaling pathway:

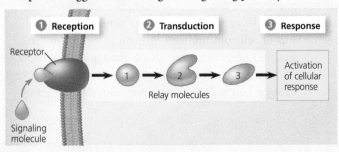

? *What determines whether a cell responds to a hormone such as epinephrine? What determines how a cell responds to such a hormone?*

CONCEPT 11.2

Reception: A signaling molecule binds to a receptor protein, causing it to change shape (pp. 214–218)

- The binding between signaling molecule (**ligand**) and receptor is highly specific. A specific shape change in a receptor is often the initial transduction of the signal.
- There are three major types of cell-surface transmembrane receptors: (1) **G protein-coupled receptors (GPCRs)** work with cytoplasmic **G proteins**. Ligand binding activates the receptor, which then activates a specific G protein, which activates yet another protein, thus propagating the signal. (2) **Receptor tyrosine kinases (RTKs)** react to the binding of signaling molecules by forming dimers and then adding phosphate groups to tyrosines on the cytoplasmic part of the other monomer making up the dimer. Relay proteins in the cell can then be activated by binding to different phosphorylated tyrosines, allowing this receptor to trigger several pathways at once. (3) **Ligand-gated ion channels** open or close in response to binding by specific signaling molecules, regulating the flow of specific ions across the membrane.
- The activity of all three types of receptors is crucial; abnormal GPCRs and RTKs are associated with many human diseases.
- Intracellular receptors are cytoplasmic or nuclear proteins. Signaling molecules that are hydrophobic or small enough to cross the plasma membrane bind to these receptors inside the cell.

? *How are the structures of a GPCR and an RTK similar? How does initiation of signal transduction differ for these two types of receptors?*

CONCEPT 11.3

Transduction: Cascades of molecular interactions relay signals from receptors to target molecules in the cell (pp. 218–222)

- At each step in a signal transduction pathway, the signal is transduced into a different form, which commonly involves a shape change in a protein. Many signal transduction pathways include **phosphorylation cascades**, in which a series of **protein kinases** each add a phosphate group to the next one in line, activating it. Enzymes called **protein phosphatases** remove the phosphate groups. The balance between phosphorylation and dephosphorylation regulates the activity of proteins involved in the sequential steps of a signal transduction pathway.
- **Second messengers**, such as the small molecule **cyclic AMP (cAMP)** and the ion Ca^{2+}, diffuse readily through the cytosol and thus help broadcast signals quickly. Many G proteins activate **adenylyl cyclase**, which makes cAMP from ATP. Cells use Ca^{2+} as a second messenger in both GPCR and RTK pathways. The tyrosine kinase pathways can also involve two other second messengers, **diacylglycerol (DAG)** and **inositol trisphosphate (IP$_3$)**. IP$_3$ can trigger a subsequent increase in Ca^{2+} levels.

? *What is the difference between a protein kinase and a second messenger? Can both operate in the same signal transduction pathway?*

CONCEPT 11.4

Response: Cell signaling leads to regulation of transcription or cytoplasmic activities (pp. 223–227)

- Some pathways lead to a nuclear response: Specific genes are turned on or off by activated transcription factors. In others, the response involves cytoplasmic regulation.
- Cellular responses are not simply on or off; they are regulated at many steps. Each protein in a signaling pathway amplifies the signal by activating multiple copies of the next component; for long pathways, the total amplification may be over a millionfold. The combination of proteins in a cell confers specificity in the signals it detects and the responses it carries out. **Scaffolding proteins** increase signaling efficiency. Pathway branching further helps the cell coordinate signals and responses. Signal response is terminated quickly by the reversal of ligand binding.

? *What mechanisms in the cell terminate its response to a signal and maintain its ability to respond to new signals?*

CONCEPT 11.5

Apoptosis integrates multiple cell-signaling pathways (pp. 227–229)

- **Apoptosis** is a type of programmed cell death in which cell components are disposed of in an orderly fashion. Studies of the soil worm *Caenorhabditis elegans* clarified molecular details of the relevant signaling pathways. A death signal leads to activation of caspases and nucleases, the main enzymes involved in apoptosis.
- Several apoptotic signaling pathways exist in the cells of humans and other mammals, triggered in different ways. Signals eliciting apoptosis can originate from outside or inside the cell.

? *What is an explanation for the similarities between genes in yeasts, nematodes, and mammals that control apoptosis?*

LEVEL 1: KNOWLEDGE/COMPREHENSION

1. Binding of a signaling molecule to which type of receptor leads directly to a change in the distribution of ions on opposite sides of the membrane?
   a. intracellular receptor
   b. G protein-coupled receptor
   c. phosphorylated receptor tyrosine kinase dimer
   d. ligand-gated ion channel

2. The activation of receptor tyrosine kinases is characterized by
   a. dimerization and phosphorylation.
   b. dimerization and IP_3 binding.
   c. a phosphorylation cascade.
   d. GTP hydrolysis.

3. Lipid-soluble signaling molecules, such as aldosterone, cross the membranes of all cells but affect only target cells because
   a. only target cells retain the appropriate DNA segments.
   b. intracellular receptors are present only in target cells.
   c. only target cells have enzymes that break down aldosterone.
   d. only in target cells is aldosterone able to initiate the phosphorylation cascade that turns genes on.

4. Consider this pathway: epinephrine → G protein-coupled receptor → G protein → adenylyl cyclase → cAMP. Identify the second messenger.
   a. cAMP
   b. G protein
   c. GTP
   d. adenylyl cyclase

5. Apoptosis involves all but which of the following?
   a. fragmentation of the DNA
   b. cell-signaling pathways
   c. lysis of the cell
   d. digestion of cellular contents by scavenger cells

LEVEL 2: APPLICATION/ANALYSIS

6. Which observation suggested to Sutherland the involvement of a second messenger in epinephrine's effect on liver cells?
   a. Enzymatic activity was proportional to the amount of calcium added to a cell-free extract.
   b. Receptor studies indicated that epinephrine was a ligand.
   c. Glycogen breakdown was observed only when epinephrine was administered to intact cells.
   d. Glycogen breakdown was observed when epinephrine and glycogen phosphorylase were combined.

7. Protein phosphorylation is commonly involved with all of the following *except*
   a. activation of receptor tyrosine kinases.
   b. activation of protein kinase molecules.
   c. activation of G protein-coupled receptors.
   d. regulation of transcription by signaling molecules.

LEVEL 3: SYNTHESIS/EVALUATION

8. **DRAW IT** Draw the following apoptotic pathway, which operates in human immune cells. A death signal is received when a molecule called Fas binds its cell-surface receptor. The binding of many Fas molecules to receptors causes receptor clustering. The intracellular regions of the receptors, when together, bind proteins called adaptor proteins. These in turn bind to inactive molecules of caspase-8, which become activated and then activate caspase-3. Once activated, caspase-3 initiates apoptosis.

9. EVOLUTION CONNECTION
   What evolutionary mechanisms might account for the origin and persistence of cell-to-cell signaling systems in prokaryotes?

10. SCIENTIFIC INQUIRY
    Epinephrine initiates a signal transduction pathway that produces cyclic AMP (cAMP) and leads to the breakdown of glycogen to glucose, a major energy source for cells. But glycogen breakdown is only part of the fight-or-flight response that epinephrine brings about; the overall effect on the body includes an increase in heart rate and alertness, as well as a burst of energy. Given that caffeine blocks the activity of cAMP phosphodiesterase, propose a mechanism by which caffeine ingestion leads to heightened alertness and sleeplessness.

11. SCIENCE, TECHNOLOGY, AND SOCIETY
    The aging process is thought to be initiated at the cellular level. Among the changes that can occur after a certain number of cell divisions is the loss of a cell's ability to respond to growth factors and other signals. Much research into aging is aimed at understanding such losses, with the ultimate goal of extending the human life span. Not everyone, however, agrees that this is a desirable goal. If life expectancy were greatly increased, what might be the social and ecological consequences?

12. WRITE ABOUT A THEME: ORGANIZATION
    The properties of life emerge at the biological level of the cell. The highly regulated process of apoptosis is not simply the destruction of a cell; it is also an emergent property. Write a short essay (about 100–150 words) that briefly explains the role of apoptosis in the development and proper functioning of an animal, and describe how this form of programmed cell death is a process that emerges from the orderly integration of signaling pathways.

13. SYNTHESIZE YOUR KNOWLEDGE

There are five basic tastes—sour, salty, sweet, bitter, and "umami." Salt is detected when the concentration of salt outside of a taste bud cell is higher than that inside of it, and ion channels allow the passive leakage of Na^+ into the cell. The resulting change in membrane potential (see Concept 7.4) sends the "salty" signal to the brain. Umami is a savory taste generated by glutamate (glutamic acid, found in monosodium glutamate, or MSG), which is used as a flavor enhancer in foods such as taco-flavored tortilla chips. The glutamate receptor is a GPCR, which, when bound, initiates a signaling pathway that ends with a cellular response, perceived by you as "taste." If you eat a regular potato chip and then rinse your mouth, you will no longer taste salt. But if you eat a flavored tortilla chip and then rinse, the taste persists. (Try it!) Propose a possible explanation for this difference.

For selected answers, see Appendix A.

MasteringBiology®

Students Go to **MasteringBiology** for assignments, the eText, and the Study Area with practice tests, animations, and activities.

Instructors Go to **MasteringBiology** for automatically graded tutorials and questions that you can assign to your students, plus Instructor Resources.

12

The Cell Cycle

▲ Chromosomes (blue) are moved by cell machinery (red) during division of a rat kangaroo cell.

▲ **Figure 12.1 How do dividing cells distribute chromosomes to daughter cells?**

The Key Roles of Cell Division

The ability of organisms to produce more of their own kind is the one characteristic that best distinguishes living things from nonliving matter. This unique capacity to procreate, like all biological functions, has a cellular basis. Rudolf Virchow, a German physician, put it this way in 1855: "Where a cell exists, there must have been a preexisting cell, just as the animal arises only from an animal and the plant only from a plant." He summarized this concept with the Latin axiom "*Omnis cellula e cellula*," meaning "Every cell from a cell." The continuity of life is based on the reproduction of cells, or **cell division**. The series of confocal fluorescence micrographs in **Figure 12.1**, starting at the upper left, follows the events of cell division as the cells of a two-celled embryo become four.

Cell division plays several important roles in life. When a prokaryotic cell divides, it is actually reproducing, since the process gives rise to a new organism (another cell). The same is true of any unicellular eukaryote, such as the amoeba shown in **Figure 12.2a**. As for multicellular eukaryotes, cell division enables each of these organisms to develop from a single cell—the fertilized egg. A two-celled embryo, the first stage in this process, is shown in **Figure 12.2b**. And cell division continues to function in renewal and repair in fully grown multicellular eukaryotes, replacing cells that die from normal wear and tear or accidents. For example, dividing cells in your bone marrow continuously make new blood cells **(Figure 12.2c)**.

(a) **Reproduction.** An amoeba, a single-celled eukaryote, is dividing into two cells. Each new cell will be an individual organism (LM).

100 μm

▶ (b) **Growth and development.** This micrograph shows a sand dollar embryo shortly after the fertilized egg divided, forming two cells (LM).

50 μm

◀ (c) **Tissue renewal.** These dividing bone marrow cells will give rise to new blood cells (LM).

20 μm

▲ Figure 12.2 **The functions of cell division.**

The cell division process is an integral part of the **cell cycle**, the life of a cell from the time it is first formed during division of a parent cell until its own division into two daughter cells. (Our use of the words *daughter* or *sister* in relation to cells is not meant to imply gender.) Passing identical genetic material to cellular offspring is a crucial function of cell division. In this chapter, you will learn how this process occurs. After studying the cellular mechanics of cell division in eukaryotes and bacteria, you will learn about the molecular control system that regulates progress through the eukaryotic cell cycle and what happens when the control system malfunctions. Because a breakdown in cell cycle control plays a major role in cancer development, this aspect of cell biology is an active area of research.

CONCEPT 12.1

Most cell division results in genetically identical daughter cells

The reproduction of a cell, with all of its complexity, cannot occur by a mere pinching in half; a cell is not like a soap bubble that simply enlarges and splits in two. In both prokaryotes and eukaryotes, most cell division involves the distribution of identical genetic material—DNA—to two daughter cells. (The exception is meiosis, the special type of eukaryotic cell division that can produce sperm and eggs.) What is most remarkable about cell division is the fidelity with which the DNA is passed from one generation of cells to the next. A dividing cell replicates its DNA, allocates the two copies to opposite ends of the cell, and only then splits into daughter cells.

Cellular Organization of the Genetic Material

A cell's endowment of DNA, its genetic information, is called its **genome**. Although a prokaryotic genome is often a single DNA molecule, eukaryotic genomes usually consist of a number of DNA molecules. The overall length of DNA in a eukaryotic cell is enormous. A typical human cell, for example, has about 2 m of DNA—a length about 250,000 times greater than the cell's diameter. Before the cell can divide to form genetically identical daughter cells, all of this DNA must be copied, or replicated, and then the two copies must be separated so that each daughter cell ends up with a complete genome.

The replication and distribution of so much DNA is manageable because the DNA molecules are packaged into structures called **chromosomes**, so named because they take up certain dyes used in microscopy (from the Greek *chroma*, color, and *soma*, body; **Figure 12.3**). Each eukaryotic chromosome consists of one very long, linear DNA molecule associated with many proteins (see Figure 6.9). The DNA molecule carries several hundred to a few thousand genes, the units of information that specify an organism's inherited traits. The associated proteins maintain the structure of the chromosome and help control the activity of the genes. Together, the entire complex of DNA and proteins that is the building material of chromosomes is referred to as **chromatin**. As you will soon see, the chromatin of a chromosome varies in its degree of condensation during the process of cell division.

Every eukaryotic species has a characteristic number of chromosomes in each cell's nucleus. For example, the nuclei of human **somatic cells** (all body cells except the reproductive cells) each contain 46 chromosomes, made up of two sets of 23, one set inherited from each parent. Reproductive

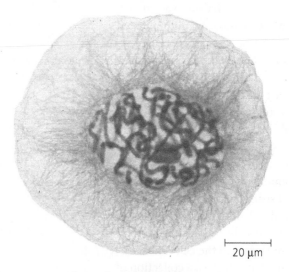

20 μm

▲ Figure 12.3 **Eukaryotic chromosomes.** Chromosomes (stained purple) are visible within the nucleus of this cell from an African blood lily. The thinner red threads in the surrounding cytoplasm are the cytoskeleton. The cell is preparing to divide (LM).

cells, or **gametes**—sperm and eggs—have one set, or half as many chromosomes as somatic cells; in our example, human gametes have one set of 23 chromosomes. The number of chromosomes in somatic cells varies widely among species: 18 in cabbage plants, 48 in chimpanzees, 56 in elephants, 90 in hedgehogs, and 148 in one species of alga. We'll now consider how these chromosomes behave during cell division.

Distribution of Chromosomes During Eukaryotic Cell Division

When a cell is not dividing, and even as it replicates its DNA in preparation for cell division, each chromosome is in the form of a long, thin chromatin fiber. After DNA replication, however, the chromosomes condense as a part of cell division: Each chromatin fiber becomes densely coiled and folded, making the chromosomes much shorter and so thick that we can see them with a light microscope.

Each duplicated chromosome has two **sister chromatids**, which are joined copies of the original chromosome **(Figure 12.4)**. The two chromatids, each containing an identical DNA molecule, are initially attached all along their lengths by protein complexes called *cohesins*; this attachment is known as *sister chromatid cohesion*. Each sister chromatid has a **centromere**, a region of the chromosomal DNA where the chromatid is attached most closely to its sister chromatid. This attachment is mediated by proteins bound to the centromeric DNA; other bound proteins condense the DNA, giving the duplicated chromosome a narrow "waist." The portion of a chromatid to either side of the centromere is referred to as an *arm* of the chromatid. (An unduplicated chromosome has a single centromere, distinguished by the proteins that bind there, and two arms.)

Later in the cell division process, the two sister chromatids of each duplicated chromosome separate and move into two new nuclei, one forming at each end of the cell. Once the sister chromatids separate, they are no longer called sister chromatids but are considered individual chromosomes; this step essentially doubles the number of chromosomes in the cell. Thus, each new nucleus receives a collection of chromosomes identical to that of the parent cell **(Figure 12.5)**. **Mitosis**, the

Sister chromatids

Centromere 0.5 μm

▲ **Figure 12.4 A highly condensed, duplicated human chromosome (SEM).**

DRAW IT *Circle one sister chromatid of the chromosome in this micrograph.*

division of the genetic material in the nucleus, is usually followed immediately by **cytokinesis**, the division of the cytoplasm. One cell has become two, each the genetic equivalent of the parent cell.

From a fertilized egg, mitosis and cytokinesis produced the 200 trillion somatic cells that now make up your body, and the same processes continue to generate new cells to

Chromosomes | Chromosomal DNA molecules

1 One of the multiple chromosomes in a eukaryotic cell is represented here, not yet duplicated. Normally it would be a long, thin chromatin fiber containing one DNA molecule and associated proteins; here its condensed form is shown for illustration purposes only.

Centromere

Chromosome arm

Chromosome duplication (including DNA replication) and condensation

2 Once duplicated, a chromosome consists of two sister chromatids connected along their entire lengths by sister chromatid cohesion. Each chromatid contains a copy of the DNA molecule.

Sister chromatids

Separation of sister chromatids into two chromosomes

3 Molecular and mechanical processes separate the sister chromatids into two chromosomes and distribute them to two daughter cells.

▲ **Figure 12.5 Chromosome duplication and distribution during cell division.**

? *How many chromatid arms does the chromosome in 2 have?*

replace dead and damaged ones. In contrast, you produce gametes—eggs or sperm—by a variation of cell division called *meiosis*, which yields daughter cells with only one set of chromosomes, half as many chromosomes as the parent cell. Meiosis in humans occurs only in special cells in the ovaries or testes (the gonads). Generating gametes, meiosis reduces the chromosome number from 46 (two sets) to 23 (one set). Fertilization fuses two gametes together and returns the chromosome number to 46 (two sets). Mitosis then conserves that number in every somatic cell nucleus of the new human individual. In Chapter 13, we will examine the role of meiosis in reproduction and inheritance in more detail. In the remainder of this chapter, we focus on mitosis and the rest of the cell cycle in eukaryotes.

CONCEPT CHECK 12.1

1. How many chromosomes are drawn in each part of Figure 12.5? (Ignore the micrograph in part 2.)

2. **WHAT IF?** A chicken has 78 chromosomes in its somatic cells. How many chromosomes did the chicken inherit from each parent? How many chromosomes are in each of the chicken's gametes? How many chromosomes will be in each somatic cell of the chicken's offspring?

For suggested answers, see Appendix A.

CONCEPT 12.2

The mitotic phase alternates with interphase in the cell cycle

In 1882, a German anatomist named Walther Flemming developed dyes that allowed him to observe, for the first time, the behavior of chromosomes during mitosis and cytokinesis. (In fact, Flemming coined the terms *mitosis* and *chromatin*.) During the period between one cell division and the next, it appeared to Flemming that the cell was simply growing larger. But we now know that many critical events occur during this stage in the life of a cell.

Phases of the Cell Cycle

Mitosis is just one part of the cell cycle (**Figure 12.6**). In fact, the **mitotic (M) phase**, which includes both mitosis and cytokinesis, is usually the shortest part of the cell cycle. The mitotic phase alternates with a much longer stage called **interphase**, which often accounts for about 90% of the cycle. Interphase can be divided into subphases: the **G_1 phase** ("first gap"), the **S phase** ("synthesis"), and the **G_2 phase** ("second gap"). The G phases were misnamed as "gaps" when they were first observed because the cells appeared inactive, but we now know that intense metabolic activity and growth occur throughout interphase. During all three

▲ **Figure 12.6 The cell cycle.** In a dividing cell, the mitotic (M) phase alternates with interphase, a growth period. The first part of interphase (G_1) is followed by the S phase, when the chromosomes duplicate; G_2 is the last part of interphase. In the M phase, mitosis distributes the daughter chromosomes to daughter nuclei, and cytokinesis divides the cytoplasm, producing two daughter cells.

subphases of interphase, in fact, a cell grows by producing proteins and cytoplasmic organelles such as mitochondria and endoplasmic reticulum. Duplication of the chromosomes, crucial for eventual division of the cell, occurs entirely during the S phase. (We will discuss synthesis of DNA in Chapter 16.) Thus, a cell grows (G_1), continues to grow as it copies its chromosomes (S), grows more as it completes preparations for cell division (G_2), and divides (M). The daughter cells may then repeat the cycle.

A particular human cell might undergo one division in 24 hours. Of this time, the M phase would occupy less than 1 hour, while the S phase might occupy about 10–12 hours, or about half the cycle. The rest of the time would be apportioned between the G_1 and G_2 phases. The G_2 phase usually takes 4–6 hours; in our example, G_1 would occupy about 5–6 hours. G_1 is the most variable in length in different types of cells. Some cells in a multicellular organism divide very infrequently or not at all. These cells spend their time in G_1 (or a related phase called G_0) doing their job in the organism—a nerve cell carries impulses, for example.

Mitosis is conventionally broken down into five stages: **prophase**, **prometaphase**, **metaphase**, **anaphase**, and **telophase**. Overlapping with the latter stages of mitosis, cytokinesis completes the mitotic phase. **Figure 12.7** describes these stages in an animal cell. Study this figure thoroughly before progressing to the next two sections, which examine mitosis and cytokinesis more closely.

The Mitotic Spindle: *A Closer Look*

Many of the events of mitosis depend on the **mitotic spindle**, which begins to form in the cytoplasm during prophase. This structure consists of fibers made of microtubules and

Exploring Mitosis in an Animal Cell

| G_2 of Interphase | Prophase | Prometaphase |

G_2 of Interphase

Centrosomes (with centriole pairs)

Chromosomes (duplicated, uncondensed)

Nucleolus

Nuclear envelope

Plasma membrane

Prophase

Early mitotic spindle

Aster

Centromere

Two sister chromatids of one chromosome

Prometaphase

Fragments of nuclear envelope

Nonkinetochore microtubules

Kinetochore

Kinetochore microtubule

G_2 of Interphase

- A nuclear envelope encloses the nucleus.
- The nucleus contains one or more nucleoli (singular, *nucleolus*).
- Two centrosomes have formed by duplication of a single centrosome. Centrosomes are regions in animal cells that organize the microtubules of the spindle. Each centrosome contains two centrioles.
- Chromosomes, duplicated during S phase, cannot be seen individually because they have not yet condensed.

The fluorescence micrographs show dividing lung cells from a newt; this species has 22 chromosomes. Chromosomes appear blue, microtubules green, and intermediate filaments red. For simplicity, the drawings show only 6 chromosomes.

Prophase

- The chromatin fibers become more tightly coiled, condensing into discrete chromosomes observable with a light microscope.
- The nucleoli disappear.
- Each duplicated chromosome appears as two identical sister chromatids joined at their centromeres and, in some species, all along their arms by cohesins (sister chromatid cohesion).
- The mitotic spindle (named for its shape) begins to form. It is composed of the centrosomes and the microtubules that extend from them. The radial arrays of shorter microtubules that extend from the centrosomes are called asters ("stars").
- The centrosomes move away from each other, propelled partly by the lengthening microtubules between them.

Prometaphase

- The nuclear envelope fragments.
- The microtubules extending from each centrosome can now invade the nuclear area.
- The chromosomes have become even more condensed.
- Each of the two chromatids of each chromosome now has a kinetochore, a specialized protein structure at the centromere.
- Some of the microtubules attach to the kinetochores, becoming "kinetochore microtubules," which jerk the chromosomes back and forth.
- Nonkinetochore microtubules interact with those from the opposite pole of the spindle.

? *How many molecules of DNA are in the prometaphase drawing? How many molecules per chromosome? How many double helices are there per chromosome? Per chromatid?*

10 μm

Metaphase

Anaphase

Telophase and Cytokinesis

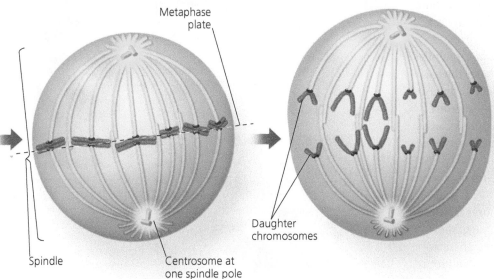

Metaphase
plate

Spindle

Centrosome at
one spindle pole

Daughter
chromosomes

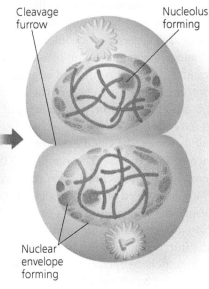

Cleavage
furrow

Nucleolus
forming

Nuclear
envelope
forming

Metaphase

- The centrosomes are now at opposite poles of the cell.
- The chromosomes have all arrived at the *metaphase plate*, a plane that is equidistant between the spindle's two poles. The chromosomes' centromeres lie at the metaphase plate.
- For each chromosome, the kinetochores of the sister chromatids are attached to kinetochore microtubules coming from opposite poles.

Anaphase

- Anaphase is the shortest stage of mitosis, often lasting only a few minutes.
- Anaphase begins when the cohesin proteins are cleaved. This allows the two sister chromatids of each pair to part suddenly. Each chromatid thus becomes a full-fledged chromosome.
- The two liberated daughter chromosomes begin moving toward opposite ends of the cell as their kinetochore microtubules shorten. Because these microtubules are attached at the centromere region, the chromosomes move centromere first (at about 1 μm/min).
- The cell elongates as the nonkinetochore microtubules lengthen.
- By the end of anaphase, the two ends of the cell have equivalent—and complete—collections of chromosomes.

Telophase

- Two daughter nuclei form in the cell. Nuclear envelopes arise from the fragments of the parent cell's nuclear envelope and other portions of the endomembrane system.
- Nucleoli reappear.
- The chromosomes become less condensed.
- Any remaining spindle microtubules are depolymerized.
- Mitosis, the division of one nucleus into two genetically identical nuclei, is now complete.

Cytokinesis

- The division of the cytoplasm is usually well under way by late telophase, so the two daughter cells appear shortly after the end of mitosis.
- In animal cells, cytokinesis involves the formation of a cleavage furrow, which pinches the cell in two.

ANIMATION **BioFlix** Visit the Study Area in **MasteringBiology** for the BioFlix® 3-D Animation on Mitosis. BioFlix Tutorials can also be assigned in MasteringBiology.

associated proteins. While the mitotic spindle assembles, the other microtubules of the cytoskeleton partially disassemble, providing the material used to construct the spindle. The spindle microtubules elongate (polymerize) by incorporating more subunits of the protein tubulin (see Table 6.1) and shorten (depolymerize) by losing subunits.

In animal cells, the assembly of spindle microtubules starts at the **centrosome**, a subcellular region containing material that functions throughout the cell cycle to organize the cell's microtubules. (It is also a type of *microtubule-organizing center*.) A pair of centrioles is located at the center of the centrosome, but they are not essential for cell division: If the centrioles are destroyed with a laser microbeam, a spindle nevertheless forms during mitosis. In fact, centrioles are not even present in plant cells, which do form mitotic spindles.

During interphase in animal cells, the single centrosome duplicates, forming two centrosomes, which remain near the nucleus. The two centrosomes move apart during prophase and prometaphase of mitosis as spindle microtubules grow out from them. By the end of prometaphase, the two centrosomes, one at each pole of the spindle, are at opposite ends of the cell. An **aster**, a radial array of short microtubules, extends from each centrosome. The spindle includes the centrosomes, the spindle microtubules, and the asters.

Each of the two sister chromatids of a duplicated chromosome has a **kinetochore**, a structure made up of proteins that have assembled on specific sections of DNA at each centromere. The chromosome's two kinetochores face in opposite directions. During prometaphase, some of the spindle microtubules attach to the kinetochores; these are called kinetochore microtubules. (The number of microtubules attached to a kinetochore varies among species, from one microtubule in yeast cells to 40 or so in some mammalian cells.) When one of a chromosome's kinetochores is "captured" by microtubules, the chromosome begins to move toward the pole from which those microtubules extend. However, this movement is checked as soon as microtubules from the opposite pole attach to the kinetochore on the other chromatid. What happens next is like a tug-of-war that ends in a draw. The chromosome moves first in one direction, then in the other, back and forth, finally settling midway between the two ends of the cell. At metaphase, the centromeres of all the duplicated chromosomes are on a plane midway between the spindle's two poles. This plane is called the **metaphase plate**, which is an imaginary plate rather than an actual cellular structure (**Figure 12.8**). Meanwhile, microtubules that do not attach to kinetochores have been elongating, and by metaphase they overlap and interact with other nonkinetochore microtubules from the opposite pole of the spindle. By metaphase, the microtubules of the asters have also grown and are in contact with the plasma membrane. The spindle is now complete.

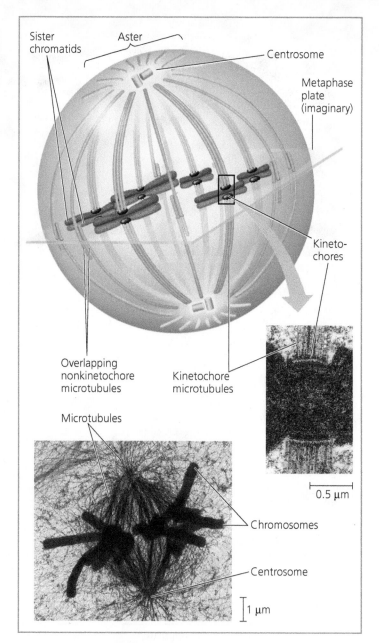

▲ **Figure 12.8 The mitotic spindle at metaphase.** The kinetochores of each chromosome's two sister chromatids face in opposite directions. Here, each kinetochore is attached to a cluster of kinetochore microtubules extending from the nearest centrosome. Nonkinetochore microtubules overlap at the metaphase plate (TEMs).

DRAW IT *On the lower micrograph, draw a line indicating the position of the metaphase plate. Circle an aster. Draw arrows indicating the directions of chromosome movement once anaphase begins.*

The structure of the spindle correlates well with its function during anaphase. Anaphase begins suddenly when the cohesins holding together the sister chromatids of each chromosome are cleaved by an enzyme called *separase*. Once separated, the chromatids become full-fledged chromosomes that move toward opposite ends of the cell.

How do the kinetochore microtubules function in this poleward movement of chromosomes? Apparently, two mechanisms are in play, both involving motor proteins. (To review how motor proteins move an object along a microtubule, see Figure 6.21.) Results of a cleverly designed experiment suggested that motor proteins on the kinetochores "walk" the chromosomes along the microtubules, which depolymerize at their kinetochore ends after the motor proteins have passed (Figure 12.9). (This is referred to as the "Pac-man" mechanism because of its resemblance to the arcade game character that moves by eating all the dots in its path.) However, other researchers, working with different cell types or cells from other species, have shown that chromosomes are "reeled in" by motor proteins at the spindle poles and that the microtubules depolymerize after they pass by these motor proteins. The general consensus now is that both mechanisms are used and that their relative contributions vary among cell types.

In a dividing animal cell, the nonkinetochore microtubules are responsible for elongating the whole cell during anaphase. Nonkinetochore microtubules from opposite poles overlap each other extensively during metaphase (see Figure 12.8). During anaphase, the region of overlap is reduced as motor proteins attached to the microtubules walk them away from one another, using energy from ATP. As the microtubules push apart from each other, their spindle poles are pushed apart, elongating the cell. At the same time, the microtubules lengthen somewhat by the addition of tubulin subunits to their overlapping ends. As a result, the microtubules continue to overlap.

At the end of anaphase, duplicate groups of chromosomes have arrived at opposite ends of the elongated parent cell. Nuclei re-form during telophase. Cytokinesis generally begins during anaphase or telophase, and the spindle eventually disassembles by depolymerization of microtubules.

Cytokinesis: *A Closer Look*

In animal cells, cytokinesis occurs by a process known as **cleavage**. The first sign of cleavage is the appearance of a **cleavage furrow**, a shallow groove in the cell surface near the old metaphase plate (Figure 12.10a). On the cytoplasmic side of the furrow is a contractile ring of actin microfilaments associated with molecules of the protein myosin. The actin microfilaments interact with the myosin molecules, causing the ring to contract. The contraction of the dividing cell's ring of microfilaments is like the pulling of a drawstring. The cleavage furrow deepens until the parent cell is pinched in two, producing two completely separated cells, each with its own nucleus and its own share of cytosol, organelles, and other subcellular structures.

Cytokinesis in plant cells, which have cell walls, is markedly different. There is no cleavage furrow. Instead, during telophase, vesicles derived from the Golgi apparatus move along microtubules to the middle of the cell, where they

▼ **Figure 12.9**   Inquiry

At which end do kinetochore microtubules shorten during anaphase?

Experiment Gary Borisy and colleagues at the University of Wisconsin wanted to determine whether kinetochore microtubules depolymerize at the kinetochore end or the pole end as chromosomes move toward the poles during mitosis. First they labeled the microtubules of a pig kidney cell in early anaphase with a yellow fluorescent dye.

Then they marked a region of the kinetochore microtubules between one spindle pole and the chromosomes by using a laser to eliminate the fluorescence from that region, while leaving the microtubules intact (see below). As anaphase proceeded, they monitored the changes in microtubule length on either side of the mark.

Results As the chromosomes moved poleward, the microtubule segments on the kinetochore side of the mark shortened, while those on the spindle pole side stayed the same length.

Conclusion During anaphase in this cell type, chromosome movement is correlated with kinetochore microtubules shortening at their kinetochore ends and not at their spindle pole ends. This experiment supports the hypothesis that during anaphase, a chromosome is walked along a microtubule as the microtubule depolymerizes at its kinetochore end, releasing tubulin subunits.

Source: G. J. Gorbsky, P. J. Sammak, and G. G. Borisy, Chromosomes move poleward in anaphase along stationary microtubules that coordinately disassemble from their kinetochore ends, *Journal of Cell Biology* 104:9–18 (1987).

WHAT IF? *If this experiment had been done on a cell type in which "reeling in" at the poles was the main cause of chromosome movement, how would the mark have moved relative to the poles? How would the microtubule lengths have changed?*

▼ Figure 12.10 Cytokinesis in animal and plant cells.

(a) Cleavage of an animal cell (SEM)

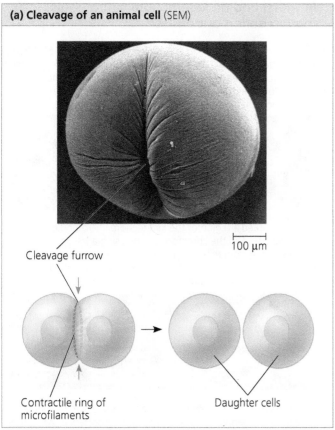

Cleavage furrow

100 μm

Contractile ring of microfilaments

Daughter cells

(b) Cell plate formation in a plant cell (TEM)

Vesicles forming cell plate

Wall of parent cell

1 μm

Cell plate

New cell wall

Daughter cells

coalesce, producing a **cell plate** (Figure 12.10b). Cell wall materials carried in the vesicles collect inside the cell plate as it grows. The cell plate enlarges until its surrounding membrane fuses with the plasma membrane along the perimeter of the cell. Two daughter cells result, each with its own plasma membrane. Meanwhile, a new cell wall arising from the contents of the cell plate has formed between the daughter cells.

Figure 12.11 is a series of micrographs of a dividing plant cell. Examining this figure will help you review mitosis and cytokinesis.

Binary Fission in Bacteria

Prokaryotes (bacteria and archaea) can undergo a type of reproduction in which the cell grows to roughly double its size and then divides to form two cells. The term **binary fission**, meaning "division in half," refers to this process and to the asexual reproduction of single-celled eukaryotes, such as the amoeba in Figure 12.2a. However, the process in eukaryotes involves mitosis, while that in prokaryotes does not.

In bacteria, most genes are carried on a single bacterial chromosome that consists of a circular DNA molecule and associated proteins. Although bacteria are smaller and simpler than eukaryotic cells, the challenge of replicating their genomes in an orderly fashion and distributing the copies equally to two daughter cells is still formidable. The chromosome of the bacterium *Escherichia coli*, for example, when it is fully stretched out, is about 500 times as long as the cell. For such a long chromosome to fit within the cell requires that it be highly coiled and folded.

In *E. coli*, the process of cell division is initiated when the DNA of the bacterial chromosome begins to replicate at a specific place on the chromosome called the **origin of replication**, producing two origins. As the chromosome continues to replicate, one origin moves rapidly toward the opposite end of the cell (Figure 12.12). While the chromosome is replicating, the cell elongates. When replication is complete and the bacterium has reached about twice its initial size, its plasma membrane pinches inward, dividing the parent *E. coli* cell into two daughter cells. In this way, each cell inherits a complete genome.

Using the techniques of modern DNA technology to tag the origins of replication with molecules that glow green in fluorescence microscopy (see Figure 6.3), researchers have directly observed the movement of bacterial chromosomes. This movement is reminiscent of the poleward movements of the centromere regions of eukaryotic chromosomes during anaphase of mitosis, but bacteria don't have visible mitotic spindles or even microtubules. In most bacterial species studied, the two origins of replication end up at opposite ends of the cell or in some other very specific location, possibly anchored there by one or more proteins. How bacterial chromosomes move and how their specific location is

Nucleus
Nucleolus
Chromosomes condensing
Chromosomes
Cell plate
10 μm

1 Prophase. The chromosomes are condensing and the nucleolus is beginning to disappear. Although not yet visible in the micrograph, the mitotic spindle is starting to form.

2 Prometaphase. Discrete chromosomes are now visible; each consists of two aligned, identical sister chromatids. Later in prometaphase, the nuclear envelope will fragment.

3 Metaphase. The spindle is complete, and the chromosomes, attached to microtubules at their kinetochores, are all at the metaphase plate.

4 Anaphase. The chromatids of each chromosome have separated, and the daughter chromosomes are moving to the ends of the cell as their kinetochore microtubules shorten.

5 Telophase. Daughter nuclei are forming. Meanwhile, cytokinesis has started: The cell plate, which will divide the cytoplasm in two, is growing toward the perimeter of the parent cell.

▲ **Figure 12.11 Mitosis in a plant cell.** These light micrographs show mitosis in cells of an onion root.

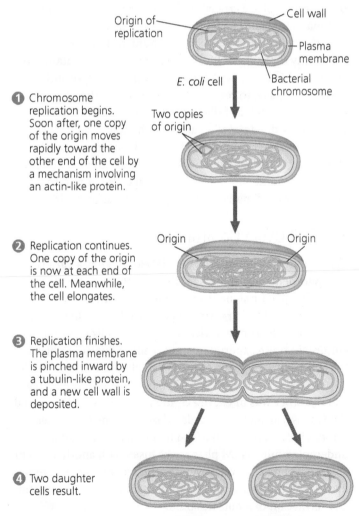

Origin of replication
Cell wall
Plasma membrane
Bacterial chromosome
E. coli cell

1 Chromosome replication begins. Soon after, one copy of the origin moves rapidly toward the other end of the cell by a mechanism involving an actin-like protein.

Two copies of origin

2 Replication continues. One copy of the origin is now at each end of the cell. Meanwhile, the cell elongates.

Origin   Origin

3 Replication finishes. The plasma membrane is pinched inward by a tubulin-like protein, and a new cell wall is deposited.

4 Two daughter cells result.

▲ **Figure 12.12 Bacterial cell division by binary fission.** The bacterium *E. coli*, shown here, has a single, circular chromosome.

established and maintained are active areas of research. Several proteins have been identified that play important roles. Polymerization of one protein resembling eukaryotic actin apparently functions in bacterial chromosome movement during cell division, and another protein that is related to tubulin helps pinch the plasma membrane inward, separating the two bacterial daughter cells.

The Evolution of Mitosis

EVOLUTION Given that prokaryotes preceded eukaryotes on Earth by more than a billion years, we might hypothesize that mitosis evolved from simpler prokaryotic mechanisms of cell reproduction. The fact that some of the proteins involved in bacterial binary fission are related to eukaryotic proteins that function in mitosis supports that hypothesis.

As eukaryotes with nuclear envelopes and larger genomes evolved, the ancestral process of binary fission, seen today in bacteria, somehow gave rise to mitosis. Variations on cell division exist in different groups of organisms. These variant processes may be similar to mechanisms used by ancestral species and thus may resemble steps in the evolution of mitosis from a binary fission-like process presumably carried out by very early bacteria. Possible intermediate stages are suggested by two unusual types of nuclear division found today in certain unicellular eukaryotes—dinoflagellates, diatoms, and some yeasts **(Figure 12.13)**. These two modes of nuclear division are thought to be cases where ancestral mechanisms have remained relatively unchanged over evolutionary time. In both types, the nuclear envelope remains intact, in contrast to what happens in most eukaryotic cells.

Bacterial chromosome

(a) Bacteria. During binary fission in bacteria, the origins of the daughter chromosomes move to opposite ends of the cell. The mechanism involves polymerization of actin-like molecules, and possibly proteins that may anchor the daughter chromosomes to specific sites on the plasma membrane.

Chromosomes

Microtubules

Intact nuclear envelope

(b) Dinoflagellates. In unicellular protists called dinoflagellates, the chromosomes attach to the nuclear envelope, which remains intact during cell division. Microtubules pass through the nucleus inside cytoplasmic tunnels, reinforcing the spatial orientation of the nucleus, which then divides in a process reminiscent of bacterial binary fission.

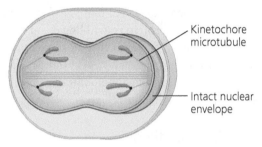

Kinetochore microtubule

Intact nuclear envelope

(c) Diatoms and some yeasts. In these two other groups of unicellular eukaryotes, the nuclear envelope also remains intact during cell division. In these organisms, the microtubules form a spindle *within* the nucleus. Microtubules separate the chromosomes, and the nucleus splits into two daughter nuclei.

Kinetochore microtubule

Fragments of nuclear envelope

(d) Most eukaryotes. In most other eukaryotes, including plants and animals, the spindle forms outside the nucleus, and the nuclear envelope breaks down during mitosis. Microtubules separate the chromosomes, and two nuclear envelopes then form.

▲ **Figure 12.13 Mechanisms of cell division in several groups of organisms.** Some unicellular eukaryotes existing today have mechanisms of cell division that may resemble intermediate steps in the evolution of mitosis. Except for (a), these schematic diagrams do not show cell walls.

1. How many chromosomes are drawn in Figure 12.8? Are they duplicated? How many chromatids are shown?
2. Compare cytokinesis in animal cells and plant cells.
3. During which stages of the cell cycle does a chromosome consist of two identical chromatids?
4. Compare the roles of tubulin and actin during eukaryotic cell division with the roles of tubulin-like and actin-like proteins during bacterial binary fission.
5. A kinetochore has been compared to a coupling device that connects a motor to the cargo that it moves. Explain.
6. **MAKE CONNECTIONS** What other functions do actin and tubulin carry out? Name the proteins they interact with to do so. (Review Figures 6.21a and 6.26a.)

For suggested answers, see Appendix A.

CONCEPT 12.3

The eukaryotic cell cycle is regulated by a molecular control system

The timing and rate of cell division in different parts of a plant or animal are crucial to normal growth, development, and maintenance. The frequency of cell division varies with the type of cell. For example, human skin cells divide frequently throughout life, whereas liver cells maintain the ability to divide but keep it in reserve until an appropriate need arises—say, to repair a wound. Some of the most specialized cells, such as fully formed nerve cells and muscle cells, do not divide at all in a mature human. These cell cycle differences result from regulation at the molecular level. The mechanisms of this regulation are of great interest, not only to understand the life cycles of normal cells but also to learn how cancer cells manage to escape the usual controls.

The Cell Cycle Control System

What controls the cell cycle? In the early 1970s, a variety of experiments led to the hypothesis that the cell cycle is driven by specific signaling molecules present in the cytoplasm. Some of the first strong evidence for this hypothesis came from experiments with mammalian cells grown in culture. In these experiments, two cells in different phases of the cell cycle were fused to form a single cell with two nuclei **(Figure 12.14)**. If one of the original cells was in the S phase and the other was in G_1, the G_1 nucleus immediately entered the S phase, as though stimulated by signaling molecules present in the cytoplasm of the first cell. Similarly, if a cell undergoing mitosis (M phase) was fused with another cell in any stage of its cell cycle, even G_1, the second nucleus immediately entered mitosis, with condensation of the chromatin and formation of a mitotic spindle.

The experiment shown in Figure 12.14 and other experiments on animal cells and yeasts demonstrated that the

▼ Figure 12.14   Inquiry

Do molecular signals in the cytoplasm regulate the cell cycle?

Experiment Researchers at the University of Colorado wondered whether a cell's progression through the cell cycle is controlled by cytoplasmic molecules. To investigate this, they selected cultured mammalian cells that were at different phases of the cell cycle and induced them to fuse. Two such experiments are shown here.

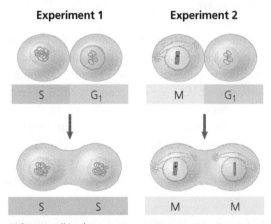

Experiment 1	Experiment 2

When a cell in the S phase was fused with a cell in G_1, the G_1 nucleus immediately entered the S phase—DNA was synthesized.

When a cell in the M phase was fused with a cell in G_1, the G_1 nucleus immediately began mitosis—a spindle formed and the chromosomes condensed, even though the chromosomes had not been duplicated.

Conclusion The results of fusing a G_1 cell with a cell in the S or M phase of the cell cycle suggest that molecules present in the cytoplasm during the S or M phase control the progression to those phases.

Source: R. T. Johnson and P. N. Rao, Mammalian cell fusion: Induction of premature chromosome condensation in interphase nuclei, *Nature* 226:717–722 (1970).

WHAT IF? *If the progression of phases did not depend on cytoplasmic molecules and, instead, each phase automatically began when the previous one was complete, how would the results have differed?*

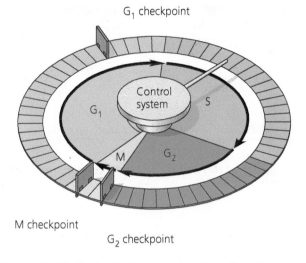

▲ **Figure 12.15 Mechanical analogy for the cell cycle control system.** In this diagram of the cell cycle, the flat "stepping stones" around the perimeter represent sequential events. Like the control device of an automatic washer, the cell cycle control system proceeds on its own, driven by a built-in clock. However, the system is subject to internal and external regulation at various checkpoints; three important checkpoints are shown (red).

sequential events of the cell cycle are directed by a distinct **cell cycle control system**, a cyclically operating set of molecules in the cell that both triggers and coordinates key events in the cell cycle. The cell cycle control system has been compared to the control device of an automatic washing machine **(Figure 12.15)**. Like the washer's timing device, the cell cycle control system proceeds on its own, according to a built-in clock. However, just as a washer's cycle is subject to both internal control (such as the sensor that detects when the tub is filled with water) and external adjustment (such as starting or stopping the machine), the cell cycle is regulated at certain checkpoints by both internal and external signals that stop or restart the machine. A **checkpoint** is a control point in the cell cycle where stop and go-ahead signals can regulate the cycle. Three important checkpoints are found in the G_1, G_2, and M phases (the red gates in Figure 12.15).

To understand how cell cycle checkpoints work, we first need to see what kinds of molecules make up the cell cycle control system (the molecular basis for the cell cycle clock) and how a cell progresses through the cycle. Then we will consider the internal and external checkpoint signals that can make the clock either pause or continue.

The Cell Cycle Clock: Cyclins and Cyclin-Dependent Kinases

Rhythmic fluctuations in the abundance and activity of cell cycle control molecules pace the sequential events of the cell cycle. These regulatory molecules are mainly proteins of two types: protein kinases and cyclins. Protein kinases are enzymes that activate or inactivate other proteins by phosphorylating them (see Chapter 11).

Many of the kinases that drive the cell cycle are actually present at a constant concentration in the growing cell, but much of the time they are in an inactive form. To be active, such a kinase must be attached to a **cyclin**, a protein that gets its name from its cyclically fluctuating concentration in the cell. Because of this requirement, these kinases are called **cyclin-dependent kinases**, or **Cdks**. The activity of a Cdk rises and falls with changes in the concentration of its cyclin partner. **Figure 12.16a** shows the fluctuating activity of **MPF**, the cyclin-Cdk complex that was discovered first (in frog eggs). Note that the peaks of MPF activity correspond to the peaks of cyclin concentration. The cyclin level rises during the S and G_2 phases and then falls abruptly during M phase.

The initials MPF stand for "maturation-promoting factor," but we can think of MPF as "M-phase-promoting factor" because it triggers the cell's passage into the M phase,

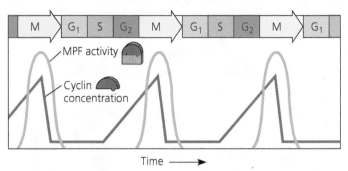

(a) **Fluctuation of MPF activity and cyclin concentration during the cell cycle**

1 Synthesis of cyclin begins in late S phase and continues through G₂. Because cyclin is protected from degradation during this stage, it accumulates.

5 During G₁, the degradation of cyclin continues, and the Cdk component of MPF is recycled.

Cdk

Degraded cyclin

Cyclin is degraded

G₂ checkpoint

Cdk

Cyclin

MPF

Cyclin accumulation

4 During anaphase, the cyclin component of MPF is degraded, terminating the M phase. The cell enters the G₁ phase.

3 MPF promotes mitosis by phosphorylating various proteins. MPF's activity peaks during metaphase.

2 Cyclin combines with Cdk, producing MPF. When enough MPF molecules accumulate, the cell passes the G₂ checkpoint and begins mitosis.

(b) **Molecular mechanisms that help regulate the cell cycle**

▲ **Figure 12.16 Molecular control of the cell cycle at the G₂ checkpoint.** The steps of the cell cycle are timed by rhythmic fluctuations in the activity of cyclin-dependent kinases (Cdks). Here we focus on a cyclin-Cdk complex in animal cells called MPF, which acts at the G₂ checkpoint as a go-ahead signal, triggering the events of mitosis.

? *Explain how the events in the diagram in (b) are related to the "Time" axis of the graph in (a), beginning at the left end.*

past the G₂ checkpoint **(Figure 12.16b)**. When cyclins that accumulate during G₂ associate with Cdk molecules, the resulting MPF complex phosphorylates a variety of proteins, initiating mitosis. MPF acts both directly as a kinase and indirectly by activating other kinases. For example, MPF causes phosphorylation of various proteins of the nuclear

lamina (see Figure 6.9), which promotes fragmentation of the nuclear envelope during prometaphase of mitosis. There is also evidence that MPF contributes to molecular events required for chromosome condensation and spindle formation during prophase.

During anaphase, MPF helps switch itself off by initiating a process that leads to the destruction of its own cyclin. The noncyclin part of MPF, the Cdk, persists in the cell, inactive until it becomes part of MPF again by associating with new cyclin molecules synthesized during the S and G₂ phases of the next round of the cycle.

The fluctuating activities of different cyclin-Cdk complexes are of major importance in controlling all the stages of the cell cycle and give the go-ahead signals at some checkpoints as well. As mentioned above, MPF controls the cell's passage through the G₂ checkpoint. Cell behavior at the G₁ checkpoint is also regulated by the activity of cyclin-Cdk protein complexes. Animal cells appear to have at least three Cdk proteins and several different cyclins that operate at this checkpoint. Next, let's consider checkpoints in more detail.

Stop and Go Signs: Internal and External Signals at the Checkpoints

Animal cells generally have built-in stop signals that halt the cell cycle at checkpoints until overridden by go-ahead signals. (The signals are transmitted within the cell by the kinds of signal transduction pathways discussed in Chapter 11.) Many signals registered at checkpoints come from cellular surveillance mechanisms inside the cell. These signals report whether crucial cellular processes that should have occurred by that point have in fact been completed correctly and thus whether or not the cell cycle should proceed. Checkpoints also register signals from outside the cell. Three important checkpoints are those in G₁, G₂, and M phases, shown in Figure 12.15.

For many cells, the G₁ checkpoint—dubbed the "restriction point" in mammalian cells—seems to be the most important. If a cell receives a go-ahead signal at the G₁ checkpoint, it will usually complete the G₁, S, G₂, and M phases and divide. If it does not receive a go-ahead signal at that point, it may exit the cycle, switching into a nondividing state called the **G₀ phase (Figure 12.17a)**. Most cells of the human body are actually in the G₀ phase. As mentioned earlier, mature nerve cells and muscle cells never divide. Other cells, such as liver cells, can be "called back" from the G₀ phase to the cell cycle by external cues, such as growth factors released during injury.

Biologists are currently working out the pathways that link signals originating inside and outside the cell with the responses by cyclin-dependent kinases and other proteins. An example of an internal signal occurs at the third important checkpoint, the M phase checkpoint **(Figure 12.17b)**.

▶ **Figure 12.17 Two important checkpoints.** At certain
checkpoints in the cell cycle (red
gates), cells do different things
depending on the signals they
receive. Events of the **(a)** G_1 and
(b) M checkpoints are shown. In
(b), the G_2 checkpoint has already
been passed by the cell.

WHAT IF? *What might be
the result if the cell ignored either checkpoint and progressed
through the cell cycle?*

In the absence of a go-ahead signal,
a cell exits the cell cycle and enters
G_0, a nondividing state.

(a) G_1 checkpoint

M checkpoint

Prometaphase

A cell in mitosis receives a stop signal
when any of its chromosomes are not
attached to spindle fibers.

(b) M checkpoint

If a cell receives a go-ahead signal, the
cell continues on in the cell cycle.

Anaphase

G_2
checkpoint

Metaphase

When all chromosomes are attached
to spindle fibers from both poles,
a go-ahead signal allows the cell to
proceed into anaphase.

Anaphase, the separation of sister chromatids,
does not begin until all the chromosomes are
properly attached to the spindle at the metaphase plate. Researchers have learned that
as long as some kinetochores are unattached
to spindle microtubules, the sister chromatids
remain together, delaying anaphase. Only when
the kinetochores of all the chromosomes are properly
attached to the spindle does the appropriate regulatory
protein complex become activated. (In this case, the regulatory molecule is not a cyclin-Cdk complex but, instead, a
different complex made up of several proteins.) Once activated, the complex sets off a chain of molecular events that
activates the enzyme separase, which cleaves the cohesins,
allowing the sister chromatids to separate. This mechanism
ensures that daughter cells do not end up with missing or
extra chromosomes.

Studies using animal cells in culture have led to the
identification of many external factors, both chemical and
physical, that can influence cell division. For example, cells
fail to divide if an essential nutrient is lacking in the culture medium. (This is analogous to trying to run a washing
machine without the water supply hooked up; an internal
sensor won't allow the machine to continue past the point
where water is needed.) And even if all other conditions are
favorable, most types of mammalian cells divide in culture
only if the growth medium includes specific growth factors.
As mentioned in Chapter 11, a **growth factor** is a protein
released by certain cells that stimulates other cells to divide.

Different cell types respond specifically to different growth
factors or combinations of growth factors.

Consider, for example, *platelet-derived growth factor
(PDGF)*, which is made by blood cell fragments called platelets. The experiment illustrated in **Figure 12.18** demonstrates
that PDGF is required for the division of cultured fibroblasts,
a type of connective tissue cell. Fibroblasts have PDGF receptors on their plasma membranes. The binding of PDGF molecules to these receptors (which are receptor tyrosine kinases;
see Figure 11.8) triggers a signal transduction pathway that
allows the cells to pass the G_1 checkpoint and divide. PDGF
stimulates fibroblast division not only in the artificial conditions of cell culture, but also in an animal's body. When an
injury occurs, platelets release PDGF in the vicinity. The resulting proliferation of fibroblasts helps heal the wound.

The effect of an external physical factor on cell division
is clearly seen in **density-dependent inhibition**, a phenomenon in which crowded cells stop dividing **(Figure 12.19a)**.
As first observed many years ago, cultured cells normally
divide until they form a single layer of cells on the inner
surface of the culture flask, at which point the cells stop dividing. If some cells are removed, those bordering the open

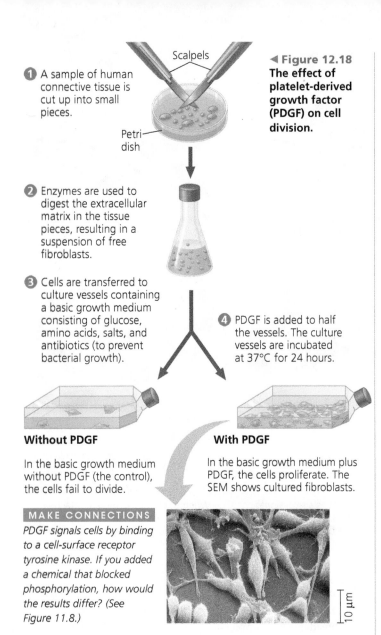

◀ **Figure 12.18 The effect of platelet-derived growth factor (PDGF) on cell division.**

❶ A sample of human connective tissue is cut up into small pieces.

Scalpels

Petri dish

❷ Enzymes are used to digest the extracellular matrix in the tissue pieces, resulting in a suspension of free fibroblasts.

❸ Cells are transferred to culture vessels containing a basic growth medium consisting of glucose, amino acids, salts, and antibiotics (to prevent bacterial growth).

❹ PDGF is added to half the vessels. The culture vessels are incubated at 37°C for 24 hours.

Without PDGF

In the basic growth medium without PDGF (the control), the cells fail to divide.

With PDGF

In the basic growth medium plus PDGF, the cells proliferate. The SEM shows cultured fibroblasts.

MAKE CONNECTIONS

PDGF signals cells by binding to a cell-surface receptor tyrosine kinase. If you added a chemical that blocked phosphorylation, how would the results differ? (See Figure 11.8.)

10 μm

Cells anchor to dish surface and divide (anchorage dependence).

When cells have formed a complete single layer, they stop dividing (density-dependent inhibition).

If some cells are scraped away, the remaining cells divide to fill the gap and then stop once they contact each other (density-dependent inhibition).

20 μm

(a) Normal mammalian cells. Contact with neighboring cells and the availability of nutrients, growth factors, and a substratum for attachment limit cell density to a single layer.

20 μm

(b) Cancer cells. Cancer cells usually continue to divide well beyond a single layer, forming a clump of overlapping cells. They do not exhibit anchorage dependence or density-dependent inhibition.

▲ **Figure 12.19 Density-dependent inhibition and anchorage dependence of cell division.** Individual cells are shown disproportionately large in the drawings.

space begin dividing again and continue until the vacancy is filled. Follow-up studies revealed that the binding of a cell-surface protein to its counterpart on an adjoining cell sends a cell division-inhibiting signal forward in the cell cycle, even in the presence of growth factors.

Most animal cells also exhibit **anchorage dependence** (see Figure 12.19a). To divide, they must be attached to a substratum, such as the inside of a culture flask or the extracellular matrix of a tissue. Experiments suggest that like cell density, anchorage is signaled to the cell cycle control system via pathways involving plasma membrane proteins and elements of the cytoskeleton linked to them.

Density-dependent inhibition and anchorage dependence appear to function not only in cell culture but also in the body's tissues, checking the growth of cells at some optimal density and location during embryonic development and throughout an organism's life. Cancer cells, which we discuss next, exhibit neither density-dependent inhibition nor anchorage dependence **(Figure 12.19b).**

Loss of Cell Cycle Controls in Cancer Cells

Cancer cells do not heed the normal signals that regulate the cell cycle. In culture, they do not stop dividing when growth factors are depleted. A logical hypothesis is that cancer cells do not need growth factors in their culture medium to grow and divide. They may make a required growth factor themselves, or they may have an abnormality in the signaling pathway that conveys the growth factor's signal to the cell cycle control system even in the absence of that factor. Another possibility is an abnormal cell cycle control system. In these scenarios, the underlying basis of the abnormality is almost always a change in one or more genes (for example, a mutation) that alters the function of their protein products, resulting in faulty cell cycle control.

There are other important differences between normal cells and cancer cells that reflect derangements of the cell cycle. If and when they stop dividing, cancer cells do so at random points in the cycle, rather than at the normal checkpoints. Moreover, cancer cells can go on dividing indefinitely in culture if they are given a continual supply of nutrients; in essence, they are "immortal." A striking example is a cell line that has been reproducing in culture since 1951. Cells of this line are called HeLa cells because their original source was a tumor removed from a woman named *Henrietta Lacks*. Cells in culture that acquire the ability to divide indefinitely are said to have undergone **transformation**, the process that causes them to behave like cancer cells. By contrast, nearly all normal, nontransformed mammalian cells growing in culture divide only about 20 to 50 times before they stop dividing, age, and die. Finally, cancer cells evade the normal controls that trigger a cell to undergo apoptosis when something is wrong—for example, when an irreparable mistake has occurred during DNA replication preceding mitosis.

The abnormal behavior of cancer cells can be catastrophic when it occurs in the body. The problem begins when a single cell in a tissue undergoes the first changes of the multistep process that converts a normal cell to a cancer cell. Such a cell often has altered proteins on its surface, and the body's immune system normally recognizes the cell as "nonself"— an insurgent—and destroys it. However, if the cell evades destruction, it may proliferate and form a tumor, a mass of abnormal cells within otherwise normal tissue. The abnormal cells may remain at the original site if they have too few genetic and cellular changes to survive at another site. In that case, the tumor is called a **benign tumor**. Most benign tumors do not cause serious problems and can be removed by surgery. In contrast, a **malignant tumor** includes cells whose genetic and cellular changes enable them to spread to new tissues and impair the functions of one or more organs; these cells are also considered *transformed* cells. An individual with a malignant tumor is said to have cancer; **Figure 12.20** shows the development of breast cancer, as well as a typical breast cancer cell.

The changes that have occurred in cells of malignant tumors show up in many ways besides excessive proliferation. These cells may have unusual numbers of chromosomes, though whether this is a cause or an effect of transformation is a topic of debate. Their metabolism may be altered, and they may cease to function in any constructive way. Abnormal changes on the cell surface cause cancer cells to lose attachments to neighboring cells and the extracellular matrix, allowing them to spread into nearby tissues. Cancer cells may also secrete signaling molecules that cause blood vessels to grow toward the tumor. A few tumor cells may separate from the original tumor, enter blood vessels and lymph vessels, and travel to other parts of the body. There, they may proliferate and form a new tumor. This spread of cancer cells to locations distant from their original site is called **metastasis** (see Figure 12.20).

A tumor that appears to be localized may be treated with high-energy radiation, which damages DNA in cancer cells much more than it does in normal cells, apparently because the majority of cancer cells have lost the ability to repair such damage. To treat known or suspected metastatic tumors, chemotherapy is used, in which drugs that are toxic to actively dividing cells are administered through the circulatory system. As you might expect, chemotherapeutic drugs interfere with specific steps in the cell cycle. For example, the drug Taxol freezes the mitotic spindle by preventing microtubule depolymerization, which stops actively dividing cells from proceeding past metaphase and leads to their destruction. The side effects of chemotherapy are due to the effects of the drugs on normal cells that divide often, due to the function of that cell type in the organism. For example, nausea results from chemotherapy's effects on intestinal cells, hair loss from effects on hair follicle cells, and susceptibility to infection from effects on immune system cells. You'll work

▼ **Figure 12.20 The growth and metastasis of a malignant breast tumor.** A series of genetic and cellular changes contribute to a tumor becoming malignant (cancerous). The cells of malignant tumors grow in an uncontrolled way and can spread to neighboring tissues and, via lymph and blood vessels, to other parts of the body. The spread of cancer cells beyond their original site is called metastasis.

Breast cancer cell (colorized SEM)

❶ A tumor grows from a single cancer cell.

❷ Cancer cells invade neighboring tissue.

❸ Cancer cells spread through lymph and blood vessels to other parts of the body.

❹ A small percentage of cancer cells may metastasize to another part of the body.

with data from an experiment involving a potential chemotherapeutic agent in the Scientific Skills Exercise.

Over the past several decades, researchers have produced a flood of valuable information about cell-signaling pathways and how their malfunction contributes to the development of cancer through effects on the cell cycle. Coupled with new molecular techniques, such as the ability to rapidly sequence the DNA of cells in a particular tumor, medical treatments for cancer are beginning to become more "personalized" to a particular patient's tumor (see Figure 18.27).

For example, the cells of roughly 20% of breast cancer tumors show abnormally high amounts of a cell-surface receptor tyrosine kinase called HER2, and many show an increase in the number of estrogen receptor (ER) molecules, intracellular receptors that can trigger cell division. Based on lab findings, a physician can prescribe chemotherapy with a molecule that blocks the function of the specific protein (Herceptin for HER2 and tamoxifen for ERs). Treatment using these agents, when appropriate, has led to increased survival rates and fewer cancer recurrences.

CONCEPT CHECK 12.3

1. In Figure 12.14, why do the nuclei resulting from experiment 2 contain different amounts of DNA?

2. How does MPF allow a cell to pass the G_2 phase checkpoint and enter mitosis? (See Figure 12.16.)

3. MAKE CONNECTIONS Explain in general how receptor tyrosine kinases and intracellular receptors might function in triggering cell division. (Review Figures 11.8 and 11.9 and Chapter 11.)

For suggested answers, see Appendix A.

SCIENTIFIC SKILLS EXERCISE

Interpreting Histograms

At What Phase Is the Cell Cycle Arrested by an Inhibitor? Many medical treatments are aimed at stopping cancer cell proliferation by blocking the cell cycle of cancerous tumor cells. One potential treatment is a cell cycle inhibitor derived from human umbilical cord stem cells. In this exercise, you will compare two histograms to determine where in the cell cycle the inhibitor blocks the division of cancer cells.

How the Experiment Was Done In the treated sample, human glioblastoma (brain cancer) cells were grown in tissue culture in the presence of the inhibitor, while control sample cells were grown in its absence. After 72 hours of growth, the two cell samples were harvested. To get a "snapshot" of the phase of the cell cycle each cell was in at that time, the samples were treated with a fluorescent chemical that binds to DNA and then run through a flow cytometer, an instrument that records the fluorescence level of each cell. Computer software then graphed the number of cells in each sample with a particular fluorescence level, as shown below.

Data from the Experiment

The data are plotted in a type of graph called a histogram (above), which groups values for a numeric variable on the x-axis into intervals. A histogram allows you to see how all the experimental subjects (cells, in this case) are distributed along a continuous variable (amount of fluorescence). In these histograms, the bars are so narrow that the data appear to follow a curve for which you can detect peaks and dips. Each narrow bar represents the number of cells observed to have a level of fluorescence in the range of that interval. This in turn indicates the relative amount of DNA in those cells. Overall, comparing the two histograms allows you to see how the DNA content of this cell population is altered by the treatment.

Interpret the Data

1. Familiarize yourself with the data shown in the histograms. (a) Which axis indirectly shows the relative amount of DNA per cell? Explain your answer. (b) In the control sample, compare the first peak in the histogram (in region A) to the second peak (in region C). Which peak shows the population of cells with the higher amount of DNA per cell? Explain. (For additional information about graphs, see the Scientific Skills Review in Appendix F and in the Study Area in MasteringBiology.)

2. (a) In the control sample histogram, identify the phase of the cell cycle (G_1, S, or G_2) of the population of cells in each region delineated by vertical lines. Label the histogram with these phases and explain your answer. (b) Does the S phase population of cells show a distinct peak in the histogram? Why or why not?

3. The histogram representing the treated sample shows the effect of growing the cancer cells alongside human umbilical cord stem cells that produce the potential inhibitor. (a) Label the histogram with the cell cycle phases. Which phase of the cell cycle has the greatest number of cells in the treated sample? Explain. (b) Compare the distribution of cells among G_1, S, and G_2 phases in the control and treated samples. What does this tell you about the cells in the treated sample? (c) Based on what you learned in Concept 12.3, propose a mechanism by which the stem cell-derived inhibitor might arrest the cancer cell cycle at this stage. (More than one answer is possible.)

MB A version of this Scientific Skills Exercise can be assigned in MasteringBiology.

Data from K. K. Velpula et al., Regulation of glioblastoma progression by cord blood stem cells is mediated by downregulation of cyclin D1, *PLoS ONE* 6(3): e18017 (2011).

SUMMARY OF KEY CONCEPTS

- Unicellular organisms reproduce by **cell division**; multicellular organisms depend on cell division for their development from a fertilized egg and for growth and repair. Cell division is part of the **cell cycle**, an ordered sequence of events in the life of a cell.

CONCEPT 12.1

Most cell division results in genetically identical daughter cells (pp. 233–235)

- The genetic material (DNA) of a cell—its **genome**—is partitioned among **chromosomes**. Each eukaryotic chromosome consists of one DNA molecule associated with many proteins. Together, the complex of DNA and associated proteins is called **chromatin**. The chromatin of a chromosome exists in different states of condensation at different times. In animals, **gametes** have one set of chromosomes and **somatic cells** have two sets.
- Cells replicate their genetic material before they divide, each daughter cell receiving a copy of the DNA. Prior to cell division, chromosomes are duplicated. Each one then consists of two identical **sister chromatids** joined along their lengths by sister chromatid cohesion and held most tightly together at a constricted region at the **centromeres**. When this cohesion is broken, the chromatids separate during cell division, becoming the chromosomes of the daughter cells. Eukaryotic cell division consists of **mitosis** (division of the nucleus) and **cytokinesis** (division of the cytoplasm).

? *Differentiate between these terms: chromosome, chromatin, and chromatid.*

CONCEPT 12.2

The mitotic phase alternates with interphase in the cell cycle (pp. 235–242)

- Between divisions, a cell is in **interphase**: the G_1, **S**, and G_2 phases. The cell grows throughout interphase, with DNA being replicated only during the synthesis (S) phase. Mitosis and cytokinesis make up the **mitotic (M) phase** of the cell cycle.

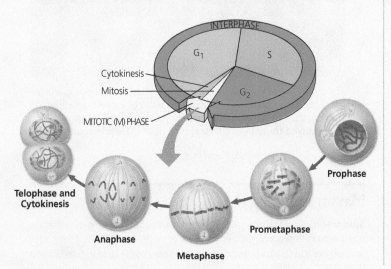

- The **mitotic spindle**, made up of microtubules, controls chromosome movement during mitosis. In animal cells, it arises from the **centrosomes** and includes spindle microtubules and **asters**. Some spindle microtubules attach to the **kinetochores** of chromosomes and move the chromosomes to the **metaphase plate**. After sister chromatids separate, motor proteins move them along kinetochore microtubules toward opposite ends of the cell. The cell elongates when motor proteins push nonkinetochore microtubules from opposite poles away from each other.
- Mitosis is usually followed by cytokinesis. Animal cells carry out cytokinesis by **cleavage**, and plant cells form a **cell plate**.
- During **binary fission** in bacteria, the chromosome replicates and the daughter chromosomes actively move apart. Some of the proteins involved in bacterial binary fission are related to eukaryotic actin and tubulin.
- Since prokaryotes preceded eukaryotes by more than a billion years, it is likely that mitosis evolved from prokaryotic cell division. Certain unicellular eukaryotes exhibit mechanisms of cell division that may be similar to those of ancestors of existing eukaryotes. Such mechanisms might represent intermediate steps in the evolution of mitosis.

? *In which of the three subphases of interphase and the stages of mitosis do chromosomes exist as single DNA molecules?*

CONCEPT 12.3

The eukaryotic cell cycle is regulated by a molecular control system (pp. 242–248)

- Signaling molecules present in the cytoplasm regulate progress through the cell cycle.
- The **cell cycle control system** is molecularly based. Cyclic changes in regulatory proteins work as a cell cycle clock. The key molecules are **cyclins** and **cyclin-dependent kinases (Cdks)**. The clock has specific **checkpoints** where the cell cycle stops until a go-ahead signal is received; important checkpoints occur in G_1, G_2, and M phases. Cell culture has enabled researchers to study the molecular details of cell division. Both internal signals and external signals control the cell cycle checkpoints via signal transduction pathways. Most cells exhibit **density-dependent inhibition** of cell division as well as **anchorage dependence**.
- Cancer cells elude normal cell cycle regulation and divide unchecked, forming tumors. **Malignant tumors** invade nearby tissues and can undergo **metastasis**, exporting cancer cells to other sites, where they may form secondary tumors. Recent cell cycle and cell signaling research, and new techniques for sequencing DNA, have led to improved cancer treatments.

? *Explain the significance of the G_1, G_2, and M checkpoints and the go-ahead signals involved in the cell cycle control system.*

TEST YOUR UNDERSTANDING

LEVEL 1: KNOWLEDGE/COMPREHENSION

1. Through a microscope, you can see a cell plate beginning to develop across the middle of a cell and nuclei forming on either side of the cell plate. This cell is most likely
   a. an animal cell in the process of cytokinesis.
   b. a plant cell in the process of cytokinesis.
   c. a bacterial cell dividing.
   d. a plant cell in metaphase.

2. Vinblastine is a standard chemotherapeutic drug used to treat cancer. Because it interferes with the assembly of microtubules, its effectiveness must be related to
   a. disruption of mitotic spindle formation.
   b. suppression of cyclin production.
   c. myosin denaturation and inhibition of cleavage furrow formation.
   d. inhibition of DNA synthesis.

3. One difference between cancer cells and normal cells is that cancer cells
   a. are unable to synthesize DNA.
   b. are arrested at the S phase of the cell cycle.
   c. continue to divide even when they are tightly packed together.
   d. cannot function properly because they are affected by density-dependent inhibition.

4. The decline of MPF activity at the end of mitosis is due to
   a. the destruction of the protein kinase Cdk.
   b. decreased synthesis of Cdk.
   c. the degradation of cyclin.
   d. the accumulation of cyclin.

5. In the cells of some organisms, mitosis occurs without cytokinesis. This will result in
   a. cells with more than one nucleus.
   b. cells that are unusually small.
   c. cells lacking nuclei.
   d. cell cycles lacking an S phase.

6. Which of the following does *not* occur during mitosis?
   a. condensation of the chromosomes
   b. replication of the DNA
   c. separation of sister chromatids
   d. spindle formation

LEVEL 2: APPLICATION/ANALYSIS

7. A particular cell has half as much DNA as some other cells in a mitotically active tissue. The cell in question is most likely in
   a. G_1.   c. prophase.
   b. G_2.   d. metaphase.

8. The drug cytochalasin B blocks the function of actin. Which of the following aspects of the animal cell cycle would be most disrupted by cytochalasin B?
   a. spindle formation
   b. spindle attachment to kinetochores
   c. cell elongation during anaphase
   d. cleavage furrow formation and cytokinesis

9. In the light micrograph below of dividing cells near the tip of an onion root, identify a cell in each of the following stages: prophase, prometaphase, metaphase, anaphase, and telophase. Describe the major events occurring at each stage.

10. **DRAW IT** Draw one eukaryotic chromosome as it would appear during interphase, during each of the stages of mitosis, and during cytokinesis. Also draw and label the nuclear envelope and any microtubules attached to the chromosome(s).

LEVEL 3: SYNTHESIS/EVALUATION

11. **EVOLUTION CONNECTION**
   The result of mitosis is that the daughter cells end up with the same number of chromosomes that the parent cell had. Another way to maintain the number of chromosomes would be to carry out cell division first and then duplicate the chromosomes in each daughter cell. Do you think this would be an equally good way of organizing the cell cycle? Why do you suppose that evolution has not led to this alternative?

12. **SCIENTIFIC INQUIRY**
   Although both ends of a microtubule can gain or lose subunits, one end (called the plus end) polymerizes and depolymerizes at a higher rate than the other end (the minus end). For spindle microtubules, the plus ends are in the center of the spindle, and the minus ends are at the poles. Motor proteins that move along microtubules specialize in walking either toward the plus end or toward the minus end; the two types are called plus end–directed and minus end–directed motor proteins, respectively. Given what you know about chromosome movement and spindle changes during anaphase, predict which type of motor proteins would be present on (a) kinetochore microtubules and (b) nonkinetochore microtubules.

13. **WRITE ABOUT A THEME: INFORMATION**
   Continuity of life is based on heritable information in the form of DNA. In a short essay (100–150 words), explain how the process of mitosis faithfully parcels out exact copies of this heritable information in the production of genetically identical daughter cells.

14. **SYNTHESIZE YOUR KNOWLEDGE**

Shown here are two HeLa cancer cells that are just completing cytokinesis. Explain how the cell division of cancer cells like these is misregulated. What genetic and other changes might have caused these cells to escape normal cell cycle regulation?

For selected answers, see Appendix A.

MasteringBiology®

Students Go to **MasteringBiology** for assignments, the eText, and the Study Area with practice tests, animations, and activities.

Instructors Go to **MasteringBiology** for automatically graded tutorials and questions that you can assign to your students, plus Instructor Resources.

AN INTERVIEW WITH

Charles Rotimi

Charles Rotimi was born in Nigeria and received a B.S. in biochemistry from the University of Benin. He also received advanced degrees in health care administration from the University of Mississippi and in public health from the University of Alabama. As a professor at the medical schools of Loyola University (Chicago) and Howard University, Dr. Rotimi focused his research on health disparities in populations of African ancestry. He is now the Director of the Center for Research on Genomics and Global Health at the National Institutes of Health.

How did you become interested in public health?

After arriving in Mississippi for graduate study in biochemistry, I learned that African-Americans in the local community were disproportionately affected by hypertension (high blood pressure), diabetes, and obesity. "Why was that?" I wondered. I started thinking I should go into public health, and I applied to study epidemiology at the University of Alabama. Epidemiology is the branch of medicine that studies diseases at the population level. Research in epidemiology can help determine the risk factors for various diseases and can influence public health policy. I realized I wanted to devote my career to investigating health disparities worldwide.

> " **Our ability to query the whole genome at once, for a large number of people, puts biology on a completely new scale.** "

My research career has been driven by a few fundamental questions: Why would a group of people be disproportionately affected by multiple conditions that cut across many metabolic pathways? For example, a person with diabetes tends to have hypertension, is often overweight, and may also have abnormal blood lipid levels and kidney function. Why is there such a clustering of metabolic disorders?

How did you get involved in genetics—and genomics?

One day I saw an exciting ad from Loyola University, seeking an assistant professor to study why we see different distributions of diseases across different populations of African ancestry. I said to myself, "This ad was written for me," and I got the position.

My mentor, Richard S. Cooper, had funding to look at the distribution of hypertension in selected populations in Africa, the Caribbean, and the United States. In the first study, we found that the prevalence of hypertension increases from rural West Africa to African urban centers to the black nations of the Caribbean to Maywood, Illinois. We were able to explain much of the observed increase by differences in factors like salt intake, physical activity, and weight. But we couldn't explain everything. We knew that our study subjects shared relatively recent ancestry but had varying genetic contributions from parental African and European populations. (For example, African-Americans have, on average, about 20% of their DNA from Europe.) These understandings led us to realize that we needed to incorporate genetics in our attempts to explain the residual variability.

Today, we use genomics on a routine basis. I can sequence all the genes of study participants. I feel like a kid in a candy store! Our ability to query the whole genome at once, for a large number of people, puts biology on a completely new scale.

What is the role of genetics in personalized medicine?

One of the things genomics is teaching us is that diseases such as hypertension or diabetes or cancer can be very different on the molecular level from person to person. Being able to use genetics to subclassify these diseases will enable us to treat individuals with specific drugs that will help them.

In my center here at NIH we are studying variation in important drug-metabolizing enzymes in people from various populations. Using a new chip that analyzes the genes for these enzymes, we have looked at 19 different populations across the world. We've found that people can belong to the same ethnic group yet have very different responses to a drug because of individual variation. These data really caution against using easy labels like "black," "African," or "European" for drug prescription at the individual level.

(MB) For an extended interview and video clip, go to the Study Area in MasteringBiology.

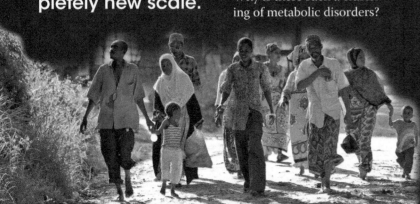

13

Meiosis and Sexual Life Cycles

▲ **Figure 13.1 What accounts for family resemblance?**

Variations on a Theme

We all know that offspring resemble their parents more than they do unrelated individuals. If you examine the family members shown in **Figure 13.1**, you can pick out some similar features among them. The transmission of traits from one generation to the next is called inheritance, or **heredity** (from the Latin *heres*, heir). However, sons and daughters are not identical copies of either parent or of their siblings. Along with inherited similarity, there is also **variation**. What are the biological mechanisms leading to the "family resemblance" evident among the family members in the photo above? The answer to this question eluded biologists until the advance of genetics in the 20th century.

Genetics is the scientific study of heredity and hereditary variation. In this unit, you'll learn about genetics at multiple levels, from organisms to cells to molecules. We begin by examining how chromosomes pass from parents to offspring in sexually reproducing organisms. The processes of meiosis (a special type of cell division) and fertilization (the fusion of sperm and egg, as seen in the photo at the left) maintain a species' chromosome count during the sexual life cycle. We will describe the cellular mechanics of meiosis and explain how this process differs from mitosis. Finally, we will consider how both meiosis and fertilization contribute to genetic variation, such as that seen in Figure 13.1.

CONCEPT 13.1

Offspring acquire genes from parents by inheriting chromosomes

Family friends may tell you that you have your mother's freckles or your father's eyes. Of course, parents do not, in any literal sense, give their children freckles, eyes, hair, or any other traits. What, then, *is* actually inherited?

Inheritance of Genes

Parents endow their offspring with coded information in the form of hereditary units called **genes**. The genes we inherit from our mothers and fathers are our genetic link to our parents, and they account for family resemblances such as shared eye color or freckles. Our genes program the specific traits that emerge as we develop from fertilized eggs into adults.

The genetic program is written in the language of DNA, the polymer of four different nucleotides you learned about in Concepts 1.1 and 5.5. Inherited information is passed on in the form of each gene's specific sequence of DNA nucleotides, much as printed information is communicated in the form of meaningful sequences of letters. In both cases, the language is symbolic. Just as your brain translates the word *apple* into a mental image of the fruit, cells translate genes into freckles and other features. Most genes program cells to synthesize specific enzymes and other proteins, whose cumulative action produces an organism's inherited traits. The programming of these traits in the form of DNA is one of the unifying themes of biology.

The transmission of hereditary traits has its molecular basis in the replication of DNA, which produces copies of genes that can be passed from parents to offspring. In animals and plants, reproductive cells called **gametes** are the vehicles that transmit genes from one generation to the next. During fertilization, male and female gametes (sperm and eggs) unite, passing on genes of both parents to their offspring.

Except for small amounts of DNA in mitochondria and chloroplasts, the DNA of a eukaryotic cell is packaged into chromosomes within the nucleus. Every species has a characteristic number of chromosomes. For example, humans have 46 chromosomes in their **somatic cells**—all cells of the body except the gametes and their precursors. Each chromosome consists of a single long DNA molecule elaborately coiled in association with various proteins. One chromosome includes several hundred to a few thousand genes, each of which is a specific sequence of nucleotides within the DNA molecule. A gene's specific location along the length of a chromosome is called the gene's **locus** (plural, *loci*; from the Latin, meaning "place"). Our genetic endowment (our genome) consists of the genes and other DNA that make up the chromosomes we inherited from our parents.

Comparison of Asexual and Sexual Reproduction

Only organisms that reproduce asexually have offspring that are exact genetic copies of themselves. In **asexual reproduction**, a single individual is the sole parent and passes copies of all its genes to its offspring without the fusion of gametes. For example, single-celled eukaryotic organisms can reproduce asexually by mitotic cell division, in which DNA is copied and allocated equally to two daughter cells. The genomes of the offspring are virtually exact copies of the parent's genome. Some multicellular organisms are also capable of reproducing asexually (**Figure 13.2**). Because the cells of the offspring are derived by mitosis in the parent, the "chip off the old block" is usually genetically identical to its parent. An individual that reproduces asexually gives rise to a **clone**, a group of genetically identical individuals. Genetic differences occasionally arise in asexually reproducing organisms as a result of changes in the DNA called mutations, which we will discuss in Chapter 17.

In **sexual reproduction**, two parents give rise to offspring that have unique combinations of genes inherited from the two parents. In contrast to a clone, offspring of sexual reproduction vary genetically from their siblings and both parents: They are variations on a common theme of family resemblance, not exact replicas. Genetic variation like that shown in Figure 13.1 is an important consequence of sexual reproduction. What mechanisms generate this genetic variation? The key is the behavior of chromosomes during the sexual life cycle.

(a) Hydra   **(b) Redwoods**

▲ **Figure 13.2 Asexual reproduction in two multicellular organisms. (a)** This relatively simple animal, a hydra, reproduces by budding. The bud, a localized mass of mitotically dividing cells, develops into a small hydra, which detaches from the parent (LM). **(b)** All the trees in this circle of redwoods arose asexually from a single parent tree, whose stump is in the center of the circle.

1. **MAKE CONNECTIONS** Using what you know of gene expression in a cell, explain what causes the traits of parents (such as hair color) to show up in their offspring. (See Concept 5.5.)

2. How do asexually reproducing eukaryotic organisms produce offspring that are genetically identical to each other and to their parents?

3. **WHAT IF?** A horticulturalist breeds orchids, trying to obtain a plant with a unique combination of desirable traits. After many years, she finally succeeds. To produce more plants like this one, should she cross-breed it with another plant or clone it? Why?

For suggested answers, see Appendix A.

CONCEPT 13.2

Fertilization and meiosis alternate in sexual life cycles

A **life cycle** is the generation-to-generation sequence of stages in the reproductive history of an organism, from conception to production of its own offspring. In this section, we use humans as an example to track the behavior of chromosomes through the sexual life cycle. We begin by considering the chromosome count in human somatic cells and gametes. We will then explore how the behavior of chromosomes relates to the human life cycle and other types of sexual life cycles.

Sets of Chromosomes in Human Cells

In humans, each somatic cell has 46 chromosomes. During mitosis, the chromosomes become condensed enough to be visible under a light microscope. At this point, they can be distinguished from one another by their size, the positions of their centromeres, and the pattern of colored bands produced by certain chromatin-binding stains.

Careful examination of a micrograph of the 46 human chromosomes from a single cell in mitosis reveals that there are two chromosomes of each of 23 types. This becomes clear when images of the chromosomes are arranged in pairs, starting with the longest chromosomes. The resulting ordered display is called a **karyotype (Figure 13.3)**. The two chromosomes of a pair have the same length, centromere position, and staining pattern: These are called **homologous chromosomes**, or **homologs**. Both chromosomes of each pair carry genes controlling the same inherited characters. For example, if a gene for eye color is situated at a particular locus on a certain chromosome, then the homolog of that chromosome will also have a version of the same gene specifying eye color at the equivalent locus.

The two distinct chromosomes referred to as X and Y are an important exception to the general pattern of homologous chromosomes in human somatic cells. Human females

▼ **Figure 13.3** | **Research Method**

Preparing a Karyotype

Application A karyotype is a display of condensed chromosomes arranged in pairs. Karyotyping can be used to screen for defective chromosomes or abnormal numbers of chromosomes associated with certain congenital disorders, such as Down syndrome.

Technique Karyotypes are prepared from isolated somatic cells, which are treated with a drug to stimulate mitosis and then grown in culture for several days. Cells arrested in metaphase, when chromosomes are most highly condensed, are stained and then viewed with a microscope equipped with a digital camera. An image of the chromosomes is displayed on a computer monitor, and digital software is used to arrange them in pairs according to their appearance.

Pair of homologous duplicated chromosomes

Centromere

5 µm

Sister chromatids

Metaphase chromosome

Results This karyotype shows the chromosomes from a normal human male, digitally colored to emphasize their banding patterns. The size of the chromosome, position of the centromere, and pattern of stained bands help identify specific chromosomes. Although difficult to discern in the karyotype, each metaphase chromosome consists of two closely attached sister chromatids (see the diagram of a pair of homologous duplicated chromosomes).

have a homologous pair of X chromosomes (XX), but males have one X and one Y chromosome (XY). Only small parts of the X and Y are homologous. Most of the genes carried on the X chromosome do not have counterparts on the tiny Y, and the Y chromosome has genes lacking on the X. Because they determine an individual's sex, the X and Y chromosomes are called **sex chromosomes**. The other chromosomes are called **autosomes**.

The pairs of homologous chromosomes in each human somatic cell is a consequence of our sexual origins. We inherit one chromosome of a pair from each parent. Thus, the 46 chromosomes in our somatic cells are actually two sets of 23 chromosomes—a maternal set (from our mother) and a paternal set (from our father). The number of chromosomes in a single set is represented by n. Any cell with two chromosome sets is called a **diploid cell** and has a diploid number of chromosomes, abbreviated $2n$. For humans, the diploid number is 46 ($2n = 46$), the number of chromosomes in our somatic cells. In a cell in which DNA synthesis has occurred, all the chromosomes are duplicated, and therefore each consists of two identical sister chromatids, associated closely at the centromere and along the arms. (Even though the chromosomes are duplicated, we still say the cell is diploid ($2n$) because it has only two sets of information.) **Figure 13.4** helps clarify the various terms that we use to describe duplicated chromosomes in a diploid cell.

Unlike somatic cells, gametes contain a single set of chromosomes. Such cells are called **haploid cells**, and each has a haploid number of chromosomes (n). For humans, the

haploid number is 23 ($n = 23$). The set of 23 consists of the 22 autosomes plus a single sex chromosome. An unfertilized egg contains an X chromosome, but a sperm may contain an X or a Y chromosome.

Each sexually reproducing species has a characteristic diploid and haploid number. For example, the fruit fly *Drosophila melanogaster* has a diploid number ($2n$) of 8 and a haploid number (n) of 4, while for dogs, $2n$ is 78 and n is 39. Now let's consider chromosome behavior during sexual life cycles. We'll use the human life cycle as an example.

Behavior of Chromosome Sets in the Human Life Cycle

The human life cycle begins when a haploid sperm from the father fuses with a haploid egg from the mother (**Figure 13.5**). This union of gametes, culminating in fusion of their nuclei, is called **fertilization**. The resulting fertilized egg, or **zygote**, is diploid because it contains two haploid sets of chromosomes bearing genes representing the maternal and paternal family

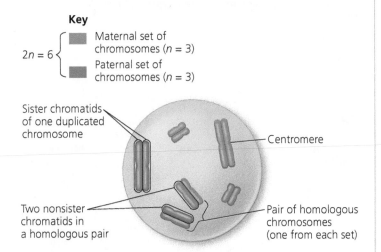

▲ **Figure 13.4 Describing chromosomes.** A cell from an organism with a diploid number of 6 ($2n = 6$) is depicted here following chromosome duplication and condensation. Each of the six duplicated chromosomes consists of two sister chromatids associated closely along their lengths. Each homologous pair is composed of one chromosome from the maternal set (red) and one from the paternal set (blue). Each set is made up of three chromosomes in this example (long, medium, and short). Together, one maternal and one paternal chromatid in a pair of homologous chromosomes are called nonsister chromatids.

? *How many sets of chromosomes are present in this diagram? How many pairs of homologous chromosomes are present?*

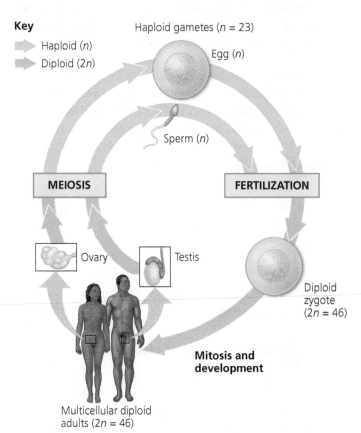

▲ **Figure 13.5 The human life cycle.** In each generation, the number of chromosome sets doubles at fertilization but is halved during meiosis. For humans, the number of chromosomes in a haploid cell is 23, consisting of one set ($n = 23$); the number of chromosomes in the diploid zygote and all somatic cells arising from it is 46, consisting of two sets ($2n = 46$).

This figure introduces a color code that will be used for other life cycles later in this book. The aqua arrows identify haploid stages of a life cycle, and the tan arrows identify diploid stages.

lines. As a human develops into a sexually mature adult, mitosis of the zygote and its descendant cells generates all the somatic cells of the body. Both chromosome sets in the zygote and all the genes they carry are passed with precision to the somatic cells.

The only cells of the human body not produced by mitosis are the gametes, which develop from specialized cells called *germ cells* in the gonads—ovaries in females and testes in males. Imagine what would happen if human gametes were made by mitosis: They would be diploid like the somatic cells. At the next round of fertilization, when two gametes fused, the normal chromosome number of 46 would double to 92, and each subsequent generation would double the number of chromosomes yet again. This does not happen, however, because in sexually reproducing organisms, gamete formation involves a type of cell division called **meiosis**. This type of cell division reduces the number of sets of chromosomes from two to one in the gametes, counterbalancing the doubling that occurs at fertilization. As a result of meiosis, each human sperm and egg is haploid ($n = 23$). Fertilization restores the diploid condition by combining two haploid sets of chromosomes, and the human life cycle is repeated, generation after generation (see Figure 13.5).

In general, the steps of the human life cycle are typical of many sexually reproducing animals. Indeed, the processes of fertilization and meiosis are the hallmarks of sexual reproduction in plants, fungi, and protists as well as in animals. Fertilization and meiosis alternate in sexual life cycles, maintaining a constant number of chromosomes in each species from one generation to the next.

The Variety of Sexual Life Cycles

Although the alternation of meiosis and fertilization is common to all organisms that reproduce sexually, the timing of these two events in the life cycle varies, depending on the species. These variations can be grouped into three main types of life cycles. In the type that occurs in humans and most other animals, gametes are the only haploid cells (**Figure 13.6a**). Meiosis occurs in germ cells during the production of gametes, which undergo no further cell division prior to fertilization. After fertilization, the diploid zygote divides by mitosis, producing a multicellular organism that is diploid.

Plants and some species of algae exhibit a second type of life cycle called **alternation of generations** (**Figure 13.6b**). This type includes both diploid and haploid stages that are multicellular. The multicellular diploid stage is called the *sporophyte*. Meiosis in the sporophyte produces haploid cells called *spores*. Unlike a gamete, a haploid spore doesn't fuse with another cell but divides mitotically, generating a multicellular haploid stage called the *gametophyte*. Cells of the gametophyte give rise to gametes by mitosis. Fusion of two haploid gametes at fertilization results in a diploid zygote, which develops into the next sporophyte generation. Therefore, in this type of life cycle, the sporophyte generation produces a gametophyte as its offspring, and the gametophyte generation produces the next sporophyte generation (see Figure 13.6b). The term *alternation of generations* fits well as a name for this type of life cycle.

A third type of life cycle occurs in most fungi and some protists, including some algae (**Figure 13.6c**). After gametes

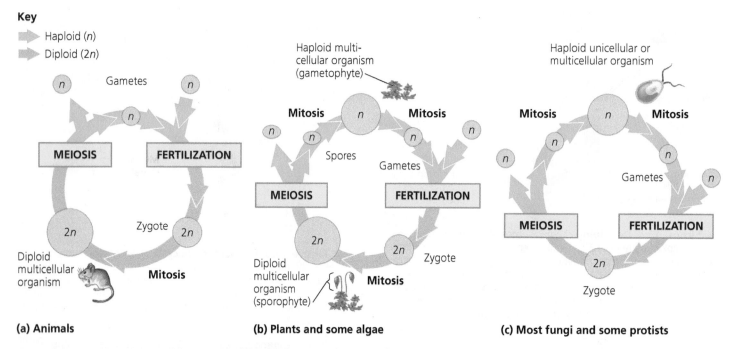

▲ Figure 13.6 **Three types of sexual life cycles.** The common feature of all three cycles is the alternation of meiosis and fertilization, key events that contribute to genetic variation among offspring. The cycles differ in the timing of these two key events.

fuse and form a diploid zygote, meiosis occurs without a multicellular diploid offspring developing. Meiosis produces not gametes but haploid cells that then divide by mitosis and give rise to either unicellular descendants or a haploid multicellular adult organism. Subsequently, the haploid organism carries out further mitoses, producing the cells that develop into gametes. The only diploid stage found in these species is the single-celled zygote.

Note that *either* haploid or diploid cells can divide by mitosis, depending on the type of life cycle. Only diploid cells, however, can undergo meiosis because haploid cells have only a single set of chromosomes that cannot be further reduced. Though the three types of sexual life cycles differ in the timing of meiosis and fertilization, they share a fundamental result: genetic variation among offspring.

CONCEPT CHECK 13.2

1. **MAKE CONNECTIONS** In Figure 13.4, how many DNA molecules (double helices) are present (see Figure 12.5)? What is the haploid number of this cell? Is a set of chromosomes haploid or diploid?

2. In the karyotype shown in Figure 13.3, how many pairs of chromosomes are present? How many sets?

3. **WHAT IF?** A certain eukaryote lives as a unicellular organism, but during environmental stress, it produces gametes. The gametes fuse, and the resulting zygote undergoes meiosis, generating new single cells. What type of organism could this be?

For suggested answers, see Appendix A.

CONCEPT 13.3

Meiosis reduces the number of chromosome sets from diploid to haploid

Many of the steps of meiosis closely resemble corresponding steps in mitosis. Meiosis, like mitosis, is preceded by the duplication of chromosomes. However, this single duplication is followed by not one but two consecutive cell divisions, called **meiosis I** and **meiosis II**. These two divisions result in four daughter cells (rather than the two daughter cells of mitosis), each with only half as many chromosomes as the parent cell—one set, rather than two.

The Stages of Meiosis

The overview of meiosis in **Figure 13.7** shows, for a single pair of homologous chromosomes in a diploid cell, that both members of the pair are duplicated and the copies sorted into four haploid daughter cells. Recall that sister chromatids are two copies of *one* chromosome, closely associated all

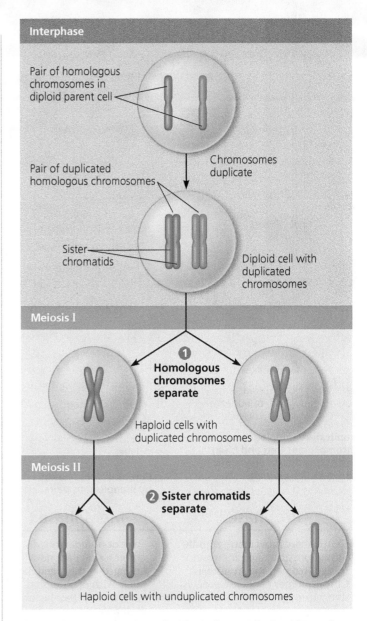

▲ **Figure 13.7 Overview of meiosis: how meiosis reduces chromosome number.** After the chromosomes duplicate in interphase, the diploid cell divides *twice*, yielding four haploid daughter cells. This overview tracks just one pair of homologous chromosomes, which for the sake of simplicity are drawn in the condensed state throughout.

DRAW IT *Redraw the cells in this figure using a simple double helix to represent each DNA molecule.*

along their lengths; this association is called *sister chromatid cohesion*. Together, the sister chromatids make up one duplicated chromosome (see Figure 13.4). In contrast, the two chromosomes of a homologous pair are individual chromosomes that were inherited from different parents. Homologs appear alike in the microscope, but they may have different versions of genes, each called an *allele*, at corresponding loci. Homologs are not associated with each other in any obvious way except during meiosis.

Figure 13.8 describes in detail the stages of the two divisions of meiosis for an animal cell whose diploid number is 6. Study this figure thoroughly before going on.

Exploring Meiosis in an Animal Cell

MEIOSIS I: Separates homologous chromosomes

Prophase I	Metaphase I	Anaphase I	Telophase I and Cytokinesis

Centrosome (with centriole pair)

Sister chromatids

Chiasmata

Spindle

Homologous chromosomes

Fragments of nuclear envelope

Duplicated homologous chromosomes (red and blue) pair and exchange segments; 2n = 6 in this example.

Centromere (with kinetochore)

Metaphase plate

Microtubules attached to kinetochore

Chromosomes line up by homologous pairs.

Sister chromatids remain attached

Homologous chromosomes separate

Each pair of homologous chromosomes separates.

Cleavage furrow

Two haploid cells form; each chromosome still consists of two sister chromatids.

Prophase I

- Centrosome movement, spindle formation, and nuclear envelope breakdown occur as in mitosis. Chromosomes condense progressively throughout prophase I.

- During early prophase I, before the stage shown above, each chromosome pairs with its homolog, aligned gene by gene, and **crossing over** occurs: The DNA molecules of non-sister chromatids are broken (by proteins) and are rejoined to each other.

- At the stage shown above, each homologous pair has one or more X-shaped regions called **chiasmata** (singular, *chiasma*), where crossovers have occurred.

- Later in prophase I, after the stage shown above, microtubules from one pole or the other will attach to the two kinetochores, one at the centromere of each homolog. (The two kinetochores of a homolog, not yet visible above, act as a single kinetochore.) The homologous pairs will then move toward the metaphase plate.

Metaphase I

- Pairs of homologous chromosomes are now arranged at the metaphase plate, with one chromosome in each pair facing each pole.

- Both chromatids of one homolog are attached to kinetochore microtubules from one pole; those of the other homolog are attached to microtubules from the opposite pole.

Anaphase I

- Breakdown of proteins that are responsible for sister chromatid cohesion along chromatid arms allows homologs to separate.

- The homologs move toward opposite poles, guided by the spindle apparatus.

- Sister chromatid cohesion persists at the centromere, causing chromatids to move as a unit toward the same pole.

Telophase I and Cytokinesis

- When telophase I begins, each half of the cell has a complete haploid set of duplicated chromosomes. Each chromosome is composed of two sister chromatids; one or both chromatids include regions of nonsister chromatid DNA.

- Cytokinesis (division of the cytoplasm) usually occurs simultaneously with telophase I, forming two haploid daughter cells.

- In animal cells like these, a cleavage furrow forms. (In plant cells, a cell plate forms.)

- In some species, chromosomes decondense and nuclear envelopes form.

- No chromosome duplication occurs between meiosis I and meiosis II.

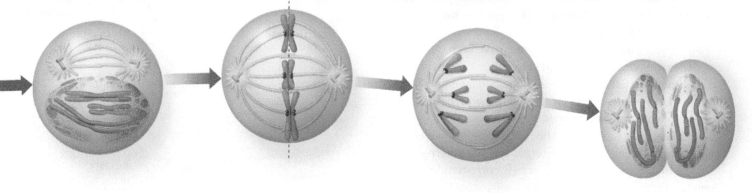

MEIOSIS II: Separates sister chromatids

| Prophase II | Metaphase II | Anaphase II | Telophase II and Cytokinesis |

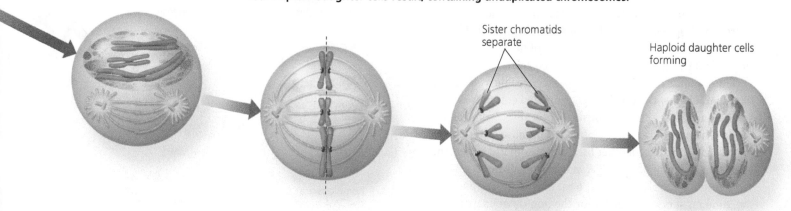

During another round of cell division, the sister chromatids finally separate; four haploid daughter cells result, containing unduplicated chromosomes.

Sister chromatids separate

Haploid daughter cells forming

Prophase II

• A spindle apparatus forms.

• In late prophase II (not shown here), chromosomes, each still composed of two chromatids associated at the centromere, move toward the metaphase II plate.

Metaphase II

• The chromosomes are positioned at the metaphase plate as in mitosis.

• Because of crossing over in meiosis I, the two sister chromatids of each chromosome are *not* genetically identical.

• The kinetochores of sister chromatids are attached to microtubules extending from opposite poles.

Anaphase II

• Breakdown of proteins holding the sister chromatids together at the centromere allows the chromatids to separate. The chromatids move toward opposite poles as individual chromosomes.

Telophase II and Cytokinesis

• Nuclei form, the chromosomes begin decondensing, and cytokinesis occurs.

• The meiotic division of one parent cell produces four daughter cells, each with a haploid set of (unduplicated) chromosomes.

• The four daughter cells are genetically distinct from one another and from the parent cell.

MAKE CONNECTIONS *Look at Figure 12.7 and imagine the two daughter cells undergoing another round of mitosis, yielding four cells. Compare the number of chromosomes in each of those four cells, after mitosis, with the number in each cell in Figure 13.8, after meiosis. What is it about the process of meiosis that accounts for this difference, even though meiosis also includes two cell divisions?*

ANIMATION ***BioFlix*** Visit the Study Area in **MasteringBiology** for the BioFlix® 3-D Animation on Meiosis. BioFlix Tutorials can also be assigned in MasteringBiology.

Crossing Over and Synapsis During Prophase I

Prophase I of meiosis is a very busy time. The prophase I cell shown in Figure 13.8 is at a point fairly late in prophase I, when homologous pairing, crossing over, and chromosome condensation have already taken place. The sequence of events leading up to that point is shown in more detail in **Figure 13.9.**

After interphase, the chromosomes have been duplicated and the sister chromatids are held together by proteins called *cohesins*. Early in prophase I, the two members of a homologous pair associate loosely along their length. Each gene on one homolog is aligned precisely with the corresponding gene on the other homolog. The DNA of two nonsister chromatids—one maternal and one paternal—is broken by specific proteins at precisely corresponding points. Next, the formation of a zipper-like structure called the **synaptonemal complex** holds one homolog tightly to the other. During this association, called **synapsis**, the DNA breaks are closed up so that each broken end is joined to the corresponding segment of the *nonsister* chromatid. Thus, a paternal chromatid is joined to a piece of maternal chromatid beyond the crossover point, and vice versa.

These points of crossing over become visible as chiasmata (singular, *chiasma*) after the synaptonemal complex disassembles and the homologs move slightly apart from each other. The homologs remain attached because sister chromatids are still held together by sister chromatid cohesion, even though some of the DNA may no longer be attached to its original chromosome. At least one crossover per chromosome must occur in order for the homologous pair to stay together as it moves to the metaphase I plate.

A Comparison of Mitosis and Meiosis

Figure 13.10 summarizes the key differences between meiosis and mitosis in diploid cells. Basically, meiosis reduces the number of chromosome sets from two (diploid) to one (haploid), whereas mitosis conserves the number of chromosome sets. Therefore, meiosis produces cells that differ genetically from their parent cell and from each other, whereas mitosis produces daughter cells that are genetically identical to their parent cell and to each other.

Three events unique to meiosis occur during meiosis I:

1. **Synapsis and crossing over.** During prophase I, duplicated homologs pair up and crossing over occurs, as described above. Synapsis and crossing over normally do not occur during prophase of mitosis.
2. **Homologous pairs at the metaphase plate.** At metaphase I of meiosis, chromosomes are positioned at the metaphase plate as pairs of homologs, rather than individual chromosomes, as in metaphase of mitosis.

1 After interphase, the chromosomes have been duplicated and sister chromatids are held together by proteins called cohesins (purple). Each pair of homologs associate along their length. The DNA molecules of two nonsister chromatids are broken at precisely corresponding points. The chromatin of the chromosomes is beginning to condense.

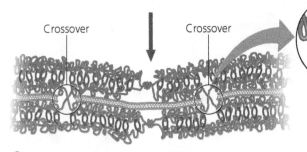

2 A zipperlike protein complex, the synaptonemal complex (green), begins to form, attaching one homolog to the other. The chromatin continues to condense.

3 The synaptonemal complex is fully formed; the two homologs are said to be in synapsis. During synapsis, the DNA breaks are closed up when each broken end is joined to the corresponding segment of the nonsister chromatid, producing crossovers.

4 After the synaptonemal complex disassembles, the homologs move slightly apart from each other but remain attached because of sister chromatid cohesion, even though some of the DNA may no longer be attached to its original chromosome. The points of attachment where crossovers have occurred show up as chiasmata. The chromosomes continue to condense as they move toward the metaphase plate.

▲ **Figure 13.9 Crossing over and synapsis in prophase I: a closer look.** For simplicity, the four chromatids of the homologous pair shown here are depicted side by side, but in reality, the blue chromosome would be right on top of the red one (see the top cell in Figure 13.12).

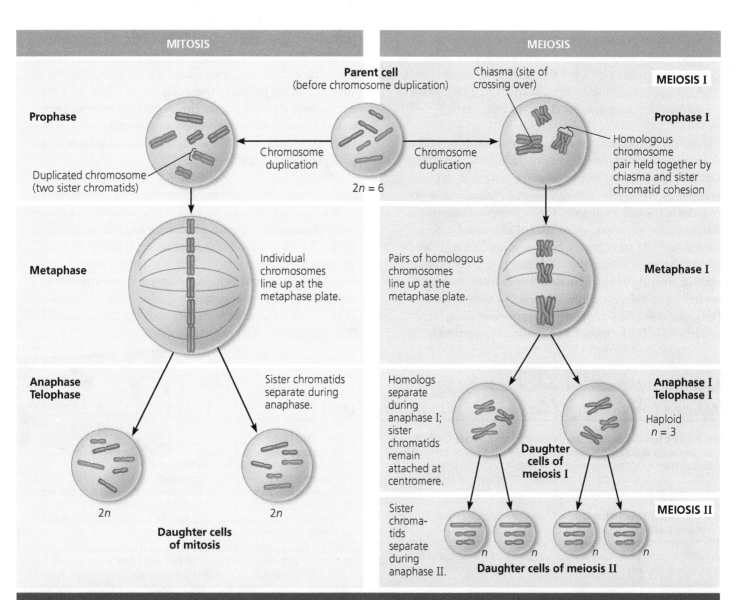

	MITOSIS			MEIOSIS	

Parent cell (before chromosome duplication)

Chiasma (site of crossing over)

MEIOSIS I

Prophase

Duplicated chromosome (two sister chromatids)

Chromosome duplication

$2n = 6$

Chromosome duplication

Prophase I

Homologous chromosome pair held together by chiasma and sister chromatid cohesion

Metaphase

Individual chromosomes line up at the metaphase plate.

Pairs of homologous chromosomes line up at the metaphase plate.

Metaphase I

Anaphase Telophase

Sister chromatids separate during anaphase.

Homologs separate during anaphase I; sister chromatids remain attached at centromere.

Anaphase I Telophase I

Haploid $n = 3$

Daughter cells of meiosis I

Anaphase I Telophase I

$2n$

$2n$

Daughter cells of mitosis

Sister chromatids separate during anaphase II.

MEIOSIS II

n n n n

Daughter cells of meiosis II

SUMMARY

Property	Mitosis (occurs in both diploid and haploid cells)	Meiosis (can only occur in diploid cells)
DNA replication	Occurs during interphase before mitosis begins	Occurs during interphase before meiosis I begins
Number of divisions	One, including prophase, prometaphase, metaphase, anaphase, and telophase	Two, each including prophase, metaphase, anaphase, and telophase
Synapsis of homologous chromosomes	Does not occur	Occurs during prophase I along with crossing over between nonsister chromatids; resulting chiasmata hold pairs together due to sister chromatid cohesion
Number of daughter cells and genetic composition	Two, each genetically identical to the parent cell, with the same number of chromosomes	Four, each haploid (n); genetically different from the parent cell and from each other
Role in the animal or plant body	Enables multicellular animal or plant (gametophyte or sporophyte) to arise from a single cell; produces cells for growth, repair, and, in some species, asexual reproduction; produces gametes in the gametophyte plant	Produces gametes (in animals) or spores (in the sporophyte plant); reduces number of chromosome sets by half and introduces genetic variability among the gametes or spores

▲ **Figure 13.10 A comparison of mitosis and meiosis.**

DRAW IT *Could any other combinations of chromosomes be generated during meiosis II from the specific cells shown in telophase I? Explain. (Hint: Draw the cells as they would appear in metaphase II.)*

3. **Separation of homologs.** At anaphase I of meiosis, the duplicated chromosomes of each homologous pair move toward opposite poles, but the sister chromatids of each duplicated chromosome remain attached. In anaphase of mitosis, by contrast, sister chromatids separate.

Sister chromatids stay together due to sister chromatid cohesion, mediated by cohesin proteins. In mitosis, this attachment lasts until the end of metaphase, when enzymes cleave the cohesins, freeing the sister chromatids to move to opposite poles of the cell. In meiosis, sister chromatid cohesion is released in two steps, one at the start of anaphase I and one at anaphase II. In metaphase I, homologs are held together by cohesion between sister chromatid arms in regions beyond points of crossing over, where stretches of sister chromatids now belong to different chromosomes. The combination of crossing over and sister chromatid cohesion along the arms results in the formation of a chiasma. Chiasmata hold homologs together as the spindle forms for the first meiotic division. At the onset of anaphase I, the release of cohesion along sister chromatid *arms* allows homologs to separate. At anaphase II, the release of sister chromatid cohesion at the *centromeres* allows the sister chromatids to separate. Thus, sister chromatid cohesion and crossing over, acting together, play an essential role in the lining up of chromosomes by homologous pairs at metaphase I.

Meiosis I is called the *reductional division* because it reduces the number of chromosome sets from two (diploid) to one (haploid). During meiosis II (the *equational division*), sister chromatids separate, producing haploid daughter cells. The mechanism for separating sister chromatids is virtually identical in meiosis II and mitosis. The molecular basis of chromosome behavior during meiosis continues to be a focus of intense research. In the **Scientific Skills Exercise**, you can work with data tracking the amount of DNA in cells as they progress through meiosis.

SCIENTIFIC SKILLS EXERCISE

Making a Line Graph and Converting Between Units of Data

How Does DNA Content Change as Budding Yeast Cells Proceed Through Meiosis? When nutrients are low, cells of the budding yeast (*Saccharomyces cerevisiae*) exit the mitotic cell cycle and enter meiosis. In this exercise, you will track the DNA content of a population of yeast cells as they progress through meiosis.

How the Experiment Was Done Researchers grew a culture of yeast cells in a nutrient-rich medium and then transferred them to a nutrient-poor medium to induce meiosis. At different times after induction, the DNA content per cell was measured in a sample of the cells, and the average DNA content per cell was recorded in femtograms (fg; 1 femtogram = 1×10^{-15} gram).

Data from the Experiment

Time After Induction (hours)	Average Amount of DNA per Cell (fg)
0.0	24.0
1.0	24.0
2.0	40.0
3.0	47.0
4.0	47.5
5.0	48.0
6.0	48.0
7.0	47.5
7.5	25.0
8.0	24.0
9.0	23.5
9.5	14.0
10.0	13.0
11.0	12.5
12.0	12.0
13.0	12.5
14.0	12.0

Interpret the Data

1. First, set up your graph. (a) Place the labels for the independent variable and the dependent variable on the appropriate axes, followed by units of measurement in parentheses. Explain your choices. (b) Add tick marks and values for each axis in your graph. Explain your choices. (For additional information about graphs, see the Scientific Skills Review in Appendix F and in the Study Area in MasteringBiology.)

2. Because the variable on the *x*-axis varies continuously, it makes sense to plot the data on a line graph. (a) Plot each data point from the table onto the graph. (b) Connect the data points with line segments.

3. Most of the yeast cells in the culture were in G_1 of the cell cycle before being moved to the nutrient-poor medium. (a) How many femtograms of DNA are there in each yeast cell in G_1? Estimate this value from the data in your graph. (b) How many femtograms of DNA should be present in each cell in G_2? (See Concept 12.2 and Figure 12.6.) At the end of meiosis I (MI)? At the end of meiosis II (MII)? (See Figure 13.7.) (c) Using these values as a guideline, distinguish the different phases by inserting vertical dashed lines in the graph between phases and label each phase (G_1, S, G_2, MI, MII). You can figure out where to put the dividing lines based on what you know about the DNA content of each phase (see Figure 13.7). (d) Think carefully about the point where the line at the highest value begins to slope downward. What specific point of meiosis does this "corner" represent? What stage(s) correspond to the downward sloping line?

4. Given the fact that 1 fg of DNA = 9.78×10^5 base pairs (on average), you can convert the amount of DNA per cell to the length of DNA in numbers of base pairs. (a) Calculate the number of base pairs of DNA in the haploid yeast genome. Express your answer in millions of base pairs (Mb), a standard unit for expressing genome size. Show your work. (b) How many base pairs per minute were synthesized during the S phase of these yeast cells?

(MB) A version of this Scientific Skills Exercise can be assigned in MasteringBiology.

Further Reading G. Simchen, Commitment to meiosis: what determines the mode of division in budding yeast? *BioEssays* 31:169–177 (2009).

14

Mendel and the Gene Idea

▲ **Figure 14.1 What principles of inheritance did Gregor Mendel discover by breeding pea plants?**

Drawing from the Deck of Genes

The crowd at a soccer match attests to the marvelous variety and diversity of humankind. Brown, blue, or gray eyes; black, brown, or blond hair—these are just a few examples of heritable variations that we may observe. What principles account for the transmission of such traits from parents to offspring?

The explanation of heredity most widely in favor during the 1800s was the "blending" hypothesis, the idea that genetic material contributed by the two parents mixes just as blue and yellow paints blend to make green. This hypothesis predicts that over many generations, a freely mating population will give rise to a uniform population of individuals, something we don't see. The blending hypothesis also fails to explain the reappearance of traits after they've skipped a generation.

An alternative to the blending model is a "particulate" hypothesis of inheritance: the gene idea. In this model, parents pass on discrete heritable units—genes—that retain their separate identities in offspring. An organism's collection of genes is more like a deck of cards than a pail of paint. Like playing cards, genes can be shuffled and passed along, generation after generation, in undiluted form.

Modern genetics had its genesis in an abbey garden, where a monk named Gregor Mendel documented a particulate mechanism for inheritance using pea plants **(Figure 14.1)**. Mendel developed his theory of inheritance several

◀ **Mendel (third from right, holding a sprig of fuchsia) with his fellow monks.**

267

decades before chromosomes were observed under the microscope and the significance of their behavior was understood. In this chapter, we'll step into Mendel's garden to re-create his experiments and explain how he arrived at his theory of inheritance. We'll also explore inheritance patterns more complex than those observed by Mendel in garden peas. Finally, we will see how the Mendelian model applies to the inheritance of human variations, including hereditary disorders such as sickle-cell disease.

Mendel used the scientific approach to identify two laws of inheritance

Mendel discovered the basic principles of heredity by breeding garden peas in carefully planned experiments. As we retrace his work, you will recognize the key elements of the scientific process that were introduced in Chapter 1.

Mendel's Experimental, Quantitative Approach

Mendel grew up on his parents' small farm in a region of Austria that is now part of the Czech Republic. In this agricultural area, Mendel and the other children received agricultural training in school along with their basic education. As an adolescent, Mendel overcame financial hardship and illness to excel in high school and, later, at the Olmutz Philosophical Institute.

In 1843, at the age of 21, Mendel entered an Augustinian monastery, a reasonable choice at that time for someone who valued the life of the mind. He considered becoming a teacher but failed the necessary examination. In 1851, he left the monastery to pursue two years of study in physics and chemistry at the University of Vienna. These were very important years for Mendel's development as a scientist, in large part due to the strong influence of two professors. One was the physicist Christian Doppler, who encouraged his students to learn science through experimentation and trained Mendel to use mathematics to help explain natural phenomena. The other was a botanist named Franz Unger, who aroused Mendel's interest in the causes of variation in plants.

After attending the university, Mendel returned to the monastery and was assigned to teach at a local school, where several other instructors were enthusiastic about scientific research. In addition, his fellow monks shared a long-standing fascination with the breeding of plants. Around 1857, Mendel began breeding garden peas in the abbey garden to study inheritance. Although the question of heredity had long been a focus of curiosity at the monastery, Mendel's fresh approach allowed him to deduce principles that had remained elusive to others.

One reason Mendel probably chose to work with peas is that there are many varieties. For example, one variety has purple flowers, while another variety has white flowers. A heritable feature that varies among individuals, such as flower color, is called a **character**. Each variant for a character, such as purple or white color for flowers, is called a **trait**.

Other advantages of using peas are their short generation time and the large number of offspring from each mating. Furthermore, Mendel could strictly control mating between plants **(Figure 14.2)**. Each pea flower has both pollen-producing organs (stamens) and an egg-bearing organ (carpel). In nature, pea plants usually self-fertilize: Pollen grains from the stamens land on the carpel of the same flower, and sperm released from the pollen grains fertilize

▼ **Figure 14.2** | Research Method

Crossing Pea Plants

Application By crossing (mating) two true-breeding varieties of an organism, scientists can study patterns of inheritance. In this example, Mendel crossed pea plants that varied in flower color.

Technique

① Removed stamens from purple flower

② Transferred sperm-bearing pollen from stamens of white flower to egg-bearing carpel of purple flower

Parental generation (P)

Carpel

Stamens

③ Waited for pollinated carpel to mature into pod

④ Planted seeds from pod

Results When pollen from a white flower was transferred to a purple flower, the first-generation hybrids all had purple flowers. The result was the same for the reciprocal cross, which involved the transfer of pollen from purple flowers to white flowers.

First filial generation offspring (F₁)

⑤ Examined offspring: all purple flowers

eggs present in the carpel.* To achieve cross-pollination of two plants, Mendel removed the immature stamens of a plant before they produced pollen and then dusted pollen from another plant onto the altered flowers (see Figure 14.2). Each resulting zygote then developed into a plant embryo encased in a seed (pea). Mendel could thus always be sure of the parentage of new seeds.

Mendel chose to track only those characters that occurred in two distinct, alternative forms, such as purple or white flower color. He also made sure that he started his experiments with varieties that, over many generations of self-pollination, had produced only the same variety as the parent plant. Such plants are said to be **true-breeding**. For example, a plant with purple flowers is true-breeding if the seeds produced by self-pollination in successive generations all give rise to plants that also have purple flowers.

In a typical breeding experiment, Mendel cross-pollinated two contrasting, true-breeding pea varieties—for example, purple-flowered plants and white-flowered plants (see Figure 14.2). This mating, or *crossing*, of two true-breeding varieties is called **hybridization**. The true-breeding parents are referred to as the **P generation** (parental generation), and their hybrid offspring are the **F_1 generation** (first filial generation, the word *filial* from the Latin word for "son"). Allowing these F_1 hybrids to self-pollinate (or to cross-pollinate with other F_1 hybrids) produces an **F_2 generation** (second filial generation). Mendel usually followed traits for at least the P, F_1, and F_2 generations. Had Mendel stopped his experiments with the F_1 generation, the basic patterns of inheritance would have eluded him. Mendel's quantitative analysis of the F_2 plants from thousands of genetic crosses like these allowed him to deduce two fundamental principles of heredity, which have come to be called the law of segregation and the law of independent assortment.

The Law of Segregation

If the blending model of inheritance were correct, the F_1 hybrids from a cross between purple-flowered and white-flowered pea plants would have pale purple flowers, a trait intermediate between those of the P generation. Notice in Figure 14.2 that the experiment produced a very different result: All the F_1 offspring had flowers just as purple as the purple-flowered parents.

What happened to the white-flowered plants' genetic contribution to the hybrids? If it were lost, then the F_1 plants could produce only purple-flowered offspring in the F_2 generation. But when Mendel allowed the F_1 plants to

self-pollinate and planted their seeds, the white-flower trait reappeared in the F_2 generation. Mendel used very large sample sizes and kept accurate records of his results: 705 of the F_2 plants had purple flowers, and 224 had white flowers. These data fit a ratio of approximately three purple to one white (Figure 14.3). Mendel reasoned that the heritable factor for white flowers did not disappear in the F_1 plants but was somehow hidden, or masked, when the purple-flower factor was present. In Mendel's terminology, purple flower color is a *dominant* trait, and white flower color is a *recessive* trait. The reappearance of white-flowered plants in the

▼ **Figure 14.3** Inquiry

When F_1 hybrid pea plants self- or cross-pollinate, which traits appear in the F_2 generation?

Experiment Mendel crossed true-breeding purple-flowered plants and white-flowered plants (crosses are symbolized by ×). The resulting F_1 hybrids were allowed to self-pollinate or were cross-pollinated with other F_1 hybrids. The F_2 generation plants were then observed for flower color.

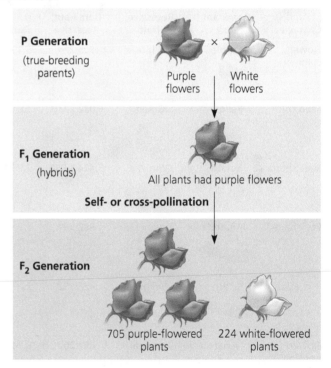

P Generation (true-breeding parents)

Purple flowers   ×   White flowers

F_1 Generation (hybrids)

All plants had purple flowers

Self- or cross-pollination

F_2 Generation

705 purple-flowered plants   224 white-flowered plants

Results Both purple-flowered and white-flowered plants appeared in the F_2 generation, in a ratio of approximately 3:1.

Conclusion The "heritable factor" for the recessive trait (white flowers) had not been destroyed, deleted, or "blended" in the F_1 generation but was merely masked by the presence of the factor for purple flowers, which is the dominant trait.

Source: G. Mendel, Experiments in plant hybridization, *Proceedings of the Natural History Society of Brünn* 4:3–47 (1866).

WHAT IF? *If you mated two purple-flowered plants from the P generation, what ratio of traits would you expect to observe in the offspring? Explain.*

*As you learned in Figure 13.6b, meiosis in plants produces spores, not gametes. In flowering plants like the pea, each spore develops into a microscopic haploid gametophyte that contains only a few cells and is located on the parent plant. The gametophyte produces sperm, in pollen grains, and eggs, in the carpel. For simplicity, we will not include the gametophyte stage in our discussion of fertilization in plants.

F_2 generation was evidence that the heritable factor causing white flowers had not been diluted or destroyed by coexisting with the purple-flower factor in the F_1 hybrids. Instead, it had been hidden when in the presence of the purple flower factor.

Mendel observed the same pattern of inheritance in six other characters, each represented by two distinctly different traits (Table 14.1). For example, when Mendel crossed a true-breeding variety that produced smooth, round pea seeds with one that produced wrinkled seeds, all the F_1 hybrids produced round seeds; this is the dominant trait for seed shape. In the F_2 generation, approximately 75% of the seeds were round and 25% were wrinkled—a 3:1 ratio, as in Figure 14.3. Now let's see how Mendel deduced the law of segregation from his experimental results. In the discussion that follows, we will use modern terms instead of some of the terms used by Mendel. (For example, we'll use "gene" instead of Mendel's "heritable factor.")

Mendel's Model

Mendel developed a model to explain the 3:1 inheritance pattern that he consistently observed among the F_2 offspring in his pea experiments. We describe four related concepts making up this model, the fourth of which is the law of segregation.

First, *alternative versions of genes account for variations in inherited characters.* The gene for flower color in pea plants, for example, exists in two versions, one for purple flowers and the other for white flowers. These alternative versions of a gene are called **alleles**. Today, we can relate this concept to chromosomes and DNA. As shown in **Figure 14.4**, each gene is a sequence of nucleotides at a specific place, or locus, along a particular chromosome. The DNA at that locus, however, can vary slightly in its nucleotide sequence. This variation in information content can affect the function of the encoded protein and thus the phenotype of the organism. The purple-flower allele and the white-flower allele are two DNA sequence variations possible at the flower-color locus on one of a pea plant's chromosomes, one that allows synthesis of purple pigment and one that does not.

Second, *for each character, an organism inherits two copies (that is, two alleles) of a gene, one from each parent.* Remarkably, Mendel made this deduction without knowing about the role, or even the existence, of chromosomes. Each somatic cell in a diploid organism has two sets of chromosomes, one set inherited from each parent (see Concept 13.2). Thus, a genetic locus is actually represented twice in a diploid cell, once on each homolog of a specific pair of chromosomes. The two alleles at a particular locus may be identical, as in the true-breeding plants of Mendel's P generation. Or the alleles may differ, as in the F_1 hybrids (see Figure 14.4).

Third, *if the two alleles at a locus differ, then one, the* **dominant allele**, *determines the organism's appearance; the other, the* **recessive allele**, *has no noticeable effect on the organism's appearance.* Accordingly, Mendel's F_1 plants had purple flowers because the allele for that trait is dominant and the allele for white flowers is recessive.

The fourth and final part of Mendel's model, the **law of segregation**, states that *the two alleles for a heritable character segregate (separate from each other) during gamete formation and end up in different gametes.* Thus, an egg or a sperm gets only one of the two alleles that are present in the somatic cells of the organism making the gamete. In terms of chromosomes, this segregation corresponds to the distribution of the two members of a pair of homologous chromosomes to different gametes in meiosis (see Figure 13.7). Note that if an organism has identical alleles for a particular character—that is, the organism is true-breeding for that character—then that allele is present in all gametes. But if different alleles are present, as in the F_1 hybrids, then 50% of the gametes receive the dominant allele and 50% receive the recessive allele.

Table 14.1	The Results of Mendel's F_1 Crosses for Seven Characters in Pea Plants				
Character	Dominant Trait	×	Recessive Trait	F_2 Generation Dominant: Recessive	Ratio
Flower color	Purple	×	White	705:224	3.15:1
Seed color	Yellow	×	Green	6,022:2,001	3.01:1
Seed shape	Round	×	Wrinkled	5,474:1,850	2.96:1
Pod shape	Inflated	×	Constricted	882:299	2.95:1
Pod color	Green	×	Yellow	428:152	2.82:1
Flower position	Axial	×	Terminal	651:207	3.14:1
Stem length	Tall	×	Dwarf	787:277	2.84:1

► **Figure 14.4 Alleles, alternative versions of a gene.** Shown is a pair of homologous chromosomes in an F₁ hybrid pea plant, with the DNA sequence from the flower color allele of each. The paternally inherited chromosome (blue) has an allele for purple flowers, which codes for a protein that indirectly controls synthesis of purple pigment. The maternally inherited chromosome (red) has an allele for white flowers, which results in no functional protein being made.

Allele for purple flowers

DNA with nucleotide sequence CTAAATCGGT

Locus for flower-color gene

Pair of homologous chromosomes

Allele for white flowers

DNA with nucleotide sequence ATAAATCGGT

Enzyme

Through a series of steps, this DNA sequence results in production of an enzyme that helps synthesize purple pigment.

This DNA sequence results in the absence of the enzyme.

One purple-flower allele results in sufficient pigment for purple flowers.

Does Mendel's segregation model account for the 3:1 ratio he observed in the F₂ generation of his numerous crosses? For the flower-color character, the model predicts that the two different alleles present in an F₁ individual will segregate into gametes such that half the gametes will have the purple-flower allele and half will have the white-flower allele. During self-pollination, gametes of each class unite randomly. An egg with a purple-flower allele has an equal chance of being fertilized by a sperm with a purple-flower allele or one with a white-flower allele. Since the same is true for an egg with a white-flower allele, there are four equally likely combinations of sperm and egg. **Figure 14.5** illustrates these combinations using a **Punnett square**, a handy diagrammatic device for predicting the allele composition of offspring from a cross between individuals of known genetic makeup. Notice that we use a capital letter to symbolize a dominant allele and a lowercase letter for a recessive allele. In our example, *P* is the purple-flower allele, and *p* is the white-flower allele; it is often useful as well to be able to refer to the gene itself as the *P/p* gene.

In the F₂ offspring, what color will the flowers be? One-fourth of the plants have inherited two purple-flower alleles; clearly, these plants will have purple flowers. One-half of the F₂ offspring

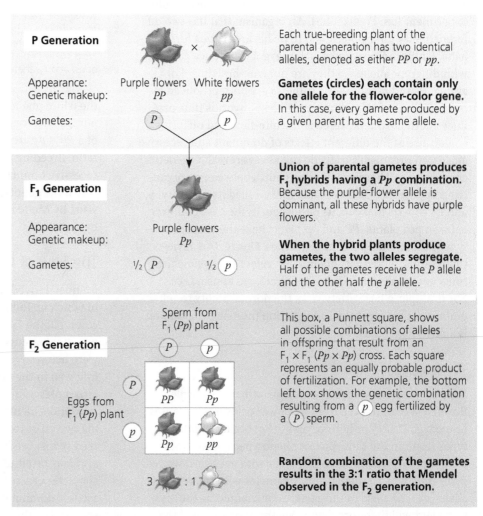

P Generation

Appearance: Purple flowers   White flowers
Genetic makeup: *PP*   *pp*

Gametes: *P*   *p*

Each true-breeding plant of the parental generation has two identical alleles, denoted as either *PP* or *pp*.

Gametes (circles) each contain only one allele for the flower-color gene. In this case, every gamete produced by a given parent has the same allele.

F₁ Generation

Appearance: Purple flowers
Genetic makeup: *Pp*

Gametes: ½ *P*   ½ *p*

Union of parental gametes produces F₁ hybrids having a *Pp* combination. Because the purple-flower allele is dominant, all these hybrids have purple flowers.

When the hybrid plants produce gametes, the two alleles segregate. Half of the gametes receive the *P* allele and the other half the *p* allele.

F₂ Generation

Sperm from F₁ (*Pp*) plant

P   *p*

Eggs from F₁ (*Pp*) plant

P   *p*

PP   *Pp*

Pp   *pp*

3 : 1

This box, a Punnett square, shows all possible combinations of alleles in offspring that result from an F₁ × F₁ (*Pp* × *Pp*) cross. Each square represents an equally probable product of fertilization. For example, the bottom left box shows the genetic combination resulting from a *p* egg fertilized by a *P* sperm.

Random combination of the gametes results in the 3:1 ratio that Mendel observed in the F₂ generation.

▲ **Figure 14.5 Mendel's law of segregation.** This diagram shows the genetic makeup of the generations in Figure 14.3. It illustrates Mendel's model for inheritance of the alleles of a single gene. Each plant has two alleles for the gene controlling flower color, one allele inherited from each of the plant's parents. To construct a Punnett square that predicts the F₂ generation offspring, we list all the possible gametes from one parent (here, the F₁ female) along the left side of the square and all the possible gametes from the other parent (here, the F₁ male) along the top. The boxes represent the offspring resulting from all the possible unions of male and female gametes.

have inherited one purple-flower allele and one white-flower allele; these plants will also have purple flowers, the dominant trait. Finally, one-fourth of the F₂ plants have inherited two white-flower alleles and will express the recessive trait. Thus, Mendel's model accounts for the 3:1 ratio of traits that he observed in the F₂ generation.

Useful Genetic Vocabulary

An organism that has a pair of identical alleles for a character is said to be **homozygous** for the gene controlling that character. In the parental generation in Figure 14.5, the purple pea plant is homozygous for the dominant allele (*PP*), while the white plant is homozygous for the recessive allele (*pp*). Homozygous plants "breed true" because all of their gametes contain the same allele—either *P* or *p* in this example. If we cross dominant homozygotes with recessive homozygotes, every offspring will have two different alleles—*Pp* in the case of the F₁ hybrids of our flower-color experiment (see Figure 14.5). An organism that has two different alleles for a gene is said to be **heterozygous** for that gene. Unlike homozygotes, heterozygotes produce gametes with different alleles, so they are not true-breeding. For example, *P*- and *p*-containing gametes are both produced by our F₁ hybrids. Self-pollination of the F₁ hybrids thus produces both purple-flowered and white-flowered offspring.

Because of the different effects of dominant and recessive alleles, an organism's traits do not always reveal its genetic composition. Therefore, we distinguish between an organism's appearance or observable traits, called its **phenotype**, and its genetic makeup, its **genotype**. In the case of flower color in pea plants, *PP* and *Pp* plants have the same phenotype (purple) but different genotypes. **Figure 14.6** reviews these terms. Note that "phenotype" refers to physiological traits as well as traits that relate directly to appearance. For example, a pea variety lacks the normal ability to self-pollinate. This physiological variation (non-self-pollination) is a phenotypic trait.

The Testcross

Suppose we have a "mystery" pea plant that has purple flowers. We cannot tell from its flower color if this plant is homozygous (*PP*) or heterozygous (*Pp*) because both genotypes result in the same purple phenotype. To determine the genotype, we can cross this plant with a white-flowered plant (*pp*), which will make only gametes with the recessive allele (*p*). The allele in the gamete contributed by the mystery plant will therefore determine the appearance of the offspring **(Figure 14.7)**. If all the offspring of the cross have purple flowers, then the purple-flowered mystery plant must be homozygous for the dominant allele, because a *PP* × *pp* cross produces all *Pp* offspring. But if both the purple and

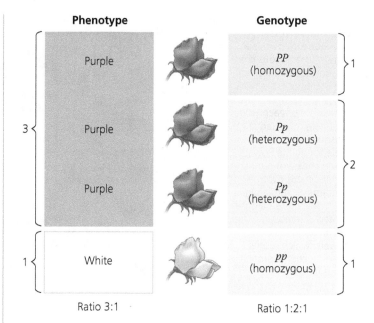

▲ **Figure 14.6 Phenotype versus genotype.** Grouping F₂ offspring from a cross for flower color according to phenotype results in the typical 3:1 phenotypic ratio. In terms of genotype, however, there are actually two categories of purple-flowered plants, *PP* (homozygous) and *Pp* (heterozygous), giving a 1:2:1 genotypic ratio.

the white phenotypes appear among the offspring, then the purple-flowered parent must be heterozygous. The offspring of a *Pp* × *pp* cross will be expected to have a 1:1 phenotypic ratio. Breeding an organism of unknown genotype with a recessive homozygote is called a **testcross** because it can reveal the genotype of that organism. The testcross was devised by Mendel and continues to be an important tool used by geneticists.

The Law of Independent Assortment

Mendel derived the law of segregation from experiments in which he followed only a *single* character, such as flower color. All the F₁ progeny produced in his crosses of true-breeding parents were **monohybrids**, meaning that they were heterozygous for the one particular character being followed in the cross. We refer to a cross between such heterozygotes as a **monohybrid cross**.

Mendel identified his second law of inheritance by following *two* characters at the same time, such as seed color and seed shape. Seeds (peas) may be either yellow or green. They also may be either round (smooth) or wrinkled. From single-character crosses, Mendel knew that the allele for yellow seeds is dominant (*Y*), and the allele for green seeds is recessive (*y*). For the seed-shape character, the allele for round is dominant (*R*), and the allele for wrinkled is recessive (*r*).

Imagine crossing two true-breeding pea varieties that differ in *both* of these characters—a cross between a plant with yellow-round seeds (*YYRR*) and a plant with green-wrinkled

Research Method

The Testcross

Application An organism that exhibits a dominant trait, such as purple flowers in pea plants, can be either homozygous for the dominant allele or heterozygous. To determine the organism's genotype, geneticists can perform a testcross.

Technique In a testcross, the individual with the unknown genotype is crossed with a homozygous individual expressing the recessive trait (white flowers in this example), and Punnett squares are used to predict the possible outcomes.

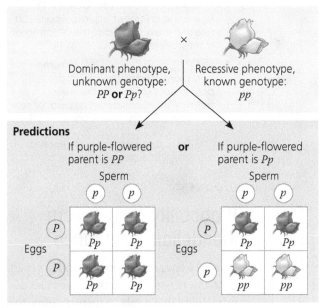

Results Matching the results to either prediction identifies the unknown parental genotype (either *PP* or *Pp* in this example). In this testcross, we transferred pollen from a white-flowered plant to the carpels of a purple-flowered plant; the opposite (reciprocal) cross would have led to the same results.

seeds (*yyrr*). The F₁ plants will be **dihybrids**, individuals heterozygous for the two characters being followed in the cross (*YyRr*). But are these two characters transmitted from parents to offspring as a package? That is, will the *Y* and *R* alleles always stay together, generation after generation? Or are seed color and seed shape inherited independently? **Figure 14.8** shows how a **dihybrid cross**, a cross between F₁ dihybrids, can determine which of these two hypotheses is correct.

The F₁ plants, of genotype *YyRr*, exhibit both dominant phenotypes, yellow seeds with round shapes, no matter which hypothesis is correct. The key step in the experiment is to see what happens when F₁ plants self-pollinate

and produce F₂ offspring. If the hybrids must transmit their alleles in the same combinations in which the alleles were inherited from the P generation, then the F₁ hybrids will produce only two classes of gametes: *YR* and *yr*. This "dependent assortment" hypothesis predicts that the phenotypic ratio of the F₂ generation will be 3:1, just as in a monohybrid cross (see Figure 14.8, left side).

The alternative hypothesis is that the two pairs of alleles segregate independently of each other. In other words, genes are packaged into gametes in all possible allelic combinations, as long as each gamete has one allele for each gene (see Figure 13.11). In our example, an F₁ plant will produce four classes of gametes in equal quantities: *YR*, *Yr*, *yR*, and *yr*. If sperm of the four classes fertilize eggs of the four classes, there will be 16 (4 × 4) equally probable ways in which the alleles can combine in the F₂ generation, as shown in Figure 14.8, right side. These combinations result in four phenotypic categories with a ratio of 9:3:3:1 (nine yellow-round to three green-round to three yellow-wrinkled to one green-wrinkled). When Mendel did the experiment and classified the F₂ offspring, his results were close to the predicted 9:3:3:1 phenotypic ratio, supporting the hypothesis that the alleles for one gene—controlling seed color or seed shape, in this example—are sorted into gametes independently of the alleles of other genes.

Mendel tested his seven pea characters in various dihybrid combinations and always observed a 9:3:3:1 phenotypic ratio in the F₂ generation. Is this consistent with the 3:1 phenotypic ratio seen for the monohybrid cross shown in Figure 14.5? To investigate this question, let's consider one of the two dihybrid characters by itself: Looking only at pea color, we see that there are 416 yellow and 140 green peas—a 2.97:1 ratio, or roughly 3:1. In the dihybrid cross, the pea color alleles segregate as if this were a monohybrid cross. The results of Mendel's dihybrid experiments are the basis for what we now call the **law of independent assortment**, which states that *two or more genes assort independently—that is, each pair of alleles segregates independently of each other pair of alleles—during gamete formation.*

This law applies only to genes (allele pairs) located on different chromosomes (that is to say, on chromosomes that are not homologous) or, alternatively, to genes that are very far apart on the same chromosome. (The latter case will be explained in Chapter 15, along with the more complex inheritance patterns of genes located near each other, which tend to be inherited together.) All the pea characters Mendel chose for analysis were controlled by genes on different chromosomes or were far apart on the same chromosome; this situation greatly simplified interpretation of his multicharacter pea crosses. All the examples we consider in the rest of this chapter involve genes located on different chromosomes.

Do the alleles for one character assort into gametes dependently or independently of the alleles for a different character?

Experiment To follow the characters of seed color and seed shape through the F₂ generation, Mendel crossed a true-breeding plant with yellow-round seeds with a true-breeding plant with green-wrinkled seeds, producing dihybrid F₁ plants. Self-pollination of the F₁ dihybrids produced the F₂ generation. The two hypotheses (dependent and independent assortment) predict different phenotypic ratios.

Results

315 ◯   108 ◯   101 ▣   32 ▣   Phenotypic ratio approximately 9:3:3:1

Conclusion Only the hypothesis of independent assortment predicts two of the observed phenotypes: green-round seeds and yellow-wrinkled seeds (see the right-hand Punnett square). The alleles for each gene segregate independently of those of the other, and the two genes are said to assort independently.

Source: G. Mendel, Experiments in plant hybridization, *Proceedings of the Natural History Society of Brünn* 4:3–47 (1866).

WHAT IF? *Suppose Mendel had transferred pollen from an F₁ plant to the carpel of a plant that was homozygous recessive for both genes. Set up the cross and draw Punnett squares that predict the offspring for both hypotheses. Would this cross have supported the hypothesis of independent assortment equally well?*

---

1. **DRAW IT** Pea plants heterozygous for flower position and stem length (*AaTt*) are allowed to self-pollinate, and 400 of the resulting seeds are planted. Draw a Punnett square for this cross. How many offspring would be predicted to have terminal flowers and be dwarf? (See Table 14.1.)

2. **WHAT IF?** List all gametes that could be made by a pea plant heterozygous for seed color, seed shape, and pod shape (*YyRrIi*; see Table 14.1). How large a Punnett square would you need to draw to predict the offspring of a self-pollination of this "trihybrid"?

3. **MAKE CONNECTIONS** In some pea plant crosses, the plants are self-pollinated. Explain whether self-pollination is considered asexual or sexual reproduction. (See Concept 13.1.)

For suggested answers, see Appendix A.

CONCEPT 14.2

Probability laws govern Mendelian inheritance

Mendel's laws of segregation and independent assortment reflect the same rules of probability that apply to tossing coins, rolling dice, and drawing cards from a deck. The probability scale ranges from 0 to 1. An event that is certain to occur has a probability of 1, while an event that is certain *not* to occur has a probability of 0. With a coin that has heads on both sides, the probability of tossing heads is 1, and the probability of tossing tails is 0. With a normal coin, the chance of tossing heads is ½, and the chance of tossing tails is ½. The probability of drawing the ace of spades from a 52-card deck is 1/52. The probabilities of all possible outcomes for an event must add up to 1. With a deck of cards, the chance of picking a card other than the ace of spades is 51/52.

Tossing a coin illustrates an important lesson about probability. For every toss, the probability of heads is ½. The outcome of any particular toss is unaffected by what has happened on previous trials. We refer to phenomena such as coin tosses as independent events. Each toss of a coin, whether done sequentially with one coin or simultaneously with many, is independent of every other toss. And like two separate coin tosses, the alleles of one gene segregate into gametes independently of another gene's alleles (the law of independent assortment). Two basic rules of probability can help us predict the outcome of the fusion of such gametes in simple monohybrid crosses and more complicated crosses as well.

The Multiplication and Addition Rules Applied to Monohybrid Crosses

How do we determine the probability that two or more independent events will occur together in some specific combination? For example, what is the chance that two coins tossed simultaneously will both land heads up? The **multiplication rule** states that to determine this probability, we multiply the probability of one event (one coin coming up heads) by the probability of the other event (the other coin coming up heads). By the multiplication rule, then, the probability that both coins will land heads up is $\frac{1}{2} \times \frac{1}{2} = \frac{1}{4}$.

We can apply the same reasoning to an F_1 monohybrid cross. With seed shape in pea plants as the heritable character, the genotype of F_1 plants is Rr. Segregation in a heterozygous plant is like flipping a coin in terms of calculating the probability of each outcome: Each egg produced has a $\frac{1}{2}$ chance of carrying the dominant allele (R) and a $\frac{1}{2}$ chance of carrying the recessive allele (r). The same odds apply to each sperm cell produced. For a particular F_2 plant to have wrinkled seeds, the recessive trait, both the egg and the sperm that come together must carry the r allele. The probability that an r allele will be present in both gametes at fertilization is found by multiplying $\frac{1}{2}$ (the probability that the egg will have an r) $\times$ $\frac{1}{2}$ (the probability that the sperm will have an r). Thus, the multiplication rule tells us that the probability of an F_2 plant having wrinkled seeds (rr) is $\frac{1}{4}$ (**Figure 14.9**). Likewise, the probability of an F_2 plant carrying both dominant alleles for seed shape (RR) is $\frac{1}{4}$.

To figure out the probability that an F_2 plant from a monohybrid cross will be heterozygous rather than homozygous, we need to invoke a second rule. Notice in Figure 14.9 that the dominant allele can come from the egg and the recessive allele from the sperm, or vice versa. That is, F_1 gametes can combine to produce Rr offspring in two *mutually exclusive* ways: For any particular heterozygous F_2 plant, the dominant allele can come from the egg *or* the sperm, but not from both. According to the **addition rule**, the probability that any one of two or more mutually exclusive events will occur is calculated by adding their individual probabilities. As we have just seen, the multiplication rule gives us the individual probabilities that we will now add together. The probability for one possible way of obtaining an F_2 heterozygote—the dominant allele from the egg and the recessive allele from the sperm—

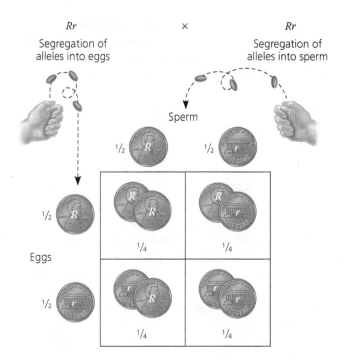

▲ **Figure 14.9 Segregation of alleles and fertilization as chance events.** When a heterozygote (Rr) forms gametes, whether a particular gamete ends up with an R or an r is like the toss of a coin. We can determine the probability for any genotype among the offspring of two heterozygotes by multiplying together the individual probabilities of an egg and sperm having a particular allele (R or r in this example).

is $\frac{1}{4}$. The probability for the other possible way—the recessive allele from the egg and the dominant allele from the sperm—is also $\frac{1}{4}$ (see Figure 14.9). Using the rule of addition, then, we can calculate the probability of an F_2 heterozygote as $\frac{1}{4} + \frac{1}{4} = \frac{1}{2}$.

Solving Complex Genetics Problems with the Rules of Probability

We can also apply the rules of probability to predict the outcome of crosses involving multiple characters. Recall that each allelic pair segregates independently during gamete formation (the law of independent assortment). Thus, a dihybrid or other multicharacter cross is equivalent to two or more independent monohybrid crosses occurring simultaneously. By applying what we have learned about monohybrid crosses, we can determine the probability of specific genotypes occurring in the F_2 generation without having to construct unwieldy Punnett squares.

Consider the dihybrid cross between $YyRr$ heterozygotes shown in Figure 14.8. We will focus first on the seed-color character. For a monohybrid cross of Yy plants, we can use a simple Punnett square to determine that the probabilities of the offspring genotypes are $\frac{1}{4}$ for YY, $\frac{1}{2}$ for Yy, and $\frac{1}{4}$ for yy. We can draw a second Punnett square to determine that the same probabilities apply to the offspring genotypes for seed shape: $\frac{1}{4}$ RR, $\frac{1}{2}$ Rr, and $\frac{1}{4}$ rr. Knowing these probabilities, we can simply use the multiplication rule to determine the probability of each of the genotypes in the F_2 generation. To give two examples, the calculations for finding the probabilities of two of the possible F_2 genotypes ($YYRR$ and $YyRR$) are shown below:

Probability of $YYRR$ = $\frac{1}{4}$(probability of YY) $\times$ $\frac{1}{4}$ (RR) = $\frac{1}{16}$

Probability of $YyRR$ = $\frac{1}{2}$(Yy) $\quad\quad\quad\quad$ $\times \frac{1}{4}$ (RR) = $\frac{1}{8}$

The $YYRR$ genotype corresponds to the upper left box in the larger Punnett square in Figure 14.8 (one box = $\frac{1}{16}$). Looking closely at the larger Punnett square in Figure 14.8, you will see that 2 of the 16 boxes ($\frac{1}{8}$) correspond to the $YyRR$ genotype.

Now let's see how we can combine the multiplication and addition rules to solve even more complex problems in Mendelian genetics. Imagine a cross of two pea varieties in which we track the inheritance of three characters. Let's cross a trihybrid with purple flowers and yellow, round seeds (heterozygous for all three genes) with a plant with purple flowers and green, wrinkled seeds (heterozygous for flower color but homozygous recessive for the other two characters). Using Mendelian symbols, our cross is $PpYyRr \times Ppyyrr$. What fraction of offspring from this cross are predicted to exhibit the recessive phenotypes for *at least two* of the three characters?

To answer this question, we can start by listing all genotypes we could get that fulfill this condition: $ppyyRr$, $ppYyrr$, $Ppyyrr$, $PPyyrr$, and $ppyyrr$. (Because the condition is *at least two* recessive traits, it includes the last genotype, which shows all three recessive traits.) Next, we calculate the probability for each of these genotypes resulting from our $PpYyRr \times Ppyyrr$ cross by multiplying together the individual probabilities for the allele pairs, just as we did in our dihybrid example. Note that in a cross involving heterozygous and homozygous allele pairs (for example, $Yy \times yy$), the probability of heterozygous offspring is $\frac{1}{2}$ and the probability of homozygous offspring is $\frac{1}{2}$. Finally, we use the addition rule to add the probabilities for all the different genotypes that fulfill the condition of at least two recessive traits, as shown below:

$ppyyRr$	$\frac{1}{4}$ (probability of pp) $\times \frac{1}{2}$ (yy) $\times \frac{1}{2}$(Rr) =	$\frac{1}{16}$
$ppYyrr$	$\frac{1}{4} \times \frac{1}{2} \times \frac{1}{2}$ =	$\frac{1}{16}$
$Ppyyrr$	$\frac{1}{2} \times \frac{1}{2} \times \frac{1}{2}$ =	$\frac{2}{16}$
$PPyyrr$	$\frac{1}{4} \times \frac{1}{2} \times \frac{1}{2}$ =	$\frac{1}{16}$
$ppyyrr$	$\frac{1}{4} \times \frac{1}{2} \times \frac{1}{2}$ =	$\frac{1}{16}$
Chance of *at least two* recessive traits		= $\frac{6}{16}$ or $\frac{3}{8}$

In time, you'll be able to solve genetics problems faster by using the rules of probability than by filling in Punnett squares.

We cannot predict with certainty the exact numbers of progeny of different genotypes resulting from a genetic cross. But the rules of probability give us the *chance* of various outcomes. Usually, the larger the sample size, the closer the results will conform to our predictions. Mendel understood this statistical feature of inheritance and had a keen sense of the rules of chance. It was for this reason that he set up his experiments so as to generate, and then count, large numbers of offspring from his crosses.

CONCEPT CHECK 14.2

1. For any gene with a dominant allele A and recessive allele a, what proportions of the offspring from an $AA \times Aa$ cross are expected to be homozygous dominant, homozygous recessive, and heterozygous?

2. Two organisms, with genotypes $BbDD$ and $BBDd$, are mated. Assuming independent assortment of the B/b and D/d genes, write the genotypes of all possible offspring from this cross and use the rules of probability to calculate the chance of each genotype occurring.

3. **WHAT IF?** Three characters (flower color, seed color, and pod shape) are considered in a cross between two pea plants: $PpYyIi \times ppYyii$. What fraction of offspring are predicted to be homozygous recessive for at least two of the three characters?

For suggested answers, see Appendix A.

CONCEPT 14.3

Inheritance patterns are often more complex than predicted by simple Mendelian genetics

In the 20th century, geneticists extended Mendelian principles not only to diverse organisms, but also to patterns of inheritance more complex than those described by Mendel. For the work that led to his two laws of inheritance, Mendel chose pea plant characters that turn out to have a relatively simple genetic basis: Each character is determined by one gene, for which there are only two alleles, one completely dominant and the other completely recessive. (There is one exception: Mendel's pod-shape character is actually determined by two genes.) Not all heritable characters are determined so simply, and the relationship between genotype and phenotype is rarely so straightforward. Mendel himself realized that he could not explain the more complicated patterns he observed in crosses involving other pea characters or other plant species. This does not diminish the utility of Mendelian genetics, however, because the basic principles of segregation and independent assortment apply even to more complex patterns of inheritance. In this section, we will extend Mendelian genetics to hereditary patterns that were not reported by Mendel.

Extending Mendelian Genetics for a Single Gene

The inheritance of characters determined by a single gene deviates from simple Mendelian patterns when alleles are not completely dominant or recessive, when a particular gene has more than two alleles, or when a single gene produces multiple phenotypes. We will describe examples of each of these situations in this section.

Degrees of Dominance

Alleles can show different degrees of dominance and recessiveness in relation to each other. In Mendel's classic pea crosses, the F_1 offspring always looked like one of the two parental varieties because one allele in a pair showed **complete dominance** over the other. In such situations, the phenotypes of the heterozygote and the dominant homozygote are indistinguishable.

For some genes, however, neither allele is completely dominant, and the F_1 hybrids have a phenotype somewhere between those of the two parental varieties. This phenomenon, called **incomplete dominance**, is seen when red snapdragons are crossed with white snapdragons: All the F_1 hybrids have pink flowers **(Figure 14.10)**. This third, intermediate phenotype results from flowers of the heterozygotes having less red pigment than the red homozygotes. (This is unlike the case of Mendel's pea plants, where the *Pp* heterozygotes make enough pigment for the flowers to be purple, indistinguishable from those of *PP* plants.)

At first glance, incomplete dominance of either allele seems to provide evidence for the blending hypothesis of inheritance, which would predict that the red or white trait could never reappear among offspring from the pink hybrids. In fact, interbreeding F_1 hybrids produces F_2 offspring with a phenotypic ratio of one red to two pink to one white. (Because heterozygotes have a separate phenotype, the genotypic and phenotypic ratios for the F_2 generation are the same, 1:2:1.) The segregation of the red-flower and white-flower alleles in the gametes produced by the pink-flowered plants confirms that the alleles for flower color are heritable factors that maintain their identity in the hybrids; that is, inheritance is particulate.

Another variation on dominance relationships between alleles is called **codominance**; in this variation, the two alleles each affect the phenotype in separate, distinguishable ways. For example, the human MN blood group is determined by codominant alleles for two specific molecules located on the surface of red blood cells, the M and N molecules. A single gene locus, at which two allelic variations are possible, determines the phenotype of this blood group. Individuals homozygous for the *M* allele (*MM*) have red blood cells with only M molecules; individuals homozygous for the *N* allele (*NN*) have red blood cells with only N

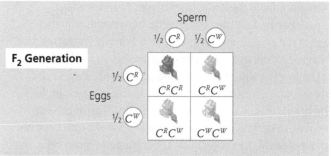

▲ **Figure 14.10 Incomplete dominance in snapdragon color.** When red snapdragons are crossed with white ones, the F_1 hybrids have pink flowers. Segregation of alleles into gametes of the F_1 plants results in an F_2 generation with a 1:2:1 ratio for both genotype and phenotype. Neither allele is dominant, so rather than using upper- and lowercase letters, we use the letter C with a superscript to indicate an allele for flower color: C^R for red and C^W for white.

? *Suppose a classmate argues that this figure supports the blending hypothesis for inheritance. What might your classmate say, and how would you respond?*

molecules. But *both* M and N molecules are present on the red blood cells of individuals heterozygous for the *M* and *N* alleles (*MN*). Note that the MN phenotype is *not* intermediate between the M and N phenotypes, which distinguishes codominance from incomplete dominance. Rather, *both* M and N phenotypes are exhibited by heterozygotes, since both molecules are present.

The Relationship Between Dominance and Phenotype We've now seen that the relative effects of two alleles range from complete dominance of one allele, through incomplete dominance of either allele, to codominance of both alleles. It is important to understand that an allele is called *dominant* because it is seen in the phenotype, not because it somehow subdues a recessive allele. Alleles are simply variations in a gene's nucleotide sequence (see Figure 14.4). When a dominant allele coexists with a recessive allele in a heterozygote, they do not actually interact at all. It is in the pathway from genotype to phenotype that dominance and recessiveness come into play.

To illustrate the relationship between dominance and phenotype, we can use one of the characters Mendel studied—round versus wrinkled pea seed shape. The dominant allele (round) codes for an enzyme that helps convert an unbranched form of starch to a branched form in the seed. The recessive allele (wrinkled) codes for a defective form of this enzyme, leading to an accumulation of unbranched starch, which causes excess water to enter the seed by osmosis. Later, when the seed dries, it wrinkles. If a dominant allele is present, no excess water enters the seed and it does not wrinkle when it dries. One dominant allele results in enough of the enzyme to synthesize adequate amounts of branched starch, which means that dominant homozygotes and heterozygotes have the same phenotype: round seeds.

A closer look at the relationship between dominance and phenotype reveals an intriguing fact: For any character, the observed dominant/recessive relationship of alleles depends on the level at which we examine phenotype. **Tay-Sachs disease**, an inherited disorder in humans, is an example. The brain cells of a child with Tay-Sachs disease cannot metabolize certain lipids because a crucial enzyme does not work properly. As these lipids accumulate in brain cells, the child begins to suffer seizures, blindness, and degeneration of motor and mental performance and dies within a few years.

Only children who inherit two copies of the Tay-Sachs allele (homozygotes) have the disease. Thus, at the *organismal* level, the Tay-Sachs allele qualifies as recessive. However, the activity level of the lipid-metabolizing enzyme in heterozygotes is intermediate between that in individuals homozygous for the normal allele and that in individuals with Tay-Sachs disease. The intermediate phenotype observed at the *biochemical* level is characteristic of incomplete dominance of either allele. Fortunately, the heterozygote condition does not lead to disease symptoms, apparently because half the normal enzyme activity is sufficient to prevent lipid accumulation in the brain. Extending our analysis to yet another level, we find that heterozygous individuals produce equal numbers of normal and dysfunctional enzyme molecules. Thus, at the *molecular* level, the normal allele and the Tay-Sachs allele are codominant. As you can see, whether alleles appear to be completely dominant, incompletely dominant, or codominant depends on the level at which the phenotype is analyzed.

Frequency of Dominant Alleles Although you might assume that the dominant allele for a particular character would be more common than the recessive allele, this is not a given. For example, about one baby out of 400 in the United States is born with extra fingers or toes, a condition known as polydactyly. Some cases are caused by the presence of a dominant allele. The low frequency of polydactyly indicates that the recessive allele, which results in five digits per appendage, is far more prevalent than the dominant allele in the population. In Chapter 23, you will learn how relative frequencies of alleles in a population are affected by natural selection.

Multiple Alleles

Only two alleles exist for the pea characters that Mendel studied, but most genes exist in more than two allelic forms. The ABO blood groups in humans, for instance, are determined by three alleles of a single gene: I^A, I^B, and i. A person's blood group may be one of four types: A, B, AB, or O. These letters refer to two carbohydrates—A and B—that may be found on the surface of red blood cells. A person's blood cells may have carbohydrate A (type A blood), carbohydrate B (type B), both (type AB), or neither (type O), as shown in **Figure 14.11**. Matching compatible blood groups is critical for safe blood transfusions (see Chapter 43).

Pleiotropy

So far, we have treated Mendelian inheritance as though each gene affects only one phenotypic character. Most genes, however, have multiple phenotypic effects, a property called **pleiotropy** (from the Greek *pleion*, more). In humans, for example, pleiotropic alleles are responsible for the multiple symptoms associated with certain hereditary diseases, such as cystic fibrosis and sickle-cell disease, discussed later

(a) The three alleles for the ABO blood groups and their carbohydrates. Each allele codes for an enzyme that may add a specific carbohydrate (designated by the superscript on the allele and shown as a triangle or circle) to red blood cells.

Allele	I^A	I^B	i
Carbohydrate	A △	B ○	none

(b) Blood group genotypes and phenotypes. There are six possible genotypes, resulting in four different phenotypes.

Genotype	$I^A I^A$ or $I^A i$	$I^B I^B$ or $I^B i$	$I^A I^B$	ii
Red blood cell appearance				
Phenotype (blood group)	A	B	AB	O

▲ **Figure 14.11 Multiple alleles for the ABO blood groups.** The four blood groups result from different combinations of three alleles.

? *Based on the surface carbohydrate phenotype in (b), what are the dominance relationships among the alleles?*

in this chapter. In the garden pea, the gene that determines flower color also affects the color of the coating on the outer surface of the seed, which can be gray or white. Given the intricate molecular and cellular interactions responsible for an organism's development and physiology, it isn't surprising that a single gene can affect a number of characteristics.

Extending Mendelian Genetics for Two or More Genes

Dominance relationships, multiple alleles, and pleiotropy all have to do with the effects of the alleles of a single gene. We now consider two situations in which two or more genes are involved in determining a particular phenotype: epistasis, where one gene affects the phenotype of another because the two gene products interact; and polygenic inheritance, where multiple genes independently affect a single trait.

Epistasis

In **epistasis** (from the Greek for "standing upon"), the phenotypic expression of a gene at one locus alters that of a gene at a second locus. An example will help clarify this concept. In Labrador retrievers (commonly called "Labs"), black coat color is dominant to brown. Let's designate B and b as the two alleles for this character. For a Lab to have brown fur, its genotype must be bb; these dogs are called chocolate Labs. But there is more to the story. A second gene determines whether or not pigment will be deposited in the hair. The dominant allele, symbolized by E, results in the deposition of either black or brown pigment, depending on the genotype at the first locus. But if the Lab is homozygous recessive for the second locus (ee), then the coat is yellow, regardless of the genotype at the black/brown locus (so-called golden Labs). In this case, the gene for pigment deposition (E/e) is said to be epistatic to the gene that codes for black or brown pigment (B/b).

What happens if we mate black Labs that are heterozygous for both genes ($BbEe$)? Although the two genes affect the same phenotypic character (coat color), they follow the law of independent assortment. Thus, our breeding experiment represents an F_1 dihybrid cross, like those that produced a 9:3:3:1 ratio in Mendel's experiments. We can use a Punnett square to represent the genotypes of the F_2 offspring (**Figure 14.12**). As a result of epistasis, the phenotypic ratio among the F_2 offspring is 9 black to 3 chocolate to 4 golden Labs. Other types of epistatic interactions produce different ratios, but all are modified versions of 9:3:3:1.

Polygenic Inheritance

Mendel studied characters that could be classified on an either-or basis, such as purple versus white flower color. But many characters, such as human skin color and height, are not one of two discrete characters, but instead vary in the

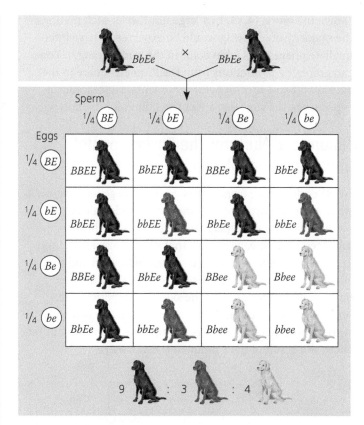

▲ **Figure 14.12 An example of epistasis.** This Punnett square illustrates the genotypes and phenotypes predicted for offspring of matings between two black Labrador retrievers of genotype $BbEe$. The E/e gene, which is epistatic to the B/b gene coding for hair pigment, controls whether or not pigment of any color will be deposited in the hair.

? *Explain the genetic basis for the difference between the ratio (9:3:4) of phenotypes seen in this cross and that seen in Figure 14.8.*

population in gradations along a continuum. These are called **quantitative characters**. Quantitative variation usually indicates **polygenic inheritance**, an additive effect of two or more genes on a single phenotypic character. (In a way, this is the converse of pleiotropy, where a single gene affects several phenotypic characters.) Height is a good example of polygenic inheritance: A recent study using genomic methods identified at least 180 genes that affect height.

Skin pigmentation in humans is also controlled by many separately inherited genes. Here, we'll simplify the story in order to understand the concept of polygenic inheritance. Let's consider three genes, with a dark-skin allele for each gene (A, B, or C) contributing one "unit" of darkness (also a simplification) to the phenotype and being incompletely dominant to the other allele (a, b, or c). In our model, an $AABBCC$ person would be very dark, while an $aabbcc$ individual would be very light. An $AaBbCc$ person would have skin of an intermediate shade. Because the alleles have a cumulative effect, the genotypes $AaBbCc$ and $AABbcc$ would make the same genetic contribution (three units) to skin darkness. There are seven skin-color phenotypes that could result from a mating between $AaBbCc$ heterozygotes, as shown in **Figure 14.13**. In a large number of such matings, the majority of offspring would be expected to have intermediate phenotypes (skin color in the middle range). You can graph the predictions from the Punnett square in the **Scientific Skills Exercise**. Environmental factors, such as exposure to the sun, also affect the skin-color phenotype.

Nature and Nurture: The Environmental Impact on Phenotype

Another departure from simple Mendelian genetics arises when the phenotype for a character depends on environment as well as genotype. A single tree, locked into its inherited genotype, has leaves that vary in size, shape, and greenness, depending on their exposure to wind and sun. For humans, nutrition influences height, exercise alters build, sun-tanning darkens the skin, and experience improves performance on intelligence tests. Even identical twins, who are genetic equals, accumulate phenotypic differences as a result of their unique experiences.

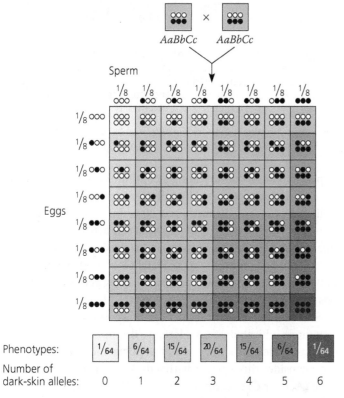

Phenotypes: $\frac{1}{64}$ $\frac{6}{64}$ $\frac{15}{64}$ $\frac{20}{64}$ $\frac{15}{64}$ $\frac{6}{64}$ $\frac{1}{64}$

Number of dark-skin alleles: 0 1 2 3 4 5 6

▲ **Figure 14.13 A simplified model for polygenic inheritance of skin color.** In this model, three separately inherited genes affect skin color. The heterozygous individuals (*AaBbCc*) represented by the two rectangles at the top of this figure each carry three dark-skin alleles (black circles, which represent *A*, *B*, or *C*) and three light-skin alleles (white circles, which represent *a*, *b*, or *c*). The Punnett square shows all the possible genetic combinations in gametes and offspring of many hypothetical matings between these heterozygotes. The results are summarized by the phenotypic frequencies (fractions) under the Punnett square. (The phenotypic ratio of the skin colors shown in the boxes is 1:6:15:20:15:6:1.)

▲ **Figure 14.14 The effect of environment on phenotype.** The outcome of a genotype lies within a phenotypic range that depends on the environment in which the genotype is expressed. For example, the acidity and free aluminum content of the soil affect the color range of hydrangea flowers of the same genetic variety. The color ranges from pink (basic soil) to blue-violet (acidic soil), and free aluminum is necessary for bluer colors.

Whether human characteristics are more influenced by genes or the environment—in everyday terms, nature versus nurture—is a debate that we will not attempt to settle here. We can say, however, that a genotype generally is not associated with a rigidly defined phenotype, but rather with a range of phenotypic possibilities due to environmental influences (**Figure 14.14**). For some characters, such as the ABO blood group system, the phenotypic range has no breadth whatsoever; that is, a given genotype mandates a very specific phenotype. Other characteristics, such as a person's blood count of red and white cells, vary quite a bit, depending on such factors as the altitude, the customary level of physical activity, and the presence of infectious agents.

Generally, the phenotypic range is broadest for polygenic characters. Environment contributes to the quantitative nature of these characters, as we have seen in the continuous variation of skin color. Geneticists refer to such characters as **multifactorial**, meaning that many factors, both genetic and environmental, collectively influence phenotype.

A Mendelian View of Heredity and Variation

We have now broadened our view of Mendelian inheritance by exploring degrees of dominance as well as multiple alleles, pleiotropy, epistasis, polygenic inheritance, and the phenotypic impact of the environment. How can we integrate these refinements into a comprehensive theory of Mendelian genetics? The key is to make the transition from the reductionist emphasis on single genes and phenotypic characters to the emergent properties of the organism as a whole, one of the themes of this book.

The term *phenotype* can refer not only to specific characters, such as flower color and blood group, but also to an organism in its entirety—*all* aspects of its physical appearance, internal anatomy, physiology, and behavior. Similarly, the term *genotype* can refer to an organism's entire genetic makeup, not just its alleles for a single genetic locus. In most

Making a Histogram and Analyzing a Distribution Pattern

What Is the Distribution of Phenotypes Among Offspring of Two Parents Who Are Both Heterozygous for Three Additive Genes?
Human skin color is a polygenic trait that is determined by the additive effects of many different genes. In this exercise, you will work with a simplified model of skin-color genetics where only three genes are assumed to affect the darkness of skin color and where each gene has two alleles—dark or light (see Figure 14.13). In this model, each dark allele contributes equally to the darkness of skin color, and each pair of alleles segregates independently of each other pair. Using a type of graph called a histogram, you will determine the distribution of phenotypes of offspring with different numbers of dark-skin alleles. (For additional information about graphs, see the Scientific Skills Review in Appendix F and in the Study Area in MasteringBiology.)

How This Model Is Analyzed To predict the phenotypes of the offspring of parents heterozygous for the three genes in our simplified model, we can use the Punnett square in Figure 14.13. The heterozygous individuals (*AaBbCc*) represented by the two rectangles at the top of this figure each carry three dark-skin alleles (black circles, which represent *A*, *B*, or *C*) and three light-skin alleles (white circles, which represent *a*, *b*, or *c*). The Punnett square shows all the possible genetic combinations in gametes and in offspring of a large number of hypothetical matings between these heterozygotes.

Predictions from the Punnett Square If we assume that each square in the Punnett square represents one offspring of the heterozygous *AaBbCc* parents, then the squares below show the frequencies of all seven possible phenotypes of offspring, with each phenotype having a specific number of dark-skin alleles.

Phenotypes:	$1/64$	$6/64$	$15/64$	$20/64$	$15/64$	$6/64$	$1/64$
Number of dark-skin alleles:	0	1	2	3	4	5	6

Interpret the Data
1. A histogram is a bar graph that shows the distribution of numeric data (here, the number of dark-skin alleles). To make a histogram of

the allele distribution, put skin color (as the number of dark-skin alleles) along the *x*-axis and number of offspring (out of 64) with each phenotype on the *y*-axis. There are no gaps in our allele data, so draw the bars next to each other with no space in between.

2. You can see that the skin-color phenotypes are not distributed uniformly. (a) Which phenotype has the highest frequency? Draw a vertical dashed line through that bar. (b) Distributions of values like this one tend to show one of several common patterns. Sketch a rough curve that approximates the values and look at its shape. Is it symmetrically distributed around a central peak value (a "normal distribution," sometimes called a bell curve); is it skewed to one end of the *x*-axis or the other (a "skewed distribution"); or does it show two apparent groups of frequencies (a "bimodal distribution")? Explain the reason for the curve's shape. (It will help to read the text description that supports Figure 14.13.)

3. If one of the three genes were lethal when homozygous recessive, what would happen to the distribution of phenotype frequencies? To determine this, use *bb* as an example of a lethal genotype. Using Figure 14.13, identify offspring where the center circle (the *B/b* gene) in both the top and bottom rows of the square is white, representing the homozygous state *bb*. Because *bb* individuals would not survive, cross out those squares, then count the phenotype frequencies of the surviving offspring according to the number of dark-skin alleles (0–6) and graph the new data. What happens to the shape of the curve compared with the curve in question 2? What does this indicate about the distribution of phenotype frequencies?

(MB) A version of this Scientific Skills Exercise can be assigned in MasteringBiology.

Further Reading R. A. Sturm, A golden age of human pigmentation genetics, *Trends in Genetics* 22:464–468 (2006).

---

cases, a gene's impact on phenotype is affected by other genes and by the environment. In this integrated view of heredity and variation, an organism's phenotype reflects its overall genotype and unique environmental history.

Considering all that can occur in the pathway from genotype to phenotype, it is indeed impressive that Mendel could uncover the fundamental principles governing the transmission of individual genes from parents to offspring. Mendel's two laws, of segregation and of independent assortment, explain heritable variations in terms of alternative forms of genes (hereditary "particles," now known as the alleles of genes) that are passed along, generation after generation, according to simple rules of probability. This theory of inheritance is equally valid for peas, flies, fishes, birds, and human beings—indeed, for any organism with a sexual life cycle. Furthermore, by extending the principles of segregation and independent assortment to help explain such hereditary patterns as epistasis and quantitative characters, we begin to see how broadly Mendelian genetics applies. From Mendel's

abbey garden came a theory of particulate inheritance that anchors modern genetics. In the last section of this chapter, we will apply Mendelian genetics to human inheritance, with emphasis on the transmission of hereditary diseases.

CONCEPT CHECK 14.3

1. *Incomplete dominance* and *epistasis* are both terms that define genetic relationships. What is the most basic distinction between these terms?

2. If a man with type AB blood marries a woman with type O, what blood types would you expect in their children? What fraction would you expect of each type?

3. **WHAT IF?** A rooster with gray feathers and a hen of the same phenotype produce 15 gray, 6 black, and 8 white chicks. What is the simplest explanation for the inheritance of these colors in chickens? What phenotypes would you expect in the offspring of a cross between a gray rooster and a black hen?

For suggested answers, see Appendix A.

CONCEPT 14.4

Many human traits follow Mendelian patterns of inheritance

Peas are convenient subjects for genetic research, but humans are not. The human generation span is long—about 20 years—and human parents produce many fewer offspring than peas and most other species. Even more important, it wouldn't be ethical to ask pairs of humans to breed so that the phenotypes of their offspring could be analyzed! In spite of these constraints, the study of human genetics continues, spurred on by our desire to understand our own inheritance. New molecular biological techniques have led to many breakthrough discoveries, as we will see in Chapter 20, but basic Mendelian genetics endures as the foundation of human genetics.

Pedigree Analysis

Unable to manipulate the mating patterns of people, geneticists instead analyze the results of matings that have already occurred. They do so by collecting information about a family's history for a particular trait and assembling this information into a family tree describing the traits of parents and children across the generations—the family **pedigree**.

Figure 14.15a shows a three-generation pedigree that traces the occurrence of a pointed contour of the hairline on the forehead. This trait, called a widow's peak, is due to a dominant allele, *W*. Because the widow's-peak allele is dominant, all individuals who lack a widow's peak must be homozygous recessive (*ww*). The two grandparents with widow's peaks must have the *Ww* genotype, since some of their offspring are homozygous recessive. The offspring in the second generation who *do* have widow's peaks must also be heterozygous, because they are the products of *Ww* × *ww* matings. The third generation in this pedigree consists of two sisters. The one who has a widow's peak could be either homozygous (*WW*) or heterozygous (*Ww*), given what we know about the genotypes of her parents (both *Ww*).

Figure 14.15b is a pedigree of the same family, but this time we focus on a recessive trait, attached earlobes. We'll use *f* for the recessive allele and *F* for the dominant allele, which results in free earlobes. As you work your way through the pedigree, notice once again that you can apply what you have learned about Mendelian inheritance to understand the genotypes shown for the family members.

An important application of a pedigree is to help us calculate the probability that a future child will have a particular genotype and phenotype. Suppose that the couple represented in the second generation of Figure 14.15 decides to have one more child. What is the probability that the child will have a widow's peak? This is equivalent to a

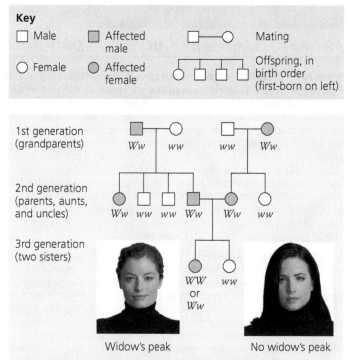

(a) Is a widow's peak a dominant or recessive trait?
Tips for pedigree analysis: Notice in the third generation that the second-born daughter lacks a widow's peak, although both of her parents had the trait. Such a pattern of inheritance supports the hypothesis that the trait is due to a dominant allele. If the trait were due to a *recessive* allele, and both parents had the recessive phenotype, then *all* of their offspring would also have the recessive phenotype.

(b) Is an attached earlobe a dominant or recessive trait?
Tips for pedigree analysis: Notice that the first-born daughter in the third generation has attached earlobes, although both of her parents lack that trait (they have free earlobes). Such a pattern is easily explained if the attached-lobe phenotype is due to a recessive allele. If it were due to a *dominant* allele, then at least one parent would also have had the trait.

▲ **Figure 14.15 Pedigree analysis.** Each of these pedigrees traces a trait through three generations of the same family. The two traits have different inheritance patterns, as shown by the pedigrees.

Mendelian F_1 monohybrid cross ($Ww \times Ww$), and thus the probability that a child will inherit a dominant allele and have a widow's peak is ¾ (¼ WW + ½ Ww). What is the probability that the child will have attached earlobes? Again, we can treat this as a monohybrid cross ($Ff \times Ff$), but this time we want to know the chance that the offspring will be homozygous recessive (ff). That probability is ¼. Finally, what is the chance that the child will have a widow's peak *and* attached earlobes? Assuming that the genes for these two characters are on different chromosomes, the two pairs of alleles will assort independently in this dihybrid cross ($WwFf \times WwFf$). Thus, we can use the multiplication rule: ¾ (chance of widow's peak) × ¼ (chance of attached earlobes) = ³⁄₁₆ (chance of widow's peak and attached earlobes).

Pedigrees are a more serious matter when the alleles in question cause disabling or deadly diseases instead of innocuous human variations such as hairline or earlobe configuration. However, for disorders inherited as simple Mendelian traits, the same techniques of pedigree analysis apply.

Recessively Inherited Disorders

Thousands of genetic disorders are known to be inherited as simple recessive traits. These disorders range in severity from relatively mild, such as albinism (lack of pigmentation, which results in susceptibility to skin cancers and vision problems), to life-threatening, such as cystic fibrosis.

The Behavior of Recessive Alleles

How can we account for the behavior of alleles that cause recessively inherited disorders? Recall that genes code for proteins of specific function. An allele that causes a genetic disorder (let's call it allele *a*) codes for either a malfunctioning protein or no protein at all. In the case of disorders classified as recessive, heterozygotes (Aa) are typically normal in phenotype because one copy of the normal allele (A) produces a sufficient amount of the specific protein. Thus, a recessively inherited disorder shows up only in the homozygous individuals (aa) who inherit one recessive allele from each parent. Although phenotypically normal with regard to the disorder, heterozygotes may transmit the recessive allele to their offspring and thus are called **carriers**. **Figure 14.16** illustrates these ideas using albinism as an example.

Most people who have recessive disorders are born to parents who are carriers of the disorder but have a normal phenotype, as is the case shown in the Punnett square in Figure 14.16. A mating between two carriers corresponds to a Mendelian F_1 monohybrid cross, so the predicted genotypic ratio for the offspring is 1 AA : 2 Aa : 1 aa. Thus, each child has a ¼ chance of inheriting a double dose of the recessive allele; in the case of albinism, such a child will be albino. From the genotypic ratio, we also can see that out of three offspring with the *normal* phenotype (one AA plus

▲ **Figure 14.16 Albinism: a recessive trait.** One of the two sisters shown here has normal coloration; the other is albino. Most recessive homozygotes are born to parents who are carriers of the disorder but themselves have a normal phenotype, the case shown in the Punnett square.

? *What is the probability that the sister with normal coloration is a carrier of the albinism allele?*

two Aa), two are predicted to be heterozygous carriers, a ²⁄₃ chance. Recessive homozygotes could also result from $Aa \times aa$ and $aa \times aa$ matings, but if the disorder is lethal before reproductive age or results in sterility (neither of which is true for albinism), no aa individuals will reproduce. Even if recessive homozygotes are able to reproduce, this will occur relatively rarely, since such individuals account for a much smaller percentage of the population than heterozygous carriers (for reasons we'll examine in Chapter 23).

In general, genetic disorders are not evenly distributed among all groups of people. For example, the incidence of Tay-Sachs disease, which we described earlier in this chapter, is disproportionately high among Ashkenazic Jews, Jewish people whose ancestors lived in central Europe. In that population, Tay-Sachs disease occurs in one out of 3,600 births, an incidence about 100 times greater than that among non-Jews or Mediterranean (Sephardic) Jews. This uneven distribution results from the different genetic histories of the world's peoples during less technological times, when populations were more geographically (and hence genetically) isolated.

When a disease-causing recessive allele is rare, it is relatively unlikely that two carriers of the same harmful allele will meet and mate. The probability of passing on recessive traits increases greatly, however, if the man and woman are close relatives (for example, siblings or first cousins). This is because people with recent common ancestors are more likely to carry the same recessive alleles than are unrelated people. Thus, these consanguineous ("same blood") matings, indicated in pedigrees by double lines, are more likely to produce offspring homozygous for recessive traits— including harmful ones. Such effects can be observed in many types of domesticated and zoo animals that have become inbred.

There is debate among geneticists about the extent to which human consanguinity increases the risk of inherited diseases. Many deleterious alleles have such severe effects that a homozygous embryo spontaneously aborts long before birth. Still, most societies and cultures have laws or taboos forbidding marriages between close relatives. These rules may have evolved out of empirical observation that in most populations, stillbirths and birth defects are more common when parents are closely related. Social and economic factors have also influenced the development of customs and laws against consanguineous marriages.

Cystic Fibrosis

The most common lethal genetic disease in the United States is **cystic fibrosis**, which strikes one out of every 2,500 people of European descent but is much rarer in other groups. Among people of European descent, one out of 25 (4%) are carriers of the cystic fibrosis allele. The normal allele for this gene codes for a membrane protein that functions in the transport of chloride ions between certain cells and the extracellular fluid. These chloride transport channels are defective or absent in the plasma membranes of children who inherit two recessive alleles for cystic fibrosis. The result is an abnormally high concentration of extracellular chloride, which causes the mucus that coats certain cells to become thicker and stickier than normal. The mucus builds up in the pancreas, lungs, digestive tract, and other organs, leading to multiple (pleiotropic) effects, including poor absorption of nutrients from the intestines, chronic bronchitis, and recurrent bacterial infections.

Untreated, cystic fibrosis can cause death by the age of 5. Daily doses of antibiotics to stop infection, gentle pounding on the chest to clear mucus from clogged airways, and other therapies can prolong life. In the United States, more than half of those with cystic fibrosis now survive into their 30s and beyond.

Sickle-Cell Disease: A Genetic Disorder with Evolutionary Implications

EVOLUTION The most common inherited disorder among people of African descent is **sickle-cell disease**, which affects one out of 400 African-Americans. Sickle-cell disease is caused by the substitution of a single amino acid in the hemoglobin protein of red blood cells; in homozygous individuals, all hemoglobin is of the sickle-cell (abnormal) variety. When the oxygen content of an affected individual's blood is low (at high altitudes or under physical stress, for instance), the sickle-cell hemoglobin proteins aggregate into long fibers that deform the red cells into a sickle shape (see Figure 5.19). Sickled cells may clump and clog small blood vessels, often leading to other symptoms throughout the body, including physical weakness, pain, organ damage, and even paralysis. Regular blood transfusions can ward off brain damage in children with sickle-cell disease, and new drugs can help prevent or treat other problems, but there is currently no widely available cure.

Although two sickle-cell alleles are necessary for an individual to manifest full-blown sickle-cell disease, the presence of one sickle-cell allele can affect the phenotype. Thus, at the organismal level, the normal allele is incompletely dominant to the sickle-cell allele (Figure 14.17). At the molecular level, the two alleles are codominant; both normal and abnormal (sickle-cell) hemoglobins are made in heterozygotes (carriers), who are said to have *sickle-cell trait*. Heterozygotes are usually healthy but may suffer some symptoms during long periods of reduced blood oxygen.

About one out of ten African-Americans have sickle-cell trait, an unusually high frequency of heterozygotes for an allele with severe detrimental effects in homozygotes. Why haven't evolutionary processes resulted in the disappearance of this allele among this population? One explanation is that having a single copy of the sickle-cell allele reduces the frequency and severity of malaria attacks, especially among young children. The malaria parasite spends part of its life cycle in red blood cells (see Figure 28.16), and the presence of even heterozygous amounts of sickle-cell hemoglobin results in lower parasite densities and hence reduced malaria symptoms. Thus, in tropical Africa, where infection with the

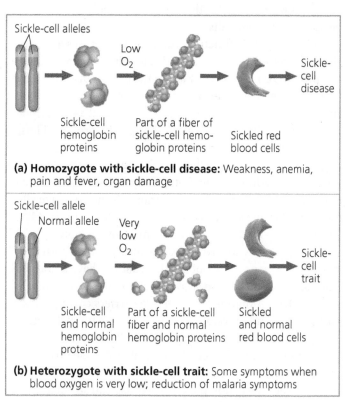

Sickle-cell alleles

Sickle-cell hemoglobin proteins → Low O₂ → Part of a fiber of sickle-cell hemoglobin proteins → Sickled red blood cells → Sickle-cell disease

(a) Homozygote with sickle-cell disease: Weakness, anemia, pain and fever, organ damage

Sickle-cell allele
Normal allele

Sickle-cell and normal hemoglobin proteins → Very low O₂ → Part of a sickle-cell fiber and normal hemoglobin proteins → Sickled and normal red blood cells → Sickle-cell trait

(b) Heterozygote with sickle-cell trait: Some symptoms when blood oxygen is very low; reduction of malaria symptoms

▲ Figure 14.17 Sickle-cell disease and sickle-cell trait.

malaria parasite is common, the sickle-cell allele confers an advantage to heterozygotes even though it is harmful in the homozygous state. (The balance between these two effects will be discussed in Chapter 23; see Figure 23.17.) The relatively high frequency of African-Americans with sickle-cell trait is a vestige of their African roots.

Dominantly Inherited Disorders

Although many harmful alleles are recessive, a number of human disorders are due to dominant alleles. One example is *achondroplasia*, a form of dwarfism that occurs in one of every 25,000 people. Heterozygous individuals have the dwarf phenotype (Figure 14.18). Therefore, all people who are not achondroplastic dwarfs—99.99% of the population—are homozygous for the recessive allele. Like the presence of extra fingers or toes mentioned earlier, achondroplasia is a trait for which the recessive allele is much more prevalent than the corresponding dominant allele.

Dominant alleles that cause a lethal disease are much less common than recessive alleles that have lethal effects. All lethal alleles arise by mutations (changes to the DNA) in cells that produce sperm or eggs; presumably, such mutations are equally likely to be recessive or dominant. A lethal recessive allele can be passed from one generation to the next by heterozygous carriers because the carriers themselves have normal phenotypes. A lethal dominant allele, however, often causes the death of afflicted individuals before they can mature and reproduce, so the allele is not passed on to future generations.

In cases of late-onset diseases, however, a lethal dominant allele may be passed on. If symptoms first appear after reproductive age, the individual may already have transmitted the allele to his or her children. For example, a degenerative disease of the nervous system, called **Huntington's disease**, is caused by a lethal dominant allele that has no obvious phenotypic effect until the individual is about 35 to 45 years old. Once the deterioration of the nervous system begins, it is irreversible and inevitably fatal. As with other dominant traits, a child born to a parent with the Huntington's disease allele has a 50% chance of inheriting the allele and the disorder (see the Punnett square in Figure 14.18). In the United States, this disease afflicts about one in 10,000 people.

At one time, the onset of symptoms was the only way to know if a person had inherited the Huntington's allele, but this is no longer the case. By analyzing DNA samples from a large family with a high incidence of the disorder, geneticists tracked the Huntington's allele to a locus near the tip of chromosome 4, and the gene was sequenced in 1993. This information led to the development of a test that could detect the presence of the Huntington's allele in an individual's genome. (The methods that make such tests possible are discussed in Chapter 20.) The availability of this test poses an agonizing dilemma for those with a family history of Huntington's disease. Some individuals may want to be tested for this disease, whereas others may decide it would be too stressful to find out whether they carry the allele.

Multifactorial Disorders

The hereditary diseases we have discussed so far are sometimes described as simple Mendelian disorders because they result from abnormality of one or both alleles at a single genetic locus. Many more people are susceptible to diseases that have a multifactorial basis—a genetic component plus a significant environmental influence. Heart disease, diabetes, cancer, alcoholism, certain mental illnesses such as schizophrenia and bipolar disorder, and many other diseases are multifactorial. In these cases, the hereditary component is polygenic. For example, many genes affect cardiovascular health, making some of us more prone than others to heart attacks and strokes. No matter what our genotype, however, our lifestyle has a tremendous effect on phenotype for cardiovascular health and other multifactorial characters. Exercise, a healthful diet, abstinence from smoking, and an ability to handle stressful situations all reduce our risk of heart disease and some types of cancer.

Genetic Testing and Counseling

Avoiding simple Mendelian disorders is possible when the risk of a particular genetic disorder can be assessed before a child is conceived or during the early stages of the pregnancy. Many hospitals have genetic counselors who can provide information to prospective parents concerned about a family history for a specific disease. Fetal and newborn testing can also reveal genetic disorders.

▲ **Figure 14.18 Achondroplasia: a dominant trait.** Dr. Michael C. Ain has achondroplasia, a form of dwarfism caused by a dominant allele. This has inspired his work: He is a specialist in the repair of bone defects caused by achondroplasia and other disorders. The dominant allele (*D*) might have arisen as a mutation in the egg or sperm of a parent or could have been inherited from an affected parent, as shown for an affected father in the Punnett square.

Parents

Dwarf   Normal
Dd   ×   *dd*

Sperm

D d

Eggs

d | *Dd* Dwarf | *dd* Normal

d | *Dd* Dwarf | *dd* Normal

Counseling Based on Mendelian Genetics and Probability Rules

Consider the case of a hypothetical couple, John and Carol. Each had a brother who died from the same recessively inherited lethal disease. Before conceiving their first child, John and Carol seek genetic counseling to determine the risk of having a child with the disease. From the information about their brothers, we know that both parents of John and both parents of Carol must have been carriers of the recessive allele. Thus, John and Carol are both products of $Aa \times Aa$ crosses, where a symbolizes the allele that causes this particular disease. We also know that John and Carol are not homozygous recessive (aa), because they do not have the disease. Therefore, their genotypes are either AA or Aa.

Given a genotypic ratio of 1 AA : 2 Aa : 1 aa for offspring of an $Aa \times Aa$ cross, John and Carol each have a $\frac{2}{3}$ chance of being carriers (Aa). According to the rule of multiplication, the overall probability of their firstborn having the disorder is $\frac{2}{3}$ (the chance that John is a carrier) times $\frac{2}{3}$ (the chance that Carol is a carrier) times $\frac{1}{4}$ (the chance of two carriers having a child with the disease), which equals $\frac{1}{9}$. Suppose that Carol and John decide to have a child—after all, there is an $\frac{8}{9}$ chance that their baby will not have the disorder. If, despite these odds, their child is born with the disease, then we would know that *both* John and Carol are, in fact, carriers (Aa genotype). If both John and Carol are carriers, there is a $\frac{1}{4}$ chance that any subsequent child this couple has will have the disease. The probability is higher for subsequent children because the diagnosis of the disease in the first child established that both parents are carriers, not because the genotype of the first child affects in any way that of future children.

When we use Mendel's laws to predict possible outcomes of matings, it is important to remember that each child represents an independent event in the sense that its genotype is unaffected by the genotypes of older siblings. Suppose that John and Carol have three more children, and *all three* have the hypothetical hereditary disease. There is only one chance in 64 ($\frac{1}{4} \times \frac{1}{4} \times \frac{1}{4}$) that such an outcome will occur. Despite this run of misfortune, the chance that still another child of this couple will have the disease remains $\frac{1}{4}$.

Tests for Identifying Carriers

Most children with recessive disorders are born to parents with normal phenotypes. The key to accurately assessing the genetic risk for a particular disease is therefore to find out whether the prospective parents are heterozygous carriers of the recessive allele. For an increasing number of heritable disorders, tests are available that can distinguish individuals of normal phenotype who are dominant homozygotes from those who are heterozygous carriers. There are now tests that can identify carriers of the alleles for Tay-Sachs disease, sickle-cell disease, and the most common form of cystic fibrosis.

These tests for identifying carriers enable people with family histories of genetic disorders to make informed decisions about having children, but raise other issues. Could carriers be denied health or life insurance or lose the jobs providing those benefits, even though they themselves are healthy? The Genetic Information Nondiscrimination Act, signed into law in the United States in 2008, allays these concerns by prohibiting discrimination in employment or insurance coverage based on genetic test results. A question that remains is whether sufficient genetic counseling is available to help large numbers of individuals understand their genetic test results. Even when test results are clearly understood, affected individuals may still face difficult decisions. Advances in biotechnology offer the potential to reduce human suffering, but along with them come ethical issues that require conscientious deliberation.

Fetal Testing

Suppose a couple expecting a child learns that they are both carriers of the Tay-Sachs allele. In the 14th–16th week of pregnancy, tests performed along with a technique called **amniocentesis** can determine whether the developing fetus has Tay-Sachs disease (**Figure 14.19a**). In this procedure, a physician inserts a needle into the uterus and extracts about 10 mL of amniotic fluid, the liquid that bathes the fetus. Some genetic disorders can be detected from the presence of certain molecules in the amniotic fluid itself. Tests for other disorders, including Tay-Sachs disease, are performed on the DNA of cells cultured in the laboratory, descendants of fetal cells sloughed off into the amniotic fluid. A karyotype of these cultured cells can also identify certain chromosomal defects (see Figure 13.3).

In an alternative technique called **chorionic villus sampling (CVS)**, a physician inserts a narrow tube through the cervix into the uterus and suctions out a tiny sample of tissue from the placenta, the organ that transmits nutrients and fetal wastes between the fetus and the mother (**Figure 14.19b**). The cells of the chorionic villi of the placenta, the portion sampled, are derived from the fetus and have the same genotype and DNA sequence as the new individual. These cells are proliferating rapidly enough to allow karyotyping to be carried out immediately. This rapid analysis represents an advantage over amniocentesis, in which the cells must be cultured for several weeks before karyotyping. Another advantage of CVS is that it can be performed as early as the 8th–10th week of pregnancy.

Medical scientists have also developed methods for isolating fetal cells, or even fetal DNA, that have escaped into the mother's blood. Although very few are present,

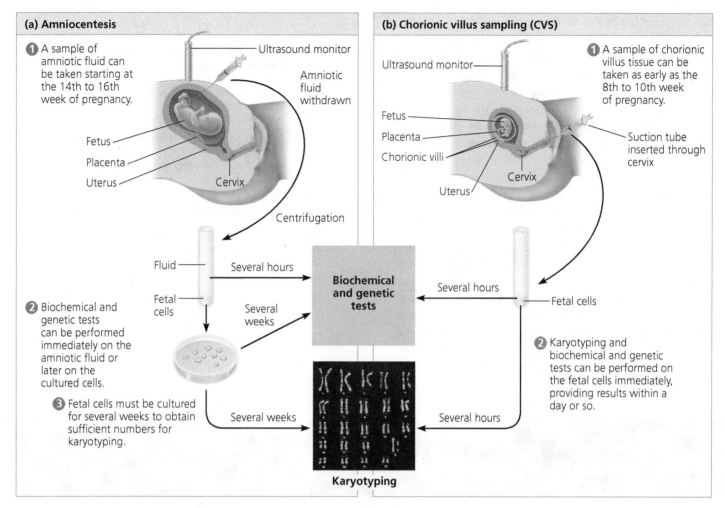

(a) Amniocentesis

1 A sample of amniotic fluid can be taken starting at the 14th to 16th week of pregnancy.

Ultrasound monitor

Amniotic fluid withdrawn

Fetus

Placenta

Uterus

Cervix

Centrifugation

Fluid

Several hours

Fetal cells

Several weeks

Biochemical and genetic tests

2 Biochemical and genetic tests can be performed immediately on the amniotic fluid or later on the cultured cells.

3 Fetal cells must be cultured for several weeks to obtain sufficient numbers for karyotyping.

Several weeks

(b) Chorionic villus sampling (CVS)

Ultrasound monitor

1 A sample of chorionic villus tissue can be taken as early as the 8th to 10th week of pregnancy.

Fetus

Placenta

Chorionic villi

Cervix

Suction tube inserted through cervix

Uterus

Several hours

Fetal cells

2 Karyotyping and biochemical and genetic tests can be performed on the fetal cells immediately, providing results within a day or so.

Several hours

Several hours

Karyotyping

▲ **Figure 14.19 Testing a fetus for genetic disorders.** Biochemical tests may detect substances associated with particular disorders, and genetic testing can detect many genetic abnormalities. Karyotyping shows whether the chromosomes of the fetus are normal in number and appearance.

the cells can be cultured and tested, and the fetal DNA can be analyzed. In 2012, researchers were able to analyze the entire genome of a fetus, comparing sequences of samples obtained from both parents and fetal DNA found in the mother's blood. This noninvasive method will likely become the method of choice in diagnosing most genetically based disorders.

Imaging techniques allow a physician to examine a fetus directly for major anatomical abnormalities that might not show up in genetic tests. In the *ultrasound* technique, reflected sound waves are used to produce an image of the fetus by a simple noninvasive procedure. In *fetoscopy*, a needle-thin tube containing a viewing scope and fiber optics (to transmit light) is inserted into the uterus.

Ultrasound and isolation of fetal cells or DNA from maternal blood pose no known risk to either mother or fetus, while the other procedures can cause complications in a small percentage of cases. Amniocentesis or CVS for

diagnostic testing is generally offered to women over age 35, due to their increased risk of bearing a child with Down syndrome, and may also be offered to younger women if there are known concerns. If the fetal tests reveal a serious disorder like Tay-Sachs, the parents face the difficult choice of either terminating the pregnancy or preparing to care for a child with a genetic disorder, one that might even be fatal. Parental and fetal screening for Tay-Sachs alleles done since 1980 has reduced the number of children born with this incurable disease by 90%.

Newborn Screening

Some genetic disorders can be detected at birth by simple biochemical tests that are now routinely performed in most hospitals in the United States. One common screening program is for phenylketonuria (PKU), a recessively inherited disorder that occurs in about one out of every 10,000–15,000 births in the United States. Children with this disease cannot properly metabolize the amino acid phenylalanine. This compound and its by-product, phenylpyruvate, can accumulate to toxic levels in the blood, causing severe intellectual disability (mental retardation). However, if PKU is detected in the newborn, a special diet low in phenylalanine will usually allow normal development. (Among many other substances, this diet excludes the artificial sweetener aspartame, which contains phenylalanine.) Unfortunately, few other genetic disorders are treatable at present.

Fetal and newborn screening for serious inherited diseases, tests for identifying carriers, and genetic counseling all rely on the Mendelian model of inheritance. We owe the "gene idea"—the concept of heritable factors transmitted according to simple rules of chance—to the elegant quantitative experiments of Gregor Mendel. The importance of his discoveries was overlooked by most biologists until early in the 20th century, decades after he reported his findings. In the next chapter, you will learn how Mendel's laws have their physical basis in the behavior of chromosomes during sexual life cycles and how the synthesis of Mendelian genetics and a chromosome theory of inheritance catalyzed progress in genetics.

CONCEPT CHECK 14.4

1. Beth and Tom each have a sibling with cystic fibrosis, but neither Beth nor Tom nor any of their parents have the disease. Calculate the probability that if this couple has a child, the child will have cystic fibrosis. What would be the probability if a test revealed that Tom is a carrier but Beth is not? Explain your answers.

2. MAKE CONNECTIONS Explain how the change of a single amino acid in hemoglobin leads to the aggregation of hemoglobin into long fibers. (Review Figures 5.14, 5.18, and 5.19.)

3. Joan was born with six toes on each foot, a dominant trait called polydactyly. Two of her five siblings and her mother, but not her father, also have extra digits. What is Joan's genotype for the number-of-digits character? Explain your answer. Use D and d to symbolize the alleles for this character.

4. MAKE CONNECTIONS In Table 14.1, note the phenotypic ratio of the dominant to recessive trait in the F_2 generation for the monohybrid cross involving flower color. Then determine the phenotypic ratio for the offspring of the second-generation couple in Figure 14.15b. What accounts for the difference in the two ratios?

For suggested answers, see Appendix A.

14 Chapter Review

SUMMARY OF KEY CONCEPTS

CONCEPT 14.1

Mendel used the scientific approach to identify two laws of inheritance (pp. 268–274)

- Gregor Mendel formulated a theory of inheritance based on experiments with garden peas, proposing that parents pass on to their offspring discrete genes that retain their identity through generations. This theory includes two "laws."
- The **law of segregation** states that genes have alternative forms, or **alleles**. In a diploid organism, the two alleles of a gene segregate (separate) during meiosis and gamete formation; each sperm or egg carries only one allele of each pair. This law explains the 3:1 ratio of F_2 phenotypes observed when **monohybrids** self-pollinate. Each organism inherits one allele for each gene from each parent. In **heterozygotes**, the two alleles are different; expression of the **dominant allele** masks the phenotypic effect of the **recessive allele**. **Homozygotes** have identical alleles of a given gene and are **true-breeding**.
- The **law of independent assortment** states that the pair of alleles for a given gene segregates into gametes independently of the pair of alleles for any other gene. In a cross between **dihybrids** (individuals heterozygous for two genes), the offspring have four phenotypes in a 9:3:3:1 ratio.

? *When Mendel did crosses of true-breeding purple- and white-flowered pea plants, the white-flowered trait disappeared from the F_1 generation but reappeared in the F_2 generation. Use genetic terms to explain why that happened.*

CONCEPT 14.2

Probability laws govern Mendelian inheritance (pp. 274–276)

Rr
Segregation of alleles into sperm

Sperm

$1/2$ *R* $1/2$ *r*

- The **multiplication rule** states that the probability of two or more events occurring together is equal to the product of the individual probabilities of the independent single events. The **addition rule** states that the probability of an event that can occur in two or more independent, mutually exclusive ways is the sum of the individual probabilities.
- The rules of probability can be used to solve complex genetics problems. A dihybrid or other multicharacter cross is equivalent to two or more independent monohybrid crosses occurring simultaneously. In calculating the chances of the various offspring genotypes from such crosses, each character is first considered separately and then the individual probabilities are multiplied.

DRAW IT *Redraw the Punnett square on the right side of Figure 14.8 as two smaller monohybrid Punnett squares, one for each gene. Below each square, list the fractions of each phenotype produced. Use the rule of multiplication to compute the overall fraction of each possible dihybrid phenotype. What is the phenotypic ratio?*

CONCEPT 14.3

Inheritance patterns are often more complex than predicted by simple Mendelian genetics (pp. 276–281)

- Extensions of Mendelian genetics for a single gene:

Relationship among alleles of a single gene	Description	Example
Complete dominance of one allele	Heterozygous phenotype same as that of homozygous dominant	PP Pp
Incomplete dominance of either allele	Heterozygous phenotype intermediate between the two homozygous phenotypes	$C^R C^R$ $C^R C^W$ $C^W C^W$
Codominance	Both phenotypes expressed in heterozygotes	$I^A I^B$
Multiple alleles	In the population, some genes have more than two alleles	ABO blood group alleles I^A, I^B, i
Pleiotropy	One gene affects multiple phenotypic characters	Sickle-cell disease

- Extensions of Mendelian genetics for two or more genes:

Relationship among two or more genes	Description	Example
Epistasis	The phenotypic expression of one gene affects the expression of another gene	$BbEe$ × $BbEe$ ... 9 : 3 : 4
Polygenic inheritance	A single phenotypic character is affected by two or more genes	$AaBbCc$ × $AaBbCc$

- The expression of a genotype can be affected by environmental influences, resulting in a range of phenotypes. Polygenic characters that are also influenced by the environment are called **multifactorial** characters.
- An organism's overall phenotype, including its physical appearance, internal anatomy, physiology, and behavior, reflects its overall genotype and unique environmental history. Even in more complex inheritance patterns, Mendel's fundamental laws of segregation and independent assortment still apply.

? *Which of the following are demonstrated by the inheritance patterns of the ABO blood group alleles: complete dominance, incomplete dominance, codominance, multiple alleles, pleiotropy, epistasis, and/or polygenic inheritance? Explain each of your answers.*

CONCEPT 14.4

Many human traits follow Mendelian patterns of inheritance (pp. 282–288)

- Analysis of family **pedigrees** can be used to deduce the possible genotypes of individuals and make predictions about future offspring. Such predictions are statistical probabilities rather than certainties.

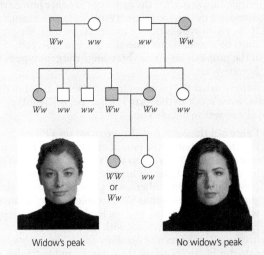

Widow's peak   No widow's peak

- Many genetic disorders are inherited as simple recessive traits. Most affected (homozygous recessive) individuals are children of phenotypically normal, heterozygous **carriers**.
- The sickle-cell allele has probably persisted for evolutionary reasons: Heterozygotes have an advantage because one copy of the sickle-cell allele reduces both the frequency and severity of malaria attacks.

- Lethal dominant alleles are eliminated from the population if affected people die before reproducing. Nonlethal dominant alleles and lethal ones that strike relatively late in life can be inherited in a Mendelian way.
- Many human diseases are multifactorial—that is, they have both genetic and environmental components and do not follow simple Mendelian inheritance patterns.
- Using family histories, genetic counselors help couples determine the probability that their children will have genetic disorders. Genetic testing of prospective parents to reveal whether they are carriers of recessive alleles associated with specific disorders has become widely available. **Amniocentesis** and **chorionic villus sampling** can indicate whether a suspected genetic disorder is present in a fetus. Other genetic tests can be performed after birth.

? *Both members of a couple know that they are carriers of the cystic fibrosis allele. None of their three children has cystic fibrosis, but any one of them might be a carrier. They would like to have a fourth child but are worried that he or she would very likely have the disease, since the first three do not. What would you tell the couple? Would it remove some uncertainty from their prediction if they could find out from genetic tests whether the three children are carriers?*

1. Write down symbols for the alleles. (These may be given in the problem.) When represented by single letters, the dominant allele is uppercase and the recessive is lowercase.

2. Write down the possible genotypes, as determined by the phenotype.
   a. If the phenotype is that of the dominant trait (for example, purple flowers), then the genotype is either homozygous dominant or heterozygous (*PP* or *Pp*, in this example).
   b. If the phenotype is that of the recessive trait, the genotype must be homozygous recessive (for example, *pp*).
   c. If the problem says "true-breeding," the genotype is homozygous.

3. Determine what the problem is asking for. If asked to do a cross, write it out in the form [Genotype] × [Genotype], using the alleles you've decided on.

4. To figure out the outcome of a cross, set up a Punnett square.
   a. Put the gametes of one parent at the top and those of the other on the left. To determine the allele(s) in each gamete for a given genotype, set up a systematic way to list all the possibilities. (Remember, each gamete has one allele of each gene.) Note that there are 2^n possible types of gametes, where *n* is the number of gene loci that are heterozygous. For example, an individual with genotype *AaBbCc* would produce $2^3 = 8$ types of gametes. Write the genotypes of the gametes in circles above the columns and to the left of the rows.
   b. Fill in the Punnett square as if each possible sperm were fertilizing each possible egg, making all of the possible offspring. In a cross of *AaBbCc* × *AaBbCc*, for example, the Punnett square would have 8 columns and 8 rows, so there are 64 different offspring; you would know the genotype of each and thus the phenotype. Count genotypes and phenotypes to obtain the genotypic and phenotypic ratios. Because the Punnett square is so large, this method is not the most efficient. See tip 5.

5. You can use the rules of probability if the Punnett square would be too big. (For example, see the question at the end of the summary for Concept 14.2 and question 7 below.) You can consider each gene separately (see Concept 14.2).

6. If, instead, the problem gives you the phenotypic ratios of offspring but not the genotypes of the parents in a given cross, the phenotypes can help you deduce the parents' unknown genotypes.
   a. For example, if ½ of the offspring have the recessive phenotype and ½ the dominant, you know that the cross was between a heterozygote and a homozygous recessive.
   b. If the ratio is 3:1, the cross was between two heterozygotes.
   c. If two genes are involved and you see a 9:3:3:1 ratio in the offspring, you know that each parent is heterozygous for both genes. Caution: Don't assume that the reported numbers will exactly equal the predicted ratios. For example, if there are 13 offspring with the dominant trait and 11 with the recessive, assume that the ratio is one dominant to one recessive.

7. For pedigree problems, use the tips in Figure 14.15 and below to determine what kind of trait is involved.
   a. If parents without the trait have offspring with the trait, the trait must be recessive and the parents both carriers.
   b. If the trait is seen in every generation, it is most likely dominant (see the next possibility, though).
   c. If both parents have the trait and the trait is recessive, all offspring will show the trait.
   d. To determine the likely genotype of a certain individual in a pedigree, first label the genotypes of all the family members you can. Even if some of the genotypes are incomplete, label what you do know. For example, if an individual has the dominant phenotype, the genotype must be *AA* or *Aa*; you can write this as *A−*. Try different possibilities to see which fits the results. Use the rules of probability to calculate the probability of each possible genotype being the correct one.

LEVEL 1: KNOWLEDGE/COMPREHENSION

1. **DRAW IT** Two pea plants heterozygous for the characters of pod color and pod shape are crossed. Draw a Punnett square to determine the phenotypic ratios of the offspring.

2. A man with type A blood marries a woman with type B blood. Their child has type O blood. What are the genotypes of these three individuals? What genotypes, and in what frequencies, would you expect in future offspring from this marriage?

3. A man has six fingers on each hand and six toes on each foot. His wife and their daughter have the normal number of digits. Remember that extra digits is a dominant trait. What fraction of this couple's children would be expected to have extra digits?

4. **DRAW IT** A pea plant heterozygous for inflated pods (*Ii*) is crossed with a plant homozygous for constricted pods (*ii*). Draw a Punnett square for this cross to predict genotypic and phenotypic ratios. Assume that pollen comes from the *ii* plant.

LEVEL 2: APPLICATION/ANALYSIS

5. Flower position, stem length, and seed shape are three characters that Mendel studied. Each is controlled by an independently assorting gene and has dominant and recessive expression as indicated in Table 14.1. If a plant that is heterozygous for all three characters is allowed to self-fertilize, what proportion of the offspring would you expect to be as follows? (*Note*: Use the rules of probability instead of a huge Punnett square.)
   (a) homozygous for the three dominant traits
   (b) homozygous for the three recessive traits
   (c) heterozygous for all three characters
   (d) homozygous for axial and tall, heterozygous for seed shape

6. Phenylketonuria (PKU) is an inherited disease caused by a recessive allele. If a woman and her husband, who are both carriers, have three children, what is the probability of each of the following?
   (a) All three children are of normal phenotype.
   (b) One or more of the three children have the disease.
   (c) All three children have the disease.
   (d) At least one child is phenotypically normal.

   (*Note:* It will help to remember that the probabilities of all possible outcomes always add up to 1.)

7. The genotype of F_1 individuals in a tetrahybrid cross is *AaBbCcDd*. Assuming independent assortment of these four genes, what are the probabilities that F_2 offspring will have the following genotypes?
   (a) *aabbccdd*
   (b) *AaBbCcDd*
   (c) *AABBCCDD*
   (d) *AaBBccDd*
   (e) *AaBBCCdd*

8. What is the probability that each of the following pairs of parents will produce the indicated offspring? (Assume independent assortment of all gene pairs.)
   (a) $AABBCC \times aabbcc \rightarrow AaBbCc$
   (b) $AABbCc \times AaBbCc \rightarrow AAbbCC$
   (c) $AaBbCc \times AaBbCc \rightarrow AaBbCc$
   (d) $aaBbCC \times AABbcc \rightarrow AaBbCc$

9. Karen and Steve each have a sibling with sickle-cell disease. Neither Karen nor Steve nor any of their parents have the disease, and none of them have been tested to see if they have the sickle-cell trait. Based on this incomplete information, calculate the probability that if this couple has a child, the child will have sickle-cell disease.

10. In 1981, a stray black cat with unusual rounded, curled-back ears was adopted by a family in California. Hundreds of descendants of the cat have since been born, and cat fanciers hope to develop the curl cat into a show breed. Suppose you owned the first curl cat and wanted to develop a true-breeding variety. How would you determine whether the curl allele is dominant or recessive? How would you obtain true-breeding curl cats? How could you be sure they are true-breeding?

11. In tigers, a recessive allele of a particular gene causes both an absence of fur pigmentation (a white tiger) and a cross-eyed condition. If two phenotypically normal tigers that are heterozygous at this locus are mated, what percentage of their offspring will be cross-eyed? What percentage of cross-eyed tigers will be white?

12. In maize (corn) plants, a dominant allele I inhibits kernel color, while the recessive allele i permits color when homozygous. At a different locus, the dominant allele P causes purple kernel color, while the homozygous recessive genotype pp causes red kernels. If plants heterozygous at both loci are crossed, what will be the phenotypic ratio of the offspring?

13. The pedigree below traces the inheritance of alkaptonuria, a biochemical disorder. Affected individuals, indicated here by the colored circles and squares, are unable to metabolize a substance called alkapton, which colors the urine and stains body tissues. Does alkaptonuria appear to be caused by a dominant allele or by a recessive allele? Fill in the genotypes of the individuals whose genotypes can be deduced. What genotypes are possible for each of the other individuals?

14. Imagine that you are a genetic counselor, and a couple planning to start a family comes to you for information. Charles was married once before, and he and his first wife had a child with cystic fibrosis. The brother of his current wife, Elaine, died of cystic fibrosis. What is the probability that Charles and Elaine will have a baby with cystic fibrosis? (Neither Charles, Elaine, nor their parents have cystic fibrosis.)

LEVEL 3: SYNTHESIS/EVALUATION

15. **EVOLUTION CONNECTION**
   Over the past half century, there has been a trend in the United States and other developed countries for people to marry and start families later in life than did their parents and grandparents. What effects might this trend have on the incidence (frequency) of late-acting dominant lethal alleles in the population?

16. **SCIENTIFIC INQUIRY**
   You are handed a mystery pea plant with tall stems and axial flowers and asked to determine its genotype as quickly as possible. You know that the allele for tall stems (T) is dominant to that for dwarf stems (t) and that the allele for axial flowers (A) is dominant to that for terminal flowers (a).
   (a) What are *all* the possible genotypes for your mystery plant?
   (b) Describe the *one* cross you would do, out in your garden, to determine the exact genotype of your mystery plant.
   (c) While waiting for the results of your cross, you predict the results for each possible genotype listed in part a. How do you do this? Why is this not called "performing a cross"?
   (d) Explain how the results of your cross and your predictions will help you learn the genotype of your mystery plant.

17. **WRITE ABOUT A THEME: INFORMATION**
   The continuity of life is based on heritable information in the form of DNA. In a short essay (100–150 words), explain how the passage of genes from parents to offspring, in the form of particular alleles, ensures perpetuation of parental traits in offspring and, at the same time, genetic variation among offspring. Use genetic terms in your explanation.

18. **SYNTHESIZE YOUR KNOWLEDGE**

Just for fun, imagine that "shirt-striping" is a phenotypic character caused by a single gene. Make up a genetic explanation for the appearance of the family in the above photograph, consistent with their "shirt phenotypes." Include in your answer the presumed allele combinations for "shirt-striping" in each family member. What is the inheritance pattern shown by the child?

For selected answers, see Appendix A.

MasteringBiology®

Students Go to **MasteringBiology** for assignments, the eText, and the Study Area with practice tests, animations, and activities.

Instructors Go to **MasteringBiology** for automatically graded tutorials and questions that you can assign to your students, plus Instructor Resources.

15

The Chromosomal Basis of Inheritance

▲ **Figure 15.1 Where are Mendel's hereditary factors located in the cell?**

Locating Genes Along Chromosomes

Today, we know that genes—Mendel's "factors"—are segments of DNA located along chromosomes. We can see the location of a particular gene by tagging chromosomes with a fluorescent dye that highlights that gene. For example, the two yellow spots in **Figure 15.1** mark a specific gene on human chromosome 6. (The chromosome has duplicated, so the allele on that chromosome is present as two copies, one per sister chromatid.) However, Gregor Mendel's "hereditary factors" were purely an abstract concept when he proposed their existence in 1860. At that time, no cellular structures had been identified that could house these imaginary units, and most biologists were skeptical about Mendel's proposed laws of inheritance.

Using improved techniques of microscopy, cytologists worked out the process of mitosis in 1875 (see the drawing at the lower left) and meiosis in the 1890s. Cytology and genetics converged as biologists began to see parallels between the behavior of Mendel's proposed hereditary factors during sexual life cycles and the behavior of chromosomes: As shown in **Figure 15.2**, chromosomes and genes are both present in pairs in diploid cells, and homologous chromosomes separate and alleles segregate during the process of meiosis. Furthermore, after meiosis, fertilization restores the paired condition for both chromosomes and genes.

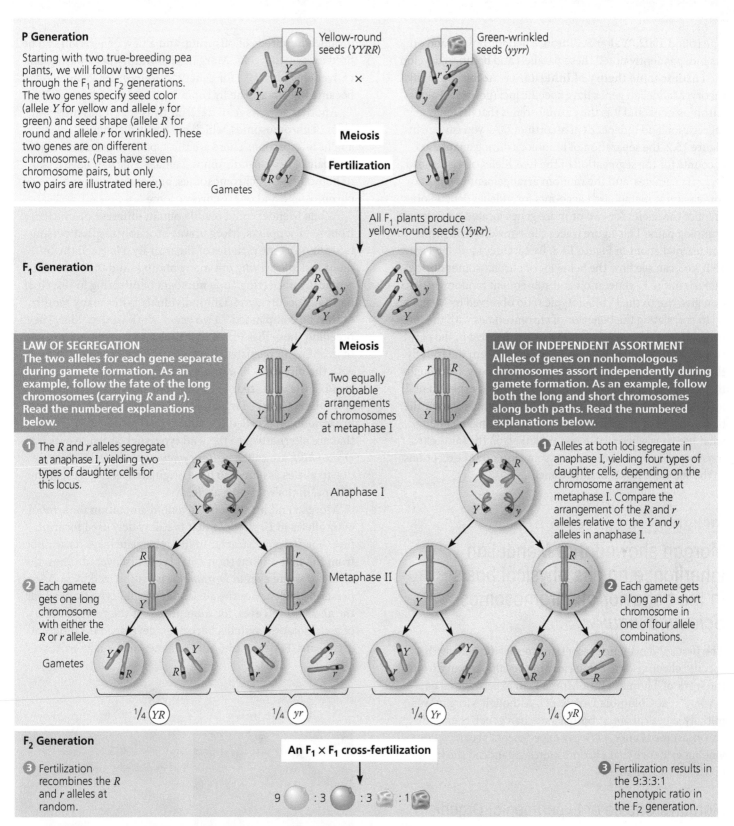

P Generation

Starting with two true-breeding pea plants, we will follow two genes through the F_1 and F_2 generations. The two genes specify seed color (allele *Y* for yellow and allele *y* for green) and seed shape (allele *R* for round and allele *r* for wrinkled). These two genes are on different chromosomes. (Peas have seven chromosome pairs, but only two pairs are illustrated here.)

Yellow-round seeds (*YYRR*)

×

Green-wrinkled seeds (*yyrr*)

Meiosis

Fertilization

Gametes

All F_1 plants produce yellow-round seeds (*YyRr*).

F_1 Generation

Meiosis

Two equally probable arrangements of chromosomes at metaphase I

LAW OF SEGREGATION
The two alleles for each gene separate during gamete formation. As an example, follow the fate of the long chromosomes (carrying *R* and *r*). Read the numbered explanations below.

LAW OF INDEPENDENT ASSORTMENT
Alleles of genes on nonhomologous chromosomes assort independently during gamete formation. As an example, follow both the long and short chromosomes along both paths. Read the numbered explanations below.

1 The *R* and *r* alleles segregate at anaphase I, yielding two types of daughter cells for this locus.

Anaphase I

1 Alleles at both loci segregate in anaphase I, yielding four types of daughter cells, depending on the chromosome arrangement at metaphase I. Compare the arrangement of the *R* and *r* alleles relative to the *Y* and *y* alleles in anaphase I.

Metaphase II

2 Each gamete gets one long chromosome with either the *R* or *r* allele.

2 Each gamete gets a long and a short chromosome in one of four allele combinations.

Gametes

¼ *YR*   ¼ *yr*   ¼ *Yr*   ¼ *yR*

F_2 Generation

3 Fertilization recombines the *R* and *r* alleles at random.

An F_1 × F_1 cross-fertilization

9   : 3   : 3   : 1

3 Fertilization results in the 9:3:3:1 phenotypic ratio in the F_2 generation.

▲ **Figure 15.2 The chromosomal basis of Mendel's laws.** Here we correlate the results of one of Mendel's dihybrid crosses (see Figure 14.8) with the behavior of chromosomes during meiosis (see Figure 13.8). The arrangement of chromosomes at metaphase I of meiosis and their movement during anaphase I account, respectively, for the independent assortment and segregation of the alleles for seed color and shape. Each cell that undergoes meiosis in an F_1 plant produces two kinds of gametes. If we count the results for all cells, however, each F_1 plant produces equal numbers of all four kinds of gametes because the alternative chromosome arrangements at metaphase I are equally likely.

? *If you crossed an F_1 plant with a plant that was homozygous recessive for both genes (yyrr), how would the phenotypic ratio of the offspring compare with the 9:3:3:1 ratio seen here?*

Around 1902, Walter S. Sutton, Theodor Boveri, and others independently noted these parallels and began to develop the **chromosome theory of inheritance**. According to this theory, Mendelian genes have specific loci (positions) along chromosomes, and it is the chromosomes that undergo segregation and independent assortment. As you can see in Figure 15.2, the separation of homologs during anaphase I accounts for the segregation of the two alleles of a gene into separate gametes, and the random arrangement of chromosome pairs at metaphase I accounts for independent assortment of the alleles for two or more genes located on different homolog pairs. This figure traces the same dihybrid pea cross you learned about in Figure 14.8. By carefully studying Figure 15.2, you can see how the behavior of chromosomes during meiosis in the F_1 generation and subsequent random fertilization give rise to the F_2 phenotypic ratio observed by Mendel.

In correlating the behavior of chromosomes with that of genes, this chapter will extend what you learned in the past two chapters. First, we'll describe evidence from the fruit fly that strongly supported the chromosome theory. (Although this theory made a lot of sense, it still required experimental evidence.) Next, we'll explore the chromosomal basis for the transmission of genes from parents to offspring, including what happens when two genes are linked on the same chromosome. Finally, we will discuss some important exceptions to the standard mode of inheritance.

CONCEPT 15.1

Morgan showed that Mendelian inheritance has its physical basis in the behavior of chromosomes: *Scientific inquiry*

The first solid evidence associating a specific gene with a specific chromosome came early in the 20th century from the work of Thomas Hunt Morgan, an experimental embryologist at Columbia University. Although Morgan was initially skeptical about both Mendelian genetics and the chromosome theory, his early experiments provided convincing evidence that chromosomes are indeed the location of Mendel's heritable factors.

Morgan's Choice of Experimental Organism

Many times in the history of biology, important discoveries have come to those insightful or lucky enough to choose an experimental organism suitable for the research problem being tackled. Mendel chose the garden pea because a number of distinct varieties were available. For his work, Morgan selected a species of fruit fly, *Drosophila melanogaster*, a common insect that feeds on the fungi growing on fruit. Fruit flies are prolific breeders; a single mating will produce hundreds of offspring, and a new generation can be bred every two weeks. Morgan's laboratory began using this convenient organism for genetic studies in 1907 and soon became known as "the fly room."

Another advantage of the fruit fly is that it has only four pairs of chromosomes, which are easily distinguishable with a light microscope. There are three pairs of autosomes and one pair of sex chromosomes. Female fruit flies have a pair of homologous X chromosomes, and males have one X chromosome and one Y chromosome.

While Mendel could readily obtain different pea varieties from seed suppliers, Morgan was probably the first person to want different varieties of the fruit fly. He faced the tedious task of carrying out many matings and then microscopically inspecting large numbers of offspring in search of naturally occurring variant individuals. After many months of this, he complained, "Two years' work wasted. I have been breeding those flies for all that time and I've got nothing out of it." Morgan persisted, however, and was finally rewarded with the discovery of a single male fly with white eyes instead of the usual red. The phenotype for a character most commonly observed in natural populations, such as red eyes in *Drosophila*, is called the **wild type** (Figure 15.3). Traits that are alternatives to the wild type, such as white eyes in *Drosophila*, are called *mutant phenotypes* because they are due to alleles assumed to have originated as changes, or mutations, in the wild-type allele.

Morgan and his students invented a notation for symbolizing alleles in *Drosophila* that is still widely used for fruit flies. For a given character in flies, the gene takes its symbol from the first mutant (non–wild type) discovered. Thus, the allele for white eyes in *Drosophila* is symbolized by w. A superscript + identifies the allele for the wild-type trait: w^+ for the allele for red eyes, for example. Over the years, a variety of gene notation systems have been developed for different organisms. For example, human genes are usually written

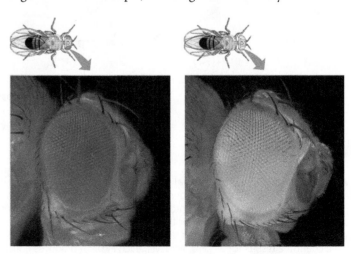

▲ **Figure 15.3 Morgan's first mutant.** Wild-type *Drosophila* flies have red eyes (left). Among his flies, Morgan discovered a mutant male with white eyes (right). This variation made it possible for Morgan to trace a gene for eye color to a specific chromosome (LMs).

in all capitals, such as *HD* for the allele for Huntington's disease.

Correlating Behavior of a Gene's Alleles with Behavior of a Chromosome Pair

Morgan mated his white-eyed male fly with a red-eyed female. All the F_1 offspring had red eyes, suggesting that the wild-type allele is dominant. When Morgan bred the F_1 flies to each other, he observed the classical 3:1 phenotypic ratio among the F_2 offspring. However, there was a surprising additional result: The white-eye trait showed up only in males. All the F_2 females had red eyes, while half the males had red eyes and half had white eyes. Therefore, Morgan concluded that somehow a fly's eye color was linked to its sex. (If the eye-color gene were unrelated to sex, half of the white-eyed flies would have been male and half female.)

Recall that a female fly has two X chromosomes (XX), while a male fly has an X and a Y (XY). The correlation between the trait of white eye color and the male sex of the affected F_2 flies suggested to Morgan that the gene involved in his white-eyed mutant was located exclusively on the X chromosome, with no corresponding allele present on the Y chromosome. His reasoning can be followed in **Figure 15.4**. For a male, a single copy of the mutant allele would confer white eyes; since a male has only one X chromosome, there can be no wild-type allele (w^+) present to mask the recessive allele. However, a female could have white eyes only if both her X chromosomes carried the recessive mutant allele (w). This was impossible for the F_2 females in Morgan's experiment because all the F_1 fathers had red eyes, so each F_2 female received a w^+ allele on the X chromosome inherited from her father.

Morgan's finding of the correlation between a particular trait and an individual's sex provided support for the chromosome theory of inheritance: namely, that a specific gene is carried on a specific chromosome (in this case, an eye-color gene on the X chromosome). In addition, Morgan's work indicated that genes located on a sex chromosome exhibit unique inheritance patterns, which we will discuss in the next section. Recognizing the importance of Morgan's early work, many bright students were attracted to his fly room.

CONCEPT CHECK 15.1

1. Which one of Mendel's laws relates to the inheritance of alleles for a single character? Which law relates to the inheritance of alleles for two characters in a dihybrid cross?

2. MAKE CONNECTIONS Review the description of meiosis (see Figure 13.8) and Mendel's laws of segregation and independent assortment (see Concept 14.1). What is the physical basis for each of Mendel's laws?

3. WHAT IF? Propose a possible reason that the first naturally occurring mutant fruit fly Morgan saw involved a gene on a sex chromosome.

For suggested answers, see Appendix A.

▼ Figure 15.4   Inquiry

In a cross between a wild-type female fruit fly and a mutant white-eyed male, what color eyes will the F_1 and F_2 offspring have?

Experiment Thomas Hunt Morgan wanted to analyze the behavior of two alleles of a fruit fly eye-color gene. In crosses similar to those done by Mendel with pea plants, Morgan and his colleagues mated a wild-type (red-eyed) female with a mutant white-eyed male.

Morgan then bred an F_1 red-eyed female to an F_1 red-eyed male to produce the F_2 generation.

Results The F_2 generation showed a typical Mendelian ratio of 3 red-eyed flies : 1 white-eyed fly. However, all white-eyed flies were males; no females displayed the white-eye trait.

Conclusion All F_1 offspring had red eyes, so the mutant white-eye trait (w) must be recessive to the wild-type red-eye trait (w^+). Since the recessive trait—white eyes—was expressed only in males in the F_2 generation, Morgan deduced that this eye-color gene is located on the X chromosome and that there is no corresponding locus on the Y chromosome.

Source: T. H. Morgan, Sex-limited inheritance in *Drosophila, Science* 32:120–122 (1910).

(MB) A related Experimental Inquiry Tutorial can be assigned in MasteringBiology.

WHAT IF? *Suppose this eye-color gene were located on an autosome. Predict the phenotypes (including gender) of the F_2 flies in this hypothetical cross. (Hint: Draw a Punnett square.)*

Sex-linked genes exhibit unique patterns of inheritance

As you just learned, Morgan's discovery of a trait (white eyes) that correlated with the sex of flies was a key episode in the development of the chromosome theory of inheritance. Because the identity of the sex chromosomes in an individual could be inferred by observing the sex of the fly, the behavior of the two members of the pair of sex chromosomes could be correlated with the behavior of the two alleles of the eye-color gene. In this section, we'll take a closer look at the role of sex chromosomes in inheritance.

The Chromosomal Basis of Sex

Although the anatomical and physiological differences between women and men are numerous, the chromosomal basis for determining sex is rather simple. Humans and other mammals have two types of sex chromosomes, designated X and Y. The Y chromosome is much smaller than the X chromosome (Figure 15.5). A person who inherits two X chromosomes, one from each parent, usually develops as a female; a male inherits one X chromosome and one Y chromosome (Figure 15.6a). Short segments at either end

▲ Figure 15.5 Human sex chromosomes.

of the Y chromosome are the only regions that are homologous with regions of the X. These homologous regions allow the X and Y chromosomes in males to pair and behave like homologs during meiosis in the testes.

In mammalian testes and ovaries, the two sex chromosomes segregate during meiosis. Each egg receives one X chromosome. In contrast, sperm fall into two categories: Half the sperm cells a male produces receive an X chromosome, and half receive a Y chromosome. We can trace the sex of each offspring to the events of conception: If a sperm cell bearing an X chromosome fertilizes an egg, the zygote is XX, a female; if a sperm cell containing a Y chromosome fertilizes an egg, the zygote is XY, a male (see Figure 15.6a). Thus, sex determination is a matter of chance—a fifty-fifty chance. Note that the mammalian X-Y system isn't the only chromosomal system for determining sex. Figure 15.6b–d illustrates three other systems.

In humans, the anatomical signs of sex begin to emerge when the embryo is about 2 months old. Before then, the rudiments of the gonads are generic—they can develop into either testes or ovaries, depending on whether or not a Y chromosome is present. In 1990, a British research team

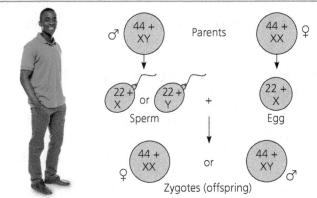

(a) **The X-Y system.** In mammals, the sex of an offspring depends on whether the sperm cell contains an X chromosome or a Y.

(b) **The X-0 system.** In grasshoppers, cockroaches, and some other insects, there is only one type of sex chromosome, the X. Females are XX; males have only one sex chromosome (X0). Sex of the offspring is determined by whether the sperm cell contains an X chromosome or no sex chromosome.

(c) **The Z-W system.** In birds, some fishes, and some insects, the sex chromosomes present in the egg (not the sperm) determine the sex of offspring. The sex chromosomes are designated Z and W. Females are ZW and males are ZZ.

(d) **The haplo-diploid system.** There are no sex chromosomes in most species of bees and ants. Females develop from fertilized eggs and are thus diploid. Males develop from unfertilized eggs and are haploid; they have no fathers.

▲ Figure 15.6 **Some chromosomal systems of sex determination.** Numerals indicate the number of autosomes in the species pictured. In *Drosophila*, males are XY, but sex depends on the ratio between the number of X chromosomes and the number of autosome sets, not simply on the presence of a Y chromosome.

identified a gene on the Y chromosome required for the development of testes. They named the gene *SRY*, for *s*ex-determining *r*egion of *Y*. In the absence of *SRY*, the gonads develop into ovaries. The biochemical, physiological, and anatomical features that distinguish males and females are complex, and many genes are involved in their development. In fact, *SRY* codes for a protein that regulates other genes.

Researchers have sequenced the human Y chromosome and have identified 78 genes that code for about 25 proteins (some genes are duplicates). About half of these genes are expressed only in the testis, and some are required for normal testicular functioning and the production of normal sperm. A gene located on either sex chromosome is called a **sex-linked gene**; those located on the Y chromosome are called *Y-linked genes*. The Y chromosome is passed along virtually intact from a father to all his sons. Because there are so few Y-linked genes, very few disorders are transferred from father to son on the Y chromosome. A rare example is that in the absence of certain Y-linked genes, an XY individual is male but does not produce normal sperm.

The human X chromosome contains approximately 1,100 genes, which are called **X-linked genes**. The fact that males and females inherit a different number of X chromosomes leads to a pattern of inheritance different from that produced by genes located on autosomes.

Inheritance of X-Linked Genes

While most Y-linked genes help determine sex, the X chromosomes have genes for many characters unrelated to sex. X-linked genes in humans follow the same pattern of inheritance that Morgan observed for the eye-color locus he studied in *Drosophila* (see Figure 15.4). Fathers pass X-linked alleles to all of their daughters but to none of their sons. In contrast, mothers can pass X-linked alleles to both sons and daughters, as shown in **Figure 15.7** for the inheritance of a mild X-linked disorder, red-green color blindness.

If an X-linked trait is due to a recessive allele, a female will express the phenotype only if she is homozygous for

that allele. Because males have only one locus, the terms *homozygous* and *heterozygous* lack meaning for describing their X-linked genes; the term *hemizygous* is used in such cases. Any male receiving the recessive allele from his mother will express the trait. For this reason, far more males than females have X-linked recessive disorders. However, even though the chance of a female inheriting a double dose of the mutant allele is much less than the probability of a male inheriting a single dose, there *are* females with X-linked disorders. For instance, color blindness is almost always inherited as an X-linked trait. A color-blind daughter may be born to a color-blind father whose mate is a carrier (see Figure 15.7c). Because the X-linked allele for color blindness is relatively rare, though, the probability that such a man and woman will mate is low.

A number of human X-linked disorders are much more serious than color blindness, such as **Duchenne muscular dystrophy**, which affects about one out of 3,500 males born in the United States. The disease is characterized by a progressive weakening of the muscles and loss of coordination. Affected individuals rarely live past their early 20s. Researchers have traced the disorder to the absence of a key muscle protein called dystrophin and have mapped the gene for this protein to a specific locus on the X chromosome.

Hemophilia is an X-linked recessive disorder defined by the absence of one or more of the proteins required for blood clotting. When a person with hemophilia is injured, bleeding is prolonged because a firm clot is slow to form. Small cuts in the skin are usually not a problem, but bleeding in the muscles or joints can be painful and can lead to serious damage. In the 1800s, hemophilia was widespread among the royal families of Europe. Queen Victoria of

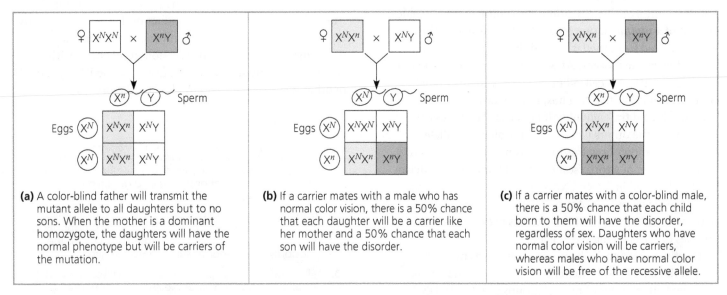

(a) A color-blind father will transmit the mutant allele to all daughters but to no sons. When the mother is a dominant homozygote, the daughters will have the normal phenotype but will be carriers of the mutation.

(b) If a carrier mates with a male who has normal color vision, there is a 50% chance that each daughter will be a carrier like her mother and a 50% chance that each son will have the disorder.

(c) If a carrier mates with a color-blind male, there is a 50% chance that each child born to them will have the disorder, regardless of sex. Daughters who have normal color vision will be carriers, whereas males who have normal color vision will be free of the recessive allele.

▲ **Figure 15.7 The transmission of X-linked recessive traits.** In this diagram, red-green color blindness is used as an example. The superscript *N* represents the dominant allele for normal color vision carried on the X chromosome, while *n* represents the recessive allele, which has a mutation for color blindness. White boxes indicate unaffected individuals, light orange boxes indicate carriers, and dark orange boxes indicate color-blind individuals.

? *If a color-blind woman married a man who had normal color vision, what would be the probable phenotypes of their children?*

England is known to have passed the allele to several of her descendants. Subsequent intermarriage with royal family members of other nations, such as Spain and Russia, further spread this X-linked trait, and its incidence is well documented in royal pedigrees. A few years ago, new genomic techniques allowed sequencing of DNA from tiny amounts isolated from the buried remains of royal family members. The genetic basis of the mutation, and how it resulted in a nonfunctional blood-clotting factor, is now understood. Today, people with hemophilia are treated as needed with intravenous injections of the protein that is missing.

X Inactivation in Female Mammals

Female mammals, including human females, inherit two X chromosomes—twice the number inherited by males—so you may wonder whether females make twice as much as males of the proteins encoded by X-linked genes. In fact, almost all of one X chromosome in each cell in female mammals becomes inactivated during early embryonic development. As a result, the cells of females and males have the same effective dose (one copy) of most X-linked genes. The inactive X in each cell of a female condenses into a compact object called a **Barr body** (discovered by Canadian anatomist Murray Barr), which lies along the inside of the nuclear envelope. Most of the genes of the X chromosome that forms the Barr body are not expressed. In the ovaries, however, Barr-body chromosomes are reactivated in the cells that give rise to eggs, such that following meiosis, every female gamete (egg) has an active X.

British geneticist Mary Lyon demonstrated that the selection of which X chromosome will form the Barr body occurs randomly and independently in each embryonic cell present at the time of X inactivation. As a consequence, females consist of a *mosaic* of two types of cells: those with the active X derived from the father and those with the active X derived from the mother. After an X chromosome is inactivated in a particular cell, all mitotic descendants of that cell have the same inactive X. Thus, if a female is heterozygous for a sex-linked trait, about half her cells will express one allele, while the others will express the alternate allele. **Figure 15.8** shows how this mosaicism results in the mottled coloration of a tortoiseshell cat. In humans, mosaicism can be observed in a recessive X-linked mutation that prevents the development of sweat glands. A woman who is heterozygous for this trait has patches of normal skin and patches of skin lacking sweat glands.

Inactivation of an X chromosome involves modification of the DNA and proteins bound to it, called histones, including attachment of methyl groups (—CH₃) to DNA nucleotides. (The regulatory role of DNA methylation is discussed in Chapter 18.) A particular region of each X chromosome contains several genes involved in the inactivation process. The two regions, one on each X chromosome,

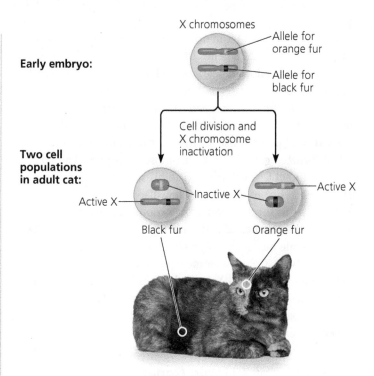

▲ **Figure 15.8 X inactivation and the tortoiseshell cat.** The tortoiseshell gene is on the X chromosome, and the tortoiseshell phenotype requires the presence of two different alleles, one for orange fur and one for black fur. Normally, only females can have both alleles, because only they have two X chromosomes. If a female cat is heterozygous for the tortoiseshell gene, she is tortoiseshell. Orange patches are formed by populations of cells in which the X chromosome with the orange allele is active; black patches have cells in which the X chromosome with the black allele is active. ("Calico" cats also have white areas, which are determined by another gene.)

associate briefly with each other in each cell at an early stage of embryonic development. Then one of the genes, called *XIST* (for X-inactive specific transcript) becomes active *only* on the chromosome that will become the Barr body. Multiple copies of the RNA product of this gene apparently attach to the X chromosome on which they are made, eventually almost covering it. Interaction of this RNA with the chromosome initiates X inactivation, and the RNA products of other nearby genes help to regulate the process.

CONCEPT CHECK 15.2

1. A white-eyed female *Drosophila* is mated with a red-eyed (wild-type) male, the reciprocal cross of the one shown in Figure 15.4. What phenotypes and genotypes do you predict for the offspring?

2. Neither Tim nor Rhoda has Duchenne muscular dystrophy, but their firstborn son does. What is the probability that a second child will have the disease? What is the probability if the second child is a boy? A girl?

3. MAKE CONNECTIONS Consider what you learned about dominant and recessive alleles in Concept 14.1. If a disorder were caused by a dominant X-linked allele, how would the inheritance pattern differ from what we see for recessive X-linked disorders?

For suggested answers, see Appendix A.

Linked genes tend to be inherited together because they are located near each other on the same chromosome

The number of genes in a cell is far greater than the number of chromosomes; in fact, each chromosome (except the Y) has hundreds or thousands of genes. Genes located near each other on the same chromosome tend to be inherited together in genetic crosses; such genes are said to be genetically linked and are called **linked genes**. When geneticists follow linked genes in breeding experiments, the results deviate from those expected from Mendel's law of independent assortment.

How Linkage Affects Inheritance

To see how linkage between genes affects the inheritance of two different characters, let's examine another of Morgan's *Drosophila* experiments. In this case, the characters are body color and wing size, each with two different phenotypes. Wild-type flies have gray bodies and normal-sized wings. In addition to these flies, Morgan had managed to obtain, through breeding, doubly mutant flies with black bodies and wings much smaller than normal, called vestigial wings. The mutant alleles are recessive to the wild-type alleles, and neither gene is on a sex chromosome. In his investigation of these two genes, Morgan carried out the crosses shown in **Figure 15.9**. The first was a P generation cross to generate F_1 dihybrid flies, and the second was a testcross.

▼ **Figure 15.9** Inquiry

How does linkage between two genes affect inheritance of characters?

Experiment Morgan wanted to know whether the genes for body color and wing size are genetically linked, and if so, how this affects their inheritance. The alleles for body color are b^+ (gray) and b (black), and those for wing size are vg^+ (normal) and vg (vestigial).

Morgan mated true-breeding P (parental) generation flies—wild-type flies with black, vestigial-winged flies—to produce heterozygous F_1 dihybrids ($b^+ b\ vg^+ vg$), all of which are wild-type in appearance.

He then mated wild-type F_1 dihybrid females with homozygous recessive males. This testcross will reveal the genotype of the eggs made by the dihybrid female.

The testcross male's sperm contributes only recessive alleles, so the phenotype of the offspring reflects the genotype of the female's eggs.

Note: Although only females (with pointed abdomens) are shown, half the offspring in each class would be males (with rounded abdomens).

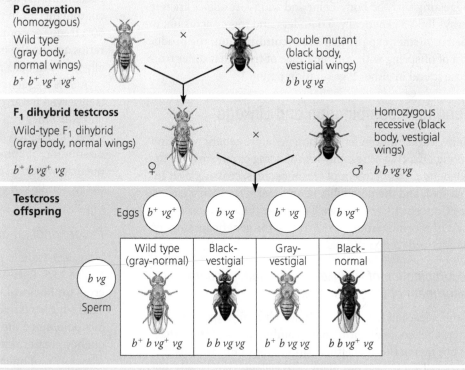

P Generation (homozygous)

Wild type (gray body, normal wings)
$b^+ b^+ vg^+ vg^+$

× Double mutant (black body, vestigial wings)
$b\ b\ vg\ vg$

F_1 dihybrid testcross

Wild-type F_1 dihybrid (gray body, normal wings)
$b^+ b\ vg^+ vg$ ♀

× Homozygous recessive (black body, vestigial wings)
♂ $b\ b\ vg\ vg$

Testcross offspring

Eggs: $b^+ vg^+$ | $b\ vg$ | $b^+ vg$ | $b\ vg^+$

Sperm: $b\ vg$

Wild type (gray-normal)	Black-vestigial	Gray-vestigial	Black-normal
$b^+ b\ vg^+ vg$	$b\ b\ vg\ vg$	$b^+ b\ vg\ vg$	$b\ b\ vg^+ vg$

PREDICTED RATIOS

Predicted ratio if genes are located on different chromosomes:	1	:	1	:	1	:	1
Predicted ratio if genes are located on the same chromosome *and* parental alleles are always inherited together:	1	:	1	:	0	:	0
Results Data from Morgan's experiment:	965	:	944	:	206	:	185

Conclusion Since most offspring had a parental (P generation) phenotype, Morgan concluded that the genes for body color and wing size are genetically linked on the same chromosome. However, the production of a relatively small number of offspring with nonparental phenotypes indicated that some mechanism occasionally breaks the linkage between specific alleles of genes on the same chromosome.

Source: T. H. Morgan and C. J. Lynch, The linkage of two factors in *Drosophila* that are not sex-linked, *Biological Bulletin* 23:174–182 (1912).

WHAT IF? *If the parental (P generation) flies had been true-breeding for gray body with vestigial wings and black body with normal wings, which phenotypic class(es) would be largest among the testcross offspring?*

The resulting flies had a much higher proportion of the combinations of traits seen in the P generation flies (called parental phenotypes) than would be expected if the two genes assorted independently. Morgan thus concluded that body color and wing size are usually inherited together in specific (parental) combinations because the genes for these characters are near each other on the same chromosome:

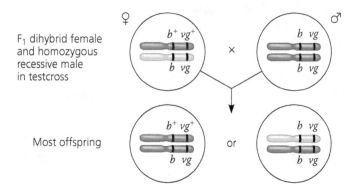

F₁ dihybrid female and homozygous recessive male in testcross

Most offspring

However, as Figure 15.9 shows, both of the combinations of traits not seen in the P generation (called nonparental phenotypes) were also produced in Morgan's experiments, suggesting that the body-color and wing-size alleles are not always linked genetically. To understand this conclusion, we need to further explore **genetic recombination**, the production of offspring with combinations of traits that differ from those found in either P generation parent.*

Genetic Recombination and Linkage

Meiosis and random fertilization generate genetic variation among offspring of sexually reproducing organisms due to independent assortment of chromosomes, crossing over in meiosis I, and the possibility of any sperm fertilizing any egg (see Concept 13.4). Here we'll examine the chromosomal basis of recombination in relation to the genetic findings of Mendel and Morgan.

Recombination of Unlinked Genes: Independent Assortment of Chromosomes

Mendel learned from crosses in which he followed two characters that some offspring have combinations of traits that do not match those of either parent. For example, consider a cross of a dihybrid pea plant with yellow-round seeds, heterozygous for both seed color and seed shape (*YyRr*), with a plant homozygous for both recessive alleles (with green-wrinkled seeds, *yyrr*). (This acts as a testcross because the results will reveal the genotype of the gametes made in the

---

* As you proceed, be sure to keep in mind the distinction between the terms *linked genes* (two or more genes on the same chromosome that tend to be inherited together) and *sex-linked gene* (a single gene on a sex chromosome).

dihybrid *YyRr* plant.) Let's represent the cross by the following Punnett square:

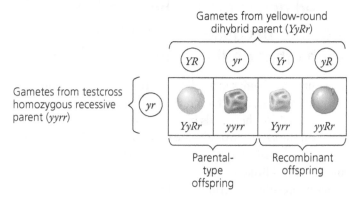

Notice in this Punnett square that one-half of the offspring are expected to inherit a phenotype that matches either of the phenotypes of the P (parental) generation originally crossed to produce the F₁ dihybrid (see Figure 15.2). These matching offspring are called **parental types**. But two non-parental phenotypes are also found among the offspring. Because these offspring have new combinations of seed shape and color, they are called **recombinant types**, or **recombinants** for short. When 50% of all offspring are recombinants, as in this example, geneticists say that there is a 50% frequency of recombination. The predicted phenotypic ratios among the offspring are similar to what Mendel actually found in his *YyRr* × *yyrr* crosses.

A 50% frequency of recombination in such testcrosses is observed for any two genes that are located on different chromosomes and thus cannot be linked. The physical basis of recombination between unlinked genes is the random orientation of homologous chromosomes at metaphase I of meiosis, which leads to the independent assortment of the two unlinked genes (see Figure 13.11 and the question in the Figure 15.2 legend).

Recombination of Linked Genes: Crossing Over

Now, let's explain the results of the *Drosophila* testcross in Figure 15.9. Recall that most of the offspring from the testcross for body color and wing size had parental phenotypes. That suggested that the two genes were on the same chromosome, since the occurrence of parental types with a frequency greater than 50% indicates that the genes are linked. About 17% of offspring, however, were recombinants.

Seeing these results, Morgan proposed that some process must occasionally break the physical connection between specific alleles of genes on the same chromosome. Later experiments showed that this process, now called **crossing over**, accounts for the recombination of linked genes. In crossing over, which occurs while replicated homologous chromosomes are paired during prophase of meiosis I, a set of proteins orchestrates an exchange of corresponding segments of one maternal and one paternal chromatid (see

► **Figure 15.10 Chromosomal basis for recombination of linked genes.** In these diagrams re-creating the testcross in Figure 15.9, we track chromosomes as well as genes. The maternal chromosomes (present in the wild-type F_1 dihybrid) are color-coded red and pink to distinguish one homolog from the other before any meiotic crossing over has occurred. Because crossing over between the b^+/b and vg^+/vg loci occurs in some, but not all, egg-producing cells, more eggs with parental-type chromosomes than with recombinant ones are produced in the mating females. Fertilization of the eggs by sperm of genotype $b\ vg$ gives rise to some recombinant offspring. The recombination frequency is the percentage of recombinant flies in the total pool of offspring.

DRAW IT *Suppose, as in the question at the bottom of Figure 15.9, the parental (P generation) flies were true-breeding for gray body with vestigial wings and black body with normal wings. Draw the chromosomes in each of the four possible kinds of eggs from an F_1 female, and label each chromosome as "parental" or "recombinant."*

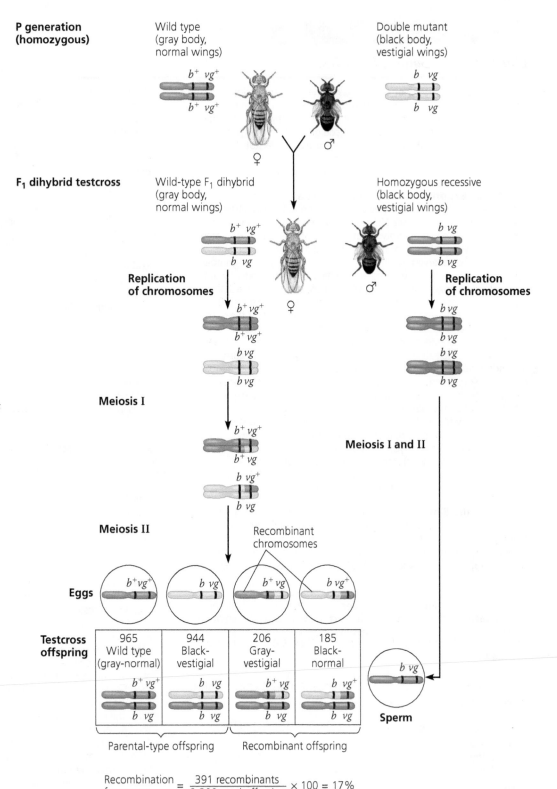

$$\text{Recombination frequency} = \frac{391 \text{ recombinants}}{2,300 \text{ total offspring}} \times 100 = 17\%$$

Figure 13.9). In effect, when a single crossover occurs, end portions of two nonsister chromatids trade places.

Figure 15.10 shows how crossing over in a dihybrid female fly resulted in recombinant eggs and ultimately recombinant offspring in Morgan's testcross. Most eggs had a chromosome with either the $b^+\ vg^+$ or $b\ vg$ parental genotype, but some had a recombinant chromosome ($b^+\ vg$ or $b\ vg^+$). Fertilization of

all classes of eggs by homozygous recessive sperm ($b\ vg$) produced an offspring population in which 17% exhibited a nonparental, recombinant phenotype, reflecting combinations of alleles not seen before in either P generation parent. In the Scientific Skills Exercise, you can use a statistical test to analyze the results from an F_1 dihybrid testcross and see whether the two genes assort independently or are linked.

Using the Chi-Square (χ^2) Test

Are Two Genes Linked or Unlinked? Genes that are in close proximity on the same chromosome will result in the linked alleles being inherited together more often than not. But how can you tell if certain alleles are inherited together due to linkage or whether they just happen to assort together? In this exercise, you will use a simple statistical test, the chi-square (χ^2) test, to analyze phenotypes of F_1 testcross progeny in order to see whether two genes are linked or unlinked.

How These Experiments Are Done If genes are unlinked and assorting independently, the phenotypic ratio of offspring from an F_1 testcross is expected to be 1:1:1:1 (see Figure 15.9). If the two genes are linked, however, the observed phenotypic ratio of the offspring will not match that ratio. Given that random fluctuations in the data do occur, how much must the observed numbers deviate from the expected numbers for us to conclude that the genes are not assorting independently but may instead be linked? To answer this question, scientists use a statistical test. This test, called a chi-square (χ^2) test, compares an observed data set to an expected data set predicted by a hypothesis (here, that the genes are unlinked) and measures the discrepancy between the two, thus determining the "goodness of fit." If the discrepancy between the observed and expected data sets is so large that it is unlikely to have occurred by random fluctuation, we say there is statistically significant evidence against the hypothesis (or, more specifically, evidence for the genes being linked). If the discrepancy is small, then our observations are well explained by random variation alone. In this case, we say the observed data are consistent with our hypothesis, or that the discrepancy is statistically insignificant. Note, however, that consistency with our hypothesis is not the same as proof of our hypothesis. Also, the size of the experimental data set is important: With small data sets like this one, even if the genes are linked, discrepancies might be small by chance alone if the linkage is weak. For simplicity, we overlook the effect of sample size here.

Data from the Simulated Experiment In cosmos plants, purple stem (A) is dominant to green stem (a), and short petals (B) is dominant to long petals (b). In a simulated cross, $AABB$ plants were crossed with $aabb$ plants to generate F_1 dihybrids ($AaBb$), which were then testcrossed ($AaBb \times aabb$). A total of 900 offspring plants were scored for stem color and flower petal length.

Offspring from test-cross of $AaBb$ (F_1) × $aabb$	Purple stem/short petals (A–B–)	Green stem/short petals (aaB–)	Purple stem/long petals (A–bb)	Green stem/long petals ($aabb$)
Expected ratio if the genes are unlinked	1	1	1	1
Expected number of offspring (of 900)				
Observed number of offspring (of 900)	220	210	231	239

Interpret the Data

1. The results in the data table are from a simulated F_1 dihybrid testcross. The hypothesis that the two genes are unlinked predicts the offspring phenotypic ratio will be 1:1:1:1. Using this ratio, calculate

the expected number of each phenotype out of the 900 total offspring, and enter the values in the data table.

▲ Cosmos plants

2. The goodness of fit is measured by χ^2. This statistic measures the amounts by which the observed values differ from their respective predictions to indicate how closely the two sets of values match. The formula for calculating this value is

$$\chi^2 = \sum \frac{(o - e)^2}{e}$$

where o = observed and e = expected. Calculate the χ^2 value for the data using the table below. Fill out the table, carrying out the operations indicated in the top row. Then add up the entries in the last column to find the χ^2 value.

Testcross Offspring	Expected (e)	Observed (o)	Deviation (o−e)	(o−e)²	(o−e)²/e
(A–B–)		220			
(aaB–)		210			
(A–bb)		231			
($aabb$)		239			
				χ^2 = Sum	

3. The χ^2 value means nothing on its own—it is used to find the probability that, assuming the hypothesis is true, the observed data set could have resulted from random fluctuations. A low probability suggests that the observed data are not consistent with the hypothesis, and thus the hypothesis should be rejected. A standard cutoff point used by biologists is a probability of 0.05 (5%). If the probability corresponding to the χ^2 value is 0.05 or less, the differences between observed and expected values are considered statistically significant and the hypothesis (that the genes are unlinked) should be rejected. If the probability is above 0.05, the results are not statistically significant; the observed data are consistent with the hypothesis. To find the probability, locate your χ^2 value in the χ^2 Distribution Table in Appendix F. The "degrees of freedom" (df) of your data set is the number of categories (here, 4 phenotypes) minus 1, so df = 3. (a) Determine which values on the df = 3 line of the table your calculated χ^2 value lies between. (b) The column headings for these values show the probability range for your χ^2 number. Based on whether there are nonsignificant ($p > 0.05$) or significant ($p \leq 0.05$) differences between the observed and expected values, are the data consistent with the hypothesis that the two genes are unlinked and assorting independently, or is there enough evidence to reject this hypothesis?

MB A version of this Scientific Skills Exercise can be assigned in MasteringBiology.

New Combinations of Alleles: Variation for Natural Selection

EVOLUTION The physical behavior of chromosomes during meiosis contributes to the generation of variation in offspring (see Concept 13.4). Each pair of homologous chromosomes lines up independently of other pairs during metaphase I, and crossing over prior to that, during prophase I, can mix and match parts of maternal and paternal homologs. Mendel's elegant experiments show that the behavior of the abstract entities known as genes—or, more concretely, alleles of genes—also leads to variation in offspring (see Concept 14.1). Now, putting these different ideas together, you can see that the recombinant chromosomes resulting from crossing over may bring alleles together in new combinations, and the subsequent events of meiosis distribute to gametes the recombinant chromosomes in a multitude of combinations, such as the new variants seen in Figures 15.9 and 15.10. Random fertilization then increases even further the number of variant allele combinations that can be created.

This abundance of genetic variation provides the raw material on which natural selection works. If the traits conferred by particular combinations of alleles are better suited for a given environment, organisms possessing those genotypes will be expected to thrive and leave more offspring, ensuring the continuation of their genetic complement. In the next generation, of course, the alleles will be shuffled anew. Ultimately, the interplay between environment and genotype will determine which genetic combinations persist over time.

Mapping the Distance Between Genes Using Recombination Data: *Scientific Inquiry*

The discovery of linked genes and recombination due to crossing over motivated one of Morgan's students, Alfred H. Sturtevant, to work out a method for constructing a **genetic map**, an ordered list of the genetic loci along a particular chromosome.

Sturtevant hypothesized that the percentage of recombinant offspring, the *recombination frequency*, calculated from experiments like the one in Figures 15.9 and 15.10, depends on the distance between genes on a chromosome. He assumed that crossing over is a random event, with the chance of crossing over approximately equal at all points along a chromosome. Based on these assumptions, Sturtevant predicted that *the farther apart two genes are, the higher the probability that a crossover will occur between them and therefore the higher the recombination frequency.* His reasoning was simple: The greater the distance between two genes, the more points there are between them where crossing over can occur. Using recombination data from various fruit fly crosses, Sturtevant proceeded to assign relative positions to genes on the same chromosomes—that is, to *map* genes.

A genetic map based on recombination frequencies is called a **linkage map**. **Figure 15.11** shows Sturtevant's linkage map of three genes: the body-color (*b*) and wing-size (*vg*) genes depicted in Figure 15.10 and a third gene, called cinnabar (*cn*). Cinnabar is one of many *Drosophila* genes affecting eye color. Cinnabar eyes, a mutant phenotype, are a brighter red than the wild-type color. The recombination frequency between *cn* and *b* is 9%; that between *cn* and *vg*, 9.5%; and that between *b* and *vg*, 17%. In other words, crossovers between *cn* and *b* and between *cn* and *vg* are about half as frequent as crossovers between *b* and *vg*. Only a map that locates *cn* about midway between *b* and *vg* is consistent with these data, as you can prove to yourself by drawing alternative maps. Sturtevant expressed the distances between genes in **map units**, defining one map unit as equivalent to a 1% recombination frequency.

In practice, the interpretation of recombination data is more complicated than this example suggests. Some genes on a chromosome are so far from each other that a crossover between them is virtually certain. The observed frequency of recombination in crosses involving two such

---

▼ **Figure 15.11** | **Research Method**

Constructing a Linkage Map

Application A linkage map shows the relative locations of genes along a chromosome.

Technique A linkage map is based on the assumption that the probability of a crossover between two genetic loci is proportional to the distance separating the loci. The recombination frequencies used to construct a linkage map for a particular chromosome are obtained from experimental crosses, such as the cross depicted in Figures 15.9 and 15.10. The distances between genes are expressed as map units, with one map unit equivalent to a 1% recombination frequency. Genes are arranged on the chromosome in the order that best fits the data.

Results In this example, the observed recombination frequencies between three *Drosophila* gene pairs (*b–cn* 9%, *cn–vg* 9.5%, and *b–vg* 17%) best fit a linear order in which *cn* is positioned about halfway between the other two genes:

The *b–vg* recombination frequency (17%) is slightly less than the sum of the *b–cn* and *cn–vg* frequencies (9 + 9.5 = 18.5%) because of the few times that one crossover occurs between *b* and *cn* and another crossover occurs between *cn* and *vg*. The second crossover would "cancel out" the first, reducing the observed *b–vg* recombination frequency while contributing to the frequency between each of the closer pairs of genes. The value of 18.5% (18.5 map units) is closer to the actual distance between the genes. In practice, a geneticist would add the smaller distances in constructing a map.

genes can have a maximum value of 50%, a result indistinguishable from that for genes on different chromosomes. In this case, the physical connection between genes on the same chromosome is not reflected in the results of genetic crosses. Despite being on the same chromosome and thus being *physically connected*, the genes are *genetically unlinked*; alleles of such genes assort independently, as if they were on different chromosomes. In fact, at least two of the genes for pea characters that Mendel studied are now known to be on the same chromosome, but the distance between them is so great that linkage is not observed in genetic crosses. Consequently, the two genes behaved as if they were on different chromosomes in Mendel's experiments. Genes located far apart on a chromosome are mapped by adding the recombination frequencies from crosses involving closer pairs of genes lying between the two distant genes.

Using recombination data, Sturtevant and his colleagues were able to map numerous *Drosophila* genes in linear arrays. They found that the genes clustered into four groups of linked genes (*linkage groups*). Light microscopy had revealed four pairs of chromosomes in *Drosophila*, so the linkage map provided additional evidence that genes are located on chromosomes. Each chromosome has a linear array of specific genes, each gene with its own locus (**Figure 15.12**).

Because a linkage map is based strictly on recombination frequencies, it gives only an approximate picture of a chromosome. The frequency of crossing over is not actually uniform over the length of a chromosome, as Sturtevant assumed, and therefore map units do not correspond to actual physical distances (in nanometers, for instance). A linkage map does portray the order of genes along a chromosome, but it does not accurately portray the precise locations of those genes. Other methods enable geneticists to construct *cytogenetic maps* of chromosomes, which locate genes with respect to chromosomal features, such as stained bands, that can be seen in the microscope. Technical advances over the last two decades have enormously increased the rate and affordability of DNA sequencing. Today, most researchers sequence whole genomes to map the locations of genes of a given species. The entire nucleotide sequence is the ultimate physical map of a chromosome, revealing the physical distances between gene loci in DNA nucleotides (see Concept 21.1). Comparing a linkage map with such a physical map or with a cytogenetic map of the same chromosome, we find that the linear order of genes is identical in all the maps, but the spacing between genes is not.

CONCEPT CHECK 15.3

1. When two genes are located on the same chromosome, what is the physical basis for the production of recombinant offspring in a testcross between a dihybrid parent and a double-mutant (recessive) parent?

2. For each type of offspring of the testcross in Figure 15.9, explain the relationship between its phenotype and the alleles contributed by the female parent. (It will be useful to draw out the chromosomes of each fly and follow the alleles throughout the cross.)

3. **WHAT IF?** Genes *A*, *B*, and *C* are located on the same chromosome. Testcrosses show that the recombination frequency between *A* and *B* is 28% and between *A* and *C* is 12%. Can you determine the linear order of these genes? Explain.

For suggested answers, see Appendix A.

CONCEPT 15.4

Alterations of chromosome number or structure cause some genetic disorders

As you have learned so far in this chapter, the phenotype of an organism can be affected by small-scale changes involving individual genes. Random mutations are the source of all new alleles, which can lead to new phenotypic traits.

Large-scale chromosomal changes can also affect an organism's phenotype. Physical and chemical disturbances, as well as errors during meiosis, can damage chromosomes in major ways or alter their number in a cell. Large-scale chromosomal alterations in humans and other mammals often lead to spontaneous abortion (miscarriage) of a fetus, and individuals born with these types of genetic defects commonly exhibit various developmental disorders. Plants may tolerate such genetic defects better than animals do.

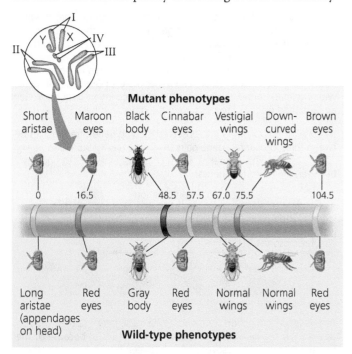

▲ **Figure 15.12 A partial genetic (linkage) map of a *Drosophila* chromosome.** This simplified map shows just seven of the genes that have been mapped on *Drosophila* chromosome II. (DNA sequencing has revealed over 9,000 genes on that chromosome.) The number at each gene locus indicates the number of map units between that locus and the locus for arista length (left). Notice that more than one gene can affect a given phenotypic characteristic, such as eye color.

Abnormal Chromosome Number

Ideally, the meiotic spindle distributes chromosomes to daughter cells without error. But there is an occasional mishap, called a **nondisjunction**, in which the members of a pair of homologous chromosomes do not move apart properly during meiosis I or sister chromatids fail to separate during meiosis II **(Figure 15.13)**. In nondisjunction, one gamete receives two of the same type of chromosome and another gamete receives no copy. The other chromosomes are usually distributed normally.

If either of the aberrant gametes unites with a normal one at fertilization, the zygote will also have an abnormal number of a particular chromosome, a condition known as **aneuploidy**. Fertilization involving a gamete that has no copy of a particular chromosome will lead to a missing chromosome in the zygote (so that the cell has $2n - 1$ chromosomes); the aneuploid zygote is said to be **monosomic** for that chromosome. If a chromosome is present in triplicate in the zygote (so that the cell has $2n + 1$ chromosomes), the aneuploid cell is **trisomic** for that chromosome. Mitosis will subsequently transmit the anomaly to all embryonic cells. Monosomy and trisomy are estimated to occur in between 10 and 25% of human conceptions, and is the main reason for pregnancy loss. If the organism survives, it usually has a set of traits caused by the abnormal dose of the genes associated with the extra or missing chromosome. Down syndrome is an example of trisomy in humans that will be discussed later. Nondisjunction can also occur during mitosis. If such an error takes place early in embryonic development, then the aneuploid condition is passed along by mitosis to a large number of cells and is likely to have a substantial effect on the organism.

Some organisms have more than two complete chromosome sets in all somatic cells. The general term for this chromosomal alteration is **polyploidy**; the specific terms *triploidy* (3n) and *tetraploidy* (4n) indicate three or four chromosomal sets, respectively. One way a triploid cell may arise is by the fertilization of an abnormal diploid egg produced by nondisjunction of all its chromosomes. Tetraploidy could result from the failure of a 2n zygote to divide after replicating its chromosomes. Subsequent normal mitotic divisions would then produce a 4n embryo.

Polyploidy is fairly common in the plant kingdom. The spontaneous origin of polyploid individuals plays an important role in plant evolution (see Chapter 24). Many species we eat are polyploid: Bananas are triploid, wheat hexaploid (6n), and strawberries octoploid (8n). Polyploid animal species are much less common, but there are a few fishes and amphibians known to be polyploid. In general, polyploids are more nearly normal in appearance than aneuploids. One extra (or missing) chromosome apparently disrupts genetic balance more than does an entire extra set of chromosomes.

Alterations of Chromosome Structure

Errors in meiosis or damaging agents such as radiation can cause breakage of a chromosome, which can lead to four types of changes in chromosome structure **(Figure 15.14)**. A **deletion** occurs when a chromosomal fragment is lost. The affected chromosome is then missing certain genes. The "deleted" fragment may become attached as an extra segment to a sister chromatid, producing a **duplication**. Alternatively, a detached fragment could attach to a nonsister chromatid of a homologous chromosome. In that case, though, the "duplicated" segments might not be identical because the homologs could carry different alleles of certain genes. A chromosomal fragment may also reattach to the original chromosome but in the reverse orientation, producing an **inversion**. A fourth possible result of chromosomal breakage is for the fragment to join a nonhomologous chromosome, a rearrangement called a **translocation**.

Deletions and duplications are especially likely to occur during meiosis. In crossing over, nonsister chromatids sometimes exchange unequal-sized segments of DNA, so that one partner gives up more genes than it receives. The products of such an unequal crossover are one chromosome with a deletion and one chromosome with a duplication.

A diploid embryo that is homozygous for a large deletion (or has a single X chromosome with a large deletion, in a male) is usually missing a number of essential genes, a condition typically lethal. Duplications and translocations also tend

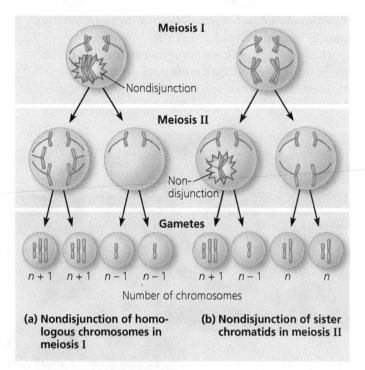

▲ **Figure 15.13 Meiotic nondisjunction.** Gametes with an abnormal chromosome number can arise by nondisjunction in either meiosis I or meiosis II. For simplicity, the figure does not show the spores formed by meiosis in plants. Ultimately, spores form gametes that have the defects shown. (See Figure 13.6.)

Within figure:

Meiosis I

Nondisjunction

Meiosis II

Non-disjunction

Gametes

$n + 1$ $n + 1$ $n - 1$ $n - 1$ $n + 1$ $n - 1$ n n

Number of chromosomes

(a) Nondisjunction of homologous chromosomes in meiosis I

(b) Nondisjunction of sister chromatids in meiosis II

▼ **Figure 15.14 Alterations of chromosome structure.** Red arrows indicate breakage points. Dark purple highlights the chromosomal parts affected by the rearrangements.

(a) Deletion

A **deletion** removes a chromosomal segment.

(b) Duplication

A **duplication** repeats a segment.

(c) Inversion

An **inversion** reverses a segment within a chromosome.

(d) Translocation

A **translocation** moves a segment from one chromosome to a nonhomologous chromosome. In a reciprocal translocation, the most common type, nonhomologous chromosomes exchange fragments.

Less often, a nonreciprocal translocation occurs: A chromosome transfers a fragment but receives none in return (not shown).

Human Disorders Due to Chromosomal Alterations

Alterations of chromosome number and structure are associated with a number of serious human disorders. As described earlier, nondisjunction in meiosis results in aneuploidy in gametes and any resulting zygotes. Although the frequency of aneuploid zygotes may be quite high in humans, most of these chromosomal alterations are so disastrous to development that the affected embryos are spontaneously aborted long before birth. However, some types of aneuploidy appear to upset the genetic balance less than others, where individuals with certain aneuploid conditions can survive to birth and beyond. These individuals have a set of traits—a *syndrome*—characteristic of the type of aneuploidy. Genetic disorders caused by aneuploidy can be diagnosed before birth by fetal testing (see Figure 14.19).

Down Syndrome (Trisomy 21)

One aneuploid condition, **Down syndrome**, affects approximately one out of every 830 children born in the United States **(Figure 15.15)**. Down syndrome is usually the result of an extra chromosome 21, so that each body cell has a total of 47 chromosomes. Because the cells are trisomic for chromosome 21, Down syndrome is often called *trisomy 21*. Down syndrome includes characteristic facial features, short stature, correctable heart defects, and developmental delays. Individuals with Down syndrome have an increased chance of developing leukemia and Alzheimer's disease but have a lower rate of high blood pressure, atherosclerosis (hardening of the arteries), stroke, and many types of solid tumors. Although people with Down syndrome, on average, have a life span shorter than normal, most, with proper medical treatment, live to middle age and beyond. Many live independently or at home with their families, are employed, and are valuable contributors to their communities. Almost all males and about half of females with Down syndrome are sexually underdeveloped and sterile.

The frequency of Down syndrome increases with the age of the mother. While the disorder occurs in just 0.04% of children born to women under age 30, the risk climbs to be harmful. In reciprocal translocations, in which segments are exchanged between nonhomologous chromosomes, and in inversions, the balance of genes is not abnormal—all genes are present in their normal doses. Nevertheless, translocations and inversions can alter phenotype because a gene's expression can be influenced by its location among neighboring genes, which can have devastating effects.

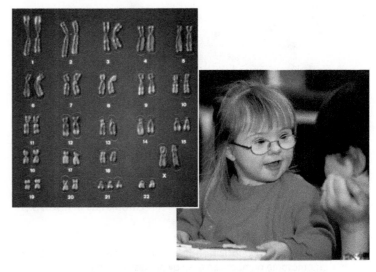

▲ **Figure 15.15 Down syndrome.** The karyotype shows trisomy 21, the most common cause of Down syndrome. The child exhibits the facial features characteristic of this disorder.

to 0.92% for mothers at age 40 and is even higher for older mothers. The correlation of Down syndrome with maternal age has not yet been explained. Most cases result from nondisjunction during meiosis I, and some research points to an age-dependent abnormality in meiosis. Trisomies of some other chromosomes also increase in incidence with maternal age, although infants with other autosomal trisomies rarely survive for long. Due to its low risk and its potential for providing useful information, prenatal screening for trisomies in the embryo is now offered to all pregnant women. In 2008, the Prenatally and Postnatally Diagnosed Conditions Awareness Act was signed into law in the United States. This law stipulates that medical practitioners give accurate, up-to-date information about any prenatal or postnatal diagnosis received by parents and that they connect parents with appropriate support services.

Aneuploidy of Sex Chromosomes

Aneuploid conditions involving sex chromosomes appear to upset the genetic balance less than those involving autosomes. This may be because the Y chromosome carries relatively few genes. Also, extra copies of the X chromosome simply become inactivated as Barr bodies.

An extra X chromosome in a male, producing XXY, occurs approximately once in every 500 to 1,000 live male births. People with this disorder, called *Klinefelter syndrome*, have male sex organs, but the testes are abnormally small and the man is sterile. Even though the extra X is inactivated, some breast enlargement and other female body characteristics are common. Affected individuals may have subnormal intelligence. About 1 of every 1,000 males is born with an extra Y chromosome (XYY). These males undergo normal sexual development and do not exhibit any well-defined syndrome, but tend to be taller than average.

Females with trisomy X (XXX), which occurs once in approximately 1,000 live female births, are healthy and have no unusual physical features other than being slightly taller than average. Triple-X females are at risk for learning disabilities but are fertile. Monosomy X, which is called *Turner syndrome*, occurs about once in every 2,500 female births and is the only known viable monosomy in humans. Although these X0 individuals are phenotypically female, they are sterile because their sex organs do not mature. When provided with estrogen replacement therapy, girls with Turner syndrome do develop secondary sex characteristics. Most have normal intelligence.

Disorders Caused by Structurally Altered Chromosomes

Many deletions in human chromosomes, even in a heterozygous state, cause severe problems. One such syndrome, known as *cri du chat* ("cry of the cat"), results from a specific deletion in chromosome 5. A child born with this deletion is severely intellectually disabled, has a small head with

▲ **Figure 15.16 Translocation associated with chronic myelogenous leukemia (CML).** The cancerous cells in nearly all CML patients contain an abnormally short chromosome 22, the so-called Philadelphia chromosome, and an abnormally long chromosome 9. These altered chromosomes result from the reciprocal translocation shown here, which presumably occurred in a single white blood cell precursor undergoing mitosis and was then passed along to all descendant cells.

unusual facial features, and has a cry that sounds like the mewing of a distressed cat. Such individuals usually die in infancy or early childhood.

Chromosomal translocations have been implicated in certain cancers, including *chronic myelogenous leukemia* (*CML*). This disease occurs when a reciprocal translocation happens during mitosis of cells that will become white blood cells. In these cells, the exchange of a large portion of chromosome 22 with a small fragment from a tip of chromosome 9 produces a much shortened, easily recognized chromosome 22, called the *Philadelphia chromosome* (**Figure 15.16**). Such an exchange causes cancer by activating a gene that leads to uncontrolled cell cycle progression. (The mechanism of gene activation will be discussed in Chapter 18.)

CONCEPT CHECK 15.4

1. About 5% of individuals with Down syndrome have a chromosomal translocation in which a third copy of chromosome 21 is attached to chromosome 14. If this translocation occurred in a parent's gonad, how could it lead to Down syndrome in a child?

2. **WHAT IF?** The ABO blood type locus has been mapped on chromosome 9. A father who has type AB blood and a mother who has type O blood have a child with trisomy 9 and type A blood. Using this information, can you tell in which parent the nondisjunction occurred? Explain your answer. (See Figure 14.11.)

3. **MAKE CONNECTIONS** The gene that is activated on the Philadelphia chromosome codes for an intracellular tyrosine kinase. Review the discussion of cell cycle control in Concept 12.3, and explain how the activation of this gene could contribute to the development of cancer.

For suggested answers, see Appendix A.

CONCEPT 15.5

Some inheritance patterns are exceptions to standard Mendelian inheritance

In the previous section, you learned about deviations from the usual patterns of chromosomal inheritance due to abnormal events in meiosis and mitosis. We conclude this chapter by describing two normally occurring exceptions to Mendelian genetics, one involving genes located in the nucleus and the other involving genes located outside the nucleus. In both cases, the sex of the parent contributing an allele is a factor in the pattern of inheritance.

Genomic Imprinting

Throughout our discussions of Mendelian genetics and the chromosomal basis of inheritance, we have assumed that a given allele will have the same effect whether it was inherited from the mother or the father. This is probably a safe assumption most of the time. For example, when Mendel crossed purple-flowered pea plants with white-flowered pea plants, he observed the same results regardless of whether the purple-flowered parent supplied the eggs or the sperm. In recent years, however, geneticists have identified a number of traits in mammals that depend on which parent passed along the alleles for those traits. Such variation in phenotype depending on whether an allele is inherited from the male or female parent is called **genomic imprinting**. (Note that unlike sex-linked genes, most imprinted genes are on autosomes.) Using newer DNA sequence-based methods, over 60 imprinted genes have been identified, with hundreds more suspected.

Genomic imprinting occurs during gamete formation and results in the silencing of a particular allele of certain genes. Because these genes are imprinted differently in sperm and eggs, the offspring expresses only one allele of an imprinted gene, the one that has been inherited from either the female or the male parent. The imprints are then transmitted to all body cells during development. In each generation, the old imprints are "erased" in gamete-producing cells, and the chromosomes of the developing gametes are newly imprinted according to the sex of the individual forming the gametes. In a given species, the imprinted genes are always imprinted in the same way. For instance, a gene imprinted for maternal allele expression is always imprinted this way, generation after generation.

Consider, for example, the mouse gene for insulin-like growth factor 2 (*Igf2*), one of the first imprinted genes to be identified. Although this growth factor is required for normal prenatal growth, only the paternal allele is expressed (Figure 15.17a). Evidence that the *Igf2* gene is imprinted

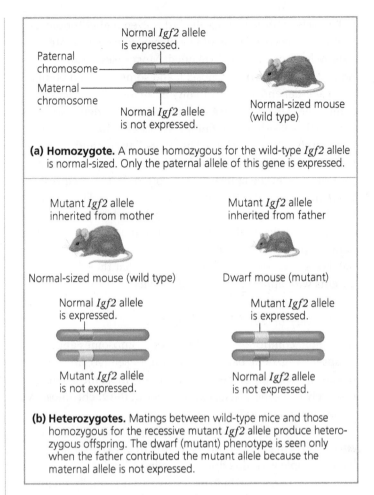

(a) Homozygote. A mouse homozygous for the wild-type *Igf2* allele is normal-sized. Only the paternal allele of this gene is expressed.

(b) Heterozygotes. Matings between wild-type mice and those homozygous for the recessive mutant *Igf2* allele produce heterozygous offspring. The dwarf (mutant) phenotype is seen only when the father contributed the mutant allele because the maternal allele is not expressed.

▲ **Figure 15.17 Genomic imprinting of the mouse *Igf2* gene.**

came initially from crosses between normal-sized (wild-type) mice and dwarf (mutant) mice homozygous for a recessive mutation in the *Igf2* gene. The phenotypes of heterozygous offspring (with one normal allele and one mutant) differed depending on whether the mutant allele came from the mother or the father (**Figure 15.17b**).

What exactly is a genomic imprint? In many cases, it seems to consist of methyl (—CH$_3$) groups that are added to cytosine nucleotides of one of the alleles. Such methylation may silence the allele, an effect consistent with evidence that heavily methylated genes are usually inactive (see Concept 18.2). However, for a few genes, methylation has been shown to *activate* expression of the allele. This is the case for the *Igf2* gene: Methylation of certain cytosines on the paternal chromosome leads to expression of the paternal *Igf2* allele, by an indirect mechanism involving chromatin condensation.

Genomic imprinting is thought to affect only a small fraction of the genes in mammalian genomes, but most of the known imprinted genes are critical for embryonic development. In experiments with mice, embryos engineered to inherit both copies of certain chromosomes from the same parent usually die before birth, whether that parent is male or female. A few years ago, however, scientists in Japan combined the genetic material from two eggs in a zygote while allowing expression of the *Igf2* gene from only one of the egg nuclei. The zygote developed into an apparently healthy mouse. Normal development seems to require that embryonic cells have exactly one active copy—not zero, not two—of certain genes. The association of improper imprinting with abnormal development and certain cancers has stimulated ongoing studies of how different genes are imprinted.

Inheritance of Organelle Genes

Although our focus in this chapter has been on the chromosomal basis of inheritance, we end with an important amendment: Not all of a eukaryotic cell's genes are located on nuclear chromosomes, or even in the nucleus; some genes are located in organelles in the cytoplasm. Because they are outside the nucleus, these genes are sometimes called *extranuclear genes* or *cytoplasmic genes*. Mitochondria, as well as chloroplasts and other plastids in plants, contain small circular DNA molecules that carry a number of genes. These organelles reproduce themselves and transmit their genes to daughter organelles. Organelle genes are not distributed to offspring according to the same rules that direct the distribution of nuclear chromosomes during meiosis, so they do not display Mendelian inheritance.

The first hint that extranuclear genes exist came from studies by the German scientist Carl Correns on the inheritance of yellow or white patches on the leaves of an otherwise green plant. In 1909, he observed that the coloration of the offspring was determined only by the maternal parent (the source of eggs) and not by the paternal parent (the source of sperm). Subsequent research showed that such coloration patterns, or variegation, are due to mutations in plastid genes that control pigmentation (Figure 15.18). In most plants, a zygote receives all its plastids from the cytoplasm of the egg and none from the sperm, which contributes little more than a haploid set of chromosomes. An egg may contain plastids with different alleles for a pigmentation gene. As the zygote develops, plastids containing wild-type or mutant pigmentation genes are distributed randomly to

daughter cells. The pattern of leaf coloration exhibited by a plant depends on the ratio of wild-type to mutant plastids in its various tissues.

Similar maternal inheritance is also the rule for mitochondrial genes in most animals and plants, because almost all the mitochondria passed on to a zygote come from the cytoplasm of the egg. (The few mitochondria contributed by the sperm appear to be destroyed in the egg by autophagy; see Figure 6.13.) The products of most mitochondrial genes help make up the protein complexes of the electron transport chain and ATP synthase (see Figure 9.15). Defects in one or more of these proteins, therefore, reduce the amount of ATP the cell can make and have been shown to cause a number of rare human disorders. Because the parts of the body most susceptible to energy deprivation are the nervous system and the muscles, most mitochondrial diseases primarily affect these systems. For example, *mitochondrial myopathy* causes weakness, intolerance of exercise, and muscle deterioration. Another mitochondrial disorder is *Leber's hereditary optic neuropathy*, which can produce sudden blindness in people as young as their 20s or 30s. The four mutations found thus far to cause this disorder affect oxidative phosphorylation during cellular respiration, a crucial function for the cell (see Concept 9.4).

In addition to the rare diseases clearly caused by defects in mitochondrial DNA, mitochondrial mutations inherited from a person's mother may contribute to at least some types of diabetes and heart disease, as well as to other disorders that commonly debilitate the elderly, such as Alzheimer's disease. In the course of a lifetime, new mutations gradually accumulate in our mitochondrial DNA, and some researchers think that these mutations play a role in the normal aging process.

Wherever genes are located in the cell—in the nucleus or in cytoplasmic organelles—their inheritance depends on the precise replication of DNA. In the next chapter, you will learn how this molecular reproduction occurs.

▼ **Figure 15.18 A painted nettle coleus plant.** The variegated (patterned) leaves on this coleus plant (*Solenostemon scutellarioides*) result from mutations that affect expression of pigment genes located in plastids, which generally are inherited from the maternal parent.

CONCEPT CHECK 15.5

1. Gene dosage—the number of copies of a gene that are actively being expressed—is important to proper development. Identify and describe two processes that establish the proper dosage of certain genes.

2. Reciprocal crosses between two primrose varieties, A and B, produced the following results: A female × B male → offspring with all green (nonvariegated) leaves; B female × A male → offspring with patterned (variegated) leaves. Explain these results.

3. **WHAT IF?** Mitochondrial genes are critical to the energy metabolism of cells, but mitochondrial disorders caused by mutations in these genes are generally not lethal. Why not?

For suggested answers, see Appendix A.

CONCEPT 15.1

Morgan showed that Mendelian inheritance has its physical basis in the behavior of chromosomes: *scientific inquiry* (pp. 294–295)

- Morgan's work with an eye color gene in *Drosophila* led to the **chromosome theory of inheritance**, which states that genes are located on chromosomes and that the behavior of chromosomes during meiosis accounts for Mendel's laws.

> ? *What characteristic of the sex chromosomes allowed Morgan to correlate their behavior with that of the alleles of the eye-color gene?*

CONCEPT 15.2

Sex-linked genes exhibit unique patterns of inheritance (pp. 296–298)

- Sex is often chromosomally based. Humans and other mammals have an X-Y system in which sex is determined by whether a Y chromosome is present. Other systems are found in birds, fishes, and insects.
- The sex chromosomes carry **sex-linked genes**, virtually all of which are on the X chromosome (X-linked). Any male who inherits a recessive X-linked allele (from his mother) will express the trait, such as color blindness.
- In mammalian females, one of the two X chromosomes in each cell is randomly inactivated during early embryonic development, becoming highly condensed into a **Barr body**.

> ? *Why are males affected much more often than females by X-linked disorders?*

CONCEPT 15.3

Linked genes tend to be inherited together because they are located near each other on the same chromosome (pp. 299–304)

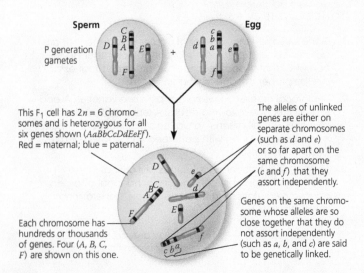

P generation gametes

Sperm | Egg

This F$_1$ cell has 2n = 6 chromosomes and is heterozygous for all six genes shown (*AaBbCcDdEeFf*). Red = maternal; blue = paternal.

The alleles of unlinked genes are either on separate chromosomes (such as *d* and *e*) or so far apart on the same chromosome (*c* and *f*) that they assort independently.

Genes on the same chromosome whose alleles are so close together that they do not assort independently (such as *a*, *b*, and *c*) are said to be genetically linked.

Each chromosome has hundreds or thousands of genes. Four (*A, B, C, F*) are shown on this one.

- Among offspring from an F$_1$ dihybrid testcross, **parental types** have the same combination of traits as those in the P generation parents. **Recombinant types** (**recombinants**) exhibit new combinations of traits not seen in either P generation parent. Because of the independent assortment of chromosomes, unlinked genes exhibit a 50% frequency of recombination in the gametes. For genetically **linked genes**, **crossing over** between nonsister chromatids during meiosis I accounts for the observed recombinants, always less than 50% of the total.
- The order of genes on a chromosome and the relative distances between them can be deduced from recombination frequencies observed in genetic crosses. These data allow construction of a **linkage map** (a type of **genetic map**). The farther apart genes are, the more likely their allele combinations will be recombined during crossing over.

> ? *Why are specific alleles of two distant genes more likely to show recombination than those of two closer genes?*

CONCEPT 15.4

Alterations of chromosome number or structure cause some genetic disorders (pp. 304–307)

- **Aneuploidy**, an abnormal chromosome number, can result from **nondisjunction** during meiosis. When a normal gamete unites with one containing two copies or no copies of a particular chromosome, the resulting zygote and its descendant cells either have one extra copy of that chromosome (**trisomy**, 2n + 1) or are missing a copy (**monosomy**, 2n − 1). **Polyploidy** (more than two complete sets of chromosomes) can result from complete nondisjunction during gamete formation.
- Chromosome breakage can result in alterations of chromosome structure: **deletions**, **duplications**, **inversions**, and **translocations**. Translocations can be reciprocal or nonreciprocal.
- Changes in the number of chromosomes per cell or in the structure of individual chromosomes can affect the phenotype and, in some cases, lead to disorders. Such alterations cause **Down syndrome** (usually due to trisomy of chromosome 21), certain cancers associated with chromosomal translocations, and various other human disorders.

> ? *Why are inversions and reciprocal translocations less likely to be lethal than are aneuploidy, duplications, deletions, and nonreciprocal translocations?*

CONCEPT 15.5

Some inheritance patterns are exceptions to standard Mendelian inheritance (pp. 308–309)

- In mammals, the phenotypic effects of a small number of particular genes depend on which allele is inherited from each parent, a phenomenon called **genomic imprinting**. Imprints are formed during gamete production, with the result that one allele (either maternal or paternal) is not expressed in offspring.
- The inheritance of traits controlled by the genes present in mitochondria and plastids depends solely on the maternal parent because the zygote's cytoplasm containing these organelles comes from the egg. Some diseases affecting the nervous and muscular systems are caused by defects in mitochondrial genes that prevent cells from making enough ATP.

> ? *Explain how genomic imprinting and inheritance of mitochondrial and chloroplast DNA are exceptions to standard Mendelian inheritance.*

LEVEL 1: KNOWLEDGE/COMPREHENSION

1. A man with hemophilia (a recessive, sex-linked condition) has a daughter of normal phenotype. She marries a man who is normal for the trait. What is the probability that a daughter of this mating will have hemophilia? That a son will have hemophilia? If the couple has four sons, what is the probability that all four will be born with hemophilia?

2. Pseudohypertrophic muscular dystrophy is an inherited disorder that causes gradual deterioration of the muscles. It is seen almost exclusively in boys born to apparently normal parents and usually results in death in the early teens. Is this disorder caused by a dominant or a recessive allele? Is its inheritance sex-linked or autosomal? How do you know? Explain why this disorder is almost never seen in girls.

3. A wild-type fruit fly (heterozygous for gray body color and normal wings) is mated with a black fly with vestigial wings. The offspring have the following phenotypic distribution: wild-type, 778; black-vestigial, 785; black-normal, 158; gray-vestigial, 162. What is the recombination frequency between these genes for body color and wing size? Is this consistent with the results of the experiment in Figure 15.9?

4. A planet is inhabited by creatures that reproduce with the same hereditary patterns seen in humans. Three phenotypic characters are height (T = tall, t = dwarf), head appendages (A = antennae, a = no antennae), and nose morphology (S = upturned snout, s = downturned snout). Since the creatures are not "intelligent," Earth scientists are able to do some controlled breeding experiments using various heterozygotes in testcrosses. For tall heterozygotes with antennae, the offspring are tall-antennae, 46; dwarf-antennae, 7; dwarf-no antennae, 42; tall-no antennae, 5. For heterozygotes with antennae and an upturned snout, the offspring are antennae-upturned snout, 47; antennae-downturned snout, 2; no antennae-downturned snout, 48; no antennae-upturned snout, 3. Calculate the recombination frequencies for both experiments.

LEVEL 2: APPLICATION/ANALYSIS

5. Using the information from problem 4, scientists do a further testcross using a heterozygote for height and nose morphology. The offspring are tall-upturned snout, 40; dwarf-upturned snout, 9; dwarf-downturned snout, 42; tall-downturned snout, 9. Calculate the recombination frequency from these data, and then use your answer from problem 4 to determine the correct order of the three linked genes.

6. A wild-type fruit fly (heterozygous for gray body color and red eyes) is mated with a black fruit fly with purple eyes. The offspring are wild-type, 721; black-purple, 751; gray-purple, 49; black-red, 45. What is the recombination frequency between these genes for body color and eye color? Using information from problem 3, what fruit flies (genotypes and phenotypes) would you mate to determine the order of the body-color, wing-size, and eye-color genes on the chromosome?

7. Assume that genes A and B are on the same chromosome and are 50 map units apart. An animal heterozygous at both loci is crossed with one that is homozygous recessive at both loci. What percentage of the offspring will show recombinant phenotypes resulting from crossovers? Without knowing these genes are on the same chromosome, how would you interpret the results of this cross?

8. Two genes of a flower, one controlling blue (B) versus white (b) petals and the other controlling round (R) versus oval (r) stamens, are linked and are 10 map units apart. You cross a homozygous blue-oval plant with a homozygous white-round plant. The resulting F_1 progeny are crossed with homozygous white-oval plants, and 1,000 F_2 progeny are obtained. How many F_2 plants of each of the four phenotypes do you expect?

9. You design *Drosophila* crosses to provide recombination data for gene *a*, which is located on the chromosome shown in Figure 15.12. Gene *a* has recombination frequencies of 14% with the vestigial-wing locus and 26% with the brown-eye locus. Approximately where is *a* located along the chromosome?

LEVEL 3: SYNTHESIS/EVALUATION

10. Banana plants, which are triploid, are seedless and therefore sterile. Propose a possible explanation.

11. **EVOLUTION CONNECTION**
Crossing over is thought to be evolutionarily advantageous because it continually shuffles genetic alleles into novel combinations. Until recently, it was thought that the genes on the Y chromosome might degenerate because they lack homologous genes on the X chromosome with which to pair up prior to crossing over. However, when the Y chromosome was sequenced, eight large regions were found to be internally homologous to each other, and quite a few of the 78 genes represent duplicates. (Y chromosome researcher David Page has called it a "hall of mirrors.") What might be a benefit of these regions?

12. **SCIENTIFIC INQUIRY**
DRAW IT Assume you are mapping genes A, B, C, and D in *Drosophila*. You know that these genes are linked on the same chromosome, and you determine the recombination frequencies between each pair of genes to be as follows: A–B, 8%; A–C, 28%; A–D, 25%; B–C, 20%; B–D, 33%.
(a) Describe how you determined the recombination frequencies for each pair of genes.
(b) Draw a chromosome map based on your data.

13. **WRITE ABOUT A THEME: INFORMATION**
The continuity of life is based on heritable information in the form of DNA. In a short essay (100–150 words), relate the structure and behavior of chromosomes to inheritance in both asexually and sexually reproducing species.

14. **SYNTHESIZE YOUR KNOWLEDGE**

Butterflies have an X-Y sex determination system that is different from that of flies or humans. Female butterflies may be either XY or XO, while butterflies with two or more X chromosomes are males. This photograph shows a tiger swallowtail *gynandromorph*, which is half male (left side) and half female (right side). Given that the first division of the zygote divides the embryo into the future right and left halves of the butterfly, propose a hypothesis that explains how nondisjunction during the first mitosis might have produced this unusual-looking butterfly.

For selected answers, see Appendix A.

MasteringBiology®

Students Go to **MasteringBiology** for assignments, the eText, and the Study Area with practice tests, animations, and activities.

Instructors Go to **MasteringBiology** for automatically graded tutorials and questions that you can assign to your students, plus Instructor Resources.

16

The Molecular Basis of Inheritance

▲ Figure 16.1 **What is the structure of DNA?**

Life's Operating Instructions

In April 1953, James Watson and Francis Crick shook the scientific world by proposing an elegant double-helical model for the structure of deoxyribonucleic acid, or DNA (Figure 16.1). The photo at the lower left shows the DNA model they constructed from sheet metal and wire. Over the past 60 years, their model has become an icon of modern biology. Gregor Mendel's heritable factors and Thomas Hunt Morgan's genes on chromosomes are, in fact, composed of DNA. Chemically speaking, your genetic endowment is the DNA you inherited from your parents. DNA, the substance of inheritance, is the most celebrated molecule of our time.

Of all nature's molecules, nucleic acids are unique in their ability to direct their own replication from monomers. Indeed, the resemblance of offspring to their parents has its basis in the accurate replication of DNA and its transmission from one generation to the next. Hereditary information in DNA directs the development of your biochemical, anatomical, physiological, and, to some extent, behavioral traits. In this chapter, you will discover how biologists deduced that DNA is the genetic material and how Watson and Crick worked out its structure. You will also learn how a molecule of DNA is copied during **DNA replication** and how cells repair their DNA. Finally, you will explore how a molecule of DNA is packaged together with proteins in a chromosome.

▲ James Watson (left) and Francis Crick with their DNA model.

DNA is the genetic material

Today, even schoolchildren have heard of DNA, and scientists routinely manipulate DNA in the laboratory, often to change the heritable traits of cells in their experiments. Early in the 20th century, however, identifying the molecules of inheritance loomed as a major challenge to biologists.

The Search for the Genetic Material: *Scientific Inquiry*

Once T. H. Morgan's group showed that genes exist as parts of chromosomes (described in Chapter 15), the two chemical components of chromosomes—DNA and protein—emerged as the leading candidates for the genetic material. Until the 1940s, the case for proteins seemed stronger: Biochemists had identified proteins as a class of macromolecules with great heterogeneity and specificity of function, essential requirements for the hereditary material. Moreover, little was known about nucleic acids, whose physical and chemical properties seemed far too uniform to account for the multitude of specific inherited traits exhibited by every organism. This view gradually changed as the role of DNA in heredity was worked out in studies of bacteria and the viruses that infect them, systems far simpler than fruit flies or humans. Let's trace the search for the genetic material as a case study in scientific inquiry.

Evidence That DNA Can Transform Bacteria

In 1928, a British medical officer named Frederick Griffith was trying to develop a vaccine against pneumonia. He was studying *Streptococcus pneumoniae*, a bacterium that causes pneumonia in mammals. Griffith had two strains (varieties) of the bacterium, one pathogenic (disease-causing) and one nonpathogenic (harmless). He was surprised to find that when he killed the pathogenic bacteria with heat and then mixed the cell remains with living bacteria of the nonpathogenic strain, some of the living cells became pathogenic (Figure 16.2). Furthermore, this newly acquired trait of pathogenicity was inherited by all the descendants of the transformed bacteria. Apparently, some chemical component of the dead pathogenic cells caused this heritable change, although the identity of the substance was not known. Griffith called the phenomenon **transformation**, now defined as a change in genotype and phenotype due to the assimilation of external DNA by a cell. Later work by Oswald Avery, Maclyn McCarty, and Colin MacLeod identified the transforming substance as DNA.

Scientists remained skeptical, however, many still viewing proteins as better candidates for the genetic material. Also, many biologists were not convinced that bacterial genes would be similar in composition and function to those of

---

▼ Figure 16.2 | Inquiry

Can a genetic trait be transferred between different bacterial strains?

Experiment Frederick Griffith studied two strains of the bacterium *Streptococcus pneumoniae*. The S (smooth) strain can cause pneumonia in mice; it is pathogenic because the cells have an outer capsule that protects them from an animal's immune system. Cells of the R (rough) strain lack a capsule and are nonpathogenic. To test for the trait of pathogenicity, Griffith injected mice with the two strains:

Living S cells (pathogenic control)	Living R cells (nonpathogenic control)	Heat-killed S cells (nonpathogenic control)	Mixture of heat-killed S cells and living R cells

Results

Mouse dies	Mouse healthy	Mouse healthy	Mouse dies

In blood sample, living S cells were found. They could reproduce, yielding more S cells.

Conclusion The living R bacteria had been transformed into pathogenic S bacteria by an unknown, heritable substance from the dead S cells that enabled the R cells to make capsules.

Source: F. Griffith, The significance of pneumococcal types, *Journal of Hygiene* 27:113–159 (1928).

WHAT IF? *How did this experiment rule out the possibility that the R cells simply used the dead S cells' capsules to become pathogenic?*

---

more complex organisms. But the major reason for the continued doubt was that so little was known about DNA.

Evidence That Viral DNA Can Program Cells

Additional evidence that DNA was the genetic material came from studies of viruses that infect bacteria (Figure 16.3). These viruses are called **bacteriophages** (meaning "bacteria-eaters"), or **phages** for short. Viruses are much simpler than

► Figure 16.3 **A virus infecting a bacterial cell.** A phage called T2 attaches to a host cell and injects its genetic material through the plasma membrane, while the head and tail parts remain on the outer bacterial surface (colorized TEM).

Phage head
DNA
Tail sheath
Tail fiber
Genetic material
Bacterial cell
100 nm

cells. A **virus** is little more than DNA (or sometimes RNA) enclosed by a protective coat, which is often simply protein. To produce more viruses, a virus must infect a cell and take over the cell's metabolic machinery.

Phages have been widely used as tools by researchers in molecular genetics. In 1952, Alfred Hershey and Martha Chase performed experiments showing that DNA is the genetic material of a phage known as T2. This is one of many phages that infect *Escherichia coli* (*E. coli*), a bacterium that normally lives in the intestines of mammals and is a model organism for molecular biologists. At that time,

biologists already knew that T2, like many other phages, was composed almost entirely of DNA and protein. They also knew that the T2 phage could quickly turn an *E. coli* cell into a T2-producing factory that released many copies of new phages when the cell ruptured. Somehow, T2 could reprogram its host cell to produce viruses. But which viral component—protein or DNA—was responsible?

Hershey and Chase answered this question by devising an experiment showing that only one of the two components of T2 actually enters the *E. coli* cell during infection **(Figure 16.4)**. In their experiment, they used a radioactive

---

▼ **Figure 16.4** | Inquiry

Is protein or DNA the genetic material of phage T2?

Experiment Alfred Hershey and Martha Chase used radioactive sulfur and phosphorus to trace the fates of protein and DNA, respectively, of T2 phages that infected bacterial cells. They wanted to see which of these molecules entered the cells and could reprogram them to make more phages.

❶ Mixed radioactively labeled phages with bacteria. The phages infected the bacterial cells.

❷ Agitated the mixture in a blender to free phage parts outside the bacteria from the cells.

❸ Centrifuged the mixture so that bacteria formed a pellet at the bottom of the test tube; free phages and phage parts, which are lighter, remained suspended in the liquid.

❹ Measured the radioactivity in the pellet and the liquid.

Phage
Radioactive protein
Bacterial cell
DNA
Empty protein shell
Phage DNA
Radioactivity (phage protein) found in liquid
Centrifuge
Pellet (bacterial cells and contents)

Batch 1: Phages were grown with radioactive sulfur (^{35}S), which was incorporated into phage protein (pink).

Radioactive DNA
Batch 2: Phages were grown with radioactive phosphorus (^{32}P), which was incorporated into phage DNA (blue).
Centrifuge
Pellet
Radioactivity (phage DNA) found in pellet

Results When proteins were labeled (batch 1), radioactivity remained outside the cells, but when DNA was labeled (batch 2), radioactivity was found inside the cells. Bacterial cells containing radioactive phage DNA released new phages with some radioactive phosphorus.

Conclusion Phage DNA entered bacterial cells, but phage proteins did not. Hershey and Chase concluded that DNA, not protein, functions as the genetic material of phage T2.

Source: A. D. Hershey and M. Chase, Independent functions of viral protein and nucleic acid in growth of bacteriophage, *Journal of General Physiology* 36:39–56 (1952).

WHAT IF? *How would the results have differed if proteins carried the genetic information?*

---

isotope of sulfur to tag protein in one batch of T2 and a radioactive isotope of phosphorus to tag DNA in a second batch. Because protein, but not DNA, contains sulfur, radioactive sulfur atoms were incorporated only into the protein of the phage. In a similar way, the atoms of radioactive phosphorus labeled only the DNA, not the protein, because nearly all the phage's phosphorus is in its DNA. In the experiment, separate samples of nonradioactive *E. coli* cells were infected with the protein-labeled and DNA-labeled batches of T2. The researchers then tested the two samples shortly after the onset of infection to see which type of molecule—protein or DNA—had entered the bacterial cells and would therefore be capable of reprogramming them.

Hershey and Chase found that the phage DNA entered the host cells but the phage protein did not. Moreover, when these bacteria were returned to a culture medium, and the infection ran its course, the *E. coli* released phages that contained some radioactive phosphorus. This result further showed that the DNA inside the cell played an ongoing role during the infection process.

Hershey and Chase concluded that the DNA injected by the phage must be the molecule carrying the genetic information that makes the cells produce new viral DNA and proteins. The Hershey-Chase experiment was a landmark study because it provided powerful evidence that nucleic acids, rather than proteins, are the hereditary material, at least for certain viruses.

Additional Evidence That DNA Is the Genetic Material

Further evidence that DNA is the genetic material came from the laboratory of biochemist Erwin Chargaff. It was already known that DNA is a polymer of nucleotides, each consisting of three components: a nitrogenous (nitrogen-containing) base, a pentose sugar called deoxyribose, and a phosphate group (Figure 16.5). The base can be adenine (A), thymine (T), guanine (G), or cytosine (C). Chargaff analyzed the base composition of DNA from a number of different organisms. In 1950, he reported that the base composition of DNA varies from one species to another. For example, he found that 32.8% of sea urchin DNA nucleotides have the base A, whereas only 30.4% of human DNA nucleotides have the base A and only 24.7% of the DNA nucleotides from the bacterium *E. coli* have the base A. Chargaff's evidence of molecular diversity among species, which most scientists had presumed to be absent from DNA, made DNA a more credible candidate for the genetic material.

Chargaff also noticed a peculiar regularity in the ratios of nucleotide bases. In the DNA of each species he studied, the number of adenines approximately equaled the number

▲ **Figure 16.5 The structure of a DNA strand.** Each of the four DNA nucleotide monomers consists of a nitrogenous base (T, A, C, or G), the sugar deoxyribose (blue), and a phosphate group (yellow). The phosphate group of one nucleotide is attached to the sugar of the next, forming a "backbone" of alternating phosphates and sugars from which the bases project. The polynucleotide strand has directionality, from the 5′ end (with the phosphate group) to the 3′ end (with the —OH group of the sugar). 5′ and 3′ refer to the numbers assigned to the carbons in the sugar ring.

of thymines, and the number of guanines approximately equaled the number of cytosines. In sea urchin DNA, for example, Chargaff's analysis found the four bases in these percentages: A = 32.8% and T = 32.1%; G = 17.7% and C = 17.3%. (The percentages are not exactly the same because of limitations in Chargaff's techniques.)

These two findings became known as *Chargaff's rules*: (1) the base composition v of DNA aries between species, and (2) for each species, the percentages of A and T bases are roughly equal and the percentages of G and C bases are roughly equal. In the Scientific Skills Exercise, you can use Chargaff's rules to predict unknown percentages of nucleotide bases. The basis for these rules remained unexplained until the discovery of the double helix.

Working with Data in a Table

Given the Percentage Composition of One Nucleotide in a Genome, Can We Predict the Percentages of the Other Three Nucleotides? Even before the structure of DNA was elucidated, Erwin Chargaff and his coworkers noticed a pattern in the base composition of nucleotides from different organisms: The percentage of adenine (A) bases roughly equaled that of thymine (T) bases, and the percentage of cytosine (C) bases roughly equaled that of guanine (G) bases. Further, the percentage of each pair (A/T or C/G) varied from species to species. We now know that the 1:1 A/T and C/G ratios are due to complementary base pairing between A and T and between C and G in the DNA double helix, and interspecies differences are due to the unique sequences of bases along a DNA strand. In this exercise, you will apply Chargaff's rules to predict the composition of bases in a genome.

How the Experiments Were Done In Chargaff's experiments, DNA was extracted from the given organism, hydrolyzed to break apart the individual nucleotides, and then analyzed chemically. (These experiments provided approximate values for each type of nucleotide. Today, whole-genome sequencing allows base composition analysis to be done more precisely directly from the sequence data.)

Data from the Experiments Tables are useful for organizing sets of data representing a common set of values (here, percentages of A, G, C, and T) for a number of different samples (in this case, from different species). You can apply the patterns that you see in the known data to predict unknown values. In the table at the upper right, complete base distribution data are given for sea urchin DNA and salmon DNA; you will use Chargaff's rules to fill in the rest of the table with predicted values.

Source of DNA	Base Percentage			
	Adenine	Guanine	Cytosine	Thymine
Sea urchin	32.8	17.7	17.3	32.1
Salmon	29.7	20.8	20.4	29.1
Wheat	28.1	21.8	22.7	
E. coli	24.7	26.0		
Human	30.4			30.1
Ox	29.0			

Interpret the Data

1. Explain how the sea urchin and salmon data demonstrate both of Chargaff's rules.
2. Using Chargaff's rules, fill in the table with your predictions of the missing percentages of bases, starting with the wheat genome and proceeding through *E. coli*, human, and ox. Show how you arrived at your answers.
3. If Chargaff's rule—that the amount of A equals the amount of T and the amount of C equals the amount of G—is valid, then hypothetically we could extrapolate this to the combined DNA of all species on Earth (like one huge Earth genome). To see whether the data in the table support this hypothesis, calculate the average percentage for each base in your completed table by averaging the values in each column. Does Chargaff's equivalence rule still hold true?

(MB) A version of this Scientific Skills Exercise can be assigned in MasteringBiology.

Data from several papers by Chargaff: for example, E. Chargaff et al., Composition of the desoxypentose nucleic acids of four genera of sea-urchin, *Journal of Biological Chemistry* 195:155–160 (1952).

Building a Structural Model of DNA: *Scientific Inquiry*

Once most biologists were convinced that DNA was the genetic material, the challenge was to determine how the structure of DNA could account for its role in inheritance. By the early 1950s, the arrangement of covalent bonds in a nucleic acid polymer was well established (see Figure 16.5), and researchers focused on discovering the three-dimensional structure of DNA. Among the scientists working on the problem were Linus Pauling, at the California Institute of Technology, and Maurice Wilkins and Rosalind Franklin, at King's College in London. First to come up with the correct answer, however, were two scientists who were relatively unknown at the time—the American James Watson and the Englishman Francis Crick.

The brief but celebrated partnership that solved the puzzle of DNA structure began soon after Watson journeyed to Cambridge University, where Crick was studying protein structure with a technique called X-ray crystallography (see Figure 5.22). While visiting the laboratory of Maurice Wilkins, Watson saw an X-ray diffraction image of DNA produced by Wilkins's accomplished colleague Rosalind Franklin (Figure 16.6a). Images produced by X-ray crystallography are not actually pictures of molecules. The spots

and smudges in **Figure 16.6b** were produced by X-rays that were diffracted (deflected) as they passed through aligned fibers of purified DNA. Watson was familiar with the type of X-ray diffraction pattern that helical molecules produce, and an examination of the photo that Wilkins showed him confirmed that DNA was helical in shape. It also augmented earlier data obtained by Franklin and others suggesting the

(a) Rosalind Franklin   **(b) Franklin's X-ray diffraction photograph of DNA**

▲ **Figure 16.6 Rosalind Franklin and her X-ray diffraction photo of DNA.** Franklin, a very accomplished X-ray crystallographer, conducted critical experiments resulting in the photo that allowed Watson and Crick to deduce the double-helical structure of DNA.

width of the helix and the spacing of the nitrogenous bases along it. The pattern in this photo implied that the helix was made up of two strands, contrary to a three-stranded model that Linus Pauling had proposed a short time earlier. The presence of two strands accounts for the now-familiar term **double helix** (Figure 16.7).

Watson and Crick began building models of a double helix that would conform to the X-ray measurements and what was then known about the chemistry of DNA, including Chargaff's rule of base equivalences. Having also read an unpublished annual report summarizing Franklin's work, they knew she had concluded that the sugar-phosphate backbones were on the outside of the DNA molecule, contrary to their working model. Franklin's arrangement was appealing because it put the relatively hydrophobic nitrogenous bases in the molecule's interior, away from the surrounding aqueous solution, and the negatively charged phosphate groups wouldn't be forced together in the interior. Watson constructed such a model, shown in the lower photo on the first page of this chapter.

In this model, the two sugar-phosphate backbones are **antiparallel**—that is, their subunits run in opposite directions (see Figure 16.7b). You can imagine the overall arrangement as a rope ladder with rigid rungs. The side ropes represent the sugar-phosphate backbones, and the rungs represent pairs of nitrogenous bases. Now imagine twisting the ladder to form a helix. Franklin's X-ray data indicated that the helix makes one full turn every 3.4 nm along its length. With the bases stacked just 0.34 nm apart, there are ten layers of base pairs, or rungs of the ladder, in each full turn of the helix.

The nitrogenous bases of the double helix are paired in specific combinations: adenine (A) with thymine (T), and guanine (G) with cytosine (C). It was mainly by trial and error that Watson and Crick arrived at this key feature of DNA. At first, Watson imagined that the bases paired like with like—for example, A with A and C with C. But this model did not fit the X-ray data, which suggested that the double helix had a uniform diameter. Why is this requirement inconsistent with like-with-like pairing of bases? Adenine and guanine are purines, nitrogenous bases with two organic rings, while cytosine and thymine are nitrogenous bases called pyrimidines, which have a single ring. Thus, purines (A and G) are about twice as wide as pyrimidines (C and T). A purine-purine pair is too wide and a pyrimidine-pyrimidine pair too narrow to account for the 2-nm

(a) **Key features of DNA structure.** The "ribbons" in this diagram represent the sugar-phosphate backbones of the two DNA strands. The helix is "right-handed," curving up to the right. The two strands are held together by hydrogen bonds (dotted lines) between the nitrogenous bases, which are paired in the interior of the double helix.

(b) **Partial chemical structure.** For clarity, the two DNA strands are shown untwisted in this partial chemical structure. Strong covalent bonds link the units of each strand, while weaker hydrogen bonds between the bases hold one strand to the other. Notice that the strands are antiparallel, meaning that they are oriented in opposite directions, like the lanes of a divided highway.

(c) **Space-filling model.** The tight stacking of the base pairs is clear in this computer-generated, space-filling model. Van der Waals interactions between the stacked pairs play a major role in holding the molecule together.

▲ Figure 16.7 **The structure of the double helix.**

diameter of the double helix. Always pairing a purine with a pyrimidine, however, results in a uniform diameter:

Purine + purine: too wide

Pyrimidine + pyrimidine: too narrow

Purine + pyrimidine: width consistent with X-ray data

Watson and Crick reasoned that there must be additional specificity of pairing dictated by the structure of the bases. Each base has chemical side groups that can form hydrogen bonds with its appropriate partner: Adenine can form two hydrogen bonds with thymine and only thymine; guanine forms three hydrogen bonds with cytosine and only cytosine. In shorthand, A pairs with T, and G pairs with C **(Figure 16.8)**.

The Watson-Crick model took into account Chargaff's ratios and ultimately explained them. Wherever one strand of a DNA molecule has an A, the partner strand has a T. Similarly, a G in one strand is always paired with a C in the complementary strand. Therefore, in the DNA of any organism, the amount of adenine equals the amount of thymine, and the amount of guanine equals the amount of cytosine. (Modern DNA sequencing techniques have confirmed that the amounts are exactly equal.) Although the base-pairing rules dictate the combinations of nitrogenous bases that form the "rungs" of the double helix, they do not restrict the sequence of nucleotides *along* each DNA strand. The linear sequence of the four bases can be varied in countless ways, and each gene has a unique base sequence.

Adenine (A)   Thymine (T)

Guanine (G)   Cytosine (C)

▲ **Figure 16.8 Base pairing in DNA.** The pairs of nitrogenous bases in a DNA double helix are held together by hydrogen bonds, shown here as black dotted lines.

In April 1953, Watson and Crick surprised the scientific world with a succinct, one-page paper that reported their molecular model for DNA: the double helix, which has since become the symbol of molecular biology. Watson and Crick, along with Maurice Wilkins, were awarded the Nobel Prize in 1962 for this work. (Sadly, Rosalind Franklin had died at the age of 38 in 1958 and was thus ineligible for the prize.) The beauty of the double helix model was that the structure of DNA suggested the basic mechanism of its replication.

CONCEPT 16.2

Many proteins work together in DNA replication and repair

The relationship between structure and function is manifest in the double helix. The idea that there is specific pairing of nitrogenous bases in DNA was the flash of inspiration that led Watson and Crick to the double helix. At the same time, they saw the functional significance of the base-pairing rules. They ended their classic paper with this wry statement: "It has not escaped our notice that the specific pairing we have postulated immediately suggests a possible copying mechanism for the genetic material."* In this section, you will learn about the basic principle of DNA replication, as well as some important details of the process.

The Basic Principle: Base Pairing to a Template Strand

In a second paper, Watson and Crick stated their hypothesis for how DNA replicates:

Now our model for deoxyribonucleic acid is, in effect, a pair of templates, each of which is complementary to the other. We imagine that prior to duplication the hydrogen bonds are broken, and the two chains unwind and separate. Each chain then acts as a template for the formation on to itself of a new companion chain, so that eventually we shall have two pairs of chains, where we only had one before. Moreover, the sequence of the pairs of bases will have been duplicated exactly.†

*J. D. Watson and F. H. C. Crick, Molecular structure of nucleic acids: a structure for deoxyribose nucleic acids, *Nature* 171:737–738 (1953).

†J. D. Watson and F. H. C. Crick, Genetical implications of the structure of deoxyribonucleic acid, *Nature* 171:964–967 (1953).

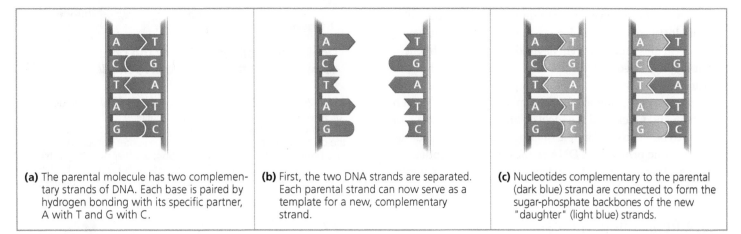

(a) The parental molecule has two complementary strands of DNA. Each base is paired by hydrogen bonding with its specific partner, A with T and G with C.

(b) First, the two DNA strands are separated. Each parental strand can now serve as a template for a new, complementary strand.

(c) Nucleotides complementary to the parental (dark blue) strand are connected to form the sugar-phosphate backbones of the new "daughter" (light blue) strands.

▲ **Figure 16.9 A model for DNA replication: the basic concept.** In this simplified illustration, a short segment of DNA has been untwisted. Simple shapes symbolize the four kinds of bases. Dark blue represents DNA strands present in the parental molecule; light blue represents newly synthesized DNA.

Figure 16.9 illustrates Watson and Crick's basic idea. To make it easier to follow, we show only a short section of double helix in untwisted form. Notice that if you cover one of the two DNA strands of Figure 16.9a, you can still determine its linear sequence of nucleotides by referring to the uncovered strand and applying the base-pairing rules. The two strands are complementary; each stores the information necessary to reconstruct the other. When a cell copies a DNA molecule, each strand serves as a template for ordering nucleotides into a new, complementary strand. Nucleotides line up along the template strand according to the base-pairing rules and are linked to form the new strands. Where there was one double-stranded DNA molecule at the beginning of the process, there are soon two, each an exact replica of the "parental" molecule. The copying mechanism is analogous to using a photographic negative to make a positive image, which can in turn be used to make another negative, and so on.

This model of DNA replication remained untested for several years following publication of the DNA structure. The requisite experiments were simple in concept but difficult to perform. Watson and Crick's model predicts that when a double helix replicates, each of the two daughter molecules will have one old strand, from the parental molecule, and one newly made strand. This **semiconservative model** can be distinguished from a conservative model of replication, in which the two parental strands somehow come back together after the process (that is, the parental molecule is conserved). In yet a third model, called the dispersive model, all four strands of DNA following replication have a mixture of old and new DNA. These three models are shown in **Figure 16.10**. Although mechanisms for conservative or dispersive DNA replication are not easy to devise, these models remained possibilities until they could be

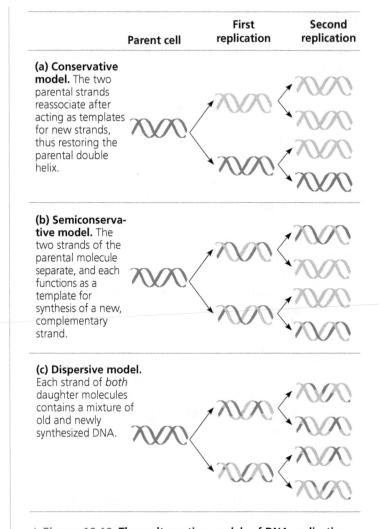

(a) **Conservative model.** The two parental strands reassociate after acting as templates for new strands, thus restoring the parental double helix.

(b) **Semiconservative model.** The two strands of the parental molecule separate, and each functions as a template for synthesis of a new, complementary strand.

(c) **Dispersive model.** Each strand of *both* daughter molecules contains a mixture of old and newly synthesized DNA.

▲ **Figure 16.10 Three alternative models of DNA replication.** Each short segment of double helix symbolizes the DNA within a cell. Beginning with a parent cell, we follow the DNA for two more generations of cells—two rounds of DNA replication. Parental DNA is dark blue; newly made DNA is light blue.

ruled out. After two years of preliminary work at the California Institute of Technology in the late 1950s, Matthew Meselson and Franklin Stahl devised a clever experiment that distinguished between the three models, described in **Figure 16.11**. The results of their experiment supported the semiconservative model of DNA replication, as predicted by Watson and Crick, and is widely acknowledged among biologists to be a classic example of elegant experimental design.

The basic principle of DNA replication is conceptually simple. However, the actual process involves some complicated biochemical gymnastics, as we will now see.

DNA Replication: *A Closer Look*

The bacterium *E. coli* has a single chromosome of about 4.6 million nucleotide pairs. In a favorable environment, an *E. coli* cell can copy all this DNA and divide to form two genetically identical daughter cells in less than an hour. Each of *your* cells has 46 DNA molecules in its nucleus, one long double-helical molecule per chromosome. In all, that represents about 6 billion nucleotide pairs, or over a thousand times more DNA than is found in a bacterial cell. If we were to print the one-letter symbols for these bases (A, G, C, and T) the size of the type you are now reading, the 6 billion nucleotide pairs of information in a diploid human cell would fill about 1,400 biology textbooks. Yet it takes one of your cells just a few hours to copy all of this DNA. This replication of an enormous amount of genetic information is achieved with very few errors—only about one per 10 billion nucleotides. The copying of DNA is remarkable in its speed and accuracy.

More than a dozen enzymes and other proteins participate in DNA replication. Much more is known about how this "replication machine" works in bacteria (such as *E. coli*) than in eukaryotes, and we will describe the basic steps of the process for *E. coli*, except where otherwise noted. What scientists have learned about eukaryotic DNA replication suggests, however, that most of the process is fundamentally similar for prokaryotes and eukaryotes.

Getting Started

The replication of a chromosome begins at particular sites called **origins of replication**, short stretches of DNA having a specific sequence of nucleotides. The *E. coli* chromosome, like many other bacterial chromosomes, is circular and has a single origin. Proteins that initiate DNA replication recognize this sequence and attach to the DNA, separating the two strands and opening up a replication "bubble." Replication of DNA then proceeds in both directions until the entire molecule is copied **(Figure 16.12a)**. In contrast to a bacterial chromosome, a eukaryotic chromosome may have hundreds or even a few thousand replication origins. Multiple replication bubbles form and eventually fuse, thus speeding up the copying of the very long DNA molecules

---

▼ Figure 16.11 | Inquiry

Does DNA replication follow the conservative, semiconservative, or dispersive model?

Experiment Matthew Meselson and Franklin Stahl cultured *E. coli* for several generations in a medium containing nucleotide precursors labeled with a heavy isotope of nitrogen, ^{15}N. They then transferred the bacteria to a medium with only ^{14}N, a lighter isotope. A sample was taken after the first DNA replication; another sample was taken after the second replication. They extracted DNA from the bacteria in the samples and then centrifuged each DNA sample to separate DNA of different densities.

① Bacteria cultured in medium with ^{15}N (heavy isotope)

② Bacteria transferred to medium with ^{14}N (lighter isotope)

Results

③ DNA sample centrifuged after first replication

④ DNA sample centrifuged after second replication

Less dense

More dense

Conclusion Meselson and Stahl compared their results to those predicted by each of the three models in Figure 16.10, as shown below. The first replication in the ^{14}N medium produced a band of hybrid (^{15}N-^{14}N) DNA. This result eliminated the conservative model. The second replication produced both light and hybrid DNA, a result that refuted the dispersive model and supported the semiconservative model. They therefore concluded that DNA replication is semiconservative.

Predictions:	**First replication**	**Second replication**
Conservative model		
Semiconservative model		
Dispersive model		

Source: M. Meselson and F. W. Stahl, The replication of DNA in *Escherichia coli*, *Proceedings of the National Academy of Sciences USA* 44:671–682 (1958).

Inquiry in Action Read and analyze the original paper in *Inquiry in Action: Interpreting Scientific Papers*.

(MB) A related Experimental Inquiry Tutorial can be assigned in MasteringBiology.

WHAT IF? *If Meselson and Stahl had first grown the cells in ^{14}N-containing medium and then moved them into ^{15}N-containing medium before taking samples, what would have been the result?*

Bacterial chromosome

Origin of replication
Parental (template) strand
Daughter (new) strand
Double-stranded DNA molecule
Replication bubble
Replication fork
Two daughter DNA molecules

0.5 μm

(a) Origin of replication in an *E. coli* cell. In the circular chromosome of *E. coli* and many other bacteria, only one origin of replication is present. The parental strands separate at the origin, forming a replication bubble with two forks (red arrows). Replication proceeds in both directions until the forks meet on the other side, resulting in two daughter DNA molecules. The TEM shows a bacterial chromosome with a large replication bubble. New and old strands cannot be seen individually in the TEM.

Eukaryotic chromosome

Origin of replication
Double-stranded DNA molecule
Parental (template) strand
Daughter (new) strand
Bubble
Replication fork
Two daughter DNA molecules

0.25 μm

(b) Origins of replication in a eukaryotic cell. In each linear chromosome of a eukaryote, DNA replication begins when replication bubbles form at many sites along the giant DNA molecule. The bubbles expand as replication proceeds in both directions (red arrows). Eventually, the bubbles fuse and synthesis of the daughter strands is complete. The TEM shows three replication bubbles along the DNA of a cultured Chinese hamster cell.

DRAW IT *In the TEM, add arrows in the forks of the third bubble.*

▲ **Figure 16.12 Origins of replication in *E. coli* and eukaryotes.** The red arrows indicate the movement of the replication forks and thus the overall directions of DNA replication within each bubble.

(Figure 16.12b). As in bacteria, eukaryotic DNA replication proceeds in both directions from each origin.

At each end of a replication bubble is a **replication fork**, a Y-shaped region where the parental strands of DNA are being unwound. Several kinds of proteins participate in the unwinding **(Figure 16.13)**. **Helicases** are enzymes that untwist the double helix at the replication forks, separating the two parental strands and making them available as template strands. After the parental strands separate, **single-strand binding proteins** bind to the unpaired DNA strands, keeping them from re-pairing. The untwisting of the double helix causes tighter twisting and strain ahead of the replication fork. **Topoisomerase** helps relieve this strain by breaking, swiveling, and rejoining DNA strands.

The unwound sections of parental DNA strands are now available to serve as templates for the synthesis of new

Topoisomerase breaks, swivels, and rejoins the parental DNA ahead of the replication fork, relieving the strain caused by unwinding.

Primase synthesizes RNA primers, using the parental DNA as a template.

3′
RNA primer
3′ 5′
5′
3′
Replication fork
5′

Helicase unwinds and separates the parental DNA strands.

Single-strand binding proteins stabilize the unwound parental strands.

▲ **Figure 16.13 Some of the proteins involved in the initiation of DNA replication.** The same proteins function at both replication forks in a replication bubble. For simplicity, only the left-hand fork is shown, and the DNA bases are drawn much larger in relation to the proteins than they are in reality.

complementary DNA strands. However, the enzymes that synthesize DNA cannot *initiate* the synthesis of a polynucleotide; they can only add DNA nucleotides to the end of an already existing chain that is base-paired with the template strand. The initial nucleotide chain that is produced during DNA synthesis is actually a short stretch of RNA, not DNA. This RNA chain is called a **primer** and is synthesized by the enzyme **primase** (see Figure 16.13). Primase starts a complementary RNA chain from a single RNA nucleotide, adding more RNA nucleotides one at a time, using the parental DNA strand as a template. The completed primer, generally 5–10 nucleotides long, is thus base-paired to the template strand. The new DNA strand will start from the 3′ end of the RNA primer.

Synthesizing a New DNA Strand

Enzymes called **DNA polymerases** catalyze the synthesis of new DNA by adding nucleotides to a preexisting chain. In *E. coli*, there are several different DNA polymerases, but two appear to play the major roles in DNA replication: DNA polymerase III and DNA polymerase I. The situation in eukaryotes is more complicated, with at least 11 different DNA polymerases discovered so far; however, the general principles are the same.

Most DNA polymerases require a primer and a DNA template strand, along which complementary DNA nucleotides are lined up. In *E. coli*, DNA polymerase III (abbreviated DNA pol III) adds a DNA nucleotide to the RNA primer and then continues adding DNA nucleotides, complementary to the parental DNA template strand, to the growing end of the new DNA strand. The rate of elongation is about 500 nucleotides per second in bacteria and 50 per second in human cells.

Each nucleotide to be added to a growing DNA strand consists of a sugar attached to a base and to three phosphate groups. You have already encountered such a molecule—ATP (adenosine triphosphate; see Figure 8.9). The only difference between the ATP of energy metabolism and dATP, the adenine nucleotide used to make DNA, is the sugar component, which is deoxyribose in the building block of DNA but ribose in ATP. Like ATP, the nucleotides used for DNA synthesis are chemically reactive, partly because their triphosphate tails have an unstable cluster of negative charge. As each monomer joins the growing end of a DNA strand, two phosphate groups are lost as a molecule of pyrophosphate (P—P_i). Subsequent hydrolysis of the pyrophosphate to two molecules of inorganic phosphate (P_i) is a coupled exergonic reaction that helps drive the polymerization reaction **(Figure 16.14)**.

Antiparallel Elongation

As we have noted previously, the two ends of a DNA strand are different, giving each strand directionality, like a one-way street (see Figure 16.5). In addition, the two strands of

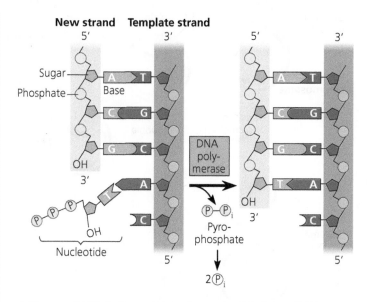

▲ **Figure 16.14 Incorporation of a nucleotide into a DNA strand.** DNA polymerase catalyzes the addition of a nucleotide to the 3′ end of a growing DNA strand, with the release of two phosphates.

? *Use this diagram to explain what we mean when we say that each DNA strand has directionality.*

DNA in a double helix are antiparallel, meaning that they are oriented in opposite directions to each other, like the lanes of a divided highway (see Figure 16.14). Therefore, the two new strands formed during DNA replication must also be antiparallel to their template strands.

How does the antiparallel arrangement of the double helix affect replication? Because of their structure, DNA polymerases can add nucleotides only to the free 3′ end of a primer or growing DNA strand, never to the 5′ end (see Figure 16.14). Thus, a new DNA strand can elongate only in the 5′ → 3′ direction. With this in mind, let's examine one of the two replication forks in a bubble **(Figure 16.15)**. Along one template strand, DNA polymerase III can synthesize a complementary strand continuously by elongating the new DNA in the mandatory 5′ → 3′ direction. DNA pol III remains in the replication fork on that template strand and continuously adds nucleotides to the new complementary strand as the fork progresses. The DNA strand made by this mechanism is called the **leading strand**. Only one primer is required for DNA pol III to synthesize the entire leading strand (see Figure 16.15).

To elongate the other new strand of DNA in the mandatory 5′ → 3′ direction, DNA pol III must work along the other template strand in the direction *away from* the replication fork. The DNA strand elongating in this direction is called the **lagging strand**.* In contrast to the leading strand,

---

*Synthesis of the leading strand and synthesis of the lagging strand occur concurrently and at the same rate. The lagging strand is so named because its synthesis is delayed slightly relative to synthesis of the leading strand; each new fragment of the lagging strand cannot be started until enough template has been exposed at the replication fork.

Overview

Origin of replication

Leading strand

Lagging strand

Primer

Lagging strand

Leading strand

Overall directions
of replication

① After RNA primer is made,
DNA pol III starts to synthesize
the leading strand.

Origin of
replication

3′

5′

RNA primer

3′

Sliding clamp

5′

DNA pol III

5′
3′

Parental DNA

3′
5′

5′
3′

3′

5′

② The leading strand is
elongated continuously
in the 5′ → 3′ direction
as the fork progresses.

▲ **Figure 16.15 Synthesis of the leading strand during DNA
replication.** This diagram focuses on the left replication fork shown
in the overview box. DNA polymerase III (DNA pol III), shaped like
a cupped hand, is shown closely associated with a protein called the
"sliding clamp" that encircles the newly synthesized double helix like
a doughnut. The sliding clamp moves DNA pol III along the DNA template strand.

which elongates continuously, the lagging strand is synthesized discontinuously, as a series of segments. These segments of the lagging strand are called **Okazaki fragments**,
after the Japanese scientist who discovered them. The fragments are about 1,000–2,000 nucleotides long in *E. coli* and
100–200 nucleotides long in eukaryotes.

Figure 16.16 illustrates the steps in the synthesis of the
lagging strand at one fork. Whereas only one primer is required on the leading strand, each Okazaki fragment on the
lagging strand must be primed separately (steps and ④).
After DNA pol III forms an Okazaki fragment (steps ②–④),
another DNA polymerase, DNA polymerase I (DNA pol I),
replaces the RNA nucleotides of the adjacent primer with
DNA nucleotides (step ⑤). But DNA pol I cannot join the
final nucleotide of this replacement DNA segment to the
first DNA nucleotide of the adjacent Okazaki fragment. Another enzyme, **DNA ligase**, accomplishes this task, joining
the sugar-phosphate backbones of all the Okazaki fragments
into a continuous DNA strand (step ⑥).

Overview

Origin of replication

Leading strand

Lagging strand

Lagging strand

Leading strand

Overall directions
of replication

① Primase joins RNA
nucleotides into a primer.

Origin of replication

Template
strand

3′

5′   3′

5′   3′
5′

② DNA pol III adds
DNA nucleotides to
the primer, forming
Okazaki fragment 1.

RNA primer
for fragment 1

3′

5′

3′   5′   3′
5′

③ After reaching the
next RNA primer to
the right, DNA pol III
detaches.

3′

Okazaki fragment 1

5′

3′
5′

RNA primer
for fragment 2

5′
3′

Okazaki
fragment 2

④ Fragment 2 is primed.
Then DNA pol III adds DNA
nucleotides, detaching when it
reaches the fragment 1 primer.

3′
5′

5′
3′

⑤ DNA pol I replaces the RNA
with DNA, adding nucleotides
to the 3′ end of fragment 2
(and, earlier, of fragment 1).

3′
5′

⑥ DNA ligase forms
a bond between the
newest DNA and the
DNA of fragment 1.

5′
3′

⑦ The lagging
strand in this region
is now complete.

3′
5′

Overall direction of replication

▲ **Figure 16.16 Synthesis of the lagging strand.**

Figure 16.17 and Table 16.1 summarize DNA replication. Please study them carefully before proceeding.

The DNA Replication Complex

It is traditional—and convenient—to represent DNA polymerase molecules as locomotives moving along a DNA railroad track, but such a model is inaccurate in two important ways. First, the various proteins that participate in DNA replication actually form a single large complex, a "DNA replication machine." Many protein-protein interactions facilitate the efficiency of this complex. For example, by interacting with other proteins at the fork, primase apparently acts as a molecular brake, slowing progress of the replication fork and coordinating the placement of primers and

the rates of replication on the leading and lagging strands. Second, the DNA replication complex may not move along the DNA; rather, the DNA may move through the complex during the replication process. In eukaryotic cells, multiple copies of the complex, perhaps grouped into "factories," may be anchored to the nuclear matrix, a framework of fibers extending through the interior of the nucleus. Experimental evidence supports a model in which two DNA polymerase molecules, one on each template strand, "reel in" the parental DNA and extrude newly made daughter DNA molecules. In this so-called trombone model, the lagging strand is also looped back through the complex (Figure 16.18).

1 Helicase unwinds the parental double helix.

2 Molecules of single-strand binding protein stabilize the unwound template strands.

3 The leading strand is synthesized continuously in the 5' to 3' direction by DNA pol III.

DNA pol III

Primer Primase

Parental DNA

4 Primase begins synthesis of the RNA primer for the fifth Okazaki fragment.

DNA pol III

Lagging strand

Lagging strand template

DNA pol I

DNA ligase

Overview

Origin of replication

Leading strand

Lagging strand

Lagging strand

Leading strand

Overall directions of replication

Leading strand template

Leading strand

5 DNA pol III is completing synthesis of fragment 4. When it reaches the RNA primer on fragment 3, it will detach and begin adding DNA nucleotides to the 3' end of the fragment 5 primer in the replication fork.

6 DNA pol I removes the primer from the 5' end of fragment 2, replacing it with DNA nucleotides added one by one to the 3' end of fragment 3. After the last addition, the backbone is left with a free 3' end.

7 DNA ligase joins the 3' end of fragment 2 to the 5' end of fragment 1.

▲ **Figure 16.17 A summary of bacterial DNA replication.** The detailed diagram shows the left-hand replication fork of the replication bubble shown in the overview (upper right). Viewing each daughter strand in its entirety in the overview, you can see that half of it is made continuously as the leading strand, while the other half (on the other side of the origin) is synthesized in fragments as the lagging strand.

DRAW IT *Draw a similar diagram showing the right-hand fork of this bubble, numbering the Okazaki fragments appropriately. Label all 5' and 3' ends.*

Table 16.1	Bacterial DNA Replication Proteins and Their Functions	
Protein	**Function**	
Helicase 	Unwinds parental double helix at replication forks	
Single-strand binding protein 	Binds to and stabilizes single-stranded DNA until it is used as a template	
Topoisomerase 	Relieves overwinding strain ahead of replication forks by breaking, swiveling, and rejoining DNA strands	
Primase 	Synthesizes an RNA primer at 5′ end of leading strand and at 5′ end of each Okazaki fragment of lagging strand	
DNA pol III 	Using parental DNA as a template, synthesizes new DNA strand by adding nucleotides to an RNA primer or a pre-existing DNA strand	
DNA pol I 	Removes RNA nucleotides of primer from 5′ end and replaces them with DNA nucleotides	
DNA ligase 	Joins Okazaki fragments of lagging strand; on leading strand, joins 3′ end of DNA that replaces primer to rest of leading strand DNA	

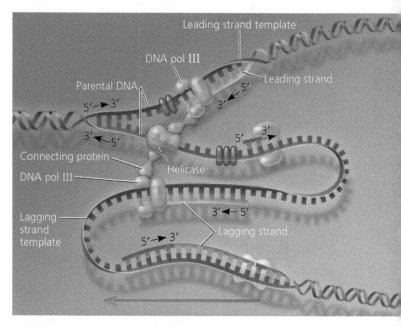

▲ **Figure 16.18 A current model of the DNA replication complex.** Two DNA polymerase III molecules work together in a complex with helicase and other proteins. One DNA polymerase acts on each template strand. The lagging strand template DNA loops through the complex, resembling the slide of a trombone. (This is often called the trombone model.)

DRAW IT *Draw a line tracing the lagging strand template along the entire stretch of DNA shown here.*

ANIMATION **BioFlix** Visit the Study Area in **MasteringBiology** for the BioFlix® 3-D Animation on DNA Replication. BioFlix Tutorials can also be assigned in MasteringBiology.

Proofreading and Repairing DNA

We cannot attribute the accuracy of DNA replication solely to the specificity of base pairing. Initial pairing errors between incoming nucleotides and those in the template strand occur at a rate of one in 10^5 nucleotides. However, errors in the completed DNA molecule amount to only one in 10^{10} (10 billion) nucleotides, an error rate that is 100,000 times lower. This is because during DNA replication, DNA polymerases proofread each nucleotide against its template as soon as it is covalently bonded to the growing strand. Upon finding an incorrectly paired nucleotide, the polymerase removes the nucleotide and then resumes synthesis. (This action is similar to fixing a word processing error by deleting the wrong letter and then entering the correct letter.)

Mismatched nucleotides sometimes evade proofreading by a DNA polymerase. In **mismatch repair**, other enzymes remove and replace incorrectly paired nucleotides that have resulted from replication errors. Researchers spotlighted the importance of such repair enzymes when they found that a hereditary defect in one of them is associated with a form of colon cancer. Apparently, this defect allows cancer-causing errors to accumulate in the DNA faster than normal.

Incorrectly paired or altered nucleotides can also arise after replication. In fact, maintenance of the genetic

information encoded in DNA requires frequent repair of various kinds of damage to existing DNA. DNA molecules are constantly subjected to potentially harmful chemical and physical agents, such as X-rays, as we'll discuss in Chapter 17. In addition, DNA bases often undergo spontaneous chemical changes under normal cellular conditions. However, these changes in DNA are usually corrected before they become permanent changes—*mutations*—perpetuated through successive replications. Each cell continuously monitors and repairs its genetic material. Because repair of damaged DNA is so important to the survival of an organism, it is no surprise that many different DNA repair enzymes have evolved. Almost 100 are known in *E. coli*, and about 130 have been identified so far in humans.

Most cellular systems for repairing incorrectly paired nucleotides, whether they are due to DNA damage or to replication errors, use a mechanism that takes advantage of the base-paired structure of DNA. In many cases, a segment of the strand containing the damage is cut out (excised) by a DNA-cutting enzyme—a **nuclease**—and the resulting gap is then filled in with nucleotides, using the undamaged strand as a template. The enzymes involved in filling the gap are

① Teams of enzymes detect and repair damaged DNA, such as this thymine dimer (often caused by ultraviolet radiation), which distorts the DNA molecule.

Nuclease

② A nuclease enzyme cuts the damaged DNA strand at two points, and the damaged section is removed.

DNA polymerase

③ Repair synthesis by a DNA polymerase fills in the missing nucleotides.

DNA ligase

④ DNA ligase seals the free end of the new DNA to the old DNA, making the strand complete.

▲ **Figure 16.19 Nucleotide excision repair of DNA damage.**

a DNA polymerase and DNA ligase. One such DNA repair system is called **nucleotide excision repair (Figure 16.19)**.

An important function of the DNA repair enzymes in our skin cells is to repair genetic damage caused by the ultraviolet rays of sunlight. One type of damage, shown in Figure 16.19, is the covalent linking of thymine bases that are adjacent on a DNA strand. Such *thymine dimers* cause the DNA to buckle and interfere with DNA replication. The importance of repairing this kind of damage is underscored by a disorder called xeroderma pigmentosum, which in most cases is caused by an inherited defect in a nucleotide excision repair enzyme. Individuals with this disorder are hypersensitive to sunlight; mutations in their skin cells caused by ultraviolet light are left uncorrected, resulting in skin cancer.

Evolutionary Significance of Altered DNA Nucleotides

EVOLUTION Faithful replication of the genome and repair of DNA damage are important for the functioning of the organism and for passing on a complete, accurate genome to the next generation. The error rate after proofreading and repair is extremely low, but rare mistakes do slip through. Once a mismatched nucleotide pair is replicated, the sequence change is permanent in the daughter molecule that has the incorrect nucleotide as well as in any subsequent copies. As we mentioned earlier, a permanent change in the DNA sequence is called a mutation.

Mutations can change the phenotype of an organism (as you'll learn in Chapter 17). And if they occur in germ cells, which give rise to gametes, mutations can be passed on from generation to generation. The vast majority of such changes either have no effect or are harmful, but a very small percentage can be beneficial. In either case, mutations are the original source of the variation on which natural selection operates during evolution and are ultimately responsible for the appearance of new species. (You'll learn more about this process in Unit Four.) The balance between complete fidelity of DNA replication or repair and a low mutation rate has, over long periods of time, allowed the evolution of the rich diversity of species we see on Earth today.

Replicating the Ends of DNA Molecules

For linear DNA, such as the DNA of eukaryotic chromosomes, the usual replication machinery cannot complete the 5′ ends of daughter DNA strands. This is a consequence of the fact that a DNA polymerase can add nucleotides only to the 3′ end of a preexisting polynucleotide. Even if an Okazaki fragment can be started with an RNA primer bound to the very end of the template strand, once that primer is removed, it cannot be replaced with DNA because there is no 3′ end available for nucleotide addition (**Figure 16.20**). As a result, repeated rounds of replication produce shorter and shorter DNA molecules with uneven ("staggered") ends.

Most prokaryotes have a circular chromosome, with no ends, so the shortening of DNA does not occur. But what protects the genes of linear eukaryotic chromosomes from being eroded away during successive rounds of DNA replication? Eukaryotic chromosomal DNA molecules have special nucleotide sequences called **telomeres** at their ends (**Figure 16.21**). Telomeres do not contain genes; instead, the DNA typically consists of multiple repetitions of one short nucleotide sequence. In each human telomere, for example, the six-nucleotide sequence TTAGGG is repeated between 100 and 1,000 times. Telomeres have two protective functions.

First, specific proteins associated with telomeric DNA prevent the staggered ends of the daughter molecule from activating the cell's systems for monitoring DNA damage. (Staggered ends of a DNA molecule, which often result from double-strand breaks, can trigger signal transduction pathways leading to cell cycle arrest or cell death.) Second, telomeric DNA acts as a kind of buffer zone that provides some protection against the organism's genes shortening, somewhat like how the plastic-wrapped ends of a shoelace slow its unraveling. However, telomeres do not prevent the erosion of genes near the ends of chromosomes; they merely postpone it.

As shown in Figure 16.20, telomeres become shorter during every round of replication. Thus, as expected, telomeric DNA tends to be shorter in dividing somatic cells of older

▲ **Figure 16.21 Telomeres.** Eukaryotes have repetitive, noncoding sequences called telomeres at the ends of their DNA. Telomeres are stained orange in these mouse chromosomes (LM).

▲ **Figure 16.20 Shortening of the ends of linear DNA molecules.** Here we follow the end of one strand of a DNA molecule through two rounds of replication. After the first round, the new lagging strand is shorter than its template. After a second round, both the leading and lagging strands have become shorter than the original parental DNA. Although not shown here, the other ends of these DNA molecules also become shorter.

individuals and in cultured cells that have divided many times. It has been proposed that shortening of telomeres is somehow connected to the aging process of certain tissues and even to aging of the organism as a whole.

But what about cells whose genome must persist virtually unchanged from an organism to its offspring over many generations? If the chromosomes of germ cells became shorter in every cell cycle, essential genes would eventually be missing from the gametes they produce. However, this does not occur: An enzyme called *telomerase* catalyzes the lengthening of telomeres in eukaryotic germ cells, thus restoring their original length and compensating for the shortening that occurs during DNA replication. Telomerase is not active in most human somatic cells, but its activity varies from tissue to tissue. The activity of telomerase in germ cells results in telomeres of maximum length in the zygote.

Normal shortening of telomeres may protect organisms from cancer by limiting the number of divisions that somatic cells can undergo. Cells from large tumors often have unusually short telomeres, as we would expect for cells that have undergone many cell divisions. Further shortening would presumably lead to self-destruction of the tumor cells. Telomerase activity is abnormally high in cancerous somatic cells, suggesting that its ability to stabilize telomere length may allow these cancer cells to persist. Many cancer cells do seem capable of unlimited cell division, as do immortal strains of cultured cells (see Chapter 12). For several years, researchers have studied inhibition of telomerase as a possible cancer therapy. Thus far, while studies that inhibited telomerase in mice with tumors have led to the death of cancer cells, eventually the cells have restored the length of their telomeres by an alternative pathway. This is an area of ongoing research that may eventually yield useful cancer treatments.

Thus far in this chapter, you have learned about the structure and replication of a DNA molecule. In the next section, we'll take a step back and examine how DNA is packaged into chromosomes, the structures that carry the genetic information.

CONCEPT CHECK 16.2

1. What role does complementary base pairing play in the replication of DNA?

2. Identify two major functions of DNA pol III in DNA replication.

3. **MAKE CONNECTIONS** What is the relationship between DNA replication and the S phase of the cell cycle? See Figure 12.6.

4. **WHAT IF?** If the DNA pol I in a given cell were nonfunctional, how would that affect the synthesis of a *leading* strand? In the overview box in Figure 16.17, point out where DNA pol I would normally function on the top leading strand.

For suggested answers, see Appendix A.

A chromosome consists of a DNA molecule packed together with proteins

The main component of the genome in most bacteria is one double-stranded, circular DNA molecule that is associated with a small amount of protein. Although we refer to this structure as the bacterial chromosome, it is very different from a eukaryotic chromosome, which consists of one linear DNA molecule associated with a large amount of protein. In *E. coli*, the chromosomal DNA consists of about 4.6 million nucleotide pairs, representing about 4,400 genes. This is 100 times more DNA than is found in a typical virus, but only about one-thousandth as much DNA as in a human somatic cell. Still, that is a tremendous amount of DNA to be packaged in such a small container.

Stretched out, the DNA of an *E. coli* cell would measure about a millimeter in length, which is 500 times longer than the cell. Within a bacterium, however, certain proteins

---

▼ **Figure 16.22**

Exploring Chromatin Packing in a Eukaryotic Chromosome

This series of diagrams and transmission electron micrographs depicts a current model for the progressive levels of DNA coiling and folding. The illustration zooms out from a single molecule of DNA to a metaphase chromosome, which is large enough to be seen with a light microscope.

Nucleosome
(10 nm in diameter)

DNA
double helix
(2 nm in diameter)

Histone tail

H1

Histones

DNA, the double helix

Shown here is a ribbon model of DNA, with each ribbon representing one of the sugar-phosphate backbones. Recall that the phosphate groups along the backbone contribute a negative charge along the outside of each strand. The TEM shows a molecule of naked (protein-free) DNA; the double helix alone is 2 nm across.

Histones

Proteins called **histones** are responsible for the first level of DNA packing in chromatin. Although each histone is small—containing only about 100 amino acids—the total mass of histone in chromatin roughly equals the mass of DNA. More than a fifth of a histone's amino acids are positively charged (lysine or arginine) and therefore bind tightly to the negatively charged DNA.

Four types of histones are most common in chromatin: H2A, H2B, H3, and H4. The histones are very similar among eukaryotes; for example, all but two of the amino acids in cow H4 are identical to those in pea H4. The apparent conservation of histone genes during evolution probably reflects the important role of histones in organizing DNA within cells.

These four types of histones are critical to the next level of DNA packing. (A fifth type of histone, called H1, is involved in a further stage of packing.)

Nucleosomes, or "beads on a string" (10-nm fiber)

In electron micrographs, unfolded chromatin is 10 nm in diameter (the *10-nm fiber*). Such chromatin resembles beads on a string (see the TEM). Each "bead" is a **nucleosome**, the basic unit of DNA packing; the "string" between beads is called *linker DNA*.

A nucleosome consists of DNA wound twice around a protein core of eight histones, two each of the main histone types (H2A, H2B, H3, and H4). The amino end (N-terminus) of each histone (the *histone tail*) extends outward from the nucleosome.

In the cell cycle, the histones leave the DNA only briefly during DNA replication. Generally, they do the same during transcription, another process that requires access to the DNA by the cell's molecular machinery. Nucleosomes, and in particular their histone tails, are involved in the regulation of gene expression.

cause the chromosome to coil and "supercoil," densely packing it so that it fills only part of the cell. Unlike the nucleus of a eukaryotic cell, this dense region of DNA in a bacterium, called the nucleoid, is not bounded by membrane (see Figure 6.5).

Each eukaryotic chromosome contains a single linear DNA double helix that, in humans, averages about 1.5×10^8 nucleotide pairs. This is an enormous amount of DNA relative to a chromosome's condensed length. If completely stretched out, such a DNA molecule would be about 4 cm long, thousands of times the diameter of a cell nucleus—and that's not even considering the DNA of the other 45 human chromosomes!

In the cell, eukaryotic DNA is precisely combined with a large amount of protein. Together, this complex of DNA and protein, called **chromatin**, fits into the nucleus through an elaborate, multilevel system of packing. Our current view of the successive levels of DNA packing in a chromosome is outlined in **Figure 16.22**. Study this figure carefully before reading further.

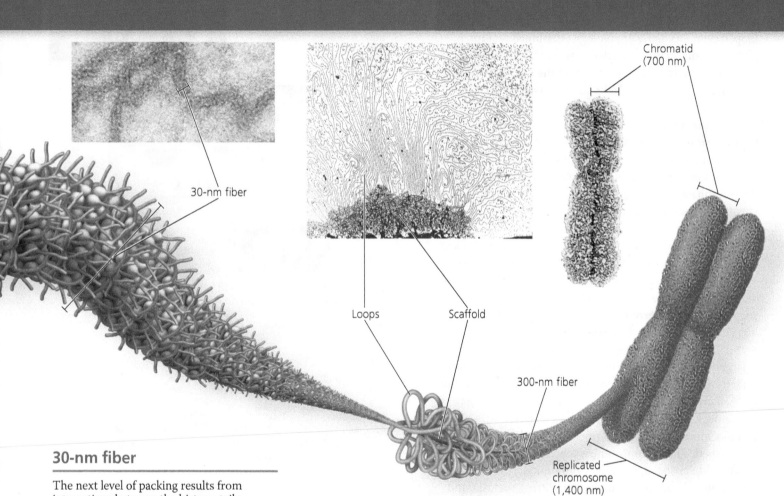

30-nm fiber

Chromatid (700 nm)

Loops   Scaffold

300-nm fiber

Replicated chromosome (1,400 nm)

30-nm fiber

The next level of packing results from interactions between the histone tails of one nucleosome and the linker DNA and nucleosomes on either side. The fifth histone, H1, is involved at this level. These interactions cause the extended 10-nm fiber to coil or fold, forming a chromatin fiber roughly 30 nm in thickness, the *30-nm fiber*. Although the 30-nm fiber is quite prevalent in the interphase nucleus, the packing arrangement of nucleosomes in this form of chromatin is still a matter of some debate.

Looped domains (300-nm fiber)

The 30-nm fiber, in turn, forms loops called *looped domains* attached to a chromosome scaffold composed of proteins, thus making up a *300-nm fiber*. The scaffold is rich in one type of topoisomerase, and H1 molecules also appear to be present.

Metaphase chromosome

In a mitotic chromosome, the looped domains themselves coil and fold in a manner not yet fully understood, further compacting all the chromatin to produce the characteristic metaphase chromosome (also shown in the micrograph above). The width of one chromatid is 700 nm. Particular genes always end up located at the same places in metaphase chromosomes, indicating that the packing steps are highly specific and precise.

Chromatin undergoes striking changes in its degree of packing during the course of the cell cycle (see Figure 12.7). In interphase cells stained for light microscopy, the chromatin usually appears as a diffuse mass within the nucleus, suggesting that the chromatin is highly extended. As a cell prepares for mitosis, its chromatin coils and folds up (condenses), eventually forming a characteristic number of short, thick metaphase chromosomes that are distinguishable from each other with the light microscope (**Figure 16.23a**).

Though interphase chromatin is generally much less condensed than the chromatin of mitotic chromosomes, it shows several of the same levels of higher-order packing. Some of the chromatin comprising a chromosome seems to be present as a 10-nm fiber, but much is compacted into a 30-nm fiber, which in some regions is further folded into looped domains. Early on, biologists assumed that interphase chromatin was a tangled mass in the nucleus, like a bowl of spaghetti, but this is far from the case. Although an interphase chromosome lacks an obvious scaffold, its looped domains appear to be attached to the nuclear lamina, on the inside of the nuclear envelope, and perhaps also to fibers of the nuclear matrix. These attachments may help organize regions of chromatin where genes are active. The chromatin of each chromosome occupies a specific restricted area within the interphase nucleus, and the chromatin fibers of different chromosomes do not appear to be entangled (**Figure 16.23b**).

Even during interphase, the centromeres and telomeres of chromosomes, as well as other chromosomal regions in some cells, exist in a highly condensed state similar to that seen in a metaphase chromosome. This type of interphase chromatin, visible as irregular clumps with a light microscope, is called **heterochromatin**, to distinguish it from the less compacted, more dispersed **euchromatin** ("true chromatin"). Because of its compaction, heterochromatic DNA is largely inaccessible to the machinery in the cell responsible for transcribing the genetic information coded in the DNA, a crucial early step in gene expression. In contrast, the looser packing of euchromatin makes its DNA accessible to this machinery, so the genes present in euchromatin can be transcribed. The chromosome is a dynamic structure that is condensed, loosened, modified, and remodeled as necessary for various cell processes, including mitosis, meiosis, and gene activity. Chemical modifications of histones affect the state of chromatin condensation and also have multiple effects on gene activity, as you'll see in Chapter 18.

In this chapter, you have learned how DNA molecules are arranged in chromosomes and how DNA replication provides the copies of genes that parents pass to offspring. However, it is not enough that genes be copied and transmitted; the information they carry must be used by the cell. In other words, genes must also be expressed. In the next chapter, we will examine how the cell expresses the genetic information encoded in DNA.

(a) These metaphase chromosomes have been "painted" so that the two homologs of a pair are the same color. Above is a spread of treated chromosomes; on the right, they have been organized into a karyotype.

(b) The ability to visually distinguish among chromosomes makes it possible to see how the chromosomes are arranged in the interphase nucleus. Each chromosome appears to occupy a specific territory during interphase. In general, the two homologs of a pair are not located together.

▲ **Figure 16.23 "Painting" chromosomes.** Researchers can treat ("paint") human chromosomes with molecular tags that cause each chromosome pair to appear a different color.

MAKE CONNECTIONS *If you arrested a human cell in metaphase I of meiosis and applied this technique, what would you observe? How would this differ from what you would see in metaphase of mitosis? Review Figure 13.8 and Figure 12.7.*

CONCEPT CHECK 16.3

1. Describe the structure of a nucleosome, the basic unit of DNA packing in eukaryotic cells.

2. What two properties, one structural and one functional, distinguish heterochromatin from euchromatin?

3. **MAKE CONNECTIONS** Interphase chromosomes appear to be attached to the nuclear lamina and perhaps also the nuclear matrix. Describe these two structures. See Figure 6.9 and the associated text.

For suggested answers, see Appendix A.

16 Chapter Review

SUMMARY OF KEY CONCEPTS

CONCEPT 16.1

DNA is the genetic material (pp. 313–318)

- Experiments with bacteria and with **phages** provided the first strong evidence that the genetic material is DNA.
- Watson and Crick deduced that DNA is a **double helix** and built a structural model. Two **antiparallel** sugar-phosphate chains wind around the outside of the molecule; the nitrogenous bases project into the interior, where they hydrogen-bond in specific pairs, A with T, G with C.

Nitrogenous bases

Sugar-phosphate backbone

Hydrogen bond

> **?** *What does it mean when we say that the two DNA strands in the double helix are antiparallel? What would an end of the double helix look like if the strands were parallel?*

CONCEPT 16.2

Many proteins work together in DNA replication and repair (pp. 318–327)

- The Meselson-Stahl experiment showed that **DNA replication** is **semiconservative**: The parental molecule unwinds, and each strand then serves as a template for the synthesis of a new strand according to base-pairing rules.
- DNA replication at one **replication fork** is summarized here:

DNA pol III synthesizes **leading strand** continuously

Parental DNA

DNA pol III starts DNA synthesis at 3′ end of primer, continues in 5′ → 3′ direction

Origin of replication

Lagging strand synthesized in short **Okazaki fragments**, later joined by **DNA ligase**

Helicase

Primase synthesizes a short RNA **primer**

DNA pol I replaces the RNA primer with DNA nucleotides

3′
5′

5′
3′

3′
5′

- DNA polymerases proofread new DNA, replacing incorrect nucleotides. In **mismatch repair**, enzymes correct errors that persist. **Nucleotide excision repair** is a process by which **nucleases** cut out and other enzymes replace damaged stretches of DNA.
- The ends of eukaryotic chromosomal DNA get shorter with each round of replication. The presence of **telomeres**, repetitive sequences at the ends of linear DNA molecules, postpones the erosion of genes. Telomerase catalyzes the lengthening of telomeres in germ cells.

> **?** *Compare DNA replication on the leading and lagging strands, including both similarities and differences.*

CONCEPT 16.3

A chromosome consists of a DNA molecule packed together with proteins (pp. 328–330)

- The chromosome of most bacterial species is a circular DNA molecule with some associated proteins, making up the nucleoid. The **chromatin** making up a eukaryotic chromosome is composed of DNA, **histones**, and other proteins. The histones bind to each other and to the DNA to form **nucleosomes**, the most basic units of DNA packing. Histone tails extend outward from each bead-like nucleosome core. Additional coiling and folding lead ultimately to the highly condensed chromatin of the metaphase chromosome. Chromosomes occupy restricted areas in the interphase nucleus. In interphase cells, most chromatin is less compacted (**euchromatin**), but some remains highly condensed (**heterochromatin**). Euchromatin, but not heterochromatin, is generally accessible for transcription of genes.

> **?** *Describe the levels of chromatin packing you'd expect to see in an interphase nucleus.*

TEST YOUR UNDERSTANDING

LEVEL 1: KNOWLEDGE/COMPREHENSION

1. In his work with pneumonia-causing bacteria and mice, Griffith found that
   a. the protein coat from pathogenic cells was able to transform nonpathogenic cells.
   b. heat-killed pathogenic cells caused pneumonia.
   c. some substance from pathogenic cells was transferred to nonpathogenic cells, making them pathogenic.
   d. the polysaccharide coat of bacteria caused pneumonia.

2. What is the basis for the difference in how the leading and lagging strands of DNA molecules are synthesized?
   a. The origins of replication occur only at the 5′ end.
   b. Helicases and single-strand binding proteins work at the 5′ end.
   c. DNA polymerase can join new nucleotides only to the 3′ end of a pre-existing strand.
   d. DNA ligase works only in the 3′ → 5′ direction.

3. In analyzing the number of different bases in a DNA sample, which result would be consistent with the base-pairing rules?
   a. $A = G$
   b. $A + G = C + T$
   c. $A + T = G + C$
   d. $A = C$

4. The elongation of the leading strand during DNA synthesis
   a. progresses away from the replication fork.
   b. occurs in the 3′ → 5′ direction.
   c. does not require a template strand.
   d. depends on the action of DNA polymerase.

5. In a nucleosome, the DNA is wrapped around
   a. histones.
   b. ribosomes.
   c. polymerase molecules.
   d. a thymine dimer.

6. *E. coli* cells grown on ^{15}N medium are transferred to ^{14}N medium and allowed to grow for two more generations (two rounds of DNA replication). DNA extracted from these cells is centrifuged. What density distribution of DNA would you expect in this experiment?
   a. one high-density and one low-density band
   b. one intermediate-density band
   c. one high-density and one intermediate-density band
   d. one low-density and one intermediate-density band

7. A biochemist isolates, purifies, and combines in a test tube a variety of molecules needed for DNA replication. When she adds some DNA to the mixture, replication occurs, but each DNA molecule consists of a normal strand paired with numerous segments of DNA a few hundred nucleotides long. What has she probably left out of the mixture?
   a. DNA polymerase
   b. DNA ligase
   c. Okazaki fragments
   d. primase

8. The spontaneous loss of amino groups from adenine in DNA results in hypoxanthine, an uncommon base, opposite thymine. What combination of proteins could repair such damage?
   a. nuclease, DNA polymerase, DNA ligase
   b. telomerase, primase, DNA polymerase
   c. telomerase, helicase, single-strand binding protein
   d. DNA ligase, replication fork proteins, adenylyl cyclase

9. MAKE CONNECTIONS Although the proteins that cause the *E. coli* chromosome to coil are not histones, what property would you expect them to share with histones, given their ability to bind to DNA (see Figure 5.14)?

LEVEL 3: SYNTHESIS/EVALUATION

10. EVOLUTION CONNECTION
    Some bacteria may be able to respond to environmental stress by increasing the rate at which mutations occur during cell division. How might this be accomplished? Might there be an evolutionary advantage of this ability? Explain.

11. SCIENTIFIC INQUIRY

DRAW IT Model building can be an important part of the scientific process. The illustration shown above is a computer-generated model of a DNA replication complex. The parental and newly synthesized DNA strands are color-coded differently, as are each of the following three proteins: DNA pol III, the sliding clamp, and single-strand binding protein. Use what you've learned in this chapter to clarify this model by labeling each DNA strand and each protein and indicating the overall direction of DNA replication.

12. WRITE ABOUT A THEME: INFORMATION
    The continuity of life is based on heritable information in the form of DNA, and structure and function are correlated at all levels of biological organization. In a short essay (100–150 words), describe how the structure of DNA is correlated with its role as the molecular basis of inheritance.

13. SYNTHESIZE YOUR KNOWLEDGE

This image shows DNA interacting with a computer-generated model of a TAL protein, one of a family of proteins found only in a species of the bacterium *Xanthomonas*. The bacterium uses proteins like this one to find particular gene sequences in cells of the organisms it infects, such as tomatoes, rice, and citrus fruits. Researchers are excited about working with this family of proteins. Their goal is to generate modified versions that can home in on specific gene sequences. Such proteins could then be used in an approach called gene therapy to "fix" mutated genes in individuals with genetic diseases. Given what you know about DNA structure and considering the image above, discuss how the TAL protein's structure suggests that it functions.

For selected answers, see Appendix A.

MasteringBiology®

Students Go to **MasteringBiology** for assignments, the eText, and the Study Area with practice tests, animations, and activities.

Instructors Go to **MasteringBiology** for automatically graded tutorials and questions that you can assign to your students, plus Instructor Resources.

17

Gene Expression: From Gene to Protein

▲ Figure 17.1 How does a single faulty gene result in the dramatic appearance of an albino animal?

The Flow of Genetic Information

In 2006, a young albino deer seen frolicking with several brown deer in the mountains of eastern Germany elicited a public outcry (Figure 17.1). A local hunting organization announced that the albino deer suffered from a "genetic disorder" and should be shot. Some argued that the deer should merely be prevented from mating with other deer to safeguard the population's gene pool. Others favored relocating the albino deer to a nature reserve because they worried that it might be more noticeable to predators if left in the wild. A German rock star even held a benefit concert to raise funds for the relocation. What led to the striking phenotype of this deer, the cause of this lively debate?

You learned in Chapter 14 that inherited traits are determined by genes, and that the trait of albinism is caused by a recessive allele of a pigmentation gene. The information content of genes is in the form of specific sequences of nucleotides along strands of DNA, the genetic material. But how does this information determine an organism's traits? Put another way, what does a gene actually say? And how is its message translated by cells into a specific trait, such as brown hair, type A blood, or, in the case of an albino deer, a total lack of pigment? The albino deer has a faulty version of a key protein, an enzyme required for pigment synthesis, and this protein is faulty because the gene that codes for it contains incorrect information.

◀ An albino raccoon.

This example illustrates the main point of this chapter: The DNA inherited by an organism leads to specific traits by dictating the synthesis of proteins and of RNA molecules involved in protein synthesis. In other words, proteins are the link between genotype and phenotype. **Gene expression** is the process by which DNA directs the synthesis of proteins (or, in some cases, just RNAs). The expression of genes that code for proteins includes two stages: transcription and translation. This chapter describes the flow of information from gene to protein and explains how genetic mutations affect organisms through their proteins. Understanding the processes of gene expression, which are similar in all three domains of life, will allow us to revisit the concept of the gene in more detail at the end of the chapter.

CONCEPT 17.1

Genes specify proteins via transcription and translation

Before going into the details of how genes direct protein synthesis, let's step back and examine how the fundamental relationship between genes and proteins was discovered.

Evidence from the Study of Metabolic Defects

In 1902, British physician Archibald Garrod was the first to suggest that genes dictate phenotypes through enzymes that catalyze specific chemical reactions in the cell. Garrod postulated that the symptoms of an inherited disease reflect a person's inability to make a particular enzyme. He later referred to such diseases as "inborn errors of metabolism." Garrod gave as one example the hereditary condition called alkaptonuria. In this disorder, the urine is black because it contains the chemical alkapton, which darkens upon exposure to air. Garrod reasoned that most people have an enzyme that metabolizes alkapton, whereas people with alkaptonuria have inherited an inability to make that metabolic enzyme.

Garrod may have been the first to recognize that Mendel's principles of heredity apply to humans as well as peas. Garrod's realization was ahead of its time, but research several decades later supported his hypothesis that a gene dictates the production of a specific enzyme, later named the *one gene–one enzyme hypothesis*. Biochemists accumulated much evidence that cells synthesize and degrade most organic molecules via metabolic pathways, in which each chemical reaction in a sequence is catalyzed by a specific enzyme (see Concept 8.1). Such metabolic pathways lead, for instance, to the synthesis of the pigments that give the brown deer in Figure 17.1 their fur color or fruit flies (*Drosophila*) their eye color (see Figure 15.3). In the 1930s, the American biochemist and geneticist George Beadle and his French colleague

Boris Ephrussi speculated that in *Drosophila*, each of the various mutations affecting eye color blocks pigment synthesis at a specific step by preventing production of the enzyme that catalyzes that step. But neither the chemical reactions nor the enzymes that catalyze them were known at the time.

Nutritional Mutants in Neurospora: Scientific Inquiry

A breakthrough in demonstrating the relationship between genes and enzymes came a few years later at Stanford University, where Beadle and Edward Tatum began working with a bread mold, *Neurospora crassa.* They bombarded *Neurospora* with X-rays, shown in the 1920s to cause genetic changes, and then looked among the survivors for mutants that differed in their nutritional needs from the wild-type bread mold. Wild-type *Neurospora* has modest food requirements. It can grow in the laboratory on a simple solution of inorganic salts, glucose, and the vitamin biotin, incorporated into agar, a support medium. From this minimal medium, the mold cells use their metabolic pathways to produce all the other molecules they need. Beadle and Tatum identified mutants that could not survive on minimal medium, apparently because they were unable to synthesize certain essential molecules from the minimal ingredients. To ensure survival of these nutritional mutants, Beadle and Tatum allowed them to grow on a complete growth medium, which consisted of minimal medium supplemented with all 20 amino acids and a few other nutrients. The complete growth medium could support any mutant that couldn't synthesize one of the supplements.

To characterize the metabolic defect in each nutritional mutant, Beadle and Tatum took samples from the mutant growing on complete medium and distributed them to a number of different vials. Each vial contained minimal medium plus a single additional nutrient. The particular supplement that allowed growth indicated the metabolic defect. For example, if the only supplemented vial that supported growth of the mutant was the one fortified with the amino acid arginine, the researchers could conclude that the mutant was defective in the biochemical pathway that wild-type cells use to synthesize arginine.

In fact, such arginine-requiring mutants were obtained and studied by two colleagues of Beadle and Tatum, Adrian Srb and Norman Horowitz, who wanted to investigate the biochemical pathway for arginine synthesis in *Neurospora* **(Figure 17.2)**. Srb and Horowitz pinned down each mutant's defect more specifically, using additional tests to distinguish among three classes of arginine-requiring mutants. Mutants in each class required a different set of compounds along the arginine-synthesizing pathway, which has three steps. These results, and those of many similar experiments done by Beadle and Tatum, suggested that each class was blocked at a different step in this pathway because mutants in that class lacked the enzyme that catalyzes the blocked step.

Inquiry

Do individual genes specify the enzymes that function in a biochemical pathway?

Experiment Working with the mold *Neurospora crassa*, Adrian Srb and Norman Horowitz, then at Stanford University, used Beadle and Tatum's experimental approach to isolate mutants that required arginine in their growth medium. The researchers showed that these mutants fell into three classes, each defective in a different gene. From studies by others on mammalian liver cells, they suspected that the metabolic pathway of arginine biosynthesis involved a precursor nutrient and the intermediate molecules ornithine and citrulline, as shown in the diagram on the right.

Their most famous experiment, shown here, tested both the *one gene–one enzyme hypothesis* and their postulated arginine-synthesizing pathway. In this experiment, they grew their three classes of mutants under the four different conditions shown in the Results Table below. They included minimal medium (MM) as a control, knowing that wild-type cells could grow on MM but mutant cells could not. (See test tubes below.)

Growth: Wild-type cells growing and dividing

No growth: Mutant cells cannot grow and divide

Control: Minimal medium

Results As shown in the table on the right, the wild-type strain was capable of growth under all experimental conditions, requiring only the minimal medium. The three classes of mutants each had a specific set of growth requirements. For example, class II mutants could not grow when ornithine alone was added but could grow when either citrulline or arginine was added.

Results Table	Classes of *Neurospora crassa*			
Condition	**Wild type**	**Class I mutants**	**Class II mutants**	**Class III mutants**
Minimal medium (MM) (control)				
MM + ornithine				
MM + citrulline				
MM + arginine (control)				
Summary of results	Can grow with or without any supplements	Can grow on ornithine, citrulline, or arginine	Can grow only on citrulline or arginine	Require arginine to grow

Conclusion From the growth requirements of the mutants, Srb and Horowitz deduced that each class of mutant was unable to carry out one step in the pathway for synthesizing arginine, presumably because it lacked the necessary enzyme, as shown in the table on the right. Because each of their mutants was mutated in a single gene, they concluded that each mutated gene must normally dictate the production of one enzyme. Their results supported the one gene–one enzyme hypothesis, proposed by Beadle and Tatum, and also confirmed that the arginine pathway described in the mammalian liver also operates in *Neurospora*. (Notice in the Results Table that a mutant can grow only if supplied with a compound made *after* the defective step because this bypasses the defect.)

Source: A. M. Srb and N. H. Horowitz, The ornithine cycle in *Neurospora* and its genetic control, *Journal of Biological Chemistry* 154:129–139 (1944).

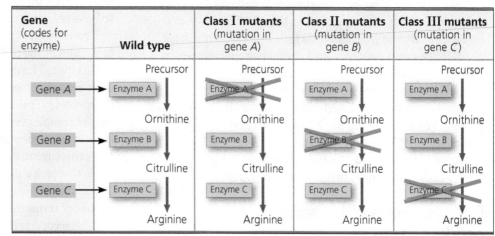

WHAT IF? *Suppose the experiment had shown that class I mutants could grow only in MM supplemented by ornithine or arginine and that class II mutants could grow in MM supplemented by citrulline, ornithine, or arginine. What conclusions would the researchers have drawn from those results regarding the biochemical pathway and the defect in class I and class II mutants?*

Because each mutant was defective in a single gene, Beadle and Tatum saw that, taken together, the collected results provided strong support for a working hypothesis they had proposed earlier. The one gene–one enzyme hypothesis, as they dubbed it, states that the function of a gene is to dictate the production of a specific enzyme. Further support for this hypothesis came from experiments that identified the specific enzymes lacking in the mutants. Beadle and Tatum shared a Nobel Prize in 1958 for "their discovery that genes act by regulating definite chemical events" (in the words of the Nobel committee).

Today, we know of countless examples in which a mutation in a gene causes a faulty enzyme that in turn leads to an identifiable condition. The albino deer in Figure 17.1 lacks a key enzyme called tyrosinase in the metabolic pathway that produces melanin, a dark pigment. The absence of melanin causes white fur and other effects throughout the deer's body. Its nose, ears, and hooves, as well as its eyes, are pink because no melanin is present to mask the reddish color of the blood vessels that run through those structures.

The Products of Gene Expression: A Developing Story

As researchers learned more about proteins, they made revisions to the one gene–one enzyme hypothesis. First of all, not all proteins are enzymes. Keratin, the structural protein of animal hair, and the hormone insulin are two examples of nonenzyme proteins. Because proteins that are not enzymes are nevertheless gene products, molecular biologists began to think in terms of one gene–one protein. However, many proteins are constructed from two or more different polypeptide chains, and each polypeptide is specified by its own gene. For example, hemoglobin, the oxygen-transporting protein of vertebrate red blood cells, contains two kinds of polypeptides, and thus two genes code for this protein (see Figure 5.18). Beadle and Tatum's idea was therefore restated as the *one gene–one polypeptide hypothesis*. Even this description is not entirely accurate, though. First, in many cases, a eukaryotic gene can code for a set of closely related polypeptides via a process called alternative splicing, which you will learn about later in this chapter. Second, quite a few genes code for RNA molecules that have important functions in cells even though they are never translated into protein. For now, we will focus on genes that do code for polypeptides. (Note that it is common to refer to these gene products as proteins—a practice you will encounter in this book—rather than more precisely as polypeptides.)

Basic Principles of Transcription and Translation

Genes provide the instructions for making specific proteins. But a gene does not build a protein directly. The bridge between DNA and protein synthesis is the nucleic acid RNA.

RNA is chemically similar to DNA except that it contains ribose instead of deoxyribose as its sugar and has the nitrogenous base uracil rather than thymine (see Figure 5.24). Thus, each nucleotide along a DNA strand has A, G, C, or T as its base, and each nucleotide along an RNA strand has A, G, C, or U as its base. An RNA molecule usually consists of a single strand.

It is customary to describe the flow of information from gene to protein in linguistic terms because both nucleic acids and proteins are polymers with specific sequences of monomers that convey information, much as specific sequences of letters communicate information in a language like English. In DNA or RNA, the monomers are the four types of nucleotides, which differ in their nitrogenous bases. Genes are typically hundreds or thousands of nucleotides long, each gene having a specific sequence of nucleotides. Each polypeptide of a protein also has monomers arranged in a particular linear order (the protein's primary structure), but its monomers are amino acids. Thus, nucleic acids and proteins contain information written in two different chemical languages. Getting from DNA to protein requires two major stages: transcription and translation.

Transcription is the synthesis of RNA using information in the DNA. The two nucleic acids are written in different forms of the same language, and the information is simply transcribed, or "rewritten," from DNA to RNA. Just as a DNA strand provides a template for making a new complementary strand during DNA replication, it also can serve as a template for assembling a complementary sequence of RNA nucleotides. For a protein-coding gene, the resulting RNA molecule is a faithful transcript of the gene's protein-building instructions. This type of RNA molecule is called **messenger RNA (mRNA)** because it carries a genetic message from the DNA to the protein-synthesizing machinery of the cell. (Transcription is the general term for the synthesis of *any* kind of RNA on a DNA template. Later, you will learn about some other types of RNA produced by transcription.)

Translation is the synthesis of a polypeptide using the information in the mRNA. During this stage, there is a change in language: The cell must translate the nucleotide sequence of an mRNA molecule into the amino acid sequence of a polypeptide. The sites of translation are **ribosomes**, molecular complexes that facilitate the orderly linking of amino acids into polypeptide chains.

Transcription and translation occur in all organisms—those that lack a membrane-bounded nucleus (bacteria and archaea) and those that have one (eukaryotes). Because most studies of transcription and translation have used bacteria and eukaryotic cells, they are our main focus in this chapter. Our understanding of transcription and translation in archaea lags behind, but we do know that archaeal cells share some features of gene expression with bacteria and others with eukaryotes.

The basic mechanics of transcription and translation are similar for bacteria and eukaryotes, but there is an important difference in the flow of genetic information within the cells. Because bacteria do not have nuclei, their DNA is not separated by nuclear membranes from ribosomes and the other protein-synthesizing equipment (**Figure 17.3a**). As you will see later, this lack of compartmentalization allows translation of an mRNA to begin while its transcription is still in progress. In a eukaryotic cell, by contrast, the nuclear envelope separates transcription from translation in space and time (**Figure 17.3b**). Transcription occurs in the nucleus, and mRNA is then transported to the cytoplasm, where translation occurs. But before eukaryotic RNA transcripts from protein-coding genes can leave the nucleus, they are modified in various ways to produce the final, functional mRNA. The transcription of a protein-coding eukaryotic gene results in *pre-mRNA*, and further processing yields the finished mRNA. The initial RNA transcript from any gene, including those specifying RNA that is not translated into protein, is more generally called a **primary transcript**.

To summarize: Genes program protein synthesis via genetic messages in the form of messenger RNA. Put another way, cells are governed by a molecular chain of command with a directional flow of genetic information, shown here by arrows:

This concept was dubbed the *central dogma* by Francis Crick in 1956. How has the concept held up over time? In the 1970s, scientists were surprised to discover that some enzymes exist that use RNA molecules as templates for DNA synthesis (a process you'll read about in Chapter 19). However, these exceptions do not invalidate the idea that, in general, genetic information flows from DNA to RNA to protein. In the next section, we discuss how the instructions for assembling amino acids into a specific order are encoded in nucleic acids.

The Genetic Code

When biologists began to suspect that the instructions for protein synthesis were encoded in DNA, they recognized a problem: There are only four nucleotide bases to specify 20 amino acids. Thus, the genetic code cannot be a language like Chinese, where each written symbol corresponds to a word. How many nucleotides, then, correspond to an amino acid?

Codons: Triplets of Nucleotides

If each kind of nucleotide base were translated into an amino acid, only four amino acids could be specified, one per nucleotide base. Would a language of two-letter code

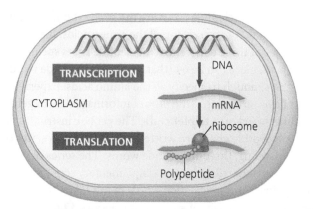

(a) Bacterial cell. In a bacterial cell, which lacks a nucleus, mRNA produced by transcription is immediately translated without additional processing.

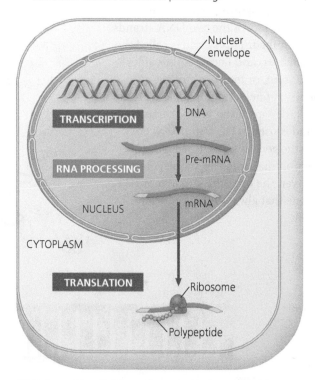

(b) Eukaryotic cell. The nucleus provides a separate compartment for transcription. The original RNA transcript, called pre-mRNA, is processed in various ways before leaving the nucleus as mRNA.

▲ **Figure 17.3 Overview: the roles of transcription and translation in the flow of genetic information.** In a cell, inherited information flows from DNA to RNA to protein. The two main stages of information flow are transcription and translation. A miniature version of part (a) or (b) accompanies several figures later in the chapter as an orientation diagram to help you see where a particular figure fits into the overall scheme.

words suffice? The two-nucleotide sequence AG, for example, could specify one amino acid, and GT could specify another. Since there are four possible nucleotide bases in each position, this would give us 16 (that is, 4×4, or 4^2) possible arrangements—still not enough to code for all 20 amino acids.

Triplets of nucleotide bases are the smallest units of uniform length that can code for all the amino acids. If each arrangement of three consecutive nucleotide bases specifies an amino acid, there can be 64 (that is, 4^3) possible code words—more than enough to specify all the amino acids. Experiments have verified that the flow of information from gene to protein is based on a **triplet code**: The genetic instructions for a polypeptide chain are written in the DNA as a series of nonoverlapping, three-nucleotide words. The series of words in a gene is transcribed into a complementary series of nonoverlapping, three-nucleotide words in mRNA, which is then translated into a chain of amino acids **(Figure 17.4)**.

During transcription, the gene determines the sequence of nucleotide bases along the length of the RNA molecule that is being synthesized. For each gene, only one of the two DNA strands is transcribed. This strand is called the **template strand** because it provides the pattern, or template, for the sequence of nucleotides in an RNA transcript. For any given gene, the same strand is used as the template every time the gene is transcribed. For other genes on the same DNA molecule, however, the opposite strand may be the one that always functions as the template.

DNA molecule

Gene 1

Gene 2

Gene 3

▲ **Figure 17.4 The triplet code.** For each gene, one DNA strand functions as a template for transcription of RNAs, such as mRNA. The base-pairing rules for DNA synthesis also guide transcription, except that uracil (U) takes the place of thymine (T) in RNA. During translation, the mRNA is read as a sequence of nucleotide triplets, called codons. Each codon specifies an amino acid to be added to the growing polypeptide chain. The mRNA is read in the 5′ → 3′ direction.

? *Write the sequence of the mRNA strand and the nontemplate DNA strand—in both cases reading from 5′ to 3′—and compare them.*

An mRNA molecule is complementary rather than identical to its DNA template because RNA nucleotides are assembled on the template according to base-pairing rules (see Figure 17.4). The pairs are similar to those that form during DNA replication, except that U (the RNA substitute for T) pairs with A and the mRNA nucleotides contain ribose instead of deoxyribose. Like a new strand of DNA, the RNA molecule is synthesized in an antiparallel direction to the template strand of DNA. (To review what is meant by "antiparallel" and the 5′ and 3′ ends of a nucleic acid chain, see Figure 16.7.) In the example in Figure 17.4, the nucleotide triplet ACC along the DNA (written as 3′-ACC-5′) provides a template for 5′-UGG-3′ in the mRNA molecule. The mRNA nucleotide triplets are called **codons**, and they are customarily written in the 5′ → 3′ direction. In our example, UGG is the codon for the amino acid tryptophan (abbreviated Trp). The term *codon* is also used for the DNA nucleotide triplets along the *nontemplate* strand. These codons are complementary to the template strand and thus identical in sequence to the mRNA, except that they have a T wherever there is a U in the mRNA. (For this reason, the nontemplate DNA strand is often called the *coding strand*.)

During translation, the sequence of codons along an mRNA molecule is decoded, or translated, into a sequence of amino acids making up a polypeptide chain. The codons are read by the translation machinery in the 5′ → 3′ direction along the mRNA. Each codon specifies which one of the 20 amino acids will be incorporated at the corresponding position along a polypeptide. Because codons are nucleotide triplets, the number of nucleotides making up a genetic message must be three times the number of amino acids in the protein product. For example, it takes 300 nucleotides along an mRNA strand to code for the amino acids in a polypeptide that is 100 amino acids long.

Cracking the Code

Molecular biologists cracked the genetic code of life in the early 1960s when a series of elegant experiments disclosed the amino acid translations of each of the RNA codons. The first codon was deciphered in 1961 by Marshall Nirenberg, of the National Institutes of Health, along with his colleagues. Nirenberg synthesized an artificial mRNA by linking identical RNA nucleotides containing uracil as their base. No matter where this message started or stopped, it could contain only one codon in repetition: UUU. Nirenberg added this "poly-U" to a test-tube mixture containing amino acids, ribosomes, and the other components required for protein synthesis. His artificial system translated the poly-U into a polypeptide containing many units of the amino acid phenylalanine (Phe), strung together as a long polyphenylalanine chain. Thus, Nirenberg determined that the mRNA codon UUU specifies the amino acid phenylalanine. Soon, the amino acids specified by the codons AAA, GGG, and CCC were also determined.

Although more elaborate techniques were required to decode mixed triplets such as AUA and CGA, all 64 codons were deciphered by the mid-1960s. As **Figure 17.5** shows, 61 of the 64 triplets code for amino acids. The three codons that do not designate amino acids are "stop" signals, or termination codons, marking the end of translation. Notice that the codon AUG has a dual function: It codes for the amino acid methionine (Met) and also functions as a "start" signal, or initiation codon. Genetic messages usually begin with the mRNA codon AUG, which signals the protein-synthesizing machinery to begin translating the mRNA at that location. (Because AUG also stands for methionine, polypeptide chains begin with methionine when they are synthesized. However, an enzyme may subsequently remove this starter amino acid from the chain.)

Notice in Figure 17.5 that there is redundancy in the genetic code, but no ambiguity. For example, although codons GAA and GAG both specify glutamic acid (redundancy), neither of them ever specifies any other amino acid (no ambiguity). The redundancy in the code is not altogether random. In many cases, codons that are synonyms for a particular amino acid differ only in the third nucleotide base of the triplet. We will consider the significance of this redundancy later in the chapter.

Our ability to extract the intended message from a written language depends on reading the symbols in the correct groupings—that is, in the correct **reading frame**. Consider this statement: "The red dog ate the bug." Group the letters incorrectly by starting at the wrong point, and the result will probably be gibberish: for example, "her edd oga tet heb ug." The reading frame is also important in the molecular language of cells. The short stretch of polypeptide shown in Figure 17.4, for instance, will be made correctly only if the mRNA nucleotides are read from left to right (5′ → 3′) in the groups of three shown in the figure: UGG UUU GGC UCA. Although a genetic message is written with no spaces between the codons, the cell's protein-synthesizing machinery reads the message as a series of nonoverlapping three-letter words. The message is *not* read as a series of overlapping words—UGGUUU, and so on—which would convey a very different message.

Evolution of the Genetic Code

EVOLUTION The genetic code is nearly universal, shared by organisms from the simplest bacteria to the most complex plants and animals. The RNA codon CCG, for instance, is translated as the amino acid proline in all organisms whose genetic code has been examined. In laboratory experiments, genes can be transcribed and translated after being transplanted from one species to another, sometimes with quite striking results, as shown in **Figure 17.6**. Bacteria can

Second mRNA base

	U	C	A	G	
U	UUU ⎤ Phe UUC ⎦ UUA ⎤ Leu UUG ⎦	UCU ⎤ UCC ⎥ Ser UCA ⎥ UCG ⎦	UAU ⎤ Tyr UAC ⎦ UAA Stop UAG Stop	UGU ⎤ Cys UGC ⎦ UGA Stop UGG Trp	U C A G
C	CUU ⎤ CUC ⎥ Leu CUA ⎥ CUG ⎦	CCU ⎤ CCC ⎥ Pro CCA ⎥ CCG ⎦	CAU ⎤ His CAC ⎦ CAA ⎤ Gln CAG ⎦	CGU ⎤ CGC ⎥ Arg CGA ⎥ CGG ⎦	U C A G
A	AUU ⎤ AUC ⎥ Ile AUA ⎦ AUG Met or start	ACU ⎤ ACC ⎥ Thr ACA ⎥ ACG ⎦	AAU ⎤ Asn AAC ⎦ AAA ⎤ Lys AAG ⎦	AGU ⎤ Ser AGC ⎦ AGA ⎤ Arg AGG ⎦	U C A G
G	GUU ⎤ GUC ⎥ Val GUA ⎥ GUG ⎦	GCU ⎤ GCC ⎥ Ala GCA ⎥ GCG ⎦	GAU ⎤ Asp GAC ⎦ GAA ⎤ Glu GAG ⎦	GGU ⎤ GGC ⎥ Gly GGA ⎥ GGG ⎦	U C A G

First mRNA base (5′ end of codon) ... Third mRNA base (3′ end of codon)

▲ **Figure 17.5 The codon table for mRNA.** The three nucleotide bases of an mRNA codon are designated here as the first, second, and third bases, reading in the 5′ → 3′ direction along the mRNA. (Practice using this table by finding the codons in Figure 17.4.) The codon AUG not only stands for the amino acid methionine (Met) but also functions as a "start" signal for ribosomes to begin translating the mRNA at that point. Three of the 64 codons function as "stop" signals, marking where ribosomes end translation. See Figure 5.14 for a list of the full names of all the amino acids.

(a) Tobacco plant expressing a firefly gene. The yellow glow is produced by a chemical reaction catalyzed by the protein product of the firefly gene.

(b) Pig expressing a jellyfish gene. Researchers injected a jellyfish gene for a fluorescent protein into fertilized pig eggs. One developed into this fluorescent pig.

▲ **Figure 17.6 Expression of genes from different species.** Because diverse forms of life share a common genetic code, one species can be programmed to produce proteins characteristic of a second species by introducing DNA from the second species into the first.

be programmed by the insertion of human genes to synthesize certain human proteins for medical use, such as insulin. Such applications have produced many exciting developments in the area of biotechnology (see Chapter 20).

Despite a small number of exceptions in which a few codons differ from the standard ones, the evolutionary significance of the code's near universality is clear. A language shared by all living things must have been operating very early in the history of life—early enough to be present in the common ancestor of all present-day organisms. A shared genetic vocabulary is a reminder of the kinship that bonds all life on Earth.

CONCEPT CHECK 17.1

1. **MAKE CONNECTIONS** In a research article about alkaptonuria published in 1902, Garrod suggested that humans inherit two "characters" (alleles) for a particular enzyme and that both parents must contribute a faulty version for the offspring to have the disorder. Today, would this disorder be called dominant or recessive? (See Concept 14.4.)

2. What polypeptide product would you expect from a poly-G mRNA that is 30 nucleotides long?

3. **DRAW IT** The template strand of a gene contains the sequence 3'-TTCAGTCGT-5'. Draw the nontemplate sequence and mRNA sequence, indicating the 5' and 3' ends of each. Compare the two sequences.

4. **DRAW IT** Imagine that the nontemplate sequence in question 3 had been transcribed instead of the template sequence. Draw the mRNA sequence and translate it using Figure 17.5. (Be sure to pay attention to the 5' and 3' ends.) Predict how well the protein synthesized from the nontemplate strand would function, if at all.

For suggested answers, see Appendix A.

CONCEPT 17.2

Transcription is the DNA-directed synthesis of RNA: *A closer look*

Now that we have considered the linguistic logic and evolutionary significance of the genetic code, we are ready to reexamine transcription, the first stage of gene expression, in more detail.

Molecular Components of Transcription

Messenger RNA, the carrier of information from DNA to the cell's protein-synthesizing machinery, is transcribed from the template strand of a gene. An enzyme called an **RNA polymerase** pries the two strands of DNA apart and joins together RNA nucleotides complementary to the DNA template strand, thus elongating the RNA polynucleotide **(Figure 17.7).** Like the DNA polymerases that function in

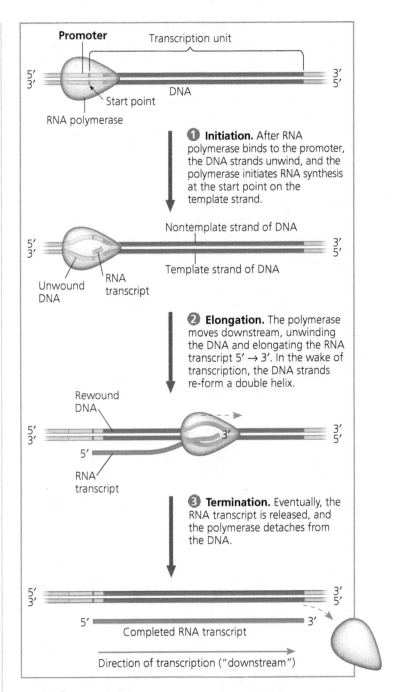

Promoter — **Transcription unit**

RNA polymerase / Start point / DNA

❶ **Initiation.** After RNA polymerase binds to the promoter, the DNA strands unwind, and the polymerase initiates RNA synthesis at the start point on the template strand.

Nontemplate strand of DNA
Template strand of DNA
Unwound DNA / RNA transcript

❷ **Elongation.** The polymerase moves downstream, unwinding the DNA and elongating the RNA transcript 5' → 3'. In the wake of transcription, the DNA strands re-form a double helix.

Rewound DNA
RNA transcript

❸ **Termination.** Eventually, the RNA transcript is released, and the polymerase detaches from the DNA.

Completed RNA transcript
Direction of transcription ("downstream")

▲ **Figure 17.7 The stages of transcription: initiation, elongation, and termination.** This general depiction of transcription applies to both bacteria and eukaryotes, but the details of termination differ, as described in the text. Also, in a bacterium, the RNA transcript is immediately usable as mRNA; in a eukaryote, the RNA transcript must first undergo processing.

MAKE CONNECTIONS *Compare the use of a template strand during transcription and replication. See Figure 16.17.*

DNA replication, RNA polymerases can assemble a polynucleotide only in its 5' → 3' direction. Unlike DNA polymerases, however, RNA polymerases are able to start a chain from scratch; they don't need a primer.

Specific sequences of nucleotides along the DNA mark where transcription of a gene begins and ends. The DNA sequence where RNA polymerase attaches and initiates transcription is known as the **promoter**; in bacteria, the sequence that signals the end of transcription is called the **terminator**. (The termination mechanism is different in eukaryotes; we'll describe it later.) Molecular biologists refer to the direction of transcription as "downstream" and the other direction as "upstream." These terms are also used to describe the positions of nucleotide sequences within the DNA or RNA. Thus, the promoter sequence in DNA is said to be upstream from the terminator. The stretch of DNA downstream from the promoter that is transcribed into an RNA molecule is called a **transcription unit**.

Bacteria have a single type of RNA polymerase that synthesizes not only mRNA but also other types of RNA that function in protein synthesis, such as ribosomal RNA. In contrast, eukaryotes have at least three types of RNA polymerase in their nuclei; the one used for pre-mRNA synthesis is called RNA polymerase II. The other RNA polymerases transcribe RNA molecules that are not translated into protein. In the discussion that follows, we start with the features of mRNA synthesis common to both bacteria and eukaryotes and then describe some key differences.

Synthesis of an RNA Transcript

The three stages of transcription, as shown in Figure 17.7 and described next, are initiation, elongation, and termination of the RNA chain. Study Figure 17.7 to familiarize yourself with the stages and the terms used to describe them.

RNA Polymerase Binding and Initiation of Transcription

The promoter of a gene includes within it the transcription **start point** (the nucleotide where RNA synthesis actually begins) and typically extends several dozen or more nucleotide pairs upstream from the start point. RNA polymerase binds in a precise location and orientation on the promoter, therefore determining where transcription starts and which of the two strands of the DNA helix is used as the template.

Certain sections of a promoter are especially important for binding RNA polymerase. In bacteria, part of the RNA polymerase itself specifically recognizes and binds to the promoter. In eukaryotes, a collection of proteins called **transcription factors** mediate the binding of RNA polymerase and the initiation of transcription. Only after transcription factors are attached to the promoter does RNA polymerase II bind to it. The whole complex of transcription factors and RNA polymerase II bound to the promoter is called a **transcription initiation complex**. Figure 17.8 shows the role of transcription factors and a crucial promoter DNA sequence called a **TATA box** in forming the initiation complex at a eukaryotic promoter.

The interaction between eukaryotic RNA polymerase II and transcription factors is an example of the importance

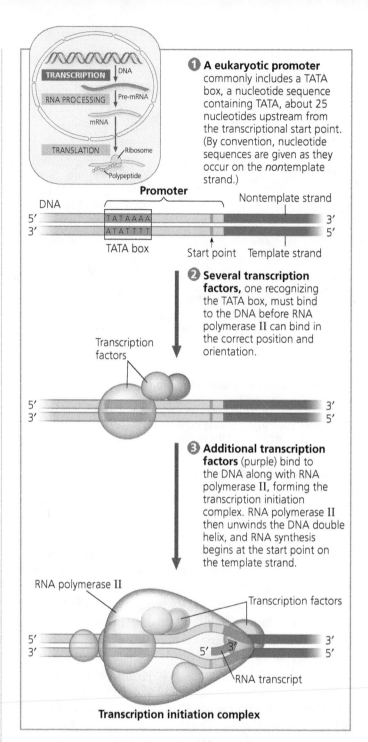

1 **A eukaryotic promoter** commonly includes a TATA box, a nucleotide sequence containing TATA, about 25 nucleotides upstream from the transcriptional start point. (By convention, nucleotide sequences are given as they occur on the *non*template strand.)

2 **Several transcription factors,** one recognizing the TATA box, must bind to the DNA before RNA polymerase II can bind in the correct position and orientation.

3 **Additional transcription factors** (purple) bind to the DNA along with RNA polymerase II, forming the transcription initiation complex. RNA polymerase II then unwinds the DNA double helix, and RNA synthesis begins at the start point on the template strand.

Transcription initiation complex

▲ **Figure 17.8 The initiation of transcription at a eukaryotic promoter.** In eukaryotic cells, proteins called transcription factors mediate the initiation of transcription by RNA polymerase II.

? *Explain how the interaction of RNA polymerase with the promoter would differ if the figure showed transcription initiation for bacteria.*

of protein-protein interactions in controlling eukaryotic transcription. Once the appropriate transcription factors are firmly attached to the promoter DNA and the polymerase is bound in the correct orientation, the enzyme unwinds the two DNA strands and begins transcribing the template strand at the start point.

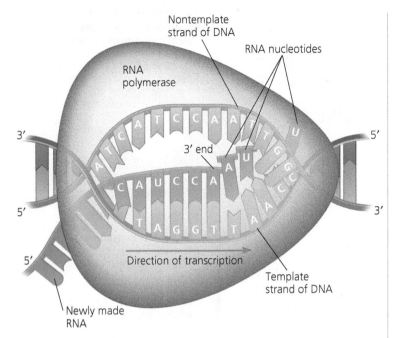

Nontemplate strand of DNA

RNA nucleotides

RNA polymerase

3′

5′

5′

3′

3′ end

3′

5′

Direction of transcription

5′

Newly made RNA

Template strand of DNA

▲ **Figure 17.9 Transcription elongation.** RNA polymerase moves along the DNA template strand, joining complementary RNA nucleotides to the 3′ end of the growing RNA transcript. Behind the polymerase, the new RNA peels away from the template strand, which re-forms a double helix with the nontemplate strand.

Elongation of the RNA Strand

As RNA polymerase moves along the DNA, it untwists the double helix, exposing about 10–20 DNA nucleotides at a time for pairing with RNA nucleotides **(Figure 17.9)**. The enzyme adds nucleotides to the 3′ end of the growing RNA molecule as it continues along the double helix. In the wake of this advancing wave of RNA synthesis, the new RNA molecule peels away from its DNA template, and the DNA double helix re-forms. Transcription progresses at a rate of about 40 nucleotides per second in eukaryotes.

A single gene can be transcribed simultaneously by several molecules of RNA polymerase following each other like trucks in a convoy. A growing strand of RNA trails off from each polymerase, with the length of each new strand reflecting how far along the template the enzyme has traveled from the start point (see the mRNA molecules in Figure 17.22). The congregation of many polymerase molecules simultaneously transcribing a single gene increases the amount of mRNA transcribed from it, which helps the cell make the encoded protein in large amounts.

Termination of Transcription

The mechanism of termination differs between bacteria and eukaryotes. In bacteria, transcription proceeds through a terminator sequence in the DNA. The transcribed terminator (an RNA sequence) functions as the termination signal, causing the polymerase to detach from the DNA and release the transcript, which requires no further modification before translation. In eukaryotes, RNA polymerase II

transcribes a sequence on the DNA called the polyadenylation signal sequence, which specifies a polyadenylation signal (AAUAAA) in the pre-mRNA. This is called a "signal" because once this stretch of six RNA nucleotides appears, it is immediately bound by certain proteins in the nucleus. Then, at a point about 10–35 nucleotides downstream from the AAUAAA, these proteins cut it free from the polymerase, releasing the pre-mRNA. The pre-mRNA then undergoes processing, the topic of the next section. Although that cleavage marks the end of the mRNA, the RNA polymerase II continues to transcribe. Since the new 5′ end isn't protected by a cap, however, enzymes degrade the RNA from the 5′ end. The polymerase continues transcribing, pursued by the enzymes, until they catch up to the polymerase and it dissociates from the DNA.

CONCEPT CHECK 17.2

1. What is a promoter? Is it located at the upstream or downstream end of a transcription unit?

2. What enables RNA polymerase to start transcribing a gene at the right place on the DNA in a bacterial cell? In a eukaryotic cell?

3. **WHAT IF?** Suppose X-rays caused a sequence change in the TATA box of a particular gene's promoter. How would that affect transcription of the gene? (See Figure 17.8.)

For suggested answers, see Appendix A.

CONCEPT 17.3

Eukaryotic cells modify RNA after transcription

Enzymes in the eukaryotic nucleus modify pre-mRNA in specific ways before the genetic message is dispatched to the cytoplasm. During this **RNA processing**, both ends of the primary transcript are altered. Also, in most cases, certain interior sections of the RNA molecule are cut out and the remaining parts spliced together. These modifications produce an mRNA molecule ready for translation.

Alteration of mRNA Ends

Each end of a pre-mRNA molecule is modified in a particular way **(Figure 17.10)**. The 5′ end, which is synthesized first, receives a **5′ cap**, a modified form of a guanine (G) nucleotide added onto the 5′ end after transcription of the first 20–40 nucleotides. The 3′ end of the pre-mRNA molecule is also modified before the mRNA exits the nucleus. Recall that the pre-mRNA is released soon after the polyadenylation signal, AAUAAA, is transcribed. At the 3′ end, an enzyme then adds 50–250 more adenine (A) nucleotides, forming a **poly-A tail**. The 5′ cap and poly-A tail share several important functions. First, they seem to facilitate the

A modified guanine nucleotide added to the 5' end

Region that includes protein-coding segments

Polyadenylation signal

50–250 adenine nucleotides added to the 3' end

5'

3'

G—Ⓟ—Ⓟ—Ⓟ—

AAUAAA

AAA···AAA

5' Cap   5' UTR   Start codon   Stop codon   3' UTR   **Poly-A tail**

▲ **Figure 17.10 RNA processing: Addition of the 5' cap and poly-A tail.** Enzymes modify the two ends of a eukaryotic pre-mRNA molecule. The modified ends may promote the export of mRNA from the nucleus, and they help protect the mRNA from degradation. When the mRNA reaches the cytoplasm, the modified ends, in conjunction with certain cytoplasmic proteins, facilitate ribosome attachment. The 5' cap and poly-A tail are not translated into protein, nor are the regions called the 5' untranslated region (5' UTR) and 3' untranslated region (3' UTR). The pink segments will be described shortly (see Figure 17.11).

export of the mature mRNA from the nucleus. Second, they help protect the mRNA from degradation by hydrolytic enzymes. And third, they help ribosomes attach to the 5' end of the mRNA once the mRNA reaches the cytoplasm. Figure 17.10 shows a diagram of a eukaryotic mRNA molecule with cap and tail. The figure also shows the untranslated regions (UTRs) at the 5' and 3' ends of the mRNA (referred to as the 5' UTR and 3' UTR). The UTRs are parts of the mRNA that will not be translated into protein, but they have other functions, such as ribosome binding.

Split Genes and RNA Splicing

A remarkable stage of RNA processing in the eukaryotic nucleus is the removal of large portions of the RNA molecule that is initially synthesized. This cut-and-paste job, called **RNA splicing**, is similar to editing a video **(Figure 17.11)**. The average length of a transcription unit along a human DNA molecule is about 27,000 nucleotide pairs, so the primary RNA transcript is also that long. However, the average-sized protein of 400 amino acids requires only 1,200 nucleotides in RNA to code for it. (Remember, each amino acid is encoded by a *triplet* of nucleotides.) This means that most eukaryotic genes and their RNA transcripts have long noncoding stretches of nucleotides, regions that are not translated. Even more surprising is that most of these noncoding sequences are interspersed between coding segments of the gene and thus between coding segments of the pre-mRNA. In other words, the sequence of DNA nucleotides that codes for a eukaryotic polypeptide is usually not continuous; it is split into segments. The noncoding segments of nucleic acid that lie between coding regions are called *inter*vening sequences, or **introns**. The other regions are called **exons**, because they are eventually *ex*pressed, usually by being translated into amino acid sequences. (Exceptions include the UTRs of the exons at the ends of the RNA, which make up part of the mRNA but are not translated into protein. Because of these exceptions, you may prefer to think of exons as sequences of RNA that *ex*it the nucleus.) The terms *intron* and *exon* are used for both RNA sequences and the DNA sequences that encode them.

In making a primary transcript from a gene, RNA polymerase II transcribes both introns and exons from the DNA, but the mRNA molecule that enters the cytoplasm is an abridged version. The introns are cut out from the molecule

© Pearson Education, Inc.

Pre-mRNA   5' Cap   5' Exon Intron Exon   Intron   Exon 3'   Poly-A tail

Codon numbers: 1–30   31–104   105–146

Introns cut out and exons spliced together

mRNA   5' Cap   Poly-A tail

5' UTR   1–146   3' UTR

Coding segment

▲ **Figure 17.11 RNA processing: RNA splicing.** The RNA molecule shown here codes for β-globin, one of the polypeptides of hemoglobin. The numbers under the RNA refer to codons; β-globin is 146 amino acids long. The β-globin gene and its pre-mRNA transcript have three exons, corresponding to sequences that will leave the nucleus as mRNA. (The 5' UTR and 3' UTR are parts of exons because they are included in the mRNA; however, they do not code for protein.) During RNA processing, the introns are cut out and the exons spliced together. In many genes, the introns are much longer than the exons.

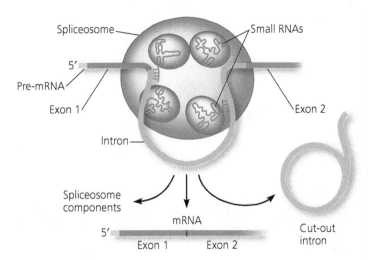

▲ **Figure 17.12 A spliceosome splicing a pre-mRNA.** The diagram shows a portion of a pre-mRNA transcript, with an intron (pink) flanked by two exons (red). Small RNAs within the spliceosome base-pair with nucleotides at specific sites along the intron. Next, the spliceosome catalyzes cutting of the pre-mRNA and the splicing together of the exons, releasing the intron for rapid degradation.

and the exons joined together, forming an mRNA molecule with a continuous coding sequence. This is the process of RNA splicing.

How is pre-mRNA splicing carried out? The removal of introns is accomplished by a large complex made of proteins and small RNAs called a **spliceosome**. This complex binds to several short nucleotide sequences along an intron, including key sequences at each end **(Figure 17.12)**. The intron is then released (and rapidly degraded), and the spliceosome joins together the two exons that flanked the intron. It turns out that the small RNAs in the spliceosome not only participate in spliceosome assembly and splice site recognition, but also catalyze the splicing reaction.

Ribozymes

The idea of a catalytic role for the RNAs in the spliceosome arose from the discovery of **ribozymes**, RNA molecules that function as enzymes. In some organisms, RNA splicing can occur without proteins or even additional RNA molecules: The intron RNA functions as a ribozyme and catalyzes its own excision! For example, in the ciliate protist *Tetrahymena*, self-splicing occurs in the production of ribosomal RNA (rRNA), a component of the organism's ribosomes. The pre-rRNA actually removes its own introns. The discovery of ribozymes rendered obsolete the idea that all biological catalysts are proteins.

Three properties of RNA enable some RNA molecules to function as enzymes. First, because RNA is single-stranded, a region of an RNA molecule may base-pair, in an antiparallel arrangement, with a complementary region elsewhere in the same molecule; this gives the molecule a particular three-dimensional structure. A specific structure is essential to the catalytic function of ribozymes, just as it is

for enzymatic proteins. Second, like certain amino acids in an enzymatic protein, some of the bases in RNA contain functional groups that can participate in catalysis. Third, the ability of RNA to hydrogen-bond with other nucleic acid molecules (either RNA or DNA) adds specificity to its catalytic activity. For example, complementary base pairing between the RNA of the spliceosome and the RNA of a primary RNA transcript precisely locates the region where the ribozyme catalyzes splicing. Later in this chapter, you will see how these properties of RNA also allow it to perform important noncatalytic roles in the cell, such as recognition of the three-nucleotide codons on mRNA.

The Functional and Evolutionary Importance of Introns

EVOLUTION Whether or not RNA splicing and the presence of introns have provided selective advantages during evolutionary history is a matter of some debate. In any case, it is informative to consider their possible adaptive benefits. Specific functions have not been identified for most introns, but at least some contain sequences that regulate gene expression, and many affect gene products.

One important consequence of the presence of introns in genes is that a single gene can encode more than one kind of polypeptide. Many genes are known to give rise to two or more different polypeptides, depending on which segments are treated as exons during RNA processing; this is called **alternative RNA splicing** (see Figure 18.13). For example, sex differences in fruit flies are largely due to differences in how males and females splice the RNA transcribed from certain genes. Results from the Human Genome Project (discussed in Concept 21.1) suggest that alternative RNA splicing is one reason humans can get along with about the same number of genes as a nematode (roundworm). Because of alternative splicing, the number of different protein products an organism produces can be much greater than its number of genes.

Proteins often have a modular architecture consisting of discrete structural and functional regions called **domains**. One domain of an enzyme, for example, might include the active site, while another might allow the enzyme to bind to a cellular membrane. In quite a few cases, different exons code for the different domains of a protein **(Figure 17.13)**.

The presence of introns in a gene may facilitate the evolution of new and potentially beneficial proteins as a result of a process known as *exon shuffling*. Introns increase the probability of crossing over between the exons of alleles of a gene—simply by providing more terrain for crossovers without interrupting coding sequences. This might result in new combinations of exons and proteins with altered structure and function. We can also imagine the occasional mixing and matching of exons between completely different (nonallelic) genes. Exon shuffling of either sort could lead to new proteins with novel combinations of functions. While most of the shuffling would result in nonbeneficial changes, occasionally a beneficial variant might arise.

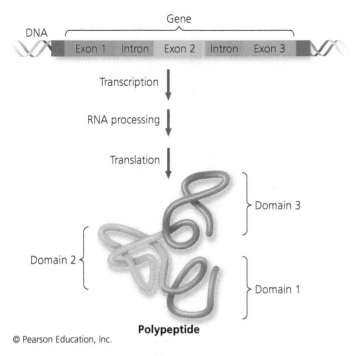

© Pearson Education, Inc.

▲ **Figure 17.13 Correspondence between exons and protein domains.**

CONCEPT CHECK 17.3

1. There are fewer than 21,000 human genes. How, then, can human cells make 75,000–100,000 different proteins?

2. How is RNA splicing similar to how you would watch a television show recorded earlier using a DVR? What would introns correspond to in this analogy?

3. **WHAT IF?** What would be the effect of treating cells with an agent that removed the cap from mRNAs?

For suggested answers, see Appendix A.

CONCEPT 17.4

Translation is the RNA-directed synthesis of a polypeptide: *A closer look*

We will now examine in greater detail how genetic information flows from mRNA to protein—the process of translation. As we did for transcription, we'll concentrate on the basic steps of translation that occur in both bacteria and eukaryotes, while pointing out key differences.

Molecular Components of Translation

In the process of translation, a cell "reads" a genetic message and builds a polypeptide accordingly. The message is a series of codons along an mRNA molecule, and the translator is called **transfer RNA (tRNA)**. The function of tRNA is to transfer amino acids from the cytoplasmic pool of amino acids to a growing polypeptide in a ribosome. A cell keeps its cytoplasm stocked with all 20 amino acids, either by synthesizing them from other compounds or by taking them up from the surrounding solution. The ribosome, a structure

▲ **Figure 17.14 Translation: the basic concept.** As a molecule of mRNA is moved through a ribosome, codons are translated into amino acids, one by one. The interpreters are tRNA molecules, each type with a specific nucleotide triplet called an anticodon at one end and a corresponding amino acid at the other end. A tRNA adds its amino acid cargo to a growing polypeptide chain when the anticodon hydrogen-bonds to the complementary codon on the mRNA. The figures that follow show some of the details of translation in a bacterial cell.

ANIMATION **BioFlix** Visit the Study Area in **MasteringBiology** for the BioFlix® 3-D Animation on Protein Synthesis. BioFlix Tutorials can also be assigned in MasteringBiology.

made of proteins and RNAs, adds each amino acid brought to it by tRNA to the growing end of a polypeptide chain **(Figure 17.14)**.

Translation is simple in principle but complex in its biochemistry and mechanics, especially in the eukaryotic cell. In dissecting translation, we'll focus on the slightly less complicated version of the process that occurs in bacteria. We'll first look at the major players in this process and then see how they act together in making a polypeptide.

The Structure and Function of Transfer RNA

The key to translating a genetic message into a specific amino acid sequence is the fact that each tRNA molecule translates a given mRNA codon into a certain amino acid. This is possible because a tRNA bears a specific amino acid at one end, while at the other end is a nucleotide triplet that can base-pair with the complementary codon on mRNA.

A tRNA molecule consists of a single RNA strand that is only about 80 nucleotides long (whereas most mRNA molecules have hundreds of nucleotides). Because of the presence of complementary stretches of nucleotide bases that can hydrogen-bond to each other, this single strand can fold back on itself and form a molecule with a three-dimensional structure. Flattened into one plane to clarify this base pairing, a tRNA molecule looks like a cloverleaf (Figure 17.15a). The tRNA actually twists and folds into a compact three-dimensional structure that is roughly L-shaped (Figure 17.15b). The loop extending from one end of the L includes the **anticodon**, the particular nucleotide triplet that base-pairs to a specific mRNA codon. From the other end of the L-shaped tRNA molecule protrudes its 3' end, which is the attachment site for an amino acid.

As an example, consider the mRNA codon 5'-GGC-3', which is translated as the amino acid glycine. The tRNA that base-pairs with this codon by hydrogen bonding has 3'-CCG-5' as its anticodon and carries glycine at its other end (see the incoming tRNA approaching the ribosome in Figure 17.14). As an mRNA molecule is moved through a ribosome, glycine will be added to the polypeptide chain whenever the codon GGC is presented for translation. Codon by codon, the genetic message is translated as tRNAs deposit amino acids in the order prescribed, and the ribosome joins the amino acids into a chain. The tRNA molecule is a translator in the sense that it can read a nucleic acid word (the mRNA codon) and interpret it as a protein word (the amino acid).

Like mRNA and other types of cellular RNA, transfer RNA molecules are transcribed from DNA templates. In a eukaryotic cell, tRNA, like mRNA, is made in the nucleus and then travels from the nucleus to the cytoplasm, where it will participate in the process of translation. In both bacterial and eukaryotic cells, each tRNA molecule is used repeatedly, picking up its designated amino acid in the cytosol, depositing this cargo onto a polypeptide chain at the ribosome, and then leaving the ribosome, ready to pick up another of the same amino acid.

The accurate translation of a genetic message requires two instances of molecular recognition. First, a tRNA that binds to an mRNA codon specifying a particular amino acid must carry that amino acid, and no other, to the ribosome. The correct matching up of tRNA and amino acid is carried out by a family of related enzymes called **aminoacyl-tRNA synthetases (Figure 17.16)**. The active site of each type of aminoacyl-tRNA synthetase fits only a specific combination of amino acid and tRNA. There are 20 different synthetases, one for each amino acid; each synthetase is able to bind to all the different tRNAs that code for its particular amino acid. The synthetase catalyzes the covalent attachment of the amino acid to its tRNA in a process driven by the hydrolysis of ATP. The resulting aminoacyl tRNA, also called a charged tRNA, is released from the enzyme and is then

(a) **Two-dimensional structure.** The four base-paired regions and three loops are characteristic of all tRNAs, as is the base sequence of the amino acid attachment site at the 3' end. The anticodon triplet is unique to each tRNA type, as are some sequences in the other two loops. (The asterisks mark bases that have been chemically modified, a characteristic of tRNA. The modified bases contribute to tRNA function in a way that is not yet understood.)

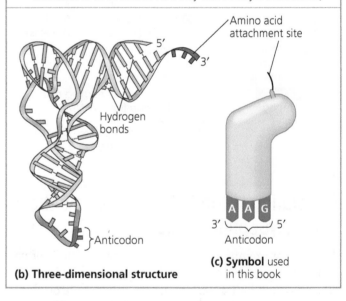

(b) **Three-dimensional structure**

(c) **Symbol** used in this book

▲ Figure 17.15 **The structure of transfer RNA (tRNA).** Anticodons are conventionally written 3' → 5' to align properly with codons written 5' → 3' (see Figure 17.14). For base pairing, RNA strands must be antiparallel, like DNA. For example, anticodon 3'-AAG-5' pairs with mRNA codon 5'-UUC-3'.

available to deliver its amino acid to a growing polypeptide chain on a ribosome.

The second instance of molecular recognition is the pairing of the tRNA anticodon with the appropriate mRNA codon. If one tRNA variety existed for each mRNA codon specifying an amino acid, there would be 61 tRNAs (see Figure 17.5). In fact, there are only about 45, signifying that some tRNAs must be able to bind to more than one codon.

① The amino acid and the appropriate tRNA enter the active site of the specific synthetase.

Tyrosine (Tyr) (amino acid)

Tyrosyl-tRNA synthetase (enzyme), which can only bind tyrosine and Tyr-tRNA

Tyr-tRNA

Anticodon on tRNA complementary to the Tyr codon on mRNA

ATP

AMP + 2 ℗$_i$

② Using ATP, the synthetase catalyzes the covalent bonding of the amino acid to its specific tRNA.

Aminoacyl-tRNA synthetase

tRNA

Amino acid

③ The tRNA, charged with its amino acid, is released by the synthetase.

Computer model

▲ **Figure 17.16 Aminoacyl-tRNA synthetases provide specificity in joining amino acids to their tRNAs.** Linkage of a tRNA to its amino acid is an endergonic process that occurs at the expense of ATP, which loses two phosphate groups, becoming AMP (adenosine monophosphate).

Such versatility is possible because the rules for base pairing between the third nucleotide base of a codon and the corresponding base of a tRNA anticodon are relaxed compared to those at other codon positions. For example, the nucleotide base U at the 5′ end of a tRNA anticodon can pair with either A or G in the third position (at the 3′ end) of an mRNA codon. The flexible base pairing at this codon position is called **wobble**. Wobble explains why the synonymous codons for a given amino acid most often differ in their third nucleotide base, but not in the other bases. A case in point is that a tRNA with the anticodon 3′-UCU-5′ can base-pair with either the mRNA codon 5′-AGA-3′ or 5′-AGG-3′, both of which code for arginine (see Figure 17.5).

Ribosomes

Ribosomes facilitate the specific coupling of tRNA anticodons with mRNA codons during protein synthesis. A ribosome consists of a large subunit and a small subunit, each made up of proteins and one or more **ribosomal RNAs (rRNAs) (Figure 17.17)**. In eukaryotes, the subunits are

Growing polypeptide

Exit tunnel

tRNA molecules

E P A

Large subunit

Small subunit

5′

mRNA

3′

(a) Computer model of functioning ribosome. This is a model of a bacterial ribosome, showing its overall shape. The eukaryotic ribosome is roughly similar. A ribosomal subunit is a complex of ribosomal RNA molecules and proteins.

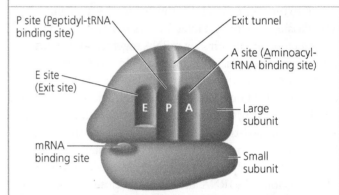

P site (Peptidyl-tRNA binding site)

Exit tunnel

E site (Exit site)

A site (Aminoacyl-tRNA binding site)

E P A

Large subunit

mRNA binding site

Small subunit

(b) Schematic model showing binding sites. A ribosome has an mRNA binding site and three tRNA binding sites, known as the A, P, and E sites. This schematic ribosome will appear in later diagrams.

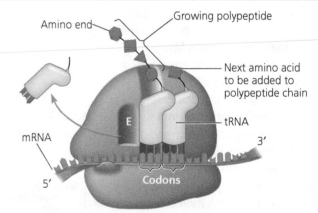

Amino end

Growing polypeptide

Next amino acid to be added to polypeptide chain

tRNA

mRNA

E

3′

5′

Codons

(c) Schematic model with mRNA and tRNA. A tRNA fits into a binding site when its anticodon base-pairs with an mRNA codon. The P site holds the tRNA attached to the growing polypeptide. The A site holds the tRNA carrying the next amino acid to be added to the polypeptide chain. Discharged tRNAs leave from the E site. The polypeptide grows at its carboxyl end.

▲ **Figure 17.17 The anatomy of a functioning ribosome.**

made in the nucleolus. Ribosomal RNA genes are transcribed, and the RNA is processed and assembled with proteins imported from the cytoplasm. Completed ribosomal subunits are then exported via nuclear pores to the cytoplasm. In both bacteria and eukaryotes, a large and a small subunit join to form a functional ribosome only when attached to an mRNA molecule. About one-third of the mass of a ribosome is made up of proteins; the rest consists of rRNAs, either three molecules (in bacteria) or four (in eukaryotes). Because most cells contain thousands of ribosomes, rRNA is the most abundant type of cellular RNA.

Although the ribosomes of bacteria and eukaryotes are very similar in structure and function, eukaryotic ribosomes are slightly larger, as well as differing somewhat from bacterial ribosomes in their molecular composition. The differences are medically significant. Certain antibiotic drugs can inactivate bacterial ribosomes without affecting eukaryotic ribosomes. These drugs, including tetracycline and streptomycin, are used to combat bacterial infections.

The structure of the bacterial ribosome has been determined to the atomic level (see the interview with Venki Ramakrishnan before Chapter 2). This structure clearly reflects its function of bringing mRNA together with tRNAs carrying amino acids. In addition to a binding site for mRNA, each ribosome has three binding sites for tRNA, as described in Figure 17.17. The **P site** (peptidyl-tRNA binding site) holds the tRNA carrying the growing polypeptide chain, while the **A site** (aminoacyl-tRNA binding site) holds the tRNA carrying the next amino acid to be added to the chain. Discharged tRNAs leave the ribosome from the **E site** (exit site). The ribosome holds the tRNA and mRNA in close proximity and positions the new amino acid so that it can be added to the carboxyl end of the growing polypeptide. It then catalyzes the formation of the peptide bond. As the polypeptide becomes longer, it passes through an *exit tunnel* in the ribosome's large subunit. When the polypeptide is complete, it is released through the exit tunnel.

There is strong evidence supporting the hypothesis that rRNA, not protein, is primarily responsible for both the structure and the function of the ribosome. The proteins, which are largely on the exterior, support the shape changes of the rRNA molecules as they carry out catalysis during translation. Ribosomal RNA is the main constituent of the A and P sites and of the interface between the two subunits; it also acts as the catalyst of peptide bond formation. Thus, a ribosome can be regarded as one colossal ribozyme!

Building a Polypeptide

We can divide translation, the synthesis of a polypeptide chain, into three stages: initiation, elongation, and termination. All three stages require protein "factors" that aid in the translation process. For certain aspects of chain initiation and elongation, energy is also required. It is provided by the hydrolysis of guanosine triphosphate (GTP).

Ribosome Association and Initiation of Translation

The initiation stage of translation brings together mRNA, a tRNA bearing the first amino acid of the polypeptide, and the two subunits of a ribosome **(Figure 17.18)**. First, a small ribosomal subunit binds to both mRNA and a specific initiator tRNA, which carries the amino acid methionine. In bacteria, the small subunit can bind these two in either order; it binds the mRNA at a specific RNA sequence, just upstream of the start codon, AUG. In eukaryotes, the small subunit, with the initiator tRNA already bound, binds to the 5' cap of the mRNA and then moves, or *scans*, downstream along the mRNA until it reaches the start codon; the initiator tRNA then hydrogen-bonds to the AUG start codon. In either case, the start codon signals the start of translation; this is important because it establishes the codon reading frame for the mRNA. In the Scientific Skills Exercise, you can work with DNA sequences encoding the ribosomal binding sites on the mRNAs of a group of *E. coli* genes.

The union of mRNA, initiator tRNA, and a small ribosomal subunit is followed by the attachment of a large ribosomal subunit, completing the *translation initiation complex*. Proteins called *initiation factors* are required to

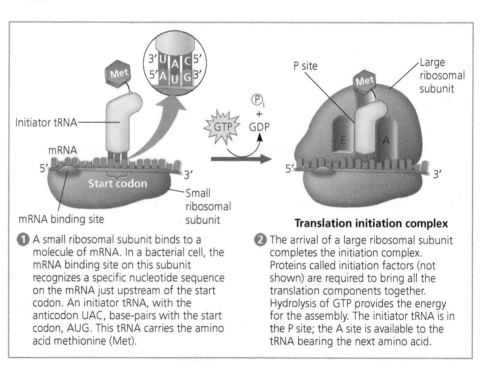

1 A small ribosomal subunit binds to a molecule of mRNA. In a bacterial cell, the mRNA binding site on this subunit recognizes a specific nucleotide sequence on the mRNA just upstream of the start codon. An initiator tRNA, with the anticodon UAC, base-pairs with the start codon, AUG. This tRNA carries the amino acid methionine (Met).

2 The arrival of a large ribosomal subunit completes the initiation complex. Proteins called initiation factors (not shown) are required to bring all the translation components together. Hydrolysis of GTP provides the energy for the assembly. The initiator tRNA is in the P site; the A site is available to the tRNA bearing the next amino acid.

▲ **Figure 17.18 The initiation of translation.**

Interpreting a Sequence Logo

How Can a Sequence Logo Be Used to Identify Ribosome Binding Sites? When initiating translation, ribosomes bind to an mRNA at a ribosome binding site upstream of the AUG start codon. Because mRNAs from different genes all bind to a ribosome, the genes encoding these mRNAs are likely to have a similar base sequence where the ribosomes bind. Therefore, candidate ribosome binding sites on mRNA can be identified by comparing DNA sequences (and thus the mRNA sequences) of multiple genes in a species, searching the region upstream of the start codon for shared ("conserved") stretches of bases. In this exercise, you will analyze DNA sequences from multiple such genes, represented by a visual graphic called a sequence logo.

How the Experiment Was Done The DNA sequences of 149 genes from the *E. coli* genome were aligned using computer software. The aim was to identify similar base sequences—at the appropriate location in each gene—as potential ribosome binding sites. Rather than presenting the data as a series of 149 sequences aligned in a column (a sequence alignment), the researchers used a sequence logo.

Data from the Experiment To show how sequence logos are made, the potential ribosome binding regions from 10 *E. coli* genes are shown in a sequence alignment, followed by the sequence logo derived from the aligned sequences. Note that the DNA shown is the nontemplate (coding) strand, which is how DNA sequences are typically presented.

thrA	G G T A A C G A G G T A A C A A C C A T G C G A G T G
lacA	C A T A A C G G A G T G A T C G C A T T G A A C A T G
lacY	C G C G T A A G G A A A T C C A T T A T G T A C T A T
lacZ	T T C A C A C A G G A A A C A G C T A T G A C C A T G
lacI	C A A T T C A G G G T G G T G A A T G T G A A A C C A
recA	G G C A T G A C A G G A G T A A A A A T G G C T A T C
galR	A C C C A C T A A G G T A T T T T C A T G G C G A C C
metJ	A A G A G G A T T A A G T A T C T C A T G G C T G A A
lexA	A T A C A C C C A G G G G G C G G A A T G A A A G C G
trpR	T A A C A A T G G C G A C A T A T T A T G G C C C A A

5'—(positions −18 to 8)—3'

▲ Sequence alignment

▲ Sequence logo

Interpret the Data

1. In the sequence logo (bottom, left), the horizontal axis shows the primary sequence of the DNA by nucleotide position. Letters for each base are stacked on top of each other according to their relative frequency at that position among the aligned sequences, with the most common base as the largest letter at the top of the stack. The height of each letter represents the relative frequency of that base *at that position*. (a) In the sequence alignment, count the number of each base at position −9 and order them from most to least frequent. Compare this to the size and placement of each base at −9 in the logo. (b) Do the same for positions 0 and 1.

2. The height of a stack of letters in a logo indicates the predictive power of that stack (determined statistically). If the stack is tall, we can be more confident in predicting what base will be in that position if a new sequence is added to the logo. For example, at position 2, all 10 sequences have a G; the probability of finding a G there in a new sequence is very high, as is the stack. For short stacks, the bases all have about the same frequency, so it's hard to predict a base at those positions. (a) Which two positions have the most predictable bases? What bases do you predict would be at those positions in a newly sequenced gene? (b) Which 12 positions have the least predictable bases? How do you know? How does this reflect the relative frequencies of the bases shown in the 10 sequences? Use the two leftmost positions of the 12 as examples in your answer.

3. In the actual experiment, the researchers used 149 sequences to build their sequence logo, which is shown below. There is a stack at each position, even if short, because the sequence logo includes more data. (a) Which three positions in this sequence logo have the most predictable bases? Name the most frequent base at each. (b) Which positions have the least predictable bases? How can you tell?

4. A consensus sequence identifies the base occurring most often at each position in the set of sequences. (a) Write out the consensus sequence of this (the nontemplate) strand. In any position where the base can't be determined, put a dash. (b) Which provides more information—the consensus sequence or the sequence logo? What is lost in the less informative method?

5. (a) Based on the logo, what five adjacent base positions in the 5' UTR region are most likely to be involved in ribosome binding? Explain. (b) What is represented by the bases in positions 0–2?

(MB) A version of this Scientific Skills Exercise can be assigned in MasteringBiology.

Further Reading T. D. Schneider and R. M. Stephens, Sequence logos: A new way to display consensus sequences, *Nucleic Acids Research* 18:6097–6100 (1990).

bring all these components together. The cell also expends energy obtained by hydrolysis of a GTP molecule to form the initiation complex. At the completion of the initiation process, the initiator tRNA sits in the P site of the ribosome, and the vacant A site is ready for the next aminoacyl tRNA. Note that a polypeptide is always synthesized in one direction, from the initial methionine at the amino end, also called the N-terminus, toward the final amino acid at the carboxyl end, also called the C-terminus (see Figure 5.15).

Elongation of the Polypeptide Chain

In the elongation stage of translation, amino acids are added one by one to the previous amino acid at the C-terminus of the growing chain. Each addition involves the participation of several proteins called *elongation factors* and occurs in a

three-step cycle described in **Figure 17.19**. Energy expenditure occurs in the first and third steps. Codon recognition requires hydrolysis of one molecule of GTP, which increases the accuracy and efficiency of this step. One more GTP is hydrolyzed to provide energy for the translocation step.

The mRNA is moved through the ribosome in one direction only, 5′ end first; this is equivalent to the ribosome moving 5′ → 3′ on the mRNA. The important point is that the ribosome and the mRNA move relative to each other, unidirectionally, codon by codon. The elongation cycle takes less than a tenth of a second in bacteria and is repeated as each amino acid is added to the chain until the polypeptide is completed. The empty tRNAs that are released from the E site return to the cytoplasm, where they will be reloaded with the appropriate amino acid (see Figure 17.16).

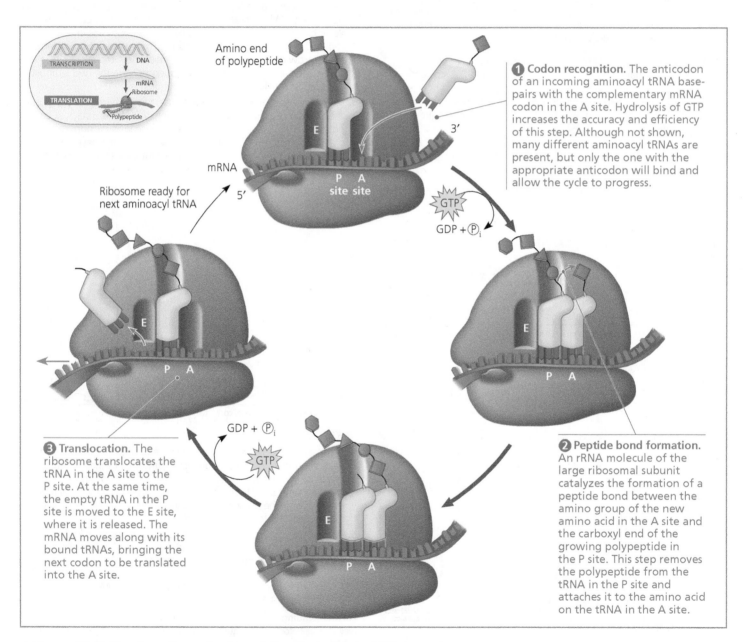

▲ **Figure 17.19 The elongation cycle of translation.** The hydrolysis of GTP plays an important role in the elongation process. Not shown are the proteins called elongation factors.

Mutations of one or a few nucleotides can affect protein structure and function

Now that you have explored the process of gene expression, you are ready to understand the effects of changes to the genetic information of a cell. These changes, called **mutations**, are responsible for the huge diversity of genes found among organisms because mutations are the ultimate source of new genes. Earlier, we considered chromosomal rearrangements that affect long segments of DNA (see Figure 15.14); these are considered large-scale mutations. Here we examine small-scale mutations of one or a few nucleotide pairs, including **point mutations**, changes in a single nucleotide pair of a gene.

If a point mutation occurs in a gamete or in a cell that gives rise to gametes, it may be transmitted to offspring and to future generations. If the mutation has an adverse effect on the phenotype of a person, the mutant condition is referred to as a genetic disorder or hereditary disease. For example, we can trace the genetic basis of sickle-cell disease to the mutation of a single nucleotide pair in the gene that encodes the β-globin polypeptide of hemoglobin. The change of a single nucleotide in the DNA's template strand leads to the production of an abnormal protein (**Figure 17.25**; also see Figure 5.19). In individuals who are homozygous for the mutant allele, the sickling of red blood cells caused by the altered hemoglobin produces the multiple symptoms associated with sickle-cell disease (see Concept 14.4 and Figure 23.17). Another disorder caused by a point mutation is a heart condition called familial cardiomyopathy that is responsible for some incidents of sudden death in young athletes. Point mutations in several genes that encode muscle proteins have been identified, any of which can lead to this disorder.

Types of Small-Scale Mutations

Let's now consider how small-scale mutations affect proteins. Point mutations within a gene can be divided into two general categories: (1) single nucleotide-pair substitutions and (2) nucleotide-pair insertions or deletions. Insertions and deletions can involve one or more nucleotide pairs.

Substitutions

A **nucleotide-pair substitution** is the replacement of one nucleotide and its partner with another pair of nucleotides (**Figure 17.26a**). Some substitutions have no effect on the encoded protein, owing to the redundancy of the genetic code. For example, if 3′-CCG-5′ on the template strand mutated to 3′-CCA-5′, the mRNA codon that used to be GGC would become GGU, but a glycine would still be inserted at the proper location in the protein (see Figure 17.5). In other words, a change in a nucleotide pair may transform one codon into another that is translated into the same amino acid. Such a change is an example of a **silent mutation**, which has no observable effect on the phenotype. (Silent mutations can occur outside genes as well.) Substitutions that change one amino acid to another one are called **missense mutations**. Such a mutation may have little effect on the protein: The new amino acid may have properties similar to those of the amino acid it replaces, or it may be in a region of the protein where the exact sequence of amino acids is not essential to the protein's function.

However, the nucleotide-pair substitutions of greatest interest are those that cause a major change in a protein. The alteration of a single amino acid in a crucial area of a protein—such as in the part of the β-globin subunit of hemoglobin shown in Figure 17.25 or in the active site of an enzyme as shown in Figure 8.19—can significantly alter protein activity. Occasionally, such a mutation leads to an improved protein or one with novel capabilities, but much more often such mutations are neutral or detrimental, leading to a useless or less active protein that impairs cellular function.

Substitution mutations are usually missense mutations; that is, the altered codon still codes for an amino acid and thus makes sense, although not necessarily the *right* sense. But a point mutation can also change a codon for an amino acid into a stop codon. This is called a **nonsense mutation**,

Wild-type β-globin	Sickle-cell β-globin	
Wild-type β-globin DNA	**Mutant β-globin DNA**	In the DNA, the mutant (sickle-cell) template strand (top) has an A where the wild-type template has a T.
3′ C T C 5′ 5′ G A G 3′	3′ C A C 5′ 5′ G T G 3′	
mRNA	**mRNA**	The mutant mRNA has a U instead of an A in one codon.
5′ G A G 3′	5′ G U G 3′	
Normal hemoglobin	**Sickle-cell hemoglobin**	The mutant β-globin has a valine (Val) instead of a glutamic acid (Glu).
Glu	Val	

▲ **Figure 17.25 The molecular basis of sickle-cell disease: a point mutation.** The allele that causes sickle-cell disease differs from the wild-type (normal) allele by a single DNA nucleotide pair. The micrographs are SEMs of a normal red blood cell (on the left) and a sickled red blood cell (right) from individuals homozygous for either wild-type or mutant alleles, respectively.

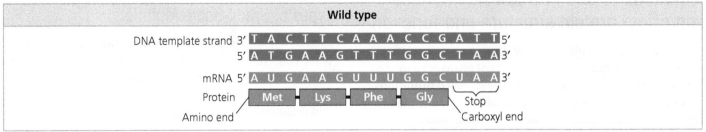

▼ **Figure 17.26 Types of small-scale mutations that affect mRNA sequence.** All but one of the types shown here also affect the amino acid sequence of the encoded polypeptide.

Wild type

and it causes translation to be terminated prematurely; the resulting polypeptide will be shorter than the polypeptide encoded by the normal gene. Nearly all nonsense mutations lead to nonfunctional proteins.

Insertions and Deletions

Insertions and **deletions** are additions or losses of nucleotide pairs in a gene **(Figure 17.26b)**. These mutations have a disastrous effect on the resulting protein more often than substitutions do. Insertion or deletion of nucleotides may alter the reading frame of the genetic message, the triplet grouping of nucleotides on the mRNA that is read during translation. Such a mutation, called a **frameshift mutation**, occurs whenever the number of nucleotides inserted or deleted is not a multiple of three. All nucleotides downstream of the deletion or insertion will be improperly grouped into codons; the result will be extensive missense, usually ending sooner or later in nonsense and premature termination. Unless the frameshift is very near the end of the gene, the protein is almost certain to be nonfunctional.

New Mutations and Mutagens

Mutations can arise in a number of ways. Errors during DNA replication or recombination can lead to nucleotide-pair substitutions, insertions, or deletions, as well as to mutations affecting longer stretches of DNA. If an incorrect nucleotide is added to a growing chain during replication, for example, the base on that nucleotide will then be mismatched with the nucleotide base on the other strand. In many cases, the error will be corrected by DNA proofreading and repair systems (see Concept 16.2). Otherwise, the incorrect base will be used as a template in the next round of replication, resulting in a mutation. Such mutations are called *spontaneous mutations*. It is difficult to calculate the rate at which such mutations occur. Rough estimates have been made of the rate of mutation during DNA replication for both *E. coli* and eukaryotes, and the numbers are similar: About one nucleotide in every 10^{10} is altered, and the change is passed on to the next generation of cells.

A number of physical and chemical agents, called **mutagens**, interact with DNA in ways that cause mutations. In the 1920s, Hermann Muller discovered that X-rays caused genetic changes in fruit flies, and he used X-rays to make *Drosophila* mutants for his genetic studies. But he also recognized an alarming implication of his discovery: X-rays and other forms of high-energy radiation pose hazards to the genetic material of people as well as laboratory organisms. Mutagenic radiation, a physical mutagen, includes ultraviolet (UV) light, which can cause disruptive thymine dimers in DNA (see Figure 16.19).

Chemical mutagens fall into several categories. Nucleotide analogs are chemicals similar to normal DNA nucleotides but that pair incorrectly during DNA replication. Other chemical mutagens interfere with correct DNA replication by inserting themselves into the DNA and distorting the double helix. Still other mutagens cause chemical changes in bases that change their pairing properties.

Researchers have developed a variety of methods to test the mutagenic activity of chemicals. A major application of these tests is the preliminary screening of chemicals to identify those that may cause cancer. This approach makes sense because most carcinogens (cancer-causing chemicals) are mutagenic, and conversely, most mutagens are carcinogenic.

What Is a Gene? *Revisiting the Question*

Our definition of a gene has evolved over the past few chapters, as it has through the history of genetics. We began with the Mendelian concept of a gene as a discrete unit of inheritance that affects a phenotypic character (Chapter 14). We saw that Morgan and his colleagues assigned such genes to specific loci on chromosomes (Chapter 15). We went on to view a gene as a region of specific nucleotide sequence along the length of the DNA molecule of a chromosome (Chapter 16). Finally, in this chapter, we have considered a functional definition of a gene as a DNA sequence that codes for a specific polypeptide chain. All these definitions are useful, depending on the context in which genes are being studied.

We now realize that saying a gene codes for a polypeptide is an oversimplification. Most eukaryotic genes contain noncoding segments (such as introns), so large portions of these genes have no corresponding segments in polypeptides. Molecular biologists also often include promoters and certain other regulatory regions of DNA within the boundaries of a gene. These DNA sequences are not transcribed, but they can be considered part of the functional gene because they must be present for transcription to occur. Our definition of a gene must also be broad enough to include the DNA that is transcribed into rRNA, tRNA, and other RNAs that are not translated. These genes have no polypeptide products but play crucial roles in the cell. Thus, we arrive at the following definition: *A gene is a region of DNA that can be expressed to produce a final functional product that is either a polypeptide or an RNA molecule.*

When considering phenotypes, however, it is often useful to start by focusing on genes that code for polypeptides. In this chapter, you have learned in molecular terms how a typical gene is expressed—by transcription into RNA and then translation into a polypeptide that forms a protein of specific structure and function. Proteins, in turn, bring about an organism's observable phenotype.

A given type of cell expresses only a subset of its genes. This is an essential feature in multicellular organisms: You'd be in trouble if the lens cells in your eyes started expressing the genes for hair proteins, which are normally expressed only in hair follicle cells! Gene expression is precisely regulated, which we'll explore in the next chapter, beginning with the simpler case of bacteria and continuing with eukaryotes.

CONCEPT CHECK 17.5

1. What happens when one nucleotide pair is lost from the middle of the coding sequence of a gene?

2. MAKE CONNECTIONS Individuals heterozygous for the sickle-cell allele are generally healthy but show phenotypic effects of the allele under some circumstances (see Figure 14.17). Explain in terms of gene expression.

3. WHAT IF? DRAW IT The template strand of a gene includes this sequence:

   3'-TACTTGTCCGATATC-5'. It is mutated to

   3'-TACTTGTCCAATATC-5'. For both normal and mutant sequences, draw the double-stranded DNA, the resulting mRNA, and the amino acid sequence each encodes. What is the effect of the mutation on the amino acid sequence?

For suggested answers, see Appendix A.

17 Chapter Review

SUMMARY OF KEY CONCEPTS

CONCEPT 17.1

Genes specify proteins via transcription and translation (pp. 334–340)

- Beadle and Tatum's studies of mutant strains of *Neurospora* led to the one gene–one polypeptide hypothesis. During **gene expression**, the information encoded in genes is used to make specific polypeptide chains (enzymes and other proteins) or RNA molecules.
- **Transcription** is the synthesis of RNA complementary to a **template strand** of DNA. **Translation** is the synthesis of a polypeptide whose amino acid sequence is specified by the nucleotide sequence in **mRNA**.
- Genetic information is encoded as a sequence of nonoverlapping nucleotide triplets, or **codons**. A codon in messenger RNA (mRNA) either is translated into an amino acid (61 of the 64 codons) or serves as a stop signal (3 codons). Codons must be read in the correct **reading frame**.

? *Describe the process of gene expression, by which a gene affects the phenotype of an organism.*

CONCEPT 17.2

Transcription is the DNA-directed synthesis of RNA: *A closer look* (pp. 340–342)

- RNA synthesis is catalyzed by **RNA polymerase**, which links together RNA nucleotides complementary to a DNA template strand. This process follows the same base-pairing rules as DNA replication, except that in RNA, uracil substitutes for thymine.

- The three stages of transcription are initiation, elongation, and termination. A **promoter**, often including a **TATA box** in eukaryotes, establishes where RNA synthesis is initiated. **Transcription factors** help eukaryotic RNA polymerase recognize promoter sequences, forming a **transcription initiation complex**. Termination differs in bacteria and eukaryotes.

? *What are the similarities and differences in the initiation of gene transcription in bacteria and eukaryotes?*

CONCEPT 17.3

Eukaryotic cells modify RNA after transcription (pp. 342–345)

- Eukaryotic mRNAs undergo **RNA processing**, which includes RNA splicing, the addition of a modified nucleotide **5′ cap** to the 5′ end, and the addition of a **poly-A tail** to the 3′ end.

- Most eukaryotic genes are split into segments: They have **introns** interspersed among the **exons** (the regions included in the mRNA). In **RNA splicing**, introns are removed and exons joined. RNA splicing is typically carried out by **spliceosomes**, but in some cases, RNA alone catalyzes its own splicing. The catalytic ability of some RNA molecules, called **ribozymes**, derives from the inherent properties of RNA. The presence of introns allows for **alternative RNA splicing**.

? *What function do the 5′ cap and the poly-A tail serve on a eukaryotic mRNA?*

CONCEPT 17.4

Translation is the RNA-directed synthesis of a polypeptide: *A closer look* (pp. 345–354)

- A cell translates an mRNA message into protein using **transfer RNAs (tRNAs)**. After being bound to a specific amino acid by an **aminoacyl-tRNA synthetase**, a tRNA lines up via its **anticodon** at the complementary codon on mRNA. A **ribosome**, made up of **ribosomal RNAs (rRNAs)** and proteins, facilitates this coupling with binding sites for mRNA and tRNA.
- Ribosomes coordinate the three stages of translation: initiation, elongation, and termination. The formation of peptide bonds between amino acids is catalyzed by rRNA as tRNAs move through the **A and P sites** and exit through the **E site**.

- After translation, modifications to proteins can affect their shape. Free ribosomes in the cytosol initiate synthesis of all proteins, but proteins with a **signal peptide** are synthesized on the ER.
- A gene can be transcribed by multiple RNA polymerases simultaneously. A single mRNA molecule can be translated simultaneously by a number of ribosomes, forming a **polyribosome**. In bacteria, these processes are coupled, but in eukaryotes they are separated in space and time by the nuclear membrane.

? *What function do tRNAs serve in the process of translation?*

CONCEPT 17.5

Mutations of one or a few nucleotides can affect protein structure and function (pp. 355–357)

- Small-scale **mutations** include **point mutations**, changes in one DNA nucleotide pair, which may lead to production of nonfunctional proteins. **Nucleotide-pair substitutions** can cause **missense** or **nonsense mutations**. Nucleotide-pair **insertions** or **deletions** may produce **frameshift mutations**.
- Spontaneous mutations can occur during DNA replication, recombination, or repair. Chemical and physical **mutagens** cause DNA damage that can alter genes.

? *What will be the results of chemically modifying one nucleotide base of a gene? What role is played by DNA repair systems in the cell?*

TEST YOUR UNDERSTANDING

LEVEL 1: KNOWLEDGE/COMPREHENSION

1. In eukaryotic cells, transcription cannot begin until
   a. the two DNA strands have completely separated and exposed the promoter.
   b. several transcription factors have bound to the promoter.
   c. the 5′ caps are removed from the mRNA.
   d. the DNA introns are removed from the template.

2. Which of the following is *not* true of a codon?
   a. It may code for the same amino acid as another codon.
   b. It never codes for more than one amino acid.
   c. It extends from one end of a tRNA molecule.
   d. It is the basic unit of the genetic code.

3. The anticodon of a particular tRNA molecule is
   a. complementary to the corresponding mRNA codon.
   b. complementary to the corresponding triplet in rRNA.
   c. the part of tRNA that bonds to a specific amino acid.
   d. catalytic, making the tRNA a ribozyme.

4. Which of the following is *not* true of RNA processing?
   a. Exons are cut out before mRNA leaves the nucleus.
   b. Nucleotides may be added at both ends of the RNA.
   c. Ribozymes may function in RNA splicing.
   d. RNA splicing can be catalyzed by spliceosomes.

5. Which component is *not* directly involved in translation?
   a. GTP
   b. DNA
   c. tRNA
   d. ribosomes

LEVEL 2: APPLICATION/ANALYSIS

6. Using Figure 17.5, identify a 5′ → 3′ sequence of nucleotides in the DNA template strand for an mRNA coding for the polypeptide sequence Phe-Pro-Lys.
   a. 5′-UUUGGGAAA-3′
   b. 5′-GAACCCCTT-3′
   c. 5′-CTTCGGGAA-3′
   d. 5′-AAACCCUUU-3′

7. Which of the following mutations would be *most* likely to have a harmful effect on an organism?
   a. a deletion of three nucleotides near the middle of a gene
   b. a single nucleotide deletion in the middle of an intron
   c. a single nucleotide deletion near the end of the coding sequence
   d. a single nucleotide insertion downstream of, and close to, the start of the coding sequence

8. Would the coupling of the processes shown in Figure 17.23 be found in a eukaryotic cell? Explain why or why not.

9. **DRAW IT** Fill in the following table:

Type of RNA	Functions
Messenger RNA (mRNA)	
Transfer RNA (tRNA)	
	Plays catalytic (ribozyme) roles and structural roles in ribosomes
Primary transcript	
Small RNAs in the spliceosome	

LEVEL 3: SYNTHESIS/EVALUATION

10. **EVOLUTION CONNECTION**
    Most amino acids are coded for by a set of similar codons (see Figure 17.5). What evolutionary explanations can you give for this pattern? (*Hint:* There is one explanation relating to ancestry, and some less obvious ones of a "form-fits-function" type.)

11. **SCIENTIFIC INQUIRY**
    Knowing that the genetic code is almost universal, a scientist uses molecular biological methods to insert the human β-globin gene (shown in Figure 17.11) into bacterial cells, hoping the cells will express it and synthesize functional β-globin protein. Instead, the protein produced is nonfunctional and is found to contain many fewer amino acids than does β-globin made by a eukaryotic cell. Explain why.

12. **WRITE ABOUT A THEME: INFORMATION**
    Evolution accounts for the unity and diversity of life, and the continuity of life is based on heritable information in the form of DNA. In a short essay (100–150 words), discuss how the fidelity with which DNA is inherited is related to the processes of evolution. (Review the discussion of proofreading and DNA repair in Concept 16.2.)

13. **SYNTHESIZE YOUR KNOWLEDGE**

Some mutations result in proteins that function well at one temperature but are nonfunctional at a different (usually higher) temperature. Siamese cats have such a "temperature-sensitive" mutation in a gene encoding an enzyme that makes dark pigment in the fur. The mutation results in the breed's distinctive point markings and lighter body color (see the photo). Using this information and what you learned in the chapter, explain the pattern of the cat's fur pigmentation.

For selected answers, see Appendix A.

MasteringBiology®

Students Go to **MasteringBiology** for assignments, the eText, and the Study Area with practice tests, animations, and activities.

Instructors Go to **MasteringBiology** for automatically graded tutorials and questions that you can assign to your students, plus Instructor Resources.

18

Regulation of Gene Expression

▲ Figure 18.1 **How can this fish's eyes see equally well in both air and water?**

Differential Expression of Genes

The fish in **Figure 18.1** is keeping an eye out for predators above—or, more precisely, half of each eye! *Anableps anableps*, commonly known as "cuatro ojos" ("four eyes"), glides through freshwater lakes and ponds in Central and South America with the upper half of each eye protruding from the water. The eye's upper half is particularly well-suited for aerial vision and the lower half for aquatic vision. The molecular basis of this specialization has recently been revealed: The cells of the two parts of the eye express a slightly different set of genes involved in vision, even though these two groups of cells are quite similar and contain identical genomes. What is the biological mechanism underlying the difference in gene expression that makes this remarkable feat possible?

A hallmark of prokaryotic and eukaryotic cells alike—from a bacterium to the cells of a fish—is their intricate and precise regulation of gene expression. In this chapter, we first explore how bacteria regulate expression of their genes in response to different environmental conditions. We then examine how eukaryotes regulate gene expression to maintain different cell types, including the many roles played by RNA molecules. In the final two sections, we explore the role of gene regulation in both embryonic development, as the ultimate example of proper gene regulation, and cancer, as an illustration of what happens when regulation goes awry. Orchestrating proper gene expression by all cells is crucial to the functions of life.

CONCEPT 18.1

Bacteria often respond to environmental change by regulating transcription

Bacterial cells that can conserve resources and energy have a selective advantage over cells that are unable to do so. Thus, natural selection has favored bacteria that express only the genes whose products are needed by the cell.

Consider, for instance, an individual *Escherichia coli* cell living in the erratic environment of a human colon, dependent for its nutrients on the whimsical eating habits of its host. If the environment is lacking in the amino acid tryptophan, which the bacterium needs to survive, the cell responds by activating a metabolic pathway that makes tryptophan from another compound. Later, if the human host eats a tryptophan-rich meal, the bacterial cell stops producing tryptophan, thus avoiding wasting resources to produce a substance readily available in prefabricated form from the surrounding solution. This is just one example of how bacteria tune their metabolism to changing environments.

Metabolic control occurs on two levels, as shown for the synthesis of tryptophan in **Figure 18.2**. First, cells can adjust the activity of enzymes already present. This is a fairly fast response, which relies on the sensitivity of many enzymes to chemical cues that increase or decrease their catalytic activity (see Concept 8.5). The activity of the first enzyme in the pathway is inhibited by the pathway's end product **(Figure 18.2a)**. Thus, if tryptophan accumulates in a cell, it shuts down the synthesis of more tryptophan by inhibiting enzyme activity. Such *feedback inhibition*, typical of anabolic (biosynthetic) pathways, allows a cell to adapt to short-term fluctuations in the supply of a substance it needs.

Second, cells can adjust the production level of certain enzymes; that is, they can regulate the expression of the genes encoding the enzymes. If, in our example, the environment provides all the tryptophan the cell needs, the cell stops making the enzymes that catalyze the synthesis of tryptophan **(Figure 18.2b)**. In this case, the control of enzyme production occurs at the level of transcription, the synthesis of messenger RNA coding for these enzymes. More generally, many genes of the bacterial genome are switched on or off by changes in the metabolic status of the cell. One basic mechanism for this control of gene expression in bacteria, described as the *operon model*, was discovered in 1961 by François Jacob and Jacques Monod at the Pasteur Institute in Paris. Let's see what an operon is and how it works.

Operons: The Basic Concept

E. coli synthesizes the amino acid tryptophan from a precursor molecule in the three-step pathway shown in Figure 18.2. Each reaction in the pathway is catalyzed by a specific enzyme, and the five genes that code for the

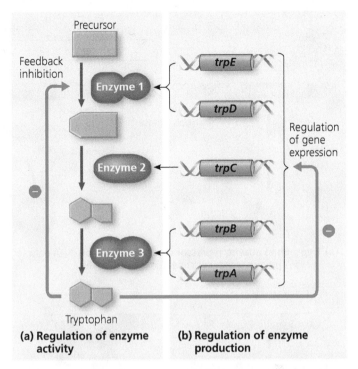

(a) Regulation of enzyme activity

(b) Regulation of enzyme production

▲ **Figure 18.2 Regulation of a metabolic pathway.** In the pathway for tryptophan synthesis, an abundance of tryptophan can both **(a)** inhibit the activity of the first enzyme in the pathway (feedback inhibition), a rapid response, and **(b)** repress expression of the genes encoding all subunits of the enzymes in the pathway, a longer-term response. Genes *trpE* and *trpD* encode the two subunits of enzyme 1, and genes *trpB* and *trpA* encode the two subunits of enzyme 3. (The genes were named before the order in which they functioned in the pathway was determined.) The ⊖ symbol stands for inhibition.

subunits of these enzymes are clustered together on the bacterial chromosome. A single promoter serves all five genes, which together constitute a transcription unit. (Recall from Concept 17.2 that a promoter is a site where RNA polymerase can bind to DNA and begin transcription.) Thus, transcription gives rise to one long mRNA molecule that codes for the five polypeptides making up the enzymes in the tryptophan pathway **(Figure 18.3a)**. The cell can translate this one mRNA into five separate polypeptides because the mRNA is punctuated with start and stop codons that signal where the coding sequence for each polypeptide begins and ends.

A key advantage of grouping genes of related function into one transcription unit is that a single "on-off switch" can control the whole cluster of functionally related genes; in other words, these genes are *coordinately controlled.* When an *E. coli* cell must make tryptophan for itself because the nutrient medium lacks this amino acid, all the enzymes for the metabolic pathway are synthesized at one time. The switch is a segment of DNA called an **operator**. Both its location and name suit its function: Positioned within the promoter or, in some cases, between the promoter and the enzyme-coding genes, the operator controls the access of RNA polymerase to the genes. All together, the operator,

(a) Tryptophan absent, repressor inactive, operon on. RNA polymerase attaches to the DNA at the operon's promoter and transcribes the operon's genes.

(b) Tryptophan present, repressor active, operon off. As tryptophan accumulates, it inhibits its own production by activating the repressor protein, which binds to the operator, blocking transcription.

▲ **Figure 18.3 The *trp* operon in *E. coli*: regulated synthesis of repressible enzymes.** Tryptophan is an amino acid produced by an anabolic pathway catalyzed by repressible enzymes. **(a)** The five genes encoding the polypeptide subunits of the enzymes in this pathway (see Figure 18.2) are grouped, along with a promoter, into the *trp* operon. The *trp* operator (the repressor binding site) is located within the *trp* promoter (the RNA polymerase binding site). **(b)** Accumulation of tryptophan, the end product of the pathway, represses transcription of the *trp* operon, thus blocking synthesis of all the enzymes in the pathway and shutting down tryptophan production.

? *Describe what happens to the* trp *operon as the cell uses up its store of tryptophan.*

the promoter, and the genes they control—the entire stretch of DNA required for enzyme production for the tryptophan pathway—constitute an **operon**. The *trp* operon (*trp* for tryptophan) is one of many operons in the *E. coli* genome (see Figure 18.3).

If the operator is the operon's switch for controlling transcription, how does this switch work? By itself, the *trp* operon is turned on; that is, RNA polymerase can bind to the promoter and transcribe the genes of the operon. The operon can be switched off by a protein that is called the *trp* **repressor**. The repressor binds to the operator and blocks attachment of RNA polymerase to the promoter, preventing transcription of the genes **(Figure 18.3b)**. A repressor protein is specific for the operator of a particular operon. For example, the repressor that switches off the *trp* operon by binding to the *trp* operator has no effect on other operons in the *E. coli* genome.

The *trp* repressor is the protein product of a **regulatory gene** called *trpR*, which is located some distance from the *trp* operon and has its own promoter. Regulatory genes are

expressed continuously, although at a low rate, and a few *trp* repressor molecules are always present in *E. coli* cells. Why, then, is the *trp* operon not switched off permanently? First, the binding of repressors to operators is reversible. An operator alternates between two states: one with the repressor bound and one without the repressor bound. The relative duration of the repressor-bound state increases when there are more active repressor molecules present. Second, the *trp* repressor, like most regulatory proteins, is an allosteric protein, with two alternative shapes—one active and the other inactive (see Figure 8.20). The *trp* repressor is synthesized in the inactive form, which has little affinity for the *trp* operator. Only when a tryptophan molecule binds to the *trp* repressor at an allosteric site does the repressor protein change its shape to the active form, which can attach to the operator, turning the operon off.

Tryptophan functions in this system as a **corepressor**, a small molecule that cooperates with a repressor protein to switch an operon off. As tryptophan accumulates, more tryptophan molecules associate with *trp* repressor molecules, which can then bind to the *trp* operator and shut down production of the tryptophan pathway enzymes. If the cell's tryptophan level drops, transcription of the operon's genes resumes. The *trp* operon is one example of how gene expression can respond to changes in the cell's internal and external environment.

Repressible and Inducible Operons: Two Types of Negative Gene Regulation

The *trp* operon is said to be a *repressible operon* because its transcription is usually on but can be inhibited (repressed) when a specific small molecule (in this case, tryptophan) binds allosterically to a regulatory protein. In contrast, an *inducible operon* is usually off but can be stimulated (induced) when a specific small molecule interacts with a regulatory protein. The classic example of an inducible operon is the *lac* operon (*lac* for lactose).

The disaccharide lactose (milk sugar) is available to *E. coli* in the human colon if the host drinks milk. Lactose metabolism begins with hydrolysis of the disaccharide into its component monosaccharides (glucose and galactose), a reaction catalyzed by the enzyme β-galactosidase. Only a few molecules of this enzyme are present in an *E. coli* cell growing in the absence of lactose. If lactose is added to the bacterium's

environment, however, the number of β-galactosidase molecules in the cell can increase a thousandfold within about 15 minutes.

The gene for β-galactosidase (*lacZ*) is part of the *lac* operon (Figure 18.4), which includes two other genes coding for enzymes that function in the use of lactose. The entire transcription unit is under the command of one main operator and promoter. The regulatory gene, *lacI*, located outside the operon, codes for an allosteric repressor protein that can switch off the *lac* operon by binding to the operator. So far, this sounds just like regulation of the *trp* operon, but there is one important difference. Recall that the *trp* repressor protein is inactive by itself and requires tryptophan as a co-repressor in order to bind to the operator. The *lac* repressor, in contrast, is active by itself, binding to the operator and switching the *lac* operon off. In this case, a specific small molecule, called an **inducer**, *inactivates* the repressor.

For the *lac* operon, the inducer is allolactose, an isomer of lactose formed in small amounts from lactose that enters the cell. In the absence of lactose (and hence allolactose), the *lac* repressor is in its active shape, and the genes of the *lac* operon are silenced (Figure 18.4a). If lactose is present, allolactose binds to the *lac* repressor and alters its shape, nullifying the repressor's ability to attach to the operator. Without the repressor bound, the *lac* operon is transcribed into mRNA for the lactose-utilizing enzymes (Figure 18.4b).

In the context of gene regulation, the enzymes of the lactose pathway are referred to as *inducible enzymes* because their synthesis is induced by a chemical signal (allolactose, in this case). Analogously, the enzymes for tryptophan synthesis are said to be repressible. *Repressible enzymes* generally function in anabolic pathways, which synthesize essential end products from raw materials (precursors). By

(a) Lactose absent, repressor active, operon off. The *lac* repressor is innately active, and in the absence of lactose it switches off the operon by binding to the operator.

(b) Lactose present, repressor inactive, operon on. Allolactose, an isomer of lactose, derepresses the operon by inactivating the repressor. In this way, the enzymes for lactose utilization are induced.

◀ **Figure 18.4 The *lac* operon in *E. coli*: regulated synthesis of inducible enzymes.** *E. coli* uses three enzymes to take up and metabolize lactose, the genes for which are clustered in the *lac* operon. The first gene, *lacZ*, codes for β-galactosidase, which hydrolyzes lactose to glucose and galactose. The second, *lacY*, codes for a permease, the membrane protein that transports lactose into the cell. The third, *lacA*, codes for transacetylase, whose function in lactose metabolism is unclear. Unusually, the gene for the *lac* repressor, *lacI*, is adjacent to the *lac* operon; the function of the teal region within the promoter will be revealed in Figure 18.5.

suspending production of an end product when it is already present in sufficient quantity, the cell can allocate its organic precursors and energy for other uses. In contrast, inducible enzymes usually function in catabolic pathways, which break down a nutrient to simpler molecules. By producing the appropriate enzymes only when the nutrient is available, the cell avoids wasting energy and precursors making proteins that are not needed.

Regulation of both the *trp* and *lac* operons involves the *negative* control of genes, because the operons are switched off by the active form of the repressor protein. It may be easier to see this for the *trp* operon, but it is also true for the *lac* operon. Allolactose induces enzyme synthesis not by directly activating the *lac* operon, but by freeing it from the negative effect of the repressor. Gene regulation is said to be *positive* only when a regulatory protein interacts directly with the genome to switch transcription on.

Positive Gene Regulation

When glucose and lactose are both present in its environment, *E. coli* preferentially uses glucose. The enzymes for glucose breakdown in glycolysis (see Figure 9.9) are continually present. Only when lactose is present *and* glucose is in short supply does *E. coli* use lactose as an energy source, and only then does it synthesize appreciable quantities of the enzymes for lactose breakdown.

How does the *E. coli* cell sense the glucose concentration and relay this information to the *lac* operon? Again, the mechanism depends on the interaction of an allosteric regulatory protein with a small organic molecule, in this case **cyclic AMP (cAMP)**, which accumulates when glucose is scarce (see Figure 11.11 for the structure of cAMP). The regulatory protein, called *catabolite activator protein (CAP)*, is an **activator**, a protein that binds to DNA and stimulates transcription of a gene. When cAMP binds to this regulatory protein, CAP assumes its active shape and can attach to a specific site at the upstream end of the *lac* promoter **(Figure 18.5a)**. This attachment increases the affinity of RNA polymerase for the promoter, which is actually rather low even when no repressor is bound to the operator. By facilitating the binding of RNA polymerase to the promoter and thereby increasing the rate of transcription, the attachment of CAP to the promoter directly stimulates gene expression. Therefore, this mechanism qualifies as positive regulation.

If the amount of glucose in the cell increases, the cAMP concentration falls, and without cAMP, CAP detaches from the operon. Because CAP is inactive, RNA polymerase binds less efficiently to the promoter, and transcription of the *lac* operon proceeds only at a low level, even when lactose is present **(Figure 18.5b)**. Thus, the *lac* operon is under dual control: negative control by the *lac* repressor and positive control by CAP. The state of the *lac* repressor (with or without bound allolactose) determines whether or not

transcription of the *lac* operon's genes occurs at all; the state of CAP (with or without bound cAMP) controls the *rate* of transcription if the operon is repressor-free. It is as though the operon has both an on-off switch and a volume control.

In addition to regulating the *lac* operon, CAP helps regulate other operons that encode enzymes used in catabolic pathways. All told, it may affect the expression of more than 100 genes in *E. coli*. When glucose is plentiful and CAP is inactive, the synthesis of enzymes that catabolize compounds other than glucose generally slows down. The ability to catabolize other compounds, such as lactose, enables a cell deprived of glucose to survive. The compounds present in the cell at the moment determine which operons are switched on—the result of simple interactions of activator and repressor proteins with the promoters of the genes in question.

(a) Lactose present, glucose scarce (cAMP level high): abundant *lac* mRNA synthesized. If glucose is scarce, the high level of cAMP activates CAP, and the *lac* operon produces large amounts of mRNA coding for the enzymes in the lactose pathway.

(b) Lactose present, glucose present (cAMP level low): little *lac* mRNA synthesized. When glucose is present, cAMP is scarce, and CAP is unable to stimulate transcription at a significant rate, even though no repressor is bound.

▲ **Figure 18.5 Positive control of the lac operon by catabolite activator protein (CAP).** RNA polymerase has high affinity for the *lac* promoter only when CAP is bound to a DNA site at the upstream end of the promoter. CAP, in turn, attaches to its DNA site only when associated with cyclic AMP (cAMP), whose concentration in the cell rises when the glucose concentration falls. Thus, when glucose is present, even if lactose is also available, the cell preferentially catabolizes glucose and makes very little of the lactose-utilizing enzymes.

1. How does binding of the *trp* corepressor to its repressor alter repressor function and transcription? What about the binding of the *lac* inducer to its repressor?

2. Describe the binding of RNA polymerase, repressors, and activators to the *lac* operon when both lactose and glucose are scarce. What is the effect of these scarcities on transcription of the *lac* operon?

3. **WHAT IF?** A certain mutation in *E. coli* changes the *lac* operator so that the active repressor cannot bind. How would this affect the cell's production of β-galactosidase?

For suggested answers, see Appendix A.

CONCEPT 18.2

Eukaryotic gene expression is regulated at many stages

All organisms, whether prokaryotes or eukaryotes, must regulate which genes are expressed at any given time. Both unicellular organisms and the cells of multicellular organisms continually turn genes on and off in response to signals from their external and internal environments. Regulation of gene expression is also essential for cell specialization in multicellular organisms, which are made up of different types of cells. To perform its own distinct role, each cell type must maintain a specific program of gene expression in which certain genes are expressed and others are not.

Differential Gene Expression

A typical human cell might express about 20% of its protein-coding genes at any given time. Highly differentiated cells, such as muscle or nerve cells, express an even smaller fraction of their genes. Almost all the cells in a multicellular organism contain an identical genome. (Cells of the immune system are one exception, as you will see in Chapter 43.) However, the subset of genes expressed in the cells of each type is unique, allowing these cells to carry out their specific function. The differences between cell types, therefore, are due not to different genes being present, but to **differential gene expression**, the expression of different genes by cells with the same genome.

The function of any cell, whether a single-celled eukaryote or a particular cell type in a multicellular organism, depends on the appropriate set of genes being expressed. The transcription factors of a cell must locate the right genes at the right time, a task on a par with finding a needle in a haystack. When gene expression proceeds abnormally, serious imbalances and diseases, including cancer, can arise.

Figure 18.6 summarizes the process of gene expression in a eukaryotic cell, highlighting key stages in the expression of a protein-coding gene. Each stage depicted in Figure 18.6

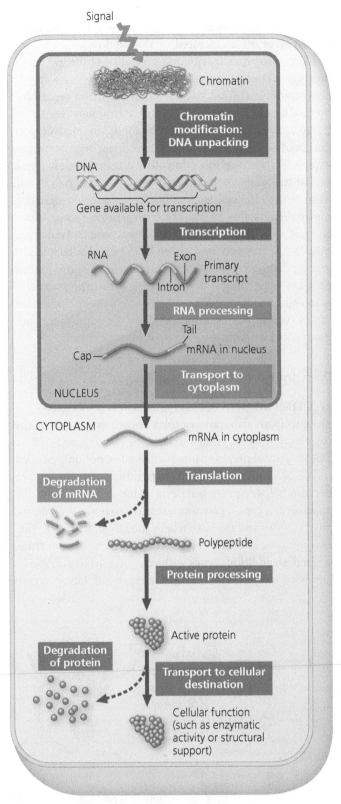

▲ **Figure 18.6 Stages in gene expression that can be regulated in eukaryotic cells.** In this diagram, the colored boxes indicate the processes most often regulated; each color indicates the type of molecule that is affected (blue = DNA, red/orange = RNA, purple = protein). The nuclear envelope separating transcription from translation in eukaryotic cells offers an opportunity for post-transcriptional control in the form of RNA processing that is absent in prokaryotes. In addition, eukaryotes have a greater variety of control mechanisms operating before transcription and after translation. The expression of any given gene, however, does not necessarily involve every stage shown; for example, during processing, some but not all polypeptides are cleaved.

is a potential control point at which gene expression can be turned on or off, accelerated, or slowed down.

Fifty or so years ago, an understanding of the mechanisms that control gene expression in eukaryotes seemed almost hopelessly out of reach. Since then, new research methods, notably advances in DNA technology (see Chapter 20), have enabled molecular biologists to uncover many details of eukaryotic gene regulation. In all organisms, gene expression is commonly controlled at transcription; regulation at this stage often occurs in response to signals coming from outside the cell, such as hormones or other signaling molecules. For this reason, the term *gene expression* is often equated with transcription for both bacteria and eukaryotes. While this may most often be the case for bacteria, the greater complexity of eukaryotic cell structure and function provides opportunities for regulating gene expression at many additional stages (see Figure 18.6). In the remainder of this section, we'll examine some of the important control points of eukaryotic gene expression more closely.

Regulation of Chromatin Structure

Recall that the DNA of eukaryotic cells is packaged with proteins in an elaborate complex known as chromatin, the basic unit of which is the nucleosome (see Figure 16.22). The structural organization of chromatin not only packs a cell's DNA into a compact form that fits inside the nucleus, but also helps regulate gene expression in several ways. The location of a gene's promoter, relative to both placement of nucleosomes and the sites where the DNA attaches to the chromosome scaffold, can affect whether the gene is transcribed. In addition, genes within heterochromatin, which is highly condensed, are usually not expressed. Lastly, certain chemical modifications to the histone proteins and to the DNA of chromatin can influence both chromatin structure and gene expression. Here we examine the effects of these modifications, which are catalyzed by specific enzymes.

Histone Modifications and DNA Methylation

There is abundant evidence that chemical modifications to histones, the proteins around which the DNA is wrapped in nucleosomes, play a direct role in the regulation of gene transcription. The N-terminus of each histone molecule in a nucleosome protrudes outward from the nucleosome **(Figure 18.7a)**. These histone tails are accessible to various modifying enzymes that catalyze the addition or removal of specific chemical groups, such as acetyl ($—COCH_3$), methyl, and phosphate groups. Generally, **histone acetylation** appears to promote transcription by opening up the chromatin structure **(Figure 18.7b)**, while addition of methyl groups can lead to the condensation of chromatin and reduced transcription.

While some enzymes methylate the tails of histone proteins, a different set of enzymes can methylate certain bases in the DNA itself, usually cytosine. Such **DNA methylation** occurs in most plants, animals, and fungi. Long stretches of inactive DNA, such as that of inactivated mammalian X chromosomes (see Figure 15.8), are generally more methylated than regions of actively transcribed DNA. On a smaller scale, individual genes are usually more heavily methylated in cells in which they are not expressed. Removal of the extra methyl groups can turn on some of these genes.

Once methylated, genes usually stay that way through successive cell divisions in a given individual. At DNA sites where one strand is already methylated, enzymes methylate the correct daughter strand after each round of DNA replication.

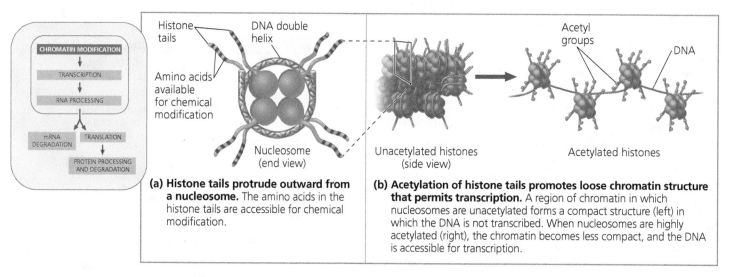

(a) Histone tails protrude outward from a nucleosome. The amino acids in the histone tails are accessible for chemical modification.

(b) Acetylation of histone tails promotes loose chromatin structure that permits transcription. A region of chromatin in which nucleosomes are unacetylated forms a compact structure (left) in which the DNA is not transcribed. When nucleosomes are highly acetylated (right), the chromatin becomes less compact, and the DNA is accessible for transcription.

▲ **Figure 18.7 A simple model of histone tails and the effect of histone acetylation.** In addition to acetylation, histones can undergo several other types of modifications that also help determine the chromatin configuration in a region.

Methylation patterns are thus passed on, and cells forming specialized tissues keep a chemical record of what occurred during embryonic development. A methylation pattern maintained in this way also accounts for *genomic imprinting* in mammals, where methylation permanently regulates expression of either the maternal or paternal allele of particular genes at the start of development (see Figure 15.17).

Epigenetic Inheritance

The chromatin modifications that we have just discussed do not entail a change in the DNA sequence, yet they still may be passed along to future generations of cells. Inheritance of traits transmitted by mechanisms not involving the nucleotide sequence itself is called **epigenetic inheritance**. Whereas mutations in the DNA are permanent changes, modifications to the chromatin can be reversed. For example, DNA methylation patterns are largely erased and reestablished during gamete formation.

Researchers are amassing more and more evidence for the importance of epigenetic information in the regulation of gene expression. Epigenetic variations might help explain why one identical twin acquires a genetically based disease, such as schizophrenia, but the other does not, despite their identical genomes. Alterations in normal patterns of DNA methylation are seen in some cancers, where they are associated with inappropriate gene expression. Evidently, enzymes that modify chromatin structure are integral parts of the eukaryotic cell's machinery for regulating transcription.

Regulation of Transcription Initiation

Chromatin-modifying enzymes provide initial control of gene expression by making a region of DNA either more or less able to bind the transcription machinery. Once the chromatin of a gene is optimally modified for expression, the initiation of transcription is the next major step at which gene expression is regulated. As in bacteria, the regulation of transcription initiation in eukaryotes involves proteins that bind to DNA and either facilitate or inhibit binding of RNA polymerase. The process is more complicated in eukaryotes, however. Before looking at how eukaryotic cells control their transcription, let's review the structure of a typical eukaryotic gene and its transcript.

Organization of a Typical Eukaryotic Gene

A eukaryotic gene and the DNA elements (segments) that control it are typically organized as shown in **Figure 18.8**, which extends what you learned about eukaryotic genes in Chapter 17. Recall that a cluster of proteins called a *transcription initiation complex* assembles on the promoter sequence at the "upstream" end of the gene. One of these proteins, RNA polymerase II, then proceeds to transcribe

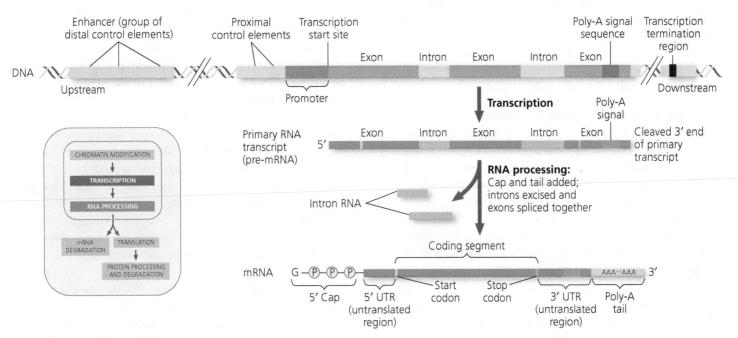

▲ **Figure 18.8 A eukaryotic gene and its transcript.** Each eukaryotic gene has a promoter, a DNA sequence where RNA polymerase binds and starts transcription, proceeding "downstream." A number of control elements (gold) are involved in regulating the initiation of transcription; these are DNA sequences located near (proximal to) or far from (distal to) the promoter. Distal control elements can be grouped together as enhancers, one of which is shown for this gene. A polyadenylation (poly-A) signal sequence in the last exon of the gene is transcribed into an RNA sequence that signals where the transcript is cleaved and the poly-A tail added. Transcription may continue for hundreds of nucleotides beyond the poly-A signal before terminating. RNA processing of the primary transcript into a functional mRNA involves three steps: addition of the 5' cap, addition of the poly-A tail, and splicing. In the cell, the 5' cap is added soon after transcription is initiated, and splicing occurs while transcription is still under way (see Figure 17.10).

the gene, synthesizing a primary RNA transcript (pre-mRNA). RNA processing includes enzymatic addition of a 5′ cap and a poly-A tail, as well as splicing out of introns, to yield a mature mRNA. Associated with most eukaryotic genes are multiple **control elements**, segments of noncoding DNA that serve as binding sites for the proteins called transcription factors, which in turn regulate transcription. Control elements and the transcription factors they bind are critical to the precise regulation of gene expression seen in different cell types.

The Roles of Transcription Factors

To initiate transcription, eukaryotic RNA polymerase requires the assistance of transcription factors. Some transcription factors (such as those illustrated in Figure 17.8) are essential for the transcription of *all* protein-coding genes; therefore, they are often called *general transcription factors*. A few general transcription factors bind to a DNA sequence such as the TATA box within the promoter, but most bind to proteins, including other transcription factors and RNA polymerase II. Protein-protein interactions are crucial to the initiation of eukaryotic transcription. Only when the complete initiation complex has assembled can the polymerase begin to move along the DNA template strand, producing a complementary strand of RNA.

The interaction of general transcription factors and RNA polymerase II with a promoter usually leads to a low rate of initiation and production of few RNA transcripts. In eukaryotes, high levels of transcription of particular genes at the appropriate time and place depend on the interaction of control elements with another set of proteins, which can be thought of as *specific transcription factors*.

Enhancers and Specific Transcription Factors As you can see in Figure 18.8, some control elements, named *proximal control elements*, are located close to the promoter. (Although some biologists consider proximal control elements part of the promoter, in this book we do not.) The more distant *distal control elements*, groupings of which are called **enhancers**, may be thousands of nucleotides upstream or downstream of a gene or even within an intron. A given gene may have multiple enhancers, each active at a different time or in a different cell type or location in the organism. Each enhancer, however, is generally associated with only that gene and no other.

In eukaryotes, the rate of gene expression can be strongly increased or decreased by the binding of specific transcription factors, either activators or repressors, to the control elements of enhancers. Hundreds of transcription activators have been discovered in eukaryotes; the structure of one example is shown in **Figure 18.9**. Researchers have identified two types of structural domains that are commonly found

▲ **Figure 18.9 The structure of MyoD, an activator.** The MyoD protein is made up of two subunits (purple and salmon) with extensive regions of α helix. Each subunit has one DNA-binding domain and one activation domain. The latter includes binding sites for the other subunit and for other proteins. MyoD is involved in muscle development in vertebrate embryos (see Concept 18.4).

in a large number of activator proteins. The first is a DNA-binding domain—a part of the protein's three-dimensional structure that binds to DNA—and the second is an activation domain. Activation domains bind other regulatory proteins or components of the transcription machinery, facilitating a series of protein-protein interactions that result in enhanced transcription of a given gene. A transcription factor can have one or more of either type of domain.

Figure 18.10 shows the currently accepted model for how binding of activators to an enhancer located far from the promoter can influence transcription. Protein-mediated bending of the DNA is thought to bring the bound activators into contact with a group of *mediator proteins*, which in turn interact with proteins at the promoter. These protein-protein interactions help assemble and position the initiation complex on the promoter. Many studies support this model, including one showing that the proteins regulating a mouse globin gene contact both the gene's promoter and an enhancer located about 50,000 nucleotides upstream. Protein interactions allow these two regions in the DNA to come together in a very specific fashion, in spite of the large number of nucleotide pairs between them. In the Scientific Skills Exercise, you can work with data from an experiment that identified the control elements in an enhancer of a particular human gene.

Specific transcription factors that function as repressors can inhibit gene expression in several different ways. Some repressors bind directly to control element DNA (in enhancers or elsewhere), blocking activator binding. Other repressors interfere with the activator itself so it can't bind the DNA.

In addition to influencing transcription directly, some activators and repressors act indirectly by affecting chromatin

1 Activator proteins bind to distal control elements grouped as an enhancer in the DNA. This enhancer has three binding sites, each called a distal control element.

DNA

Activators

Promoter

Gene

Enhancer

Distal control element

TATA box

CHROMATIN MODIFICATION

TRANSCRIPTION

RNA PROCESSING

mRNA DEGRADATION

TRANSLATION

PROTEIN PROCESSING AND DEGRADATION

2 A DNA-bending protein brings the bound activators closer to the promoter. General transcription factors, mediator proteins, and RNA polymerase II are nearby.

DNA-bending protein

General transcription factors

Group of mediator proteins

RNA polymerase II

3 The activators bind to certain mediator proteins and general transcription factors, helping them form an active transcription initiation complex on the promoter.

RNA polymerase II

Transcription initiation complex

RNA synthesis

▲ **Figure 18.10 A model for the action of enhancers and transcription activators.** Bending of the DNA by a protein enables enhancers to influence a promoter hundreds or even thousands of nucleotides away. Specific transcription factors called activators bind to the enhancer DNA sequences and then to a group of mediator proteins, which in turn bind to general transcription factors and ultimately RNA polymerase II, assembling the transcription initiation complex. These protein-protein interactions facilitate the correct positioning of the complex on the promoter and the initiation of RNA synthesis. Only one enhancer (with three gold control elements) is shown here, but a gene may have several enhancers that act at different times or in different cell types.

structure. Studies using yeast and mammalian cells show that some activators recruit proteins that acetylate histones near the promoters of specific genes, thus promoting transcription (see Figure 18.7). Similarly, some repressors recruit proteins that remove acetyl groups from histones, leading to reduced transcription, a phenomenon referred to as *silencing*. Indeed, recruitment of chromatin-modifying proteins seems to be the most common mechanism of repression in eukaryotic cells.

Combinatorial Control of Gene Activation In eukaryotes, the precise control of transcription depends largely on the binding of activators to DNA control elements. Considering the great number of genes that must be regulated in a typical animal or plant cell, the number of completely different nucleotide sequences found in control elements is surprisingly small. A dozen or so short nucleotide sequences appear again and again in the control elements for different genes. On average, each enhancer is composed of about ten control

Analyzing DNA Deletion Experiments

What Control Elements Regulate Expression of the *mPGES-1* Gene?

The promoter of a gene includes the DNA immediately upstream of the transcription start site, but the control elements regulating the level at which the gene is transcribed may be thousands of base pairs upstream of the promoter, grouped in an enhancer. Because the distance and spacing of control elements make them difficult to identify, scientists begin by deleting possible control elements and measuring the effect on gene expression. In this exercise, you will analyze data obtained from DNA deletion experiments that tested possible control elements for the human gene *mPGES-1*. This gene codes for an enzyme that synthesizes a type of prostaglandin, a chemical made during inflammation.

How the Experiment Was Done The researchers hypothesized that there were three possible control elements in an enhancer region located 8–9 kilobases upstream of the *mPGES-1* gene. Control elements regulate whatever gene is in the appropriate downstream location. Thus, to test the activity of the possible elements, researchers first synthesized molecules of DNA ("constructs") with the intact enhancer region upstream of a "reporter gene," a gene whose mRNA product could be easily measured experimentally. Next, they synthesized three more DNA constructs but deleted one of the three proposed control elements in each (see left side of figure). The researchers then introduced each DNA construct into a separate human cell culture, where the cells took up the artificial DNA molecules. After 48 hours, the amount of reporter gene mRNA made by the cells was measured. Comparing these amounts allowed researchers to determine if any of the deletions had an effect on expression of the reporter gene, mimicking the effect that deletions would have had on *mPGES-1* gene expression. (The *mPGES-1* gene itself couldn't be used to measure expression levels because the cells express their own *mPGES-1* gene, mRNA from which would otherwise confuse the results.)

Data from the Experiment The diagrams on the left side of the figure show the intact DNA sequence (top) and the three experimental DNA constructs. A red X is located on the possible control element (1, 2, or 3) that was deleted in each experimental DNA construct. The area between the slashes represents the approximately 8 kilobases of DNA located between the promoter and the enhancer region. The horizontal bar graph on the right shows the amount of reporter gene mRNA that was present in each cell culture after 48 hours relative to the amount that was in the culture containing the intact enhancer region (top bar = 100%).

Enhancer with possible control elements 1 2 3 · Promoter · Reporter gene

© 2012 The Biochemical Society

Relative level of reporter mRNA (% of control)

Interpret the Data

1. (a) What is the independent variable in the graph (that is, what variable was manipulated by the scientists)? (b) What is the dependent variable (that is, what variable responded to the changes in the independent variable)? (c) What was the control treatment in this experiment? Label it on the diagram.

2. Do the data suggest that any of these possible control elements are actual control elements? Explain.

3. (a) Did deletion of any of the possible control elements cause a *reduction* in reporter gene expression? If so, which one(s), and how can you tell? (b) If loss of a control element causes a reduction in gene expression, what must be the normal role of that control element? Provide a biological explanation for how the loss of such a control element could lead to a reduction in gene expression.

4. (a) Did deletion of any of the possible control elements cause an *increase* in reporter gene expression relative to the control? If so, which one(s), and how can you tell? (b) If loss of a control element causes an increase in gene expression, what must be the normal role of that control element? Propose a biological explanation for how the loss of such a control element could lead to an increase in gene expression.

(MB) A version of this Scientific Skills Exercise can be assigned in MasteringBiology.

Data from J. N. Walters et al., Regulation of human microsomal prostaglandin E synthase-1 by IL-1b requires a distal enhancer element with a unique role for C/EBPb, *Biochemical Journal* 443:561–571 (2012).

elements, each of which can bind only one or two specific transcription factors. It is the particular *combination* of control elements in an enhancer associated with a gene, rather than the presence of a single unique control element, that is important in regulating transcription of the gene.

Even with only a dozen control element sequences available, a very large number of combinations are possible. Each combination of control elements will be able to activate transcription only when the appropriate activator proteins are present, which may occur at a precise time during development or in a particular cell type. **Figure 18.11** illustrates how the use of different combinations of just a few control elements can allow differential regulation of transcription in two representative cell types—liver cells and lens cells. This can occur because each cell type contains a different group of activator proteins. Although the cells of an embryo all arise from one cell (the fertilized egg), diverse paths during embryonic development lead to different mixes of activator proteins in each type of cell. How cell types come to differ during this process will be explored in Concept 18.4.

▶ **Figure 18.11 Cell type–specific transcription.** Both liver cells and lens cells have the genes for making the proteins albumin and crystallin, but only liver cells make albumin (a blood protein) and only lens cells make crystallin (the main protein of the lens of the eye). The specific transcription factors made in a cell determine which genes are expressed. In this example, the genes for albumin and crystallin are shown at the top, each with an enhancer made up of three different control elements. Although the enhancers for the two genes both have a gray control element, each enhancer has a unique combination of elements. All the activator proteins required for high-level expression of the albumin gene are present only in liver cells **(a)**, whereas the activators needed for expression of the crystallin gene are present only in lens cells **(b)**. For simplicity, we consider only the role of specific transcription factors that are activators here, although repressors may also influence transcription in certain cell types.

? *Describe the enhancer for the albumin gene in each type of cell. How would the nucleotide sequence of this enhancer in the liver cell compare with that in the lens cell?*

(a) Liver cell. The albumin gene is expressed, and the crystallin gene is not.

(b) Lens cell. The crystallin gene is expressed, and the albumin gene is not.

Coordinately Controlled Genes in Eukaryotes

How does the eukaryotic cell deal with a group of genes of related function that need to be turned on or off at the same time? Earlier in this chapter, you learned that in bacteria, such coordinately controlled genes are often clustered into an operon, which is regulated by a single promoter and transcribed into a single mRNA molecule. Thus, the genes are expressed together, and the encoded proteins are produced concurrently. With a few exceptions, operons that work in this way have *not* been found in eukaryotic cells.

Co-expressed eukaryotic genes, such as genes coding for the enzymes of a metabolic pathway, are typically scattered over different chromosomes. Here, coordinate gene expression depends on the association of a specific combination of control elements with every gene of a dispersed group. Activator proteins in the nucleus that recognize the control elements bind to them, promoting simultaneous transcription of the genes, no matter where they are in the genome.

Coordinate control of dispersed genes in a eukaryotic cell often occurs in response to chemical signals from outside the cell. A steroid hormone, for example, enters a cell and binds to a specific intracellular receptor protein, forming a hormone-receptor complex that serves as a transcription activator (see Figure 11.9). Every gene whose transcription is stimulated by a particular steroid hormone, regardless of its chromosomal location, has a control element recognized by that hormone-receptor complex. This is how estrogen activates a group of genes that stimulate cell division in uterine cells, preparing the uterus for pregnancy.

Many signaling molecules, such as nonsteroid hormones and growth factors, bind to receptors on a cell's surface and never actually enter the cell. Such molecules can control gene expression indirectly by triggering signal transduction pathways that lead to activation of particular transcription activators or repressors (see Figure 11.15). Coordinate regulation in such pathways is the same as for steroid hormones: Genes with the same sets of control elements are activated by the same chemical signals. Because this system for coordinating gene regulation is so widespread, scientists think that it probably arose early in evolutionary history.

Nuclear Architecture and Gene Expression

You saw in Figure 16.23b that each chromosome in the interphase nucleus occupies a distinct territory. The chromosomes are not completely isolated, however. Recently, techniques have been developed that allow researchers to cross-link and identify regions of chromosomes that associate with each other during interphase. These studies reveal that loops of chromatin extend from individual chromosomal territories into specific sites in the nucleus **(Figure 18.12)**. Different loops from the same chromosome and loops from other chromosomes may congregate in such sites, some of which are rich in RNA polymerases and other transcription-associated proteins. Like a recreation center that draws members from many different neighborhoods, these so-called *transcription factories* are thought to be areas specialized for a common function.

The old view that the nuclear contents are like a bowl of amorphous chromosomal spaghetti has given way to a new model of a nucleus with a defined architecture and regulated movements of chromatin. Relocation of particular genes from their chromosomal territories to transcription factories may be part of the process of readying genes for transcription. This is an exciting area of current research that raises many fascinating questions for consideration.

▲ **Figure 18.12 Chromosomal interactions in the interphase nucleus.** Although each chromosome has its own territory (see Figure 16.23b), loops of chromatin may extend into other sites in the nucleus. Some of these sites are transcription factories that are occupied by multiple chromatin loops from the same chromosome (blue loops) or other chromosomes (red and green loops).

Mechanisms of Post-Transcriptional Regulation

Transcription alone does not constitute gene expression. The expression of a protein-coding gene is ultimately measured by the amount of functional protein a cell makes, and much happens between the synthesis of the RNA transcript and the activity of the protein in the cell. Many regulatory mechanisms operate at the various stages after transcription (see Figure 18.6). These mechanisms allow a cell to fine-tune gene expression rapidly in response to environmental changes without altering its transcription patterns. Here we discuss how cells can regulate gene expression once a gene has been transcribed.

RNA Processing

RNA processing in the nucleus and the export of mature RNA to the cytoplasm provide several opportunities for regulating gene expression that are not available in prokaryotes. One example of regulation at the RNA-processing level is **alternative RNA splicing**, in which different mRNA molecules are produced from the same primary transcript, depending on which RNA segments are treated as exons and which as introns. Regulatory proteins specific to a cell type control intron-exon choices by binding to regulatory sequences within the primary transcript.

A simple example of alternative RNA splicing is shown in **Figure 18.13** for the troponin T gene, which encodes two different (though related) proteins. Other genes code

▼ **Figure 18.13 Alternative RNA splicing of the troponin T gene.** The primary transcript of this gene can be spliced in more than one way, generating different mRNA molecules. Notice that one mRNA molecule has ended up with exon 3 (green) and the other with exon 4 (purple). These two mRNAs are translated into different but related muscle proteins.

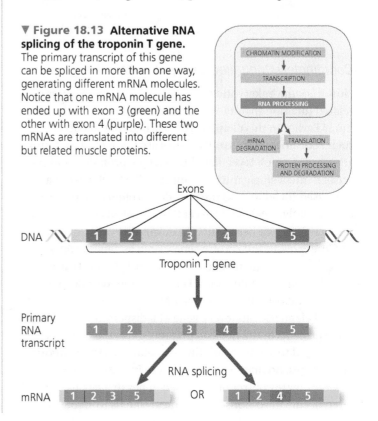

for many more possible products. For instance, researchers have found a *Drosophila* gene with enough alternatively spliced exons to generate about 19,000 membrane proteins that have different extracellular domains. At least 17,500 (94%) of the alternative mRNAs are actually synthesized. Each developing nerve cell in the fly appears to synthesize a unique form of the protein, which acts as an identification badge on the cell surface.

It is clear that alternative RNA splicing can significantly expand the repertoire of a eukaryotic genome. In fact, alternative splicing was proposed as one explanation for the surprisingly low number of human genes counted when the human genome was sequenced. The number of human genes was found to be similar to that of a soil worm (nematode), a mustard plant, or a sea anemone. This discovery prompted questions about what, if not the number of genes, accounts for the more complex morphology (external form) of humans. It turns out that 75–100% of human genes that have multiple exons probably undergo alternative splicing. Thus, the extent of alternative splicing greatly multiplies the number of possible human proteins, which may be better correlated with complexity of form.

Initiation of Translation and mRNA Degradation

Translation presents another opportunity for regulating gene expression; such regulation occurs most commonly at the initiation stage (see Figure 17.18). For some mRNAs, the initiation of translation can be blocked by regulatory proteins that bind to specific sequences or structures within the untranslated region (UTR) at the 5' or 3' end, preventing the attachment of ribosomes. (Recall from Chapter 17 that both the 5' cap and the poly-A tail of an mRNA molecule are important for ribosome binding.)

Alternatively, translation of *all* the mRNAs in a cell may be regulated simultaneously. In a eukaryotic cell, such "global" control usually involves the activation or inactivation of one or more of the protein factors required to initiate translation. This mechanism plays a role in starting translation of mRNAs that are stored in eggs. Just after fertilization, translation is triggered by the sudden activation of translation initiation factors. The response is a burst of synthesis of the proteins encoded by the stored mRNAs. Some plants and algae store mRNAs during periods of darkness; light then triggers the reactivation of the translational apparatus.

The life span of mRNA molecules in the cytoplasm is important in determining the pattern of protein synthesis in a cell. Bacterial mRNA molecules typically are degraded by enzymes within a few minutes of their synthesis. This short life span of mRNAs is one reason bacteria can change their patterns of protein synthesis so quickly in response to environmental changes. In contrast, mRNAs in multicellular eukaryotes typically survive for hours, days, or even weeks. For instance, the mRNAs for the hemoglobin polypeptides

(α-globin and β-globin) in developing red blood cells are unusually stable, and these long-lived mRNAs are translated repeatedly in red blood cells.

Nucleotide sequences that affect how long an mRNA remains intact are often found in the untranslated region (UTR) at the 3' end of the molecule (see Figure 18.8). In one experiment, researchers transferred such a sequence from the short-lived mRNA for a growth factor to the 3' end of a normally stable globin mRNA. The globin mRNA was quickly degraded.

During the past few years, other mechanisms that degrade or block expression of mRNA molecules have come to light. These mechanisms involve an important group of newly discovered RNA molecules that regulate gene expression at several levels, and we will discuss them later in this chapter.

Protein Processing and Degradation

The final opportunities for controlling gene expression occur after translation. Often, eukaryotic polypeptides must be processed to yield functional protein molecules. For instance, cleavage of the initial insulin polypeptide (proinsulin) forms the active hormone. In addition, many proteins undergo chemical modifications that make them functional. Regulatory proteins are commonly activated or inactivated by the reversible addition of phosphate groups, and proteins destined for the surface of animal cells acquire sugars. Cell-surface proteins and many others must also be transported to target destinations in the cell in order to function. Regulation might occur at any of the steps involved in modifying or transporting a protein.

Finally, the length of time each protein functions in the cell is strictly regulated by means of selective degradation. Many proteins, such as the cyclins involved in regulating the cell cycle, must be relatively short-lived if the cell is to function appropriately (see Figure 12.16). To mark a particular protein for destruction, the cell commonly attaches molecules of a small protein called ubiquitin to the protein. Giant protein complexes called proteasomes then recognize the ubiquitin-tagged proteins and degrade them.

CONCEPT CHECK 18.2

1. In general, what are the effects of histone acetylation and DNA methylation on gene expression?

2. Compare the roles of general and specific transcription factors in regulating gene expression.

3. **WHAT IF?** Suppose you compared the nucleotide sequences of the distal control elements in the enhancers of three genes that are expressed only in muscle cells. What would you expect to find? Why?

4. Once mRNA encoding a particular protein reaches the cytoplasm, what are four mechanisms that can regulate the amount of the protein that is active in the cell?

For suggested answers, see Appendix A.

CONCEPT 18.3

Noncoding RNAs play multiple roles in controlling gene expression

Genome sequencing has revealed that protein-coding DNA accounts for only 1.5% of the human genome and a similarly small percentage of the genomes of many other multicellular eukaryotes. A very small fraction of the non-protein-coding DNA consists of genes for RNAs such as ribosomal RNA and transfer RNA. Until recently, most of the remaining DNA was assumed to be untranscribed. The idea was that since it didn't specify proteins or the few known types of RNA, such DNA didn't contain meaningful genetic information. However, a flood of recent data has contradicted this idea. For example, a massive study of the entire human genome completed in 2012 showed that roughly 75% of the genome is transcribed at some point in any given cell. Introns account for only a fraction of this transcribed, nontranslated RNA. These and other results suggest that a significant amount of the genome may be transcribed into non-protein-coding RNAs—also called *noncoding RNAs*, or *ncRNAs*—including a variety of small RNAs. While many questions about the functions of these RNAs remain unanswered, researchers are uncovering more evidence of their biological roles every day.

Biologists are excited about these recent discoveries, which hint at a large, diverse population of RNA molecules in the cell that play crucial roles in regulating gene expression—but have gone largely unnoticed until now. Subsequent research has impelled revision of the long-standing view that because mRNAs code for proteins, they are the most important RNAs functioning in the cell. This represents a major shift in the thinking of biologists, one that you are witnessing as students entering this field of study. It's as if our exclusive focus on a famous rock star has blinded us to the many backup musicians and songwriters working behind the scenes.

Effects on mRNAs by MicroRNAs and Small Interfering RNAs

Regulation by both small and large ncRNAs is known to occur at several points in the pathway of gene expression, including mRNA translation and chromatin modification. We will focus mainly on two types of small ncRNAs that have been extensively studied in the past few years. The importance of these RNAs was acknowledged when they were the focus of the 2006 Nobel Prize in Physiology or Medicine, which was awarded for work completed only 8 years earlier.

Since 1993, a number of research studies have uncovered small single-stranded RNA molecules, called **microRNAs**

(**miRNAs**), capable of binding to complementary sequences in mRNA molecules. A longer RNA precursor is processed by cellular enzymes into an miRNA, a single-stranded RNA of about 22 nucleotides that forms a complex with one or more proteins. The miRNA allows the complex to bind to any mRNA molecule with at least 7 or 8 nucleotides of complementary sequence. The miRNA-protein complex then either degrades the target mRNA or blocks its translation (**Figure 18.14**). It has been estimated that expression of at least one-half of all human genes may be regulated by miRNAs, a remarkable figure given that the existence of miRNAs was unknown a mere two decades ago.

Another class of small RNAs are called **small interfering RNAs (siRNAs)**. These are similar in size and function to miRNAs—both can associate with the same proteins, producing similar results. In fact, if siRNA precursor RNA molecules are injected into a cell, the cell's machinery can process them into siRNAs that turn off expression of genes with related sequences, similarly to how miRNAs function. The distinction between miRNAs and siRNAs is based on subtle differences in the structure of their precursors, which

1 The miRNA binds to a target mRNA with at least 7 complementary bases.

mRNA degraded   OR   Translation blocked

2 If miRNA and mRNA bases are complementary all along their length, the mRNA is degraded (left); if the match is less complete, translation is blocked (right).

▲ **Figure 18.14 Regulation of gene expression by miRNAs.** A 22-nucleotide miRNA, formed by enzymatic processing of an RNA precursor, associates with one or more proteins in a complex. The complex can then degrade or block translation of target mRNAs.

in both cases are RNA molecules that are mostly double-stranded. The blocking of gene expression by siRNAs is called **RNA interference (RNAi)**, and it is used in the laboratory as a means of disabling specific genes to investigate their function.

How did the RNAi pathway evolve? As you will learn in Chapter 19, some viruses have double-stranded RNA genomes. Given that the cellular RNAi pathway can process double-stranded RNAs into homing devices that lead to destruction of related RNAs, some scientists think that this pathway may have evolved as a natural defense against infection by such viruses. However, the fact that RNAi can also affect the expression of nonviral cellular genes may reflect a different evolutionary origin for the RNAi pathway. Moreover, many species, including mammals, apparently produce their own long, double-stranded RNA precursors to small RNAs such as siRNAs. Once produced, these RNAs can interfere with gene expression at stages other than translation, as we'll discuss next.

Chromatin Remodeling by ncRNAs

The pervasive function of noncoding RNAs in regulating gene expression is becoming increasingly obvious, and one more effect of ncRNAs is worth discussing here. In addition to regulating mRNAs, some ncRNAs act to bring about remodeling of chromatin structure. One example occurs during formation of heterochromatin at the centromere, as studied in a species of yeast.

In the S phase of the cell cycle, the centromeric regions of DNA must be loosened for chromosomal replication and then re-condensed into heterochromatin in preparation for mitosis. In some yeasts, siRNAs produced by the yeast cells themselves are required to re-form the heterochromatin at the centromeres. A model for how this happens is shown in **Figure 18.15**. Exactly how the process starts and the order of the steps are still being debated, but biologists all agree on the general idea: The siRNA system in yeast interacts with other noncoding RNAs and with chromatin-modifying enzymes to remodel chromatin structure at the centromere. In most mammalian cells, siRNAs are not known to occur, and the mechanism for centromere DNA condensation is not yet understood. However, it may turn out to involve other small ncRNAs.

A newly discovered class of small ncRNAs is called *piwi-interacting RNAs*, or *piRNAs*. (Dr. Haifan Lin, whose interview appears before Chapter 6, discovered and named piRNAs.) These RNAs also induce formation of heterochromatin, blocking expression of some parasitic DNA elements in the genome known as transposons. (Transposons are discussed in Chapter 21.) Usually 24–31 nucleotides in length, piRNAs are processed from a longer, single-stranded RNA

① RNA transcripts (red) are produced from centromeric DNA.

② Each RNA transcript is used as a template by a yeast enzyme that synthesizes the complementary strand, forming double-stranded RNA.

③ The double-stranded RNA is processed into short, single-stranded siRNAs that associate with proteins, forming siRNA-protein complexes.

④ The siRNA-protein complexes bind the RNA transcripts being produced from the centromeric DNA and, in this way, are tethered to the centromere region.

⑤ Proteins in the siRNA-protein complexes recruit enzymes (green) that chemically modify the histones within the chromatin and initiate chromatin condensation.

⑥ Ultimately, this process leads to formation of heterochromatin at the centromere.

▲ **Figure 18.15 Condensation of chromatin at the centromere.** In one type of yeast, siRNAs and longer noncoding RNAs cooperate in the pathway that leads to re-formation of highly condensed heterochromatin at the centromere of each chromatid after DNA replication.

precursor. They play an indispensable role in the germ cells of many animal species, where they appear to help reestablish appropriate methylation patterns in the genome during gamete formation.

Finally, ncRNAs are responsible for X chromosome inactivation, which, in most female mammals, prevents expression of genes located on one of the X chromosomes (see Figure 15.8). In this case, transcripts of the XIST gene located on the chromosome to be inactivated bind back to and coat that chromosome, and this binding leads to condensation of the entire chromosome into heterochromatin.

The cases we have just described involve chromatin remodeling in large regions of the chromosome. Because chromatin structure affects transcription and thus gene expression, RNA-based regulation of chromatin structure is likely to play an important role in gene regulation.

The Evolutionary Significance of Small ncRNAs

EVOLUTION Small ncRNAs can regulate gene expression at multiple steps and in many ways. In general, extra levels of gene regulation might allow evolution of a higher degree of complexity of form. The versatility of miRNA regulation has therefore led some biologists to hypothesize that an increase in the number of different miRNAs specified by the genome of a given species has allowed morphological complexity to increase over evolutionary time. While this hypothesis is still being evaluated, it is logical to expand the discussion to include all small ncRNAs. Exciting new techniques for rapidly sequencing genomes have allowed biologists to begin asking how many genes for ncRNAs are present in the genome of any given species. A survey of different species supports the notion that siRNAs evolved first, followed by miRNAs and later piRNAs, which are found only in animals. And while there are hundreds of types of miRNAs, there appear to be 60,000 or so types of piRNAs, allowing the potential for very sophisticated gene regulation by piRNAs.

Given the extensive functions of ncRNAs, it is not surprising that many of the ncRNAs characterized thus far play important roles in embryonic development—the topic we turn to in the next section. Embryonic development is perhaps the ultimate example of precisely regulated gene expression.

CONCEPT CHECK 18.3

1. Compare miRNAs and siRNAs, including their functions.
2. **WHAT IF?** Suppose the mRNA being degraded in Figure 18.14 coded for a protein that promotes cell division in a multicellular organism. What would happen if a mutation disabled the gene for the miRNA that triggers this degradation?

For suggested answers, see Appendix A.

A program of differential gene expression leads to the different cell types in a multicellular organism

In the embryonic development of multicellular organisms, a fertilized egg (a zygote) gives rise to cells of many different types, each with a different structure and corresponding function. Typically, cells are organized into tissues, tissues into organs, organs into organ systems, and organ systems into the whole organism. Thus, any developmental program must produce cells of different types that form higher-level structures arranged in a particular way in three dimensions. The processes that occur during development in plants and animals are detailed in Chapters 35 and 47, respectively. In this chapter, we focus on the program of regulation of gene expression that orchestrates development, using a few animal species as examples.

A Genetic Program for Embryonic Development

The photos in **Figure 18.16** illustrate the dramatic difference between a frog zygote and the tadpole it becomes. This remarkable transformation results from three interrelated processes: cell division, cell differentiation, and morphogenesis. Through a succession of mitotic cell divisions, the zygote gives rise to a large number of cells. Cell division alone, however, would merely produce a great ball of identical cells, nothing like a tadpole. During embryonic development, cells not only increase in number, but also undergo cell **differentiation**, the process by which cells become specialized in structure and function. Moreover, the different kinds of cells are not randomly distributed but are organized into tissues and organs in a particular three-dimensional

(a) Fertilized eggs of a frog   (b) Newly hatched tadpole

▲ Figure 18.16 **From fertilized egg to animal: What a difference four days makes.** It takes just four days for cell division, differentiation, and morphogenesis to transform each of the fertilized frog eggs shown in **(a)** into a tadpole like the one in **(b)**.

arrangement. The physical processes that give an organism its shape constitute **morphogenesis**, the development of the form of an organism and its structures.

All three processes are rooted in cellular behavior. Even morphogenesis, the shaping of the organism, can be traced back to changes in the shape, motility, and other characteristics of the cells that make up various regions of the embryo. As you have seen, the activities of a cell depend on the genes it expresses and the proteins it produces. Almost all cells in an organism have the same genome; therefore, differential gene expression results from the genes being regulated differently in each cell type.

In Figure 18.11, you saw a simplified view of how differential gene expression occurs in two cell types, a liver cell and a lens cell. Each of these fully differentiated cells has a particular mix of specific activators that turn on the collection of genes whose products are required in the cell. The fact that both cells arose through a series of mitoses from a common fertilized egg inevitably leads to a question: How do different sets of activators come to be present in the two cells?

It turns out that materials placed into the egg by the mother set up a sequential program of gene regulation that is carried out as cells divide, and this program coordinates cell differentiation during embryonic development. To understand how this works, we will consider two basic developmental processes: First, we'll explore how cells that arise from early embryonic mitoses develop the differences that start each cell along its own differentiation pathway. Second, we'll see how cellular differentiation leads to one particular cell type, using muscle development as an example.

Cytoplasmic Determinants and Inductive Signals

What generates the first differences among cells in an early embryo? And what controls the differentiation of all the various cell types as development proceeds? By this point in the chapter, you can probably deduce the answer: The specific genes expressed in any particular cell of a developing organism determine its path. Two sources of information, used to varying extents in different species, "tell" a cell which genes to express at any given time during embryonic development.

One important source of information early in development is the egg's cytoplasm, which contains both RNA and proteins encoded by the mother's DNA. The cytoplasm of an unfertilized egg is not homogeneous. Messenger RNA, proteins, other substances, and organelles are distributed unevenly in the unfertilized egg, and this unevenness has a profound impact on the development of the future embryo in many species. Maternal substances in the egg that influence the course of early development are called **cytoplasmic determinants** (Figure 18.17a). After fertilization, early mitotic divisions distribute the zygote's cytoplasm

▼ **Figure 18.17** **Sources of developmental information for the early embryo.**

(a) Cytoplasmic determinants in the egg

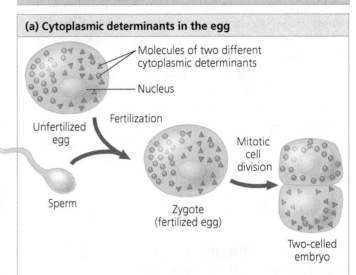

The unfertilized egg has molecules in its cytoplasm, encoded by the mother's genes, that influence development. Many of these cytoplasmic determinants, like the two shown here, are unevenly distributed in the egg. After fertilization and mitotic division, the cell nuclei of the embryo are exposed to different sets of cytoplasmic determinants and, as a result, express different genes.

(b) Induction by nearby cells

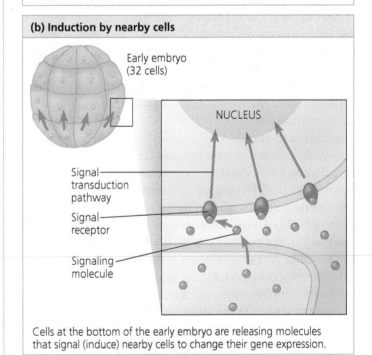

Cells at the bottom of the early embryo are releasing molecules that signal (induce) nearby cells to change their gene expression.

into separate cells. The nuclei of these cells may thus be exposed to different cytoplasmic determinants, depending on which portions of the zygotic cytoplasm a cell received. The combination of cytoplasmic determinants in a cell helps determine its developmental fate by regulating expression of the cell's genes during the course of cell differentiation.

The other major source of developmental information, which becomes increasingly important as the number of embryonic cells increases, is the environment around a particular cell. Most influential are the signals impinging on an embryonic cell from other embryonic cells in the vicinity, including contact with cell-surface molecules on neighboring cells and the binding of growth factors secreted by neighboring cells (see Chapter 11). Such signals cause changes in the target cells, a process called **induction** (Figure 18.17b). The molecules conveying these signals within the target cell are cell-surface receptors and other signaling pathway proteins. In general, the signaling molecules send a cell down a specific developmental path by causing changes in its gene expression that eventually result in observable cellular changes. Thus, interactions between embryonic cells help induce differentiation into the many specialized cell types making up a new organism.

Sequential Regulation of Gene Expression During Cellular Differentiation

The earliest changes that set a cell on its path to specialization are subtle ones, showing up only at the molecular level. Before biologists knew much about the molecular changes occurring in embryos, they coined the term **determination** to refer to the point at which an embryonic cell is irreversibly committed to becoming a particular cell type. Once it has undergone determination, an embryonic cell can be experimentally placed in another location in the embryo and it will still differentiate into the cell type that is its normal fate. Differentiation, then, is the process by which a cell attains its determined fate. As the tissues and organs of an embryo develop and their cells differentiate, the cells become more noticeably different in structure and function.

Today we understand determination in terms of molecular changes. The outcome of determination, observable cell differentiation, is marked by the expression of genes for *tissue-specific proteins*. These proteins are found only in a specific cell type and give the cell its characteristic structure and function. The first evidence of differentiation is the appearance of mRNAs for these proteins. Eventually, differentiation is observable with a microscope as changes in cellular structure. On the molecular level, different sets of genes are sequentially expressed in a regulated manner as new cells arise from division of their precursors. A number of the steps in gene expression may be regulated during differentiation, with transcription among the most common. In the fully differentiated cell, transcription remains the principal regulatory point for maintaining appropriate gene expression.

Differentiated cells are specialists at making tissue-specific proteins. For example, as a result of transcriptional regulation, liver cells specialize in making albumin, and lens cells specialize in making crystallin (see Figure 18.11). Skeletal muscle cells in vertebrates are another instructive example. Each of these cells is a long fiber containing many nuclei within a single plasma membrane. Skeletal muscle cells have high concentrations of muscle-specific versions of the contractile proteins myosin and actin, as well as membrane receptor proteins that detect signals from nerve cells.

Muscle cells develop from embryonic precursor cells that have the potential to develop into a number of cell types, including cartilage cells and fat cells, but particular conditions commit them to becoming muscle cells. Although the committed cells appear unchanged under the microscope, determination has occurred, and they are now *myoblasts*. Eventually, myoblasts start to churn out large amounts of muscle-specific proteins and fuse to form mature, elongated, multinucleate skeletal muscle cells.

Researchers have worked out what happens at the molecular level during muscle cell determination by growing myoblasts in culture and analyzing them using molecular techniques you will learn about in Chapter 20. In a series of experiments, they isolated different genes, caused each to be expressed in a separate embryonic precursor cell, and then looked for differentiation into myoblasts and muscle cells. In this way, they identified several so-called "master regulatory genes" whose protein products commit the cells to becoming skeletal muscle. Thus, in the case of muscle cells, the molecular basis of determination is the expression of one or more of these master regulatory genes.

To understand more about how determination occurs in muscle cell differentiation, let's focus on the master regulatory gene called *myoD* (Figure 18.18). This gene encodes MyoD protein, a transcription factor that binds to specific control elements in the enhancers of various target genes and stimulates their expression (see Figure 18.9). Some target genes for MyoD encode still other muscle-specific transcription factors. MyoD also stimulates expression of the *myoD* gene itself, an example of positive feedback that perpetuates MyoD's effect in maintaining the cell's differentiated state. Presumably, all the genes activated by MyoD have enhancer control elements recognized by MyoD and are thus coordinately controlled. Finally, the secondary transcription factors activate the genes for proteins such as myosin and actin that confer the unique properties of skeletal muscle cells.

The *myoD* gene deserves its designation as a master regulatory gene. Researchers have shown that MyoD is capable of changing some kinds of fully differentiated nonmuscle cells, such as fat cells and liver cells, into muscle cells. Why doesn't it work on *all* kinds of cells? One likely explanation is that activation of the muscle-specific genes is not solely dependent on MyoD but requires a particular *combination* of regulatory proteins, some of which are lacking in cells that do not respond to MyoD. The determination and differentiation of other kinds of tissues may play out in a similar fashion.

We have now seen how different programs of gene expression that are activated in the fertilized egg can result in differentiated cells and tissues. But for the tissues to function effectively in the organism as a whole, the organism's

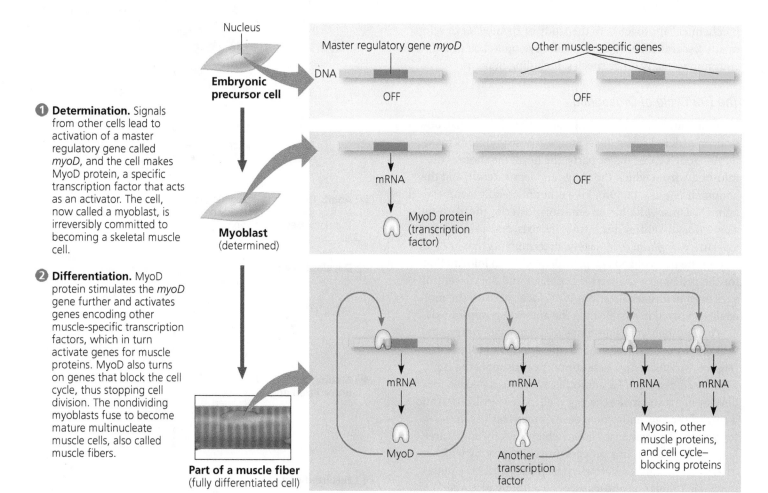

① Determination. Signals from other cells lead to activation of a master regulatory gene called *myoD*, and the cell makes MyoD protein, a specific transcription factor that acts as an activator. The cell, now called a myoblast, is irreversibly committed to becoming a skeletal muscle cell.

② Differentiation. MyoD protein stimulates the *myoD* gene further and activates genes encoding other muscle-specific transcription factors, which in turn activate genes for muscle proteins. MyoD also turns on genes that block the cell cycle, thus stopping cell division. The nondividing myoblasts fuse to become mature multinucleate muscle cells, also called muscle fibers.

Nucleus

Embryonic precursor cell

Master regulatory gene *myoD*

Other muscle-specific genes

DNA

OFF

OFF

Myoblast (determined)

mRNA

OFF

MyoD protein (transcription factor)

mRNA

mRNA

mRNA

mRNA

Part of a muscle fiber (fully differentiated cell)

MyoD

Another transcription factor

Myosin, other muscle proteins, and cell cycle–blocking proteins

▲ **Figure 18.18 Determination and differentiation of muscle cells.** Skeletal muscle cells arise from embryonic cells as a result of changes in gene expression. (In this depiction, the process of gene activation is greatly simplified.)

WHAT IF? *What would happen if a mutation in the* myoD *gene resulted in a MyoD protein that could not activate the* myoD *gene?*

body plan—its overall three-dimensional arrangement—must be established and superimposed on the differentiation process. Next we'll investigate the molecular basis for the establishment of the body plan, using the well-studied fruit fly *Drosophila melanogaster* as an example.

Pattern Formation: Setting Up the Body Plan

Cytoplasmic determinants and inductive signals both contribute to the development of a spatial organization in which the tissues and organs of an organism are all in their characteristic places. This process is called **pattern formation**.

Just as the locations of the front, back, and sides of a new building are determined before construction begins, pattern formation in animals begins in the early embryo, when the major axes of an animal are established. In a bilaterally symmetrical animal, the relative positions of head and tail, right and left sides, and back and front—the three major body axes—are set up before the organs appear. The molecular cues that control pattern formation, collectively called

positional information, are provided by cytoplasmic determinants and inductive signals (see Figure 18.17). These cues tell a cell its location relative to the body axes and to neighboring cells and determine how the cell and its progeny will respond to future molecular signals.

During the first half of the 20th century, classical embryologists made detailed anatomical observations of embryonic development in a number of species and performed experiments in which they manipulated embryonic tissues. Although this research laid the groundwork for understanding the mechanisms of development, it did not reveal the specific molecules that guide development or determine how patterns are established.

Then, in the 1940s, scientists began using the genetic approach—the study of mutants—to investigate *Drosophila* development. That approach has had spectacular success. These studies have established that genes control development and have led to an understanding of the key roles that specific molecules play in defining position and directing differentiation. By combining anatomical, genetic, and biochemical approaches to the study of *Drosophila* develop-ment, researchers have discovered developmental principles common to many other species, including humans.

The Life Cycle of Drosophila

Fruit flies and other arthropods have a modular construc-tion, an ordered series of segments. These segments make up the body's three major parts: the head, the thorax (the mid-body, from which the wings and legs extend), and the abdomen (**Figure 18.19a**). Like other bilaterally symmetrical animals, *Drosophila* has an anterior-posterior (head-to-tail) axis, a dorsal-ventral (back-to-belly) axis, and a right-left axis. In *Drosophila*, cytoplasmic determinants that are local-ized in the unfertilized egg provide positional information for the placement of anterior-posterior and dorsal-ventral axes even before fertilization. We'll focus here on the mol-ecules involved in establishing the anterior-posterior axis.

The *Drosophila* egg develops in the female's ovary, sur-rounded by ovarian cells called nurse cells and follicle cells (**Figure 18.19b**, top). These support cells supply the egg with nutrients, mRNAs, and other substances needed for development and make the egg shell. After fertilization and laying of the egg, embryonic development results in the formation of a segmented larva, which goes through three larval stages. Then, in a process much like that by which a caterpillar becomes a butterfly, the fly larva forms a pupa in which it metamorphoses into the adult fly pictured in Figure 18.19a.

Genetic Analysis of Early Development: Scientific Inquiry

Edward B. Lewis was a visionary American biologist who, in the 1940s, first showed the value of the genetic approach to studying embryonic development in *Drosophila*. Lewis studied bizarre mutant flies with developmental defects that led to extra wings or legs in the wrong place (**Figure 18.20**). He located the mutations on the fly's genetic map, thus con-necting the developmental abnormalities to specific genes. This research supplied the first concrete evidence that genes somehow direct the developmental processes studied by embryologists. The genes Lewis discovered, called **homeotic genes**, control pattern formation in the late embryo, larva, and adult.

Further insight into pattern formation during early em-bryonic development did not come for another 30 years, when two researchers in Germany, Christiane Nüsslein-Volhard and Eric Wieschaus, set out to identify *all* the genes that affect segment formation in *Drosophila*. The project was daunting for three reasons. The first was the sheer num-ber of *Drosophila* genes, now known to total about 14,000. The genes affecting segmentation might be just a few needles in a haystack or might be so numerous and varied that the scientists would be unable to make sense of them.

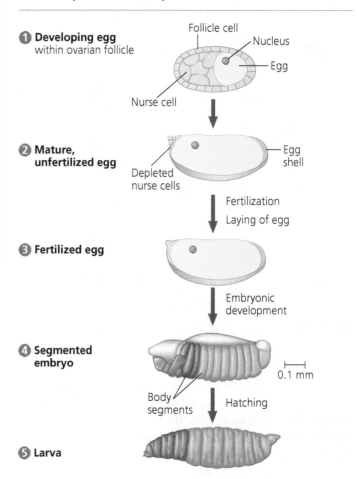

(a) Adult. The adult fly is segmented, and multiple segments make up each of the three main body parts—head, thorax, and abdomen. The body axes are shown by arrows.

① **Developing egg** within ovarian follicle

② **Mature, unfertilized egg**

③ **Fertilized egg**

④ **Segmented embryo**

⑤ **Larva**

(b) Development from egg to larva. ① The egg (yellow) is surrounded by support cells (follicle cells) within one of the mother's ovaries. ② The developing egg enlarges as nutrients and mRNAs are supplied to it by other support cells (nurse cells), which shrink. Eventually, the mature egg fills the egg shell that is secreted by the follicle cells. ③ The egg is fertilized within the mother and then laid. It develops into ④ a segmented embryo and then ⑤ a larva, which has three stages. The third stage forms a pupa (not shown), within which the larva metamorphoses into the adult shown in (a).

▲ **Figure 18.19 Key developmental events in the life cycle of *Drosophila*.**

Second, mutations affecting a process as fundamental as segmentation would surely be **embryonic lethals**, mutations with phenotypes causing death at the embryonic or larval stage. Because organisms with embryonic lethal mutations

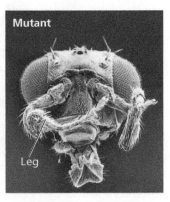

▲ **Figure 18.20 Abnormal pattern formation in *Drosophila*.** Mutations in certain regulatory genes, called homeotic genes, cause abnormal placement of structures in an animal. These colorized scanning electron micrographs contrast the head of a wild-type fruit fly, bearing a pair of small antennae, with that of a homeotic mutant (a fly with a mutation in a single gene), bearing a pair of legs in place of antennae.

never reproduce, they cannot be bred for study. The researchers dealt with this problem by looking for recessive mutations, which can be propagated in heterozygous flies that act as genetic carriers. Third, cytoplasmic determinants in the egg were known to play a role in axis formation, so the researchers knew they would have to study the mother's genes as well as those of the embryo. It is the mother's genes that we will discuss further as we focus on how the anterior-posterior body axis is set up in the developing egg.

Nüsslein-Volhard and Wieschaus began their search for segmentation genes by exposing flies to a mutagenic chemical that affected the flies' gametes. They mated the mutagenized flies and then scanned their descendants for dead embryos or larvae with abnormal segmentation or other defects. For example, to find genes that might set up the anterior-posterior axis, they looked for embryos or larvae with abnormal ends, such as two heads or two tails, predicting that such abnormalities would arise from mutations in maternal genes required for correctly setting up the offspring's head or tail end.

Using this approach, Nüsslein-Volhard and Wieschaus eventually identified about 1,200 genes essential for pattern formation during embryonic development. Of these, about 120 were essential for normal segmentation. Over several years, the researchers were able to group these segmentation genes by general function, to map them, and to clone many of them for further study in the lab. The result was a detailed molecular understanding of the early steps in pattern formation in *Drosophila*.

When the results of Nüsslein-Volhard and Wieschaus were combined with Lewis's earlier work, a coherent picture of *Drosophila* development emerged. In recognition of their discoveries, the three researchers were awarded a Nobel Prize in 1995. Next, let's consider a specific example of the genes that Nüsslein-Volhard, Wieschaus, and co-workers found.

Axis Establishment

As we mentioned earlier, cytoplasmic determinants in the egg are the substances that initially establish the axes of the *Drosophila* body. These substances are encoded by genes of the mother, fittingly called maternal effect genes. A **maternal effect gene** is a gene that, when mutant in the mother, results in a mutant phenotype in the offspring, regardless of the offspring's own genotype. In fruit fly development, the mRNA or protein products of maternal effect genes are placed in the egg while it is still in the mother's ovary. When the mother has a mutation in such a gene, she makes a defective gene product (or none at all), and her eggs are defective; when these eggs are fertilized, they fail to develop properly.

Because they control the orientation (polarity) of the egg and consequently that of the fly, these maternal effect genes are also called **egg-polarity genes**. One group of these genes sets up the anterior-posterior axis of the embryo, while a second group establishes the dorsal-ventral axis. Like mutations in segmentation genes, mutations in maternal effect genes are generally embryonic lethals.

Bicoid: A Morphogen that Determines Head Structures To see how maternal effect genes determine the body axes of the offspring, we will focus on one such gene, called *bicoid*, a term meaning "two-tailed." An embryo or larva whose mother has two mutant *bicoid* alleles lacks the front half of its body and has posterior structures at both ends **(Figure 18.21)**. This phenotype suggested to Nüsslein-Volhard and her colleagues that the product of the mother's *bicoid* gene is essential for setting up the anterior end of the fly and might be concentrated at the future anterior end of

▲ **Figure 18.21 Effect of the *bicoid* gene on *Drosophila* development.** A wild-type fruit fly larva has a head, three thoracic (T) segments, eight abdominal (A) segments, and a tail. A larva whose mother has two mutant alleles of the *bicoid* gene has two tails and lacks all anterior structures (LMs).

the embryo. This hypothesis is an example of the *morphogen gradient hypothesis* first proposed by embryologists a century ago, where gradients of substances called **morphogens** establish an embryo's axes and other features of its form.

DNA technology and other modern biochemical methods enabled the researchers to test whether the *bicoid* product, a protein called Bicoid, is in fact a morphogen that determines the anterior end of the fly. The first question they asked was whether the mRNA and protein products of this gene are located in the egg in a position consistent with the hypothesis. They found that *bicoid* mRNA is highly concentrated at the extreme anterior end of the mature egg (**Figure 18.22**). After the egg is fertilized, the mRNA is translated into protein. The Bicoid protein then diffuses from the anterior end toward the posterior, resulting in a gradient of protein within the early embryo, with the highest concentration at the anterior end. These results are consistent with the hypothesis that Bicoid protein specifies the fly's anterior end. To test the hypothesis more specifically, scientists injected pure *bicoid* mRNA into various regions of early embryos. The protein that resulted from its translation caused anterior structures to form at the injection sites.

The *bicoid* research was groundbreaking for several reasons. First, it led to the identification of a specific protein required for some of the earliest steps in pattern formation. It thus helped us understand how different regions of the egg can give rise to cells that go down different developmental pathways. Second, it increased our understanding of the mother's critical role in the initial phases of embryonic development. Finally, the principle that a gradient of morphogens can determine polarity and position has proved to be a key developmental concept for a number of species, just as early embryologists had thought.

Maternal mRNAs are crucial during development of many species. In *Drosophila*, gradients of specific proteins encoded by maternal mRNAs not only determine the posterior and anterior ends but also establish the dorsal-ventral axis. As the fly embryo grows, it reaches a point when the embryonic program of gene expression takes over, and the maternal mRNAs must be destroyed. (This process involves miRNAs in *Drosophila* and other species.) Later, positional information encoded by the embryo's genes, operating on an ever finer scale, establishes a specific number of correctly oriented segments and triggers the formation of each segment's characteristic structures. When the genes operating in this final step are abnormal, the pattern of the adult is abnormal, as you saw in Figure 18.20.

Evolutionary Developmental Biology ("Evo-Devo")

EVOLUTION The fly with legs emerging from its head in Figure 18.20 is the result of a single mutation in one gene. The gene does not encode an antenna protein, however. Instead, it encodes a transcription factor that regulates other

---

▼ Figure 18.22 | Inquiry

Could Bicoid be a morphogen that determines the anterior end of a fruit fly?

Experiment Using a genetic approach to study *Drosophila* development, Christiane Nüsslein-Volhard and colleagues at two research institutions in Germany analyzed expression of the *bicoid* gene. The researchers hypothesized that *bicoid* normally codes for a morphogen that specifies the head (anterior) end of the embryo. To begin to test this hypothesis, they used molecular techniques to determine whether the mRNA and protein encoded by this gene were found in the anterior end of the fertilized egg and early embryo of wild-type flies.

Results *Bicoid* mRNA (dark blue in the light micrographs and drawings) was confined to the anterior end of the unfertilized egg. Later in development, Bicoid protein (dark orange) was seen to be concentrated in cells at the anterior end of the embryo.

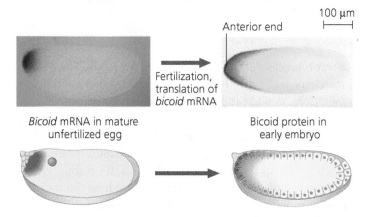

Bicoid mRNA in mature unfertilized egg

Bicoid protein in early embryo

Conclusion The location of *bicoid* mRNA and the diffuse gradient of Bicoid protein seen later are consistent with the hypothesis that Bicoid protein is a morphogen specifying formation of head-specific structures.

Source: C. Nüsslein-Volhard et al., Determination of anteroposterior polarity in *Drosophila, Science* 238:1675–1681 (1987); W. Driever and C. Nüsslein-Volhard, A gradient of *bicoid* protein in *Drosophila* embryos, *Cell* 54:83–93 (1988); T. Berleth et al., The role of localization of *bicoid* RNA in organizing the anterior pattern of the *Drosophila* embryo, *EMBO Journal* 7:1749–1756 (1988).

WHAT IF? *The researchers needed further evidence, so they injected* bicoid *mRNA into the anterior end of an egg from a female with a mutation disabling the* bicoid *gene. Given that the hypothesis was supported, what do you think were their results?*

---

genes, and its malfunction leads to misplaced structures, such as legs instead of antennae. The observation that a change in gene regulation during development could lead to such a fantastic change in body form prompted some scientists to consider whether these types of mutations could contribute to evolution by generating novel body shapes. Ultimately this line of inquiry gave rise to the field of evolutionary developmental biology, so-called "evo-devo," which will be further discussed in Chapter 21.

In this section, we have seen how a carefully orchestrated program of sequential gene regulation controls the transformation of a fertilized egg into a multicellular organism. The program is carefully balanced between turning on the genes for differentiation in the right place and turning off other genes. Even when an organism is fully developed, gene expression is regulated in a similarly fine-tuned manner. In the final section of the chapter, we'll consider how fine this tuning is by looking at how specific changes in expression of just a few genes can lead to the development of cancer.

CONCEPT CHECK 18.4

1. MAKE CONNECTIONS As you learned in Chapter 12, mitosis gives rise to two daughter cells that are genetically identical to the parent cell. Yet you, the product of many mitotic divisions, are not composed of identical cells. Why?

2. MAKE CONNECTIONS Explain how the signaling molecules released by an embryonic cell can induce changes in a neighboring cell without entering the cell. (See Figures 11.15 and 11.16.)

3. Why are fruit fly maternal effect genes also called egg-polarity genes?

4. WHAT IF? In Figure 18.17b, the lower cell is synthesizing signaling molecules, whereas the upper cell is expressing receptors for these molecules. In terms of gene regulation and cytoplasmic determinants, explain how these cells came to synthesize different molecules.

For suggested answers, see Appendix A.

CONCEPT 18.5

Cancer results from genetic changes that affect cell cycle control

In Chapter 12, we considered cancer as a type of disease in which cells escape from the control mechanisms that normally limit their growth. Now that we have discussed the molecular basis of gene expression and its regulation, we are ready to look at cancer more closely. The gene regulation systems that go wrong during cancer turn out to be the very same systems that play important roles in embryonic development, the immune response, and many other biological processes. Thus, research into the molecular basis of cancer has both benefited from and informed many other fields of biology.

Types of Genes Associated with Cancer

The genes that normally regulate cell growth and division during the cell cycle include genes for growth factors, their receptors, and the intracellular molecules of signaling pathways. (To review cell signaling, see Chapter 11; for the cell cycle, see Chapter 12.) Mutations that alter any of these genes in somatic cells can lead to cancer. The agent of such change can be random spontaneous mutation. However, it is also likely that many cancer-causing mutations result from environmental influences, such as chemical carcinogens, X-rays and other high-energy radiation, and some viruses.

Cancer research led to the discovery of cancer-causing genes called **oncogenes** (from the Greek *onco*, tumor) in certain types of viruses (see Chapter 19). Subsequently, close counterparts of viral oncogenes were found in the genomes of humans and other animals. The normal versions of the cellular genes, called **proto-oncogenes**, code for proteins that stimulate normal cell growth and division.

How might a proto-oncogene—a gene that has an essential function in normal cells—become an oncogene, a cancer-causing gene? In general, an oncogene arises from a genetic change that leads to an increase either in the amount of the proto-oncogene's protein product or in the intrinsic activity of each protein molecule. The genetic changes that convert proto-oncogenes to oncogenes fall into three main categories: movement of DNA within the genome, amplification of a proto-oncogene, and point mutations in a control element or in the proto-oncogene itself **(Figure 18.23)**.

▲ Figure 18.23 **Genetic changes that can turn proto-oncogenes into oncogenes.**

Cancer cells are frequently found to contain chromosomes that have broken and rejoined incorrectly, translocating fragments from one chromosome to another (see Figure 15.14). Having learned how gene expression is regulated, you can now see the possible consequences of such translocations. If a translocated proto-oncogene ends up near an especially active promoter (or other control element), its transcription may increase, making it an oncogene. The second main type of genetic change, amplification, increases the number of copies of the proto-oncogene in the cell through repeated gene duplication (discussed in Chapter 21). The third possibility is a point mutation either (1) in the promoter or an enhancer that controls a proto-oncogene, causing an increase in its expression, or (2) in the coding sequence of the proto-oncogene, changing the gene's product to a protein that is more active or more resistant to degradation than the normal protein. These mechanisms can lead to abnormal stimulation of the cell cycle and put the cell on the path to becoming a cancer cell.

Tumor-Suppressor Genes

In addition to genes whose products normally promote cell division, cells contain genes whose normal products *inhibit* cell division. Such genes are called **tumor-suppressor genes** because the proteins they encode help prevent uncontrolled cell growth. Any mutation that decreases the normal activity of a tumor-suppressor protein may contribute to the onset of cancer, in effect stimulating growth through the absence of suppression.

The protein products of tumor-suppressor genes have various functions. Some tumor-suppressor proteins repair damaged DNA, a function that prevents the cell from accumulating cancer-causing mutations. Other tumor-suppressor proteins control the adhesion of cells to each other or to the extracellular matrix; proper cell anchorage is crucial in normal tissues—and is often absent in cancers. Still other tumor-suppressor proteins are components of cell-signaling pathways that inhibit the cell cycle.

Interference with Normal Cell-Signaling Pathways

The proteins encoded by many proto-oncogenes and tumor-suppressor genes are components of cell-signaling pathways. Let's take a closer look at how such proteins function in normal cells and what goes wrong with their function in cancer cells. We will focus on the products of two key genes, the *ras* proto-oncogene and the *p53* tumor-suppressor gene. Mutations in *ras* occur in about 30% of human cancers, and mutations in *p53* in more than 50%.

The Ras protein, encoded by the ***ras* gene** (named for rat sarcoma, a connective tissue cancer), is a G protein that relays a signal from a growth factor receptor on the plasma membrane to a cascade of protein kinases (see Figure 11.8). The cellular response at the end of the pathway is the synthesis of a protein that stimulates the cell cycle (**Figure 18.24a**). Normally, such a pathway will not operate unless triggered by the appropriate growth factor. But certain mutations in the *ras* gene can lead to production of a hyperactive Ras protein that triggers the kinase cascade even in the absence of growth factor, resulting in increased cell division (**Figure 18.24b**). In fact, hyperactive versions or excess amounts of any of the pathway's components can have the same outcome: excessive cell division.

Figure 18.25a shows a pathway in which an intracellular signal leads to the synthesis of a protein that suppresses the cell cycle. In this case, the signal is damage to the cell's DNA, perhaps as the result of exposure to ultraviolet light. Operation of this signaling pathway blocks the cell cycle until the damage has been repaired. Otherwise, the damage might contribute to tumor formation by causing mutations or chromosomal abnormalities. Thus, the genes for the components of the pathway act as tumor-suppressor genes. The ***p53* gene**, named for the 53,000-dalton molecular weight of its protein product, is a tumor-suppressor gene. The protein it encodes is a specific transcription factor that promotes the synthesis of cell cycle–inhibiting proteins. That is why a mutation that knocks out the *p53* gene, like a mutation that leads to a hyperactive Ras protein, can lead to excessive cell growth and cancer (**Figure 18.25b**).

The *p53* gene has been called the "guardian angel of the genome." Once the gene is activated—for example, by DNA damage—the p53 protein functions as an activator for several other genes. Often it activates a gene called *p21*, whose product halts the cell cycle by binding to cyclin-dependent kinases, allowing time for the cell to repair the DNA. Researchers recently showed that p53 also activates expression of a group of miRNAs, which in turn inhibit the cell cycle. In addition, the p53 protein can turn on genes directly involved in DNA repair. Finally, when DNA damage is irreparable, p53 activates "suicide" genes, whose protein products bring about programmed cell death (apoptosis; see Figure 11.20). Thus, p53 acts in several ways to prevent a cell from passing on mutations due to DNA damage. If mutations do accumulate and the cell survives through many divisions—as is more likely if the *p53* tumor-suppressor gene is defective or missing—cancer may ensue. The many functions of p53 suggest a complex picture of regulation in normal cells, one that we do not yet fully understand.

For the present, the diagrams in Figure 18.24 and Figure 18.25 are an accurate view of how mutations can contribute to cancer, but we still don't know exactly how a particular cell becomes a cancer cell. As we discover previously unknown aspects of gene regulation, it is informative

▶ **Figure 18.24 Normal and mutant cell cycle–stimulating pathway.**
(a) The normal pathway is triggered by ❶ a growth factor that binds to ❷ its receptor in the plasma membrane. The signal is relayed to ❸ a G protein called Ras. Like all G proteins, Ras is active when GTP is bound to it. Ras passes the signal to ❹ a series of protein kinases. The last kinase activates ❺ a transcription factor (activator) that turns on one or more genes for ❻ a protein that stimulates the cell cycle. **(b)** If a mutation makes Ras or any other pathway component abnormally active, excessive cell division and cancer may result.

(a) Normal cell cycle–stimulating pathway.

(b) Mutant cell cycle–stimulating pathway.

▶ **Figure 18.25 Normal and mutant cell cycle–inhibiting pathway. (a)** In the normal pathway, ❶ DNA damage is an intracellular signal that is passed via ❷ protein kinases, leading to activation of ❸ p53. Activated p53 promotes ❹ transcription of the gene for ❺ a protein that inhibits the cell cycle. The resulting suppression of cell division ensures that the damaged DNA is not replicated. If the DNA damage is irreparable, then the p53 signal leads to programmed cell death (apoptosis). **(b)** Mutations causing deficiencies in any pathway component can contribute to the development of cancer.

❓ *Explain whether a cancer-causing mutation in a tumor-suppressor gene, such as p53, is more likely to be a recessive or a dominant mutation.*

(a) Normal cell cycle–inhibiting pathway

(b) Mutant cell cycle–inhibiting pathway

to study their role in the onset of cancer. Such studies have shown, for instance, that DNA methylation and histone modification patterns differ in normal and cancer cells and that miRNAs probably participate in cancer development. While we've learned a lot about cancer by studying cell-signaling pathways, there is still a lot left to learn.

The Multistep Model of Cancer Development

More than one somatic mutation is generally needed to produce all the changes characteristic of a full-fledged cancer cell. This may help explain why the incidence of cancer increases greatly with age. If cancer results from an accumulation of mutations and if mutations occur throughout life, then the longer we live, the more likely we are to develop cancer.

The model of a multistep path to cancer is well supported by studies of one of the best-understood types of human cancer: colorectal cancer, which affects the colon and/or rectum. About 140,000 new cases of colorectal cancer are diagnosed each year in the United States, and the disease causes 50,000 deaths per year. Like most cancers, colorectal cancer develops gradually **(Figure 18.26)**. The first sign is often a polyp, a small, benign growth in the colon lining. The cells of the polyp look normal, although they divide unusually frequently. The tumor grows and may eventually become malignant, invading other tissues. The development of a malignant tumor is paralleled by a gradual accumulation of mutations that convert proto-oncogenes to oncogenes and knock out tumor-suppressor genes. A *ras* oncogene and a mutated *p53* tumor-suppressor gene are often involved.

About half a dozen changes must occur at the DNA level for a cell to become fully cancerous. These changes usually include the appearance of at least one active oncogene and the mutation or loss of several tumor-suppressor genes. Furthermore, since mutant tumor-suppressor alleles are usually recessive, in most cases mutations must knock out *both* alleles in a cell's genome to block tumor suppression. (Most oncogenes, on the other hand, behave as dominant alleles.) The order in which these changes must occur is still under investigation, as is the relative importance of different mutations.

Since we understand the progression of this type of cancer, routine screenings are recommended to identify and remove any suspicious polyps. The colorectal cancer mortality rate has been declining for the past 20 years, due in part to increased screening and in part to improved treatments. Treatments for other cancers have improved as well. Dramatic technical advances in the sequencing of DNA and mRNA have allowed medical researchers to compare the genes expressed by different types of tumors and by the same type in different individuals. These comparisons have led to personalized cancer treatments based on the molecular characteristics of an individual's tumor.

Breast cancer is the second most common form of cancer in the United States, and the first among women. Each year, this cancer strikes over 230,000 women (and some men) in the United States and kills 40,000 (450,000 worldwide). A major problem with understanding breast cancer is its heterogeneity: Tumors differ in significant ways. Identifying differences between types of breast cancer is expected to improve treatment and decrease the mortality rate. In November of 2012, The Cancer Genome Atlas Network, sponsored by the National Institutes of Health, published the results of a multi-team effort that used a genomics approach to profile subtypes of breast cancer based on their molecular signatures. Four major types of breast cancer were identified **(Figure 18.27)**.

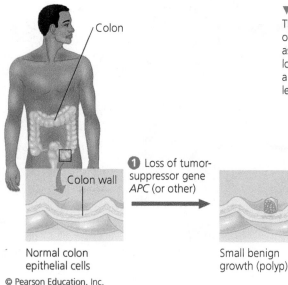

▼ **Figure 18.26 A multistep model for the development of colorectal cancer.** This type of cancer is one of the best understood. Changes in a tumor parallel a series of genetic changes, including mutations affecting several tumor-suppressor genes (such as *p53*) and the *ras* proto-oncogene. Mutations of tumor-suppressor genes often entail loss (deletion) of the gene. *APC* stands for "adenomatous polyposis coli," and *SMAD4* is a gene involved in signaling that results in apoptosis. Other mutation sequences can also lead to colorectal cancer.

Colon

Colon wall

1 Loss of tumor-suppressor gene *APC* (or other)

Normal colon epithelial cells

2 Activation of *ras* oncogene

3 Loss of tumor-suppressor gene *SMAD4*

Small benign growth (polyp)

4 Loss of tumor-suppressor gene *p53*

5 Additional mutations

Larger benign growth (adenoma)

Malignant tumor (carcinoma)

© Pearson Education, Inc.

▼ Figure 18.27

MAKE CONNECTIONS

Genomics, Cell Signaling, and Cancer

Modern medicine that melds genome-wide molecular studies with cell-signaling research is transforming the treatment of many diseases, such as breast cancer. Using micro-array analysis (*see Figure 20.13*) and other techniques, researchers measured the relative levels of mRNA transcripts for every gene in many different breast cancer tumor samples. They identified four major subtypes of breast cancer, shown below, that differ in their expression of three signal receptors involved in regulating cell growth and division (*see Figures 11.8 and 11.9*). Normal levels of these signal receptors (indicated by +) are represented in a normal breast cell at the right. The absence (–) or excess expression (++ or +++) of these receptors can cause aberrant cell signaling, leading in some cases to inappropriate cell division, which may contribute to cancer (*see Figure 18.24*). Breast cancer treatments are becoming more effective because they can be tailored to the specific cancer subtype.

Normal Breast Cells in a Milk Duct

- ERα⁺
- PR⁺
- HER2⁺

Duct interior

Estrogen receptor alpha (ERα)

Progesterone receptor (PR)

HER2 (a receptor tyrosine kinase)

Support cell

Extracellular matrix

Breast Cancer Subtypes

Luminal A	Luminal B	HER2	Basal-like

Luminal A
- ERα⁺⁺⁺
- PR⁺⁺
- HER2⁻
- 40% of breast cancers
- Best prognosis

Luminal B
- ERα⁺⁺
- PR⁺⁺
- HER2⁻ (shown); some HER2⁺⁺
- 15–20% of breast cancers
- Poorer prognosis than luminal A subtype

HER2
- ERα⁻
- PR⁻
- HER2⁺⁺
- 10–15% of breast cancers
- Poorer prognosis than luminal A subtype

Basal-like
- ERα⁻
- PR⁻
- HER2⁻
- 15–20% of breast cancers
- More aggressive; poorer prognosis than other subtypes

Both luminal subtypes overexpress ERα (luminal A more than luminal B) and PR, and usually lack expression of HER2. Both can be treated with drugs that target ERα and inactivate it, the most well-known drug being Tamoxifen. These subtypes can also be treated with drugs that inhibit estrogen synthesis.

The HER2 subtype overexpresses HER2. Because it does not express either ERα or PR at normal levels, the cells are unresponsive to therapies aimed against those two receptors. However, patients with the HER2 subtype can be treated with Herceptin, an antibody protein that inactivates the tyrosine kinase activity of HER2 (*see Concept 12.3*).

The basal-like subtype is "triple negative"—it does not express ERα, PR, or HER2. It often has a mutation in the tumor suppressor gene BRCA1 (*see Concept 18.5*). Treatments that target ER, PR, or HER2 are not effective, but new treatments are being developed. Currently, patients are treated with cytotoxic chemotherapy, which selectively kills fast-growing cells.

MAKE CONNECTIONS *When researchers compared gene expression in normal breast cells and cells from breast cancers, they found that the genes showing the most significant differences in expression encoded signal receptors, as shown here. Given what you learned in Chapters 11, 12, and this chapter, explain why this result is not surprising.*

Inherited Predisposition and Environmental Factors Contributing to Cancer

The fact that multiple genetic changes are required to produce a cancer cell helps explain the observation that cancers can run in families. An individual inheriting an oncogene or a mutant allele of a tumor-suppressor gene is one step closer to accumulating the necessary mutations for cancer to develop than is an individual without any such mutations.

Geneticists are devoting significant effort to identifying inherited cancer alleles so that predisposition to certain cancers can be detected early in life. About 15% of colorectal cancers, for example, involve inherited mutations. Many of these affect the tumor-suppressor gene called *adenomatous polyposis coli*, or *APC* (see Figure 18.26). This gene has multiple functions in the cell, including regulation of cell migration and adhesion. Even in patients with no family history of the disease, the *APC* gene is mutated in 60% of colorectal cancers. In these individuals, new mutations must occur in both *APC* alleles before the gene's function is lost. Since only 15% of colorectal cancers are associated with known inherited mutations, researchers continue in their efforts to identify "markers" that could predict the risk of developing this type of cancer.

Given the prevalence and significance of breast cancer, it is not surprising that it was one of the first cancers for which the role of inheritance was investigated. It turns out that for 5–10% of patients with breast cancer, there is evidence of a strong inherited predisposition. Geneticist Mary-Claire King began working on this problem in the mid-1970s. After 16 years of research, she convincingly demonstrated that mutations in one gene—*BRCA1*—were associated with increased susceptibility to breast cancer, a finding that flew in the face of medical opinion at the time. (*BRCA* stands for breast cancer.) Mutations in that gene or a gene called *BRCA2* are found in at least half of inherited breast cancers, and tests using DNA sequencing can detect these mutations. A woman who inherits one mutant *BRCA1* allele has a 60% probability of developing breast cancer before the age of 50, compared with only a 2% probability for an individual homozygous for the normal allele.

BRCA1 and *BRCA2* are considered tumor-suppressor genes because their wild-type alleles protect against breast cancer and their mutant alleles are recessive. (Note that mutations in *BRCA1* are commonly found in the genomes of cells from basal-like breast cancers; see Figure 18.27.) The BRCA1 and BRCA2 proteins both appear to function in the cell's DNA damage repair pathway. More is known about BRCA2, which, in association with another protein, helps repair breaks that occur in both strands of DNA; this repair function is crucial for maintaining undamaged DNA in a cell's nucleus.

Because DNA breakage can contribute to cancer, it makes sense that the risk of cancer can be lowered by minimizing exposure to DNA-damaging agents, such as the ultraviolet radiation in sunlight and chemicals found in cigarette smoke. Novel genomics-based analyses of specific cancers, such as the approach described in Figure 18.27, are contributing to both early diagnosis and development of treatments that interfere with expression of key genes in tumors. Ultimately, such approaches are expected to lower the death rate from cancer.

The Role of Viruses in Cancer

The study of genes associated with cancer, inherited or not, increases our basic understanding of how disruption of normal gene regulation can result in this disease. In addition to the mutations and other genetic alterations described in this section, a number of *tumor viruses* can cause cancer in various animals, including humans. In fact, one of the earliest breakthroughs in understanding cancer came in 1911, when Peyton Rous, an American pathologist, discovered a virus that causes cancer in chickens. The Epstein-Barr virus, which causes infectious mononucleosis, has been linked to several types of cancer in humans, notably Burkitt's lymphoma. Papillomaviruses are associated with cancer of the cervix, and a virus called HTLV-1 causes a type of adult leukemia. Worldwide, viruses seem to play a role in about 15% of the cases of human cancer.

Viruses may at first seem very different from mutations as a cause of cancer. However, we now know that viruses can interfere with gene regulation in several ways if they integrate their genetic material into the DNA of a cell. Viral integration may donate an oncogene to the cell, disrupt a tumor-suppressor gene, or convert a proto-oncogene to an oncogene. In addition, some viruses produce proteins that inactivate p53 and other tumor-suppressor proteins, making the cell more prone to becoming cancerous. Viruses are powerful biological agents, and you'll learn more about their function in Chapter 19.

CONCEPT CHECK 18.5

1. **MAKE CONNECTIONS** The p53 protein can activate genes involved in apoptosis, or programmed cell death. Discuss how mutations in genes coding for proteins that function in apoptosis could contribute to cancer. (Review Concept 11.5.)

2. Under what circumstances is cancer considered to have a hereditary component?

3. **WHAT IF?** Cancer-promoting mutations are likely to have different effects on the activity of proteins encoded by proto-oncogenes than they do on proteins encoded by tumor-suppressor genes. Explain.

For suggested answers, see Appendix A.

CONCEPT 18.1

Bacteria often respond to environmental change by regulating transcription (pp. 361–365)

- Cells control metabolism by regulating enzyme activity or the expression of genes coding for enzymes. In bacteria, genes are often clustered into operons, with one promoter serving several adjacent genes. An operator site on the DNA switches the operon on or off, resulting in coordinate regulation of the genes.

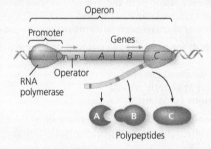

- Both repressible and inducible operons are examples of negative gene regulation. In either type of operon, binding of a specific **repressor** protein to the operator shuts off transcription. (The repressor is encoded by a separate **regulatory gene**.) In a repressible operon, the repressor is active when bound to a **corepressor**, usually the end product of an anabolic pathway.

Repressible operon:

In an inducible operon, binding of an **inducer** to an innately active repressor inactivates the repressor and turns on transcription. Inducible enzymes usually function in catabolic pathways.

Inducible operon:

- Some operons are also subject to positive gene regulation via a stimulatory **activator** protein, such as catabolite activator protein (CAP), which, when activated by **cyclic AMP**, binds to a site within the promoter and stimulates transcription.

? Compare and contrast the roles of a corepressor and an inducer in negative regulation of an operon.

CONCEPT 18.2

Eukaryotic gene expression is regulated at many stages (pp. 365–373)

? Describe what must happen for a cell-type-specific gene to be transcribed in a cell of that type.

CONCEPT 18.3

Noncoding RNAs play multiple roles in controlling gene expression (pp. 374–376)

? Why are miRNAs called noncoding RNAs? Explain how they participate in gene regulation.

CONCEPT 18.4

A program of differential gene expression leads to the different cell types in a multicellular organism (pp. 376–383)

- Embryonic cells become committed to a certain fate (**determination**), and undergo **differentiation**, becoming specialized in structure and function for their determined fate. Cells have different structures and functions not because they contain different genomes but because they express different genes. **Morphogenesis** encompasses the processes that give shape to the organism and its various structures.
- **Cytoplasmic determinants** in the unfertilized egg regulate the expression of genes in the zygote and embryo that affect the developmental fate of embryonic cells. In the process called **induction**, signaling molecules from embryonic cells cause transcriptional changes in nearby target cells.
- Differentiation is heralded by the appearance of tissue-specific proteins, which enable differentiated cells to carry out their specialized roles.
- In animals, **pattern formation**, the development of a spatial organization of tissues and organs, begins in the early embryo. **Positional information**, the molecular cues that control pattern formation, tells a cell its location relative to the body's axes and to other cells. In *Drosophila*, gradients of **morphogens** encoded by **maternal effect genes** determine the body axes. For example, the gradient of **Bicoid** protein determines the anterior-posterior axis.

? Describe the two main processes that cause embryonic cells to head down different pathways to their final fates.

CONCEPT 18.5

Cancer results from genetic changes that affect cell cycle control (pp. 383–388)

- The products of **proto-oncogenes** and **tumor-suppressor genes** control cell division. A DNA change that makes a proto-oncogene excessively active converts it to an **oncogene**, which may promote excessive cell division and cancer. A tumor-suppressor gene encodes a protein that inhibits abnormal cell division. A mutation in a tumor-suppressor gene that reduces the activity of its protein product may also lead to excessive cell division and possibly to cancer.
- Many proto-oncogenes and tumor-suppressor genes encode components of growth-stimulating and growth-inhibiting signaling pathways, respectively, and mutations in these genes can interfere with normal cell-signaling pathways. A hyperactive version of a protein in a stimulatory pathway, such as **Ras** (a G protein), functions as an oncogene protein. A defective version of a protein in an inhibitory pathway, such as **p53** (a transcription activator), fails to function as a tumor suppressor.

EFFECTS OF MUTATIONS

Protein overexpressed → Cell cycle overstimulated → Increased cell division ← Cell cycle not inhibited ← Protein absent

- In the multistep model of cancer development, normal cells are converted to cancer cells by the accumulation of mutations affecting proto-oncogenes and tumor-suppressor genes. Technical advances in DNA and mRNA sequencing are enabling cancer treatments that are more individually based.

- Genomics-based studies have resulted in researchers proposing four subtypes of breast cancer, based on expression of genes by tumor cells.
- Individuals who inherit a mutant allele of a proto-oncogene or tumor-suppressor gene have a predisposition to develop a particular cancer. Certain viruses promote cancer by integration of viral DNA into a cell's genome.

? Compare the usual functions of proteins encoded by proto-oncogenes with those of proteins encoded by tumor-suppressor genes.

TEST YOUR UNDERSTANDING

LEVEL 1: KNOWLEDGE/COMPREHENSION

1. If a particular operon encodes enzymes for making an essential amino acid and is regulated like the *trp* operon, then
   a. the amino acid inactivates the repressor.
   b. the repressor is active in the absence of the amino acid.
   c. the amino acid acts as a corepressor.
   d. the amino acid turns on transcription of the operon.

2. Muscle cells differ from nerve cells mainly because they
   a. express different genes.
   b. contain different genes.
   c. use different genetic codes.
   d. have unique ribosomes.

3. The functioning of enhancers is an example of
   a. a eukaryotic equivalent of prokaryotic promoter functioning.
   b. transcriptional control of gene expression.
   c. the stimulation of translation by initiation factors.
   d. post-translational control that activates certain proteins.

4. Cell differentiation always involves
   a. transcription of the *myoD* gene.
   b. the movement of cells.
   c. the production of tissue-specific proteins.
   d. the selective loss of certain genes from the genome.

5. Which of the following is an example of post-transcriptional control of gene expression?
   a. the addition of methyl groups to cytosine bases of DNA
   b. the binding of transcription factors to a promoter
   c. the removal of introns and alternative splicing of exons
   d. gene amplification contributing to cancer

LEVEL 2: APPLICATION/ANALYSIS

6. What would occur if the repressor of an inducible operon were mutated so it could not bind the operator?
   a. irreversible binding of the repressor to the promoter
   b. reduced transcription of the operon's genes
   c. buildup of a substrate for the pathway controlled by the operon
   d. continuous transcription of the operon's genes

7. Absence of *bicoid* mRNA from a *Drosophila* egg leads to the absence of anterior larval body parts and mirror-image duplication of posterior parts. This is evidence that the product of the *bicoid* gene
   a. normally leads to formation of head structures.
   b. normally leads to formation of tail structures.
   c. is transcribed in the early embryo.
   d. is a protein present in all head structures.

8. Which of the following statements about the DNA in one of your brain cells is true?
   a. Most of the DNA codes for protein.
   b. The majority of genes are likely to be transcribed.
   c. It is the same as the DNA in one of your liver cells.
   d. Each gene lies immediately adjacent to an enhancer.

9. Within a cell, the amount of protein made using a given mRNA molecule depends partly on
   a. the degree of DNA methylation.
   b. the rate at which the mRNA is degraded.
   c. the number of introns present in the mRNA.
   d. the types of ribosomes present in the cytoplasm.

10. Proto-oncogenes can change into oncogenes that cause cancer. Which of the following best explains the presence of these potential time bombs in eukaryotic cells?
    a. Proto-oncogenes first arose from viral infections.
    b. Proto-oncogenes are mutant versions of normal genes.
    c. Proto-oncogenes are genetic "junk."
    d. Proto-oncogenes normally help regulate cell division.

LEVEL 3: SYNTHESIS/EVALUATION

11. **DRAW IT** The diagram below shows five genes, including their enhancers, from the genome of a certain species. Imagine that orange, blue, green, black, red, and purple activator proteins exist that can bind to the appropriately color-coded control elements in the enhancers of these genes.

(a) Draw an X above enhancer elements (of all the genes) that would have activators bound in a cell in which only gene 5 is transcribed. Which colored activators would be present?
(b) Draw a dot above all enhancer elements that would have activators bound in a cell in which the green, blue, and orange activators are present. Which gene(s) would be transcribed?
(c) Imagine that genes 1, 2, and 4 code for nerve-specific proteins, and genes 3 and 5 are skin specific. Which activators would have to be present in each cell type to ensure transcription of the appropriate genes?

12. **EVOLUTION CONNECTION**
    DNA sequences can act as "tape measures of evolution" (see Chapter 5). Scientists analyzing the human genome sequence were surprised to find that some of the regions of the human genome that are most highly conserved (similar to comparable regions in other species) don't code for proteins. Propose a possible explanation for this observation.

13. **SCIENTIFIC INQUIRY**
    Prostate cells usually require testosterone and other androgens to survive. But some prostate cancer cells thrive despite treatments that eliminate androgens. One hypothesis is that estrogen, often considered a female hormone, may be activating genes normally controlled by an androgen in these cancer cells. Describe one or more experiments to test this hypothesis. (See Figure 11.9 to review the action of these steroid hormones.)

14. **SCIENCE, TECHNOLOGY, AND SOCIETY**
    Trace amounts of dioxin were present in Agent Orange, a defoliant sprayed on vegetation during the Vietnam War. Animal tests suggest that dioxin can cause birth defects, cancer, liver and thymus damage, and immune system suppression, sometimes leading to death. But the animal tests are equivocal; a hamster is not affected by a dose that can kill a guinea pig. Dioxin acts like a steroid hormone, entering a cell and binding to a cytoplasmic receptor that then binds the cell's DNA. How might this mechanism help explain the variety of dioxin's effects on different body systems and in different animals? How might you determine whether a type of illness is related to dioxin exposure? How might you determine whether a particular individual became ill as a result of exposure to dioxin? Which would be more difficult to demonstrate? Why?

15. **WRITE ABOUT A THEME: INTERACTIONS**
    In a short essay (100–150 words), discuss how the processes shown in Figure 18.2 are examples of feedback mechanisms regulating biological systems in bacterial cells.

16. **SYNTHESIZE YOUR KNOWLEDGE**

The flashlight fish has an organ under its eye that emits light, which serves to startle predators and attract prey, and allows the fish to communicate with other fish. Some species can rotate the organ inside and then out, so the light appears to flash on and off. The light is not actually emitted by the fish itself, however, but by bacteria that live in the organ in a mutualistic relationship with the fish. (While providing light for the fish, the bacteria receive nutrients from the fish and in fact are unable to survive anywhere else.) The bacteria must multiply until they reach a certain density in the organ (a "quorum"; see Concept 11.1), at which point they all begin emitting light at the same time. There is a group of six or so genes, called *lux* genes, whose gene products are necessary for light formation. Given that these bacterial genes are regulated together, propose a hypothesis for how the genes are organized and regulated.

For selected answers, see Appendix A.

MasteringBiology®

19

Viruses

▲ Figure 19.1 **Are the viruses (red) budding from this cell alive?**

A Borrowed Life

The image in **Figure 19.1** shows a remarkable event: On the left is a human immune cell under siege, releasing scores more of its invaders, which will go on to infect other cells. The attackers (red) are human immunodeficiency viruses (HIV). (The same scenario is shown in the micrograph at the lower left.) By injecting its genetic information into a cell, a single virus hijacks a cell, recruiting cellular machinery to manufacture many new viruses and promote further infection. Left untreated, HIV causes acquired immunodeficiency syndrome (AIDS) by destroying vital immune system cells.

Compared to eukaryotic and even prokaryotic cells, viruses are much smaller and simpler in structure. Lacking the structures and metabolic machinery found in a cell, a **virus** is an infectious particle consisting of little more than genes packaged in a protein coat.

Are viruses living or nonliving? Because viruses are capable of causing many diseases, researchers in the late 1800s saw a parallel with bacteria and proposed that viruses were the simplest of living forms. However, viruses cannot reproduce or carry out metabolism outside of a host cell. Most biologists studying viruses today would likely agree that they are not alive but exist in a shady area between life-forms and chemicals. The simple phrase used recently by two researchers describes them aptly enough: Viruses lead "a kind of borrowed life."

To a large extent, molecular biology was born in the laboratories of biologists studying viruses that infect bacteria. Experiments with these viruses provided evidence that genes are made of nucleic acids, and they were critical in working out the molecular mechanisms of the fundamental processes of DNA replication, transcription, and translation.

Beyond their value as experimental systems, viruses have unique genetic mechanisms that are interesting in their own right and that also help us understand how viruses cause disease. In addition, the study of viruses has led to the development of techniques that enable scientists to manipulate genes and transfer them from one organism to another. These techniques play an important role in basic research, biotechnology, and medical applications. For instance, viruses are used as agents of gene transfer in gene therapy (see Concept 20.4).

In this chapter, we will explore the biology of viruses, beginning with their structure and then describing how they replicate. Next, we will discuss the role of viruses as disease-causing agents, or pathogens, and conclude by considering some even simpler infectious agents called viroids and prions.

CONCEPT 19.1

A virus consists of a nucleic acid surrounded by a protein coat

Scientists were able to detect viruses indirectly long before they were actually able to see them. The story of how viruses were discovered begins near the end of the 19th century.

The Discovery of Viruses: *Scientific Inquiry*

Tobacco mosaic disease stunts the growth of tobacco plants and gives their leaves a mottled, or mosaic, coloration. In 1883, Adolf Mayer, a German scientist, discovered that he could transmit the disease from plant to plant by rubbing sap extracted from diseased leaves onto healthy plants. After an unsuccessful search for an infectious microbe in the sap, Mayer suggested that the disease was caused by unusually small bacteria that were invisible under a microscope. This hypothesis was tested a decade later by Dimitri Ivanowsky, a Russian biologist who passed sap from infected tobacco leaves through a filter designed to remove bacteria. After filtration, the sap still produced mosaic disease.

But Ivanowsky clung to the hypothesis that bacteria caused tobacco mosaic disease. Perhaps, he reasoned, the bacteria were small enough to pass through the filter or made a toxin that could do so. The second possibility was ruled out when the Dutch botanist Martinus Beijerinck carried out a classic series of experiments that showed that the infectious agent in the filtered sap could replicate (**Figure 19.2**).

In fact, the pathogen replicated only within the host it infected. In further experiments, Beijerinck showed that unlike

▼ **Figure 19.2** | Inquiry

What causes tobacco mosaic disease?

Experiment In the late 1800s, Martinus Beijerinck, of the Technical School in Delft, the Netherlands, investigated the properties of the agent that causes tobacco mosaic disease (then called spot disease).

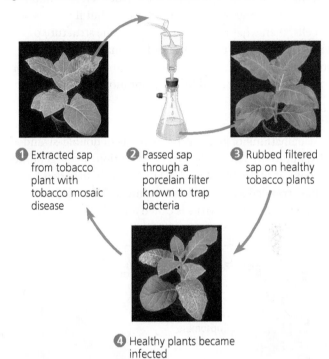

❶ Extracted sap from tobacco plant with tobacco mosaic disease

❷ Passed sap through a porcelain filter known to trap bacteria

❸ Rubbed filtered sap on healthy tobacco plants

❹ Healthy plants became infected

Results When the filtered sap was rubbed on healthy plants, they became infected. Their sap, extracted and filtered, could then act as a source of infection for another group of plants. Each successive group of plants developed the disease to the same extent as earlier groups.

Conclusion The infectious agent was apparently not a bacterium because it could pass through a bacterium-trapping filter. The pathogen must have been replicating in the plants because its ability to cause disease was undiluted after several transfers from plant to plant.

Source: M. J. Beijerinck, Concerning a contagium vivum fluidum *as cause of the spot disease of tobacco leaves,* Verhandelingen der Koninkyke akademie Wettenschappen te Amsterdam *65:3–21 (1898). Translation published in English as Phytopathological Classics Number 7 (1942), American Phytopathological Society Press, St. Paul, MN.*

WHAT IF? *If Beijerinck had observed that the infection of each group was weaker than that of the previous group and that ultimately the sap could no longer cause disease, what might he have concluded?*

bacteria used in the lab at that time, the mysterious agent of mosaic disease could not be cultivated on nutrient media in test tubes or petri dishes. Beijerinck imagined a replicating particle much smaller and simpler than a bacterium, and he is generally credited with being the first scientist to voice the concept of a virus. His suspicions were confirmed in 1935 when the American scientist Wendell Stanley crystallized the infectious particle, now known as tobacco mosaic virus (TMV). Subsequently, TMV and many other viruses were actually seen with the help of the electron microscope.

Structure of Viruses

The tiniest viruses are only 20 nm in diameter—smaller than a ribosome. Millions could easily fit on a pinhead. Even the largest known virus, which has a diameter of several hundred nanometers, is barely visible under the light microscope. Stanley's discovery that some viruses could be crystallized was exciting and puzzling news. Not even the simplest of cells can aggregate into regular crystals. But if viruses are not cells, then what are they? Examining the structure of a virus more closely reveals that it is an infectious particle consisting of nucleic acid enclosed in a protein coat and, for some viruses, surrounded by a membranous envelope.

Viral Genomes

We usually think of genes as being made of double-stranded DNA, but many viruses defy this convention. Their genomes may consist of double-stranded DNA, single-stranded DNA, double-stranded RNA, or single-stranded RNA, depending on the type of virus. A virus is called a DNA virus or an RNA virus, based on the kind of nucleic acid that makes up its genome. In either case, the genome is usually organized as a single linear or circular molecule of nucleic acid, although the genomes of some viruses consist of multiple molecules of nucleic acid. The smallest viruses known have only three genes in their genome, while the largest have several hundred to a thousand. For comparison, bacterial genomes contain about 200 to a few thousand genes.

Capsids and Envelopes

The protein shell enclosing the viral genome is called a **capsid**. Depending on the type of virus, the capsid may be rod-shaped, polyhedral, or more complex in shape. Capsids are built from a large number of protein subunits called *capsomeres*, but the number of different *kinds* of proteins in a capsid is usually small. Tobacco mosaic virus has a rigid, rod-shaped capsid made from over a thousand molecules of a single type of protein arranged in a helix; rod-shaped viruses are commonly called *helical viruses* for this reason **(Figure 19.3a)**. Adenoviruses, which infect the respiratory

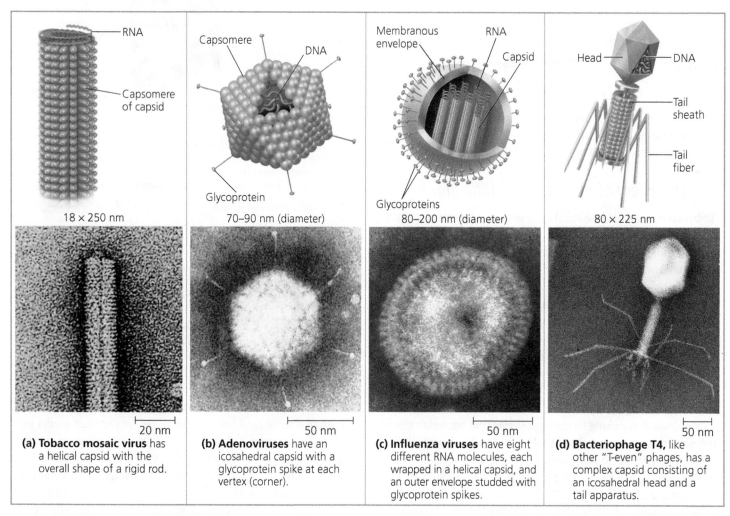

18 × 250 nm

20 nm

(a) Tobacco mosaic virus has a helical capsid with the overall shape of a rigid rod.

70–90 nm (diameter)

50 nm

(b) Adenoviruses have an icosahedral capsid with a glycoprotein spike at each vertex (corner).

80–200 nm (diameter)

50 nm

(c) Influenza viruses have eight different RNA molecules, each wrapped in a helical capsid, and an outer envelope studded with glycoprotein spikes.

80 × 225 nm

50 nm

(d) Bacteriophage T4, like other "T-even" phages, has a complex capsid consisting of an icosahedral head and a tail apparatus.

▲ **Figure 19.3 Viral structure.** Viruses are made up of nucleic acid (DNA or RNA) enclosed in a protein coat (the capsid) and sometimes further wrapped in a membranous envelope. The individual protein subunits making up the capsid are called capsomeres. Although diverse in size and shape, viruses have many common structural features. (All micrographs are colorized TEMs.)

tracts of animals, have 252 identical protein molecules arranged in a polyhedral capsid with 20 triangular facets—an icosahedron; thus, these and other similarly shaped viruses are referred to as *icosahedral viruses* (Figure 19.3b).

Some viruses have accessory structures that help them infect their hosts. For instance, a membranous envelope surrounds the capsids of influenza viruses and many other viruses found in animals (Figure 19.3c). These **viral envelopes**, which are derived from the membranes of the host cell, contain host cell phospholipids and membrane proteins. They also contain proteins and glycoproteins of viral origin. (Glycoproteins are proteins with carbohydrates covalently attached.) Some viruses carry a few viral enzyme molecules within their capsids.

Many of the most complex capsids are found among the viruses that infect bacteria, called **bacteriophages**, or simply **phages**. The first phages studied included seven that infect *Escherichia coli*. These seven phages were named type 1 (T1), type 2 (T2), and so forth, in the order of their discovery. The three T-even phages (T2, T4, and T6) turned out to be very similar in structure. Their capsids have elongated icosahedral heads enclosing their DNA. Attached to the head is a protein tail piece with fibers by which the phages attach to a bacterial cell (Figure 19.3d). In the next section, we'll examine how these few viral parts function together with cellular components to produce large numbers of viral progeny.

CONCEPT CHECK 19.1

1. Compare the structures of tobacco mosaic virus (TMV) and influenza virus (see Figure 19.3).
2. MAKE CONNECTIONS Bacteriophages were used to provide evidence that DNA carries genetic information (see Figure 16.4). Briefly describe the experiment carried out by Hershey and Chase, including in your description why the researchers chose to use phages.

For suggested answers, see Appendix A.

CONCEPT 19.2

Viruses replicate only in host cells

Viruses lack metabolic enzymes and equipment for making proteins, such as ribosomes. They are obligate intracellular parasites; in other words, they can replicate only within a host cell. It is fair to say that viruses in isolation are merely packaged sets of genes in transit from one host cell to another.

Each particular virus can infect cells of only a limited number of host species, called the **host range** of the virus. This host specificity results from the evolution of recognition systems by the virus. Viruses usually identify host cells by a "lock-and-key" fit between viral surface proteins and specific receptor molecules on the outside of cells. (According to one model, such receptor molecules originally carried out functions that benefited the host cell but were co-opted later by

viruses as portals of entry.) Some viruses have broad host ranges. For example, West Nile virus and equine encephalitis virus are distinctly different viruses that can each infect mosquitoes, birds, horses, and humans. Other viruses have host ranges so narrow that they infect only a single species. Measles virus, for instance, can infect only humans. Furthermore, viral infection of multicellular eukaryotes is usually limited to particular tissues. Human cold viruses infect only the cells lining the upper respiratory tract, and the AIDS virus binds to receptors present only on certain types of immune system cells.

General Features of Viral Replicative Cycles

A viral infection begins when a virus binds to a host cell and the viral genome makes its way inside (Figure 19.4). The

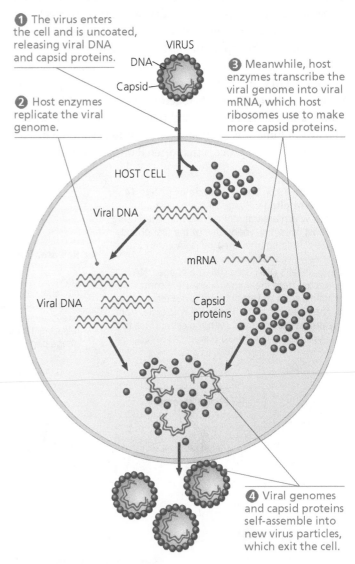

1. The virus enters the cell and is uncoated, releasing viral DNA and capsid proteins.

2. Host enzymes replicate the viral genome.

3. Meanwhile, host enzymes transcribe the viral genome into viral mRNA, which host ribosomes use to make more capsid proteins.

4. Viral genomes and capsid proteins self-assemble into new virus particles, which exit the cell.

▲ Figure 19.4 **A simplified viral replicative cycle.** A virus is an intracellular parasite that uses the equipment and small molecules of its host cell to replicate. In this simplest of viral cycles, the parasite is a DNA virus with a capsid consisting of a single type of protein.

DRAW IT *Label each of the straight black arrows with one word representing the name of the process that is occurring. Review Figure 17.24.*

mechanism of genome entry depends on the type of virus and the type of host cell. For example, T-even phages use their elaborate tail apparatus to inject DNA into a bacterium (see Figure 19.3d). Other viruses are taken up by endocytosis or, in the case of enveloped viruses, by fusion of the viral envelope with the host's plasma membrane. Once the viral genome is inside, the proteins it encodes can commandeer the host, reprogramming the cell to copy the viral genome and manufacture viral proteins. The host provides the nucleotides for making viral nucleic acids, as well as enzymes, ribosomes, tRNAs, amino acids, ATP, and other components needed for making the viral proteins. Many DNA viruses use the DNA polymerases of the host cell to synthesize new genomes along the templates provided by the viral DNA. In contrast, to replicate their genomes, RNA viruses use virally encoded RNA polymerases that can use RNA as a template. (Uninfected cells generally make no enzymes for carrying out this process.)

After the viral nucleic acid molecules and capsomeres are produced, they spontaneously self-assemble into new viruses. In fact, researchers can separate the RNA and capsomeres of TMV and then reassemble complete viruses simply by mixing the components together under the right conditions. The simplest type of viral replicative cycle ends with the exit of hundreds or thousands of viruses from the infected host cell, a process that often damages or destroys the cell. Such cellular damage and death, as well as the body's responses to this destruction, cause many of the symptoms associated with viral infections. The viral progeny that exit a cell have the potential to infect additional cells, spreading the viral infection.

There are many variations on the simplified viral replicative cycle we have just described. We will now take a look at some of these variations in bacterial viruses (phages) and animal viruses; later in the chapter, we will consider plant viruses.

Replicative Cycles of Phages

Phages are the best understood of all viruses, although some of them are also among the most complex. Research on phages led to the discovery that some double-stranded DNA viruses can replicate by two alternative mechanisms: the lytic cycle and the lysogenic cycle.

The Lytic Cycle

A phage replicative cycle that culminates in death of the host cell is known as a **lytic cycle** (**Figure 19.5**). The term refers to the last stage of infection, during which the bacterium lyses (breaks open) and releases the phages that were produced within the cell. Each of these phages can then infect a healthy cell, and a few successive lytic cycles can destroy an entire

▶ **Figure 19.5 The lytic cycle of phage T4, a virulent phage.** Phage T4 has almost 300 genes, which are transcribed and translated using the host cell's machinery. One of the first phage genes translated after the viral DNA enters the host cell codes for an enzyme that degrades the host cell's DNA (step ❷); the phage DNA is protected from breakdown because it contains a modified form of cytosine that is not recognized by the phage enzyme. The entire lytic cycle, from the phage's first contact with the cell surface to cell lysis, takes only 20–30 minutes at 37°C.

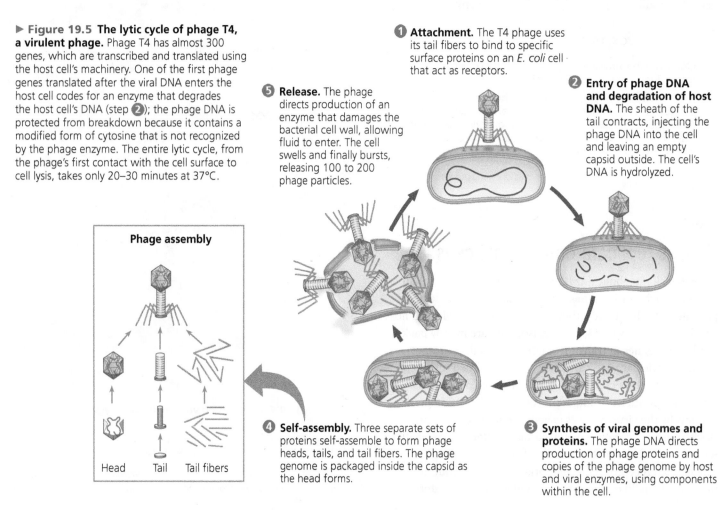

❶ **Attachment.** The T4 phage uses its tail fibers to bind to specific surface proteins on an *E. coli* cell that act as receptors.

❷ **Entry of phage DNA and degradation of host DNA.** The sheath of the tail contracts, injecting the phage DNA into the cell and leaving an empty capsid outside. The cell's DNA is hydrolyzed.

❸ **Synthesis of viral genomes and proteins.** The phage DNA directs production of phage proteins and copies of the phage genome by host and viral enzymes, using components within the cell.

❹ **Self-assembly.** Three separate sets of proteins self-assemble to form phage heads, tails, and tail fibers. The phage genome is packaged inside the capsid as the head forms.

❺ **Release.** The phage directs production of an enzyme that damages the bacterial cell wall, allowing fluid to enter. The cell swells and finally bursts, releasing 100 to 200 phage particles.

Phage assembly

Head Tail Tail fibers

bacterial population in just a few hours. A phage that replicates only by a lytic cycle is a **virulent phage**. Figure 19.5 illustrates the major steps in the lytic cycle of T4, a typical virulent phage. Study this figure before proceeding.

After reading about the lytic cycle, you may wonder why phages haven't exterminated all bacteria. The reason is that bacteria have their own defenses. First, natural selection favors bacterial mutants with surface proteins that are no longer recognized as receptors by a particular type of phage. Second, when phage DNA does enter a bacterium, the DNA often is identified as foreign and cut up by cellular enzymes called **restriction enzymes**, which are so named because their activity *restricts* the ability of the phage to replicate within the bacterium. The bacterial cell's own DNA is methylated in a way that prevents attack by its own restriction enzymes. But just as natural selection favors bacteria with receptors altered by mutation or efficient restriction enzymes, it also favors phage mutants that can bind the altered receptors or are resistant to particular restriction enzymes. Thus, the parasite-host relationship is in constant evolutionary flux.

There is yet a third important reason bacteria have been spared from extinction as a result of phage activity. Instead of lysing their host cells, many phages coexist with them in a state called lysogeny, which we'll now discuss.

The Lysogenic Cycle

In contrast to the lytic cycle, which kills the host cell, the **lysogenic cycle** allows replication of the phage genome without destroying the host. Phages capable of using both modes of replicating within a bacterium are called **temperate phages**. A temperate phage called lambda, written with the Greek letter λ, has been widely used in biological research. Phage λ resembles T4, but its tail has only one short tail fiber.

Infection of an *E. coli* cell by phage λ begins when the phage binds to the surface of the cell and injects its linear DNA genome (Figure 19.6). Within the host, the λ DNA molecule forms a circle. What happens next depends on the replicative mode: lytic cycle or lysogenic cycle. During a lytic cycle, the viral genes immediately turn the host cell into a λ-producing factory, and the cell soon lyses and releases its virus progeny. During a lysogenic cycle, however, the λ DNA molecule is incorporated into a specific site on the *E. coli* chromosome by viral proteins that break both circular DNA molecules and join them to each other. When integrated into the bacterial chromosome in this way, the viral DNA is known as a **prophage**. One prophage gene codes for a protein that prevents transcription of most of the other prophage genes. Thus, the phage genome is mostly silent

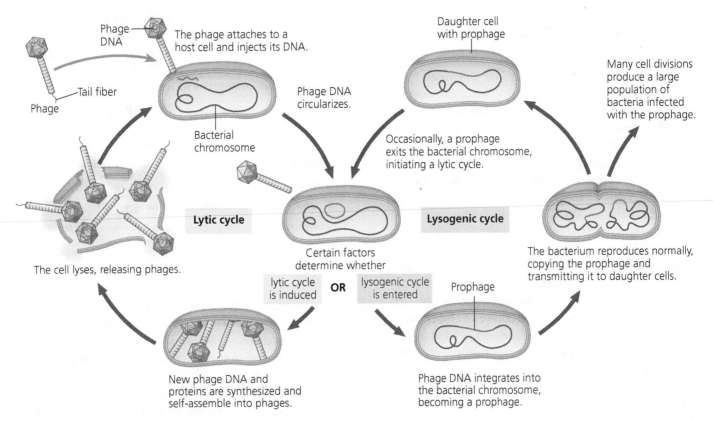

▲ **Figure 19.6 The lytic and lysogenic cycles of phage λ, a temperate phage.** After entering the bacterial cell and circularizing, the λ DNA can immediately initiate the production of a large number of progeny phages (lytic cycle) or integrate into the bacterial chromosome (lysogenic cycle). In most cases, phage λ follows the lytic pathway, which is similar to that detailed in Figure 19.5. However, once a lysogenic cycle begins, the prophage may be carried in the host cell's chromosome for many generations. Phage λ has one main tail fiber, which is short.

within the bacterium. Every time the *E. coli* cell prepares to divide, it replicates the phage DNA along with its own chromosome such that each daughter cell inherits a prophage. A single infected cell can quickly give rise to a large population of bacteria carrying the virus in prophage form. This mechanism enables viruses to propagate without killing the host cells on which they depend.

The term *lysogenic* signifiies that prophages are capable of generating active phages that lyse their host cells. This occurs when the λ genome (or that of another temperate phage) is induced to exit the bacterial chromosome and initiate a lytic cycle. An environmental signal, such as a certain chemical or high-energy radiation, usually triggers the switchover from the lysogenic to the lytic mode.

In addition to the gene for the viral protein that prevents transcription, a few other prophage genes may be expressed during lysogeny. Expression of these genes may alter the host's phenotype, a phenomenon that can have important medical significance. For example, the three species of bacteria that cause the human diseases diphtheria, botulism, and scarlet fever would not be so harmful to humans without certain prophage genes that cause the host bacteria to make toxins. And the difference between the *E. coli* strain in our intestines and the O157:H7 strain that has caused several deaths by food poisoning appears to be the presence of toxin genes of prophages in the O157:H7 strain.

Replicative Cycles of Animal Viruses

Everyone has suffered from viral infections, whether cold sores, influenza, or the common cold. Like all viruses, those that cause illness in humans and other animals can replicate only inside host cells. Many variations on the basic scheme of viral infection and replication are represented among the animal viruses. One key variable is the nature of the viral genome (double- or single-stranded DNA or RNA), which is the basis for the common classification of viruses shown in **Table 19.1**. Single-stranded RNA viruses are further classified into three classes (IV–VI) according to how the RNA genome functions in a host cell.

Whereas few bacteriophages have an envelope or RNA genome, many animal viruses have both. In fact, nearly all animal viruses with RNA genomes have an envelope, as do some with DNA genomes (see Table 19.1). Rather than consider all the mechanisms of viral infection and replication, we will focus first on the roles of viral envelopes and then on the functioning of RNA as the genetic material of many animal viruses.

Viral Envelopes

An animal virus equipped with an envelope—that is, an outer membrane—uses it to enter the host cell. Protruding from the outer surface of this envelope are viral

Table 19.1   Classes of Animal Viruses

Class/Family	Envelope?	Examples That Cause Human Diseases
I. Double-Stranded DNA (dsDNA)		
Adenovirus (see Figure 19.3b)	No	Respiratory viruses; tumor-causing viruses
Papillomavirus	No	Warts, cervical cancer
Polyomavirus	No	Tumors
Herpesvirus	Yes	Herpes simplex I and II (cold sores, genital sores); varicella zoster (shingles, chicken pox); Epstein-Barr virus (mononucleosis, Burkitt's lymphoma)
Poxvirus	Yes	Smallpox virus; cowpox virus
II. Single-Stranded DNA (ssDNA)		
Parvovirus	No	B19 parvovirus (mild rash)
III. Double-Stranded RNA (dsRNA)		
Reovirus	No	Rotavirus (diarrhea); Colorado tick fever virus
IV. Single-Stranded RNA (ssRNA); Serves as mRNA		
Picornavirus	No	Rhinovirus (common cold); poliovirus; hepatitis A virus; other intestinal viruses
Coronavirus	Yes	Severe acute respiratory syndrome (SARS)
Flavivirus	Yes	Yellow fever virus; West Nile virus; hepatitis C virus
Togavirus	Yes	Rubella virus; equine encephalitis viruses
V. ssRNA; Serves as Template for mRNA Synthesis		
Filovirus	Yes	Ebola virus (hemorrhagic fever)
Orthomyxovirus	Yes	Influenza virus (see Figures 19.3c and 19.9a)
Paramyxovirus	Yes	Measles virus; mumps virus
Rhabdovirus	Yes	Rabies virus
VI. ssRNA; Serves as Template for DNA Synthesis		
Retrovirus	Yes	Human immunodeficiency virus (HIV/AIDS; see Figure 19.8); RNA tumor viruses (leukemia)

glycoproteins that bind to specific receptor molecules on the surface of a host cell. **Figure 19.7** outlines the events in the replicative cycle of an enveloped virus with an RNA genome. Ribosomes bound to the endoplasmic reticulum (ER) of the host cell make the protein parts of the envelope glycoproteins; cellular enzymes in the ER and Golgi apparatus then add the sugars. The resulting viral glycoproteins, embedded in membrane derived from the host cell, are transported to the cell surface. In a process much like exocytosis, new viral capsids are wrapped in membrane as they bud from the cell.

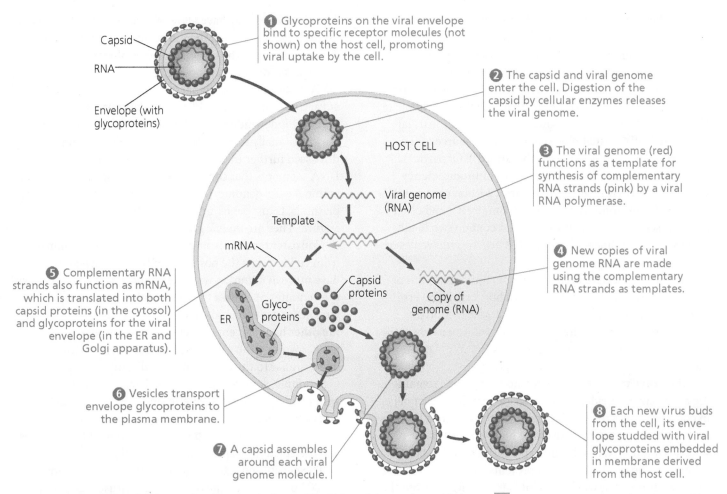

Capsid

RNA

Envelope (with glycoproteins)

1 Glycoproteins on the viral envelope bind to specific receptor molecules (not shown) on the host cell, promoting viral uptake by the cell.

2 The capsid and viral genome enter the cell. Digestion of the capsid by cellular enzymes releases the viral genome.

HOST CELL

Viral genome (RNA)

Template

mRNA

3 The viral genome (red) functions as a template for synthesis of complementary RNA strands (pink) by a viral RNA polymerase.

5 Complementary RNA strands also function as mRNA, which is translated into both capsid proteins (in the cytosol) and glycoproteins for the viral envelope (in the ER and Golgi apparatus).

Capsid proteins

Glyco-proteins

Copy of genome (RNA)

4 New copies of viral genome RNA are made using the complementary RNA strands as templates.

ER

6 Vesicles transport envelope glycoproteins to the plasma membrane.

7 A capsid assembles around each viral genome molecule.

8 Each new virus buds from the cell, its enve-lope studded with viral glycoproteins embedded in membrane derived from the host cell.

▲ **Figure 19.7 The replicative cycle of an enveloped RNA virus.** Shown here is a virus with a single-stranded RNA genome that functions as a template for synthesis of mRNA (class V of Table 19.1). Some enveloped viruses enter the host cell by fusion of the envelope with the cell's plasma membrane; others enter by endo-cytosis. For all enveloped RNA viruses, formation of new envelopes for progeny viruses occurs by the mechanism depicted in this figure.

? *Name a virus that has infected you and has a replicative cycle matching this one. (Hint: See Table 19.1.)*

In other words, the viral envelope is usually derived from the host cell's plasma membrane, although all or most of the molecules of this membrane are specified by viral genes. The enveloped viruses are now free to infect other cells. This replicative cycle does not necessarily kill the host cell, in contrast to the lytic cycles of phages.

Some viruses have envelopes that are not derived from plasma membrane. Herpesviruses, for example, are tem-porarily cloaked in membrane derived from the nuclear envelope of the host; they then shed this membrane in the cytoplasm and acquire a new envelope made from mem-brane of the Golgi apparatus. These viruses have a double-stranded DNA genome and replicate within the host cell nucleus, using a combination of viral and cellular enzymes to replicate and transcribe their DNA. In the case of herpes-viruses, copies of the viral DNA can remain behind as mini-chromosomes in the nuclei of certain nerve cells. There they remain latent until some sort of physical or emotional stress triggers a new round of active virus production. The infec-tion of other cells by these new viruses causes the blisters

characteristic of herpes, such as cold sores or genital sores. Once someone acquires a herpesvirus infection, flare-ups may recur throughout the person's life.

RNA as Viral Genetic Material

Although some phages and most plant viruses are RNA vi-ruses, the broadest variety of RNA genomes is found among the viruses that infect animals. There are three types of single-stranded RNA genomes found in animal viruses. The genome of class IV viruses can directly serve as mRNA and thus can be translated into viral protein immediately after infection. Figure 19.7 shows a virus of class V, in which the RNA genome serves instead as a *template* for mRNA syn-thesis. The RNA genome is transcribed into complemen-tary RNA strands, which function both as mRNA and as templates for the synthesis of additional copies of genomic RNA. All viruses that use an RNA genome as a template for mRNA transcription require RNA → RNA synthesis. These viruses use a viral enzyme capable of carrying out this pro-cess; there are no such enzymes in most cells. The enzyme used in this process is packaged during viral self-assembly with the genome inside the viral capsid.

The RNA animal viruses with the most complicated replicative cycles are the **retroviruses** (class VI). These viruses are equipped with an enzyme called **reverse transcriptase**, which transcribes an RNA template into DNA, providing an RNA → DNA information flow, the opposite of the usual direction. This unusual phenomenon is the source of the name retroviruses (*retro* means "backward"). Of particular medical importance is **HIV (human immunodeficiency virus)**, the retrovirus shown in Figure 19.1 that causes **AIDS (acquired immunodeficiency syndrome)**. HIV and other retroviruses are enveloped viruses that contain two identical molecules of single-stranded RNA and two molecules of reverse transcriptase.

The HIV replicative cycle (traced in **Figure 19.8**) is typical of a retrovirus. After HIV enters a host cell, its reverse transcriptase molecules are released into the cytoplasm, where they catalyze synthesis of viral DNA. The newly made viral DNA then enters the cell's nucleus and integrates into the DNA of a chromosome. The integrated viral DNA, called a **provirus**, never leaves the host's genome, remaining a permanent resident of the cell. (Recall that a prophage, in contrast, leaves the host's genome at the start of a lytic cycle.) The RNA polymerase of the host transcribes the proviral DNA into RNA molecules, which can function both as mRNA for the synthesis of viral proteins and as genomes for the new viruses that will be assembled and released from the cell. In Chapter 43, we describe how HIV causes the deterioration of the immune system that occurs in AIDS.

Evolution of Viruses

EVOLUTION We began this chapter by asking whether or not viruses are alive. Viruses do not really fit our definition of living organisms. An isolated virus is biologically inert, unable to replicate its genes or regenerate its own ATP. Yet it has a genetic program written in the universal language of life. Do we think of viruses as nature's most complex associations of molecules or as the simplest forms of life? Either way, we must bend our usual definitions. Although viruses cannot replicate or carry out metabolic activities independently, their use of the genetic code makes it hard to deny their evolutionary connection to the living world.

How did viruses originate? Viruses have been found that infect every form of life—not just bacteria, animals, and plants, but also archaea, fungi, and algae and other protists. Because they depend on cells for their own propagation, it seems likely that viruses are not the descendants of precellular forms of life but evolved—possibly multiple times—*after* the first cells appeared. Most molecular biologists favor the hypothesis that viruses originated from naked bits of cellular nucleic acids that moved from one cell to another, perhaps via injured cell surfaces. The evolution of genes coding for capsid proteins may have allowed viruses to bind cell membranes, thus facilitating the infection of uninjured cells.

Candidates for the original sources of viral genomes include plasmids and transposons. *Plasmids* are small, circular DNA molecules found in bacteria and in the unicellular eukaryotes called yeasts. Plasmids exist apart from and can replicate independently of the bacterial chromosome, and are occasionally transferred between cells; plasmids are discussed further in Chapters 20 and 27. *Transposons* are DNA segments that can move from one location to another within a cell's genome, to be detailed in Chapter 21. Thus, plasmids, transposons, and viruses all share an important feature: They are *mobile genetic elements*.

Consistent with this notion of pieces of DNA shuttling from cell to cell is the observation that a viral genome can have more in common with the genome of its host than with the genomes of viruses that infect other hosts. Indeed, some viral genes are essentially identical to genes of the host. On the other hand, recent sequencing of many viral genomes has shown that the genetic sequences of some viruses are quite similar to those of seemingly distantly related viruses; for example, some animal viruses share similar sequences with plant viruses. This genetic similarity may reflect the persistence of groups of viral genes that were favored by natural selection during the early evolution of both viruses and the eukaryotic cells that served as their hosts.

The debate about the origin of viruses was reinvigorated in 2003 by reports of one of the largest viruses yet discovered: Mimivirus is a double-stranded DNA (dsDNA) virus with an icosahedral capsid that is 400 nm in diameter, the size of a small bacterium. Its genome contains 1.2 million bases (Mb)—about 100 times as many as the influenza virus genome—and an estimated 1,000 genes. Perhaps the most surprising aspect of mimivirus, however, was that its genome included genes previously found only in cellular genomes. Some of these genes code for proteins involved in translation, DNA repair, protein folding, and polysaccharide synthesis. Whether mimivirus evolved *before* the first cells and then developed an exploitative relationship with them, or evolved more recently and simply scavenged genes from its hosts is not yet settled. In 2013 an even larger virus was discovered that cannot be classified with any existing known virus. This virus is 1 μm (1,000 nm) in diameter, with a dsDNA genome of around 2–2.5 Mb, larger than that of some small eukaryotes. What's more, over 90% of its 2,000 or so genes are unrelated to cellular genes, inspiring the naming of this virus as pandoravirus. How these and all other viruses fit in the tree of life is an intriguing, unresolved question.

The ongoing evolutionary relationship between viruses and the genomes of their host cells is an association that continues to make viruses very useful experimental systems in molecular biology. Knowledge about viruses also allows many practical applications, since viruses have a tremendous impact on all organisms through their ability to cause disease.

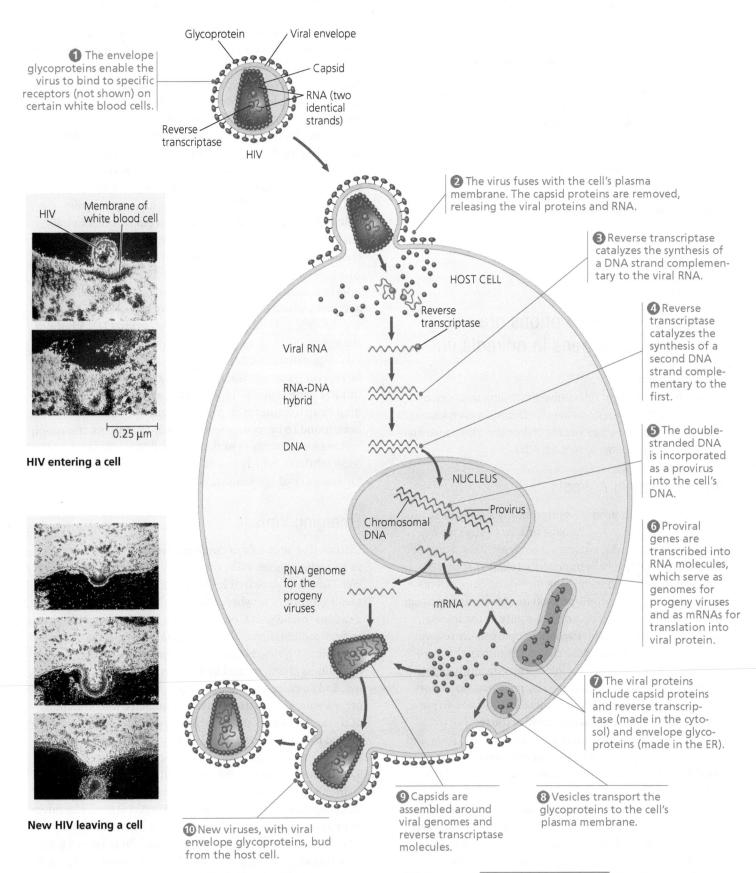

1 The envelope glycoproteins enable the virus to bind to specific receptors (not shown) on certain white blood cells.

Glycoprotein   Viral envelope

Capsid

RNA (two identical strands)

Reverse transcriptase

HIV

2 The virus fuses with the cell's plasma membrane. The capsid proteins are removed, releasing the viral proteins and RNA.

3 Reverse transcriptase catalyzes the synthesis of a DNA strand complementary to the viral RNA.

4 Reverse transcriptase catalyzes the synthesis of a second DNA strand complementary to the first.

5 The double-stranded DNA is incorporated as a provirus into the cell's DNA.

6 Proviral genes are transcribed into RNA molecules, which serve as genomes for progeny viruses and as mRNAs for translation into viral protein.

7 The viral proteins include capsid proteins and reverse transcriptase (made in the cytosol) and envelope glycoproteins (made in the ER).

8 Vesicles transport the glycoproteins to the cell's plasma membrane.

9 Capsids are assembled around viral genomes and reverse transcriptase molecules.

10 New viruses, with viral envelope glycoproteins, bud from the host cell.

HOST CELL

Reverse transcriptase

Viral RNA

RNA-DNA hybrid

DNA

NUCLEUS

Provirus

Chromosomal DNA

RNA genome for the progeny viruses

mRNA

HIV
Membrane of white blood cell

0.25 μm

HIV entering a cell

New HIV leaving a cell

▲ **Figure 19.8 The replicative cycle of HIV, the retrovirus that causes AIDS.** Note in step **5** that DNA synthesized from the viral RNA genome is integrated as a provirus into the host cell chromosomal DNA, a characteristic unique to retroviruses. For simplicity, the cell-surface proteins that act as receptors for HIV are not shown. The photos on the left (artificially colored TEMs) show HIV entering and leaving a human white blood cell.

MAKE CONNECTIONS *Describe what is known about binding of HIV to immune system cells. (See Figure 7.8.) How was this discovered?*

1. Compare the effect on the host cell of a lytic (virulent) phage and a lysogenic (temperate) phage.

2. MAKE CONNECTIONS The RNA virus in Figure 19.7 has a viral RNA polymerase that functions in step 3 of the virus's replicative cycle. Compare this with a cellular RNA polymerase in terms of template and overall function (see Figure 17.9).

3. Why is HIV called a retrovirus?

4. WHAT IF? If you were a researcher trying to combat HIV infection, what molecular processes could you attempt to block? (See Figure 19.8.)

For suggested answers, see Appendix A.

CONCEPT 19.3

Viruses, viroids, and prions are formidable pathogens in animals and plants

Diseases caused by viral infections afflict humans, agricultural crops, and livestock worldwide. Other smaller, less complex entities known as viroids and prions also cause disease in plants and animals, respectively.

Viral Diseases in Animals

A viral infection can produce symptoms by a number of different routes. Viruses may damage or kill cells by causing the release of hydrolytic enzymes from lysosomes. Some viruses cause infected cells to produce toxins that lead to disease symptoms, and some have molecular components that are toxic, such as envelope proteins. How much damage a virus causes depends partly on the ability of the infected tissue to regenerate by cell division. People usually recover completely from colds because the epithelium of the respiratory tract, which the viruses infect, can efficiently repair itself. In contrast, damage inflicted by poliovirus to mature nerve cells is permanent because these cells do not divide and usually cannot be replaced. Many of the temporary symptoms associated with viral infections, such as fever and body aches, actually result from the body's own efforts to defend itself against infection rather than from cell death caused by the virus.

The immune system is a complex and critical part of the body's natural defenses (see Chapter 43). It is also the basis for the major medical tool for preventing viral infections—vaccines. A **vaccine** is a harmless variant or derivative of a pathogen that stimulates the immune system to mount defenses against the harmful pathogen. Smallpox, a viral disease that was at one time a devastating scourge in many parts of the world, was eradicated by a vaccination program carried out by the World Health Organization (WHO). The very narrow host range of the smallpox virus—it infects only humans—was a critical factor in the success of this program. Similar worldwide vaccination campaigns are currently under way to eradicate polio and measles. Effective vaccines are also available to protect against rubella, mumps, hepatitis B, and a number of other viral diseases.

Although vaccines can prevent certain viral illnesses, medical technology can do little, at present, to cure most viral infections once they occur. The antibiotics that help us recover from bacterial infections are powerless against viruses. Antibiotics kill bacteria by inhibiting enzymes specific to bacteria but have no effect on eukaryotic or virally encoded enzymes. However, the few enzymes that are encoded only by viruses have provided targets for other drugs. Most antiviral drugs resemble nucleosides and as a result interfere with viral nucleic acid synthesis. One such drug is acyclovir, which impedes herpesvirus replication by inhibiting the viral polymerase that synthesizes viral DNA but not the eukaryotic one. Similarly, azidothymidine (AZT) curbs HIV replication by interfering with the synthesis of DNA by reverse transcriptase. In the past two decades, much effort has gone into developing drugs against HIV. Currently, multidrug treatments, sometimes called "cocktails," have been found to be most effective. Such treatments commonly include a combination of two nucleoside mimics and a protease inhibitor, which interferes with an enzyme required for assembly of the viruses.

Emerging Viruses

Viruses that suddenly become apparent are often referred to as *emerging viruses*. HIV, the AIDS virus, is a classic example: This virus appeared in San Francisco in the early 1980s, seemingly out of nowhere, although later studies uncovered a case in the Belgian Congo in 1959. The deadly Ebola virus, recognized initially in 1976 in central Africa, is one of several emerging viruses that cause *hemorrhagic fever*, an often fatal illness characterized by fever, vomiting, massive bleeding, and circulatory system collapse. A number of other dangerous emerging viruses cause encephalitis, inflammation of the brain. One example is the West Nile virus, which appeared in North America in 1999 and has now spread to all 48 contiguous states in the United States, resulting in over 5,000 cases and almost 300 deaths in 2012.

In 2009, a widespread outbreak, or **epidemic**, of a flu-like illness appeared in Mexico and the United States. The infectious agent was quickly identified as an influenza virus related to viruses that cause the seasonal flu (**Figure 19.9a**). This particular virus was named H1N1 for reasons that will be explained shortly. The illness spread rapidly, prompting WHO to declare a global epidemic, or **pandemic**, shortly thereafter. Half a year later, the disease had reached 207 countries, infecting over 600,000 people and killing almost 8,000. Public health agencies responded rapidly with

(a) **2009 pandemic H1N1 influenza A virus.** Viruses (blue) are seen on an infected cell (green) in this colorized SEM.

(b) **2009 pandemic screening.** At a South Korean airport, thermal scans were used to detect passengers with a fever who might have the H1N1 flu.

▲ **Figure 19.9 Influenza in humans.**

guidelines for shutting down schools and other public places, and vaccine development and screening efforts were accelerated (**Figure 19.9b**).

How do such viruses burst on the human scene, giving rise to harmful diseases that were previously rare or even unknown? Three processes contribute to the emergence of viral diseases. The first, and perhaps most important, is the mutation of existing viruses. RNA viruses tend to have an unusually high rate of mutation because viral RNA polymerases do not proofread and correct errors in replicating their RNA genomes. Some mutations change existing viruses into new genetic varieties (strains) that can cause disease, even in individuals who are immune to the ancestral virus. For instance, seasonal flu epidemics are caused by new strains of influenza virus genetically different enough from earlier strains that people have little immunity to them. You'll see an example of this process in the Scientific Skills Exercise, where you'll analyze genetic changes in variants of the 2009 H1N1 flu virus and correlate them with spread of the disease.

A second process that can lead to the emergence of viral diseases is the dissemination of a viral disease from a small, isolated human population. For instance, AIDS went unnamed and virtually unnoticed for decades before it began to spread around the world. In this case, technological and social factors, including affordable international travel, blood transfusions, sexual promiscuity, and the abuse of intravenous drugs, allowed a previously rare human disease to become a global scourge.

A third source of new viral diseases in humans is the spread of existing viruses from other animals. Scientists estimate that about three-quarters of new human diseases originate in this way. Animals that harbor and can transmit a particular virus but are generally unaffected by it are said to act as a natural reservoir for that virus. For example, the

H1N1 virus that caused the 2009 flu pandemic mentioned earlier was likely passed to humans from pigs; for this reason, the disease it caused was originally called "swine flu."

In general, flu epidemics provide an instructive example of the effects of viruses moving between species. There are three types of influenza virus: types B and C, which infect only humans and have never caused an epidemic, and type A, which infects a wide range of animals, including birds, pigs, horses, and humans. Influenza A strains have caused four major flu epidemics among humans in the last 100 years. The worst was the first one, the "Spanish flu" pandemic of 1918–1919, which killed 40–50 million people, including many World War I soldiers.

Different strains of influenza A are given standardized names; for example, both the strain that caused the 1918 flu and the one that caused the 2009 pandemic flu are called H1N1. The name identifies which forms of two viral surface proteins are present: hemagglutinin (H) and neuraminidase (N). There are 16 different types of hemagglutinin, a protein that helps the flu virus attach to host cells, and 9 types of neuraminidase, an enzyme that helps release new virus particles from infected cells. Waterbirds have been found that carry viruses with all possible combinations of H and N.

A likely scenario for the 1918 pandemic and others is that the virus mutated as it passed from one host species to another. When an animal like a pig or a bird is infected with more than one strain of flu virus, the different strains can undergo genetic recombination if the RNA molecules making up their genomes mix and match during viral assembly. Pigs were probably the main hosts for recombination that led to the 2009 flu virus, which turns out to contain sequences from bird, pig, and human flu viruses. Coupled with mutation, these reassortments can lead to the emergence of a viral strain capable of infecting human cells. People who have never been exposed to that particular strain before will lack immunity, and the recombinant virus has the potential to be highly pathogenic. If such a flu virus recombines with viruses that circulate widely among humans, it may acquire the ability to spread easily from person to person, dramatically increasing the potential for a major human outbreak.

One potential long-term threat is the avian flu caused by an H5N1 virus carried by wild and domestic birds. The first documented transmission from birds to humans occurred in Hong Kong in 1997. Since then, the overall mortality rate due to H5N1 has been greater than 50% of those infected—an alarming number. Also, the host range of H5N1 is expanding, which provides increasing chances for reassortment between different strains. If the H5N1 avian flu virus evolves so that it can spread easily from person to person, it could represent a major global health threat akin to that of the 1918 pandemic.

How easily could this happen? Recently, scientists working with ferrets, small mammals that are animal models

Analyzing a Sequence-Based Phylogenetic Tree to Understand Viral Evolution

How Can Sequence Data Be Used to Track Flu Virus Evolution During Pandemic Waves? In 2009, an influenza A H1N1 virus caused a pandemic, and the virus has continued to resurface in outbreaks across the world. Researchers in Taiwan were curious about why the virus kept appearing despite widespread flu vaccine initiatives. They hypothesized that newly evolved variant strains of the H1N1 virus were able to evade human immune system defenses. To test this hypothesis, they needed to determine if each wave of the flu outbreak was caused by a different H1N1 variant strain.

How the Experiment Was Done Scientists obtained the genome sequences for 4,703 virus isolates collected from patients with H1N1 flu in Taiwan. They compared the sequences in different strains for the viral hemagglutinin (HA) gene, and based on mutations that had occurred, arranged the isolates into a phylogenetic tree (see Figure 26.5 for information on how to read phylogenetic trees).

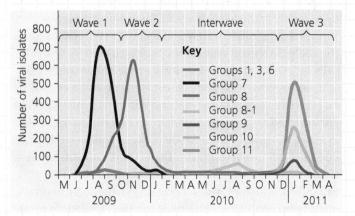

▲ H1N1 flu vaccination.

Data from the Experiment The figure at the upper left shows a phylogenetic tree; each branch tip is one variant strain of the H1N1 virus with a unique HA gene sequence. The tree is a way to visualize a working hypothesis about the evolutionary relationships between H1N1 variants.

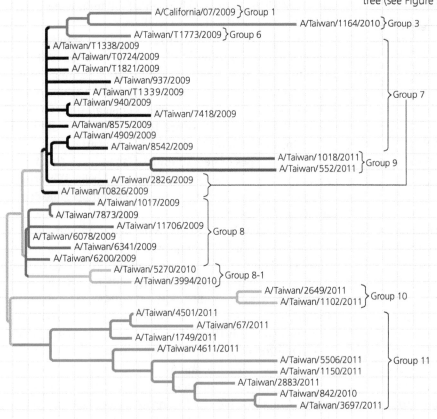

Interpret the Data

1. The phylogenetic tree shows the hypothesized evolutionary relationship between the variant strains of H1N1 virus. The more closely connected two variants are, the more alike they are in terms of HA gene sequence. Each fork in a branch, called a node, shows where two lineages separate due to different accumulated mutations. The length of the branches is a measure of how many sequence differences there are between the variants, indicating how distantly related they are. Referring to the phylogenetic tree, which variants are more closely related to each other: A/Taiwan1018/2011 and A/Taiwan/552/2011 or A/Taiwan1018/2011 and A/Taiwan/8542/2009? Explain your answer.

2. The scientists arranged the branches into groups made up of one ancestral variant and all of its descendant, mutated variants. They are color-coded in the figure. Using Group 11 as an example, trace the lineage of its variants. (a) Do all of the nodes have the same number of branches or branch tips? (b) Are all of the branches in the group the same length? (c) What do these results indicate?

3. The graph at the lower left shows the number of isolates collected (each from an ill patient) on the y-axis and the month and year that the isolates were collected on the x-axis. Each group of variants is plotted separately with a line color that matches the tree diagram. (a) Which group of variants was the earliest to cause the first wave of H1N1 flu in over 100 patients in Taiwan? (b) Once a group of variants had a peak number of infections, did members of that same group cause another (later) wave of infection? (c) One variant in Group 1 (green, uppermost branch) was used to make a vaccine that was distributed very early in the pandemic. Based on the graphed data, does it look like the vaccine was effective?

4. Groups 9, 10, and 11 all had H1N1 variants that caused a large number of infections at the same time in Taiwan. Does this mean that the scientists' hypothesis, that new variants cause new waves of infection, was incorrect? Explain your answer.

(MB) A version of this Scientific Skills Exercise can be assigned in MasteringBiology.

▲ Scientists graphed the number of isolates by the month and year of isolate collection to show the period in which each viral variant was actively causing illness in people.

Data from J.-R. Yang et al., New variants and age shift to high fatality groups contribute to severe successive waves in the 2009 influenza pandemic in Taiwan, *PLoS ONE* 6(11): e28288 (2011).

for human flu, found out that only a few mutations of the avian flu virus would allow infection of cells in the human nasal cavity and windpipe. Furthermore, when the scientists transferred nasal swabs serially from ferret to ferret, the virus became transmissible through the air. Reports of this startling discovery at a scientific conference in 2011 ignited a firestorm of debate about whether to publish the results. Ultimately, the scientific community and various governmental groups decided the benefits of potentially understanding how to prevent pandemics would outweigh the risks of the information being used for harmful purposes, and the work was published in 2012.

As we have seen, emerging viruses are generally not new; rather, they are existing viruses that mutate, disseminate more widely in the current host species, or spread to new host species. Changes in host behavior or environmental changes can increase the viral traffic responsible for emerging diseases. For instance, new roads built through remote areas can allow viruses to spread between previously isolated human populations. Also, the destruction of forests to expand cropland can bring humans into contact with other animals that may host viruses capable of infecting humans.

Viral Diseases in Plants

More than 2,000 types of viral diseases of plants are known, and together they account for an estimated annual loss of $15 billion worldwide due to their destruction of agricultural and horticultural crops. Common signs of viral infection include bleached or brown spots on leaves and fruits (as on the squash shown below, right), stunted growth, and damaged flowers or roots, all of which can diminish the yield and quality of crops.

Plant viruses have the same basic structure and mode of replication as animal viruses. Most plant viruses discovered thus far, including tobacco mosaic virus (TMV), have an RNA genome. Many have a helical capsid, like TMV, while others have an icosahedral capsid (see Figure 19.3).

Viral diseases of plants spread by two major routes. In the first route, called *horizontal transmission*, a plant is infected from an external source of the virus. Because the invading virus must get past the plant's outer protective layer of cells (the epidermis), a plant becomes more susceptible to viral infections if it has been damaged by wind, injury, or herbivores. Herbivores, especially insects, pose a double threat because they can also act as carriers of viruses, transmitting disease from plant to plant. Moreover, farmers and gardeners may transmit plant viruses inadvertently on pruning shears and other tools. The other route of viral infection is *vertical transmission*, in which a plant inherits a viral infection from a parent. Vertical transmission can occur in asexual

propagation (for example, through cuttings) or in sexual reproduction via infected seeds.

Once a virus enters a plant cell and begins replicating, viral genomes and associated proteins can spread throughout the plant by means of plasmodesmata, the cytoplasmic connections that penetrate the walls between adjacent plant cells (see Figure 36.18). The passage of viral macromolecules from cell to cell is facilitated by virally encoded proteins that cause enlargement of plasmodesmata. Scientists have not yet devised cures for most viral plant diseases. Consequently, research efforts are focused largely on reducing the transmission of such diseases and on breeding resistant varieties of crop plants.

Viroids and Prions: The Simplest Infectious Agents

As small and simple as viruses are, they dwarf another class of pathogens: **viroids**. These are circular RNA molecules, only a few hundred nucleotides long, that infect plants. Viroids do not encode proteins but can replicate in host plant cells, apparently using host cell enzymes. These small RNA molecules seem to cause errors in the regulatory systems that control plant growth; the typical signs of viroid diseases are abnormal development and stunted growth. One viroid disease, called cadang-cadang, has killed more than 10 million coconut palms in the Philippines.

An important lesson from viroids is that a single molecule can be an infectious agent that spreads a disease. But viroids are nucleic acids, whose ability to be replicated is well known. Even more surprising is the evidence for infectious *proteins*, called **prions**, which appear to cause a number of degenerative brain diseases in various animal species. These diseases include scrapie in sheep; mad cow disease, which has plagued the European beef industry in recent years; and Creutzfeldt-Jakob disease in humans, which has caused the death of some 150 people in Great Britain. Prions can be transmitted in food, as may occur when people eat prion-laden beef from cattle with mad cow disease. Kuru, another human disease caused by prions, was identified in the early 1900s among the South Fore natives of New Guinea. A kuru epidemic peaked there in the 1960s, puzzling scientists, who at first thought the disease had a genetic basis. Eventually, however, anthropological investigations ferreted out how the disease was spread: ritual cannibalism, a widespread practice among South Fore natives at that time.

Two characteristics of prions are especially alarming. First, prions act very slowly, with an incubation period of at least ten years before symptoms develop. The lengthy incubation period prevents sources of infection from being identified until long after the first cases appear, allowing many

▶ **Figure 19.10 Model for how prions propagate.** Prions are misfolded versions of normal brain proteins. When a prion contacts a normally folded version of the same protein, it may induce the normal protein to assume the abnormal shape. The resulting chain reaction may continue until high levels of prion aggregation cause cellular malfunction and eventual degeneration of the brain.

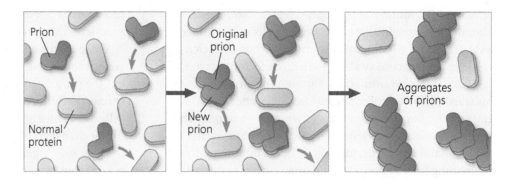

more infections to occur. Second, prions are virtually indestructible; they are not destroyed or deactivated by heating to normal cooking temperatures. To date, there is no known cure for prion diseases, and the only hope for developing effective treatments lies in understanding the process of infection.

How can a protein, which cannot replicate itself, be a transmissible pathogen? According to the leading model, a prion is a misfolded form of a protein normally present in brain cells. When the prion gets into a cell containing the normal form of the protein, the prion somehow converts normal protein molecules to the misfolded prion versions. Several prions then aggregate into a complex that can convert other normal proteins to prions, which join the chain (Figure 19.10). Prion aggregation interferes with normal cellular functions and causes disease symptoms. This model was greeted with much skepticism when it was first

proposed by Stanley Prusiner in the early 1980s, but it is now widely accepted. Prusiner was awarded the Nobel Prize in 1997 for his work on prions. He has recently proposed that prions are also involved in neurodegenerative diseases such as Alzheimer's and Parkinson disease. There are many outstanding questions about these small infectious agents.

CONCEPT CHECK 19.3

1. Describe two ways that a preexisting virus can become an emerging virus.
2. Contrast horizontal and vertical transmission of viruses in plants.
3. **WHAT IF?** TMV has been isolated from virtually all commercial tobacco products. Why, then, is TMV infection not an additional hazard for smokers?

For suggested answers, see Appendix A.

19 Chapter Review

SUMMARY OF KEY CONCEPTS

CONCEPT 19.1

A virus consists of a nucleic acid surrounded by a protein coat (pp. 393–395)

- Researchers discovered viruses in the late 1800s by studying a plant disease, tobacco mosaic disease.
- A **virus** is a small nucleic acid genome enclosed in a protein **capsid** and sometimes a membranous **viral envelope**. The genome may be single- or double-stranded DNA or RNA.

? *Are viruses generally considered living or nonliving? Explain.*

CONCEPT 19.2

Viruses replicate only in host cells (pp. 395–402)

- Viruses use enzymes, ribosomes, and small molecules of host cells to synthesize progeny viruses during replication. Each type of virus has a characteristic **host range**.
- **Phages** (viruses that infect bacteria) can replicate by two alternative mechanisms: the **lytic cycle** and the **lysogenic cycle**.

The phage attaches to a host cell and injects its DNA.

Phage DNA

Bacterial chromosome

Prophage

Lytic cycle
- **Virulent** or **temperate phage**
- Destruction of host DNA
- Production of new phages
- Lysis of host cell causes release of progeny phages

Lysogenic cycle
- **Temperate phage** only
- Genome integrates into bacterial chromosome as **prophage**, which
  (1) is replicated and passed on to daughter cells and
  (2) can be induced to leave the chromosome and initiate a lytic cycle

- Many animal viruses have an envelope. **Retroviruses** (such as **HIV**) use the enzyme **reverse transcriptase** to copy their RNA genome into DNA, which can be integrated into the host genome as a **provirus**.
- Since viruses can replicate only within cells, they probably evolved after the first cells appeared, perhaps as packaged fragments of cellular nucleic acid.

? *Describe enzymes that are not found in most cells but are necessary for the replication of viruses of certain types.*

CONCEPT 19.3

Viruses, viroids, and prions are formidable pathogens in animals and plants (pp. 402–406)

- Symptoms of viral diseases may be caused by direct viral harm to cells or by the body's immune response. **Vaccines** stimulate the immune system to defend the host against specific viruses.
- An **epidemic**, a widespread outbreak of a disease, can become a **pandemic**, a global epidemic.
- Outbreaks of emerging viral diseases in humans are usually not new, but rather are caused by existing viruses that expand their host territory. The H1N1 2009 flu virus was a new combination of pig, human, and avian viral genes that caused a pandemic. The H5N1 avian flu virus has the potential to cause a high-mortality flu pandemic.
- Viruses enter plant cells through damaged cell walls (horizontal transmission) or are inherited from a parent (vertical transmission).
- **Viroids** are naked RNA molecules that infect plants and disrupt their growth. **Prions** are slow-acting, virtually indestructible infectious proteins that cause brain diseases in mammals.

? *What aspect of an RNA virus makes it more likely than a DNA virus to become an emerging virus?*

TEST YOUR UNDERSTANDING

LEVEL 1: KNOWLEDGE/COMPREHENSION

1. Which of the following characteristics, structures, or processes is common to both bacteria and viruses?
   a. metabolism
   b. ribosomes
   c. genetic material composed of nucleic acid
   d. cell division

2. Emerging viruses arise by
   a. mutation of existing viruses.
   b. the spread of existing viruses to new host species.
   c. the spread of existing viruses more widely within their host species.
   d. all of the above.

3. To cause a human pandemic, the H5N1 avian flu virus would have to
   a. spread to primates such as chimpanzees.
   b. develop into a virus with a different host range.
   c. become capable of human-to-human transmission.
   d. become much more pathogenic.

LEVEL 2: APPLICATION/ANALYSIS

4. A bacterium is infected with an experimentally constructed bacteriophage composed of the T2 phage protein coat and T4 phage DNA. The new phages produced would have
   a. T2 protein and T4 DNA.
   b. T2 protein and T2 DNA.
   c. T4 protein and T4 DNA.
   d. T4 protein and T2 DNA.

5. RNA viruses require their own supply of certain enzymes because
   a. host cells rapidly destroy the viruses.
   b. host cells lack enzymes that can replicate the viral genome.
   c. these enzymes translate viral mRNA into proteins.
   d. these enzymes penetrate host cell membranes.

6. **DRAW IT** Redraw Figure 19.7 to show the replicative cycle of a virus with a single-stranded genome that can function as mRNA (a class IV virus).

LEVEL 3: SYNTHESIS/EVALUATION

7. **EVOLUTION CONNECTION** The success of some viruses lies in their ability to evolve rapidly within the host. Such a virus evades the host's defenses by mutating and producing many altered progeny viruses before the body can mount an attack. Thus, the viruses present late in infection differ from those that initially infected the body. Discuss this as an example of evolution in microcosm. Which viral lineages tend to predominate?

8. **SCIENTIFIC INQUIRY** When bacteria infect an animal, the number of bacteria in the body increases in an exponential fashion (graph A). After infection by a virulent animal virus with a lytic replicative cycle, there is no evidence of infection for a while. Then the number of viruses rises suddenly and subsequently increases in a series of steps (graph B). Explain the difference in the curves.

9. **WRITE ABOUT A THEME: ORGANIZATION**
   While viruses are considered by most scientists to be nonliving, they do show some characteristics of life, including the correlation of structure and function. In a short essay (100–150 words), discuss how the structure of a virus correlates with its function.

10. **SYNTHESIZE YOUR KNOWLEDGE**

Oseltamivir (Tamiflu)—an antiviral drug prescribed for influenza—acts to inhibit the enzyme neuraminidase. Explain how this drug could prevent infection in someone exposed to the flu or could shorten the course of flu in an infected patient (the two reasons for which it is prescribed).

For selected answers, see Appendix A.

MasteringBiology®

Students Go to **MasteringBiology** for assignments, the eText, and the Study Area with practice tests, animations, and activities.

Instructors Go to **MasteringBiology** for automatically graded tutorials and questions that you can assign to your students, plus Instructor Resources.

20

DNA Tools and Biotechnology

▲ Figure 20.1 How can the technique shown in this model speed up DNA sequencing?

The DNA Toolbox

The last five to ten years have seen some extraordinary feats in biology, among them determination of the complete DNA sequences of several extinct species, including woolly mammoths (see below, left), Neanderthals, and a 700,000-year-old horse. Pivotal to those discoveries was the sequencing of the human genome, essentially completed in 2003. This endeavor marked a turning point in biology because it sparked remarkable technological advances in DNA sequencing.

The first human genome sequence took several years at a cost of 1 billion dollars; the time and cost of sequencing a genome have been in free fall since then. **Figure 20.1** shows a model of a sequencing technique in which the nucleotides of a single strand of DNA are passed one by one through a tiny pore in a membrane, and the resulting tiny changes in an electrical current are used to determine the nucleotide sequence. Developers of this technique, which you will learn more about later in the chapter, claim that ultimately we will be able to sequence a human genome in about 6 hours on a $900 device the size of a pack of gum.

In this chapter, we'll first describe the main techniques for sequencing and manipulating DNA—**DNA technology**—and for using these DNA tools to analyze gene expression. Next, we'll explore advances in cloning organisms and producing stem cells, techniques that have both expanded our basic understanding of biology and enhanced our ability to apply that understanding to global problems. In the last section, we'll survey the practical applications of DNA-based **biotechnology**, the manipulation of organisms or their components to make useful products. Today, the applications of DNA technology affect everything from agriculture to criminal law to medical research. We will end by considering some of the important social and ethical issues that arise as biotechnology becomes more pervasive in our lives.

DNA sequencing and DNA cloning are valuable tools for genetic engineering and biological inquiry

The discovery of the structure of the DNA molecule, with its two complementary strands, opened the door for the development of DNA sequencing and many other techniques used in biological research today. Key to many of these techniques is **nucleic acid hybridization**, the base pairing of one strand of a nucleic acid to the complementary sequence on a strand from *another* nucleic acid molecule. In this section, we'll first describe DNA sequencing techniques. Then we'll explore other important methods used in **genetic engineering**, the direct manipulation of genes for practical purposes.

DNA Sequencing

Researchers can exploit the principle of complementary base pairing to determine the complete nucleotide sequence of a DNA molecule, a process called **DNA sequencing**. The DNA is first cut into fragments, and then each fragment is sequenced. Today, sequencing is carried out by machines **(Figure 20.2)**. The first automated procedure used a technique called *dideoxyribonucleotide* (or *dideoxy*) *chain termination sequencing*. In this technique, one strand of a DNA fragment is used as a template for synthesis of a nested set of complementary fragments; these are further analyzed to yield the sequence, as shown in detail in **Figure 20.3**. Biochemist Frederick Sanger received the Nobel Prize in 1980 for developing this method. Dideoxy sequencing is still widely used today for routine small-scale sequencing jobs, in machines like that shown in Figure 20.2a.

In the last ten years, "next-generation sequencing" techniques have been developed that do not rely on chain termination. Instead, DNA fragments are amplified (copied) to yield an enormous number of identical fragments **(Figure 20.4)**. A specific strand of each fragment is immobilized, and the complementary strand is synthesized, one nucleotide at a time. A chemical technique enables electronic monitors to identify in real time which of the four nucleotides is added; this method is thus called *sequencing by synthesis*. Thousands or hundreds of thousands of fragments, each about 400–1,000 nucleotides long, are sequenced in parallel in machines like those shown in Figure 20.2b, accounting for the high rate of nucleotides

(a) Standard sequencing machine

(b) Next-generation sequencing machines

▲ **Figure 20.2 DNA sequencing machines. (a)** This standard sequencing machine uses the dideoxy chain termination sequencing method (see Figure 20.3). It can sequence up to about 120,000 nucleotides in 10 hours and is used for sequencing small numbers of samples with shorter sequences. **(b)** Next-generation sequencing machines use "sequencing by synthesis" (see Figure 20.4). Today's machines can sequence 700–900 *million* nucleotides in 10 hours and are used for larger sequencing jobs.

sequenced per hour. This is an example of "high-throughput" DNA technology, and is currently the method of choice for studies where massive numbers of DNA samples—even representing an entire genome—are being sequenced.

Further technical developments have given rise to "third-generation sequencing," with each new technique being faster and less expensive than the previous. In these new methods, the DNA is neither cut into fragments nor amplified. Instead, a single, very long DNA molecule is sequenced on its own. Several groups have been working on the idea of moving a single strand of a DNA molecule through a very small pore (a *nanopore*) in a membrane, detecting the bases one by one by their interruption of an electrical current. One model of this concept is shown in Figure 20.1, in which the pore is a protein channel embedded in a lipid membrane. (Other researchers are using artificial membranes and nanopores.) The idea is that each type of base would interrupt the current for a slightly different length of time. This example is only one of many different approaches to further increase the rate and cut the cost of sequencing.

Research Method

Dideoxy Chain Termination Method for Sequencing DNA

Application The sequence of nucleotides in any DNA fragment of up to 800–1,000 base pairs in length can be determined rapidly with machines that carry out sequencing reactions and separate the labeled reaction products by length.

Technique This method is based on synthesis of a nested set of DNA strands complementary to one strand of a DNA fragment. Each new strand starts with the same primer and ends with a dideoxyribonucleotide (ddNTP), a modified deoxyribonucleotide (dNTP). Incorporation of a ddNTP terminates a growing DNA strand because it lacks a 3′—OH group, the site for attachment of the next nucleotide (see Figure 16.14). In the set of new strands, each nucleotide position along the original sequence is represented by strands ending at that point with the complementary ddNTP. Because each type of ddNTP is tagged with a distinct fluorescent label, the identity of the ending nucleotides of the new strands, and ultimately the entire original sequence, can be determined.

1 The fragment of DNA to be sequenced is denatured into single strands and incubated in a test tube with the necessary ingredients for DNA synthesis: a primer designed to base-pair with the known 3′ end of the template strand, DNA polymerase, the four dNTPs, and the four ddNTPs, each tagged with a specific fluorescent molecule.

2 Synthesis of each new strand starts at the 3′ end of the primer and continues until a ddNTP happens to be inserted instead of the equivalent dNTP. The incorporated ddNTP prevents further elongation of the strand. Eventually, a set of labeled strands of every possible length is generated, with the color of the tag representing the last nucleotide in the sequence.

3 The labeled strands in the mixture are separated by passage through a gel that allows shorter strands to move through more quickly than longer ones. For DNA sequencing, the gel is in a capillary tube, and its small diameter allows a fluorescence detector to sense the color of each fluorescent tag as the strands come through. Strands differing in length by as little as one nucleotide can be distinguished from each other.

Results The color of the fluorescent tag on each strand indicates the identity of the nucleotide at its 3′-end. The results can be printed out as a spectrogram, and the sequence, which is complementary to the template strand, can then be read from bottom (shortest strand) to top (longest strand). (Notice that the sequence here begins after the primer.)

Next-Generation Sequencing

① Genomic DNA is fragmented, and fragments of 400 to 1,000 base pairs are selected.

② Each fragment is isolated with a bead in a droplet of aqueous solution.

③ The fragment is copied over and over by a technique called PCR (to be described later). All the 5' ends of one strand are specifically "captured" by the bead. Eventually, 10^6 identical copies of the same single strand, which will be used as a template strand, are attached to the bead.

④ The bead is placed into a small well along with DNA polymerases and primers that can hybridize to the 3' end of the single (template) strand.

DNA polymerase

Template strand of DNA

5'   3'
       3' 5'
         Primer

A T G C

Application In current next-generation sequencing techniques, each fragment is 400–1,000 nucleotides long; by sequencing the fragments in parallel, 700–900 million nucleotides can be sequenced in 10 hours.

Technique See numbered steps and diagrams.

Results Each of the 2,000,000 wells in the multiwell plate, which holds a different fragment, yields a different sequence. The results for one fragment are shown below as a "flow-gram." The sequences of the entire set of fragments are analyzed using computer software, which "stitches" them together into a whole sequence—here, an entire genome.

4-mer { ■ A
3-mer { □ T
         ■ G
2-mer { □ C
1-mer {

TTCTGCGAA

INTERPRET THE DATA *If the template strand has two or more identical nucleotides in a row, their complementary nucleotides will be added one after the other in the same flow step. How are two or more of the same nucleotide (in a row) detected in the flow-gram? (See sample on the right.) Write out the sequence of the first 25 nucleotides in the flow-gram above, starting from the left. (Ignore the very short lines.)*

⑤ The well is one of 2 million on a multiwell plate, each containing a different DNA fragment to be sequenced. A solution of one of the four nucleotides is added to all wells and then washed off. This is done sequentially for all four nucleotides: dATP, dTTP, dGTP, and then dCTP. The entire process is then repeated.

A T G C   A T G C   A T G C   A T G C

Template strand of DNA

C C A A T G T A G C G C A G T A

dATP

PP$_i$

DNA polymerase — Primer

C C A A T G T A G C G C A G T A

dTTP

C C A A T G T A G C G C A G T A

dGTP

C C A A T G C T A G C G C A G T A

dCTP

PP$_i$

⑥ In each well, if the next base on the template strand (T in this example) is complementary to the added nucleotide (A, here), the nucleotide is joined to the growing strand, releasing PP$_i$, which causes a flash of light that is recorded.

⑦ The nucleotide is washed off and a different nucleotide (dTTP, here) is added. If the nucleotide is not complementary to the next template base (G, here), it is not joined to the strand and there is no flash.

⑧ The process of adding and washing off the four nucleotides is repeated until every fragment has a complete complementary strand. The pattern of flashes reveals the sequence of the original fragment in each well.

Improved DNA sequencing techniques have transformed the way in which we can explore fundamental biological questions about evolution and how life works. Little more than a decade after the human genome sequence was announced, researchers had completed sequencing roughly 4,000 bacterial, 190 archaeal, and 180 eukaryotic genomes, with more than 17,000 additional species under way. Complete genome sequences have been determined for cells from several cancers, for ancient humans, and for the many bacteria that live in the human intestine. In Chapter 21, you'll learn more about how this new sequencing technology has informed us about the evolution of species and the evolution of the genome itself. Now, let's consider how individual genes are studied.

Making Multiple Copies of a Gene or Other DNA Segment

A molecular biologist studying a particular gene or group of genes faces a challenge. Naturally occurring DNA molecules are very long, and a single molecule usually carries many hundreds or even thousands of genes. Moreover, in many eukaryotic genomes, protein-coding genes occupy only a small proportion of the chromosomal DNA, the rest being noncoding nucleotide sequences. A single human gene, for example, might constitute only 1/100,000 of a chromosomal DNA molecule. As a further complication, the distinctions between a gene and the surrounding DNA are subtle, consisting only of differences in nucleotide sequence. To work directly with specific genes, scientists have developed methods for preparing well-defined segments of DNA in multiple identical copies, a process called **DNA cloning**.

Most methods for cloning pieces of DNA in the laboratory share certain general features. One common approach uses bacteria, most often *Escherichia coli*. Recall from Figure 16.12 that the *E. coli* chromosome is a large circular molecule of DNA. In addition to their bacterial chromosome, *E. coli* and many other bacteria also have **plasmids**, small, circular DNA molecules that are replicated separately. A plasmid has only a small number of genes; these genes may be useful when the bacterium is in a particular environment but may not be required for survival or reproduction under most conditions

To clone pieces of DNA using bacteria, researchers first obtain a plasmid (originally isolated from a bacterial cell and genetically engineered for efficient cloning) and insert DNA from another source ("foreign" DNA) into it **(Figure 20.5)**. The resulting plasmid is now a **recombinant DNA** molecule, a molecule containing DNA from two different sources, very often different species. The plasmid is then returned to a bacterial cell, producing a *recombinant bacterium*. This single cell reproduces through repeated cell divisions to form a clone of cells, a population of genetically identical cells. Because the dividing bacteria replicate the recombinant plasmid and pass it on to their descendants, the

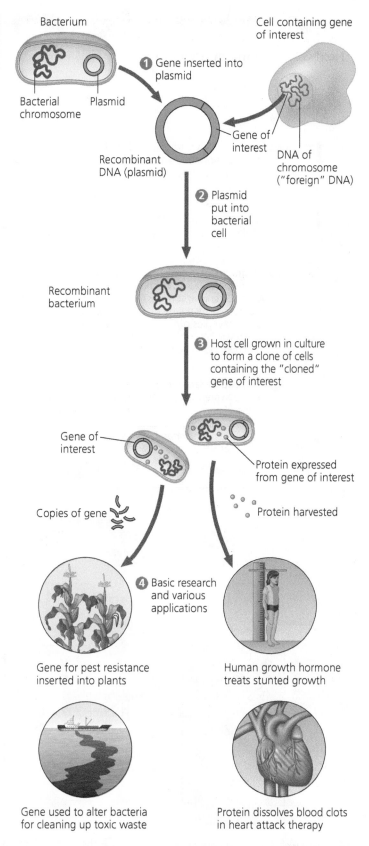

▲ **Figure 20.5 Gene cloning and some uses of cloned genes.** In this simplified diagram of gene cloning, we start with a plasmid (originally isolated from a bacterial cell) and a gene of interest from another organism. Only one plasmid and one copy of the gene of interest are shown at the top of the figure, but the starting materials would include many of each.

foreign DNA and any genes it carries are cloned at the same time. The production of multiple copies of a single gene is a type of DNA cloning called **gene cloning**.

In our example in Figure 20.5, the plasmid acts as a **cloning vector**, a DNA molecule that can carry foreign DNA into a host cell and replicate there. Bacterial plasmids are widely used as cloning vectors for several reasons: They can be readily obtained from commercial suppliers, manipulated to form recombinant plasmids by insertion of foreign DNA in a test tube (*in vitro*, from the Latin meaning "in glass"), and then easily introduced into bacterial cells. Moreover, recombinant bacterial plasmids (and the foreign DNA they carry) multiply rapidly owing to the high reproductive rate of their host (bacterial) cells. The foreign DNA in Figure 20.5 is a gene from a eukaryotic cell; we will describe in more detail how the foreign DNA segment was obtained later in this section.

Gene cloning is useful for two basic purposes: to make many copies of, or *amplify*, a particular gene and to produce a protein product (see Figure 20.5). Researchers can isolate copies of a cloned gene from bacteria for use in basic research or to endow another organism with a new metabolic capability, such as pest resistance. For example, a resistance gene present in one crop species might be cloned and transferred into plants of another species. Alternatively, a protein with medical uses, such as human growth hormone, can be harvested in large quantities from cultures of bacteria carrying a cloned gene for the protein. (We'll describe the techniques for expressing cloned genes later.) Since one gene is only a very small part of the total DNA in a cell, the ability to amplify such rare DNA fragments, by cloning or other means, is crucial for any application involving a single gene.

Using Restriction Enzymes to Make a Recombinant DNA Plasmid

Gene cloning and genetic engineering generally rely on the use of enzymes that cut DNA molecules at a limited number of specific locations. These enzymes, called restriction endonucleases, or **restriction enzymes**, were discovered in the late 1960s by biologists doing basic research on bacteria. Restriction enzymes protect the bacterial cell by cutting up foreign DNA from other organisms or phages (see Concept 19.2).

Hundreds of different restriction enzymes have been identified and isolated. Each restriction enzyme is very specific, recognizing a particular short DNA sequence, or **restriction site**, and cutting both DNA strands at precise points within this restriction site. The DNA of a bacterial cell is protected from the cell's own restriction enzymes by the addition of methyl groups ($-CH_3$) to adenines or cytosines within the sequences recognized by the enzymes.

Figure 20.6 shows how restriction enzymes are used during DNA cloning to join DNA fragments together. At the top is a bacterial plasmid (like the one in Figure 20.5) with

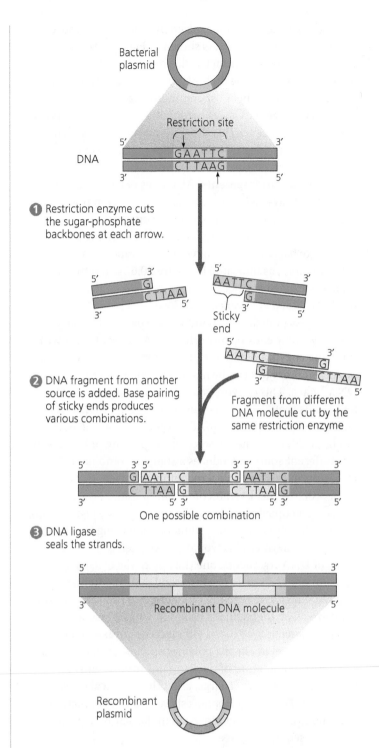

▲ **Figure 20.6 Using a restriction enzyme and DNA ligase to make a recombinant DNA plasmid.** The restriction enzyme in this example (called *Eco*RI) recognizes a specific six-base-pair sequence, the restriction site, present at one place in this plasmid. The enzyme makes staggered cuts in the sugar-phosphate backbones within this sequence, producing fragments with sticky ends. Foreign DNA fragments with complementary sticky ends can base-pair with the plasmid ends; the ligated product is a recombinant plasmid. (The two original sticky ends can also base-pair, forming a circle; ligation would result in the original non-recombinant plasmid.)

DRAW IT *The restriction enzyme* Hind*III recognizes the sequence 5'-AAGCTT-3', cutting between the two As. Draw the double-stranded sequence before and after the enzyme cuts it.*

a single restriction site recognized by a particular restriction enzyme from *E. coli*. As shown in Figure 20.6, most restriction sites are symmetrical. That is, the sequence of nucleotides is the same on both strands when read in the $5' \rightarrow 3'$ direction. The most commonly used restriction enzymes recognize sequences containing 4-8 nucleotide pairs. Because any sequence this short usually occurs (by chance) many times in a long DNA molecule, a restriction enzyme will make many cuts in such a DNA molecule, yielding a set of **restriction fragments**. All copies of a given DNA molecule always yield the same set of restriction fragments when exposed to the same restriction enzyme.

The most useful restriction enzymes cleave the sugar-phosphate backbones in the two DNA strands in a staggered manner, as indicated in Figure 20.6. The resulting double-stranded restriction fragments have at least one single-stranded end, called a **sticky end**. These short extensions can form hydrogen-bonded base pairs with complementary sticky ends on any other DNA molecules cut with the same enzyme. The associations formed in this way are only temporary but can be made permanent by the enzyme **DNA ligase**. This enzyme catalyzes the formation of covalent bonds that close up the sugar-phosphate backbones of DNA strands (see Figure 16.16). You can see at the bottom of Figure 20.6 that the ligase-catalyzed joining of DNA from two different sources produces a stable recombinant DNA molecule, in this example a recombinant plasmid.

In order to check the recombinant plasmid product after it has been copied many times in host cells (see Figure 20.5), a researcher might cut the products again using the same restriction enzyme. This would be expected to yield two kinds of DNA fragments, one the size of the original plasmid and one the size of the inserted DNA fragment, the two starting materials at the top of Figure 20.6. To separate and visualize DNA fragments of different lengths, researchers carry out a technique called **gel electrophoresis**. This technique uses a gel made of a polymer as a molecular sieve to separate out a mixture of nucleic acids (or proteins) on the basis of size, electrical charge, and other physical properties (Figure 20.7). Gel electrophoresis is used in conjunction with many different techniques in molecular biology, including DNA sequencing (see Figure 20.3).

Now that we have discussed the cloning vector in some detail, let's consider the foreign DNA to be inserted. The most common way to obtain many copies of the gene to be cloned is by PCR, described next.

Amplifying DNA: The Polymerase Chain Reaction (PCR) and Its Use in DNA Cloning

Today, most researchers have some information about the sequence of the gene or other DNA segment they want to clone. Using this information, they can start with the entire

(a) Each sample, a mixture of different DNA molecules, is placed in a separate well near one end of a thin slab of agarose gel. The gel is set into a small plastic support and immersed in an aqueous, buffered solution in a tray with electrodes at each end. The current is then turned on, causing the negatively charged DNA molecules to move toward the positive electrode.

(b) Shorter molecules are slowed down less than longer ones, so they move faster through the gel. After the current is turned off, a DNA-binding dye is added that fluoresces pink in UV light. Each pink band corresponds to many thousands of DNA molecules of the same length. The horizontal ladder of bands at the bottom of the gel is a set of restriction fragments of known sizes for comparison with samples of unknown length.

▲ **Figure 20.7 Gel electrophoresis.** A gel made of a polymer acts as a molecular sieve to separate nucleic acids or proteins differing in size, electrical charge, or other physical properties as they move in an electric field. In the example shown here, DNA molecules are separated by length in a gel made of a polysaccharide called agarose.

collection of genomic DNA from the particular species of interest and obtain many copies of the desired gene by using a technique called the **polymerase chain reaction**, or **PCR**. Figure 20.8 illustrates the steps in PCR. Within a few hours, this technique can make billions of copies of a specific target DNA segment in a sample, even if that segment makes up less than 0.001% of the total DNA in the sample.

In the PCR procedure, a three-step cycle brings about a chain reaction that produces an exponentially growing population of identical DNA molecules. During each cycle, the reaction mixture is heated to denature (separate) the strands of the double-stranded DNA and then cooled to allow annealing (hydrogen bonding) of short, single-stranded DNA primers complementary to sequences on opposite strands

Research Method

The Polymerase Chain Reaction (PCR)

Application With PCR, any specific segment (the so-called target sequence) within a DNA sample can be copied many times (amplified), completely *in vitro*.

Technique PCR requires double-stranded DNA containing the target sequence, a heat-resistant DNA polymerase, all four nucleotides, and two 15- to 20-nucleotide DNA strands that serve as primers. One primer is complementary to one end of the target sequence on one strand; the second primer is complementary to the other end of the sequence on the other strand.

Genomic DNA

Target sequence

Cycle 1 yields 2 molecules

❶ Denaturation: Heat briefly to separate DNA strands.

❷ Annealing: Cool to allow primers to form hydrogen bonds with ends of target sequence.

Primers

❸ Extension: DNA polymerase adds nucleotides to the 3′ end of each primer.

New nucleotides

Cycle 2 yields 4 molecules

Cycle 3 yields 8 molecules; 2 molecules (in white boxes) match target sequence

© Pearson Education, Inc.

Results After 3 cycles, two molecules match the target sequence exactly. After 30 more cycles, over 1 billion (10^9) molecules match the target sequence.

at each end of the target sequence; finally, a heat-stable DNA polymerase extends the primers in the 5′ → 3′ direction. If a standard DNA polymerase were used, the protein would be denatured along with the DNA during the first heating step and would have to be replaced after each cycle. The key to automating PCR was the discovery of an unusual heat-stable DNA polymerase called Taq polymerase, named after the bacterial species from which it was first isolated. This bacterial species, *Thermus aquaticus*, lives in hot springs, and the stability of its DNA polymerase at high temperatures is an evolutionary adaptation that enables the bacterium to survive and reproduce at temperatures up to 95°C.

PCR is speedy and very specific. Only minuscule amounts of DNA need be present in the starting material, and this DNA can be partially degraded, as long as a few molecules contain the complete target sequence. The key to the high specificity is the pair of primers used for each PCR amplification. The primer sequences are chosen so they hybridize *only* to sequences at opposite ends of the target segment, one on the 3′ end of each strand. (For high specificity, the primers must be at least 15 or so nucleotides long.) By the end of the third cycle, one-fourth of the molecules are identical to the target segment, with both strands the appropriate length. With each successive cycle, the number of target segment molecules of the correct length doubles, so the number of molecules equals 2^n, where n is the number of cycles. After 30 more cycles, about a billion copies of the target sequence are present!

Despite its speed and specificity, PCR amplification cannot substitute for gene cloning in cells when large amounts of a gene are required. This is because occasional errors during PCR replication limit the number of good copies and the length of DNA fragments that can be copied. Instead, PCR is used to provide a supply of the specific DNA fragment for cloning. PCR primers are synthesized to include a restriction site at each end of the DNA fragment that matches the site in the cloning vector. Then the fragment and vector are cut, allowed to hybridize, and ligated

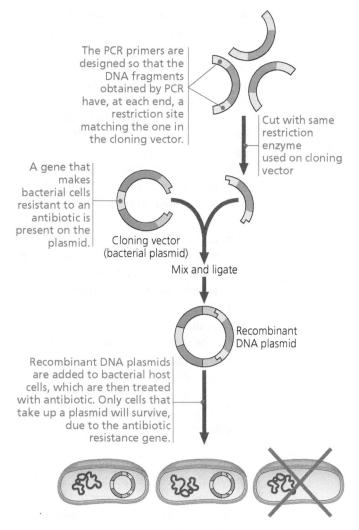

The PCR primers are designed so that the DNA fragments obtained by PCR have, at each end, a restriction site matching the one in the cloning vector.

Cut with same restriction enzyme used on cloning vector

A gene that makes bacterial cells resistant to an antibiotic is present on the plasmid.

Cloning vector (bacterial plasmid)

Mix and ligate

Recombinant DNA plasmid

Recombinant DNA plasmids are added to bacterial host cells, which are then treated with antibiotic. Only cells that take up a plasmid will survive, due to the antibiotic resistance gene.

▲ **Figure 20.9 Use of a restriction enzyme and PCR in gene cloning.** This figure takes a closer look at the process shown at the top of Figure 20.5. PCR is used to produce multiple copies of the DNA fragment or gene of interest. The ends of the fragments have the same restriction site as the cloning vector. The plasmid and the DNA fragments are cut with the same restriction enzyme, combined so the sticky ends can hybridize, ligated together, and introduced into bacterial host cells. The plasmid also contains an antibiotic resistance gene that allows only cells with a plasmid to survive when the antibiotic is present. Other genetic engineering techniques are used to ensure that cells with nonrecombinant plasmids can be eliminated.

together (**Figure 20.9**). The plasmids from the resulting bacterial clones are sequenced so that clones carrying plasmids with error-free inserts can be selected.

Devised in 1985, PCR has had a major impact on biological research and genetic engineering. PCR has been used to amplify DNA from a wide variety of sources: a 40,000-year-old frozen woolly mammoth (see the photo on the first page of this chapter); fingerprints or tiny amounts of blood, tissue, or semen found at crime scenes; single embryonic cells for rapid prenatal diagnosis of genetic disorders (see Figure 14.19); and cells infected with viruses that are difficult to detect, such as HIV. (To test for HIV, viral genes are amplified.) We'll return to applications of PCR later.

Expressing Cloned Eukaryotic Genes

Once a gene has been cloned in host cells, its protein product can be expressed in large amounts for research or for practical applications, which we'll explore in Concept 20.4. Cloned genes can be expressed in either bacterial or eukaryotic cells; each option has advantages and disadvantages.

Bacterial Expression Systems

Getting a cloned eukaryotic gene to function in bacterial host cells can be difficult because certain aspects of gene expression are different in eukaryotes and bacteria. To overcome differences in promoters and other DNA control sequences, scientists usually employ an **expression vector**, a cloning vector that contains a highly active bacterial promoter just upstream of a restriction site where the eukaryotic gene can be inserted in the correct reading frame. The bacterial host cell will recognize the promoter and proceed to express the foreign gene now linked to that promoter. Such expression vectors allow the synthesis of many eukaryotic proteins in bacterial cells.

Another problem with expressing cloned eukaryotic genes in bacteria is the presence of noncoding regions (introns; see Concept 17.3) in most eukaryotic genes. Introns can make a eukaryotic gene very long and unwieldy, and they prevent correct expression of the gene by bacterial cells, which do not have RNA-splicing machinery. This problem can be surmounted by using a form of the gene that includes only the exons. (This is called *complementary DNA*, or *cDNA*; see Figure 20.11.)

Eukaryotic DNA Cloning and Expression Systems

Molecular biologists can avoid eukaryotic-bacterial incompatibility by using eukaryotic cells such as yeasts, rather than bacteria, as hosts for cloning and expressing eukaryotic genes of interest. Yeasts, single-celled fungi, offer two advantages: They are as easy to grow as bacteria, and they have plasmids, a rarity among eukaryotes. Scientists have even constructed recombinant plasmids that combine yeast and bacterial DNA and can replicate in either type of cell.

Another reason to use eukaryotic host cells for expressing a cloned eukaryotic gene is that many eukaryotic proteins will not function unless they are modified after translation—for example, by the addition of carbohydrate groups (glycosylation) or lipid groups. Bacterial cells cannot carry out these modifications, and if the gene product requiring such processing is from a mammal, even yeast cells may not be able to modify the protein correctly. Several cultured cell types have proved successful as host cells for this purpose, including some mammalian cell lines and an insect cell line that can be infected by a virus (called baculovirus) carrying recombinant DNA.

Besides using vectors, scientists have developed a variety of other methods for introducing recombinant DNA into eukaryotic cells. In **electroporation**, a brief electrical pulse applied to a solution containing cells creates temporary holes in their plasma membranes, through which DNA can enter. (This technique is now commonly used for bacteria as well.) Alternatively, scientists can inject DNA directly into single eukaryotic cells using microscopically thin needles. Another way to get DNA into plant cells is by using the soil bacterium *Agrobacterium tumefaciens*, as we'll discuss later. Whatever the method, if the introduced DNA is incorporated into a cell's genome by genetic recombination, then it can be expressed by the cell.

To study the function of a particular protein, researchers can introduce different mutant forms of the gene for that protein into eukaryotic cells. The cells express different versions of the protein, and the resulting phenotypes provide information about the normal protein's function. For this purpose, researchers may use a cloning vector with viral DNA sequences that allow the introduced DNA to integrate into a chromosome and be stably expressed. The same approach can be used to express noncoding RNAs in order to study their role as agents of gene regulation in the cell. (Noncoding RNAs are discussed in Concept 18.3.)

Cross-Species Gene Expression and Evolutionary Ancestry

EVOLUTION The ability to express eukaryotic proteins in bacteria (even if the proteins aren't modified properly) is quite remarkable when we consider how different eukaryotic and bacterial cells are. In fact, examples abound of genes that are taken from one species and function perfectly well when transferred into another very different species. These observations underscore the shared evolutionary ancestry of species living today.

One example involves a gene called *Pax-6*, which has been found in animals as diverse as vertebrates and fruit flies. The vertebrate *Pax-6* gene product (the PAX-6 protein) triggers a complex program of gene expression resulting in formation of the vertebrate eye, which has a single lens. Expression of the fly *Pax-6* gene leads to formation of the compound fly eye, which is quite different from the vertebrate eye. When the mouse *Pax-6* gene was cloned and introduced into a fly embryo so that it replaced the fly's own *Pax-6* gene, researchers were surprised to see that the mouse version of the gene led to formation of a compound fly eye (see Figure 50.16). Conversely, when the fly *Pax-6* gene was transferred into a vertebrate embryo—a frog, in this case—a frog eye formed. Although the genetic programs triggered in vertebrates and flies generate very different eyes, the two versions of the *Pax-6* gene can substitute for each other to trigger lens development, evidence of their evolution from a gene in a very ancient common ancestor.

Simpler examples are seen in Figure 17.6, where a firefly gene is expressed in a tobacco plant and a jellyfish gene in a pig. Because of their ancient evolutionary roots, all living organisms share the same basic mechanisms of gene expression. This commonality is the basis of many recombinant DNA techniques described in this chapter.

CONCEPT CHECK **20.1**

1. The restriction site for an enzyme called *Pvu*I is the following sequence:

    5'-C G A T C G-3'
    3'-G C T A G C-5'

    Staggered cuts are made between the T and C on each strand. What type of bonds are being cleaved?

2. DRAW IT One strand of a DNA molecule has the following sequence: 5'-CCTTGACGATCGTTACCG-3'. Draw the other strand. Will *Pvu*I cut this molecule? If so, draw the products.

3. What are some potential difficulties in using plasmid vectors and bacterial host cells to produce large quantities of proteins from cloned eukaryotic genes?

4. MAKE CONNECTIONS Compare Figure 20.8 with Figure 16.20. How does replication of DNA ends during PCR proceed without shortening the fragments each time?

For suggested answers, see Appendix A.

CONCEPT 20.2

Biologists use DNA technology to study gene expression and function

To see how a biological system works, scientists seek to understand the functioning of the system's component parts. Analysis of when and where a gene or group of genes is expressed can provide important clues about their function.

Analyzing Gene Expression

Biologists driven to understand the assorted cell types of a multicellular organism, cancer cells, or the developing tissues of an embryo first try to discover which genes are expressed by the cells of interest. The most straightforward way to do this is usually to identify the mRNAs being made. We'll first examine techniques that look for patterns of expression of specific individual genes. Next, we'll explore ways to characterize groups of genes being expressed by cells or tissues of interest. As you will see, all of these procedures depend in some way on base pairing between complementary nucleotide sequences.

Studying the Expression of Single Genes

Suppose we have cloned a gene that we suspect plays an important role in the embryonic development of *Drosophila melanogaster* (the fruit fly). The first thing we might want to know is which embryonic cells express the gene—in other words, where in the embryo is the corresponding mRNA found? We can detect the mRNA by nucleic acid hybridization with molecules of complementary sequence that we can follow in some way. The complementary molecule, a short, single-stranded nucleic acid that can be either RNA or DNA, is called a **nucleic acid probe**. Using our cloned gene as a template, we can synthesize a probe complementary to the mRNA. For example, if part of the sequence on the mRNA were

5′ ···CUCAUCACCGGC··· 3′

then we would synthesize this single-stranded DNA probe:

3′ GAGTAGTGGCCG 5′

Each probe molecule is labeled during synthesis with a fluorescent tag so we can follow it. A solution containing probe molecules is applied to *Drosophila* embryos, allowing the probe to hybridize specifically with any complementary sequences on the many mRNAs in embryonic cells that are transcribing the gene. Because this technique allows us to see the mRNA in place (or *in situ*, in Latin) in the intact organism, this technique is called *in situ* **hybridization**. Different probes can be labeled with different fluorescent dyes, sometimes with strikingly beautiful results (**Figure 20.10**).

Other mRNA detection techniques may be preferable for comparing the amounts of a specific mRNA in several samples at the same time—for example, in different cell types or in embryos at different stages of development. One method that is widely used is called the **reverse transcriptase-polymerase chain reaction**, or **RT-PCR**.

RT-PCR begins by turning sample sets of mRNAs into double-stranded DNAs with the corresponding sequences. First, the enzyme reverse transcriptase (from a retrovirus; see Figure 19.8) is used *in vitro* to make a single-stranded DNA *reverse transcript* of each mRNA molecule (**Figure 20.11**). Recall that the 3′ end of the mRNA has a stretch of adenine (A) nucleotides called a poly-A tail. This allows use of a short complementary strand of thymine deoxyribonucleotides (poly-dT) as a primer for synthesis of this DNA strand. Following enzymatic degradation of the mRNA, a second DNA strand, complementary to the first, is synthesized by DNA polymerase. The resulting double-stranded DNA is called **complementary DNA (cDNA)**. (Made from mRNA, cDNA lacks introns and can be used for protein expression in bacteria, as mentioned earlier.) To analyze the timing of expression of the *Drosophila* gene of interest, for example, we would first isolate all the mRNAs from different stages of *Drosophila* embryos and make cDNA from each stage (**Figure 20.12**). Then we'd use PCR to find any cDNA derived from the gene of interest.

As you will recall from Figure 20.8, PCR is a way of rapidly making many copies of one specific stretch of double-stranded DNA, using primers that hybridize to the opposite ends of the segment of interest. In our case, we would add primers corresponding to a segment of our *Drosophila* gene,

The yellow probe hybridizes with mRNAs in cells that are expressing the *wingless* (*wg*) gene, which encodes a secreted signaling protein.

The blue probe hybridizes with mRNAs in cells that are expressing the *engrailed* (*en*) gene, which encodes a transcription factor.

3′ TAACGGTTCCAGC 5′
ATTGCCAAGGTCG
5′ 3′

wg mRNA

Cells expressing the *wg* gene

3′ CTCAAGTTGCTCT 5′
GAGTTCAACGAGA
5′ 3′

en mRNA

Cells expressing the *en* gene

Head   Thorax   Abdomen

50 μm   T1 T2 T3 A1 A2 A3 A4 A5

Segment boundary

Head   Thorax   Abdomen

▲ **Figure 20.10 Determining where genes are expressed by *in situ* hybridization analysis.** A *Drosophila* embryo was incubated in a solution containing probes for five different mRNAs, each probe labeled with a different fluorescently colored tag. The embryo was then viewed from the belly (ventral) side using fluorescence microscopy; the resulting fluorescent micrograph is shown in the middle, above. Each color marks where a specific gene is expressed as mRNA. The arrows from the groups of yellow and blue cells above the micrograph show a magnified view of nucleic acid hybridization of the appropriately colored probe to the mRNA. Yellow cells (expressing the *wg* gene) interact with blue cells (expressing the *en* gene); their interaction helps establish the pattern in a body segment. The diagram at the bottom clarifies the eight segments visible in this view.

using the cDNA from each embryonic stage as a template for PCR amplification in separate samples. When the products are analyzed on a gel, only samples that originally contained mRNA from the gene of interest will show bands containing copies of the amplified region. A recent enhancement involves using a fluorescent dye that fluoresces only when bound to a double-stranded PCR product. The newer PCR machines can detect the light and measure the PCR product, thus avoiding the need for electrophoresis while also

① Reverse transcriptase is added to a test tube containing mRNA isolated from a sample of cells.

② Reverse transcriptase makes the first DNA strand using the mRNA as a template and a short poly-dT as a DNA primer.

③ mRNA is degraded by another enzyme.

④ DNA polymerase synthesizes the second DNA strand, using a primer in the reaction mixture. (Several options exist for primers.)

⑤ The result is cDNA, which carries the complete coding sequence of the gene but no introns.

DNA in nucleus
mRNAs in cytoplasm

Reverse transcriptase
mRNA
Poly-A tail
5′ ... A A A A A A 3′
3′ ... T T T T T 5′
DNA strand
Primer (poly-dT)

5′ ... A A A A A A 3′
3′ ... T T T T T 5′

5′
3′
3′
5′
DNA polymerase

5′ ... 3′
3′ ... 5′
cDNA

▲ **Figure 20.11 Making complementary DNA (cDNA) from eukaryotic genes.** Complementary DNA is made *in vitro* using mRNA as a template for the first strand. The mRNA contains only exons, so the resulting double-stranded cDNA carries the continuous coding sequence of the gene. Only one mRNA is shown here, but the final collection of cDNAs would reflect all the mRNAs present in the cell sample. Figure 20.12 shows how the cDNA of interest is identified.

providing quantitative data, a distinct advantage. RT-PCR can also be carried out with mRNAs collected from different tissues at one time to discover which tissue is producing a specific mRNA.

In the Scientific Skills Exercise, you can work with data from an experiment that analyzed expression of a gene involved in paw formation in the mouse. The study investigated mRNA expression using two techniques. One of these methods was qualitative (*in situ* hybridization), whereas the other approach was quantitative (PCR).

Studying the Expression of Interacting Groups of Genes

A major goal of biologists is to learn how genes act together to produce and maintain a functioning organism. Now that the genomes of a number of species have been sequenced, it is possible to study the expression of large groups of genes—the so-called *systems approach*. Researchers use what is known about the whole genome to investigate which genes are transcribed in different tissues or at different stages of development. One aim is to identify networks of gene expression across an entire genome.

RT-PCR Analysis of the Expression of Single Genes

Application RT-PCR uses the enzyme reverse transcriptase (RT) in combination with PCR and gel electrophoresis. RT-PCR can be used to compare gene expression between samples—for instance, in different embryonic stages, in different tissues, or in the same type of cell under different conditions.

Technique In this example, samples containing mRNAs from six embryonic stages of *Drosophila* were analyzed for a specific mRNA as shown below. (In steps 1 and 2, the mRNA from only one stage is shown.)

① **cDNA synthesis** is carried out by incubating the mRNAs with reverse transcriptase and other necessary components.

② **PCR amplification** of the sample is performed using primers specific to the *Drosophila* gene of interest.

③ **Gel electrophoresis** will reveal amplified DNA products only in samples that contained mRNA transcribed from the specific *Drosophila* gene.

mRNAs
cDNAs
Primers
Specific gene

Embryonic stages
1 2 3 4 5 6

Results The mRNA for this gene first is expressed at stage 2 and continues to be expressed through stage 6. The size of the amplified fragment (shown by its position on the gel) depends on the distance between the primers that were used (not on the size of the mRNA).

Genome-wide expression studies can be carried out using **DNA microarray assays**. A DNA microarray consists of tiny amounts of a large number of single-stranded DNA fragments representing different genes fixed to a glass slide in a tightly spaced array, or grid. (The microarray is also called a *DNA chip* by analogy to a computer chip.) Ideally, these fragments represent all the genes of an organism.

The basic strategy in such studies is to isolate the mRNAs made in a cell of interest and use these molecules as templates for making the corresponding cDNAs by reverse transcription. In microarray assays, these cDNAs are labeled with fluorescent molecules and then allowed to hybridize to a DNA microarray. Most often, the cDNAs from two

Analyzing Quantitative and Spatial Gene Expression Data

How Is a Particular *Hox* Gene Regulated During Paw Development? *Hox* genes code for transcription factor proteins, which in turn control sets of genes important for animal development (see Concept 21.6 for more information on *Hox* genes). One group of *Hox* genes, the *Hoxd* genes, plays a role in establishing the pattern of the different digits (fingers and toes) at the end of a limb. Unlike the *mPGES-1* gene mentioned in the Chapter 18 Scientific Skills Exercise, *Hox* genes have very large, complicated regulatory regions, including control elements that may be hundreds of kilobases (kb; thousands of nucleotides) away from the gene.

In cases like this, how do biologists locate the DNA segments that contain important elements? They begin by removing (deleting) large segments of DNA and studying the effect on gene expression. In this exercise, you'll compare data from two different but complementary approaches that look at the expression of a specific *Hoxd* gene (*Hoxd13*). One approach quantifies overall expression; the other approach is less quantitative but gives important spatial localization information.

How the Experiment Was Done Researchers interested in the regulation of *Hoxd13* gene expression genetically engineered a set of mice (*transgenic* mice) that had different segments of DNA deleted upstream of the gene. They then compared levels and patterns of *Hoxd13* gene expression in the developing paws of 12.5-day-old transgenic mouse embryos (with the DNA deletions) with those seen in wild-type mouse embryos of the same age.

They used two different approaches: In some mice, they extracted the mRNA from the embryonic paws and quantified the overall level of *Hoxd13* mRNA in the whole paw using quantitative RT-PCR. In another set of the same transgenic mice, they used *in situ* hybridization to pinpoint exactly where in the paws the *Hoxd13* gene was expressed as mRNA. The particular technique that was used causes the *Hoxd13* mRNA to appear blue, or black for the highest mRNA levels.

Data from the Experiment The top-most diagram (upper right) depicts the very large regulatory region upstream of the *Hoxd13* gene. The area between the slashes represents the long stretch of DNA located between the promoter and the regulatory region.

The diagrams to the left of the bar graph show, first, the intact DNA (830 kb) and, next, the three altered DNA sequences. (Each is called a "deletion" because a particular section of DNA has been deleted from it.) A red X indicates the segment (A, B, and/or C) that was deleted in each experimental treatment.

The horizontal bar graph shows the amount of *Hoxd13* mRNA that was present in the digit-formation zone of each mutant 12.5-day-old embryo paw relative to the amount that was in the digit-formation zone of the mouse that had the intact regulatory region (top bar = 100%).

The images on the right are fluorescent micrographs of the embryo paws showing the location of the *Hoxd13* mRNA (stain appears blue or black). The white triangles show the location where the thumb will form.

Interpret the Data

1. The researchers hypothesized that all three regulatory segments (A, B, and C) were required for full expression of the *Hoxd13* gene. By measuring the amount of *Hoxd13* mRNA in the embryo paw zones where digits develop, they could measure the effect of the

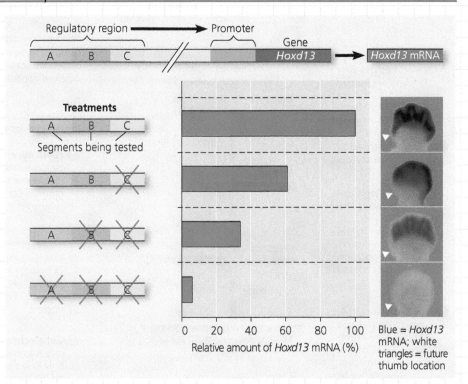

Blue = *Hoxd13* mRNA; white triangles = future thumb location

regulatory segments singly and in combination. Refer to the graph to answer these questions, noting that the segments being tested are shown on the vertical axis and the relative amount of *Hoxd13* mRNA is shown on the horizontal axis. (a) Which of the four treatments was used as a control for the experiment? (b) The hypothesis is that all three segments together are required for highest expression of the *Hoxd13* gene. Is this supported by the results? Explain your answer.

2. (a) What is the effect on the amount of *Hoxd13* mRNA when segments B and C are both deleted, compared with the control? (b) Is this effect visible in the blue-stained regions of the *in situ* hybridizations? How would you describe the spatial pattern of gene expression in the embryo paws that lack segments B and C? (You'll need to look carefully at different regions of each paw and how they differ.)

3. (a) What is the effect on the amount of *Hoxd13* mRNA when just segment C is deleted, compared with the control? (b) Is this effect visible in the *in situ* hybridizations? How would you describe the spatial pattern of gene expression in embryo paws that lack just segment C, compared with the control and with the paws that lack segments B and C?

4. If the researchers had only measured the amount of *Hoxd13* mRNA and not done the *in situ* hybridizations, what important information about the role of the regulatory segments in *Hoxd13* gene expression during paw development would have been missed? Conversely, if the researchers had only done the *in situ* hybridizations, what information would have been inaccessible?

(MB) A version of this Scientific Skills Exercise can be assigned in MasteringBiology.

Data from T. Montavon et al., A regulatory archipelago controls *Hox* genes transcription in digits, *Cell* 147:1132–1145 (2011).

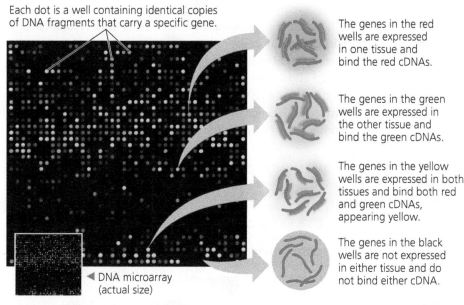

Each dot is a well containing identical copies of DNA fragments that carry a specific gene.

The genes in the red wells are expressed in one tissue and bind the red cDNAs.

The genes in the green wells are expressed in the other tissue and bind the green cDNAs.

The genes in the yellow wells are expressed in both tissues and bind both red and green cDNAs, appearing yellow.

The genes in the black wells are not expressed in either tissue and do not bind either cDNA.

◀ DNA microarray (actual size)

▲ **Figure 20.13 DNA microarray assay of gene expression levels.** Researchers synthesized two sets of cDNAs, fluorescently labeled red or green, from mRNAs from two different human tissues. These cDNAs were hybridized with a microarray containing 5,760 human genes (about 25% of human genes), resulting in the pattern shown here. The intensity of fluorescence at each spot is a measure of the relative expression in the two samples of the gene represented by that spot: Red indicates expression in one sample, green in the other, yellow in both, and black in neither.

samples (for example, different tissues) are labeled with molecules that emit different colors and tested on the same microarray. **Figure 20.13** shows the result of such an experiment, identifying the subsets of genes in the genome that are being expressed in one tissue compared with another. DNA technology makes such studies possible; with automation, they are easily performed on a large scale. Scientists can now measure the expression of thousands of genes at one time.

Alternatively, with the advent of rapid, inexpensive DNA sequencing methods, researchers can now afford to simply sequence the cDNA samples from different tissues or different embryonic stages in order to discover which genes are expressed. This straightforward method is called *RNA sequencing* or *RNA-seq* (pronounced "RNA-seek"), even though it is the cDNA that is actually sequenced. As the price of DNA sequencing plummets, this method is becoming more widely used for many applications. In most cases, however, expression of individual genes would still need to be confirmed by RT-PCR.

By uncovering gene interactions and providing clues to gene function, DNA microarray assays and RNA-seq may contribute to a better understanding of diseases and suggest new diagnostic techniques or therapies. For instance, comparing patterns of gene expression in breast cancer tumors and noncancerous breast tissue has already resulted in more informed and effective treatment protocols (see Figure 18.27). Ultimately, information from these methods should provide a grander view of how ensembles of genes interact to form an organism and maintain its vital systems.

Determining Gene Function

Once they identify a gene of interest, how do scientists determine its function? A gene's sequence can be compared with sequences in other species. If the function of a similar gene in another species is known, one might suspect that the gene product in question performs a comparable task. Data about the location and timing of gene expression may reinforce the suggested function. To obtain stronger evidence, one approach is to disable the gene and then observe the consequences in the cell or organism. In one such technique, called *in vitro* **mutagenesis**, specific mutations are introduced into a cloned gene, and the mutated gene is returned to a cell in such a way that it disables ("knocks out") the normal cellular copies of the same gene. If the introduced mutations alter or destroy the function of the gene product, the phenotype of the mutant cell may help reveal the function of the missing normal protein. Using molecular and genetic techniques worked out in the 1980s, researchers can generate mice with any given gene disabled, in order to study the role of that gene in development and in the adult. Mario Capecchi, Martin Evans, and Oliver Smithies received the Nobel Prize in 2007 for developing this technique.

A newer method for silencing expression of selected genes exploits the phenomenon of **RNA interference (RNAi)**, described in Chapter 18. This experimental approach uses synthetic double-stranded RNA molecules matching the sequence of a particular gene to trigger breakdown of the gene's messenger RNA or to block its translation. In organisms such as the nematode and the fruit fly, RNAi has already proved valuable for analyzing the functions of genes on a large scale.

In humans, ethical considerations prohibit knocking out genes to determine their functions. An alternative approach is to analyze the genomes of large numbers of people with a certain phenotypic condition or disease, such as heart disease or diabetes, to try to find differences they all share compared with people without that condition. The assumption is that these differences may be associated with one or more malfunctioning genes, thus in a sense being naturally occurring gene knockouts. Such large-scale analyses, called **genome-wide association studies**, do not require complete sequencing of all the genomes in the two groups. Instead, researchers test for *genetic markers*, DNA sequences that vary in the population. In a gene, such sequence variation is the basis of different alleles, as we have seen for sickle-cell disease (see Figure 17.25). And just like the coding sequences of genes, noncoding DNA at a specific locus on a chromosome may exhibit small nucleotide differences among individuals. Variations in coding or noncoding DNA sequence among a population are called polymorphisms (from the Greek for "many forms").

Among the most useful genetic markers in tracking down genes that contribute to diseases and disorders are single base-pair variations in the genomes of the human population. A single base-pair site where variation is found in at least 1% of the population is called a **single nucleotide polymorphism** (**SNP**, pronounced "snip"). A few million SNPs occur in the human genome, about once in 100–300 base pairs of both coding and noncoding DNA sequences. It isn't necessary to sequence the DNA of multiple individuals to find SNPs; today they can be detected by very sensitive microarray analysis or by PCR.

Once a SNP is identified that is found in all affected people, researchers focus on that region and sequence it. In nearly all cases, the SNP itself does not contribute directly to the disease in question by altering the encoded protein; in fact, most SNPs are in noncoding regions. Instead, if the SNP and a disease-causing allele are close enough, scientists can take advantage of the fact that crossing over between the marker and the gene is very unlikely during gamete formation. Therefore, the marker and gene will almost always be inherited together, even though the marker is not part of the gene (Figure 20.14). SNPs have been found that correlate with diabetes, heart disease, and several types of cancer, and the search is on for genes that might be involved.

The experimental approaches you have learned about thus far focused on working with molecules, mainly DNA and proteins. In a parallel line of inquiry, biologists have

▲ **Figure 20.14 Single nucleotide polymorphisms (SNPs) as genetic markers for disease-causing alleles.** This diagram depicts homologous segments of DNA from two groups of individuals, those in one group having a particular disease or condition with a genetic basis. Unaffected people have an A/T pair at a particular SNP locus, while affected people have a C/G pair at that locus. A SNP that varies in this way is likely to be closely linked to one or more alleles of genes that contribute to the disease in question.

MAKE CONNECTIONS *What does it mean for a SNP to be "closely linked" to a disease-causing allele, and how does this allow the SNP to be used as a genetic marker? (See Concept 15.3.)*

been developing powerful techniques for cloning whole multicellular organisms. One aim of this work is to obtain special types of cells, called stem cells, that can give rise to all types of tissues. Being able to manipulate stem cells would allow scientists to use the DNA-based methods previously discussed to alter stem cells for the treatment of diseases. Methods involving the cloning of organisms and production of stem cells are the subject of the next section.

CONCEPT CHECK 20.2

1. Describe the role of complementary base pairing during RT-PCR and DNA microarray analysis.
2. **WHAT IF?** Consider the microarray in Figure 20.13. If a sample from normal tissue is labeled with a green fluorescent dye, and a sample from cancerous tissue is labeled red, what color spots would represent genes you would be interested in if you were studying cancer? Explain.

For suggested answers, see Appendix A.

CONCEPT 20.3

Cloned organisms and stem cells are useful for basic research and other applications

Along with advances in DNA technology, scientists have been developing and refining methods for cloning whole multicellular organisms from single cells. In this context, cloning produces one or more organisms that are genetically identical to the "parent" that donated the single cell. This is often called *organismal cloning* to differentiate it from gene cloning and, more significantly, from cell cloning—the division of an asexually reproducing cell into a group of genetically identical cells. (The common theme is that the product is genetically identical to the parent. In fact, the word *clone* comes from the Greek *klon*, meaning "twig.") The current interest in organismal cloning arises primarily from its ability to generate stem cells. A **stem cell** is a relatively unspecialized cell that can both reproduce itself indefinitely and, under appropriate conditions, differentiate into specialized cells of one or more types. Stem cells have great potential for regenerating damaged tissues.

The cloning of plants and animals was first attempted over 50 years ago in experiments designed to answer basic biological questions. For example, researchers wondered if all the cells of an organism have the same genes or whether cells lose genes during the process of differentiation (see Concept 18.4). One way to answer this question is to see whether a differentiated cell can generate a whole organism—in other words, whether cloning an organism is possible. Let's discuss these early experiments before we consider more recent progress in organismal cloning and procedures for producing stem cells.

▲ Figure 20.15 The cloning of a whole carrot plant from a single carrot cell.

Fragments were cultured in nutrient medium; stirring caused single cells to shear off into the liquid.

Single cells free in suspension began to divide.

Embryonic plant developed from a cultured single cell.

Plantlet was cultured on agar medium. Later it was planted in soil.

Cross section of carrot root

Small fragments

Adult plant

Cloning Plants: Single-Cell Cultures

The successful cloning of whole plants from single differentiated cells was accomplished during the 1950s by F. C. Steward and his students at Cornell University, who worked with carrot plants (**Figure 20.15**). They found that differentiated cells taken from the root (the carrot) and incubated in culture medium could grow into normal adult plants, each genetically identical to the parent plant. These results showed that differentiation does not necessarily involve irreversible changes in the DNA. In plants, at least, mature cells can "dedifferentiate" and then give rise to all the specialized cell types of the organism. Any cell with this potential is said to be **totipotent**.

Plant cloning is used extensively in agriculture. For plants such as orchids, cloning is the only commercially practical means of reproducing plants. In other cases, cloning has been used to reproduce a plant with valuable characteristics, such as resistance to plant pathogens. In fact, you yourself may be a plant cloner: If you have ever grown a new plant from a cutting, you have practiced cloning!

Cloning Animals: Nuclear Transplantation

Differentiated cells from animals generally do not divide in culture, much less develop into the multiple cell types of a new organism. Therefore, early researchers had to use a different approach to answer the question: Are differentiated animal cells totipotent? Their approach was to remove the nucleus of an unfertilized or fertilized egg and replace it

with the nucleus of a differentiated cell, a procedure called *nuclear transplantation*. If the nucleus from the differentiated donor cell retains its full genetic capability, then it should be able to direct development of the recipient cell into all the tissues and organs of an organism.

Such experiments were conducted on one species of frog (*Rana pipiens*) by Robert Briggs and Thomas King in the 1950s and on another (*Xenopus laevis*) by John Gurdon in the 1970s (**Figure 20.16**). These researchers transplanted a

▼ Figure 20.16 | **Inquiry**

Can the nucleus from a differentiated animal cell direct development of an organism?

Experiment John Gurdon and colleagues at Oxford University, in England, destroyed the nuclei of frog (*Xenopus laevis*) eggs by exposing the eggs to ultraviolet light. They then transplanted nuclei from cells of frog embryos and tadpoles into the enucleated eggs.

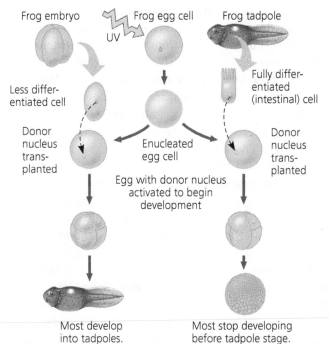

Frog embryo

Frog egg cell

Frog tadpole

UV

Less differentiated cell

Fully differentiated (intestinal) cell

Donor nucleus transplanted

Enucleated egg cell

Donor nucleus transplanted

Egg with donor nucleus activated to begin development

Most develop into tadpoles.

Most stop developing before tadpole stage.

Results When the transplanted nuclei came from an early embryo, the cells of which are relatively undifferentiated, most of the recipient eggs developed into tadpoles. But when the nuclei came from the fully differentiated intestinal cells of a tadpole, fewer than 2% of the eggs developed into normal tadpoles, and most of the embryos stopped developing at a much earlier stage.

Conclusion The nucleus from a differentiated frog cell can direct development of a tadpole. However, its ability to do so decreases as the donor cell becomes more differentiated, presumably because of changes in the nucleus.

Source: J. B. Gurdon et al., The developmental capacity of nuclei transplanted from keratinized cells of adult frogs, *Journal of Embryology and Experimental Morphology* 34:93–112 (1975).

WHAT IF? *If each cell in a four-cell embryo was already so specialized that it was not totipotent, what results would you predict for the experiment on the left side of the figure?*

nucleus from an embryonic or tadpole cell into an enucleated (nucleus-lacking) egg of the same species. In Gurdon's experiments, the transplanted nucleus was often able to support normal development of the egg into a tadpole. However, he found that the potential of a transplanted nucleus to direct normal development was inversely related to the age of the donor: the older the donor nucleus, the lower the percentage of normally developing tadpoles (see Figure 20.16).

From these results, Gurdon concluded that something in the nucleus *does* change as animal cells differentiate. In frogs and most other animals, nuclear potential tends to be restricted more and more as embryonic development and cell differentiation progress. These were foundational experiments that ultimately led to stem cell technology, and Gurdon received the 2012 Nobel Prize in Medicine for this work.

Reproductive Cloning of Mammals

In addition to cloning frogs, researchers have long been able to clone mammals by transplanting nuclei or cells from a variety of early embryos into enucleated eggs. But it was not known whether a nucleus from a fully differentiated cell could be reprogrammed successfully to act as a donor nucleus. In 1997, however, researchers at the Roslin Institute in Scotland captured newspaper headlines when they announced the birth of Dolly, a lamb cloned from an adult sheep by nuclear transplantation from a differentiated cell (Figure 20.17). These researchers achieved the necessary dedifferentiation of donor nuclei by culturing mammary cells in nutrient-poor medium. They then fused these cells with enucleated sheep eggs. The resulting diploid cells divided to form early embryos, which were implanted into surrogate mothers. Out of several hundred embryos, one successfully completed normal development, and Dolly was born.

Later analyses showed that Dolly's chromosomal DNA was indeed identical to that of the nucleus donor. (Her mitochondrial DNA came from the egg donor, as expected.) At the age of 6, Dolly suffered complications from a lung disease usually seen only in much older sheep and was euthanized. Dolly's premature death, as well as an arthritic condition, led to speculation that her cells were in some way not quite as healthy as those of a normal sheep, possibly reflecting incomplete reprogramming of the original transplanted nucleus.

Since that time, researchers have cloned numerous other mammals, including mice, cats, cows, horses, pigs, dogs, and monkeys. In most cases, their goal has been the production of new individuals; this is known as *reproductive cloning*. We have already learned a lot from such experiments. For example, cloned animals of the same species do *not* always look or behave identically. In a herd of cows cloned from the same line of cultured cells, certain cows are dominant in behavior and others are more submissive. Another example of nonidentity in clones is the first cloned cat, named CC for

▼ Figure 20.17 **Research Method**

Reproductive Cloning of a Mammal by Nuclear Transplantation

Application This method produces cloned animals with nuclear genes identical to those of the animal supplying the nucleus.

Technique Shown here is the procedure used to produce Dolly, the first reported case of a mammal cloned using the nucleus of a differentiated cell.

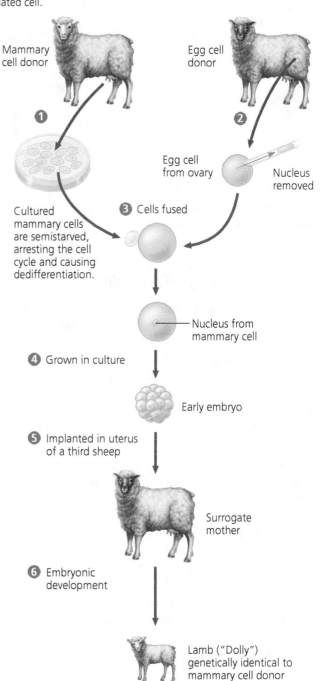

Results The genetic makeup of the cloned animal is identical to that of the animal supplying the nucleus but differs from that of the egg donor and surrogate mother. (The latter two are "Scottish blackface" sheep, with dark faces.)

▲ **Figure 20.18 CC, the first cloned cat, and her single parent.** Rainbow (left) donated the nucleus in a cloning procedure that resulted in CC (right). However, the two cats are not identical: Rainbow is a classic calico cat with orange patches on her fur and has a "reserved personality," while CC has a gray and white coat and is more playful.

Carbon Copy (**Figure 20.18**). She has a calico coat, like her single female parent, but the color and pattern are different because of random X chromosome inactivation, which is a normal occurrence during embryonic development (see Figure 15.8). And identical human twins, which are naturally occurring "clones," are always slightly different. Clearly, environmental influences and random phenomena play a significant role during development.

Faulty Gene Regulation in Cloned Animals

In most nuclear transplantation studies thus far, only a small percentage of cloned embryos develop normally to birth. And like Dolly, many cloned animals exhibit defects. Cloned mice, for instance, are prone to obesity, pneumonia, liver failure, and premature death. Scientists assert that even cloned animals that appear normal are likely to have subtle defects.

In recent years, we have begun to uncover some reasons for the low efficiency of cloning and the high incidence of abnormalities. In the nuclei of fully differentiated cells, a small subset of genes is turned on and expression of the rest is repressed. This regulation often is the result of epigenetic changes in chromatin, such as acetylation of histones or methylation of DNA (see Figure 18.7). During the nuclear transfer procedure, many of these changes must be reversed in the later-stage nucleus from a donor animal for genes to be expressed or repressed appropriately in early stages of development. Researchers have found that the DNA in cells from cloned embryos, like that of differentiated cells, often has more methyl groups than does the DNA in equivalent cells from normal embryos of the same species. This finding suggests that the reprogramming of donor nuclei requires

more accurate and complete chromatin restructuring than occurs during cloning procedures. Because DNA methylation helps regulate gene expression, misplaced or extra methyl groups in the DNA of donor nuclei may interfere with the pattern of gene expression necessary for normal embryonic development. In fact, the success of a cloning attempt may depend in large part on whether or not the chromatin in the donor nucleus can be artificially modified to resemble that of a newly fertilized egg.

Stem Cells of Animals

Progress in cloning mammalian embryos, including primates, has heightened speculation about the cloning of humans, which has not yet been achieved. The main reason researchers are trying to clone human embryos is not for reproduction, but for the production of stem cells to treat human diseases. Recall that a stem cell is a relatively unspecialized cell that can both reproduce itself indefinitely and, under appropriate conditions, differentiate into specialized cells of one or more types (**Figure 20.19**). Thus, stem cells are able both to replenish their own population and to generate cells that travel down specific differentiation pathways.

Embryonic and Adult Stem Cells

Many early animal embryos contain stem cells capable of giving rise to differentiated cells of any type. Stem cells can be isolated from early embryos at a stage called the blastula stage or its human equivalent, the blastocyst stage. In culture, these *embryonic stem (ES) cells* reproduce indefinitely; and depending on culture conditions, they can be made to differentiate

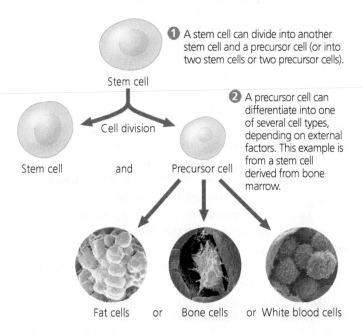

❶ A stem cell can divide into another stem cell and a precursor cell (or into two stem cells or two precursor cells).

Stem cell

Cell division

Stem cell   and   Precursor cell

❷ A precursor cell can differentiate into one of several cell types, depending on external factors. This example is from a stem cell derived from bone marrow.

Fat cells   or   Bone cells   or   White blood cells

▲ **Figure 20.19 How stem cells maintain their own population and generate differentiated cells.**

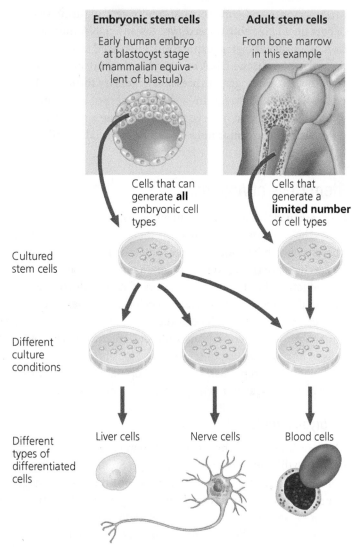

Embryonic stem cells

Early human embryo at blastocyst stage (mammalian equivalent of blastula)

Adult stem cells

From bone marrow in this example

Cells that can generate **all** embryonic cell types

Cells that generate a **limited number** of cell types

Cultured stem cells

Different culture conditions

Different types of differentiated cells

Liver cells

Nerve cells

Blood cells

▲ **Figure 20.20 Working with stem cells.** Animal stem cells, which can be isolated from early embryos or adult tissues and grown in culture, are self-perpetuating, relatively undifferentiated cells. Embryonic stem cells are easier to grow than adult stem cells and can theoretically give rise to *all* types of cells in an organism. The range of cell types that can arise from adult stem cells is not yet fully understood.

into a wide variety of specialized cells (**Figure 20.20**), including even eggs and sperm.

The adult body also has stem cells, which serve to replace nonreproducing specialized cells as needed. In contrast to ES cells, *adult stem cells* are not able to give rise to all cell types in the organism, though they can generate multiple types. For example, one of the several types of stem cells in bone marrow can generate all the different kinds of blood cells (see Figure 20.20), and another can differentiate into bone, cartilage, fat, muscle, and the linings of blood vessels. To the surprise of many, the adult brain has been found to contain stem cells that continue to produce certain kinds of nerve cells there. Researchers have also reported finding stem cells in skin, hair, eyes, and dental pulp. Although adult animals have only tiny numbers of stem cells, scientists are

learning to identify and isolate these cells from various tissues and, in some cases, to grow them in culture. With the right culture conditions (for instance, the addition of specific growth factors), cultured stem cells from adult animals have been made to differentiate into multiple types of specialized cells, although none are as versatile as ES cells.

Research with embryonic or adult stem cells is a source of valuable data about differentiation and has enormous potential for medical applications. The ultimate aim is to supply cells for the repair of damaged or diseased organs: for example, insulin-producing pancreatic cells for people with type 1 diabetes or certain kinds of brain cells for people with Parkinson's disease or Huntington's disease. Adult stem cells from bone marrow have long been used as a source of immune system cells in patients whose own immune systems are nonfunctional because of genetic disorders or radiation treatments for cancer.

The developmental potential of adult stem cells is limited to certain tissues. ES cells hold more promise than adult stem cells for most medical applications because ES cells are **pluripotent**, capable of differentiating into many different cell types. The only way to obtain ES cells thus far, however, has been to harvest them from human embryos, which raises ethical and political issues.

ES cells are currently obtained from embryos donated by patients undergoing infertility treatments or from long-term cell cultures originally established with cells isolated from donated embryos. If scientists were able to clone human embryos to the blastocyst stage, they might be able to use such clones as the source of ES cells in the future. Furthermore, with a donor nucleus from a person with a particular disease, they might be able to produce ES cells that match the patient and are thus not rejected by his or her immune system when used for treatment. When the main aim of cloning is to produce ES cells to treat disease, the process is called *therapeutic cloning*. Although most people believe that reproductive cloning of humans is unethical, opinions vary about the morality of therapeutic cloning.

Induced Pluripotent Stem (iPS) Cells

Resolving the debate now seems less urgent because researchers have learned to turn back the clock in fully differentiated cells, reprogramming them to act like ES cells. The accomplishment of this feat, which posed formidable obstacles, was announced in 2007, first by labs using mouse skin cells and then by additional groups using cells from human skin and other organs or tissues. In all these cases, researchers transformed the differentiated cells into a type of ES cell by using a retrovirus to introduce extra, cloned copies of four "stem cell" master regulatory genes. The "deprogrammed" cells are known as *induced pluripotent stem* (*iPS*) cells because, in using this fairly simple laboratory technique to return them to their undifferentiated state, pluripotency has been restored. The experiments that first transformed human differentiated cells into iPS cells are described in **Figure 20.21**. Shinya Yamanaka received the 2012 Nobel Prize in Medicine for this work, shared with John Gurdon, whose work you read about in Figure 20.16.

By many criteria, iPS cells can perform most of the functions of ES cells, but there are some differences in gene expression and other cellular functions, such as cell division. At least until these differences are fully understood, the study of ES cells will continue to make important contributions to the development of stem cell therapies. (In fact, it is likely that ES cells will always be a focus of basic research as well.) In the meantime, work is proceeding using the iPS cells that have been experimentally produced.

There are two major potential uses for human iPS cells. First, cells from patients suffering from diseases can be reprogrammed to become iPS cells, which can act as model cells for studying the disease and potential treatments. Human iPS cell lines have already been developed from individuals with type 1 diabetes, Parkinson's disease, and at least a dozen other diseases. Second, in the field of regenerative medicine, a patient's own cells could be reprogrammed into iPS cells and then used to replace nonfunctional tissues, such as insulin-producing cells of the pancreas.

Recently, in another surprising development, researchers have been able to identify genes that can directly reprogram a differentiated cell into another type of differentiated cell without passing through a pluripotent state. In the first reported example, one type of cell in the pancreas was transformed into another type. However, the two types of cells do not need to be very closely related: Another research group has been able to directly reprogram a skin fibroblast into a nerve cell. Development techniques that direct iPS cells or even fully differentiated cells to become specific cell types for regenerative medicine is an area of intense research, one that has already seen some success. The iPS cells created in this way could eventually provide tailor-made "replacement" cells for patients without using any human eggs or embryos, thus circumventing most ethical objections.

CONCEPT CHECK 20.3

1. Based on current knowledge, how would you explain the difference in the percentage of tadpoles that developed from the two kinds of donor nuclei in Figure 20.16?

2. If you were to clone a carrot using the technique shown in Figure 20.15, would all the progeny plants ("clones") look identical? Why or why not?

3. **MAKE CONNECTIONS** Compare an individual carrot cell in Figure 20.15 with the fully differentiated muscle cell in Figure 18.18 in terms of their potential to develop into different cell types.

For suggested answers, see Appendix A.

▼ Figure 20.21 **Inquiry**

Can a fully differentiated human cell be "deprogrammed" to become a stem cell?

Experiment Shinya Yamanaka and colleagues at Kyoto University, in Japan, used a retroviral vector to introduce four genes into fully differentiated human skin fibroblast cells. The cells were then cultured in a medium that would support growth of stem cells.

Stem cell

Precursor cell

Oct3/4   *Sox2*

Four "stem cell" master regulator genes were introduced, using the retroviral cloning vector.

Klf4   *c-Myc*

Skin fibroblast cell

Induced pluripotent stem (iPS) cell

Results Two weeks later, the cells resembled embryonic stem cells in appearance and were actively dividing. Their gene expression patterns, gene methylation patterns, and other characteristics were also consistent with those of embryonic stem cells. The iPS cells were able to differentiate into heart muscle cells, as well as other cell types.

Conclusion The four genes induced differentiated skin cells to become pluripotent stem cells, with characteristics of embryonic stem cells.

Source: K. Takahashi et al., Induction of pluripotent stem cells from adult human fibroblasts by defined factors, *Cell* 131:861–872 (2007).

WHAT IF? *Patients with diseases such as heart disease, diabetes, or Alzheimer's could have their own skin cells reprogrammed to become iPS cells. Once procedures have been developed for converting iPS cells into heart, pancreatic, or nervous system cells, the patients' own iPS cells might be used to treat their disease. When organs are transplanted from a donor to a diseased recipient, the recipient's immune system may reject the transplant, a condition with serious and often fatal consequences. Would using iPS cells be expected to carry the same risk? Why or why not? Given that these cells are actively dividing, undifferentiated cells, what risks might this procedure carry?*

CONCEPT 20.4

The practical applications of DNA-based biotechnology affect our lives in many ways

DNA technology is in the news almost every day. Most often, the topic is a new and promising application in medicine, but this is just one of numerous fields benefiting from DNA technology and genetic engineering.

Medical Applications

One important use of DNA technology is the identification of human genes whose mutation plays a role in genetic diseases. These discoveries may lead to ways of diagnosing, treating, and even preventing such conditions. DNA technology is also contributing to our understanding of "nongenetic" diseases, from arthritis to AIDS, since a person's genes influence susceptibility to these diseases. Furthermore, diseases of all sorts involve changes in gene expression within the affected cells and often within the patient's immune system. By using DNA microarray assays (see Figure 20.13) or other techniques to compare gene expression in healthy and diseased tissues, researchers hope to find many of the genes that are turned on or off in particular diseases. These genes and their products are potential targets for prevention or therapy.

Diagnosis and Treatment of Diseases

A new chapter in the diagnosis of infectious diseases has been opened by DNA technology, in particular the use of PCR and labeled nucleic acid probes to track down pathogens. For example, because the sequence of the RNA genome of HIV is known, RT-PCR can be used to amplify, and thus detect, HIV RNA in blood or tissue samples (see Figure 20.12). RT-PCR is often the best way to detect an otherwise elusive infective agent.

Medical scientists can now diagnose hundreds of human genetic disorders by using PCR with primers that target the genes associated with these disorders. The amplified DNA product is then sequenced to reveal the presence or absence of the disease-causing mutation. Among the genes for human diseases that have been identified are those for sickle-cell disease, hemophilia, cystic fibrosis, Huntington's disease, and Duchenne muscular dystrophy. Individuals afflicted with such diseases can often be identified before the onset of symptoms, even before birth (see Figure 14.19). PCR can also be used to identify symptomless carriers of potentially harmful recessive alleles.

As you learned earlier, genome-wide association studies have pinpointed SNPs (single nucleotide polymorphisms) that are linked to disease-causing alleles (see Figure 20.13).

Individuals can be tested by PCR and sequencing for a SNP that is correlated with the abnormal allele. The presence of particular SNPs is correlated with increased risk for conditions such as heart disease, Alzheimer's, and some types of cancer. Companies that offer individual genetic testing for risk factors like these are looking for previously identified, linked SNPs. It may be helpful for individuals to learn about their health risks, with the understanding that such genetic tests merely reflect correlations and do not make predictions.

The techniques described in this chapter have also prompted improvements in disease treatments. By analyzing the expression of many genes in breast cancer patients, researchers have been able to refine their understanding of the different subtypes of breast cancer (see Figure 18.27). Knowing the expression levels of particular genes can help physicians determine the likelihood that the cancer will recur, thus helping them design an appropriate treatment. Given that some low-risk patients have a 96% survival rate over a ten-year period with no treatment, gene expression analysis allows doctors and patients access to valuable information when they are considering treatment options.

Many envision a future of "personalized medicine" where each person's genetic profile can inform them about diseases or conditions for which they are especially at risk and help them make treatment choices. As we will discuss later in the chapter, a *genetic profile* is currently taken to mean a set of genetic markers such as SNPs. Ultimately, however, it will likely mean the complete DNA sequence of an individual—once sequencing becomes inexpensive enough. (See the interview with Charles Rotimi before Chapter 13.) Our ability to sequence a person's genome rapidly and inexpensively is advancing faster than our development of appropriate treatments for the conditions we are characterizing. Still, the identification of genes involved in these conditions provides us with good targets for therapeutic interventions.

Human Gene Therapy

Gene therapy—the introduction of genes into an afflicted individual for therapeutic purposes—holds great potential for treating the relatively small number of disorders traceable to a single defective gene. In theory, a normal allele of the defective gene could be inserted into the somatic cells of the tissue affected by the disorder.

For gene therapy of somatic cells to be permanent, the cells that receive the normal allele must be cells that multiply throughout the patient's life. Bone marrow cells, which include the stem cells that give rise to all the cells of the blood and immune system, are prime candidates. **Figure 20.22** outlines one procedure for gene therapy of an individual whose bone marrow cells do not produce a vital enzyme because of a single defective gene. One type of severe combined immunodeficiency (SCID) is caused by this kind of defect. If the treatment is successful, the patient's bone marrow cells will begin producing the missing protein, and the patient may be cured.

Cloned gene (normal allele, absent from patient's cells)

1 Insert RNA version of normal allele into retrovirus or other viral vector.

Viral RNA

Viral capsid

2 Let virus infect bone marrow cells that have been removed from the patient and cultured.

3 Viral DNA carrying the normal allele inserts into chromosome.

Bone marrow cell from patient

4 Inject engineered cells into patient.

Bone marrow

▲ **Figure 20.22 Gene therapy using a retroviral vector.** A retrovirus that has been rendered harmless is used as a vector in this procedure, which exploits the ability of a retrovirus to insert a DNA transcript of its RNA genome into the chromosomal DNA of its host cell (see Figure 19.8). If the foreign gene carried by the retroviral vector is expressed, the cell and its descendants will possess the gene product. Cells that reproduce throughout life, such as bone marrow cells, are ideal candidates for gene therapy.

The procedure shown in Figure 20.22 has been used in gene therapy trials for SCID. In a trial begun in France in 2000, ten young children with SCID were treated by the same procedure. Nine of these patients showed significant, definitive improvement after two years, the first indisputable success of gene therapy. However, three of the patients subsequently developed leukemia, a type of blood cell cancer, and one of them died. Researchers have concluded it is likely that the insertion of the retroviral vector occurred near a gene that triggers the proliferation of blood cells. Using a viral vector that does not come from a retrovirus, clinical researchers have treated at least three other genetic diseases somewhat successfully with gene therapy: a type of progressive blindness (see Concept 50.3), a degenerative disease of the nervous system, and a blood disorder involving the β-globin gene. The successful trials involve very few patients but are still cause for cautious optimism.

Gene therapy raises many technical issues. For example, how can the activity of the transferred gene be controlled so that cells make appropriate amounts of the gene product at the right time and in the right place? How can we be sure that the insertion of the therapeutic gene does not harm some other necessary cell function? As more is learned about DNA control elements and gene interactions, researchers may be able to answer such questions.

In addition to technical challenges, gene therapy provokes ethical questions. Some critics believe that tampering with human genes in any way is immoral or unethical. Other observers see no fundamental difference between the transplantation of genes into somatic cells and the transplantation of organs. You might wonder whether scientists are considering engineering human germ-line cells in the hope of correcting a defect in future generations. At present, no one in the mainstream scientific community is pursuing this goal—it is considered much too risky. Such genetic engineering is routinely done in laboratory mice, though, and the technical problems relating to similar genetic engineering in humans will eventually be solved. Under what circumstances, if any, should we alter the genomes of human germ lines? Would this inevitably lead to the practice of eugenics, a deliberate effort to control the genetic makeup of human populations? While we may not have to resolve these questions right now, considering them is worthwhile because they will probably arise at some point in the future.

Pharmaceutical Products

The pharmaceutical industry derives significant benefit from advances in DNA technology and genetic research, applying them to the development of useful drugs to treat diseases. Pharmaceutical products are synthesized using methods of either organic chemistry or biotechnology, depending on the nature of the product.

Synthesis of Small Molecules for Use as Drugs Determining the sequence and structure of proteins crucial for tumor cell survival has led to the identification of small molecules that combat certain cancers by blocking the function of these proteins. One drug, imatinib (trade name Gleevec), is a small molecule that inhibits a specific receptor tyrosine kinase (see Figure 11.8). The overexpression of this receptor, resulting from a chromosomal translocation, is instrumental in causing chronic myelogenous leukemia (CML; see Figure 15.16). Patients in the early stages of CML who are treated with imatinib have exhibited nearly complete, sustained remission from the cancer. Drugs that work in a similar way have also been used with success to treat a few types of lung and breast cancers. This approach is feasible only for cancers for which the molecular basis is fairly well understood.

In many cases of such drug-treated tumors, though, cells later arise that are resistant to the new drug. In one study, the whole genome of the tumor cells was sequenced both before and after the appearance of drug resistance. Comparison of the sequences showed genetic changes that allowed the tumor cells to "get around" the drug-inhibited protein. So we can see that cancer cells demonstrate the principles of evolution: Certain tumor cells have a random mutation that allows them to survive in the presence of a particular drug, and as a consequence of natural selection in the presence of the drug, these are the cells that survive and reproduce.

Protein Production in Cell Cultures Pharmaceutical products that are proteins are commonly synthesized on a large scale using cell cultures. You learned earlier in the chapter about DNA cloning and gene expression systems for producing large quantities of a chosen protein that is present naturally in only minute amounts. The host cells used in such expression systems can even be engineered to secrete a protein as it is made, thereby simplifying the task of purifying it by traditional biochemical methods.

Among the first pharmaceutical products manufactured in this way were human insulin and human growth hormone (HGH). Some 2 million people with diabetes in the United States depend on insulin treatment to control their disease. Human growth hormone has been a boon to children born with a form of dwarfism caused by inadequate amounts of HGH. Another important pharmaceutical product produced by genetic engineering is tissue plasminogen activator (TPA). If administered shortly after a heart attack, TPA helps dissolve blood clots and reduces the risk of subsequent heart attacks.

For the past 25 years, scientists have also been working on producing proteins in plant cell cultures. They have enjoyed recent success using carrot cells in culture to make an enzyme involved in fat breakdown that is used for treatment of a rare human disease. Plant cells are easily grown in culture (see Figure 20.15), requiring less precise conditions than animal cells. Also, they are unlikely to get contaminated by viruses that could infect animals, a situation that has on occasion held up production of the enzyme for some time. This successful accomplishment is likely to be further extended to other therapeutic proteins in the future.

Protein Production by "Pharm" Animals In some cases, instead of using cell systems to produce large quantities of protein products, pharmaceutical scientists can use whole animals. They can introduce a gene from an animal of one genotype into the genome of another individual, often of a different species. This individual is then called a **transgenic** animal. To do this, they first remove eggs from a female of the recipient species and fertilize them *in vitro*. Meanwhile, they have cloned the desired gene from the donor organism. They then inject the cloned DNA directly into the nuclei of the fertilized eggs. Some of the cells integrate the foreign DNA, the *transgene*, into their genome and are able to express the foreign gene. The engineered embryos that arise from these zygotes are then surgically implanted in a surrogate mother. If an embryo develops successfully, the result is a transgenic animal that expresses its new, "foreign" gene.

▲ **Figure 20.23 Goats as "pharm" animals.** This transgenic goat carries a gene for a human blood protein, antithrombin, which she secretes in her milk. Patients with a rare hereditary disorder in which this protein is lacking suffer from formation of blood clots in their blood vessels. Easily purified from the goat's milk, the protein is used to prevent blood clots in these patients during surgery or childbirth.

Assuming that the introduced gene encodes a protein desired in large quantities, these transgenic animals can act as pharmaceutical "factories." For example, a transgene for a human blood protein such as antithrombin, which prevents blood clots, can be inserted into the genome of a goat in such a way that the transgene's product is secreted in the animal's milk **(Figure 20.23)**. The protein is then purified from the milk (which is easier than purification from a cell culture).

Human proteins produced in transgenic farm animals for use in humans may differ in some ways from the naturally produced human proteins, possibly because of subtle differences in protein modification. Therefore, such proteins must be tested very carefully to ensure that they (or contaminants from the farm animals) will not cause allergic reactions or other adverse effects in patients who receive them.

Forensic Evidence and Genetic Profiles

In violent crimes, body fluids or small pieces of tissue may be left at the scene or on the clothes or other possessions of the victim or assailant. If enough blood, semen, or tissue is available, forensic laboratories can determine the blood type or tissue type by using antibodies to detect specific cell-surface proteins. However, such tests require fairly fresh samples in relatively large amounts. Also, because many people have the same blood or tissue type, this approach can only exclude a suspect; it cannot provide strong evidence of guilt.

DNA testing, on the other hand, can identify the guilty individual with a high degree of certainty, because the DNA sequence of every person is unique (except for identical twins). Genetic markers that vary in the population can be analyzed for a given person to determine that individual's unique set of genetic markers, or **genetic profile**. (This term is preferred over "DNA fingerprint" by forensic scientists, who want to emphasize the heritable aspect of these markers rather than the fact that they produce a pattern on a gel that, like a fingerprint, is visually recognizable.) The FBI started applying DNA technology to forensics in 1988, using a method involving gel electrophoresis and nucleic acid hybridization to detect similarities and differences in DNA samples. This method required much smaller samples of blood or tissue than earlier methods—only about 1,000 cells.

Today, forensic scientists use an even more sensitive method that takes advantage of variations in length of genetic markers called **short tandem repeats (STRs)**. These are tandemly repeated units of two- to five-nucleotide sequences in specific regions of the genome. The number of repeats present in these regions is highly variable from person to person (polymorphic), and even for a single individual, the two alleles of an STR may differ from each other. For example, one individual may have the sequence ACAT repeated 30 times at one genome locus and 15 times at the same locus on the other homolog, whereas another individual may have 18 repeats at this locus on each homolog. (These two genotypes can be expressed by the two repeat numbers: 30,15 and 18,18.) PCR is used to amplify particular STRs, using sets of primers that are labeled with different-colored fluorescent tags; the length of the region, and thus the number of repeats, can then be determined by electrophoresis. The PCR step allows use of this method even when the DNA is in poor condition or available only in minute quantities. A tissue sample containing as few as 20 cells can be sufficient for PCR amplification.

In a murder case, for example, this method can be used to compare DNA samples from the suspect, the victim, and a small amount of blood found at the crime scene. The forensic scientist tests only a few selected portions of the DNA—usually 13 STR markers. However, even this small set of markers can provide a forensically useful genetic profile because the probability that two people (who are not identical twins) would have exactly the same set of STR markers is vanishingly small. The Innocence Project, a nonprofit organization dedicated to overturning wrongful convictions, uses STR analysis of archived samples from crime scenes to revisit old cases. As of 2013, more than 300 innocent people have been released from prison as a result of forensic and legal work by this group (Figure 20.24).

Genetic profiles can also be useful for other purposes. A comparison of the DNA of a mother, her child, and the purported father can conclusively settle a question of paternity. Sometimes paternity is of historical interest: Genetic profiles provided strong evidence that Thomas Jefferson or one of his close male relatives fathered at least one of the children of his slave Sally Hemings. Genetic profiles can also identify victims of mass casualties. The largest such effort occurred after the attack on the World Trade Center in 2001; more than 10,000 samples of victims' remains were compared with DNA samples from personal items, such as tooth-brushes, provided by families. Ultimately, forensic scientists

(a) In 1984, Earl Washington was convicted and sentenced to death for the 1982 rape and murder of Rebecca Williams. His sentence was commuted to life in prison in 1993 due to new doubts about the evidence. In 2000, STR analysis by forensic scientists associated with the Innocence Project showed conclusively that he was innocent. This photo shows Washington just before his release in 2001, after 17 years in prison.

Source of sample	STR marker 1	STR marker 2	STR marker 3
Semen on victim	17,19	13,16	12,12
Earl Washington	16,18	14,15	11,12
Kenneth Tinsley	17,19	13,16	12,12

(b) In STR analysis, selected STR markers in a DNA sample are amplified by PCR, and the PCR products are separated by electrophoresis. The procedure reveals how many repeats are present for each STR locus in the sample. An individual has two alleles per STR locus, each with a certain number of repeats. This table shows the number of repeats for three STR markers in three samples: from semen found on the victim, from Washington, and from another man (Kenneth Tinsley), who was in prison because of an unrelated conviction. These and other STR data (not shown) exonerated Washington and led Tinsley to plead guilty to the murder.

▲ **Figure 20.24** STR analysis used to release an innocent man from prison.

succeeded in identifying almost 3,000 victims using these methods.

Just how reliable is a genetic profile? The greater the number of markers examined in a DNA sample, the more likely it is that the profile is unique to one individual. In forensic cases using STR analysis with 13 markers, the probability of two people having identical DNA profiles is somewhere between one chance in 10 billion and one in several trillion. (For comparison, the world's population is between 7 and 8 billion.) The exact probability depends on the frequency of those markers in the general population. Information on how common various markers are in different ethnic groups is critical because these marker frequencies may vary considerably among ethnic groups and between a particular ethnic group and the population as a whole. With the increasing availability of frequency data, forensic scientists can make extremely accurate statistical calculations. Thus, despite problems that can still arise from insufficient data, human error, or flawed evidence, genetic profiles are now accepted as compelling evidence by legal experts and scientists alike.

Environmental Cleanup

Increasingly, the remarkable ability of certain microorganisms to transform chemicals is being exploited for environmental cleanup. If the growth needs of such microbes make them unsuitable for direct use, scientists can now transfer the genes for their valuable metabolic capabilities into other microorganisms, which can then be used to treat environmental problems. For example, many bacteria can extract heavy metals, such as copper, lead, and nickel, from their environments and incorporate the metals into compounds such as copper sulfate or lead sulfate, which are readily recoverable. Genetically engineered microbes may become important in both mining (especially as ore reserves are depleted) and cleaning up highly toxic mining wastes. Biotechnologists are also trying to engineer microbes that can degrade chlorinated hydrocarbons and other harmful compounds. These microbes could be used in wastewater treatment plants or by manufacturers before the compounds are ever released into the environment.

Agricultural Applications

Scientists are working to learn more about the genomes of agriculturally important plants and animals. For a number of years, they have been using DNA technology in an effort to improve agricultural productivity. The selective breeding of both livestock (animal husbandry) and crops has exploited naturally occurring mutations and genetic recombination for thousands of years.

As we described earlier, DNA technology enables scientists to produce transgenic animals, which speeds up the selective breeding process. The goals of creating a transgenic animal are often the same as the goals of traditional breeding—for instance, to make a sheep with better quality wool, a pig with leaner meat, or a cow that will mature in a shorter time. Scientists might, for example, identify and clone a gene that causes the development of larger muscles (muscles make up most of the meat we eat) in one breed of cattle and transfer it to other cattle or even to sheep. However, problems such as low fertility or increased susceptibility to disease are not uncommon among farm animals carrying genes from other species. Animal health and welfare are important issues to consider when developing transgenic animals.

Agricultural scientists have already endowed a number of crop plants with genes for desirable traits, such as delayed ripening and resistance to spoilage and disease, as well as drought. The most commonly used vector for introducing new genes into plant cells is a plasmid, called the *Ti plasmid*, from the soil bacterium *Agrobacterium tumefaciens*. This plasmid integrates a segment of its DNA into the chromosomal DNA of its host plant cells (see Figure 35.25). To make transgenic plants, researchers engineer the plasmid to carry genes of interest and introduce it into cells. For many plant species, a single tissue cell grown in culture can give rise to an adult plant (see Figure 20.15). Thus, genetic manipulations can be performed on an ordinary somatic cell and the cell then used to generate an organism with new traits.

Genetic engineering is rapidly replacing traditional plant-breeding programs, especially for useful traits, such as herbicide or pest resistance, determined by one or a few genes. Crops engineered with a bacterial gene making the plants resistant to an herbicide can grow while weeds are destroyed, and genetically engineered crops that can resist destructive insects reduce the need for chemical insecticides. In India, the insertion of a salinity resistance gene from a coastal mangrove plant into the genomes of several rice varieties has resulted in rice plants that can grow in water three times as salty as seawater. The research foundation that carried out this feat of genetic engineering estimates that one-third of all irrigated land has high salinity owing to overirrigation and intensive use of chemical fertilizers, representing a serious threat to the food supply. Thus, salinity-resistant crop plants would be enormously valuable worldwide.

Safety and Ethical Questions Raised by DNA Technology

Early concerns about potential dangers associated with recombinant DNA technology focused on the possibility that hazardous new pathogens might be created. What might happen, for instance, if cancer cell genes were transferred into bacteria or viruses? To guard against such rogue microbes, scientists developed a set of guidelines that were adopted as formal government regulations in the United States and some other countries. One safety measure is a set of strict laboratory procedures designed to protect researchers from infection by engineered microbes and to prevent the microbes from accidentally leaving the laboratory. In addition, strains of microorganisms to be used in recombinant DNA experiments are genetically crippled to ensure that they cannot survive outside the laboratory. Finally, certain obviously dangerous experiments have been banned.

Today, most public concern about possible hazards centers not on recombinant microbes but on **genetically modified (GM) organisms** used as food. A GM organism is one that has acquired by artificial means one or more genes from another species or even from another variety of the same species. Some salmon, for example, have been genetically modified by addition of a more active salmon growth hormone gene. However, the majority of the GM organisms that contribute to our food supply are not animals, but crop plants.

GM crops are widespread in the United States, Argentina, and Brazil; together these countries account for over 80% of the world's acreage devoted to such crops. In the United States, most corn, soybean, and canola crops are genetically modified, and GM products are not required to be labeled at present. However, the same foods are an ongoing subject of controversy in Europe, where the GM revolution has met with strong opposition. Many Europeans are concerned about the safety of GM foods and the possible environmental consequences of growing GM plants. In the year 2000, negotiators from 130 countries agreed on a Biosafety Protocol that requires exporters to identify GM organisms present in bulk food shipments and allows importing countries to decide whether the products pose environmental or health risks. (Although the United States declined to sign the agreement, it went into effect anyway because the majority of countries were in favor of it.) Since then, European countries have, on occasion, refused crops from the United States and other countries, leading to trade disputes. Although a small number of GM crops have been grown on European soil, these products have generally failed in local markets, and the future of GM crops in Europe is uncertain.

Advocates of a cautious approach toward GM crops fear that transgenic plants might pass their new genes to close relatives in nearby wild areas. We know that lawn and crop grasses, for example, commonly exchange genes with wild relatives via pollen transfer. If crop plants carrying genes for resistance to herbicides, diseases, or insect pests pollinated wild ones, the offspring might become "super weeds" that are very difficult to control. Another worry concerns possible risks to human health from GM foods. Some people fear that the protein products of transgenes might lead to allergic reactions. Although there is some evidence that this could happen, advocates claim that these proteins could be tested in advance to avoid producing ones that cause allergic reactions. (For further discussion of plant biotechnology and GM crops, see Concept 38.3.)

Today, governments and regulatory agencies throughout the world are grappling with how to facilitate the use of biotechnology in agriculture, industry, and medicine while ensuring that new products and procedures are safe. In the United States, such applications of biotechnology are evaluated for potential risks by various regulatory agencies, including the Food and Drug Administration, the Environmental Protection Agency, the National Institutes of Health, and the Department of Agriculture. Meanwhile, these same agencies and the public must consider the ethical implications of biotechnology.

Advances in biotechnology have allowed us to obtain complete genome sequences for humans and many other species, providing a vast treasure trove of information about genes. We can ask how certain genes differ from species to species, as well as how genes and, ultimately, entire genomes have evolved. (These are the subjects of Chapter 21.) At the same time, the increasing speed and falling cost of sequencing the genomes of individuals are raising significant ethical questions. Who should have the right to examine someone else's genetic information? How should that information be used? Should a person's genome be a factor in determining eligibility for a job or insurance? Ethical considerations, as well as concerns about potential environmental and health hazards, will likely slow some applications of biotechnology. There is always a danger that too much regulation will stifle basic research and its potential benefits. However, the power of DNA technology and genetic engineering—our ability to profoundly and rapidly alter species that have been evolving for millennia—demands that we proceed with humility and caution.

CONCEPT CHECK 20.4

1. What is the advantage of using stem cells for gene therapy?

2. List at least three different properties that have been acquired by crop plants via genetic engineering.

3. **WHAT IF?** As a physician, you have a patient with symptoms that suggest a hepatitis A infection, but you have not been able to detect viral proteins in the blood. Knowing that hepatitis A is an RNA virus, what lab test could you perform to support your diagnosis? Explain the results that would support your hypothesis.

For suggested answers, see Appendix A.

---

20 Chapter Review

SUMMARY OF KEY CONCEPTS

CONCEPT 20.1

DNA sequencing and DNA cloning are valuable tools for genetic engineering and biological inquiry (pp. 409–417)

- **Nucleic acid hybridization**, the base pairing of one strand of a nucleic acid to the complementary sequence on a strand from another nucleic acid molecule, is widely used in DNA technology.

- **DNA sequencing** can be carried out using the *dideoxy chain termination* method in automated sequencing machines.
- Next-generation (high-throughput) techniques for sequencing DNA are based on *sequencing by synthesis*: DNA polymerase is used to synthesize a stretch of DNA from a single-stranded template, and the order in which nucleotides are added reveals the sequence.
- **Gene cloning** (or DNA cloning) produces multiple copies of a gene (or DNA fragment) that can be used in analyzing and manipulating DNA and can yield useful new products or organisms with beneficial traits.

- In **genetic engineering**, bacterial **restriction enzymes** are used to cut DNA molecules within short, specific nucleotide sequences (**restriction sites**), yielding a set of double-stranded **restriction fragments** with single-stranded **sticky ends**:

Sticky end

- The sticky ends on **restriction fragments** from one DNA source can base-pair with complementary sticky ends on fragments from other DNA molecules. Sealing the base-paired fragments with **DNA ligase** produces **recombinant DNA** molecules.
- DNA restriction fragments of different lengths can be separated by **gel electrophoresis**.
- The **polymerase chain reaction (PCR)** can produce many copies of (amplify) a specific target segment of DNA *in vitro*, using primers that bracket the desired sequence and a heat-resistant DNA polymerase.
- To clone a eukaryotic gene:

Cloning vector
(often a bacterial plasmid)

DNA fragments obtained by PCR or from another source (cut by same restriction enzyme used on cloning vector)

Mix and ligate

Recombinant DNA plasmids

Recombinant plasmids are returned to host cells, each of which divides to form a clone of cells.
- Several technical difficulties hinder the expression of cloned eukaryotic genes in bacterial host cells. The use of cultured eukaryotic cells as host cells, coupled with appropriate **expression vectors**, helps avoid these problems.

? *Describe how the process of gene cloning results in a cell clone containing a recombinant plasmid.*

CONCEPT 20.2

Biologists use DNA technology to study gene expression and function (pp. 417–422)

- Several techniques use hybridization of a **nucleic acid probe** to detect the presence of specific mRNAs.
- *In situ* **hybridization** and **RT-PCR** can detect the presence of a given mRNA in a tissue or an RNA sample, respectively.
- **DNA microarrays** are used to identify sets of genes co-expressed by a group of cells. Alternatively, their cDNAs can be sequenced (RNA-seq).
- For a gene of unknown function, experimental inactivation of the gene (a gene knockout) and observation of the resulting phenotypic effects can provide clues to its function. In humans, **genome-wide association studies** use **single nucleotide polymorphisms (SNPs)** as genetic markers for alleles that are associated with particular conditions.

? *What useful information is obtained by detecting expression of specific genes?*

CONCEPT 20.3

Cloned organisms and stem cells are useful for basic research and other applications (pp. 422–427)

- The question of whether all the cells in an organism have the same genome prompted the first attempts at organismal cloning.
- Single differentiated cells from plants are often **totipotent**: capable of generating all the tissues of a complete new plant.
- Transplantation of the nucleus from a differentiated animal cell into an enucleated egg can sometimes give rise to a new animal.
- Certain embryonic **stem cells** (ES cells) from animal embryos and particular adult stem cells from adult tissues can reproduce and differentiate both in the lab and in the organism, offering the potential for medical use. ES cells are **pluripotent** but difficult to acquire. Induced pluripotent stem (iPS) cells, generated by reprogramming differentiated cells, resemble ES cells in their capacity to differentiate. Some differentiated cells have been directly reprogrammed to become different cell types. These cells and iPS cells hold promise for medical research and regenerative medicine.

? *Describe how a researcher could carry out (1) organismal cloning, (2) production of ES cells, and (3) generation of iPS cells, focusing on how the cells are reprogrammed and using mice as an example. (The procedures are basically the same in humans and mice.)*

CONCEPT 20.4

The practical applications of DNA-based biotechnology affect our lives in many ways (pp. 428–433)

- DNA technology, including the analysis of genetic markers such as SNPs, is increasingly being used in the diagnosis of genetic and other diseases and offers potential for better treatment of genetic disorders (or even permanent cures through **gene therapy**), as well as more informed cancer therapies. DNA technology is used with cell cultures in the large-scale production of protein hormones and other proteins with therapeutic uses. Some therapeutic proteins are being produced in **transgenic** "pharm" animals.
- Analysis of genetic markers such as **short tandem repeats (STRs)** in DNA isolated from tissue or body fluids found at crime scenes leads to a **genetic profile**. Use of genetic profiles can provide definitive evidence that a suspect is innocent or strong evidence of guilt. Such analysis is also useful in parenthood disputes and in identifying the remains of crime victims.
- Genetically engineered microorganisms can be used to extract minerals from the environment or degrade various types of toxic waste materials.
- The aims of developing transgenic plants and animals are to improve agricultural productivity and food quality.
- The potential benefits of genetic engineering must be carefully weighed against the potential for harm to humans or the environment.

? *What factors affect whether a given genetic disease would be a good candidate for successful gene therapy?*

TEST YOUR UNDERSTANDING

LEVEL 1: KNOWLEDGE/COMPREHENSION

1. In DNA technology, the term *vector* can refer to
   a. the enzyme that cuts DNA into restriction fragments.
   b. the sticky end of a DNA fragment.
   c. a SNP marker.
   d. a plasmid used to transfer DNA into a living cell.

2. Which of the following tools of DNA technology is incorrectly paired with its use?
   a. electrophoresis—separation of DNA fragments
   b. DNA ligase—cutting DNA, creating sticky ends of restriction fragments
   c. DNA polymerase—polymerase chain reaction to amplify sections of DNA
   d. reverse transcriptase—production of cDNA from mRNA

3. Plants are more readily manipulated by genetic engineering than are animals because
   a. plant genes do not contain introns.
   b. more vectors are available for transferring recombinant DNA into plant cells.
   c. a somatic plant cell can often give rise to a complete plant.
   d. plant cells have larger nuclei.

4. A paleontologist has recovered a bit of tissue from the 400-year-old preserved skin of an extinct dodo (a bird). To compare a specific region of the DNA from a sample with DNA from living birds, which of the following would be most useful for increasing the amount of dodo DNA available for testing?
   a. SNP analysis
   b. polymerase chain reaction (PCR)
   c. electroporation
   d. gel electrophoresis

5. DNA technology has many medical applications. Which of the following is *not* done routinely at present?
   a. production of hormones for treating diabetes and dwarfism
   b. production of microbes that can metabolize toxins
   c. introduction of genetically engineered genes into human gametes
   d. prenatal identification of genetic disease alleles

LEVEL 2: APPLICATION/ANALYSIS

6. Which of the following would *not* be true of cDNA produced using human brain tissue as the starting material?
   a. It could be amplified by the polymerase chain reaction.
   b. It was produced from pre-mRNA using reverse transcriptase.
   c. It could be labeled and used as a probe to detect genes expressed in the brain.
   d. It lacks the introns of the pre-mRNA.

7. Expression of a cloned eukaryotic gene in a bacterial cell involves many challenges. The use of mRNA and reverse transcriptase is part of a strategy to solve the problem of
   a. post-transcriptional processing.
   b. post-translational processing.
   c. nucleic acid hybridization.
   d. restriction fragment ligation.

8. Which of the following sequences in double-stranded DNA is most likely to be recognized as a cutting site for a restriction enzyme?
   a. AAGG   c. ACCA
      TTCC   TGGT
   b. GGCC   d. AAAA
      CCGG   TTTT

LEVEL 3: SYNTHESIS/EVALUATION

9. MAKE CONNECTIONS Imagine you want to study one of the human crystallins, proteins present in the lens of the eye (see Figure 1.8). To obtain a sufficient amount of the protein of interest, you decide to clone the gene that codes for it. Assume you know the sequence of this gene. How would you go about this?

10. DRAW IT You are cloning an aardvark gene, using a bacterial plasmid as a vector. The green diagram shows the plasmid, which contains the restriction site for the enzyme used in Figure 20.6. Above the plasmid is a segment of linear aardvark DNA that was synthesized using PCR. Diagram your cloning procedure, showing what would happen to these two molecules during each step. Use one color for the aardvark DNA and its bases and another color for those of the plasmid. Label each step and all 5′ and 3′ ends.

5′ GAATTCTAAAGCGCTTATGAATTC 3′
3′ CTTAAGATTTCGCGAATACTTAAG 5′
Aardvark DNA

Plasmid

11. EVOLUTION CONNECTION
    Ethical considerations aside, if DNA-based technologies became widely used, how might they change the way evolution proceeds, as compared with the natural evolutionary mechanisms that have operated for the past 4 billion years?

12. SCIENTIFIC INQUIRY
    You hope to study a gene that codes for a neurotransmitter protein produced in human brain cells. You know the amino acid sequence of the protein. Explain how you might (a) identify what genes are expressed in a specific type of brain cell, (b) identify (and isolate) the neurotransmitter gene, (c) produce multiple copies of the gene for study, and (d) produce large quantities of the neurotransmitter for evaluation as a potential medication.

13. WRITE ABOUT A THEME: INFORMATION
    In a short essay (100–150 words), discuss how the genetic basis of life plays a central role in biotechnology.

14. SYNTHESIZE YOUR KNOWLEDGE

The water in the Yellowstone National Park hot springs shown here is around 160°F (70°C). Biologists assumed that no species of organisms could live in water above about 130°F (55°C), so they were surprised to find several species of bacteria there, now called *thermophiles* ("heat-lovers"). You've learned in this chapter how an enzyme from one species, *Thermus aquaticus*, made feasible one of the most important DNA-based techniques used in labs today. What was the enzyme, and what was the value of its being isolated from a thermophile? Can you think of reasons other enzymes from this bacterium (or other thermophiles) might also be valuable?

For selected answers, see Appendix A.

MasteringBiology®

Students Go to **MasteringBiology** for assignments, the eText, and the Study Area with practice tests, animations, and activities.

Instructors Go to **MasteringBiology** for automatically graded tutorials and questions that you can assign to your students, plus Instructor Resources.

21

Genomes and Their Evolution

▲ Figure 21.1 **What genomic information distinguishes a human from a chimpanzee?**

Reading the Leaves from the Tree of Life

The chimpanzee (*Pan troglodytes*) is our closest living relative on the evolutionary tree of life. The boy in **Figure 21.1** and his chimpanzee companion are intently studying the same leaf, but only one of them is able to talk about it. What accounts for this difference between two primates that share so much of their evolutionary history? With the advent of recent techniques for rapidly sequencing complete genomes, we have now started to address the genetic basis of intriguing questions like this.

The chimpanzee genome was sequenced two years after sequencing of the human genome was largely completed. Now that we can compare our genome, base by base, with that of the chimpanzee, we can tackle the more general issue of what differences in genetic information account for the distinct characteristics of these two species of primates.

In addition to determining the sequences of the human and chimpanzee genomes, researchers have obtained complete genome sequences for *Escherichia coli* and numerous other prokaryotes, as well as many eukaryotes, including *Zea mays* (corn), *Drosophila melanogaster* (fruit fly), *Mus musculus* (house mouse), and *Pongo pygmaeus* (orangutan). In 2010, a draft sequence was announced for the genome of *Homo neanderthalensis,* an extinct species closely related to present-day humans. These whole and partial genomes are of great interest in their own right, but they

◀ House mouse (*Mus musculus*)

also provide important insights into evolution as well as other biological processes. Broadening the human-chimpanzee comparison to the genomes of other primates and more distantly related animals should reveal the sets of genes that control group-defining characteristics. Beyond that, comparisons with the genomes of bacteria, archaea, fungi, protists, and plants should enlighten us about the long evolutionary history of shared ancient genes and their products.

With the genomes of many species fully sequenced, scientists can study whole sets of genes and their interactions, an approach called **genomics**. The sequencing efforts that feed this approach have generated, and continue to generate, enormous volumes of data. The need to deal with this ever-increasing flood of information has spawned the field of **bioinformatics**, the application of computational methods to the storage and analysis of biological data.

We will begin this chapter by discussing two approaches to genome sequencing and some of the advances in bioinformatics and its applications. We will then summarize what has been learned from the genomes that have been sequenced thus far. Next, we will describe the composition of the human genome as a representative genome of a complex multicellular eukaryote. Finally, we will explore current ideas about how genomes evolve and about how the evolution of developmental mechanisms could have generated the great diversity of life on Earth today.

CONCEPT 21.1

The Human Genome Project fostered development of faster, less expensive sequencing techniques

Sequencing of the human genome, an ambitious undertaking, officially began as the **Human Genome Project** in 1990. Organized by an international, publicly funded consortium of scientists at universities and research institutes, the project involved 20 large sequencing centers in six countries plus a host of other labs working on smaller parts of the project.

After the human genome sequence was largely completed in 2003, the sequence of each chromosome was analyzed and described in a series of papers, the last of which covered chromosome 1 and was published in 2006. With this refinement, researchers termed the sequencing "virtually complete."

The ultimate goal in mapping any genome is to determine the complete nucleotide sequence of each chromosome. For the human genome, this was accomplished by sequencing machines (see Figure 20.2), using the dideoxy chain termination method described in Figure 20.3. Even with automation, though, the sequencing of all 3 billion base pairs in a haploid set of human chromosomes presented a formidable challenge. In fact, a major thrust of the Human

Genome Project was the development of technology for faster sequencing, as described in Chapter 20. Improvements over the years chipped away at each time-consuming step, enabling the rate of sequencing to accelerate impressively: Whereas a productive lab could typically sequence 1,000 base pairs a day in the 1980s, by the year 2000 each research center working on the Human Genome Project was sequencing 1,000 base pairs *per second*, 24 hours a day, seven days a week. Methods like this that can analyze biological materials very rapidly and produce enormous volumes of data are said to be "high-throughput." Sequencing machines are an example of high-throughput devices.

Two approaches complemented each other in obtaining the complete sequence. The initial approach was a methodical one that built on an earlier storehouse of human genetic information. In 1998, however, molecular biologist J. Craig Venter set up a company (Celera Genomics) and declared his intention to sequence the entire human genome using an alternative strategy. The **whole-genome shotgun approach** starts with the cloning and sequencing of DNA fragments from randomly cut DNA. Powerful computer programs then assemble the resulting very large number of overlapping short sequences into a single continuous sequence (**Figure 21.2**).

Today, the whole-genome shotgun approach is widely used, although other approaches are required for some

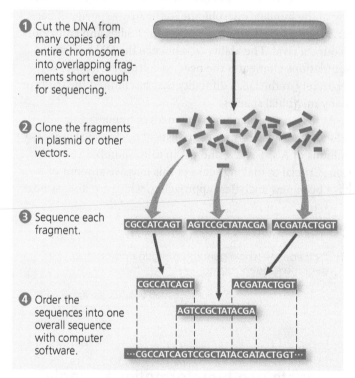

▲ **Figure 21.2 Whole-genome shotgun approach to sequencing.** In this approach, developed by J. Craig Venter and colleagues at Celera Genomics, random DNA fragments are cloned (see Figure 20.5), sequenced (see Figure 20.3), and then ordered relative to each other.

? *The fragments in stage 2 of this figure are depicted as scattered, rather than being in an ordered array. How does this depiction reflect the approach?*

regions of the genome that are difficult to sequence due to repetitive nucleotide sequences. Also, the development of newer sequencing techniques, generally called *sequencing by synthesis* (see Figure 20.4), has resulted in massive increases in speed and decreases in the cost of sequencing entire genomes. In these new techniques, many very small DNA fragments (each about 400–1,000 base pairs long) are sequenced at the same time, and computer software rapidly assembles the complete sequence. Because of the sensitivity of these techniques, the fragments can be sequenced directly; the cloning step (stage ❷ in Figure 21.2) is unnecessary. Whereas sequencing the first human genome took 13 years and cost $100 million, James Watson's genome was sequenced during four months in 2007 for about $1 million, and we are rapidly approaching the day when an individual's genome can be sequenced in a matter of hours for less than $1,000.

These technological advances have also facilitated an approach called **metagenomics** (from the Greek *meta*, beyond), in which DNA from an entire group of species (a *metagenome*) is collected from an environmental sample and sequenced. Again, computer software accomplishes the task of sorting out the partial sequences and assembling them into the individual specific genomes. So far, this approach has been applied to microbial communities found in environments as diverse as the Sargasso Sea and the human intestine. A 2012 study characterized the astounding diversity of the human "microbiome"—the many species of bacteria that coexist within and upon our bodies and contribute to our survival. The ability to sequence the DNA of mixed populations eliminates the need to culture each species separately in the lab, a difficulty that has limited the study of many microbial species.

At first glance, genome sequences of humans and other organisms are simply dry lists of nucleotide bases—millions of A's, T's, C's, and G's in mind-numbing succession. Crucial to making sense of this massive amount of data have been new analytical approaches, which we discuss next.

CONCEPT CHECK 21.1

1. Describe the whole-genome shotgun approach to genome sequencing.

For suggested answers, see Appendix A.

CONCEPT 21.2

Scientists use bioinformatics to analyze genomes and their functions

Each of the 20 or so sequencing centers around the world working on the Human Genome Project churned out voluminous amounts of DNA sequence day after day. As the data began to accumulate, the need to coordinate efforts to keep track of all the sequences became clear. Thanks to the foresight of research scientists and government officials involved in the Human Genome Project, its goals included the establishment of banks of data, or databases, and the refining of analytical software. These databases and software programs would then be centralized and made readily accessible on the Internet. Accomplishing this aim has accelerated progress in DNA sequence analysis by making bioinformatics resources available to researchers worldwide and by speeding up the dissemination of information.

Centralized Resources for Analyzing Genome Sequences

Government-funded agencies carried out their mandate to establish databases and provide software with which scientists could analyze the sequence data. For example, in the United States, a joint endeavor between the National Library of Medicine and the National Institutes of Health (NIH) created the National Center for Biotechnology Information (NCBI), which maintains a website (www.ncbi.nlm.nih.gov) with extensive bioinformatics resources. On this site are links to databases, software, and a wealth of information about genomics and related topics. Similar websites have also been established by the European Molecular Biology Laboratory, the DNA Data Bank of Japan, and BGI (formerly known as the Beijing Genome Institute) in Shenzhen, China, three genome centers with which the NCBI collaborates. These large, comprehensive websites are complemented by others maintained by individual or small groups of laboratories. Smaller websites often provide databases and software designed for a narrower purpose, such as studying genetic and genomic changes in one particular type of cancer.

The NCBI database of sequences is called GenBank. As of July 2013, it included the sequences of 165 million fragments of genomic DNA, totaling 153 billion base pairs! GenBank is constantly updated, and the amount of data it contains is estimated to double approximately every 18 months. Any sequence in the database can be retrieved and analyzed using software from the NCBI website or elsewhere.

One software program available on the NCBI website, called BLAST, allows the visitor to compare a DNA sequence with every sequence in GenBank, base by base. A researcher might search for similar regions in other genes of the same species, or among the genes of other species. Another program allows comparison of predicted protein sequences. Yet a third can search any protein sequence for common stretches of amino acids (domains) for which a function is known or suspected, and it can show a three-dimensional model of the domain alongside other relevant information (Figure 21.3). There is even a software program that can compare a collection of sequences, either nucleic acids or polypeptides, and diagram them in the form of an

1 In this window, a partial amino acid sequence from an unknown muskmelon protein ("Query") is aligned with sequences from other proteins that the computer program found to be similar. Each sequence represents a domain called WD40.

2 Four hallmarks of the WD40 domain are highlighted in yellow. (Sequence similarity is based on chemical aspects of the amino acids, so the amino acids in each hallmark region are not always identical.)

3 The Cn3D program displays a three-dimensional ribbon model of cow transducin (the protein highlighted in purple in the Sequence Alignment Viewer). This protein is the only one of those shown for which a structure has been determined. The sequence similarity of the other proteins to cow transducin suggests that their structures are likely to be similar.

6 This window displays information about the WD40 domain from the Conserved Domain Database.

WD40 - Sequence Alignment Viewer

```
                          Query  ~~~ktGGIRL~RHfksVSAVEWHRk~~gDYLSTlvLreSRAVLIHQlsk
               Cow [transducin]  ~nvrvSRELA~GHtgyLSCCRFLDd~~nQIVTs~~Sg~DTTCALWDie~
           Mustard weed [transducin]  gtvpvSRMLT~GHrgyVSCCQYVPnedaHLITs~~Sg~DQTCILWDvtt
               Corn [GNB protein]  gnmpvSRILT~GHkgyVSSCQYVPdgetRLITS~~Sg~DQTCVLWDvt~
               Human [PAFA protein]  ~~~ecIRTMH~GHdhnVSSVAIMPng~dHIVSA~~Sr~DKTIKMWEvg~
         Nematode [unknown protein #1]  ~~~rcVKTLK~GHtnyVFCCCFNPs~~gTLIAS~~GsfDETIRIWCar~
         Nematode [unknown protein #2]  ~~~rmTKTLK~GHnnyVFCCNFNPq~~sSLVVS~~GsfDESVRIWDvk~
           Fission yeast [FWDR protein]  ~~~seCISILhGHtdsVLCLTFDS~~~~TLLVS~~GsaDCTVKLWHfs~
```

WD40 - Cn3D 4.1

CDD Descriptive Items

Name: WD40

WD40 domain, found in a number of eukaryotic proteins that cover a wide variety of functions including adaptor/regulatory modules in signal transduction, pre-mRNA processing and cytoskeleton assembly; typically contains a GH dipeptide 11-24 residues from its N-terminus and the WD dipeptide at its C-terminus and is 40 residues long, hence the name WD40;

4 Cow transducin contains seven WD40 domains, one of which is highlighted here in gray.

5 The yellow segments correspond to the WD40 hallmarks highlighted in yellow in the window above.

▲ **Figure 21.3 Bioinformatics tools that are available on the Internet.** A website maintained by the National Center for Biotechnology Information (NCBI) allows scientists and the public to access DNA and protein sequences and other stored data. The site includes a link to a protein structure database (Conserved Domain Database, CDD) that can find and describe similar domains in related proteins, as well as software (Cn3D, "See in 3D") that displays three-dimensional models of domains for which the structure has been determined. Some results are shown from a search for regions of proteins similar to an amino acid sequence in a muskmelon protein. The WD40 domain is one of the most abundant domains in proteins encoded by eukaryotic genomes. Within these proteins, it often plays a key role in molecular interactions during signal transduction in cells.

evolutionary tree based on the sequence relationships. (One such diagram is shown in Figure 21.17.)

Two research institutions, Rutgers University and the University of California, San Diego, also maintain a worldwide Protein Data Bank, a database of all three-dimensional protein structures that have been determined. (The database is accessible at www.wwpdb.org.) These structures can be rotated by the viewer to show all sides of the protein. Throughout this book, you'll find images of protein structures that have been obtained from the Protein Data Bank.

There is a vast array of resources available for researchers anywhere in the world to use free of charge. Let us now consider the types of questions scientists can address using these resources.

Identifying Protein-Coding Genes and Understanding Their Functions

Using available DNA sequences, geneticists can study genes directly, rather than taking the classical genetic approach, which requires determining the genotype from the phenotype. But this more recent approach poses a new challenge: What does the gene actually do? Given a long DNA sequence from a database such as GenBank, scientists aim to identify all protein-coding genes in the sequence and ultimately their functions. This process is called **gene annotation**.

In the past, gene annotation was carried out laboriously by individual scientists interested in particular genes, but the process has now been largely automated. The usual approach is to use software to scan the stored sequences for transcriptional and translational start and stop signals, for RNA-splicing sites, and for other telltale signs of protein-coding genes. The software also looks for certain short sequences that specify known mRNAs. Thousands of such sequences, called *expressed sequence tags*, or *ESTs*, have been collected from cDNA sequences and are cataloged in computer databases. This type of analysis identifies sequences that may turn out to be previously unknown protein-coding genes.

The identities of about half of the human genes were known before the Human Genome Project began. But what about the others, the previously unknown genes revealed by analysis of DNA sequences? Clues about their identities and functions come from comparing sequences that might be genes with those of known genes from other organisms, using the software described previously. Due to redundancy in the genetic code, the DNA sequence itself may vary more among species than the protein sequence does. Thus, scientists interested in proteins often compare the predicted amino acid sequence of a protein to that of other proteins.

Sometimes a newly identified sequence will match, at least partially, the sequence of a gene or protein in another species whose function is well known. For example, a plant researcher working on signaling pathways in the muskmelon would be excited to see that a partial amino acid sequence from a gene she had identified matched with sequences in other species encoding a so-called "WD40 domain" (see Figure 21.3). These WD40 domains are present in many eukaryotes and are known to function in signal transduction pathways. Alternatively, a new gene sequence might be similar to a previously encountered sequence whose function is still unknown. Another possibility is that the sequence is entirely unlike anything ever seen before. This was true for about a third of the genes of *E. coli* when its genome was sequenced. In the last case, protein function is usually deduced through a combination of biochemical and functional studies. The biochemical approach aims to determine the three-dimensional structure of the protein as well as other attributes, such as potential binding sites for other molecules. Functional studies usually involve blocking or disabling the gene in an organism to see how the phenotype is affected. RNAi, described in Concept 18.3, is an example of an experimental technique used to block gene function.

Understanding Genes and Gene Expression at the Systems Level

The impressive computational power provided by the tools of bioinformatics allows the study of whole sets of genes and their interactions, as well as the comparison of genomes from different species. Genomics is a rich source of new insights into fundamental questions about genome organization, regulation of gene expression, embryonic development, and evolution.

One informative approach has been taken by an ongoing research project called ENCODE (Encyclopedia of DNA Elements), which began in 2003. The aim of the project is to learn everything possible about the functionally important elements in the human genome using multiple experimental techniques. Investigators have sought to identify protein-coding genes and genes for noncoding RNAs, along with sequences that regulate gene expression, such as enhancers and promoters. In addition, they have extensively characterized DNA and histone modifications and chromatin structure. The second phase of the project, involving more than

440 scientists in 32 research groups, culminated with the simultaneous publication of 30 papers in 2012, describing over 1,600 large data sets. The power of this project is that it provides the opportunity to compare results from specific projects with each other, yielding a much richer picture of the whole genome.

Perhaps the most striking finding is that about 75% of the genome is transcribed at some point in at least one of the cell types studied, even though less than 2% codes for proteins. Furthermore, biochemical functions have been assigned to DNA elements making up at least 80% of the genome. To learn more about the different types of functional elements, parallel projects are analyzing in a similar way the genomes of two model organisms, the soil nematode *Caenorhabditis elegans* and the fruit fly *Drosophila melanogaster*. Because genetic and biochemical experiments using DNA technology can be performed on these species, testing the activities of potentially functional DNA elements in their genomes is expected to illuminate the workings of the human genome.

The scientific progress resulting from sequencing genomes and studying large sets of genes has encouraged scientists to attempt similar systematic studies of sets of proteins and their properties (such as their abundance, chemical modifications, and interactions), an approach called **proteomics**. (A *proteome* is the entire set of proteins expressed by a cell or group of cells.) Proteins, not the genes that encode them, carry out most of the activities of the cell. Therefore, we must study when and where proteins are produced in an organism, as well as how they interact in networks, if we are to understand the functioning of cells and organisms.

How Systems Are Studied: An Example

Genomics and proteomics are enabling molecular biologists to approach the study of life from an increasingly global perspective. Using the tools we have described, biologists have begun to compile catalogs of genes and proteins—listings of all the "parts" that contribute to the operation of cells, tissues, and organisms. With such catalogs in hand, researchers have shifted their attention from the individual parts to their functional integration in biological systems. As you may recall, in Chapter 1 we discussed this approach, called **systems biology**, which aims to model the dynamic behavior of whole biological systems based on the study of the interactions among the system's parts. Because of the vast amounts of data generated in these types of studies, advances in computer technology and bioinformatics have been crucial in making systems biology possible.

One important use of the systems biology approach is to define gene and protein interaction networks. To map the protein interaction network in the yeast *Saccharomyces cerevisiae*, for instance, researchers used sophisticated techniques to knock out (disable) pairs of genes, one pair at a time, creating doubly mutant cells. They then compared the fitness of each double mutant (based in part on the size of

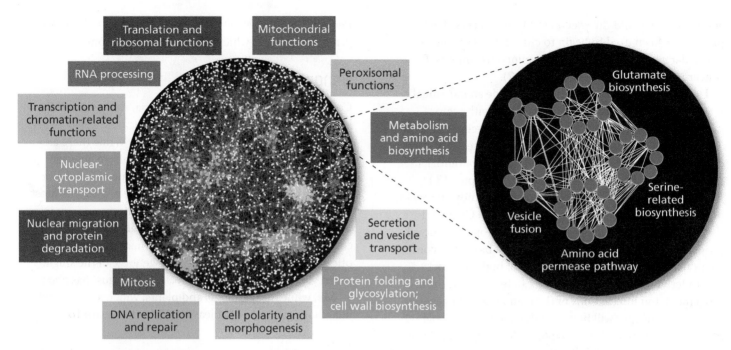

▲ **Figure 21.4 The systems biology approach to protein interactions.** This global protein interaction map shows the likely interactions (lines) among about 4,500 gene products (dots) in *Saccharomyces cerevisiae*, the budding yeast. Dots of the same color represent gene products involved in one of the 13 similarly colored cellular functions listed around the map. The white dots represent proteins that haven't been assigned to any color-coded function. The expanded area shows additional details of one map region where the gene products (blue dots) carry out amino acid biosynthesis, uptake, and related functions.

the cell colony it formed) to that predicted from the fitness of each of the two single mutants. The researchers reasoned that if the observed fitness matched the prediction, then the products of the two genes didn't interact with each other, but if the observed fitness was greater or less than predicted, then the gene products interacted in the cell. They then used computer software to build a graphic model by "mapping" the gene products to certain locations in the model, based on the similarity of their interactions. This resulted in the network-like "functional map" of protein interactions shown in **Figure 21.4**. Processing the vast number of protein-protein interactions generated by this experiment and integrating them into the completed map required powerful computers, mathematical tools, and newly developed software.

Application of Systems Biology to Medicine

The Cancer Genome Atlas is another example of systems biology in which a large group of interacting genes and gene products are analyzed together. This project, under the joint leadership of the National Cancer Institute and the NIH, aims to determine how changes in biological systems lead to cancer. A three-year pilot project ending in 2010 set out to find all the common mutations in three types of cancer—lung cancer, ovarian cancer, and glioblastoma of the brain—by comparing gene sequences and patterns of gene expression in cancer cells with those in normal cells. Work on glioblastoma confirmed the role of several suspected genes and identified a few previously unknown ones, suggesting possible new targets for therapies. The approach proved so fruitful for these three types of cancer that it has been extended to ten other types, chosen because they are common and often lethal in humans.

As high-throughput techniques become more rapid and less expensive, they are being increasingly applied to the problem of cancer. Rather than sequencing only protein-coding genes, sequencing the whole genomes of many tumors of a particular type allows scientists to uncover common chromosomal abnormalities, as well as any other consistent changes in these aberrant genomes.

In addition to whole-genome sequencing, silicon and glass "chips" that hold a microarray of most of the known human genes are now used to analyze gene expression patterns in patients suffering from various cancers and other diseases **(Figure 21.5)**. Analyzing which genes are over- or under-expressed in a particular cancer may allow physicians to tailor patients' treatment to their unique

◄ **Figure 21.5 A human gene microarray chip.** Tiny spots of DNA arranged in a grid on this silicon wafer represent almost all of the genes in the human genome. Using this chip, researchers can analyze expression patterns for all these genes at the same time.

genetic makeup and the specifics of their cancers. This approach has been used to begin to characterize subsets of particular cancers, enabling more refined treatments. Breast cancer is one example (see Figure 18.27).

Ultimately, medical records may include an individual's DNA sequence, a sort of genetic bar code, with regions highlighted that predispose the person to specific diseases. The use of such sequences for personalized medicine—disease prevention and treatment—has great potential. (See the interview with Charles Rotimi before Chapter 13.)

Systems biology is a very efficient way to study emergent properties at the molecular level. Recall from Chapter 1 that according to the theme of emergent properties, novel properties arise at each successive level of biological complexity as a result of the arrangement of building blocks at the underlying level. The more we can learn about the arrangement and interactions of the components of genetic systems, the deeper will be our understanding of whole organisms. The rest of this chapter will survey what we've learned from genomic studies thus far.

CONCEPT CHECK 21.2

1. What role does the Internet play in current genomics and proteomics research?

2. Explain the advantage of the systems biology approach to studying cancer versus the approach of studying a single gene at a time.

3. MAKE CONNECTIONS The ENCODE pilot project found that at least 75% of the genome is transcribed into RNAs, far more than could be accounted for by protein-coding genes. Review Concepts 17.3 and 18.3 and suggest some roles that these RNAs might play.

4. MAKE CONNECTIONS In Concept 20.2, you learned about genome-wide association studies. Explain how these studies use the systems biology approach.

For suggested answers, see Appendix A.

CONCEPT 21.3

Genomes vary in size, number of genes, and gene density

By April 2013, the sequencing of over 4,300 genomes had been completed and that of about 9,600 genomes and 370 metagenomes was in progress. In the completely sequenced group, about 4,000 are genomes of bacteria, and 186 are archaeal genomes. Among the 183 eukaryotic species in the group are vertebrates, invertebrates, protists, fungi, and plants. The accumulated genome sequences contain a wealth of information that we are now beginning to mine. What have we learned so far by comparing the genomes that have been sequenced? In this section, we will examine the characteristics of genome size, number of genes, and gene density.

Because these characteristics are so broad, we will focus on general trends, for which there are often exceptions.

Genome Size

Comparing the three domains (Bacteria, Archaea, and Eukarya), we find a general difference in genome size between prokaryotes and eukaryotes (Table 21.1). While there are some exceptions, most bacterial genomes have between 1 and 6 million base pairs (Mb); the genome of *E. coli*, for instance, has 4.6 Mb. Genomes of archaea are, for the most part, within the size range of bacterial genomes. (Keep in mind, however, that many fewer archaeal genomes have been completely sequenced, so this picture may change.) Eukaryotic genomes tend to be larger: The genome of the single-celled yeast *Saccharomyces cerevisiae* (a fungus) has about 12 Mb, while most animals and plants, which are multicellular, have genomes of at least 100 Mb. There are 165 Mb in

Table 21.1	Genome Sizes and Estimated Numbers of Genes*		
Organism	Haploid Genome Size (Mb)	Number of Genes	Genes per Mb
Bacteria			
Haemophilus influenzae	1.8	1,700	940
Escherichia coli	4.6	4,400	950
Archaea			
Archaeoglobus fulgidus	2.2	2,500	1,130
Methanosarcina barkeri	4.8	3,600	750
Eukaryotes			
Saccharomyces cerevisiae (yeast, a fungus)	12	6,300	525
Caenorhabditis elegans (nematode)	100	20,100	200
Arabidopsis thaliana (mustard family plant)	120	27,000	225
Daphnia pulex (water flea)	200	31,000	155
Drosophila melanogaster (fruit fly)	165	14,000	85
Oryza sativa (rice)	430	42,000	98
Zea mays (corn)	2,300	32,000	14
Ailuropoda melanoleuca (giant panda)	2,400	21,000	9
Homo sapiens (human)	3,000	<21,000	7
Paris japonica (Japanese canopy plant)	149,000	ND	ND

*Some values given here are likely to be revised as genome analysis continues. Mb = million base pairs. ND = not determined.

the fruit fly genome, while humans have 3,000 Mb, about 500 to 3,000 times as many as a typical bacterium.

Aside from this general difference between prokaryotes and eukaryotes, a comparison of genome sizes among eukaryotes fails to reveal any systematic relationship between genome size and the organism's phenotype. For instance, the genome of *Paris japonica*, the Japanese canopy plant, contains 149 billion base pairs (149,000 Mb), about 50 times the size of the human genome. Even more striking, there is a single-celled amoeba, *Polychaos dubium*, whose genome size has been estimated at 670 billion base pairs (670,000 Mb). (This genome has not yet been sequenced.) On a finer scale, comparing two insect species, the cricket (*Anabrus simplex*) genome turns out to have 11 times as many base pairs as the *Drosophila melanogaster* genome. There is a wide range of genome sizes within the groups of unicellular eukaryotes, insects, amphibians, and plants and less of a range within mammals and reptiles.

Number of Genes

The number of genes also varies between prokaryotes and eukaryotes: Bacteria and archaea, in general, have fewer genes than eukaryotes. Free-living bacteria and archaea have from 1,500 to 7,500 genes, while the number of genes in eukaryotes ranges from about 5,000 for unicellular fungi (yeasts) to at least 40,000 for some multicellular eukaryotes.

Within the eukaryotes, the number of genes in a species is often lower than expected from considering simply the size of its genome. Looking at Table 21.1, you can see that the genome of the nematode *C. elegans* is 100 Mb in size and contains roughly 20,100 genes. The *Drosophila melanogaster* genome, in comparison, is much bigger (165 Mb) but has only about two-thirds the number of genes—14,000 genes.

Considering an example closer to home, we noted that the human genome contains 3,000 Mb, well over ten times the size of either the *D. melanogaster* or *C. elegans* genome. At the outset of the Human Genome Project, biologists expected somewhere between 50,000 and 100,000 genes to be identified in the completed sequence, based on the number of known human proteins. As the project progressed, the estimate was revised downward several times, and the ENCODE project discussed above has established the number to be fewer than 21,000. This relatively low number, similar to the number of genes in the nematode *C. elegans*, surprised biologists, who had been expecting many more human genes.

What genetic attributes allow humans (and other vertebrates) to get by with no more genes than nematodes? An important factor is that vertebrate genomes "get more bang for the buck" from their coding sequences because of extensive alternative splicing of RNA transcripts. Recall that this process generates more than one polypeptide from a single gene (see Figure 18.13). A typical human gene contains about ten exons, and an estimated 90% or more of these multi-exon genes are spliced in at least two different ways. Some genes are expressed in hundreds of alternatively spliced forms, others in just two. Scientists have not yet catalogued all of the different forms, but it is clear that the number of different proteins encoded in the human genome far exceeds the proposed number of genes.

Additional polypeptide diversity could result from post-translational modifications such as cleavage or the addition of carbohydrate groups in different cell types or at different developmental stages. Finally, the discovery of miRNAs and other small RNAs that play regulatory roles have added a new variable to the mix (see Concept 18.3). Some scientists think that this added level of regulation, when present, may contribute to greater organismal complexity for a given number of genes.

Gene Density and Noncoding DNA

We can take both genome size and number of genes into account by comparing gene density in different species. In other words, we can ask: How many genes are there in a given length of DNA? When we compare the genomes of bacteria, archaea, and eukaryotes, we see that eukaryotes generally have larger genomes but fewer genes in a given number of base pairs. Humans have hundreds or thousands of times as many base pairs in their genome as most bacteria, as we already noted, but only 5 to 15 times as many genes; thus, gene density is lower in humans (see Table 21.1). Even unicellular eukaryotes, such as yeasts, have fewer genes per million base pairs than bacteria and archaea. Among the genomes that have been sequenced completely thus far, humans and other mammals have the lowest gene density.

In all bacterial genomes studied so far, most of the DNA consists of genes for protein, tRNA, or rRNA; the small amount remaining consists mainly of nontranscribed regulatory sequences, such as promoters. The sequence of nucleotides along a bacterial protein-coding gene proceeds from start to finish without interruption by noncoding sequences (introns). In eukaryotic genomes, by contrast, most of the DNA neither encodes protein nor is transcribed into RNA molecules of known function, and the DNA includes more complex regulatory sequences. In fact, humans have 10,000 times as much noncoding DNA as bacteria. Some of this DNA in multicellular eukaryotes is present as introns within genes. Indeed, introns account for most of the difference in average length between human genes (27,000 base pairs) and bacterial genes (1,000 base pairs).

In addition to introns, multicellular eukaryotes have a vast amount of non-protein-coding DNA between genes. In the next section, we will describe the composition and arrangement of these great stretches of DNA in the human genome.

CONCEPT 21.4

Multicellular eukaryotes have much noncoding DNA and many multigene families

We have spent most of this chapter, and indeed this unit, focusing on genes that code for proteins. Yet the coding regions of these genes and the genes for noncoding RNA products such as rRNA, tRNA, and miRNA make up only a small portion of the genomes of most multicellular eu-karyotes. For example, once the sequencing of the human genome was completed, it became clear that only a tiny part—about 1.5%—codes for proteins or is transcribed into rRNAs or tRNAs. **Figure 21.6** shows what is known about the makeup of the remaining 98.5% of the genome.

Gene-related regulatory sequences and introns account, respectively, for 5% and about 20% of the human genome. The rest, located between functional genes, includes some unique (single-copy) noncoding DNA, such as gene fragments and **pseudogenes**, former genes that have accumulated mu-tations over a long time and no longer produce functional proteins. (The genes that produce small noncoding RNAs are a tiny percentage of the genome, distributed between the 20% introns and the 15% unique noncoding DNA.) Most in-tergenic DNA, however, is **repetitive DNA**, which consists of sequences that are present in multiple copies in the genome. Surprisingly, about 75% of this repetitive DNA (44% of the entire human genome) is made up of units called transposable elements and sequences related to them.

The bulk of many eukaryotic genomes consists of DNA sequences that neither code for proteins nor are transcribed to produce RNAs with known functions; this noncoding DNA was often described in the past as "junk DNA." How-ever, genome comparisons over the past 10 years have re-vealed the persistence of this DNA in diverse genomes over

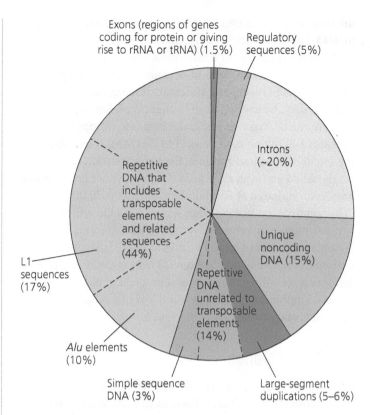

▲ **Figure 21.6 Types of DNA sequences in the human genome.** The gene sequences that code for proteins or are transcribed into rRNA or tRNA molecules make up only about 1.5% of the human genome (dark purple in the pie chart), while introns and regulatory sequences associated with genes (light purple) make up about a quarter. The vast majority of the human genome does not code for proteins or give rise to known RNAs, and much of it is repetitive DNA (dark and light green and teal). Because repetitive DNA is the most difficult to sequence and analyze, classification of some portions is tentative, and the percent-ages given here may shift slightly as genome analysis proceeds.

many hundreds of generations. For example, the genomes of humans, rats, and mice contain almost 500 regions of noncoding DNA that are *identical* in sequence in all three species. This is a higher level of sequence conservation than is seen for protein-coding regions in these species, strongly suggesting that the noncoding regions have important func-tions. The results of the ENCODE project discussed earlier have thoroughly underscored the key roles played in the cell by much of this noncoding DNA. In the next few pages, we examine how genes and noncoding DNA sequences are organized within genomes of multicellular eukaryotes, using the human genome as our main example. Genome organiza-tion tells us a lot about how genomes have evolved and con-tinue to evolve, as we'll discuss in Concept 21.5.

Transposable Elements and Related Sequences

Both prokaryotes and eukaryotes have stretches of DNA that can move from one location to another within the genome. These stretches are known as *transposable genetic elements*, or simply **transposable elements**. During the process called

▲ Figure 21.7 The effect of transposable elements on corn kernel color. Barbara McClintock first proposed the idea of mobile genetic elements after observing variegations in the color of the kernels on a corn cob (right).

transposition, a transposable element moves from one site in a cell's DNA to a different target site by a type of recombination process. Transposable elements are sometimes called "jumping genes," but actually they never completely detach from the cell's DNA. Instead, the original and new DNA sites are brought very close together by enzymes and other proteins that bend the DNA.

The first evidence for wandering DNA segments came from American geneticist Barbara McClintock's breeding experiments with Indian corn (maize) in the 1940s and 1950s **(Figure 21.7)**. As she tracked corn plants through multiple generations, McClintock identified changes in the color of corn kernels that made sense only if she postulated the existence of genetic elements capable of moving from other locations in the genome into the genes for kernel color, disrupting the genes so that the kernel color was changed. McClintock's discovery was met with great skepticism and virtually discounted at the time. Her careful work and insightful ideas were finally validated many years later when transposable elements were found in bacteria. In 1983, at the age of 81, McClintock received the Nobel Prize for her pioneering research.

Movement of Transposons and Retrotransposons

Eukaryotic transposable elements are of two types. The first type are **transposons**, which move within a genome by means of a DNA intermediate. Transposons can move by a "cut-and-paste" mechanism, which removes the element from the original site, or by a "copy-and-paste" mechanism, which leaves a copy behind **(Figure 21.8)**. Both mechanisms require an enzyme called *transposase*, which is generally encoded by the transposon.

Most transposable elements in eukaryotic genomes are of the second type, **retrotransposons**, which move by

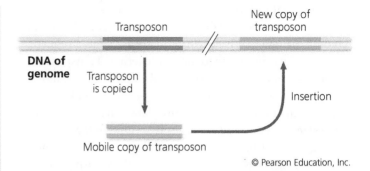

▲ Figure 21.8 Transposon movement. Movement of transposons by either the copy-and-paste mechanism (shown here) or the cut-and-paste mechanism involves a double-stranded DNA intermediate that is inserted into the genome.

? *How would this figure differ if it showed the cut-and-paste mechanism?*

means of an RNA intermediate that is a transcript of the retrotransposon DNA. Thus, retrotransposons always leave a copy at the original site during transposition **(Figure 21.9)**. To insert at another site, the RNA intermediate is first converted back to DNA by reverse transcriptase, an enzyme encoded by the retrotransposon. (Reverse transcriptase is also encoded by retroviruses, as you learned in Concept 19.2. In fact, retroviruses may have evolved from retrotransposons.) Another cellular enzyme catalyzes insertion of the reverse-transcribed DNA at a new site.

Sequences Related to Transposable Elements

Multiple copies of transposable elements and sequences related to them are scattered throughout eukaryotic genomes. A single unit is usually hundreds to thousands of base pairs long, and the dispersed "copies" are similar but usually not identical to each other. Some of these are transposable

▲ Figure 21.9 Retrotransposon movement. Movement begins with synthesis of a single-stranded RNA intermediate. The remaining steps are essentially identical to part of the retrovirus replicative cycle (see Figure 19.8).

elements that can move; the enzymes required for this movement may be encoded by any transposable element, including the one that is moving. Others are related sequences that have lost the ability to move altogether. Transposable elements and related sequences make up 25–50% of most mammalian genomes (see Figure 21.6) and even higher percentages in amphibians and many plants. In fact, the very large size of some plant genomes is accounted for not by extra genes, but by extra transposable elements. For example, sequences like these make up 85% of the corn genome!

In humans and other primates, a large portion of transposable element–related DNA consists of a family of similar sequences called *Alu elements*. These sequences alone account for approximately 10% of the human genome. *Alu* elements are about 300 nucleotides long, much shorter than most functional transposable elements, and they do not code for any protein. However, many *Alu* elements are transcribed into RNA, and at least some of these RNAs are thought to help regulate gene expression.

An even larger percentage (17%) of the human genome is made up of a type of retrotransposon called *LINE-1*, or *L1*. These sequences are much longer than *Alu* elements—about 6,500 base pairs—and typically have a very low rate of transposition. However, researchers working with rats have found L1 retrotransposons to be more active in cells of the developing brain. They have proposed that different effects on gene expression of L1 retrotransposition in developing neurons may contribute to the great diversity of neuronal cell types (see Concept 48.1).

Although many transposable elements encode proteins, these proteins do not carry out normal cellular functions. Therefore, transposable elements are usually included in the "noncoding" DNA category, along with other repetitive sequences.

Other Repetitive DNA, Including Simple Sequence DNA

Repetitive DNA that is not related to transposable elements has probably arisen from mistakes during DNA replication or recombination. Such DNA accounts for about 14% of the human genome (see Figure 21.6). About a third of this (5–6% of the human genome) consists of duplications of long stretches of DNA, with each unit ranging from 10,000 to 300,000 base pairs. These long segments seem to have been copied from one chromosomal location to another site on the same or a different chromosome and probably include some functional genes.

In contrast to scattered copies of long sequences, **simple sequence DNA** contains many copies of tandemly repeated short sequences, as in the following example (showing one DNA strand only):

... GTTACGTTACGTTACGTTACGTTACGTTAC ...

In this case, the repeated unit (GTTAC) consists of 5 nucleotides. Repeated units may contain as many as 500 nucleotides, but often contain fewer than 15 nucleotides, as in this example. When the unit contains 2–5 nucleotides, the series of repeats is called a **short tandem repeat**, or **STR**; we discussed the use of STR analysis in preparing genetic profiles in Concept 20.4. The number of copies of the repeated unit can vary from site to site within a given genome. There could be as many as several hundred thousand repetitions of the GTTAC unit at one site, but only half that number at another. STR analysis is performed on sites selected because they have relatively few repeats. The repeat number can vary from person to person, and since humans are diploid, each person has two alleles per site, which can differ. This diversity produces the variation represented in the genetic profiles that result from STR analysis. Altogether, simple sequence DNA makes up 3% of the human genome.

Much of a genome's simple sequence DNA is located at chromosomal telomeres and centromeres, suggesting that this DNA plays a structural role for chromosomes. The DNA at centromeres is essential for the separation of chromatids in cell division (see Concept 12.2). Centromeric DNA, along with simple sequence DNA located elsewhere, may also help organize the chromatin within the interphase nucleus. The simple sequence DNA located at telomeres, at the tips of chromosomes, prevents genes from being lost as the DNA shortens with each round of replication (see Concept 16.2). Telomeric DNA also binds proteins that protect the ends of a chromosome from degradation and from joining to other chromosomes.

Short repetitive sequences like those described here provide a challenge for whole-genome shotgun sequencing, because the presence of many short repeats hinders accurate reassembly of fragment sequences by computers. Regions of simple sequence DNA account for much of the uncertainty present in estimates of whole-genome sizes.

Genes and Multigene Families

We finish our discussion of the various types of DNA sequences in eukaryotic genomes with a closer look at genes. Recall that DNA sequences that code for proteins or give rise to tRNA or rRNA compose a mere 1.5% of the human genome (see Figure 21.6). If we include introns and regulatory sequences associated with genes, the total amount of DNA that is gene-related—coding and noncoding—constitutes about 25% of the human genome. Put another way, only about 6% (1.5% out of 25%) of the length of the average gene is represented in the final gene product.

Like the genes of bacteria, many eukaryotic genes are present as unique sequences, with only one copy per haploid set of chromosomes. But in the human genome and the genomes of many other animals and plants, solitary genes make up less than half of the total gene-related DNA. The rest occur in **multigene families**, collections of two or more identical or very similar genes.

In multigene families that consist of *identical* DNA sequences, those sequences are usually clustered tandemly and, with the notable exception of the genes for histone proteins, have RNAs as their final products. An example is the family of identical DNA sequences that are the genes for the three largest rRNA molecules (Figure 21.10a). These rRNA molecules are transcribed from a single transcription unit that is repeated tandemly hundreds to thousands of times in one or several clusters in the genome of a multicellular eukaryote. The many copies of this rRNA transcription unit help cells to quickly make the millions of ribosomes needed for active protein synthesis. The primary transcript is cleaved to yield the three rRNA molecules, which combine with proteins and one other kind of rRNA (5S rRNA) to form ribosomal subunits.

The classic examples of multigene families of *nonidentical* genes are two related families of genes that encode globins, a group of proteins that include the α and β polypeptide subunits of hemoglobin. One family, located on chromosome 16 in humans, encodes various forms of α-globin; the other, on chromosome 11, encodes forms of β-globin (Figure 21.10b). The different forms of each globin subunit are expressed at different times in development, allowing hemoglobin to function effectively in the changing environment of the developing animal. In humans, for example, the embryonic and fetal forms of hemoglobin have a higher affinity for oxygen than the adult forms, ensuring the efficient transfer of oxygen from mother to fetus. Also found in the globin gene family clusters are several pseudogenes. The evolution of these two globin gene families will be further discussed in Concept 21.5.

Analyzing the arrangement of the genes in gene families has given biologists insight into the evolution of genomes. We will consider some of the processes that have shaped the genomes of different species over evolutionary time in the next section.

CONCEPT CHECK 21.4

1. Discuss the characteristics of mammalian genomes that make them larger than prokaryotic genomes.

2. Which of the three mechanisms described in Figures 21.8 and 21.9 result(s) in a copy remaining at the original site as well as a copy appearing in a new location?

3. Contrast the organizations of the rRNA gene family and the globin gene families. For each, explain how the existence of a family of genes benefits the organism.

4. MAKE CONNECTIONS Assign each DNA segment at the top of Figure 18.8 to a sector in the pie chart in Figure 21.6.

For suggested answers, see Appendix A.

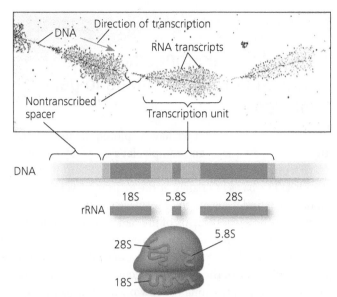

(a) **Part of the ribosomal RNA gene family.** The TEM at the top shows three of the hundreds of copies of rRNA transcription units in the rRNA gene family of a salamander genome. Each "feather" corresponds to a single unit being transcribed by about 100 molecules of RNA polymerase (dark dots along the DNA), moving left to right (red arrow). The growing RNA transcripts extend from the DNA. In the diagram of a transcription unit below the TEM, the genes for three types of rRNA (darker blue) are adjacent to regions that are transcribed but later removed (medium blue). A single transcript is processed to yield one of each of the three rRNAs (red), key components of the ribosome.

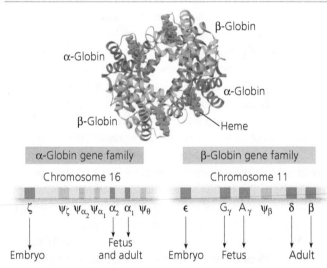

(b) **The human α-globin and β-globin gene families.** Adult hemoglobin is composed of two α-globin and two β-globin polypeptide subunits, as shown in the molecular model. The genes (darker blue) encoding α- and β-globins are found in two families, organized as shown here. The noncoding DNA (light blue) separating the functional genes within each family includes pseudogenes (ψ; gold), versions of the functional genes that no longer encode functional polypeptides. Genes and pseudogenes are named with Greek letters, as you have seen previously for the α- and β-globins. Some genes are expressed only in the embryo or fetus.

▲ **Figure 21.10 Gene families.**

? *In (a), how could you determine the direction of transcription if it weren't indicated by the red arrow?*

CONCEPT 21.5

Duplication, rearrangement, and mutation of DNA contribute to genome evolution

EVOLUTION Now that we have explored the makeup of the human genome as an example, let's see what we can learn from the composition of the genome about how it evolved. The basis of change at the genomic level is mutation, which underlies much of genome evolution. It seems likely that the earliest forms of life had a minimal number of genes—those necessary for survival and reproduction. If this were indeed the case, one aspect of evolution must have been an increase in the size of the genome, with the extra genetic material providing the raw material for gene diversification. In this section, we will first describe how extra copies of all or part of a genome can arise and then consider subsequent processes that can lead to the evolution of proteins (or RNA products) with slightly different or entirely new functions.

Duplication of Entire Chromosome Sets

An accident in meiosis can result in one or more extra sets of chromosomes, a condition known as polyploidy. Although such accidents would most often be lethal, in rare cases they could facilitate the evolution of genes. In a polyploid organism, one set of genes can provide essential functions for the organism. The genes in the one or more extra sets can diverge by accumulating mutations; these variations may persist if the organism carrying them survives and reproduces. In this way, genes with novel functions can evolve. As long as one copy of an essential gene is expressed, the divergence of another copy can lead to its encoded protein acting in a novel way, thereby changing the organism's phenotype.

The outcome of this accumulation of mutations may be the branching off of a new species. While polyploidy is rare among animals, it is relatively common among plants, especially flowering plants. Some botanists estimate that as many as 80% of the plant species that are alive today show evidence of polyploidy having occurred among their ancestral species. You'll learn more about how polyploidy leads to plant speciation in Concept 24.2.

Alterations of Chromosome Structure

With the recent explosion in genomic sequence information, we can now compare the chromosomal organizations of many different species in detail. This information allows us to make inferences about the evolutionary processes that shape chromosomes and may drive speciation. For example, scientists have long known that sometime in the

▲ **Figure 21.11 Human and chimpanzee chromosomes.** The positions of telomere-like and centromere-like sequences on human chromosome 2 (left) match those of telomeres on chimp chromosomes 12 and 13 and the centromere on chimp chromosome 13 (right). This suggests that chromosomes 12 and 13 in a human ancestor fused end to end to form human chromosome 2. The centromere from ancestral chromosome 12 remained functional on human chromosome 2, while the one from ancestral chromosome 13 did not.

last 6 million years, when the ancestors of humans and chimpanzees diverged as species, the fusion of two ancestral chromosomes in the human line led to different haploid numbers for humans ($n = 23$) and chimpanzees ($n = 24$). The banding patterns in stained chromosomes suggested that the ancestral versions of current chimp chromosomes 12 and 13 fused end to end, forming chromosome 2 in an ancestor of the human lineage. Sequencing and analysis of human chromosome 2 during the Human Genome Project provided very strong supporting evidence for the model we have just described (Figure 21.11).

In another study of broader scope, researchers compared the DNA sequence of each human chromosome with the whole-genome sequence of the mouse (Figure 21.12).

▲ **Figure 21.12 Human and mouse chromosomes.** Here, we can see that DNA sequences very similar to large blocks of human chromosome 16 (colored areas in this diagram) are found on mouse chromosomes 7, 8, 16, and 17. This finding suggests that the DNA sequence in each block has stayed together in the mouse and human lineages since the time they diverged from a common ancestor.

One part of their study showed that large blocks of genes on human chromosome 16 are found on four mouse chromosomes, indicating that the genes in each block stayed together in both the mouse and the human lineages during their divergent evolution from a common ancestor.

Performing the same comparative analysis between chromosomes of humans and six other mammalian species allowed the researchers to reconstruct the evolutionary history of chromosomal rearrangements in these eight species. They found many duplications and inversions of large portions of chromosomes, the result of errors during meiotic recombination in which the DNA broke and was rejoined incorrectly. The rate of these events seems to have begun accelerating about 100 million years ago, around 35 million years before large dinosaurs became extinct and the number of mammalian species began rapidly increasing. The apparent coincidence is interesting because chromosomal rearrangements are thought to contribute to the generation of new species. Although two individuals with different arrangements could still mate and produce offspring, the offspring would have two nonequivalent sets of chromosomes, making meiosis inefficient or even impossible. Thus, chromosomal rearrangements would lead to two populations that could not successfully mate with each other, a step on the way to their becoming two separate species. (You'll learn more about this in Concept 24.2.)

The same study also unearthed a pattern with medical relevance. Analysis of the chromosomal breakage points associated with the rearrangements showed that specific sites were used over and over again. A number of these recombination "hot spots" correspond to locations of chromosomal rearrangements within the human genome that are associated with congenital diseases (see Concept 15.4).

Duplication and Divergence of Gene-Sized Regions of DNA

Errors during meiosis can also lead to the duplication of chromosomal regions that are smaller than the ones we've just discussed, including segments the length of individual genes. Unequal crossing over during prophase I of meiosis, for instance, can result in one chromosome with a deletion and another with a duplication of a particular gene. Transposable elements can provide homologous sites where nonsister chromatids can cross over, even when other chromatid regions are not correctly aligned **Figure 21.13**.

Also, slippage can occur during DNA replication, such that the template shifts with respect to the new complementary strand, and a part of the template strand is either skipped by the replication machinery or used twice as a template. As a result, a segment of DNA is deleted or duplicated. It is easy to imagine how such errors could occur in regions of repeats. The variable number of repeated units of

▲ **Figure 21.13 Gene duplication due to unequal crossing over.** One mechanism by which a gene (or other DNA segment) can be duplicated is recombination during meiosis between copies of a transposable element flanking the gene. Such recombination between misaligned nonsister chromatids of homologous chromosomes produces one chromatid with two copies of the gene and one chromatid with no copy.

MAKE CONNECTIONS *Examine how crossing over occurs in Figure 13.9. In the middle panel above, draw a line through the portions that result in the upper chromatid in the bottom panel. Use a different color to do the same for the other chromatid.*

simple sequence DNA at a given site, used for STR analysis, is probably due to errors like these. Evidence that unequal crossing over and template slippage during DNA replication lead to duplication of genes is found in the existence of multigene families, such as the globin family.

Evolution of Genes with Related Functions: The Human Globin Genes

Figure 21.10b diagrams the organization of the α-globin and β-globin gene families as they exist in the human genome today. Now, let's consider how events such as duplications can lead to the evolution of genes with related functions like the globin genes. A comparison of gene sequences within a multigene family can suggest the order in which the genes arose. Re-creating the evolutionary history of the globin genes using this approach indicates that they all evolved from one common ancestral globin gene that underwent duplication and divergence into the α-globin and β-globin ancestral genes about 450–500 million years ago. Each of these genes was later duplicated several times, and the copies then diverged from each other in sequence, yielding the current

Figure 21.14 A model for the evolution of the human α-globin and β-globin gene families from a single ancestral globin gene.

? The gold elements are pseudogenes. Explain how they could have arisen after gene duplication.

family members (Figure 21.14). In fact, the common ancestral globin gene also gave rise to the oxygen-binding muscle protein myoglobin and to the plant protein leghemoglobin. The latter two proteins function as monomers, and their genes are included in a "globin superfamily."

After the duplication events, the differences between the genes in the globin families undoubtedly arose from mutations that accumulated in the gene copies over many generations. The current model is that the necessary function provided by an α-globin protein, for example, was fulfilled by one gene, while other copies of the α-globin gene accumulated random mutations. Many mutations may have had an adverse effect on the organism and others may have had no effect, but a few mutations must have altered the function of the protein product in a way that was advantageous to the organism at a particular life stage without substantially changing the protein's oxygen-carrying function. Presumably, natural selection acted on these altered genes, maintaining them in the population.

In the Scientific Skills Exercise, you can compare amino acid sequences of the globin family members and see how such comparisons were used to generate the model for globin gene evolution shown in Figure 21.14. The existence of several pseudogenes among the functional globin genes provides additional evidence for this model: Random mutations in these "genes" over evolutionary time have destroyed their function.

Evolution of Genes with Novel Functions

In the evolution of the globin gene families, gene duplication and subsequent divergence produced family members whose protein products performed functions similar to each other (oxygen transport). However, an alternative scenario is that one copy of a duplicated gene can undergo alterations that lead to a completely new function for the protein product. The genes for lysozyme and α-lactalbumin are good examples of this type of situation.

Lysozyme is an enzyme that helps protect animals against bacterial infection by hydrolyzing bacterial cell walls (see Figure 5.16); α-lactalbumin is a nonenzymatic protein that plays a role in milk production in mammals. The two proteins are quite similar in their amino acid sequences and three-dimensional structures (Figure 21.15). Both genes are found in mammals, whereas only the lysozyme gene is present in birds. These findings suggest that at some time after the lineages leading to mammals and birds had separated, the lysozyme gene was duplicated in the mammalian lineage but not in the avian lineage. Subsequently, one copy of the duplicated lysozyme gene evolved into a gene encoding α-lactalbumin, a protein with a completely different function. In a recent study, evolutionary biologists searched vertebrate genomes for genes with similar sequences. There appear to be at least eight members of the lysozyme family, with related genes found in other mammalian species as well. The functions of all the encoded gene products are not yet known, but it will be exciting to discover whether they are as different as the functions of lysozyme and α-lactalbumin.

Besides the duplication and divergence of whole genes, rearrangement of existing DNA sequences within genes has also contributed to genome evolution. The presence of introns may have promoted the evolution of new proteins by facilitating the duplication or shuffling of exons, as we'll discuss next.

Rearrangements of Parts of Genes: Exon Duplication and Exon Shuffling

Recall from Concept 17.3 that an exon often codes for a protein domain, a distinct structural and functional region of a protein molecule. We've already seen that unequal crossing over during meiosis can lead to duplication of a gene on one chromosome and its loss from the homologous chromosome (see Figure 21.13). By a similar process, a particular exon within a gene could be duplicated on one chromosome and deleted from the other. The gene with the duplicated exon would code for a protein containing

(a) Lysozyme

(b) α-lactalbumin

Lysozyme	1	KVFERCELAR	TLKRLGMDGY	RGISLANWMC	LAKWESGYNT	RATNYNAGDR
α-lactalbumin	1	KQFTKCELSQ	LLK--DIDGY	GGIALPELIC	TMFHTSGYDT	QAIVENN--E
Lysozyme	51	STDYGIFQIN	SRYWCNDGKT	PGAVNACHLS	CSALLQDNIA	DAVACAKRVV
α-lactalbumin	51	STEYGLFQIS	NKLWCKSSQV	PQSRNICDIS	CDKFLDDDIT	DDIMCAKKIL
Lysozyme	101	RDPQGIRAWV	AWRNRCQ-NR	DVRQYVQGCG	V	
α-lactalbumin	101	D-IKGIDYWL	AHKALCT--E	KLEQWLCEKL	-	

(c) Amino acid sequence alignments of lysozyme and α-lactalbumin

▲ **Figure 21.15 Comparison of lysozyme and α-lactalbumin proteins.** Computer-generated ribbon models of the similar structures of **(a)** lysozyme and **(b)** α-lactalbumin are shown, along with a comparison of the amino acid sequences of the two proteins. The amino acids are arranged in groups of 10 for ease of reading, and single-letter amino acid codes are used (see Figure 5.14). Identical amino acids are highlighted in yellow, and dashes indicate gaps in one sequence that have been introduced by the software to optimize the alignment.

MAKE CONNECTIONS *Even though two amino acids are not identical, they may be structurally and chemically similar and therefore behave similarly. Using Figure 5.14 as a reference, examine the non-identical amino acids in positions 1-30 and note cases where the amino acids in the two sequences are similar.*

a second copy of the encoded domain. This change in the protein's structure might augment its function by increasing its stability, enhancing its ability to bind a particular ligand, or altering some other property. Quite a few protein-coding genes have multiple copies of related exons, which presumably arose by duplication and then diverged. The gene encoding the extracellular matrix protein collagen is a good example. Collagen is a structural protein with a highly repetitive amino acid sequence, which reflects the repetitive pattern of exons in the collagen gene.

Alternatively, we can imagine the occasional mixing and matching of different exons either within a gene or between two different (nonallelic) genes owing to errors in meiotic recombination. This process, termed *exon shuffling*, could lead to new proteins with novel combinations of functions. As an example, let's consider the gene for tissue plasminogen activator (TPA). The TPA protein is an extracellular protein that helps control blood clotting. It has four domains of three types, each encoded by an exon; one exon is present in two copies. Because each type of exon is also found in other proteins, the current version of the gene for TPA is thought to have arisen by several instances of exon shuffling and duplication **(Figure 21.16).**

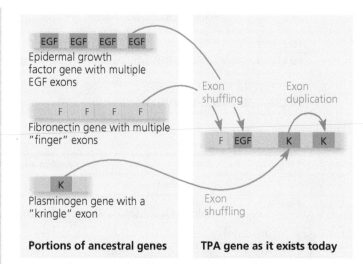

Portions of ancestral genes **TPA gene as it exists today**

▲ **Figure 21.16 Evolution of a new gene by exon shuffling.** Exon shuffling could have moved exons, each encoding a particular domain, from ancestral forms of the genes for epidermal growth factor, fibronectin, and plasminogen (left) into the evolving gene for tissue plasminogen activator, TPA (right). Duplication of the "kringle" exon (K) from the plasminogen gene after its movement could account for the two copies of this exon in the TPA gene existing today.

? *How could the presence of transposable elements within introns have facilitated the exon shuffling shown here?*

Reading an Amino Acid Sequence Identity Table

How Have Amino Acid Sequences of Human Globin Genes Diverged During Their Evolution? To build a model of the evolutionary history of the globin genes (see Figure 21.14), researchers compared the amino acid sequences of the polypeptides they encode. In this exercise, you will analyze comparisons of the amino acid sequences of globin polypeptides to shed light on their evolutionary relationships.

How the Experiment Was Done Scientists obtained the DNA sequences for each of the eight globin genes and "translated" them into amino acid sequences. They then used a computer program to align the sequences (with dashes indicating gaps in one sequence) and calculate a percent identity value for each pair of globins. The percent identity reflects the number of positions with identical amino acids relative to the total number of amino acids in a globin polypeptide. The data were displayed in a table to show the pairwise comparisons.

Data from the Experiment The following table shows an example of a pairwise alignment—that of the α_1-globin (alpha-1 globin) and ζ-globin (zeta globin) amino acid sequences—using the standard single-letter symbols for amino acids. To the left of each line of amino acid sequence is the number of the first amino acid in that line. The percent identity value for the α_1- and ζ-globin amino acid sequences was calculated by counting the number of matching amino acids (87, highlighted

in yellow), dividing by the total number of amino acid positions (143), and then multiplying by 100. This resulted in a 61% identity value for the α_1-ζ pair, as shown in the amino acid identity table at the bottom of the page. The values for other globin pairs were calculated in the same way.

▲ Hemoglobin

Interpret the Data

1. Notice that in the alignment table, the data are arranged so each globin pair can be compared. (a) Notice that some cells in the table have dashed lines. Given the pairs that are being compared for these cells, what percent identity value is implied by the dashed lines? (b) Notice that the cells in the lower left half of the table are blank. Using the information already provided in the table, fill in the missing values. Why does it make sense that these cells were left blank?

2. The earlier that two genes arose from a duplicated gene, the more their nucleotide sequences can have diverged, which may result in amino acid differences in the protein products. (a) Based on that premise, identify which two genes are most divergent from each other. What is the percent amino acid identity between their polypeptides? (b) Using the same approach, identify which two globin genes are the most recently duplicated. What is the percent identity between them?

3. The model of globin gene evolution shown in Figure 21.14 suggests that an ancestral gene duplicated and mutated to become α- and β-globin genes, and then each one was further duplicated and mutated. What features of the data set support the model?

4. Make a list of all the percent identity values from the table, starting with 100% at the top. Next to each number write the globin pair(s) with that percent identity value. Use one color for the globins from the α family and a different color for the globins from the β family. (a) Compare the order of pairs on your list with their positions in the model shown in Figure 21.14. Does the order of pairs describe the same relative "closeness" of globin family members seen in the model? (b) Compare the percent identity values for pairs within the α or β group to the values for between-group pairs.

(MB) A version of this Scientific Skills Exercise can be assigned in MasteringBiology.

Data from NCBI database. **Further Reading** R. C. Hardison, Globin genes on the move, *Journal of Biology* 7:35.1–35.5 (2008).

Globin	Alignment of Globin Amino Acid Sequences
α_1	1 MVLSPADKTNVKAAWGKVGAHAGEYGAEAL
ζ	1 MSLTKTERTIIVSMWAKISTQADTIGTETL
α_1	31 ERMFLSFPTTKTYFPHFDLSH-GSAQVKGH
ζ	31 ERLFLSHPQTKTYFPHFDL-HPGSAQLRAH
α_1	61 GKKVADALTNAVAHVDDMPNALSALSDLHA
ζ	61 GSKVVAAVGDAVKSIDDIGGALSKLSELHA
α_1	91 HKLRVDPVNFKLLSHCLLVTLAAHLPAEFT
ζ	91 YILRVDPVNFKLLSHCLLVTLAARFPADFT
α_1	121 PAVHASLDKFLASVSTVLTSKYR
ζ	121 AEAHAAWDKFLSVVSSVLTEKYR

Amino Acid Identity Table

		α Family			β Family				
		α_1 (alpha 1)	α_2 (alpha 2)	ζ (zeta)	β (beta)	δ (delta)	ϵ (epsilon)	A_γ (gamma A)	G_γ (gamma G)
α Family	α_1	-----	100	61	45	44	39	42	42
	α_2		-----	61	45	44	39	42	42
	ζ			-----	38	40	41	41	41
β Family	β				-----	93	76	73	73
	δ					-----	73	71	72
	ϵ						-----	80	80
	A_γ							-----	99
	G_γ								-----

How Transposable Elements Contribute to Genome Evolution

The persistence of transposable elements as a large fraction of some eukaryotic genomes is consistent with the idea that they play an important role in shaping a genome over evolutionary time. These elements can contribute to the evolution of the genome in several ways. They can promote recombination, disrupt cellular genes or control elements, and carry entire genes or individual exons to new locations.

Transposable elements of similar sequence scattered throughout the genome facilitate recombination between different chromosomes by providing homologous regions for crossing over. Most such recombination events are probably detrimental, causing chromosomal translocations and other changes in the genome that may be lethal to the organism. But over the course of evolutionary time, an occasional recombination event of this sort may be advantageous to the organism. (For the change to be heritable, of course, it must happen in a cell that will give rise to a gamete.)

The movement of a transposable element can have a variety of consequences. For instance, if a transposable element "jumps" into the middle of a protein-coding sequence, it will prevent the production of a normal transcript of the gene. If a transposable element inserts within a regulatory sequence, the transposition may lead to increased or decreased production of one or more proteins. Transposition caused both types of effects on the genes coding for pigment-synthesizing enzymes in McClintock's corn kernels. Again, while such changes are usually harmful, in the long run some may prove beneficial by providing a survival advantage.

During transposition, a transposable element may carry along a gene or even a group of genes to a new position in the genome. This mechanism probably accounts for the location of the α-globin and β-globin gene families on different human chromosomes, as well as the dispersion of the genes of certain other gene families. By a similar tagalong process, an exon from one gene may be inserted into another gene in a mechanism similar to that of exon shuffling during recombination. For example, an exon may be inserted by transposition into the intron of a protein-coding gene. If the inserted exon is retained in the RNA transcript during RNA splicing, the protein that is synthesized will have an additional domain, which may confer a new function on the protein.

All the processes discussed in this section most often produce either harmful effects, which may be lethal, or no effect at all. In a few cases, however, small heritable changes may occur that are beneficial. Over many generations, the resulting genetic diversity provides valuable raw material for natural selection. Diversification of genes and their products is an important factor in the evolution of new species. Thus, the accumulation of changes in the genome of each species provides a record of its evolutionary history. To read this record, we must be able to identify genomic changes. Comparing the genomes of different species allows us to do that and has increased our understanding of how genomes evolve. You will learn more about these topics next.

CONCEPT CHECK 21.5

1. Describe three examples of errors in cellular processes that lead to DNA duplications.

2. Explain how multiple exons might have arisen in the ancestral EGF and fibronectin genes shown on the left side of Figure 21.16.

3. What are three ways that transposable elements are thought to contribute to genome evolution?

4. **WHAT IF?** In 2005, Icelandic scientists reported finding a large chromosomal inversion present in 20% of northern Europeans, and they noted that Icelandic women with this inversion had significantly more children than women without it. What would you expect to happen to the frequency of this inversion in the Icelandic population in future generations?

For suggested answers, see Appendix A.

CONCEPT 21.6

Comparing genome sequences provides clues to evolution and development

EVOLUTION One researcher has likened the current state of biology to the Age of Exploration in the 15th century, which occurred soon after major improvements in navigation and ship design. In the last 25 years, we have seen rapid advances in genome sequencing and data collection, new techniques for assessing gene activity across the whole genome, and refined approaches for understanding how genes and their products work together in complex systems. We are truly poised on the brink of a new world.

Comparisons of genome sequences from different species reveal a lot about the evolutionary history of life, from very ancient to more recent. Similarly, comparative studies of the genetic programs that direct embryonic development in different species are beginning to clarify the mechanisms that generated the great diversity of life-forms present today. In this final section of the chapter, we will discuss what has been learned from these two approaches.

Comparing Genomes

The more similar in sequence the genes and genomes of two species are, the more closely related those species are in their evolutionary history. Comparing genomes of closely related species sheds light on more recent evolutionary events, whereas comparing genomes of very distantly related species helps us understand ancient evolutionary history. In

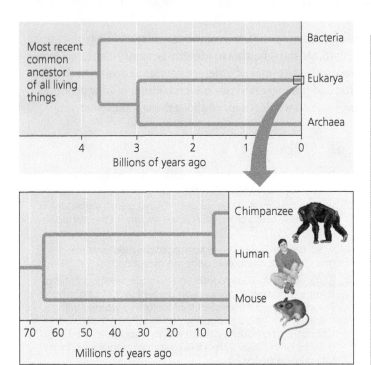

▲ **Figure 21.17 Evolutionary relationships of the three domains of life.** The tree diagram at the top shows the ancient divergence of bacteria, archaea, and eukaryotes. A portion of the eukaryote lineage is expanded in the inset to show the more recent divergence of three mammalian species discussed in this chapter.

either case, learning about characteristics that are shared or divergent between groups enhances our picture of the evolution of organisms and biological processes. As you learned in Chapter 1, the evolutionary relationships between species can be represented by a diagram in the form of a tree (often turned sideways), where each branch point marks the divergence of two lineages. **Figure 21.17** shows the evolutionary relationships of some groups and species we will discuss.

Comparing Distantly Related Species

Determining which genes have remained similar—that is, are *highly conserved*—in distantly related species can help clarify evolutionary relationships among species that diverged from each other long ago. Indeed, comparisons of the specific gene sequences of bacteria, archaea, and eukaryotes indicate that these three groups diverged between 2 and 4 billion years ago and strongly support the theory that they are the fundamental domains of life (see Figure 21.17).

In addition to their value in evolutionary biology, comparative genomic studies confirm the relevance of research on model organisms to our understanding of biology in general and human biology in particular. Very ancient genes can still be surprisingly similar in disparate species. As a case in point, several yeast genes are so similar to certain human disease genes (genes whose mutation causes disease) that researchers have deduced the functions of the human genes by studying their yeast counterparts. This striking result underscores the common origin of these two distantly related species.

Comparing Closely Related Species

The genomes of two closely related species are likely to be organized similarly because of their relatively recent divergence. In the past, this kind of similarity allowed the fully sequenced genome of one species to be used as a scaffold for assembling the genomic sequences of a closely related species, accelerating mapping of the second genome. For instance, using the human genome sequence as a guide, researchers were able to quickly sequence the chimpanzee genome. With the advent of new and faster sequencing techniques, most genomes are assembled individually, as has been done recently for the bonobo and gorilla genomes. (Along with chimpanzees, bonobos are the other African ape species that are the closest living relatives to humans.)

The recent divergence of two closely related species also underlies the small number of gene differences that are found when their genomes are compared. The particular genetic differences can therefore be more easily correlated with phenotypic differences between the two species. An exciting application of this type of analysis is seen as researchers compare the human genome with the genomes of the chimpanzee, mouse, rat, and other mammals. Identifying the genes shared by all of these species but not by nonmammals should give clues about what it takes to make a mammal, while finding the genes shared by chimpanzees and humans but not by rodents will tell us something about primates. And, of course, comparing the human genome with that of the chimpanzee will help us answer the tantalizing question we asked at the beginning of the chapter: What genomic information defines a human or a chimpanzee?

An analysis of the overall composition of the human and chimpanzee genomes, which are thought to have diverged only about 6 million years ago (see Figure 21.17), reveals some general differences. Considering single nucleotide substitutions, the two genomes differ by only 1.2%. When researchers looked at longer stretches of DNA, however, they were surprised to find a further 2.7% difference due to insertions or deletions of larger regions in the genome of one or the other species; many of the insertions were duplications or other repetitive DNA. In fact, a third of the human duplications are not present in the chimpanzee genome, and some of these duplications contain regions associated with human diseases. There are more *Alu* elements in the human genome than in the chimpanzee genome, and the latter contains many copies of a retroviral provirus not present in humans. All of these observations provide clues to the forces that might have swept the two genomes along different paths, but we don't have a complete picture yet.

The sequencing of the bonobo genome, completed in 2012, revealed that in some regions, human sequences were more closely related to either chimpanzee or bonobo sequences than chimpanzee or bonobo sequences were to each other. Such a fine-grained comparison of three closely related species allows even more detail to be worked out in reconstructing their related evolutionary history.

We also don't know how the genetic differences revealed by genome sequencing might account for the distinct characteristics of each species. To discover the basis for the phenotypic differences between chimpanzees and humans, biologists are studying specific genes and types of genes that differ between the two species and comparing them with their counterparts in other mammals. This approach has revealed a number of genes that are apparently changing (evolving) faster in the human than in either the chimpanzee or the mouse. Among them are genes involved in defense against malaria and tuberculosis as well as at least one gene that regulates brain size. When genes are classified by function, the genes that seem to be evolving the fastest are those that code for transcription factors. This discovery makes sense because transcription factors regulate gene expression and thus play a key role in orchestrating the overall genetic program.

One transcription factor whose gene shows evidence of rapid change in the human lineage is called FOXP2 **(Figure 21.18)**. Several lines of evidence suggest that the

---

▼ **Figure 21.18** | Inquiry

What is the function of a gene (*FOXP2*) that is rapidly evolving in the human lineage?

Experiment Several lines of evidence support a role for the *FOXP2* gene in the development of speech and language in humans and of vocalization in other vertebrates. In 2005, Joseph Buxbaum and collaborators at the Mount Sinai School of Medicine and several other institutions tested the function of *FOXP2*. They used the mouse, a model organism in which genes can be easily knocked out, as a representative vertebrate that vocalizes: Mice produce ultrasonic squeaks (whistles) to communicate stress. The researchers used genetic engineering to produce mice in which one or both copies of *FOXP2* were disrupted.

| Wild type: two normal copies of *FOXP2* | Heterozygote: one copy of *FOXP2* disrupted | Homozygote: both copies of *FOXP2* disrupted |

They then compared the phenotypes of these mice. Two of the characters they examined are included here: brain anatomy and vocalization.

Experiment 1: Researchers cut thin sections of brain and stained them with reagents that allow visualization of brain anatomy in a UV fluorescence microscope.

Experiment 2: Researchers separated each newborn pup from its mother and recorded the number of ultrasonic whistles produced by the pup.

Results

Experiment 1 Results: Disruption of both copies of *FOXP2* led to brain abnormalities in which the cells were disorganized. Phenotypic effects on the brain of heterozygotes, with one disrupted copy, were less severe. (Each color in the micrographs below reveals a different cell or tissue type.)

Experiment 2 Results: Disruption of both copies of *FOXP2* led to an absence of ultrasonic vocalization in response to stress. The effect on vocalization in the heterozygote was also extreme.

Wild type

Heterozygote

Homozygote

Conclusion *FOXP2* plays a significant role in the development of functional communication systems in mice. The results augment evidence from studies of birds and humans, supporting the hypothesis that *FOXP2* may act similarly in diverse organisms.

Source: W. Shu et al., Altered ultrasonic vocalization in mice with a disruption in the Foxp2 gene, *Proceedings of the National Academy of Sciences* 102:9643–9648 (2005).

WHAT IF? *Since the results support a role for mouse FOXP2 in vocalization, you might wonder whether the human FOXP2 protein is a key regulator of speech. If you were given the amino acid sequences of wild-type and mutant human FOXP2 proteins and the wild-type chimpanzee FOXP2 protein, how would you investigate this question? What further clues could you obtain by comparing these sequences to that of the mouse FOXP2 protein?*

FOXP2 gene functions in vocalization in vertebrates. For one thing, mutations in this gene can produce severe speech and language impairment in humans. Moreover, the *FOXP2* gene is expressed in the brains of zebra finches and canaries at the time when these songbirds are learning their songs. But perhaps the strongest evidence comes from a "knockout" experiment in which researchers disrupted the *FOXP2* gene in mice and analyzed the resulting phenotype (see Figure 21.18). The homozygous mutant mice had malformed brains and failed to emit normal ultrasonic vocalizations, and mice with one faulty copy of the gene also showed significant problems with vocalization. These results support the idea that the *FOXP2* gene product turns on genes involved in vocalization.

Expanding on this analysis, another research group more recently replaced the *FOXP2* gene in mice with a "humanized" copy coding for the human versions of two amino acids that differ between human and chimp; these are the changes potentially responsible for a human's ability to speak. Although the mice were generally healthy, they had subtly different vocalizations and showed changes in brain cells in circuits associated with speech in human brains.

In 2010, the Neanderthal genome was sequenced from a very small amount of preserved genomic DNA. Neanderthals (*Homo neanderthalensis*) are members of the same genus to which humans (*Homo sapiens*) belong (see Concept 34.7). A reconstruction of their evolutionary history based on genomic comparisons between the two species suggests that some groups of humans and Neanderthals co-existed and interbred for a period of time before Neanderthals went extinct about 30,000 years ago. While Neanderthals have sometimes been portrayed as primitive beings that could only grunt, their *FOXP2* gene sequence encodes an identical protein to that of humans. This suggests that Neanderthals may have been capable of speech of some type and, along with other observed genetic similarities, forces us to reevaluate our image of our recent extinct relatives.

The *FOXP2* story is an excellent example of how different approaches can complement each other in uncovering biological phenomena of widespread importance. The *FOXP2* experiments used mice as a model for humans because it would be unethical (as well as impractical) to carry out such experiments in humans. Mice and humans, which diverged about 65.5 million years ago (see Figure 21.17), share about 85% of their genes. This genetic similarity can be exploited in studying human genetic disorders. If researchers know the organ or tissue that is affected by a particular genetic disorder, they can look for genes that are expressed in these locations in mice.

Further research efforts are under way to extend genomic studies to many more species, including neglected species from diverse branches of the tree of life. These studies will advance our understanding of evolution, of course, as well as all aspects of biology, from human health to ecology.

Comparing Genomes Within a Species

Another exciting consequence of our ability to analyze genomes is our growing understanding of the spectrum of genetic variation in humans. Because the history of the human species is so short—probably about 200,000 years—the amount of DNA variation among humans is small compared to that of many other species. Much of our diversity seems to be in the form of single nucleotide polymorphisms (SNPs). SNPs are single base-pair sites where variation is found in at least 1% of the population (see Concept 20.2); they are usually detected by DNA sequencing. In the human genome, SNPs occur on average about once in 100–300 base pairs. Scientists have already identified the location of several million SNP sites in the human genome and continue to find more.

In the course of this search, they have also found other variations—including chromosomal regions with inversions, deletions, and duplications. The most surprising discovery has been the widespread occurrence of *copy-number variants* (*CNVs*), loci where some individuals have one or multiple copies of a particular gene or genetic region, rather than the standard two copies (one on each homolog). CNVs result from regions of the genome being duplicated or deleted inconsistently within the population. A recent study of 40 people found more than 8,000 CNVs involving 13% of the genes in the genome, and these CNVs probably represent just a small subset of the total. Since these variants encompass much longer stretches of DNA than the single nucleotides of SNPs, CNVs are more likely to have phenotypic consequences and to play a role in complex diseases and disorders. At the very least, the high incidence of copy-number variation casts doubt on the meaning of the phrase "a normal human genome."

Copy-number variants, SNPs, and variations in repetitive DNA such as short tandem repeats (STRs) are useful genetic markers for studying human evolution. In one study, the genomes of two Africans from different communities were sequenced: Archbishop Desmond Tutu, the South African civil rights advocate and a member of the Bantu tribe, the majority population in southern Africa; and !Gubi, a hunter-gatherer from the Khoisan community in Namibia, a minority African population that is probably the human group with the oldest known lineage. The comparison revealed many differences, as you might expect. The analysis was then broadened to compare the protein-coding regions of !Gubi's genome with those of three other Khoisan community members (self-identified Bushmen) living nearby. Remarkably, the four African genomes differed more from each other than a European would from an Asian. These data highlight the extensive diversity among African genomes. Extending this approach will help us answer important questions about the differences between human populations and the migratory routes of human populations throughout history.

Widespread Conservation of Developmental Genes Among Animals

Biologists in the field of evolutionary developmental biology, or **evo-devo** as it is often called, compare developmental processes of different multicellular organisms. Their aim is to understand how these processes have evolved and how changes in them can modify existing organismal features or lead to new ones. With the advent of molecular techniques and the recent flood of genomic information, we are beginning to realize that the genomes of related species with strikingly different forms may have only minor differences in gene sequence or, perhaps more importantly, in gene regulation. Discovering the molecular basis of these differences in turn helps us understand the origins of the myriad diverse forms that cohabit this planet, thus informing our study of evolution.

In Chapter 18, you learned about the homeotic genes in *Drosophila melanogaster*, which specify the identity of body segments in the fruit fly (see Figure 18.20). Molecular analysis of the homeotic genes in *Drosophila* has shown that they all include a 180-nucleotide sequence called a **homeobox**, which codes for a 60-amino-acid *homeodomain* in the encoded proteins. An identical or very similar nucleotide sequence has been discovered in the homeotic genes of many invertebrates and vertebrates. The sequences are so similar between humans and fruit flies, in fact, that one researcher has whimsically referred to flies as "little people with wings." The resemblance even extends to the organization of these genes: The vertebrate genes homologous to the homeotic genes of fruit flies have kept the same chromosomal arrangement **(Figure 21.19)**. Homeobox-containing sequences have also been found in regulatory genes of much more distantly related eukaryotes, including plants and yeasts. From these similarities, we can deduce that the homeobox DNA sequence evolved very early in the history of life and was sufficiently valuable to organisms to have been conserved in animals and plants virtually unchanged for hundreds of millions of years.

Homeotic genes in animals were named *Hox* genes, short for *homeobox*-containing genes, because homeotic genes were the first genes found to have this sequence. Other homeobox-containing genes were later found that do not act as homeotic genes; that is, they do not directly control the identity of body parts. However, most of these genes, in animals at least, are associated with development, suggesting their ancient and fundamental importance in that process. In *Drosophila*, for example, homeoboxes are present not only in the homeotic genes but also in the egg-polarity gene *bicoid* (see Figures 18.21 and 18.22), in several of the segmentation genes, and in a master regulatory gene for eye development.

Researchers have discovered that the homeobox-encoded homeodomain binds to DNA when the protein functions

▲ **Figure 21.19 Conservation of homeotic genes in a fruit fly and a mouse.** Homeotic genes that control the form of anterior and posterior structures of the body occur in the same linear sequence on chromosomes in *Drosophila* and mice. Each colored band on the chromosomes shown here represents a homeotic gene. In fruit flies, all homeotic genes are found on one chromosome. The mouse and other mammals have the same or similar sets of genes on four chromosomes. The color code indicates the parts of the embryos in which these genes are expressed and the adult body regions that result. All of these genes are essentially identical in flies and mice, except for those represented by black bands, which are less similar in the two animals.

as a transcription factor. Elsewhere in the protein, domains that are more variable interact with other transcription factors, allowing the homeodomain-containing protein to recognize specific enhancers and regulate the associated genes. Proteins with homeodomains probably regulate development by coordinating the transcription of batteries of developmental genes, switching them on or off. In embryos of *Drosophila* and other animal species, different combinations of homeobox genes are active in different parts of the embryo. This selective expression of regulatory genes, varying over time and space, is central to pattern formation.

Developmental biologists have found that in addition to homeotic genes, many other genes involved in development are highly conserved from species to species. These include numerous genes encoding components of signaling pathways. The extraordinary similarity among some developmental genes in different animal species raises a question: How can the same genes be involved in the development of animals whose forms are so very different from each other?

Ongoing studies are suggesting answers to this question. In some cases, small changes in regulatory sequences of particular genes cause changes in gene expression patterns that can lead to major changes in body form. For example, the differing patterns of expression of the *Hox* genes along the body axis in insects and crustaceans can explain the variation in number of leg-bearing segments among these segmented animals **(Figure 21.20)**. In other cases, similar genes direct different developmental processes in various organisms, resulting in diverse body shapes. Several *Hox* genes, for instance, are expressed in the embryonic and larval stages of the sea urchin, a nonsegmented animal that has a body plan quite different from those of insects and mice. Sea urchin adults make the pincushion-shaped shells you may have seen on the beach (see Figure 8.4); two species of live sea urchins are shown in the photo below. Sea urchins are among the organisms long used in classical embryological studies (see Chapter 47).

In this final chapter of the genetics unit, you have learned how studying genomic composition and comparing the genomes of different species can illuminate the process by which genomes evolve. Further, comparing developmental programs, we can see that the unity of life is reflected in the similarity of molecular and cellular mechanisms used to establish body pattern, although the genes directing development may differ among organisms. The similarities between genomes reflect the common ancestry of life on Earth. But the differences are also crucial, for they have created the huge diversity of organisms that have evolved. In the remainder of the book, we expand our perspective beyond the level of molecules, cells, and genes to explore this diversity on the organismal level.

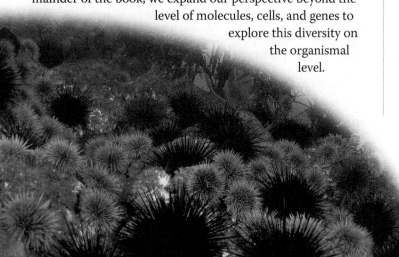

(a) Expression of four *Hox* genes in the brine shrimp *Artemia*

Thorax   Genital segments   Abdomen

Thorax   Abdomen

(b) Expression of the grasshopper versions of the same four *Hox* genes

© 1995 The Royal Society

▲ **Figure 21.20 Effect of differences in *Hox* gene expression in crustaceans and insects.** Changes in the expression patterns of *Hox* genes have occurred over evolutionary time. These changes account in part for the different body plans of the brine shrimp *Artemia*, a crustacean (top), and the grasshopper, an insect. Shown here are regions of the adult body color-coded for expression of four *Hox* genes that determine the formation of particular body parts during embryonic development. Each color represents a specific *Hox* gene. Colored stripes on the thorax of *Artemia* indicate co-expression of three *Hox* genes.

CONCEPT CHECK 21.6

1. Would you expect the genome of the macaque (a monkey) to be more similar to the mouse genome or the human genome? Why?

2. The DNA sequences called homeoboxes, which help homeotic genes in animals direct development, are common to flies and mice. Given this similarity, explain why these animals are so different.

3. **WHAT IF?** There are three times as many *Alu* elements in the human genome as in the chimpanzee genome. How do you think these extra *Alu* elements arose in the human genome? Propose a role they might have played in the divergence of these two species.

For suggested answers, see Appendix A.

SUMMARY OF KEY CONCEPTS

CONCEPT 21.1

The Human Genome Project fostered development of faster, less expensive sequencing techniques (pp. 437–438)

- The **Human Genome Project** was largely completed in 2003, aided by major advances in sequencing technology.
- In the **whole-genome shotgun** approach, the whole genome is cut into many small, overlapping fragments that are sequenced; computer software then assembles the genome sequence.

? *How did the Human Genome Project result in more rapid, less expensive DNA sequencing technology?*

CONCEPT 21.2

Scientists use bioinformatics to analyze genomes and their functions (pp. 438–442)

- Computer analysis of genome sequences aids **gene annotation**, the identification of protein-coding sequences. Methods to detemine gene function include comparing sequences of newly discovered genes with those of known genes in other species and observing the effects of experimentally inactivating the genes.
- In systems biology, scientists use the computer-based tools of **bioinformatics** to compare genomes and study sets of genes and proteins as whole systems (**genomics** and **proteomics**). Studies include large-scale analyses of protein interactions, functional DNA elements, and genes contributing to medical conditions.

? *What has been the most significant finding of the ENCODE project? Why was the project expanded to include non-human species?*

CONCEPT 21.3

Genomes vary in size, number of genes, and gene density (pp. 442–444)

	Bacteria	Archaea	Eukarya
Genome size	Most are 1–6 Mb		Most are 10–4,000 Mb, but a few are much larger
Number of genes	1,500–7,500		5,000–40,000
Gene density	Higher than in eukaryotes		Lower than in prokaryotes (Within eukaryotes, lower density is correlated with larger genomes.)
Introns	None in protein-coding genes	Present in some genes	Present in most genes of multicellular eukaryotes, but only in some genes of unicellular eukaryotes
Other noncoding DNA	Very little		Can exist in large amounts; generally more repetitive noncoding DNA in multicellular eukaryotes

? *Compare genome size, gene number, and gene density (a) in the three domains and (b) among eukaryotes.*

CONCEPT 21.4

Multicellular eukaryotes have much noncoding DNA and many multigene families (pp. 444–447)

- Only 1.5% of the human genome codes for proteins or gives rise to rRNAs or tRNAs; the rest is noncoding DNA, including **pseudogenes** and **repetitive DNA** of unknown function.
- The most abundant type of repetitive DNA in multicellular eukaryotes consists of **transposable elements** and related sequences. In eukaryotes, there are two types of transposable elements: **transposons**, which move via a DNA intermediate, and **retrotransposons**, which are more prevalent and move via an RNA intermediate.
- Other repetitive DNA includes short, noncoding sequences that are tandemly repeated thousands of times (**simple sequence DNA**, which includes **STRs**); these sequences are especially prominent in centromeres and telomeres, where they probably play structural roles in the chromosome.
- Though many eukaryotic genes are present in one copy per haploid chromosome set, others (most, in some species) are members of a gene family, such as the human globin gene families:

? *Explain how the function of transposable elements might account for their prevalence in human noncoding DNA.*

CONCEPT 21.5

Duplication, rearrangement, and mutation of DNA contribute to genome evolution (pp. 448–453)

- Errors in cell division can lead to extra copies of all or part of entire chromosome sets, which may then diverge if one set accumulates sequence changes. Polyploidy occurs more often among plants than animals, and contributes to speciation.
- The chromosomal organization of genomes can be compared among species, providing information about evolutionary relationships. Within a given species, rearrangements of chromosomes are thought to contribute to the emergence of new species.
- The genes encoding the various related but different globin proteins evolved from one common ancestral globin gene, which duplicated and diverged into α-globin and β-globin ancestral genes. Subsequent duplication and random mutation gave rise to the present globin genes, all of which code for oxygen-binding proteins. The copies of some duplicated genes have diverged so much that the functions of their encoded proteins (such as lysozyme and α-lactalbumin) are now substantially different.
- Rearrangement of exons within and between genes during evolution has led to genes containing multiple copies of similar exons and/or several different exons derived from other genes.
- Movement of transposable elements or recombination between copies of the same element can generate new sequence combinations that are beneficial to the organism. These may alter the functions of genes or their patterns of expression and regulation.

? *How could chromosomal rearrangements lead to the emergence of new species?*

Comparing genome sequences provides clues to evolution and development (pp. 453–458)

- Comparisons of genomes from widely divergent and closely related species provide valuable information about ancient and more recent evolutionary history, respectively. Analysis of single nucleotide polymorphisms (SNPs) and copy-number variants (CNVs) among individuals in a species can also shed light on the evolution of that species.

- Evolutionary developmental (**evo-devo**) biologists have shown that homeotic genes and some other genes associated with animal development contain a **homeobox** region whose sequence is highly conserved among diverse species. Related sequences are present in the genes of plants and yeasts.

? *What type of information can be obtained by comparing the genomes of closely related species? Of very distantly related species?*

TEST YOUR UNDERSTANDING

LEVEL 1: KNOWLEDGE/COMPREHENSION

1. Bioinformatics includes all of the following except
   a. using computer programs to align DNA sequences.
   b. using DNA technology to combine DNA from two different sources in a test tube.
   c. developing computer-based tools for genome analysis.
   d. using mathematical tools to make sense of biological systems.

2. Homeotic genes
   a. encode transcription factors that control the expression of genes responsible for specific anatomical structures.
   b. are found only in *Drosophila* and other arthropods.
   c. are the only genes that contain the homeobox domain.
   d. encode proteins that form anatomical structures in the fly.

LEVEL 2: APPLICATION/ANALYSIS

3. Two eukaryotic proteins have one domain in common but are otherwise very different. Which of the following processes is most likely to have contributed to this similarity?
   a. gene duplication
   b. RNA splicing
   c. exon shuffling
   d. random point mutations

4. **DRAW IT** Below are the amino acid sequences (using the single-letter code; see Figure 5.14) of four short segments of the FOXP2 protein from six species: chimpanzee (C), orangutan (O), gorilla (G), rhesus macaque (R), mouse (M), and human (H). These segments contain all of the amino acid differences between the FOXP2 proteins of these species.

   1. ATETI...PKSSD...TSSTT...NARRD

   2. ATETI...PKSSE...TSSTT...NARRD

   3. ATETI...PKSSD...TSSTT...NARRD

   4. ATETI...PKSSD...TSSNT...SARRD

   5. ATETI...PKSSD...TSSTT...NARRD

   6. VTETI...PKSSD...TSSTT...NARRD

Use a highlighter to color any amino acid that varies among the species. (Color that amino acid in all sequences.)
(a) The C, G, R sequences are identical. Which lines correspond to those sequences?
(b) The H sequence differs from that of the C, G, R species at two amino acids. Underline the two differences in the H sequence.

(c) The O sequence differs from the C, G, R sequences at one amino acid (having V instead of A) and from the H sequence at three amino acids. Which line is the O sequence?
(d) In the M sequence, circle the amino acid(s) that differ from the C, G, R sequences, and draw a square around those that differ from the H sequence.
(e) Primates and rodents diverged between 60 and 100 million years ago, and chimpanzees and humans about 6 million years ago. What can you conclude by comparing the amino acid differences between the mouse and the C, G, R species with those between the human and the C, G, R species?

LEVEL 3: SYNTHESIS/EVALUATION

5. **EVOLUTION CONNECTION**
   Genes important in the embryonic development of animals, such as homeobox-containing genes, have been relatively well conserved during evolution; that is, they are more similar among different species than are many other genes. Why is this?

6. **SCIENTIFIC INQUIRY**
   The scientists mapping the SNPs in the human genome noticed that groups of SNPs tended to be inherited together, in blocks known as haplotypes, ranging in length from 5,000 to 200,000 base pairs. There are as few as four or five commonly occurring combinations of SNPs per haplotype. Integrating what you've learned throughout this chapter and this unit, propose an explanation for this observation.

7. **WRITE ABOUT A THEME: INFORMATION**
   The continuity of life is based on heritable information in the form of DNA. In a short essay (100–150 words), explain how mutations in protein-coding genes and regulatory DNA contribute to evolution.

8. **SYNTHESIZE YOUR KNOWLEDGE**

Insects have three thoracic (trunk) segments. While researchers have found insect fossils with pairs of wings on all three segments, modern insects have wings or related structures on only the second and third segment. It turns out that in modern insects, *Hox* gene products act to inhibit wing formation on the first segment. The treehopper insect (above) is somewhat of an exception. In addition to having wings on its second segment, the treehopper's first segment has an ornate helmet that resembles a set of thorns, which a recent study has found to be a modified, fused pair of "wings." The thorn-like structure helps to camouflage the treehopper in tree branches, thus reducing its risk of predation. Explain how changes in gene regulation could have led to the evolution of such a structure.

For selected answers, see Appendix A.

MasteringBiology®

Students Go to **MasteringBiology** for assignments, the eText, and the Study Area with practice tests, animations, and activities.

Instructors Go to **MasteringBiology** for automatically graded tutorials and questions that you can assign to your students, plus Instructor Resources.

AN INTERVIEW WITH

Hopi Hoekstra

Meet the queen of the beach mice: Hopi Hoekstra, the Alexander Agassiz Professor of Zoology at Harvard University. Dr. Hoekstra received her B.A. in integrative biology from the University of California, Berkeley, and her Ph.D. in zoology from the University of Washington, Seattle. She is interested in the genetic basis of adaptation and speciation in vertebrates and has published dozens of groundbreaking papers on organisms ranging from rodents to lizards to birds of prey.

How did you first become interested in biology?

My family is from Holland, and I thought I wanted to be a political science major—my goal was to become the ambassador to Holland. But I quickly realized that wasn't my cup of tea. This led me to consider, "What do I get most excited about?" I had always been captivated by the natural world, and I wondered how what I observed in nature could all come to be. So I started taking biology courses, and eventually I worked in a lab where I was running cockroaches on treadmills. This is not glamorous, you know. But even so, this was where I fell in love with research, with the idea of discovery, of designing experiments and testing them. I was hooked.

> " **By performing experiments in the wild along with molecular genetic studies in the lab, we can tell a more complete story about how organisms evolve....** "

Much of your research concerns beach mice in the genus *Peromyscus*. What drew you to these mice?

Well, they're adorable, aren't they? Just look at the picture!

▶ Beach mouse (*Peromyscus polionotus*).

But they are also related closely enough to lab mice that we can borrow the many genetic and genomic tools that have been developed for those mice. In addition, they breed in the lab just like lab mice, so we can do well-controlled experiments. And third, and probably most importantly, biologists have studied these species in the wild for many years, dating back to the late 1800s. As a result, we have an incredible wealth of information about their ecology, reproductive biology, physiology, and behavior.

Tell us about the work you and your students are currently doing.

We're trying to uncover the genetic basis of traits that affect survival and reproduction in nature. Typically, we begin with a particular phenotype, such as coat color in beach mice, and we perform experiments in the wild to test whether the phenotype really does affect the organism's ability to survive or reproduce. Then we try to find the gene or genes that code for this trait. But we don't stop there. Once we have found the genes, we examine how particular changes in those genes affect development to produce the variation in the trait that we see in the wild—such as the different colors we see in a population of beach mice. By performing experiments in the wild along with molecular genetic studies in the lab, we can tell a more complete story about how organisms evolve in response to the challenges they face in nature.

You have a very busy laboratory, filled with students and postdoctoral researchers. What are your thoughts about mentoring students?

My day-to-day job is all about discovery. For example, we recently had a lab meeting where several students described a project they had been working on for some time, and now they were moving towards an answer to their initial question. There's something so satisfying about that. Science is like a treasure hunt. It is thrilling to ask questions that we find interesting, and then have our results contribute to our understanding of evolution. Mentoring students is about passing along that enthusiasm, that sense of wonder about how nature works. Seeing the enthusiasm of my students as they describe what they did and what it tells us—I can't think of anything more fun to do with my day!

MB For an extended interview and video clip, go to the Study Area in MasteringBiology.

22

Descent with Modification: A Darwinian View of Life

▲ **Figure 22.1 How is this caterpillar protecting itself from predators?**

Endless Forms Most Beautiful

A hungry bird would have to look very closely to spot this caterpillar of the moth *Synchlora aerata*, which blends in well with the flowers on which it feeds. The disguise is enhanced by the caterpillar's flair for "decorating"—it glues pieces of flower petals to its body, transforming itself into its own background **(Figure 22.1)**.

This distinctive caterpillar is a member of a diverse group, the more than 120,000 species of lepidopteran insects (moths and butterflies). All lepidopterans go through a juvenile stage characterized by a well-developed head and many chewing mouthparts: the ravenous, efficient feeding machines we call caterpillars. As adults, all lepidopterans share other features, such as three pairs of legs and two pairs of wings covered with small scales. But the many lepidopterans also differ from one another. How did there come to be so many different moths and butterflies, and what causes their similarities and differences? The self-decorating caterpillar and its many close relatives illustrate three key observations about life:

- the striking ways in which organisms are suited for life in their environments*
- the many shared characteristics (unity) of life
- the rich diversity of life

---

*Here and throughout this text, the term *environment* refers to other organisms as well as to the physical aspects of an organism's surroundings.

More than a century and a half ago, Charles Darwin was inspired to develop a scientific explanation for these three broad observations. When he published his hypothesis in his book *The Origin of Species*, Darwin ushered in a scientific revolution—the era of evolutionary biology.

For now, we will define **evolution** as *descent with modification*, a phrase Darwin used in proposing that Earth's many species are descendants of ancestral species that were different from the present-day species. Evolution can also be defined more narrowly as a change in the genetic composition of a population from generation to generation (see Chapter 23).

We can also view evolution in two related but different ways: as a pattern and as a process. The *pattern* of evolutionary change is revealed by data from many scientific disciplines, including biology, geology, physics, and chemistry. These data are facts—they are observations about the natural world. The *process* of evolution consists of the mechanisms that produce the observed pattern of change. These mechanisms represent natural causes of the natural phenomena we observe. Indeed, the power of evolution as a unifying theory is its ability to explain and connect a vast array of observations about the living world.

As with all general theories in science, we continue to test our understanding of evolution by examining whether it can account for new observations and experimental results. In this and the following chapters, we'll examine how ongoing discoveries shape what we know about the pattern and process of evolution. To set the stage, we'll first retrace Darwin's quest to explain the adaptations, unity, and diversity of what he called life's "endless forms most beautiful."

CONCEPT 22.1

The Darwinian revolution challenged traditional views of a young Earth inhabited by unchanging species

What impelled Darwin to challenge the prevailing views about Earth and its life? Darwin developed his revolutionary proposal over time, influenced by the work of others and by his travels **(Figure 22.2)**. As we'll see, his ideas also had deep historical roots.

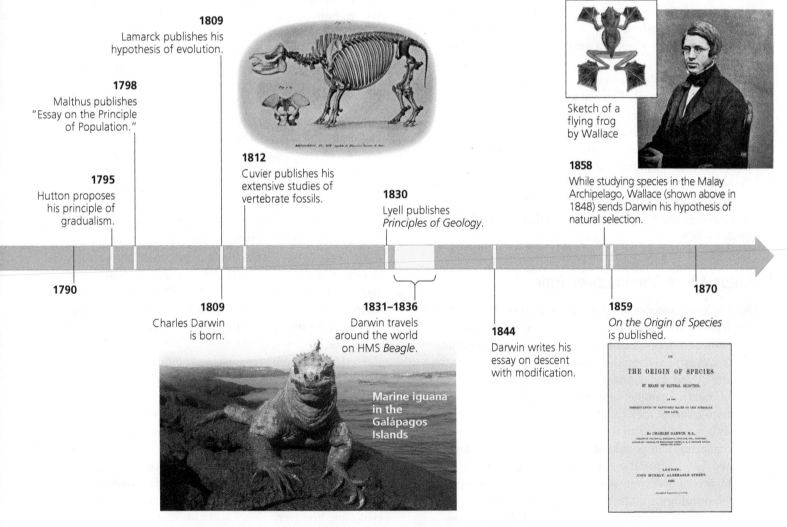

1809
Lamarck publishes his hypothesis of evolution.

1798
Malthus publishes "Essay on the Principle of Population."

1795
Hutton proposes his principle of gradualism.

1812
Cuvier publishes his extensive studies of vertebrate fossils.

1830
Lyell publishes *Principles of Geology*.

Sketch of a flying frog by Wallace

1858
While studying species in the Malay Archipelago, Wallace (shown above in 1848) sends Darwin his hypothesis of natural selection.

1790

1809
Charles Darwin is born.

1831–1836
Darwin travels around the world on HMS *Beagle*.

Marine iguana in the Galápagos Islands

1844
Darwin writes his essay on descent with modification.

1859
On the Origin of Species is published.

1870

▲ Figure 22.2 **The intellectual context of Darwin's ideas.**

Scala Naturae and Classification of Species

Long before Darwin was born, several Greek philosophers suggested that life might have changed gradually over time. But one philosopher who greatly influenced early Western science, Aristotle (384–322 BCE), viewed species as fixed (unchanging). Through his observations of nature, Aristotle recognized certain "affinities" among organisms. He concluded that life-forms could be arranged on a ladder, or scale, of increasing complexity, later called the *scala naturae* ("scale of nature"). Each form of life, perfect and permanent, had its allotted rung on this ladder.

These ideas were generally consistent with the Old Testament account of creation, which holds that species were individually designed by God and therefore perfect. In the 1700s, many scientists interpreted the often remarkable match of organisms to their environment as evidence that the Creator had designed each species for a particular purpose.

One such scientist was Carolus Linnaeus (1707–1778), a Swedish physician and botanist who sought to classify life's diversity, in his words, "for the greater glory of God." Linnaeus developed the two-part, or *binomial*, format for naming species (such as *Homo sapiens* for humans) that is still used today. In contrast to the linear hierarchy of the *scala naturae*, Linnaeus adopted a nested classification system, grouping similar species into increasingly general categories. For example, similar species are grouped in the same genus, similar genera (plural of genus) are grouped in the same family, and so on (see Figure 1.12).

Linnaeus did not ascribe the resemblances among species to evolutionary kinship, but rather to the pattern of their creation. A century later, however, Darwin argued that classification should be based on evolutionary relationships. He also noted that scientists using the Linnaean system often grouped organisms in ways that reflected those relationships.

Ideas About Change over Time

Among other sources of information, Darwin drew from the work of scientists studying **fossils**, the remains or traces of organisms from the past. Many fossils are found in sedimentary rocks formed from the sand and mud that settle to the bottom of seas, lakes, and swamps (**Figure 22.3**). New layers of sediment cover older ones and compress them into superimposed layers of rock called **strata** (singular, *stratum*). The fossils in a particular stratum provide a glimpse of some of the organisms that populated Earth at the time that layer formed. Later, erosion may carve through upper (younger) strata, revealing deeper (older) strata that had been buried.

Paleontology, the study of fossils, was developed in large part by French scientist Georges Cuvier (1769–1832). In

❶ Rivers carry sediment into aquatic habitats such as seas and swamps. Over time, sedimentary rock layers (strata) form under water. Some strata contain fossils.

❷ As water levels change and the bottom surface is pushed upward, the strata and their fossils are exposed.

Younger stratum with more recent fossils

Older stratum with older fossils

▲ **Figure 22.3 Formation of sedimentary strata with fossils.**

examining strata near Paris, Cuvier noted that the older the stratum, the more dissimilar its fossils were to current life-forms. He also observed that from one layer to the next, some new species appeared while others disappeared. He inferred that extinctions must have been a common occurrence, but he staunchly opposed the idea of evolution. Cuvier speculated that each boundary between strata represented a sudden catastrophic event, such as a flood, that had destroyed many of the species living in that area. Such regions, he reasoned, were later repopulated by different species immigrating from other areas.

In contrast, other scientists suggested that profound change could take place through the cumulative effect of slow but continuous processes. In 1795, Scottish geologist James Hutton (1726–1797) proposed that Earth's geologic features could be explained by gradual mechanisms, such as valleys being formed by rivers. The leading geologist of Darwin's time, Charles Lyell (1797–1875), incorporated Hutton's thinking into his proposal that the same geologic processes are operating today as in the past, and at the same rate.

Hutton and Lyell's ideas strongly influenced Darwin's thinking. Darwin agreed that if geologic change results from slow, continuous actions rather than from sudden events, then Earth must be much older than the widely accepted age of a few thousand years. It would, for example, take a very long time for a river to carve a canyon by erosion. He later reasoned that perhaps similarly slow and subtle processes could produce substantial biological change. Darwin was not the first to apply the idea of gradual change to biological evolution, however.

Lamarck's Hypothesis of Evolution

Although some 18th-century naturalists suggested that life evolves as environments change, only one proposed a mechanism for *how* life changes over time: French biologist Jean-Baptiste de Lamarck (1744–1829). Alas, Lamarck is primarily remembered today *not* for his visionary recognition that evolutionary change explains patterns in fossils and the match of organisms to their environments, but for the incorrect mechanism he proposed.

Lamarck published his hypothesis in 1809, the year Darwin was born. By comparing living species with fossil forms, Lamarck had found what appeared to be several lines of descent, each a chronological series of older to younger fossils leading to a living species. He explained his findings using two principles that were widely accepted at the time. The first was *use and disuse*, the idea that parts of the body that are used extensively become larger and stronger, while those that are not used deteriorate. Among many examples, he cited a giraffe stretching its neck to reach leaves on high branches. The second principle, *inheritance of acquired characteristics*, stated that an organism could pass these modifications to its offspring. Lamarck reasoned that the long, muscular neck of the living giraffe had evolved over many generations as giraffes stretched their necks ever higher.

Lamarck also thought that evolution happens because organisms have an innate drive to become more complex. Darwin rejected this idea, but he, too, thought that variation was introduced into the evolutionary process in part through inheritance of acquired characteristics. Today, however, our understanding of genetics refutes this mechanism: Experiments show that traits acquired by use during an individual's life are not inherited in the way proposed by Lamarck (Figure 22.4).

▲ **Figure 22.4 Acquired traits cannot be inherited.** This bonsai tree was "trained" to grow as a dwarf by pruning and shaping. However, seeds from this tree would produce offspring of normal size.

Lamarck was vilified in his own time, especially by Cuvier, who denied that species ever evolve. In retrospect, however, Lamarck did recognize that the match of organisms to their environments can be explained by gradual evolutionary change, and he did propose a testable explanation for how this change occurs.

CONCEPT CHECK 22.1

1. How did Hutton's and Lyell's ideas influence Darwin's thinking about evolution?
2. MAKE CONNECTIONS   Scientific hypotheses must be testable (see Concept 1.3). Applying this criterion, are Cuvier's explanation of the fossil record and Lamarck's hypothesis of evolution scientific? Explain your answer in each case.

For suggested answers, see Appendix A.

CONCEPT 22.2

Descent with modification by natural selection explains the adaptations of organisms and the unity and diversity of life

As the 19th century dawned, it was generally thought that species had remained unchanged since their creation. A few clouds of doubt about the permanence of species were beginning to gather, but no one could have forecast the thundering storm just beyond the horizon. How did Charles Darwin become the lightning rod for a revolutionary view of life?

Darwin's Research

Charles Darwin (1809–1882) was born in Shrewsbury, in western England. Even as a boy, he had a consuming interest in nature. When he was not reading nature books, he was fishing, hunting, riding, and collecting insects. However, Darwin's father, a physician, could see no future for his son as a naturalist and sent him to medical school in Edinburgh. But Charles found medicine boring and surgery before the days of anesthesia horrifying. He quit medical school and enrolled at Cambridge University, intending to become a clergyman. (At that time, many scholars of science belonged to the clergy.)

At Cambridge, Darwin became the protégé of John Henslow, a botany professor. Soon after Darwin graduated, Henslow recommended him to Captain Robert FitzRoy, who was preparing the survey ship HMS *Beagle* for a long voyage around the world. Darwin would pay his own way and serve as a conversation partner to the young captain. FitzRoy, who was himself an accomplished scientist, accepted Darwin because he was a skilled naturalist and because they were of similar age and social class.

The Voyage of the Beagle

Darwin embarked from England on the *Beagle* in December 1831. The primary mission of the voyage was to chart poorly known stretches of the South American coastline. Darwin, however, spent most of his time on shore, observing and collecting thousands of plants and animals. He described features of organisms that made them well suited to such diverse environments as the humid jungles of Brazil, the expansive grasslands of Argentina, and the towering peaks of the Andes. He also noted that the plants and animals in temperate regions of South America more closely resembled species living in the South American tropics than species living in temperate regions of Europe. Furthermore, the fossils he found, though clearly different from living species, distinctly resembled the living organisms of South America.

Darwin also spent much time thinking about geology. Despite repeated bouts of seasickness, he read Lyell's *Principles of Geology* during the voyage. He experienced geologic change firsthand when a violent earthquake shook the coast of Chile, and he observed afterward that rocks along the coast had been thrust upward by several feet. Finding fossils of ocean organisms high in the Andes, Darwin inferred that the rocks containing the fossils must have been raised there by many similar earthquakes. These observations reinforced what he had learned from Lyell: Physical evidence did not support the traditional view that Earth was only a few thousand years old.

Darwin's interest in the species (or fossils) found in an area was further stimulated by the *Beagle*'s stop at the Galápagos, a group of volcanic islands located near the equator about 900 km west of South America (Figure 22.5). Darwin was fascinated by the unusual organisms there. The birds he collected included several kinds of mockingbirds. These mockingbirds, though similar to each other, seemed to be different species. Some were unique to individual islands, while others lived on two or more adjacent islands. Furthermore, although the animals on the Galápagos resembled species living on the South American mainland, most of the Galápagos species were not known from anywhere else in the world. Darwin hypothesized that the Galápagos had been colonized by organisms that had strayed from South America and then diversified, giving rise to new species on the various islands.

Darwin's Focus on Adaptation

During the voyage of the *Beagle*, Darwin observed many examples of **adaptations**, inherited characteristics of organisms that enhance their survival and reproduction in specific environments. Later, as he reassessed his observations, he began to perceive adaptation to the environment and the origin of new species as closely related processes. Could a new species arise from an ancestral form by the gradual accumulation of adaptations to a different environment? From studies made years after Darwin's voyage, biologists have concluded that this is indeed what happened to a diverse

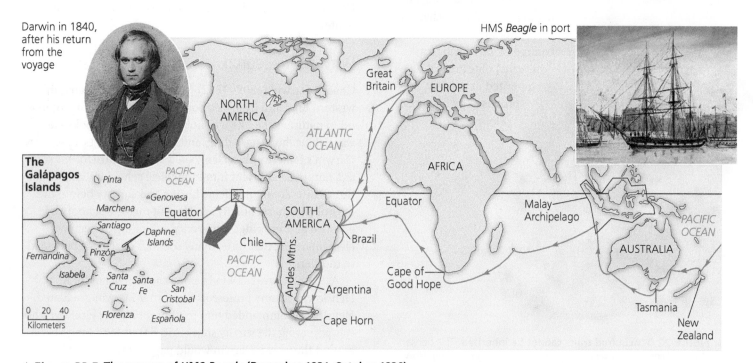

▲ Figure 22.5 **The voyage of HMS** *Beagle* **(December 1831–October 1836).**

group of finches found on the Galápagos Islands (see Figure 1.20). The finches' various beaks and behaviors are adapted to the specific foods available on their home islands (Figure 22.6). Darwin realized that explaining such adaptations was essential to understanding evolution. His explanation of how adaptations arise centered on **natural selection**, a process in which individuals that have certain inherited traits tend to survive and reproduce at higher rates than other individuals *because of* those traits.

By the early 1840s, Darwin had worked out the major features of his hypothesis. He set these ideas on paper in 1844, when he wrote a long essay on descent with modification and its underlying mechanism, natural selection. Yet he was still reluctant to publish his ideas, in part because he anticipated the uproar they would cause. During this time, Darwin continued to compile evidence in support of his hypothesis. By the mid-1850s, he had described his ideas to Lyell and a few others. Lyell, who was not yet convinced of evolution, nevertheless urged Darwin to publish on the subject before someone else came to the same conclusions and published first.

In June 1858, Lyell's prediction came true. Darwin received a manuscript from Alfred Russel Wallace (1823–1913), a British naturalist working in the South Pacific islands of the Malay Archipelago (see Figure 22.2). Wallace had developed a hypothesis of natural selection nearly identical to Darwin's. He asked Darwin to evaluate his paper and forward it to Lyell if it merited publication. Darwin complied, writing to Lyell: "Your words have come true with a vengeance. . . . I never saw a more striking coincidence . . . so all my originality, whatever it may amount to, will be smashed." On July 1, 1858, Lyell and a colleague presented Wallace's paper, along with extracts from Darwin's unpublished 1844 essay, to the Linnean Society of London. Darwin quickly finished his book, titled *On the Origin of Species by Means of Natural Selection* (commonly referred to as *The Origin of Species*), and published it the next year. Although Wallace had submitted his ideas for publication first, he admired Darwin and thought that Darwin had developed the idea of natural selection so extensively that he should be known as its main architect.

Within a decade, Darwin's book and its proponents had convinced most scientists of the time that life's diversity is the product of evolution. Darwin succeeded where previous evolutionists had failed, mainly by presenting a plausible scientific mechanism with immaculate logic and an avalanche of evidence.

The Origin of Species

In his book, Darwin amassed evidence that three broad observations about nature—the unity of life, the diversity of life, and the match between organisms and their environments—resulted from descent with modification by natural selection.

Descent with Modification

In the first edition of *The Origin of Species*, Darwin never used the word *evolution* (although the final word of the book is "evolved"). Rather, he discussed *descent with modification*, a phrase that summarized his view of life. Organisms share many characteristics, leading Darwin to perceive unity in life. He attributed the unity of life to the descent of all organisms from an ancestor that lived in the remote past. He also thought that as the descendants of that ancestral organism lived in various habitats, they gradually accumulated diverse modifications, or adaptations, that fit them to

(a) Cactus-eater. The long, sharp beak of the cactus ground finch (*Geospiza scandens*) helps it tear and eat cactus flowers and pulp.

(b) Insect-eater. The green warbler finch (*Certhidea olivacea*) uses its narrow, pointed beak to grasp insects.

(c) Seed-eater. The large ground finch (*Geospiza magnirostris*) has a large beak adapted for cracking seeds found on the ground.

▲ **Figure 22.6 Three examples of beak variation in Galápagos finches.** The Galápagos Islands are home to more than a dozen species of closely related finches, some found only on a single island. A striking difference among them is their beaks, which are adapted for specific diets.

MAKE CONNECTIONS *Review Figure 1.20. To which of the other two species shown above is the cactus-eater more closely related (that is, with which does the cactus-eater share a more recent common ancestor)?*

► Figure 22.7
"I think...." In this 1837 sketch, Darwin envisioned the branching pattern of evolution. Branches that end in twigs labeled A–D represent particular groups of living organisms; all other branches represent extinct groups.

specific ways of life. Darwin reasoned that over a long period of time, descent with modification eventually led to the rich diversity of life we see today.

Darwin viewed the history of life as a tree, with multiple branchings from a common trunk out to the tips of the youngest twigs (Figure 22.7). In his diagram, the tips of the twigs that are labeled A–D represent several groups of organisms living in the present day, while the unlabeled branches represent groups that are extinct. Each fork of the tree represents the most recent common ancestor of all the lines of evolution that subsequently branch from that point. Darwin reasoned that such a branching process, along with past extinction events, could explain the large morphological gaps that sometimes exist between related groups of organisms.

As an example, let's consider the three living species of elephants: the Asian elephant (*Elephas maximus*) and two species of African elephants (*Loxodonta africana* and *L. cyclotis*). These closely related species are very similar because they shared the same line of descent until a relatively recent split from their common ancestor, as shown in the tree diagram in **Figure 22.8**. Note that seven lineages related to elephants have become extinct over the past 32 million years. As a result, there are no living species that fill the morphological gap between the elephants and their nearest relatives today, the hyraxes and manatees. Such extinctions are not uncommon. In fact, many evolutionary branches, even some major ones, are dead ends: Scientists estimate that over 99% of all species that have ever lived are now extinct. As in Figure 22.8, fossils of extinct species can document the divergence of present-day groups by "filling in" gaps between them.

Artificial Selection, Natural Selection, and Adaptation

Darwin proposed the mechanism of natural selection to explain the observable patterns of evolution. He crafted his argument carefully, hoping to persuade even the most skeptical readers. First he discussed familiar examples of selective breeding of domesticated plants and animals. Humans

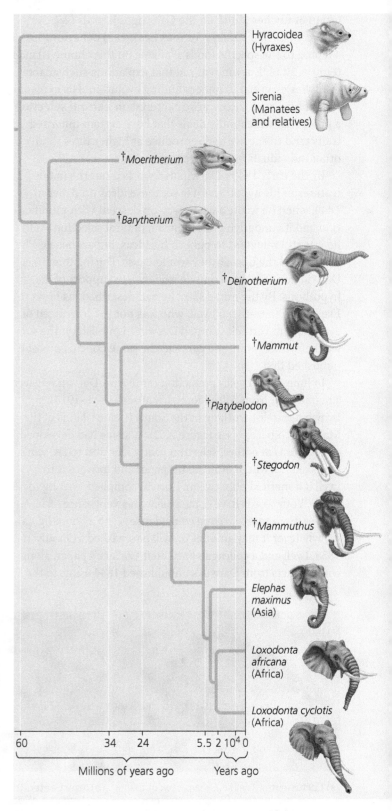

▲ Figure 22.8 **Descent with modification.** This evolutionary tree of elephants and their relatives is based mainly on fossils—their anatomy, order of appearance in strata, and geographic distribution. Note that most branches of descent ended in extinction (denoted by the dagger symbol †). (Time line not to scale.)

❓ *Based on the tree shown here, approximately when did the most recent ancestor shared by* Mammuthus *(woolly mammoths), Asian elephants, and African elephants live?*

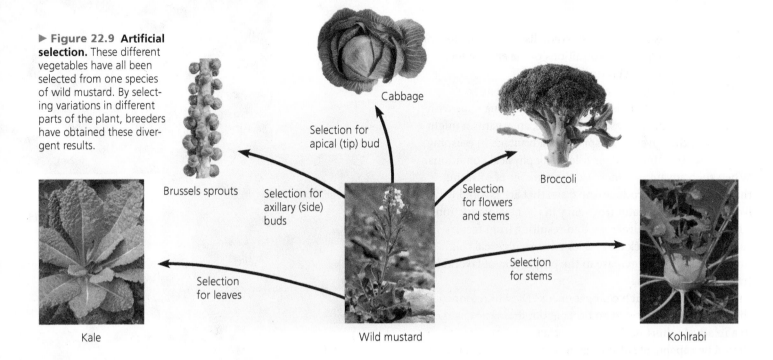

▶ **Figure 22.9 Artificial selection.** These different vegetables have all been selected from one species of wild mustard. By selecting variations in different parts of the plant, breeders have obtained these divergent results.

Brussels sprouts

Cabbage

Selection for apical (tip) bud

Selection for axillary (side) buds

Broccoli

Selection for flowers and stems

Selection for stems

Kale

Selection for leaves

Wild mustard

Kohlrabi

have modified other species over many generations by selecting and breeding individuals that possess desired traits, a process called **artificial selection (Figure 22.9)**. As a result of artificial selection, crops, livestock animals, and pets often bear little resemblance to their wild ancestors.

Darwin then argued that a similar process occurs in nature. He based his argument on two observations, from which he drew two inferences:

Observation #1: Members of a population often vary in their inherited traits **(Figure 22.10)**.

Observation #2: All species can produce more offspring than their environment can support **(Figure 22.11)**, and many of these offspring fail to survive and reproduce.

Inference #1: Individuals whose inherited traits give them a higher probability of surviving and reproducing in a given environment tend to leave more offspring than other individuals.

Inference #2: This unequal ability of individuals to survive and reproduce will lead to the accumulation of favorable traits in the population over generations.

As these two inferences suggest, Darwin saw an important connection between natural selection and the capacity of organisms to "overreproduce." He began to make this connection after reading an essay by economist Thomas Malthus, who contended that much of human suffering—disease, famine, and war—resulted from the human population's potential to increase faster than food supplies and other resources. Similarly, Darwin realized that the capacity to overreproduce was characteristic of all species. Of the many eggs laid, young born, and seeds spread, only a tiny fraction complete their development and leave offspring of

▲ **Figure 22.10 Variation in a population.** Individuals in this population of Asian ladybird beetles vary in color and spot pattern. Natural selection may act on these variations only if (1) they are heritable and (2) they affect the beetles' ability to survive and reproduce.

▶ **Figure 22.11 Overproduction of offspring.** A single puffball fungus can produce billions of offspring. If all of these offspring and their descendants survived to maturity, they would carpet the surrounding land surface.

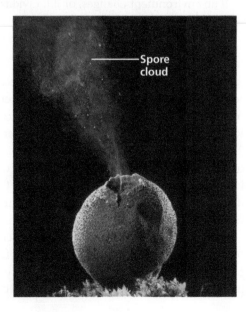

Spore cloud

their own. The rest are eaten, starved, diseased, unmated, or unable to tolerate physical conditions of the environment such as salinity or temperature.

An organism's heritable traits can influence not only its own performance, but also how well its offspring cope with environmental challenges. For example, an organism might have a trait that gives its offspring an advantage in escaping predators, obtaining food, or tolerating physical conditions. When such advantages increase the number of offspring that survive and reproduce, the traits that are favored will likely appear at a greater frequency in the next generation. Thus, over time, natural selection resulting from factors such as predators, lack of food, or adverse physical conditions can lead to an increase in the proportion of favorable traits in a population.

How rapidly do such changes occur? Darwin reasoned that if artificial selection can bring about dramatic change in a relatively short period of time, then natural selection should be capable of substantial modification of species over many hundreds of generations. Even if the advantages of some heritable traits over others are slight, the advantageous variations will gradually accumulate in the population, and less favorable variations will diminish. Over time, this process will increase the frequency of individuals with favorable adaptations and hence refine the match between organisms and their environment.

Natural Selection: *A Summary*

Let's now recap the main ideas of natural selection:

- Natural selection is a process in which individuals that have certain heritable traits survive and reproduce at a higher rate than other individuals because of those traits.
- Over time, natural selection can increase the match between organisms and their environment **(Figure 22.12)**.
- If an environment changes, or if individuals move to a new environment, natural selection may result in adaptation to these new conditions, sometimes giving rise to new species.

One subtle but important point is that although natural selection occurs through interactions between individual organisms and their environment, *individuals do not evolve.* Rather, it is the population that evolves over time.

A second key point is that natural selection can amplify or diminish only those heritable traits that differ among the individuals in a population. Thus, even if a trait is heritable, if all the individuals in a population are genetically identical for that trait, evolution by natural selection cannot occur.

Third, remember that environmental factors vary from place to place and over time. A trait that is favorable in one place or time may be useless—or even detrimental—in other places or times. Natural selection is always operating, but

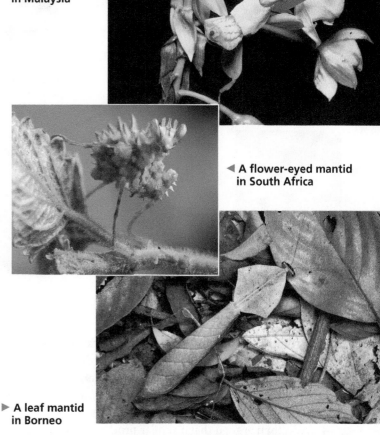

▶ **A flower mantid in Malaysia**

◀ **A flower-eyed mantid in South Africa**

▶ **A leaf mantid in Borneo**

▲ **Figure 22.12 Camouflage as an example of evolutionary adaptation.** Related species of the insects called mantids have diverse shapes and colors that evolved in different environments.

> ? *Explain how these mantids demonstrate the three key observations about life introduced at the beginning of the chapter: the match between organisms and their environments, unity, and diversity.*

which traits are favored depends on the context in which a species lives and mates.

Next, we'll survey the wide range of observations that support a Darwinian view of evolution by natural selection.

CONCEPT CHECK 22.2

1. How does the concept of descent with modification explain both the unity and diversity of life?

2. **WHAT IF?** If you discovered a fossil of an extinct mammal that lived high in the Andes, would you predict that it would more closely resemble present-day mammals from South American jungles or present-day mammals that live high in African mountains? Explain.

3. **MAKE CONNECTIONS** Review the relationship between genotype and phenotype (see Figures 14.4 and 14.6). Suppose that in a particular pea population, flowers with the white phenotype are favored by natural selection. Predict what would happen over time to the frequency of the *p* allele in the population, and explain your reasoning.

For suggested answers, see Appendix A.

CONCEPT 22.3

Evolution is supported by an overwhelming amount of scientific evidence

In *The Origin of Species*, Darwin marshaled a broad range of evidence to support the concept of descent with modification. Still—as he readily acknowledged—there were instances in which key evidence was lacking. For example, Darwin referred to the origin of flowering plants as an "abominable mystery," and he lamented the lack of fossils showing how earlier groups of organisms gave rise to new groups.

In the last 150 years, new discoveries have filled many of the gaps that Darwin identified. The origin of flowering plants, for example, is much better understood (see Chapter 30), and many fossils have been discovered that signify the origin of new groups of organisms (see Chapter 25). In this section, we'll consider four types of data that document the pattern of evolution and illuminate how it occurs: direct observations, homology, the fossil record, and biogeography.

Direct Observations of Evolutionary Change

Biologists have documented evolutionary change in thousands of scientific studies. We'll examine many such studies throughout this unit, but let's look at two examples here.

Natural Selection in Response to Introduced Species

Animals that eat plants, called herbivores, often have adaptations that help them feed efficiently on their primary food sources. What happens when herbivores switch to a new food source with different characteristics?

An opportunity to study this question in nature is provided by soapberry bugs, which use their "beak," a hollow, needlelike mouthpart, to feed on seeds located within the fruits of various plants. In southern Florida, the soapberry bug (*Jadera haematoloma*) feeds on the seeds of a native plant, the balloon vine (*Cardiospermum corindum*). In central Florida, however, balloon vines have become rare. Instead, soapberry bugs in that region now feed on the seeds of the goldenrain tree (*Koelreuteria elegans*), a species recently introduced from Asia.

Soapberry bugs feed most effectively when their beak length closely matches the depth at which seeds are found within the fruit. Goldenrain tree fruit consists of three flat lobes, and its seeds are much closer to the fruit surface than are the seeds of the plump, round fruit of the native balloon vine. These differences led researchers to predict that in populations that feed on goldenrain tree, natural selection would result in beaks that are *shorter* than those in populations that feed on balloon vine **(Figure 22.13)**. Indeed, beak

▼ **Figure 22.13** | Inquiry

Can a change in a population's food source result in evolution by natural selection?

Field Study Soapberry bugs feed most effectively when the length of their "beak" closely matches the depth of the seeds within the fruit. Scott Carroll and his colleagues measured beak lengths in soapberry bug populations feeding on the native balloon vine. They also measured beak lengths in populations feeding on the introduced goldenrain tree. The researchers then compared the measurements with those of museum specimens collected in the two areas before the goldenrain tree was introduced.

Soapberry bug with beak inserted in balloon vine fruit

Results Beak lengths were shorter in populations feeding on the introduced species than in populations feeding on the native species, in which the seeds are buried more deeply. The average beak length in museum specimens from each population (indicated by red arrows) was similar to beak lengths in populations feeding on native species.

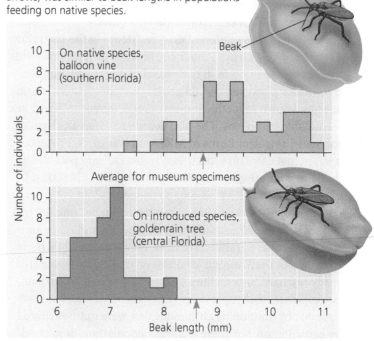

Conclusion Museum specimens and contemporary data suggest that a change in the size of the soapberry bug's food source can result in evolution by natural selection for matching beak size.

Source: S. P. Carroll and C. Boyd, Host race radiation in the soapberry bug: natural history with the history, *Evolution* 46:1052–1069 (1992).

WHAT IF? *Data from additional studies showed that when soapberry bug eggs from a population fed on balloon vine fruits were reared on goldenrain tree fruits (or vice versa), the beak lengths of the adult insects matched those in the population from which the eggs were obtained. Interpret these results.*

lengths are shorter in the populations that feed on golden-rain tree.

Researchers have also studied beak length evolution in soapberry bug populations that feed on plants introduced to Louisiana, Oklahoma, and Australia. In each of these locations, the fruit of the introduced plants is larger than the fruit of the native plant. Thus, in populations feeding on introduced species in these regions, researchers predicted that natural selection would result in the evolution of *longer* beak length. Again, data collected in field studies upheld this prediction.

The observed changes in beak lengths had important consequences: In Australia, for example, the increase in beak length nearly doubled the success with which soapberry bugs could eat the seeds of the introduced species. Furthermore, since historical data show that the goldenrain tree reached central Florida just 35 years before the scientific studies were initiated, the results demonstrate that natural selection can cause rapid evolution in a wild population.

The Evolution of Drug-Resistant Bacteria

An example of ongoing natural selection that dramatically affects humans is the evolution of drug-resistant pathogens (disease-causing organisms and viruses). This is a particular problem with bacteria and viruses because resistant strains of these pathogens can proliferate very quickly.

Consider the evolution of drug resistance in the bacterium *Staphylococcus aureus*. About one in three people harbor this species on their skin or in their nasal passages with no negative effects. However, certain genetic varieties (strains) of this species, known as methicillin-resistant *S. aureus* (MRSA), are formidable pathogens. The past decade has seen an alarming increase in virulent forms of MRSA such as clone USA300, a strain that can cause "flesh-eating disease" and potentially fatal infections (**Figure 22.14**). How did clone USA300 and other strains of MRSA become so dangerous?

The story begins in 1943, when penicillin became the first widely used antibiotic. Since then, penicillin and other antibiotics have saved millions of lives. However, by 1945, more than 20% of the *S. aureus* strains seen in hospitals were already resistant to penicillin. These bacteria had an enzyme, penicillinase, that could destroy penicillin. Researchers responded by developing antibiotics that were not destroyed by penicillinase, but some *S. aureus* populations developed resistance to each new drug within a few years.

Then, in 1959, doctors began using the powerful antibiotic methicillin. But within two years, methicillin-resistant strains of *S. aureus* appeared. How did these resistant strains emerge? Methicillin works by deactivating a protein that bacteria use to synthesize their cell walls. However, different *S. aureus* populations exhibited variations in how strongly their members were affected by the drug. In particular, some individuals were able to synthesize their cell walls using a different protein that was not affected by methicillin. These individuals survived the methicillin treatments and

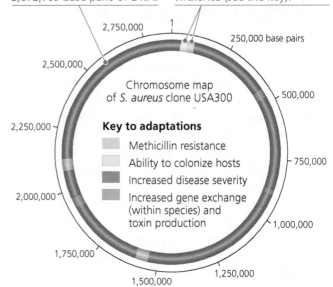

(a) Most MRSA infections are caused by recently appearing strains such as clone USA300. Resistant to multiple antibiotics and highly contagious, this strain and its close relatives can cause lethal infections of the skin, lungs, and blood. As shown here, researchers have identified key areas of the USA300 genome that code for adaptations that cause its virulent properties.

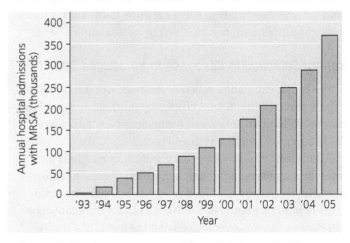

(b) MRSA infections severe enough to result in hospital admission have proliferated greatly in the past few decades.

▲ Figure 22.14 **The rise of methicillin-resistant *Staphylococcus aureus* (MRSA).**

WHAT IF? *Some drugs being developed specifically target and kill* S. aureus; *others slow the growth of MRSA but do not kill it. Based on how natural selection works and on the fact that bacterial species can exchange genes, explain why each of these strategies might be effective.*

reproduced at higher rates than did other individuals. Over time, these resistant individuals became increasingly common, leading to the spread of MRSA.

Initially, MRSA could be controlled by antibiotics that work differently from the way methicillin works. But this has become less effective because some MRSA strains are resistant to multiple antibiotics—probably because bacteria can exchange genes with members of their own and other species. Thus, the multidrug-resistant strains of today may have emerged over time as MRSA strains that were resistant to different antibiotics exchanged genes.

The *S. aureus* and soapberry bug examples highlight two key points about natural selection. First, natural selection is a process of editing, not a creative mechanism. A drug does not *create* resistant pathogens; it *selects for* resistant individuals that are already present in the population. Second, natural selection depends on time and place. It favors those characteristics in a genetically variable population that provide advantage in the current, local environment. What is beneficial in one situation may be useless or even harmful in another. Beak lengths that match the size of the typical fruit eaten by members of a particular soapberry bug population are favored by selection. However, a beak length suitable for fruit of one size can be disadvantageous when the bug is feeding on fruit of another size.

Homology

A second type of evidence for evolution comes from analyzing similarities among different organisms. As we've discussed, evolution is a process of descent with modification: Characteristics present in an ancestral organism are altered (by natural selection) in its descendants over time as they face different environmental conditions. As a result, related species can have characteristics that have an underlying similarity yet function differently. Similarity resulting from common ancestry is known as **homology**. As we'll describe in this section, an understanding of homology can be used to make testable predictions and explain observations that are otherwise puzzling.

Anatomical and Molecular Homologies

The view of evolution as a remodeling process leads to the prediction that closely related species should share similar features—and they do. Of course, closely related species share the features used to determine their relationship, but they also share many other features. Some of these shared features make little sense except in the context of evolution. For example, the forelimbs of all mammals, including humans, cats, whales, and bats, show the same arrangement of bones from the shoulder to the tips of the digits, even though the appendages have very different functions: lifting,

Humerus
Radius
Ulna
Carpals
Metacarpals
Phalanges

Human   Cat   Whale   Bat

▲ **Figure 22.15 Mammalian forelimbs: homologous structures.** Even though they have become adapted for different functions, the forelimbs of all mammals are constructed from the same basic skeletal elements: one large bone (purple), attached to two smaller bones (orange and tan), attached to several small bones (gold), attached to several metacarpals (green), attached to approximately five digits, each of which is composed of phalanges (blue).

walking, swimming, and flying (**Figure 22.15**). Such striking anatomical resemblances would be highly unlikely if these structures had arisen anew in each species. Rather, the underlying skeletons of the arms, forelegs, flippers, and wings of different mammals are **homologous structures** that represent variations on a structural theme that was present in their common ancestor.

Comparing early stages of development in different animal species reveals additional anatomical homologies not visible in adult organisms. For example, at some point in their development, all vertebrate embryos have a tail located posterior to (behind) the anus, as well as structures called pharyngeal (throat) arches (**Figure 22.16**). These homologous throat arches ultimately develop into structures with

Pharyngeal arches

Post-anal tail

Chick embryo (LM)   Human embryo

▲ **Figure 22.16 Anatomical similarities in vertebrate embryos.** At some stage in their embryonic development, all vertebrates have a tail located posterior to the anus (referred to as a post-anal tail), as well as pharyngeal (throat) arches. Descent from a common ancestor can explain such similarities.

very different functions, such as gills in fishes and parts of the ears and throat in humans and other mammals.

Some of the most intriguing homologies concern "left-over" structures of marginal, if any, importance to the organism. These **vestigial structures** are remnants of features that served a function in the organism's ancestors. For instance, the skeletons of some snakes retain vestiges of the pelvis and leg bones of walking ancestors. Another example is provided by eye remnants that are buried under scales in blind species of cave fishes. We would not expect to see these vestigial structures if snakes and blind cave fishes had origins separate from other vertebrate animals.

Biologists also observe similarities among organisms at the molecular level. All forms of life use essentially the same genetic code, suggesting that all species descended from common ancestors that used this code. But molecular homologies go beyond a shared code. For example, organisms as dissimilar as humans and bacteria share genes inherited from a very distant common ancestor. Some of these homologous genes have acquired new functions, while others, such as those coding for the ribosomal subunits used in protein synthesis (see Figure 17.17), have retained their original functions. It is also common for organisms to have genes that have lost their function, even though the homologous genes in related species may be fully functional. Like vestigial structures, it appears that such inactive "pseudogenes" may be present simply because a common ancestor had them.

Homologies and "Tree Thinking"

Some homologous characteristics, such as the genetic code, are shared by all species because they date to the deep ancestral past. In contrast, homologous characteristics that evolved more recently are shared only within smaller groups of organisms. Consider the *tetrapods* (from the Greek *tetra*, four, and *pod*, foot), the vertebrate group that consists of amphibians, mammals, and reptiles (including birds—see Figure 22.17). All tetrapods have limbs with digits (see Figure 22.15), whereas other vertebrates do not. Thus, homologous characteristics form a nested pattern: All life shares the deepest layer, and each successive smaller group adds its own homologies to those it shares with larger groups. This nested pattern is exactly what we would expect to result from descent with modification from a common ancestor.

Biologists often represent the pattern of descent from common ancestors with an **evolutionary tree**, a diagram that reflects evolutionary relationships among groups of organisms. We will explore in detail how evolutionary trees are constructed in Chapter 26, but for now, let's consider how we can interpret and use such trees.

Figure 22.17 is an evolutionary tree of tetrapods and their closest living relatives, the lungfishes. In this diagram, each branch point represents the common ancestor of all species that descended from it. For example, lungfishes and all tetrapods descended from ancestor ❶, whereas mammals, lizards and snakes, crocodiles, and birds all descended from ancestor ❸. As expected, the three homologies shown on the tree—limbs with digits, the amnion (a protective embryonic membrane), and feathers—form a nested pattern. Limbs with digits were present in common ancestor ❷ and hence are found in all of the descendants of that ancestor (the tetrapods). The amnion was present only in ancestor ❸ and hence is shared only by some tetrapods (mammals and reptiles). Feathers were present only in common ancestor ❻ and hence are found only in birds.

To explore "tree thinking" further, note that in Figure 22.17, mammals are positioned closer to amphibians than to birds. As a result, you might conclude that mammals are more closely related to amphibians than they are to birds. However, mammals are actually more closely related to birds than to amphibians because mammals and birds share a more recent

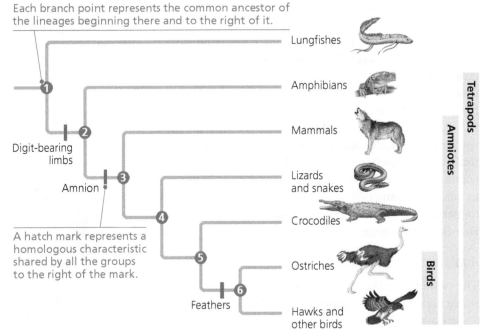

Each branch point represents the common ancestor of the lineages beginning there and to the right of it.

Digit-bearing limbs

Amnion

A hatch mark represents a homologous characteristic shared by all the groups to the right of the mark.

Feathers

Lungfishes
Amphibians
Mammals
Lizards and snakes
Crocodiles
Ostriches
Hawks and other birds

Tetrapods
Amniotes
Birds

▲ **Figure 22.17 Tree thinking: information provided in an evolutionary tree.** This evolutionary tree for tetrapods and their closest living relatives, the lungfishes, is based on anatomical and DNA sequence data. The purple bars indicate the origin of three important homologies, each of which evolved only once. Birds are nested within and evolved from reptiles; hence, the group of organisms called "reptiles" technically includes birds.

❓ *Are crocodiles more closely related to lizards or birds? Explain your answer.*

common ancestor (ancestor ❸) than do mammals and amphibians (ancestor ❷). Ancestor ❷ is also the most recent common ancestor of birds and amphibians, making mammals and birds equally related to amphibians. Finally, note that the tree in Figure 22.17 shows the relative timing of events but not their actual dates. Thus, we can conclude that ancestor ❷ lived before ancestor ❸, but we do not know when that was.

Evolutionary trees are hypotheses that summarize our current understanding of patterns of descent. Our confidence in these relationships, as with any hypothesis, depends on the strength of the supporting data. In the case of Figure 22.17, the tree is supported by many different data sets, including both anatomical and DNA sequence data. As a result, biologists are confident that it accurately reflects evolutionary history. Scientists can use such well-supported evolutionary trees to make specific and sometimes surprising predictions about organisms (see Chapter 26).

A Different Cause of Resemblance: Convergent Evolution

Although organisms that are closely related share characteristics because of common descent, distantly related organisms can resemble one another for a different reason: **convergent evolution**, the independent evolution of similar features in different lineages. Consider marsupial mammals, many of which live in Australia. Marsupials are distinct from another group of mammals—the eutherians—few of which live in Australia. (Eutherians complete their embryonic development in the uterus, whereas marsupials are born as embryos and complete their development in an external pouch.) Some Australian marsupials have eutherian look-alikes with superficially similar adaptations. For instance, a forest-dwelling Australian marsupial called the sugar glider is superficially very similar to flying squirrels, gliding eutherians that live in North American forests **(Figure 22.18)**. But the sugar glider has many other characteristics that make it a marsupial, much more closely related to kangaroos and other Australian marsupials than to flying squirrels or other eutherians. Once again, our understanding of evolution can explain these observations. Although they evolved independently from different ancestors, these two mammals have adapted to similar environments in similar ways. In such examples in which species share features because of convergent evolution, the resemblance is said to be **analogous**, not homologous. Analogous features share similar function, but not common ancestry, while homologous features share common ancestry, but not necessarily similar function.

▲ **Figure 22.18 Convergent evolution.** The ability to glide through the air evolved independently in these two distantly related mammals.

The Fossil Record

A third type of evidence for evolution comes from fossils. The fossil record documents the pattern of evolution, showing that past organisms differed from present-day organisms and that many species have become extinct. Fossils also show the evolutionary changes that have occurred in various groups of organisms. To give one of hundreds of possible examples, researchers found that the pelvic bone in fossil stickleback fish became greatly reduced in size over time in a number of different lakes. The consistent nature of this change suggests that the reduction in the size of the pelvic bone may have been driven by natural selection.

Fossils can also shed light on the origins of new groups of organisms. An example is the fossil record of cetaceans, the mammalian order that includes whales, dolphins, and porpoises. Some of these fossils **(Figure 22.19)** provided an

▲ **Figure 22.19 Ankle bones: one piece of the puzzle.** Comparing fossils and present-day examples of the astragalus (a type of ankle bone) indicates that cetaceans are closely related to even-toed ungulates. **(a)** In most mammals, the astragalus is shaped like that of a dog, with a double hump on one end (red arrows) but not at the opposite end (blue arrow). **(b)** Fossils show that the early cetacean *Pakicetus* had an astragalus with double humps at both ends, a shape otherwise found only in pigs **(c)**, deer **(d)**, and all other even-toed ungulates.

unexpected line of support for a hypothesis based on DNA sequence data: that cetaceans are closely related to even-toed ungulates, a group that includes deer, pigs, camels, and cows.

What else can fossils tell us about cetacean origins? The earliest cetaceans lived 50–60 million years ago. The fossil record indicates that prior to that time, most mammals were terrestrial. Although scientists had long realized that whales and other cetaceans originated from land mammals, few fossils had been found that revealed how cetacean limb structure had changed over time, leading eventually to the loss of hind limbs and the development of flippers and tail flukes. In the past few decades, however, a series of remarkable fossils have been discovered in Pakistan, Egypt, and North America. These fossils document steps in the transition from life on land to life in the sea, filling in some of the gaps between ancestral and living cetaceans (Figure 22.20).

Collectively, the recent fossil discoveries document the origin of a major new group of mammals, the cetaceans. These discoveries also show that cetaceans and their close living relatives (hippopotamuses, pigs, and other even-toed ungulates) are much more different from each other

▲ **Diacodexis,** an early even-toed ungulate

than were *Pakicetus* and early even-toed ungulates, such as *Diacodexis*. Similar patterns are seen in fossils documenting the origins of other major new groups of organisms, including mammals (see Chapter 25), flowering plants (see Chapter 30), and tetrapods (see Chapter 34). In each of these cases, the fossil record shows that over time, descent with modification produced increasingly large differences among related groups of organisms, ultimately resulting in the diversity of life we see today.

Biogeography

A fourth type of evidence for evolution comes from **biogeography**, the scientific study of the geographic distributions of species. The geographic distributions of organisms are influenced by many factors, including *continental drift*, the slow movement of Earth's continents over time. About 250 million years ago, these movements united all of Earth's landmasses into a single large continent called **Pangaea** (see Figure 25.16). Roughly 200 million years ago, Pangaea began to break apart; by 20 million years ago, the continents we know today were within a few hundred kilometers of their present locations.

We can use our understanding of evolution and continental drift to predict where fossils of different groups of organisms might be found. For example, scientists have constructed evolutionary trees for horses based on anatomical data. These trees and the ages of fossils of horse ancestors suggest that the genus that includes present-day horses (*Equus*) originated 5 million years ago in North America. At that time, North and South America were close to their present locations, but they were not yet connected, making it difficult for horses to travel between them. Thus, we would predict that the oldest *Equus* fossils

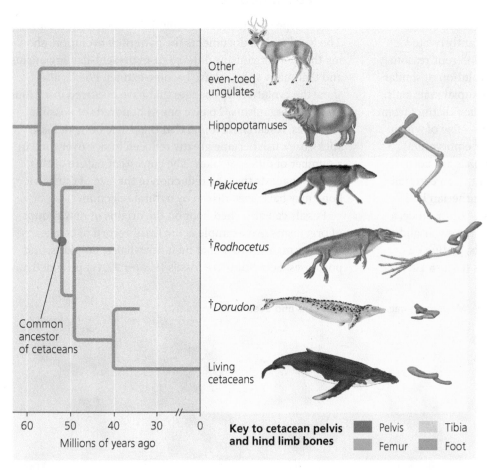

Other even-toed ungulates

Hippopotamuses

†*Pakicetus*

†*Rodhocetus*

†*Dorudon*

Living cetaceans

Common ancestor of cetaceans

| 60 | 50 | 40 | 30 | 0 |

Millions of years ago

Key to cetacean pelvis and hind limb bones

Pelvis | Tibia
Femur | Foot

▲ **Figure 22.20 The transition to life in the sea.** Cetacean lineages are highlighted in yellow in the above evolutionary tree diagram. Multiple lines of evidence support the hypothesis that cetaceans evolved from terrestrial mammals. Fossils document the reduction over time in the pelvis and hind limb bones of extinct cetacean ancestors, including *Pakicetus, Rodhocetus,* and *Dorudon*. DNA sequence data support the hypothesis that cetaceans are most closely related to hippopotamuses.

[?] *Which happened first during the evolution of cetaceans: changes in hind limb structure or the origin of tail flukes? Explain.*

should be found only on the continent on which the group originated—North America. This prediction and others like it for different groups of organisms have been upheld, providing more evidence for evolution.

We can also use our understanding of evolution to explain biogeographic data. For example, islands generally have many plant and animal species that are **endemic** (found nowhere else in the world). Yet, as Darwin described in *The Origin of Species*, most island species are closely related to species from the nearest mainland or a neighboring island. He explained this observation by suggesting that islands are colonized by species from the nearest mainland. These colonists eventually give rise to new species as they adapt to their new environments. Such a process also explains why two islands with similar environments in distant parts of the world tend to be populated not by species that are closely related to each other, but rather by species related to those of the nearest mainland, where the environment is often quite different.

What Is Theoretical About Darwin's View of Life?

Some people dismiss Darwin's ideas as "just a theory." However, as we have seen, the *pattern* of evolution—the observation that life has evolved over time—has been documented directly and is supported by a great deal of evidence. In addition, Darwin's explanation of the *process* of evolution—that natural selection is the primary cause of the observed pattern of evolutionary change—makes sense of massive amounts of data. The effects of natural selection also can be observed and tested in nature. Once such experiment is described in the Scientific Skills Exercise.

What, then, is theoretical about evolution? Keep in mind that the scientific meaning of the term *theory* is very different from its meaning in everyday use. The colloquial use of the word *theory* comes close to what scientists mean by a hypothesis. In science, a theory is more comprehensive

---

SCIENTIFIC SKILLS EXERCISE

Making and Testing Predictions

Can Predation Result in Natural Selection for Color Patterns in Guppies? What we know about evolution changes constantly as new observations lead to new hypotheses—and hence to new ways to test our understanding of evolutionary theory. Consider the wild guppies (*Poecilia reticulata*) that live in pools connected by streams on the Caribbean island of Trinidad. Male guppies have highly varied color patterns, which are controlled by genes that are only expressed in adult males. Female guppies choose males with bright color patterns as mates more often than they choose males with drab coloring. But the bright colors that attract females also make the males more conspicuous to predators. Researchers observed that in pools with few predator species, the benefits of bright colors appear to "win out," and males are more brightly colored than in pools where predation is more intense.

One guppy predator, the killifish, preys on juvenile guppies that have not yet displayed their adult coloration. Researchers predicted that if guppies with drab colors were transferred to a pool with only killifish, eventually the descendants of these guppies would be more brightly colored (because of the female preference for brightly colored males).

How the Experiment Was Done Researchers transplanted 200 guppies from pools containing pike-cichlid fish, intense guppy predators, to

pools containing killifish, less active predators that prey mainly on juvenile guppies. They tracked the number of bright-colored spots and the total area of those spots on male guppies in each generation.

Data from the Experiment After 22 months (15 generations), researchers compared the color pattern data for the source and transplanted populations.

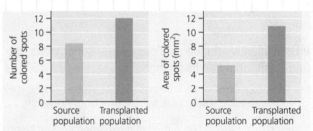

Interpret the Data

1. Identify the following elements of hypothesis-based science in this example: (a) question, (b) hypothesis, (c) prediction, (d) control group, and (e) experimental group. (For additional information about hypothesis-based science, see Chapter 1 and the Scientific Skills Review in Appendix F and the Study Area of MasteringBiology.)

2. Explain how the types of data the researchers chose to collect enabled them to test their prediction.

3. (a) What conclusion would you draw from the data presented above? (b) What additional questions might you ask to determine the strength of this conclusion?

4. Predict what would happen if, after 22 months, guppies from the transplanted population were returned to the source pool. Describe an experiment to test your prediction.

(MB) A version of this Scientific Skills Exercise can be assigned in MasteringBiology.

Data from J. A. Endler, Natural selection on color patters in *Poecilia reticulata, Evolution* 34:76–91 (1980).

Guppies transplanted

Pools with pike-cichlids and guppies

Pools with killifish, but no guppies prior to transplant

than a hypothesis. A theory, such as the theory of evolution by natural selection, accounts for many observations and explains and integrates a great variety of phenomena. Such a unifying theory does not become widely accepted unless its predictions stand up to thorough and continual testing by experiment and additional observation (see Chapter 1). As the rest of this unit demonstrates, this has certainly been the case with the theory of evolution by natural selection.

The skepticism of scientists as they continue to test theories prevents these ideas from becoming dogma. For example, although Darwin thought that evolution was a very slow process, we now know that new species sometimes form in relatively short periods of time: a few thousand years or less (see Chapter 24). Furthermore, evolutionary biologists now recognize that natural selection is not the only mechanism responsible for evolution. Indeed, the study of evolution today is livelier than ever as scientists make new discoveries using a wide range of experimental approaches and genetic analyses; you can read about one such biologist, Dr. Hopi Hoekstra, and her work in the interview before this chapter.

Although Darwin's theory attributes life's diversity to natural processes, the diverse products of evolution are nevertheless elegant and inspiring. As Darwin wrote in the final sentence of *The Origin of Species*, "There is grandeur in this view of life . . . [in which] endless forms most beautiful and most wonderful have been, and are being, evolved."

CONCEPT CHECK 22.3

1. Explain how the following statement is inaccurate: "Antibiotics have created drug resistance in MRSA."
2. How does evolution account for (a) the similar mammalian forelimbs with different functions shown in Figure 22.15 and (b) the similar forms of the two distantly related mammals shown in Figure 22.18?
3. **WHAT IF?** Dinosaurs originated 250–200 million years ago. Would you expect the geographic distribution of early dinosaur fossils to be broad (on many continents) or narrow (on one or a few continents only)? Explain.

For suggested answers, see Appendix A.

---

22 Chapter Review

SUMMARY OF KEY CONCEPTS

CONCEPT 22.1

The Darwinian revolution challenged traditional views of a young Earth inhabited by unchanging species (pp. 463–465)

- Darwin proposed that life's diversity arose from ancestral species through natural selection, a departure from prevailing views.
- Cuvier studied fossils but denied that evolution occurs; he proposed that sudden catastrophic events in the past caused species to disappear from an area.
- Hutton and Lyell thought that geologic change could result from gradual mechanisms that operated in the past in the same manner as they do today.
- Lamarck hypothesized that species evolve, but the underlying mechanisms he proposed are not supported by evidence.

? *Why was the age of Earth important for Darwin's ideas about evolution?*

CONCEPT 22.2

Descent with modification by natural selection explains the adaptations of organisms and the unity and diversity of life (pp. 465–470)

- Darwin's experiences during the voyage of the *Beagle* gave rise to his idea that new species originate from ancestral forms through the accumulation of **adaptations**. He refined his theory for many years and finally published it in 1859 after learning that Wallace had come to the same idea.

- In *The Origin of Species*, Darwin proposed that over long periods of time, descent with modification produced the rich diversity of life through the mechanism of **natural selection**.

Observations

Individuals in a population vary in their heritable characteristics.	Organisms produce more offspring than the environment can support.

Inferences

Individuals that are well suited to their environment tend to leave more offspring than other individuals.

and

Over time, favorable traits accumulate in the population.

? *Describe how overreproduction and heritable variation relate to evolution by natural selection.*

CONCEPT 22.3

Evolution is supported by an overwhelming amount of scientific evidence (pp. 471–478)

- Researchers have directly observed natural selection leading to adaptive evolution in many studies, including research on soapberry bug populations and on MRSA.
- Organisms share characteristics because of common descent (**homology**) or because natural selection affects independently

evolving species in similar environments in similar ways (**convergent evolution**).

- Fossils show that past organisms differed from living organisms, that many species have become extinct, and that species have evolved over long periods of time; fossils also document the origin of major new groups of organisms.
- Evolutionary theory can explain biogeographic patterns.

> **?** *Summarize the different lines of evidence supporting the hypothesis that cetaceans descended from land mammals and are closely related to even-toed ungulates.*

TEST YOUR UNDERSTANDING

LEVEL 1: KNOWLEDGE/COMPREHENSION

1. Which of the following is *not* an observation or inference on which natural selection is based?
   a. There is heritable variation among individuals.
   b. Poorly adapted individuals never produce offspring.
   c. Species produce more offspring than the environment can support.
   d. Only a fraction of an individual's offspring may survive.

2. Which of the following observations helped Darwin shape his concept of descent with modification?
   a. Species diversity declines farther from the equator.
   b. Fewer species live on islands than on the nearest continents.
   c. Birds live on islands located farther from the mainland than the birds' maximum nonstop flight distance.
   d. South American temperate plants are more similar to the tropical plants of South America than to the temperate plants of Europe.

LEVEL 2: APPLICATION/ANALYSIS

3. Within six months of effectively using methicillin to treat *S. aureus* infections in a community, all new *S. aureus* infections were caused by MRSA. How can this best be explained?
   a. A patient must have become infected with MRSA from another community.
   b. In response to the drug, *S. aureus* began making drug-resistant versions of the protein targeted by the drug.
   c. Some drug-resistant bacteria were present at the start of treatment, and natural selection increased their frequency.
   d. *S. aureus* evolved to resist vaccines.

4. The upper forelimbs of humans and bats have fairly similar skeletal structures, whereas the corresponding bones in whales have very different shapes and proportions. However, genetic data suggest that all three kinds of organisms diverged from a common ancestor at about the same time. Which of the following is the most likely explanation for these data?
   a. Forelimb evolution was adaptive in people and bats, but not in whales.
   b. Natural selection in an aquatic environment resulted in significant changes to whale forelimb anatomy.
   c. Genes mutate faster in whales than in humans or bats.
   d. Whales are not properly classified as mammals.

5. DNA sequences in many human genes are very similar to the sequences of corresponding genes in chimpanzees. The most likely explanation for this result is that
   a. humans and chimpanzees share a relatively recent common ancestor.
   b. humans evolved from chimpanzees.
   c. chimpanzees evolved from humans.
   d. convergent evolution led to the DNA similarities.

LEVEL 3: SYNTHESIS/EVALUATION

6. **EVOLUTION CONNECTION**
   Explain why anatomical and molecular features often fit a similar nested pattern. In addition, describe a process that can cause this not to be the case.

7. **SCIENTIFIC INQUIRY**
   DRAW IT Mosquitoes resistant to the pesticide DDT first appeared in India in 1959, but now are found throughout the world. (a) Graph the data in the table below. (b) Examining the graph, hypothesize why the percentage of mosquitoes resistant to DDT rose rapidly. (c) Suggest an explanation for the global spread of DDT resistance.

Month	0	8	12
Mosquitoes Resistant* to DDT	4%	45%	77%

Source: C. F. Curtis et al., Selection for and against insecticide resistance and possible methods of inhibiting the evolution of resistance in mosquitoes, *Ecological Entomology* 3:273–287 (1978).

*Mosquitoes were considered resistant if they were not killed within 1 hour of receiving a dose of 4% DDT.

8. **WRITE ABOUT A THEME: INTERACTIONS**
   Write a short essay (about 100–150 words) evaluating whether changes to an organism's physical environment are likely to result in evolutionary change. Use an example to support your reasoning.

9. **SYNTHESIZE YOUR KNOWLEDGE**

This honeypot ant (genus *Myrmecocystus*) can store liquid food inside its expandable abdomen. Consider other ants you are familiar with, and explain how a honeypot ant exemplifies three key features of life: adaptation, unity, and diversity.

For selected answers, see Appendix A.

MasteringBiology®

Students Go to **MasteringBiology** for assignments, the eText, and the Study Area with practice tests, animations, and activities.

Instructors Go to **MasteringBiology** for automatically graded tutorials and questions that you can assign to your students, plus Instructor Resources.

23

The Evolution of Populations

▲ Figure 23.1 **Is this finch evolving?**

The Smallest Unit of Evolution

One common misconception about evolution is that individual organisms evolve. It is true that natural selection acts on individuals: Each organism's traits affect its survival and reproductive success compared with those of other individuals. But the evolutionary impact of natural selection is only apparent in the changes in a *population* of organisms over time.

Consider the medium ground finch (*Geospiza fortis*), a seed-eating bird that inhabits the Galápagos Islands **(Figure 23.1)**. In 1977, the *G. fortis* population on the island of Daphne Major was decimated by a long period of drought: Of some 1,200 birds, only 180 survived. Researchers Peter and Rosemary Grant observed that during the drought, small, soft seeds were in short supply. The finches mostly fed on large, hard seeds that were more plentiful. Birds with larger, deeper beaks were better able to crack and eat these larger seeds, and they survived at a higher rate than finches with smaller beaks. Since beak depth is an inherited trait in these birds, the average beak depth in the next generation of *G. fortis* was greater than it had been in the pre-drought population **(Figure 23.2)**. The finch population had evolved by natural selection. However, the *individual* finches did not evolve. Each bird had a beak of a particular size, which did not grow larger during the drought. Rather, the proportion of large beaks in the population increased from generation to generation: The population evolved, not its individual members.

▶ **Figure 23.2 Evidence of selection by food source.** The data represent adult beak depth measurements of medium ground finches hatched in the generations before and after the 1977 drought. In one generation, natural selection resulted in a larger average beak size in the population.

(MB) *A related Experimental Inquiry Tutorial can be assigned in MasteringBiology.*

▲ **Figure 23.3 Phenotypic variation in horses.** In horses, coat color varies along a continuum and is influenced by multiple genes.

Focusing on evolutionary change in populations, we can define evolution on its smallest scale, called **microevolution**, as a change in allele frequencies in a population over generations. As you will see in this chapter, natural selection is not the only cause of microevolution. In fact, there are three main mechanisms that can cause allele frequency change: natural selection, genetic drift (chance events that alter allele frequencies), and gene flow (the transfer of alleles between populations). Each of these mechanisms has distinctive effects on the genetic composition of populations. However, only natural selection consistently improves the match between organisms and their environment (adaptation). Before we examine natural selection and adaptation more closely, let's revisit a prerequisite for these processes in a population: genetic variation.

CONCEPT 23.1

Genetic variation makes evolution possible

In *The Origin of Species*, Darwin provided abundant evidence that life on Earth has evolved over time, and he proposed natural selection as the primary mechanism for that change. He observed that individuals differ in their inherited traits and that selection acts on such differences, leading to evolutionary change. Although Darwin realized that variation in heritable traits is a prerequisite for evolution, he did not know precisely how organisms pass heritable traits to their offspring.

Just a few years after Darwin published *The Origin of Species*, Gregor Mendel wrote a groundbreaking paper on inheritance in pea plants (see Chapter 14). In that paper, Mendel proposed a model of inheritance in which organisms transmit discrete heritable units (now called genes) to their offspring. Although Darwin did not know about genes, Mendel's paper set the stage for understanding the genetic differences on which evolution is based. Here we'll examine such genetic differences and how they are produced.

Genetic Variation

Individuals within a species vary in their specific characteristics. Among humans, you can easily observe phenotypic variation in facial features, height, and voice. Indeed, individual variation occurs in all species. And though you cannot identify a person's blood group (A, B, AB, or O) from his or her appearance, this and many other molecular traits also vary extensively among individuals.

Such phenotypic variations often reflect **genetic variation**, differences among individuals in the composition of their genes or other DNA sequences. Some heritable phenotypic differences occur on an "either-or" basis, such as the flower colors of Mendel's pea plants: Each plant had flowers that were either purple or white (see Figure 14.3). Characters that vary in this way are typically determined by a single gene locus, with different alleles producing distinct phenotypes. In contrast, other phenotypic differences vary in gradations along a continuum. Such variation usually results from the influence of two or more genes on a single phenotypic character. In fact, many phenotypic characters are influenced by multiple genes, including coat color in horses (Figure 23.3), seed number in maize (corn), and height in humans.

How much do genes and other DNA sequences vary from one individual to another? Genetic variation at the whole-gene level (*gene variability*) can be quantified as the average percentage of loci that are heterozygous. (Recall that a heterozygous individual has two different alleles for a given locus, whereas a homozygous individual has two identical alleles for that locus.) As an example, on average the fruit fly *Drosophila melanogaster* is heterozygous for about 1,920 of its 13,700 loci (14%) and homozygous for all the rest.

Considerable genetic variation can also be measured at the molecular level of DNA (*nucleotide variability*). But little of this variation results in phenotypic variation. The reason is that many of the differences occur within *introns*, noncoding segments of DNA lying between *exons*, the regions retained

Base-pair substitutions are shown in orange.

A red arrow indicates an insertion site.

The substitution at this site results in the translation of a different amino acid.

A deletion of 26 base pairs occurred here.

1 500 1,000 1,500 2,000 2,500

Exon Intron

▲ **Figure 23.4 Extensive genetic variation at the molecular level.** This diagram summarizes data from a study comparing the DNA sequence of the alcohol dehydrogenase (*Adh*) gene in several fruit flies (*Drosophila melanogaster*). The *Adh* gene has four exons (dark blue) separated by introns (light blue);

the exons include the coding regions that are ultimately translated into the amino acids of the *Adh* enzyme (see Figure 5.1). Only one substitution has a phenotypic effect, producing a different form of the *Adh* enzyme.

MAKE CONNECTIONS *Review Figures 17.5 and 17.10. Explain how a base-pair substitution that alters a coding region of the* Adh *locus could have no effect on amino acid sequence. Then explain how an insertion in an exon could have no effect on the protein produced.*

in mRNA after RNA processing (see Figure 17.11). And of the variations that occur within exons, most do not cause a change in the amino acid sequence of the protein encoded by the gene. For example, in the sequence comparison shown in **Figure 23.4**, there are 43 nucleotide sites with variable base pairs (where substitutions have occurred), as well as several sites where insertions or deletions have occurred. Although 18 variable sites occur within the four exons of the *Adh* gene, only one of these variations (at site 1,490) results in an amino acid change. Note, however, that this single variable site is enough to cause genetic variation at the level of the gene—and hence two different forms of the *Adh* enzyme are produced.

It is important to bear in mind that some phenotypic variation does not result from genetic differences among individuals (**Figure 23.5** shows a striking example in a caterpillar of the southwestern United States). Phenotype is the product of an inherited genotype and many environmental influences (see Concept 14.3). In a human example, bodybuilders alter their phenotypes dramatically but do not pass their huge muscles on to the next generation. In general, only the genetically determined part of phenotypic variation can have evolutionary consequences. As such, genetic variation provides the raw material for evolutionary change: Without genetic variation, evolution cannot occur.

Sources of Genetic Variation

The genetic variation on which evolution depends originates when mutation, gene duplication, or other processes produce new alleles and new genes. Genetic variants can be produced rapidly in organisms with short generation times. Sexual reproduction can also result in genetic variation as existing genes are arranged in new ways.

Formation of New Alleles

New alleles can arise by *mutation*, a change in the nucleotide sequence of an organism's DNA. A mutation is like a shot in the dark—we cannot predict accurately which segments of DNA will be altered or how. In multicellular organisms, only mutations in cell lines that produce gametes can be passed to offspring. In plants and fungi, this is not as limiting as it may sound, since many different cell lines can produce gametes. But in most animals, the majority of mutations occur in somatic cells and are not passed to offspring.

A change of as little as one base in a gene—a "point mutation"—can have a significant impact on phenotype, as in sickle-cell disease (see Figure 17.25). Organisms reflect many generations of past selection, and hence their phenotypes tend to be well matched to their environments. As a result, most new mutations that alter a phenotype are at least slightly harmful. In some cases, natural selection quickly removes such harmful alleles. In diploid organisms, however, harmful alleles that are recessive can be hidden from selection. Indeed, a harmful recessive allele can persist for generations by propagation in heterozygous individuals (where its harmful effects are masked by the more favorable dominant allele). Such "heterozygote protection" maintains a huge pool of alleles that might not be favored under present conditions, but that could be beneficial if the environment changes.

▲ **Figure 23.5 Nonheritable variation.** These caterpillars of the moth *Nemoria arizonaria* owe their different appearances to chemicals in their diets, not to differences in their genotypes. **(a)** Caterpillars raised on a diet of oak flowers resemble the flowers, whereas **(b)** their siblings raised on oak leaves resemble oak twigs.

While many mutations are harmful, many others are not. Recall that much of the DNA in eukaryotic genomes does not encode proteins (see Figure 21.6). Point mutations in these noncoding regions generally result in **neutral variation**, differences in DNA sequence that do not confer a selective advantage or disadvantage. The redundancy in the genetic code is another source of neutral variation: even a point mutation in a gene that encodes a protein will have no effect on the protein's function if the amino acid composition is not changed. And even where there is a change in the amino acid, it may not affect the protein's shape and function. Finally, as you will see later in this chapter, a mutant allele may on rare occasions actually make its bearer better suited to the environment, enhancing reproductive success.

Altering Gene Number or Position

Chromosomal changes that delete, disrupt, or rearrange many loci are usually harmful. However, when such large-scale changes leave genes intact, they may not affect the organisms' phenotype. In rare cases, chromosomal rearrangements may even be beneficial. For example, the translocation of part of one chromosome to a different chromosome could link genes in a way that produces a positive effect.

A key potential source of variation is the duplication of genes due to errors in meiosis (such as unequal crossing over), slippage during DNA replication, or the activities of transposable elements (see Concept 21.5). Duplications of large chromosome segments, like other chromosomal aberrations, are often harmful, but the duplication of smaller pieces of DNA may not be. Gene duplications that do not have severe effects can persist over generations, allowing mutations to accumulate. The result is an expanded genome with new genes that may take on new functions.

Such increases in gene number appear to have played a major role in evolution. For example, the remote ancestors of mammals had a single gene for detecting odors that has since been duplicated many times. As a result, humans today have about 350 functional olfactory receptor genes, and mice have 1,000. This dramatic proliferation of olfactory genes probably helped early mammals, enabling them to detect faint odors and to distinguish among many different smells.

Rapid Reproduction

Mutation rates tend to be low in plants and animals, averaging about one mutation in every 100,000 genes per generation, and they are often even lower in prokaryotes. But prokaryotes have many more generations per unit of time, so mutations can quickly generate genetic variation in their populations. The same is true of viruses. For instance, HIV has a generation span of about two days. It also has an RNA genome, which has a much higher mutation rate than a typical DNA genome because of the lack of RNA repair mechanisms in host cells (see Chapter 19). For this reason,

single-drug treatments are unlikely to be effective against HIV; mutant forms of the virus that are resistant to a particular drug would tend to proliferate in relatively short order. The most effective AIDS treatments to date have been drug "cocktails" that combine several medications. It is less likely that a set of mutations that together confer resistance to *all* the drugs will occur in a short time period.

Sexual Reproduction

In organisms that reproduce sexually, most of the genetic variation in a population results from the unique combination of alleles that each individual receives from its parents. Of course, at the nucleotide level, all the differences among these alleles have originated from past mutations. Sexual reproduction then shuffles existing alleles and deals them at random to produce individual genotypes.

Three mechanisms contribute to this shuffling: crossing over, independent assortment of chromosomes, and fertilization (see Chapter 13). During meiosis, homologous chromosomes, one inherited from each parent, trade some of their alleles by crossing over. These homologous chromosomes and the alleles they carry are then distributed at random into gametes. Then, because myriad possible mating combinations exist in a population, fertilization brings together gametes that are likely to have different genetic backgrounds. The combined effects of these three mechanisms ensure that sexual reproduction rearranges existing alleles into fresh combinations each generation, providing much of the genetic variation that makes evolution possible.

CONCEPT CHECK 23.1

1. Explain why genetic variation within a population is a prerequisite for evolution.
2. Of all the mutations that occur in a population, why do only a small fraction become widespread?
3. MAKE CONNECTIONS If a population stopped reproducing sexually (but still reproduced asexually), how would its genetic variation be affected over time? Explain. (See Concept 13.4.)

For suggested answers, see Appendix A.

CONCEPT 23.2

The Hardy-Weinberg equation can be used to test whether a population is evolving

Although the individuals in a population must differ genetically for evolution to occur, the presence of genetic variation does not guarantee that a population will evolve. For that to happen, one of the factors that cause evolution must be at work. In this section, we'll explore one way to test whether evolution is occurring in a population. First, let's clarify what we mean by a population.

Gene Pools and Allele Frequencies

A **population** is a group of individuals of the same species that live in the same area and interbreed, producing fertile offspring. Different populations of a species may be isolated geographically from one another, exchanging genetic material only rarely. Such isolation is common for species that live on widely separated islands or in different lakes. But not all populations are isolated (**Figure 23.6**). Still, members of a population typically breed with one another and thus on average are more closely related to each other than to members of other populations.

We can characterize a population's genetic makeup by describing its **gene pool**, which consists of all copies of every type of allele at every locus in all members of the population. If only one allele exists for a particular locus in a population, that allele is said to be *fixed* in the gene pool, and all individuals are homozygous for that allele. But if there are two or more alleles for a particular locus in a population, individuals may be either homozygous or heterozygous.

For example, imagine a population of 500 wildflower plants with two alleles, C^R and C^W, for a locus that codes for flower pigment. These alleles show incomplete dominance; thus, each genotype has a distinct phenotype. Plants homozygous for the C^R allele ($C^R C^R$) produce red pigment and have red flowers; plants homozygous for the C^W allele ($C^W C^W$) produce no red pigment and have white flowers; and heterozygotes ($C^R C^W$) produce some red pigment and have pink flowers.

Each allele has a frequency (proportion) in the population. For example, suppose our population has 320 plants with red flowers, 160 with pink flowers, and 20 with white flowers. Because these are diploid organisms, these 500 individuals have a total of 1,000 copies of the gene for flower color. The C^R allele accounts for 800 of these copies ($320 \times 2 = 640$ for $C^R C^R$ plants, plus $160 \times 1 = 160$ for $C^R C^W$ plants). Thus, the frequency of the C^R allele is $800/1,000 = 0.8$ (80%).

When studying a locus with two alleles, the convention is to use p to represent the frequency of one allele and q to represent the frequency of the other allele. Thus, p, the frequency of the C^R allele in the gene pool of this population, is $p = 0.8$ (80%). And because there are only two alleles for this gene, the frequency of the C^W allele, represented by q, must be $q = 1 - p = 0.2$ (20%). For loci that have more than two alleles, the sum of all allele frequencies must still equal 1 (100%).

▲ **Figure 23.6 One species, two populations.** These two caribou populations in the Yukon are not totally isolated; they sometimes share the same area. Still, members of either population are most likely to breed within their own population.

Next we'll see how allele and genotype frequencies can be used to test whether evolution is occurring in a population.

The Hardy-Weinberg Equation

One way to assess whether natural selection or other factors are causing evolution at a particular locus is to determine what the genetic makeup of a population would be if it were *not* evolving at that locus. We can then compare that scenario with the data we actually observed for the population. If there are no differences, we can conclude that the population is not evolving. If there are differences, this suggests that the population may be evolving—and then we can try to figure out why.

Hardy-Weinberg Equilibrium

In a population that is not evolving, allele and genotype frequencies will remain constant from generation to generation, provided that only Mendelian segregation and recombination of alleles are at work. Such a population is said to be in **Hardy-Weinberg equilibrium**, named for the British mathematician and German physician, respectively, who independently developed this idea in 1908.

To determine whether a population is in Hardy-Weinberg equilibrium, it is helpful to think about genetic crosses in a new way. Previously, we used Punnett squares to determine the genotypes of offspring in a genetic cross (see Figure 14.5). Here, instead of considering the possible allele combinations from one cross, we'll consider the combination of alleles in *all* of the crosses in a population.

Imagine that all the alleles for a given locus from all the individuals in a population are placed in a large bin (**Figure 23.7**). We can think of this bin as holding the population's gene pool for that locus. "Reproduction" occurs by selecting alleles at random from the bin; somewhat similar events occur in nature when fish release sperm and eggs into the water or when pollen (containing plant

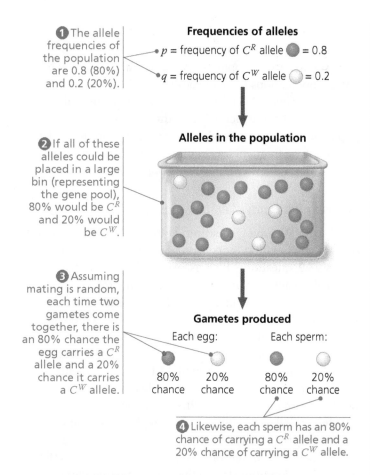

① The allele frequencies of the population are 0.8 (80%) and 0.2 (20%).

Frequencies of alleles

p = frequency of C^R allele ● = 0.8

q = frequency of C^W allele ○ = 0.2

② If all of these alleles could be placed in a large bin (representing the gene pool), 80% would be C^R and 20% would be C^W.

Alleles in the population

③ Assuming mating is random, each time two gametes come together, there is an 80% chance the egg carries a C^R allele and a 20% chance it carries a C^W allele.

Gametes produced

Each egg:

80% chance   20% chance

Each sperm:

80% chance   20% chance

④ Likewise, each sperm has an 80% chance of carrying a C^R allele and a 20% chance of carrying a C^W allele.

▲ **Figure 23.7 Selecting alleles at random from a gene pool.**

sperm) is blown about by the wind. By viewing reproduction as a process of randomly selecting and combining alleles from the bin (the gene pool), we are in effect assuming that mating occurs at random—that is, that all male-female matings are equally likely.

Let's apply the bin analogy to the hypothetical wildflower population discussed earlier. In that population of 500 flowers, the frequency of the allele for red flowers (C^R) is $p = 0.8$, and the frequency of the allele for white flowers (C^W) is $q = 0.2$. In other words, a bin holding all 1,000 copies of the flower-color gene in the population would contain 800 C^R alleles and 200 C^W alleles. Assuming that gametes are formed by selecting alleles at random from the bin, the probability that an egg or sperm contains a C^R or C^W allele is equal to the frequency of these alleles in the bin. Thus, as shown in Figure 23.7, each egg has an 80% chance of containing a C^R allele and a 20% chance of containing a C^W allele; the same is true for each sperm.

Using the rule of multiplication (see Figure 14.9), we can now calculate the frequencies of the three possible genotypes, assuming random unions of sperm and eggs. The probability that two C^R alleles will come together is $p \times p = p^2 = 0.8 \times 0.8 = 0.64$. Thus, about 64% of the plants in the next generation will have the genotype $C^R C^R$. The frequency of $C^W C^W$ individuals is expected to be about $q \times q = q^2 =$

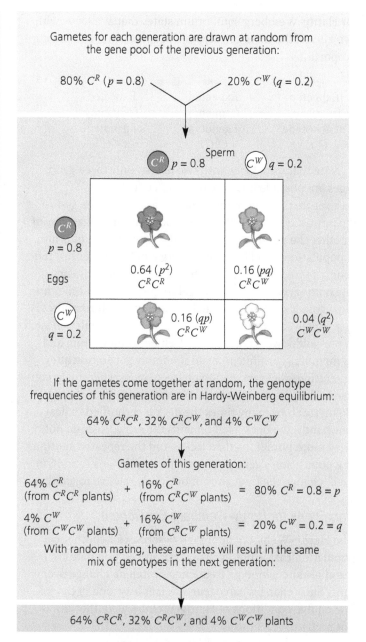

Gametes for each generation are drawn at random from the gene pool of the previous generation:

80% C^R ($p = 0.8$)   20% C^W ($q = 0.2$)

Sperm

C^R $p = 0.8$ C^W $q = 0.2$

Eggs

C^R $p = 0.8$

0.64 (p^2) $C^R C^R$ 0.16 (pq) $C^R C^W$

C^W $q = 0.2$

0.16 (qp) $C^R C^W$ 0.04 (q^2) $C^W C^W$

If the gametes come together at random, the genotype frequencies of this generation are in Hardy-Weinberg equilibrium:

64% $C^R C^R$, 32% $C^R C^W$, and 4% $C^W C^W$

Gametes of this generation:

64% C^R (from $C^R C^R$ plants) + 16% C^R (from $C^R C^W$ plants) = 80% C^R = 0.8 = p

4% C^W (from $C^W C^W$ plants) + 16% C^W (from $C^R C^W$ plants) = 20% C^W = 0.2 = q

With random mating, these gametes will result in the same mix of genotypes in the next generation:

64% $C^R C^R$, 32% $C^R C^W$, and 4% $C^W C^W$ plants

▲ **Figure 23.8 The Hardy-Weinberg principle.** In our wildflower population, the gene pool remains constant from one generation to the next. Mendelian processes alone do not alter frequencies of alleles or genotypes.

? *If the frequency of the* C^R *allele is 0.6, predict the frequencies of the* $C^R C^R$, $C^R C^W$, *and* $C^W C^W$ *genotypes.*

$0.2 \times 0.2 = 0.04$, or 4%. $C^R C^W$ heterozygotes can arise in two different ways. If the sperm provides the C^R allele and the egg provides the C^W allele, the resulting heterozygotes will be $p \times q = 0.8 \times 0.2 = 0.16$, or 16% of the total. If the sperm provides the C^W allele and the egg the C^R allele, the heterozygous offspring will make up $q \times p = 0.2 \times 0.8 = 0.16$, or 16%. The frequency of heterozygotes is thus the sum of these possibilities: $pq + qp = 2pq = 0.16 + 0.16 = 0.32$, or 32%.

As shown in **Figure 23.8**, the genotype frequencies in the next generation must add up to 1 (100%). Thus, the equation for Hardy-Weinberg equilibrium states that at a locus with two alleles, the three genotypes will appear in the following proportions:

$$\underbrace{p^2}_{\substack{\text{Expected} \\ \text{frequency} \\ \text{of genotype} \\ C^R C^R}} + \underbrace{2pq}_{\substack{\text{Expected} \\ \text{frequency} \\ \text{of genotype} \\ C^R C^W}} + \underbrace{q^2}_{\substack{\text{Expected} \\ \text{frequency} \\ \text{of genotype} \\ C^W C^W}} = 1$$

Note that for a locus with two alleles, only three genotypes are possible (in this case, $C^R C^R$, $C^R C^W$, and $C^W C^W$). As a result, the sum of the frequencies of the three genotypes must equal 1 (100%) in *any* population—regardless of whether the population is in Hardy-Weinberg equilibrium. A population is in Hardy-Weinberg equilibrium only if the genotype frequencies are such that the actual frequency of one homozygote is p^2, the actual frequency of the other homozygote is q^2, and the actual frequency of heterozygotes is $2pq$. Finally, as suggested by Figure 23.8, if a population such as our wildflowers is in Hardy-Weinberg equilibrium and its members continue to mate randomly generation after generation, allele and genotype frequencies will remain constant. The system operates somewhat like a deck of cards: No matter how many times the deck is reshuffled to deal out new hands, the deck itself remains the same. Aces do not grow more numerous than jacks. And the repeated shuffling of a population's gene pool over the generations cannot, in itself, change the frequency of one allele relative to another.

Conditions for Hardy-Weinberg Equilibrium

The Hardy-Weinberg approach describes a hypothetical population that is not evolving. But in real populations, the allele and genotype frequencies often *do* change over time. Such changes can occur when at least one of the following five conditions of Hardy-Weinberg equilibrium is not met:

1. **No mutations.** The gene pool is modified if mutations alter alleles or if entire genes are deleted or duplicated.
2. **Random mating.** If individuals tend to mate within a subset of the population, such as their near neighbors or close relatives (inbreeding), random mixing of gametes does not occur, and genotype frequencies change.
3. **No natural selection.** Differences in the survival and reproductive success of individuals carrying different genotypes can alter allele frequencies.
4. **Extremely large population size.** The smaller the population, the more likely it is that allele frequencies will fluctuate by chance from one generation to the next (a process called genetic drift).
5. **No gene flow.** By moving alleles into or out of populations, gene flow can alter allele frequencies.

Departure from these conditions usually results in evolutionary change, which, as we've already described, is common in natural populations. But it is also common for natural populations to be in Hardy-Weinberg equilibrium for specific genes. This can occur if selection alters allele frequencies at some loci but not others. In addition, some populations evolve so slowly that the changes in their allele and genotype frequencies are difficult to distinguish from those predicted for a non-evolving population.

Applying the Hardy-Weinberg Equation

The Hardy-Weinberg equation is often used as an initial test of whether evolution is occurring in a population (Concept Check 23.2, question 3 is an example). The equation also has medical applications, such as estimating the percentage of a population carrying the allele for an inherited disease. For example, consider phenylketonuria (PKU), a metabolic disorder that results from homozygosity for a recessive allele and occurs in about one out of every 10,000 babies born in the United States. Left untreated, PKU results in mental disability and other problems. (As described in Concept 14.4, newborns are now tested for PKU, and symptoms can be largely avoided with a diet very low in phenylalanine.)

To apply the Hardy-Weinberg equation, we must assume that no new PKU mutations are being introduced into the population (condition 1) and that people neither choose their mates on the basis of whether or not they carry this gene nor generally mate with close relatives (condition 2). We must also ignore any effects of differential survival and reproductive success among PKU genotypes (condition 3) and assume that there are no effects of genetic drift (condition 4) or of gene flow from other populations into the United States (condition 5). These assumptions are reasonable: The mutation rate for the PKU gene is low, inbreeding and other forms of nonrandom mating are not common in the United States, selection occurs only against the rare homozygotes (and then only if dietary restrictions are not followed), the U.S. population is very large, and populations outside the country have PKU allele frequencies similar to those seen in the United States.

If all these assumptions hold, then the frequency of individuals in the population born with PKU will correspond to q^2 in the Hardy-Weinberg equation (q^2 = frequency of homozygotes). Because the allele is recessive, we must estimate the number of heterozygotes rather than counting them directly as we did with the pink flowers. Since we know there is one PKU occurrence per 10,000 births ($q^2 = 0.0001$), the frequency (q) of the recessive allele for PKU is

$$q = \sqrt{0.0001} = 0.01$$

and the frequency of the dominant allele is

$$p = 1 - q = 1 - 0.01 = 0.99$$

The frequency of carriers, heterozygous people who do not have PKU but may pass the PKU allele to offspring, is

$$2pq = 2 \times 0.99 \times 0.01 = 0.0198$$
(approximately 2% of the U.S. population)

Remember, the assumption of Hardy-Weinberg equilibrium yields an approximation; the real number of carriers may differ. Still, our calculations suggest that harmful recessive alleles at this and other loci can be concealed in a population because they are carried by healthy heterozygotes. The Scientific Skills Exercise provides another opportunity for you to apply the Hardy-Weinberg equation to allele data.

CONCEPT CHECK 23.2

1. A population has 700 individuals, 85 of genotype *AA*, 320 of genotype *Aa*, and 295 of genotype *aa*. What are the frequencies of alleles *A* and *a*?

2. The frequency of allele *a* is 0.45 for a population in Hardy-Weinberg equilibrium. What are the expected frequencies of genotypes *AA*, *Aa*, and *aa*?

3. **WHAT IF?** A locus that affects susceptibility to a degenerative brain disease has two alleles, *V* and *v*. In a population, 16 people have genotype *VV*, 92 have genotype *Vv*, and 12 have genotype *vv*. Is this population evolving? Explain.

For suggested answers, see Appendix A.

CONCEPT 23.3

Natural selection, genetic drift, and gene flow can alter allele frequencies in a population

Note again the five conditions required for a population to be in Hardy-Weinberg equilibrium. A deviation from any of these conditions is a potential cause of evolution. New mutations (violation of condition 1) can alter allele frequencies, but because mutations are rare, the change from one generation to the next is likely to be very small. Non-random mating (violation of condition 2) can affect the frequencies of homozygous and heterozygous genotypes but by itself has no effect on allele frequencies in the gene pool. (Allele frequencies can change if individuals with certain inherited traits are more likely than other individuals to obtain mates. However, such a situation not only causes a deviation from random mating, but also violates condition 3, no natural selection.)

For the rest of this section we will focus on the three mechanisms that alter allele frequencies directly and cause most evolutionary change: natural selection, genetic drift, and gene flow (violations of conditions 3–5).

SCIENTIFIC SKILLS EXERCISE

Using the Hardy-Weinberg Equation to Interpret Data and Make Predictions

Is Evolution Occurring in a Soybean Population? One way to test whether evolution is occurring in a population is to compare the observed genotype frequencies at a locus with those expected for a non-evolving population based on the Hardy-Weinberg equation. In this exercise, you'll test whether a soybean population is evolving at a locus with two alleles, C^G and C^Y, that affect chlorophyll production and hence leaf color.

How the Experiment Was Done Students planted soybean seeds and then counted the number of seedlings of each genotype at day 7 and again at day 21. Seedlings of each genotype could be distinguished visually because the C^G and C^Y alleles show incomplete dominance: $C^G C^G$ seedlings have green leaves, $C^G C^Y$ seedlings have green-yellow leaves, and $C^Y C^Y$ seedlings have yellow leaves.

Data from the Experiment

Time (days)	Number of Seedlings			
	Green ($C^G C^G$)	Green-yellow ($C^G C^Y$)	Yellow ($C^Y C^Y$)	Total
7	49	111	56	216
21	47	106	20	173

Interpret the Data

1. Use the observed genotype frequencies from the day 7 data to calculate the frequencies of the C^G allele (*p*) and the C^Y allele (*q*).

2. Next, use the Hardy-Weinberg equation ($p^2 + 2pq + q^2 = 1$) to calculate the expected frequencies of genotypes $C^G C^G$, $C^G C^Y$, and $C^Y C^Y$ for a population in Hardy-Weinberg equilibrium.

3. Calculate the observed frequencies of genotypes $C^G C^G$, $C^G C^Y$, and $C^Y C^Y$ at day 7. Compare these frequencies to the expected frequencies calculated in step 2. Is the seedling population in Hardy-Weinberg equilibrium at day 7, or is evolution occurring? Explain your reasoning and identify which genotypes, if any, appear to be selected for or against.

4. Calculate the observed frequencies of genotypes $C^G C^G$, $C^G C^Y$, and $C^Y C^Y$ at day 21. Compare these frequencies to the expected frequencies calculated in step 2 and the observed frequencies at day 7. Is the seedling population in Hardy-Weinberg equilibrium at day 21, or is evolution occurring? Explain your reasoning and identify which genotypes, if any, appear to be selected for or against.

5. Homozygous $C^Y C^Y$ individuals cannot produce chlorophyll. The ability to photosynthesize becomes more critical as seedlings age and begin to exhaust the supply of food that was stored in the seed from which they emerged. Develop a hypothesis that explains the data for days 7 and 21. Based on this hypothesis, predict how the frequencies of the C^G and C^Y alleles will change beyond day 21.

MB A version of this Scientific Skills Exercise can be assigned in MasteringBiology.

Natural Selection

The concept of natural selection is based on differential success in survival and reproduction: Individuals in a population exhibit variations in their heritable traits, and those with traits that are better suited to their environment tend to produce more offspring than those with traits that are not as well suited (see Chapter 22).

In genetic terms, selection results in alleles being passed to the next generation in proportions that differ from those in the present generation. For example, the fruit fly *D. melanogaster* has an allele that confers resistance to several insecticides, including DDT. This allele has a frequency of 0% in laboratory strains of *D. melanogaster* established from flies collected in the wild in the early 1930s, prior to DDT use. However, in strains established from flies collected after 1960 (following 20 or more years of DDT use), the allele frequency is 37%. We can infer that this allele either arose by mutation between 1930 and 1960 or was present in 1930, but very rare. In any case, the rise in frequency of this allele most likely occurred because DDT is a powerful poison that is a strong selective force in exposed fly populations.

As the *D. melanogaster* example suggests, an allele that confers resistance to an insecticide will increase in frequency in a population exposed to that insecticide. Such changes are not coincidental. By consistently favoring some alleles over others, natural selection can cause **adaptive evolution** (evolution that results in a better match between organisms and their environment). We'll explore this process in more detail later in this chapter.

Genetic Drift

If you flip a coin 1,000 times, a result of 700 heads and 300 tails might make you suspicious about that coin. But if you flip a coin only 10 times, an outcome of 7 heads and 3 tails would not be surprising. The smaller the number of coin flips, the more likely it is that chance alone will cause a deviation from the predicted result. (In this case, the prediction is an equal number of heads and tails.) Chance events can also cause allele frequencies to fluctuate unpredictably from one generation to the next, especially in small populations—a process called **genetic drift**.

Figure 23.9 models how genetic drift might affect a small population of our wildflowers. In this example, drift leads to the loss of an allele from the gene pool, but it is a matter of chance that the C^W allele is lost and not the C^R allele. Such unpredictable changes in allele frequencies can be caused by chance events associated with survival and reproduction. Perhaps a large animal such as a moose stepped on the three $C^W C^W$ individuals in generation 2, killing them and increasing the chance that only the C^R allele would be passed to the next generation. Allele frequencies can also be affected by chance events that occur during fertilization. For example, suppose two individuals of genotype $C^R C^W$ had a small number of offspring. By chance alone, every egg and sperm pair that generated offspring could happen to have carried the C^R allele and not the C^W allele.

Certain circumstances can result in genetic drift having a significant impact on a population. Two examples are the founder effect and the bottleneck effect.

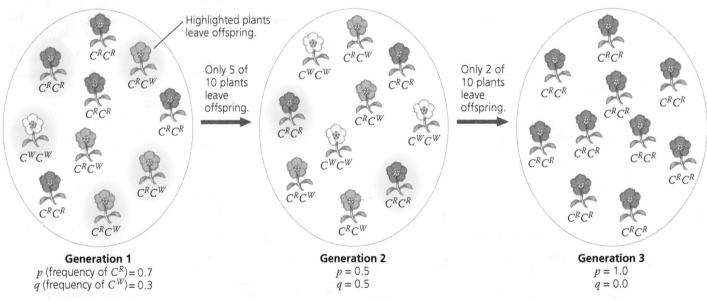

Generation 1
p (frequency of C^R) = 0.7
q (frequency of C^W) = 0.3

Generation 2
p = 0.5
q = 0.5

Generation 3
p = 1.0
q = 0.0

▲ **Figure 23.9 Genetic drift.** This small wildflower population has a stable size of ten plants. Suppose that by chance only five plants of generation 1 (those highlighted in yellow) produce fertile offspring. (This could occur, for example, if only those plants happened to grow in a location that provided enough nutrients to support the production of offspring.) Again by chance, only two plants of generation 2 leave fertile offspring. As a result, by chance the frequency of the C^W allele first increases in generation 2, then falls to zero in generation 3.

ANIMATION *BioFlix* Visit the Study Area in **MasteringBiology** for the BioFlix® 3-D Animation on Mechanisms of Evolution.

The Founder Effect

When a few individuals become isolated from a larger population, this smaller group may establish a new population whose gene pool differs from the source population; this is called the **founder effect**. The founder effect might occur, for example, when a few members of a population are blown by a storm to a new island. Genetic drift, in which chance events alter allele frequencies, will occur in such a case if the storm indiscriminately transports some individuals (and their alleles), but not others, from the source population.

The founder effect probably accounts for the relatively high frequency of certain inherited disorders among isolated human populations. For example, in 1814, 15 British colonists founded a settlement on Tristan da Cunha, a group of small islands in the Atlantic Ocean midway between Africa and South America. Apparently, one of the colonists carried a recessive allele for retinitis pigmentosa, a progressive form of blindness that afflicts homozygous individuals. Of the founding colonists' 240 descendants on the island in the late 1960s, 4 had retinitis pigmentosa. The frequency of the allele that causes this disease is ten times higher on Tristan da Cunha than in the populations from which the founders came.

The Bottleneck Effect

A sudden change in the environment, such as a fire or flood, may drastically reduce the size of a population. A severe drop in population size can cause the **bottleneck effect**, so named because the population has passed through a "bottleneck" that reduces its size **(Figure 23.10)**. By chance alone, certain alleles may be overrepresented among the survivors, others may be underrepresented, and some may be absent altogether. Ongoing genetic drift is likely to have substantial effects on the gene pool until the population becomes large enough that chance events have less impact. But even if a population that has passed through a bottleneck ultimately

recovers in size, it may have low levels of genetic variation for a long period of time—a legacy of the genetic drift that occurred when the population was small.

Human actions sometimes create severe bottlenecks for other species, as the following example shows.

Case Study: Impact of Genetic Drift on the Greater Prairie Chicken

Millions of greater prairie chickens (*Tympanuchus cupido*) once lived on the prairies of Illinois. As these prairies were converted to farmland and other uses during the 19th and 20th centuries, the number of greater prairie chickens plummeted **(Figure 23.11a)**. By 1993 fewer than 50 birds remained. These few surviving birds had low levels of genetic variation, and less than 50% of their eggs hatched, compared with much higher hatching rates of the larger populations in Kansas and Nebraska **(Figure 23.11b)**.

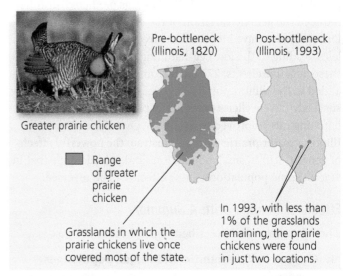

(a) The Illinois population of greater prairie chickens dropped from millions of birds in the 1800s to fewer than 50 birds in 1993.

Location	Population size	Number of alleles per locus	Percentage of eggs hatched
Illinois			
1930–1960s	1,000–25,000	5.2	93
1993	<50	3.7	<50
Kansas, 1998 (no bottleneck)	750,000	5.8	99
Nebraska, 1998 (no bottleneck)	75,000–200,000	5.8	96

(b) In the small Illinois population, genetic drift led to decreases in the number of alleles per locus and the percentage of eggs hatched.

▲ **Figure 23.11 Genetic drift and loss of genetic variation.**

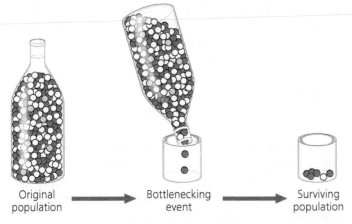

▲ **Figure 23.10 The bottleneck effect.** Shaking just a few marbles through the narrow neck of a bottle is analogous to a drastic reduction in the size of a population. By chance, blue marbles are overrepresented in the surviving population and gold marbles are absent.

These data suggest that genetic drift during the bottle-neck may have led to a loss of genetic variation and an increase in the frequency of harmful alleles. To investigate this hypothesis, researchers extracted DNA from 15 museum specimens of Illinois greater prairie chickens. Of the 15 birds, 10 had been collected in the 1930s, when there were 25,000 greater prairie chickens in Illinois, and 5 had been collected in the 1960s, when there were 1,000 greater prairie chickens in Illinois. By studying the DNA of these specimens, the researchers were able to obtain a minimum, baseline estimate of how much genetic variation was present in the Illinois population *before* the population shrank to extremely low numbers. This baseline estimate is a key piece of information that is not usually available in cases of population bottlenecks.

The researchers surveyed six loci and found that the 1993 population had fewer alleles per locus than the pre-bottleneck Illinois or the current Kansas and Nebraska populations (see Figure 23.11b). Thus, as predicted, drift had reduced the genetic variation of the small 1993 population. Drift may also have increased the frequency of harmful alleles, leading to the low egg-hatching rate. To counteract these negative effects, 271 birds from neighboring states were added to the Illinois population over four years. This strategy succeeded: New alleles entered the population, and the egg-hatching rate improved to over 90%. Overall, studies on the Illinois greater prairie chicken illustrate the powerful effects of genetic drift in small populations and provide hope that in at least some populations, these effects can be reversed.

Effects of Genetic Drift: *A Summary*

The examples we've described highlight four key points:

1. **Genetic drift is significant in small populations.** Chance events can cause an allele to be disproportionately over- or underrepresented in the next generation. Although chance events occur in populations of all sizes, they tend to alter allele frequencies substantially only in small populations.
2. **Genetic drift can cause allele frequencies to change at random.** Because of genetic drift, an allele may increase in frequency one year, then decrease the next; the change from year to year is not predictable. Thus, unlike natural selection, which in a given environment consistently favors some alleles over others, genetic drift causes allele frequencies to change at random over time.
3. **Genetic drift can lead to a loss of genetic variation within populations.** By causing allele frequencies to fluctuate randomly over time, genetic drift can eliminate alleles from a population. Because evolution depends on genetic variation, such losses can influence how effectively a population can adapt to a change in the environment.
4. **Genetic drift can cause harmful alleles to become fixed.** Alleles that are neither harmful nor beneficial can be lost or become fixed by chance through genetic drift. In very small populations, genetic drift can also cause alleles that are slightly harmful to become fixed. When this occurs, the population's survival can be threatened (as in the case of the greater prairie chicken).

Gene Flow

Natural selection and genetic drift are not the only phenomena affecting allele frequencies. Allele frequencies can also change by **gene flow**, the transfer of alleles into or out of a population due to the movement of fertile individuals or their gametes. For example, suppose that near our original hypothetical wildflower population there is another population consisting primarily of white-flowered individuals ($C^W C^W$). Insects carrying pollen from these plants may fly to and pollinate plants in our original population. The introduced C^W alleles would modify our original population's allele frequencies in the next generation. Because alleles are transferred between populations, gene flow tends to reduce the genetic differences between populations. In fact, if it is extensive enough, gene flow can result in two populations combining into a single population with a common gene pool.

Alleles transferred by gene flow can also affect how well populations are adapted to local environmental conditions. Researchers studying the songbird *Parus major* (great tit) on the small Dutch island of Vlieland noted survival differences between two populations on the island. The survival rate of females born in the eastern population is twice that of females born in the central population, regardless of where the females eventually settle and raise offspring (Figure 23.12). This finding suggests that females born in the eastern population are better adapted to life on the island than females born in the central population. But field studies also showed that the two populations are connected by high levels of gene flow (mating), which should reduce genetic differences between them. So how can the eastern population be better adapted to life on Vlieland than the central population?

The answer lies in the unequal amounts of gene flow from the mainland. In any given year, 43% of the first-time breeders in the central population are immigrants from the mainland, compared with only 13% in the eastern population. Birds with mainland genotypes survive and reproduce poorly on Vlieland, and in the eastern population, selection reduces the frequency of these genotypes. In the central population, however, gene flow from the mainland is so high that it overwhelms the effects of selection. As a result, females born in the central population have many immigrant genes, reducing the degree to which members of that population are adapted to life on the island. Researchers are currently investigating why gene flow is so much higher in the

Parus major

© 2005 Macmillan Publishers Ltd.

▲ **Figure 23.12 Gene flow and local adaptation.** In *Parus major* populations on Vlieland, the yearly survival rate of females born in the central population is lower than that of females born in the eastern population. Gene flow from the mainland is much higher to the central population than it is to the eastern population, and birds from the mainland are selected against in both populations. These data suggest that gene flow from the mainland has prevented the central population from adapting fully to its local conditions.

central population and why birds with mainland genotypes survive and reproduce poorly on Vlieland.

Gene flow can also transfer alleles that improve the ability of populations to adapt to local conditions. For example, gene flow has resulted in the worldwide spread of several insecticide-resistance alleles in the mosquito *Culex pipiens*, a vector of West Nile virus and other diseases. Each of these alleles has a unique genetic signature that allowed researchers to document that it arose by mutation in only one or a few geographic locations. In their population of origin, these alleles increased because they provided insecticide resistance. These alleles were then transferred to new populations, where again, their frequencies increased as a result of natural selection.

Finally, gene flow has become an increasingly important agent of evolutionary change in human populations. Humans today move much more freely about the world than in the past. As a result, mating is more common between members of populations that previously had very little contact, leading to an exchange of alleles and fewer genetic differences between those populations.

CONCEPT CHECK 23.3

1. In what sense is natural selection more "predictable" than genetic drift?

2. Distinguish genetic drift from gene flow in terms of (a) how they occur and (b) their implications for future genetic variation in a population.

3. **WHAT IF?** Suppose two plant populations exchange pollen and seeds. In one population, individuals of genotype *AA* are most common (9,000 *AA*, 900 *Aa*, 100 *aa*), while the opposite is true in the other population (100 *AA*, 900 *Aa*, 9,000 *aa*). If neither allele has a selective advantage, what will happen over time to the allele and genotype frequencies of these populations?

For suggested answers, see Appendix A.

CONCEPT 23.4

Natural selection is the only mechanism that consistently causes adaptive evolution

Evolution by natural selection is a blend of chance and "sorting": chance in the creation of new genetic variations (as in mutation) and sorting as natural selection favors some alleles over others. Because of this favoring process, the outcome of natural selection is *not* random. Instead, natural selection consistently increases the frequencies of alleles that provide reproductive advantage, thus leading to adaptive evolution.

Natural Selection: *A Closer Look*

In examining how natural selection brings about adaptive evolution, we'll begin with the concept of relative fitness and the different ways that an organism's phenotype is subject to natural selection.

Relative Fitness

The phrases "struggle for existence" and "survival of the fittest" are commonly used to describe natural selection, but these expressions are misleading if taken to mean direct competitive contests among individuals. There *are* animal species in which individuals, usually the males, lock horns or otherwise do combat to determine mating privilege. But reproductive success is generally more subtle and depends on many factors besides outright battle. For example, a barnacle that is more efficient at collecting food than its neighbors may have greater stores of energy and hence be able to produce a larger number of eggs. A moth may have more offspring than other moths in the same population because its body colors more effectively conceal it from predators, improving its chance of surviving long enough to produce more offspring. These examples illustrate how in a given environment, certain traits can lead to greater **relative fitness**: the contribution an individual makes to the gene pool of the next generation *relative to* the contributions of other individuals.

Although we often refer to the relative fitness of a genotype, remember that the entity that is subjected to natural selection is the whole organism, not the underlying genotype. Thus, selection acts more directly on the phenotype than on the genotype; it acts on the genotype indirectly, via how the genotype affects the phenotype.

Directional, Disruptive, and Stabilizing Selection

Natural selection can alter the frequency distribution of heritable traits in three ways, depending on which phenotypes in a population are favored. These three modes of selection are called directional selection, disruptive selection, and stabilizing selection.

Directional selection occurs when conditions favor individuals exhibiting one extreme of a phenotypic range, thereby shifting a population's frequency curve for the phenotypic character in one direction or the other **(Figure 23.13a)**.

Directional selection is common when a population's environment changes or when members of a population migrate to a new (and different) habitat. For instance, an increase in the relative abundance of large seeds over small seeds led to an increase in beak depth in a population of Galápagos finches (see Figure 23.2).

Disruptive selection (Figure 23.13b) occurs when conditions favor individuals at both extremes of a phenotypic range over individuals with intermediate phenotypes. One example is a population of black-bellied seedcracker finches in Cameroon whose members display two distinctly different beak sizes. Small-billed birds feed mainly on soft seeds, whereas large-billed birds specialize in cracking hard seeds. It appears that birds with intermediate-sized bills are relatively inefficient at cracking both types of seeds and thus have lower relative fitness.

Stabilizing selection (Figure 23.13c) acts against both extreme phenotypes and favors intermediate variants. This mode of selection reduces variation and tends to maintain the status quo for a particular phenotypic character. For example, the birth weights of most human babies lie in the range of 3–4 kg (6.6–8.8 pounds); babies who are either much smaller or much larger suffer higher rates of mortality.

Regardless of the mode of selection, however, the basic mechanism remains the same. Selection favors individuals whose heritable phenotypic traits provide higher reproductive success than do the traits of other individuals.

▶ **Figure 23.13 Modes of selection.** These cases describe three ways in which a hypothetical deer mouse population with heritable variation in fur coloration from light to dark might evolve. The graphs show how the frequencies of individuals with different fur colors change over time. The large white arrows symbolize selective pressures against certain phenotypes.

MAKE CONNECTIONS *Review Figure 22.13. Which mode of selection has occurred in soapberry bug populations that feed on the introduced goldenrain tree? Explain.*

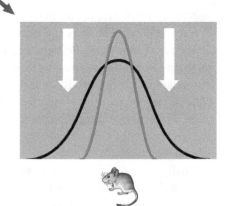

(a) Directional selection shifts the overall makeup of the population by favoring variants that are at one extreme of the distribution. In this case, lighter mice are selected against because they live among dark rocks, making it harder for them to hide from predators.

(b) Disruptive selection favors variants at both ends of the distribution. These mice have colonized a patchy habitat made up of light and dark rocks, with the result that mice of an intermediate color are selected against.

(c) Stabilizing selection removes extreme variants from the population and preserves intermediate types. If the environment consists of rocks of an intermediate color, both light and dark mice will be selected against.

The Key Role of Natural Selection in Adaptive Evolution

The adaptations of organisms include many striking examples. Certain octopuses, for example, have the ability to change color rapidly, enabling them to blend into different backgrounds. Another example is the remarkable jaws of snakes (Figure 23.14), which allow them to swallow prey much larger than their own head (a feat analogous to a person swallowing a whole watermelon). Other adaptations, such as a version of an enzyme that shows improved function in cold environments, may be less visually dramatic but just as important for survival and reproduction.

Such adaptations can arise gradually over time as natural selection increases the frequencies of alleles that enhance survival and reproduction. As the proportion of individuals that have favorable traits increases, the match between a species and its environment improves; that is, adaptive evolution occurs. However, the physical and biological components of an organism's environment may change over time. As a result, what constitutes a "good match" between an organism and its environment can be a moving target, making adaptive evolution a continuous, dynamic process.

And what about genetic drift and gene flow? Both can, in fact, increase the frequencies of alleles that improve the match between organisms and their environment, but neither does so consistently. Genetic drift can cause the frequency of a slightly beneficial allele to increase, but it also can cause the frequency of such an allele to decrease.

Similarly, gene flow may introduce alleles that are advantageous or ones that are disadvantageous. Natural selection is the only evolutionary mechanism that consistently leads to adaptive evolution.

Sexual Selection

Charles Darwin was the first to explore the implications of **sexual selection**, a form of natural selection in which individuals with certain inherited characteristics are more likely than other individuals to obtain mates. Sexual selection can result in **sexual dimorphism**, a difference in secondary sexual characteristics between males and females of the same species (Figure 23.15). These distinctions include differences in size, color, ornamentation, and behavior.

How does sexual selection operate? There are several ways. In **intrasexual selection**, meaning selection within the same sex, individuals of one sex compete directly for mates of the opposite sex. In many species, intrasexual selection occurs among males. For example, a single male may patrol a group of females and prevent other males from mating with them. The patrolling male may defend his status by defeating smaller, weaker, or less fierce males in combat. More often, this male is the psychological victor in ritualized displays that discourage would-be competitors but do not risk injury that would reduce his own fitness (see Figure 51.16). Intrasexual selection also occurs among females in a variety of species, including ring-tailed lemurs and broad-nosed pipefish.

In **intersexual selection**, also called *mate choice*, individuals of one sex (usually the females) are choosy in selecting their mates from the other sex. In many cases, the female's choice depends on the showiness of the male's appearance or behavior (see Figure 23.15). What intrigued Darwin about mate choice is that male showiness may not seem adaptive in any other way and may in fact pose some risk. For

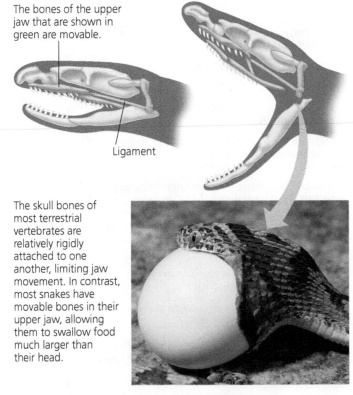

The bones of the upper jaw that are shown in green are movable.

Ligament

The skull bones of most terrestrial vertebrates are relatively rigidly attached to one another, limiting jaw movement. In contrast, most snakes have movable bones in their upper jaw, allowing them to swallow food much larger than their head.

▲ Figure 23.14 **Movable jaw bones in snakes.**

▲ Figure 23.15 **Sexual dimorphism and sexual selection.** Peacocks (above left) and peahens (above right) show extreme sexual dimorphism. There is intrasexual selection between competing males, followed by intersexual selection when the females choose among the showiest males.

example, bright plumage may make male birds more visible to predators. But if such characteristics help a male gain a mate, and if this benefit outweighs the risk from predation, then both the bright plumage and the female preference for it will be reinforced because they enhance overall reproductive success.

How do female preferences for certain male characteristics evolve in the first place? One hypothesis is that females prefer male traits that are correlated with "good genes." If the trait preferred by females is indicative of a male's overall genetic quality, both the male trait and female preference for it should increase in frequency. **Figure 23.16** describes one experiment testing this hypothesis in gray tree frogs.

Other researchers have shown that in several bird species, the traits preferred by females are related to overall male health. Here, too, female preference appears to be based on traits that reflect "good genes," in this case alleles indicative of a robust immune system.

Balancing Selection

As we've seen, genetic variation is often found at loci affected by selection. What prevents natural selection from reducing the variation at those loci by culling all unfavorable alleles? As mentioned earlier, in diploid organisms, many unfavorable recessive alleles persist because they are hidden from selection when in heterozygous individuals. In addition, selection itself may preserve variation at some loci, thus maintaining two or more forms in a population. Known as **balancing selection**, this type of selection includes heterozygote advantage and frequency-dependent selection.

Heterozygote Advantage

If individuals who are heterozygous at a particular locus have greater fitness than do both kinds of homozygotes, they exhibit **heterozygote advantage**. In such a case, natural selection tends to maintain two or more alleles at that locus. Note that heterozygote advantage is defined in terms of *genotype*, not phenotype. Thus, whether heterozygote advantage represents stabilizing or directional selection depends on the relationship between the genotype and the phenotype. For example, if the phenotype of a heterozygote is intermediate to the phenotypes of both homozygotes, heterozygote advantage is a form of stabilizing selection.

An example of heterozygote advantage occurs at the locus in humans that codes for the β polypeptide subunit of hemoglobin, the oxygen-carrying protein of red blood cells. In homozygous individuals, a certain recessive allele at that locus causes sickle-cell disease. The red blood cells of people with sickle-cell disease become distorted in shape, or *sickled*, under low-oxygen conditions (see Figure 5.19), as occurs in the capillaries. These sickled cells can clump together and block the flow of blood in the capillaries, resulting in serious

▼ Figure 23.16 | Inquiry

Do females select mates based on traits indicative of "good genes"?

Experiment Female gray tree frogs (*Hyla versicolor*) prefer to mate with males that give long mating calls. Allison Welch and colleagues, at the University of Missouri, tested whether the genetic makeup of long-calling (LC) males is superior to that of short-calling (SC) males. The researchers fertilized half the eggs of each female with sperm from an LC male and fertilized the remaining eggs with sperm from an SC male. In two separate experiments (one in 1995, the other in 1996), the resulting half-sibling offspring were raised in a common environment and their survival and growth were monitored.

Results

Offspring Performance	1995	1996
Larval survival	LC better	NSD
Larval growth	NSD	LC better
Time to metamorphosis	LC better (shorter)	LC better (shorter)

NSD = no significant difference; LC better = offspring of LC males superior to offspring of SC males.

Conclusion Because offspring fathered by an LC male outperformed their half-siblings fathered by an SC male, the team concluded that the duration of a male's mating call is indicative of the male's overall genetic quality. This result supports the hypothesis that female mate choice can be based on a trait that indicates whether the male has "good genes."

Source: A. M. Welch et al., Call duration as an indicator of genetic quality in male gray tree frogs, Science 280:1928–1930 (1998).

Inquiry in Action *Read and analyze the original paper in* Inquiry in Action: Interpreting Scientific Papers.

WHAT IF? *Why did the researchers split each female frog's eggs into two batches for fertilization by different males? Why didn't they mate each female with a single male frog?*

damage to organs such as the kidney, heart, and brain. Although some red blood cells become sickled in heterozygotes, not enough become sickled to cause sickle-cell disease.

Heterozygotes for the sickle-cell allele are protected against the most severe effects of malaria, a disease caused by a parasite that infects red blood cells (see Figure 28.16). One reason for this partial protection is that the body destroys sickled red blood cells rapidly, killing the parasites they harbor. Protection against malaria is important in tropical regions where the disease is a major killer. In such regions, selection favors heterozygotes over homozygous dominant individuals, who are more vulnerable to the effects of malaria, and also over homozygous recessive individuals, who develop sickle-cell disease. As we explore further in **Figure 23.17**, on the next two pages, these selective pressures have caused the frequency of the sickle-cell allele to reach relatively high levels in areas where the malaria parasite is common.

Frequency-Dependent Selection

In **frequency-dependent selection**, the fitness of a phenotype depends on how common it is in the population. Consider the scale-eating fish (*Perissodus microlepis*) of Lake Tanganyika, in Africa. These fish attack other fish from behind, darting in to remove a few scales from the flank of their prey. Of interest here is a peculiar feature of the scale-eating fish: Some are "left-mouthed" and some are "right-mouthed." Simple Mendelian inheritance determines these phenotypes, with the right-mouthed allele being dominant to the left-mouthed allele. Because their mouth twists to the left, left-mouthed fish always attack their prey's right flank **(Figure 23.18)**. (To see why, twist your lower jaw and lips to the left and imagine trying to take a bite from the left side of a fish, approaching it from behind.) Similarly, right-mouthed fish always attack from the left. Prey species guard against attack from whatever phenotype of scale-eating fish is most common in the lake. Thus, from year to year, selection favors whichever mouth phenotype is least common. As a result, the frequency of left- and right-mouthed fish oscillates over time, and balancing selection (due to frequency dependence) keeps the frequency of each phenotype close to 50%.

Why Natural Selection Cannot Fashion Perfect Organisms

Though natural selection leads to adaptation, nature abounds with examples of organisms that are less than ideally suited for their lifestyles. There are several reasons why.

1. **Selection can act only on existing variations.** Natural selection favors only the fittest phenotypes among those currently in the population, which may not be the ideal traits. New advantageous alleles do not arise on demand.

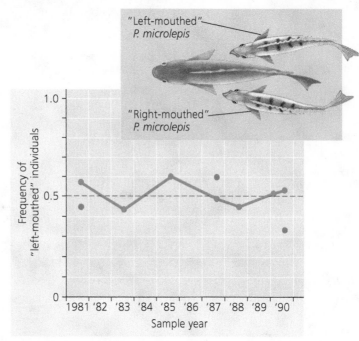

▲ **Figure 23.18** **Frequency-dependent selection.** In a population of the scale-eating fish, *Perissodus microlepis*, the frequency of left-mouthed individuals (red data points) rises and falls in a regular manner. The frequency of left-mouthed individuals among adults that reproduced was also recorded in three sample years (green data points).

INTERPRET THE DATA *For 1981, 1987, and 1990, compare the frequency of left-mouthed individuals among breeding adults to the frequency of left-mouthed individuals in the entire population. What do the data suggest about when natural selection favors left-mouthed individuals over right-mouthed individuals (or vice versa)? Explain.*

2. **Evolution is limited by historical constraints.** Each species has a legacy of descent with modification from ancestral forms. Evolution does not scrap the ancestral anatomy and build each new complex structure from scratch; rather, evolution co-opts existing structures and adapts them to new situations. We could imagine that if a terrestrial animal were to adapt to an environment in which flight would be advantageous, it might be best just to grow an extra pair of limbs that would serve as wings. However, evolution does not work this way; instead, it operates on the traits an organism already has. Thus, in birds and bats, an existing pair of limbs took on new functions for flight as these organisms evolved from nonflying ancestors.

3. **Adaptations are often compromises.** Each organism must do many different things. A seal spends part of its time on rocks; it could probably walk better if it had legs instead of flippers, but then it would not swim nearly as well. We humans owe much of our versatility and athleticism to our prehensile hands and flexible limbs, but these also make us prone to sprains, torn ligaments, and dislocations: Structural reinforcement has been compromised for agility.

▼ Figure 23.17

The Sickle-Cell Allele

This child has sickle-cell disease, a genetic disorder that strikes individuals that have two copies of the sickle-cell allele. This allele causes an abnormality in the structure and function of hemoglobin, the oxygen-carrying protein in red blood cells. Although sickle-cell disease is lethal if not treated, in some regions the sickle-cell allele can reach frequencies as high as 15–20%. How can such a harmful allele be so common?

Events at the Molecular Level

- Due to a point mutation, the sickle-cell allele differs from the wild-type allele by a single nucleotide. *See Figure 17.25.*
- The resulting change in one amino acid leads to hydrophobic interactions between the sickle-cell hemoglobin proteins under low-oxygen conditions.
- As a result, the sickle-cell proteins bind to each other in chains that together form a fiber.

Consequences for Cells

- The abnormal hemoglobin fibers distort the red blood cell into a sickle shape under low-oxygen conditions, such as those found in blood vessels returning to the heart.

Template strand

Sickle-cell allele on chromosome

An adenine replaces a thymine in the template strand of the sickle-cell allele, changing one codon in the mRNA produced during transcription. This change causes an amino-acid change in sickle-cell hemoglobin: A valine replaces a glutamic acid at one position. *See Figure 5.19.*

Sickle-cell hemoglobin

Fiber

Low-oxygen conditions

Sickled red blood cell

Wild-type allele

Normal hemoglobin
(does not aggregate into fibers)

Normal red blood cell

Infected mosquitos spread malaria when they bite people. *See Figure 28.16.*

Evolution in Populations

- Homozygotes with two sickle-cell alleles are strongly selected against because of mortality caused by sickle-cell disease. In contrast, heterozygotes experience few harmful effects from sickling yet are more likely to survive malaria than are homozygotes.
- In regions where malaria is common, the net effect of these opposing selective forces is heterozygote advantage. This has caused evolutionary change in populations—the products of which are the areas of relatively high frequencies of the sickle-cell allele shown in the map below.

Effects on Individual Organisms

- The formation of sickled red blood cells causes homozygotes with two copies of the sickle-cell allele to have sickle-cell disease.
- Some sickling also occurs in heterozygotes, but not enough to cause the disease; they have sickle-cell trait. *See Figure 14.17.*

The sickled blood cells of a homozygote block small blood vessels, causing great pain and damage to organs such as the heart, kidney, and brain.

Normal red blood cells are flexible and are able to flow freely through small blood vessels.

Key
Frequencies of the sickle-cell allele

 3.0–6.0%

 6.0–9.0%

9.0–12.0%

12.0–15.0%

>15.0%

 Distribution of malaria caused by *Plasmodium falciparum* (a parasitic unicellular eukaryote)

MAKE CONNECTIONS *In a region free of malaria, would individuals who are heterozygous for the sickle-cell allele be selected for or selected against? Explain.*

4. **Chance, natural selection, and the environment interact.** Chance events can affect the subsequent evolutionary history of populations. For instance, when a storm blows insects or birds hundreds of kilometers over an ocean to an island, the wind does not necessarily transport those individuals that are best suited to the new environment. Thus, not all alleles present in the founding population's gene pool are better suited to the new environment than the alleles that are "left behind." In addition, the environment at a particular location may change unpredictably from year to year, again limiting the extent to which adaptive evolution results in a close match between the organism and current environmental conditions.

With these four constraints, evolution does not tend to craft perfect organisms. Natural selection operates on a "better than" basis. We can, in fact, see evidence for evolution in the many imperfections of the organisms it produces.

CONCEPT CHECK 23.4

1. What is the relative fitness of a sterile mule? Explain.
2. Explain why natural selection is the only evolutionary mechanism that consistently leads to adaptive evolution.
3. **WHAT IF?** Consider a population in which heterozygotes at a certain locus have an extreme phenotype (such as being larger than homozygotes) that confers a selective advantage. Does such a situation represent directional, disruptive, or stabilizing selection? Explain.

For suggested answers, see Appendix A.

---

23 Chapter Review

SUMMARY OF KEY CONCEPTS

CONCEPT 23.1

Genetic variation makes evolution possible (pp. 481–483)

- **Genetic variation** refers to genetic differences among individuals within a population.
- The nucleotide differences that provide the basis of genetic variation originate when mutation and gene duplication produce new alleles and new genes. New genetic variants are produced rapidly in organisms with short generation times. In sexually reproducing organisms, most of the genetic differences among individuals result from crossing over, the independent assortment of chromosomes, and fertilization

? *Typically, most of the nucleotide variability that occurs within a genetic locus does not affect the phenotype. Explain why.*

CONCEPT 23.2

The Hardy-Weinberg equation can be used to test whether a population is evolving (pp. 483–487)

- A **population**, a localized group of organisms belonging to one species, is united by its **gene pool**, the aggregate of all the alleles in the population.
- For a population in **Hardy-Weinberg equilibrium**, the allele and genotype frequencies will remain constant if the population is large, mating is random, mutation is negligible, there is no gene flow, and there is no natural selection. For such a population, if p and q represent the frequencies of the only two possible alleles at a particular locus, then p^2 is the frequency of one kind of homozygote, q^2 is the frequency of the other kind of homozygote, and $2pq$ is the frequency of the heterozygous genotype.

? *Is it circular reasoning to calculate p and q from observed genotype frequencies and then use those values of p and q to test if the population is in Hardy-Weinberg equilibrium? Explain your answer.*

CONCEPT 23.3

Natural selection, genetic drift, and gene flow can alter allele frequencies in a population (pp. 487–491)

- In natural selection, individuals that have certain inherited traits tend to survive and reproduce at higher rates than other individuals *because of* those traits.
- In **genetic drift**, chance fluctuations in allele frequencies over generations tend to reduce genetic variation.
- **Gene flow**, the transfer of alleles between populations, tends to reduce genetic differences between populations over time.

? *Would two small, geographically isolated populations in very different environments be likely to evolve in similar ways? Explain.*

CONCEPT 23.4

Natural selection is the only mechanism that consistently causes adaptive evolution (pp. 491–498)

- One organism has greater **relative fitness** than another organism if it leaves more fertile descendants. The modes of natural selection differ in their effect on phenotype:

Original population   Evolved population

Directional selection   Disruptive selection   Stabilizing selection

- Unlike genetic drift and gene flow, natural selection consistently improves the match between organisms and their environment.
- **Sexual selection** influences change in secondary sex characteristics that can give individuals advantages in mating.
- **Balancing selection** occurs when natural selection maintains two or more forms in a population.

- There are constraints to evolution: Natural selection can act only on available variation; structures result from modified ancestral anatomy; adaptations are often compromises; and chance, natural selection, and the environment interact.

? *How might secondary sex characteristics differ between males and females in a species in which females compete for mates?*

TEST YOUR UNDERSTANDING

LEVEL 1: KNOWLEDGE/COMPREHENSION

1. Natural selection changes allele frequencies because some _____ survive and reproduce better than others.
   a. alleles   b. loci   c. species   d. individuals

2. No two people are genetically identical, except for identical twins. The main source of genetic variation among humans is
   a. new mutations that occurred in the preceding generation.
   b. genetic drift.
   c. the reshuffling of alleles in sexual reproduction.
   d. environmental effects.

LEVEL 2: APPLICATION/ANALYSIS

3. If the nucleotide variability of a locus equals 0%, what is the gene variability and number of alleles at that locus?
   a. gene variability = 0%; number of alleles = 0
   b. gene variability = 0%; number of alleles = 1
   c. gene variability = 0%; number of alleles = 2
   d. gene variability > 0%; number of alleles = 2

4. There are 25 individuals in population 1, all with genotype *AA*, and there are 40 individuals in population 2, all with genotype *aa*. Assume that these populations are located far from each other and that their environmental conditions are very similar. Based on the information given here, the observed genetic variation most likely resulted from
   a. genetic drift.   c. nonrandom mating.
   b. gene flow.   d. directional selection.

5. A fruit fly population has a gene with two alleles, *A1* and *A2*. Tests show that 70% of the gametes produced in the population contain the *A1* allele. If the population is in Hardy-Weinberg equilibrium, what proportion of the flies carry both *A1* and *A2*?
   a. 0.7   b. 0.49   c. 0.42   d. 0.21

LEVEL 3: SYNTHESIS/EVALUATION

6. **EVOLUTION CONNECTION**
   Using at least two examples, explain how the process of evolution is revealed by the imperfections of living organisms.

7. **SCIENTIFIC INQUIRY**
   INTERPRET THE DATA Researchers studied genetic variation in the marine mussel *Mytilus edulis* around Long Island, New York. They measured the frequency of a particular allele (*lap*^{94}) for an enzyme involved in regulating the mussel's internal saltwater balance. The researchers presented their data as a series of pie charts linked to sampling sites within Long Island Sound, where the salinity is highly variable, and along the coast of the open ocean, where salinity is constant.
   Create a data table for the 11 sampling sites by estimating the frequency of *lap*^{94} from the pie charts. (*Hint*: Think of each pie chart as a clock face to help you estimate the proportion of the shaded area.) Then graph the frequencies for sites 1–8 to show how the frequency of this allele changes with increasing salinity in Long Island Sound (from southwest to northeast). How do the data from sites 9–11 compare with the data from the sites within the Sound? Construct a hypothesis that explains the patterns you observe in the data and that accounts for the two observations listed below the map.

Sampling sites (1–8 represent pairs of sites): ① ② ③ ④ ⑤ ⑥ ⑦ ⑧ ⑨ ⑩ ⑪

Allele frequencies

■ *lap*^{94} alleles   □ Other *lap* alleles

Data from R. K. Koehn and T. J. Hilbish, The adaptive importance of genetic variation, *American Scientist* 75:134–141 (1987).

Salinity increases toward the open ocean →

Long Island Sound

Atlantic Ocean

(1) The *lap*^{94} allele helps mussels maintain osmotic balance in water with a high salt concentration but is costly to use in less salty water; and (2) mussels produce larvae that can disperse long distances before they settle on rocks and grow into adults.

8. **WRITE ABOUT A THEME: ORGANIZATION**
   Heterozygotes at the sickle-cell locus produce both normal and abnormal (sickle-cell) hemoglobin (see Concept 14.4). When hemoglobin molecules are packed into a heterozygote's red blood cells, some cells receive relatively large quantities of abnormal hemoglobin, making these cells prone to sickling. In a short essay (approximately 100–150 words), explain how these molecular and cellular events lead to emergent properties at the individual and population levels of biological organization.

9. **SYNTHESIZE YOUR KNOWLEDGE**

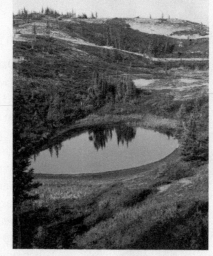

This kettle lake formed 14,000 years ago when a glacier that covered the surrounding area melted. Initially devoid of animal life, over time the lake was colonized by invertebrates and other animals. Hypothesize how mutation, natural selection, genetic drift, and gene flow may have affected populations that colonized the lake.

For suggested answers, see Appendix A.

MasteringBiology®

Students Go to **MasteringBiology** for assignments, the eText, and the Study Area with practice tests, animations, and activities.

Instructors Go to **MasteringBiology** for automatically graded tutorials and questions that you can assign to your students, plus Instructor Resources.

24

The Origin of Species

KEY CONCEPTS

24.1 The biological species concept emphasizes reproductive isolation

24.2 Speciation can take place with or without geographic separation

24.3 Hybrid zones reveal factors that cause reproductive isolation

24.4 Speciation can occur rapidly or slowly and can result from changes in few or many genes

▲ **Figure 24.1 How did this flightless bird come to live on the isolated Galápagos Islands?**

That "Mystery of Mysteries"

When Darwin came to the Galápagos Islands, he noted that these volcanic islands were teeming with plants and animals found nowhere else in the world **(Figure 24.1)**. Later he realized that these species had formed relatively recently. He wrote in his diary: "Both in space and time, we seem to be brought somewhat near to that great fact—that mystery of mysteries—the first appearance of new beings on this Earth."

The "mystery of mysteries" that captivated Darwin is **speciation,** the process by which one species splits into two or more species. Speciation fascinated Darwin (and many biologists since) because it has produced the tremendous diversity of life, repeatedly yielding new species that differ from existing ones. Speciation also helps to explain the many features that organisms share (the unity of life). When one species splits into two, the species that result share many characteristics because they are descended from this common ancestor. At the DNA sequence level, for example, such similarities indicate that the flightless cormorant (*Phalacrocorax harrisi*) in Figure 24.1 is closely related to flying cormorants found in the Americas. This suggests that the flightless cormorant originated from an ancestral cormorant species that flew from the mainland to the Galápagos.

◀ **Galápagos giant tortoise, another species unique to the islands**

Speciation also forms a conceptual bridge between **microevolution**, changes over time in allele frequencies in a population, and **macroevolution**, the broad pattern of evolution above the species level. An example of macroevolutionary change is the origin of new groups of organisms, such as mammals or flowering plants, through a series of speciation events. We examined microevolutionary mechanisms in Chapter 23, and we'll turn to macroevolution in Chapter 25. In this chapter, we'll explore the "bridge" between microevolution and macroevolution—the mechanisms by which new species originate from existing ones. First, let's establish what we actually mean by a "species."

The biological species concept emphasizes reproductive isolation

The word *species* is Latin for "kind" or "appearance." In daily life, we commonly distinguish between various "kinds" of organisms—dogs and cats, for instance—from differences in their appearance. But are organisms truly divided into the discrete units we call species, or is this classification an arbitrary attempt to impose order on the natural world? To answer this question, biologists compare not only the morphology (body form) of different groups of organisms but also less obvious differences in physiology, biochemistry, and DNA sequences. The results generally confirm that morphologically distinct species are indeed discrete groups, differing in many ways besides their body forms.

The Biological Species Concept

The primary definition of species used in this textbook is the **biological species concept**. According to this concept, a **species** is a group of populations whose members have the potential to interbreed in nature and produce viable, fertile offspring—but do not produce viable, fertile offspring with members of other such groups **(Figure 24.2)**. Thus, the members of a biological species are united by being reproductively compatible, at least potentially. All human beings, for example, belong to the same species. A businesswoman in Manhattan may be unlikely to meet a dairy farmer in Mongolia, but if the two should happen to meet and mate, they could have viable babies who develop into fertile adults. In contrast, humans and chimpanzees remain distinct biological species even where they live in the same region, because many factors keep them from interbreeding and producing fertile offspring.

What holds the gene pool of a species together, causing its members to resemble each other more than they resemble members of other species? Recall the evolutionary mechanism of *gene flow*, the transfer of alleles between populations (see Chapter 23). Typically, gene flow occurs

(a) Similarity between different species. The eastern meadowlark (*Sturnella magna*, left) and the western meadowlark (*Sturnella neglecta*, right) have similar body shapes and colorations. Nevertheless, they are distinct biological species because their songs and other behaviors are different enough to prevent interbreeding should they meet in the wild.

(b) Diversity within a species. Although diverse in appearance, all humans belong to a single biological species (*Homo sapiens*), defined by our capacity to interbreed successfully.

▲ Figure 24.2 **The biological species concept is based on the potential to interbreed, not on physical similarity.**

between the different populations of a species. This ongoing exchange of alleles tends to hold the populations together genetically. As we'll explore in this chapter, the absence of gene flow is important in the formation of new species.

Reproductive Isolation

Because biological species are defined in terms of reproductive compatibility, the formation of a new species hinges on **reproductive isolation**—the existence of biological factors (barriers) that impede members of two species from interbreeding and producing viable, fertile offspring. Such barriers block gene flow between the species and limit the formation of **hybrids**, offspring that result from an interspecific mating. Although a single barrier may not prevent all gene flow, a combination of several barriers can effectively isolate a species' gene pool.

Clearly, a fly cannot mate with a frog or a fern, but the reproductive barriers between more closely related species are not so obvious. As described in **Figure 24.3**, these barriers

Exploring Reproductive Barriers

Prezygotic barriers impede mating or hinder fertilization if mating does occur

Habitat Isolation	Temporal Isolation	Behavioral Isolation	Mechanical Isolation

Individuals of different species → MATING ATTEMPT

Two species that occupy different habitats within the same area may encounter each other rarely, if at all, even though they are not isolated by obvious physical barriers, such as mountain ranges.

Species that breed during different times of the day, different seasons, or different years cannot mix their gametes.

Courtship rituals that attract mates and other behaviors unique to a species are effective reproductive barriers, even between closely related species. Such behavioral rituals enable mate recognition—a way to identify potential mates of the same species.

Mating is attempted, but morphological differences prevent its successful completion.

Example: Two species of garter snakes in the genus *Thamnophis* occur in the same geographic areas, but one lives mainly in water (a) while the other is primarily terrestrial (b).

Example: In North America, the geographic ranges of the eastern spotted skunk (*Spilogale putorius*) (c) and the western spotted skunk (*Spilogale gracilis*) (d) overlap, but *S. putorius* mates in late winter and *S. gracilis* mates in late summer.

Example: Blue-footed boobies, inhabitants of the Galápagos, mate only after a courtship display unique to their species. Part of the "script" calls for the male to high-step (e), a behavior that calls the female's attention to his bright blue feet.

Example: The shells of two species of snails in the genus *Bradybaena* spiral in different directions: Moving inward to the center, one spirals in a counterclockwise direction (f, left), the other in a clockwise direction (f, right). As a result, the snails' genital openings (indicated by arrows) are not aligned, and mating cannot be completed.

(a)

(b)

(c)

(d)

(e)

(f)

Gametic Isolation

Reduced Hybrid Viability

Reduced Hybrid Fertility

Hybrid Breakdown

FERTILIZATION

VIABLE, FERTILE OFFSPRING

Sperm of one species may not be able to fertilize the eggs of another species. For instance, sperm may not be able to survive in the reproductive tract of females of the other species, or biochemical mechanisms may prevent the sperm from penetrating the membrane surrounding the other species' eggs.

Example: Gametic isolation separates certain closely related species of aquatic animals, such as sea urchins (g). Sea urchins release their sperm and eggs into the surrounding water, where they fuse and form zygotes. It is difficult for gametes of different species, such as the red and purple urchins shown here, to fuse because proteins on the surfaces of the eggs and sperm bind very poorly to each other.

The genes of different parent species may interact in ways that impair the hybrid's development or survival in its environment.

Example: Some salamander subspecies of the genus *Ensatina* live in the same regions and habitats, where they may occasionally hybridize. But most of the hybrids do not complete development, and those that do are frail (h).

Even if hybrids are vigorous, they may be sterile. If the chromosomes of the two parent species differ in number or structure, meiosis in the hybrids may fail to produce normal gametes. Since the infertile hybrids cannot produce offspring when they mate with either parent species, genes cannot flow freely between the species.

Example: The hybrid offspring of a male donkey (i) and a female horse (j) is a mule (k), which is robust but sterile. A "hinny" (not shown), the offspring of a female donkey and a male horse, is also sterile.

Some first-generation hybrids are viable and fertile, but when they mate with one another or with either parent species, offspring of the next generation are feeble or sterile.

Example: Strains of cultivated rice have accumulated different mutant recessive alleles at two loci in the course of their divergence from a common ancestor. Hybrids between them are vigorous and fertile (l, left and right), but plants in the next generation that carry too many of these recessive alleles are small and sterile (l, center). Although these rice strains are not yet considered different species, they have begun to be separated by postzygotic barriers.

can be classified according to whether they contribute to reproductive isolation before or after fertilization. **Prezygotic barriers** ("before the zygote") block fertilization from occurring. Such barriers typically act in one of three ways: by impeding members of different species from attempting to mate, by preventing an attempted mating from being completed successfully, or by hindering fertilization if mating is completed successfully. If a sperm cell from one species overcomes prezygotic barriers and fertilizes an ovum from another species, a variety of **postzygotic barriers** ("after the zygote") may contribute to reproductive isolation after the hybrid zygote is formed. Developmental errors may reduce survival among hybrid embryos. Or problems after birth may cause hybrids to be infertile or decrease their chance of surviving long enough to reproduce.

Limitations of the Biological Species Concept

One strength of the biological species concept is that it directs our attention to a way by which speciation can occur: by the evolution of reproductive isolation. However, the number of species to which this concept can be usefully applied is limited. There is, for example, no way to evaluate the reproductive isolation of fossils. The biological species concept also does not apply to organisms that reproduce asexually all or most of the time, such as prokaryotes. (Many prokaryotes do transfer genes among themselves, as we will discuss in Chapter 27, but this is not part of their reproductive process.) Furthermore, in the biological species concept, species are designated by the *absence* of gene flow. But there are many pairs of species that are morphologically and ecologically distinct, and yet gene flow occurs between them. An example is the grizzly bear (*Ursus arctos*) and polar bear (*Ursus maritimus*), whose hybrid offspring have been dubbed "grolar bears" **(Figure 24.4)**. As we'll discuss, natural selection can cause such species to remain distinct even though some gene flow occurs between them. Because of the limitations to the biological species concept, alternative species concepts are useful in certain situations.

Other Definitions of Species

While the biological species concept emphasizes the *separateness* of species from one another due to reproductive barriers, several other definitions emphasize the *unity within* a species. For example, the **morphological species concept** distinguishes a species by body shape and other structural features. The morphological species concept can be applied to asexual and sexual organisms, and it can be useful even without information on the extent of gene flow. In practice, scientists often distinguish species using morphological criteria. A disadvantage of this approach, however, is that it relies on subjective criteria; researchers may disagree on which structural features distinguish a species.

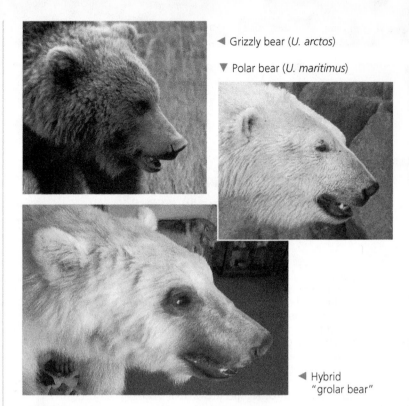

◀ Grizzly bear (*U. arctos*)

▼ Polar bear (*U. maritimus*)

◀ Hybrid "grolar bear"

▲ **Figure 24.4 Hybridization between two species of bears in the genus *Ursus*.**

The **ecological species concept** defines a species in terms of its ecological niche, the sum of how members of the species interact with the nonliving and living parts of their environment (see Concept 54.1). For example, two species of oak trees might differ in their size or in their ability to tolerate dry conditions, yet still occasionally interbreed. Because they occupy different ecological niches, these oaks would be considered separate species even though they are connected by some gene flow. Unlike the biological species concept, the ecological species concept can accommodate asexual as well as sexual species. It also emphasizes the role of disruptive natural selection as organisms adapt to different environments.

The **phylogenetic species concept** defines a species as the smallest group of individuals that share a common ancestor, forming one branch on the tree of life. Biologists trace the phylogenetic history of a species by comparing its characteristics, such as morphology or molecular sequences, with those of other organisms. Such analyses can distinguish groups of individuals that are sufficiently different to be considered separate species. Of course, the difficulty with this species concept is determining the degree of difference required to indicate separate species.

In addition to those discussed here, more than 20 other species definitions have been proposed. The usefulness of each definition depends on the situation and the research questions being asked. For our purposes of studying how species originate, the biological species concept, with its focus on reproductive barriers, is particularly helpful.

CONCEPT CHECK 24.1

1. (a) Which species concept(s) could you apply to both asexual and sexual species? (b) Which would be most useful for identifying species in the field? Explain.

2. **WHAT IF?** Suppose you are studying two bird species that live in a forest and are not known to interbreed. One species feeds and mates in the treetops and the other on the ground. But in captivity, the birds can interbreed and produce viable, fertile offspring. What type of reproductive barrier most likely keeps these species separate in nature? Explain.

For suggested answers, see Appendix A.

CONCEPT 24.2

Speciation can take place with or without geographic separation

Having discussed what constitutes a unique species, let's return to the process by which such species arise from existing species. We'll describe this process by focusing on the geographic setting in which gene flow is interrupted between populations of the existing species—in allopatric speciation the populations are geographically isolated, while in sympatric speciation they are not **(Figure 24.5)**.

Allopatric ("Other Country") Speciation

In **allopatric speciation** (from the Greek *allos*, other, and *patra*, homeland), gene flow is interrupted when a

(a) **Allopatric speciation.** A population forms a new species while geographically isolated from its parent population.

(b) **Sympatric speciation.** A subset of a population forms a new species without geographic separation.

▲ **Figure 24.5 The geography of speciation.**

population is divided into geographically isolated subpopulations. For example, the water level in a lake may subside, resulting in two or more smaller lakes that are now home to separated populations (see Figure 24.5a). Or a river may change course and divide a population of animals that cannot cross it. Allopatric speciation can also occur without geologic remodeling, such as when individuals colonize a remote area and their descendants become geographically isolated from the parent population. The flightless cormorant shown in Figure 24.1 most likely originated in this way from an ancestral flying species that reached the Galápagos Islands.

The Process of Allopatric Speciation

How formidable must a geographic barrier be to promote allopatric speciation? The answer depends on the ability of the organisms to move about. Birds, mountain lions, and coyotes can cross rivers and canyons—as can the windblown pollen of pine trees and the seeds of many flowering plants. In contrast, small rodents may find a wide river or deep canyon a formidable barrier.

Once geographic separation has occurred, the separated gene pools may diverge. Different mutations arise, and natural selection and genetic drift may alter allele frequencies in different ways in the separated populations. Reproductive isolation may then evolve as a by-product of the genetic divergence that results from selection or drift.

Figure 24.6 describes an example. On Andros Island, in the Bahamas, populations of the mosquitofish *Gambusia hubbsi* colonized a series of ponds that later became isolated from one another. Genetic analyses indicate that little or no gene flow currently occurs between the ponds. The environments of these ponds are very similar except that some contain many predatory fishes, while others do not. In the "high-predation" ponds, selection has favored the evolution of a mosquitofish body shape that enables rapid bursts of speed (see Figure 24.6a). In low-predation ponds, selection

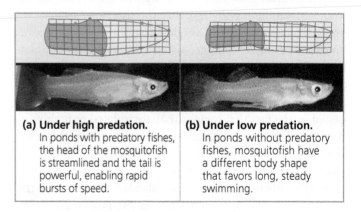

(a) **Under high predation.** In ponds with predatory fishes, the head of the mosquitofish is streamlined and the tail is powerful, enabling rapid bursts of speed.

(b) **Under low predation.** In ponds without predatory fishes, mosquitofish have a different body shape that favors long, steady swimming.

▲ **Figure 24.6 Reproductive isolation as a by-product of selection.** Bringing together mosquitofish from different ponds indicates that selection for traits that enable mosquitofish in high-predation ponds to avoid predators has isolated them reproductively from mosquitofish in low-predation ponds.

has favored a different body shape, one that improves the ability to swim for long periods of time (see Figure 24.6b). How have these different selective pressures affected the evolution of reproductive barriers? Researchers studied this question by bringing together mosquitofish from the two types of ponds. They found that female mosquitofish prefer to mate with males whose body shape is similar to their own. This preference establishes a behavioral barrier to reproduction between mosquitofish from high-predation and low-predation ponds. Thus, as a by-product of selection for avoiding predators, reproductive barriers have started to form in these allopatric populations.

Evidence of Allopatric Speciation

Many studies provide evidence that speciation can occur in allopatric populations. For example, laboratory studies show that reproductive barriers can develop when populations are isolated experimentally and subjected to different environmental conditions (**Figure 24.7**).

Field studies indicate that allopatric speciation also can occur in nature. Consider the 30 species of snapping shrimp in the genus *Alpheus* that live off the Isthmus of Panama, the land bridge that connects South and North America (**Figure 24.8**). Fifteen of these species live on the Atlantic side of the isthmus, while the other 15 live on the Pacific side. Before the isthmus formed, gene flow could occur between the Atlantic and Pacific populations of snapping shrimp. Did the species on different sides of the isthmus originate by allopatric speciation? Morphological and genetic data group these shrimp into 15 pairs of *sister species*, pairs whose member species are each other's closest relative. In each of these 15 pairs, one of the sister species lives on the Atlantic side of the isthmus, while the other lives on the Pacific side, strongly suggesting that the two species arose as a consequence of geographic separation. Furthermore, genetic analyses indicate that the *Alpheus* species originated from 9 to 3 million years ago, with the sister species that live in the deepest water diverging first. These divergence times are consistent with geologic evidence that the isthmus formed gradually, starting 10 million years ago, and closing completely about 3 million years ago.

The importance of allopatric speciation is also suggested by the fact that regions that are isolated or highly subdivided by barriers typically have more species than do otherwise similar regions that lack such features. For example, many unique plants and animals are found on the geographically isolated Hawaiian Islands (we'll return to the origin of Hawaiian species in Chapter 25). Field studies also show that reproductive isolation between two populations generally increases as the geographic distance between them increases, a finding consistent with allopatric speciation. In the Scientific Skills Exercise, you will analyze data from one such study that examined reproductive isolation

▼ Figure 24.7 | Inquiry

Can divergence of allopatric populations lead to reproductive isolation?

Experiment A researcher divided a laboratory population of the fruit fly *Drosophila pseudoobscura*, raising some flies on a starch medium and others on a maltose medium. After one year (about 40 generations), natural selection resulted in divergent evolution: Populations raised on starch digested starch more efficiently, while those raised on maltose digested maltose more efficiently. The researcher then put flies from the same or different populations in mating cages and measured mating frequencies. All flies used in the mating preference tests were reared for one generation on a standard cornmeal medium.

Initial population of fruit flies (*Drosophila pseudoobscura*)

Some flies raised on starch medium

Some flies raised on maltose medium

Mating experiments after 40 generations

Results Mating patterns among populations of flies raised on different media are shown below. When flies from "starch populations" were mixed with flies from "maltose populations," the flies tended to mate with like partners. But in the control group (shown on the right), flies from different populations adapted to starch were about as likely to mate with each other as with flies from their own population; similar results were obtained for control groups adapted to maltose.

		Female	
		Starch	Maltose
Male	Starch	22	9
	Maltose	8	20

Number of matings in experimental group

		Female	
		Starch population 1	Starch population 2
Male	Starch population 1	18	15
	Starch population 2	12	15

Number of matings in control group

Conclusion In the experimental group, the strong preference of "starch flies" and "maltose flies" to mate with like-adapted flies indicates that a reproductive barrier was forming between these fly populations. Although this reproductive barrier was not absolute (some mating between starch flies and maltose flies did occur), after 40 generations isolation appeared to be increasing. This barrier may have been caused by differences in courtship behavior that arose as an incidental by-product of differing selective pressures as these allopatric populations adapted to different sources of food.

Source: D. M. B. Dodd, Reproductive isolation as a consequence of adaptive divergence in *Drosophila pseudoobscura*, *Evolution* 43:1308–1311 (1989).

WHAT IF? *Why were all flies used in the mating preference tests reared on a standard medium (rather than on starch or maltose)?*

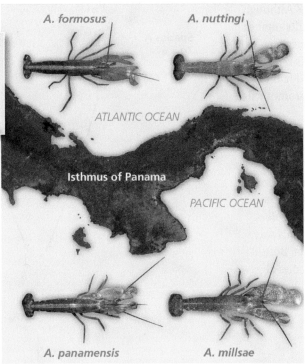

A. formosus   A. nuttingi

ATLANTIC OCEAN

Isthmus of Panama

PACIFIC OCEAN

A. panamensis   A. millsae

▶ **Figure 24.8**
Allopatric speciation in snapping shrimp (Alpheus). The shrimp pictured are just 2 of the 15 pairs of sister species that arose as populations were divided by the formation of the Isthmus of Panama. The color-coded type indicates the sister species.

in geographically separated salamander populations.

Note that while geographic isolation prevents interbreeding between members of allopatric populations, physical separation is not a biological barrier to reproduction. Biological reproductive barriers such as those described in Figure 24.3 are intrinsic to the organisms themselves. Hence, it is biological barriers that can prevent interbreeding when members of different populations come into contact with one another.

Sympatric ("Same Country") Speciation

In **sympatric speciation** (from the Greek *syn*, together), speciation occurs in populations that live in the same geographic area (see Figure 24.5b). How can reproductive barriers form between sympatric populations while

---

SCIENTIFIC SKILLS EXERCISE

Identifying Independent and Dependent Variables, Making a Scatter Plot, and Interpreting Data

Does Distance Between Salamander Populations Increase Their Reproductive Isolation? Allopatric speciation begins when populations become geographically isolated, preventing mating between individuals in different populations and thus stopping gene flow. It is logical that as distance between populations increases, so will their degree of reproductive isolation. To test this hypothesis, researchers studied populations of the dusky salamander (*Desmognathus ochrophaeus*) living on different mountain ranges in the southern Appalachians.

How the Experiment Was Done The researchers tested the reproductive isolation of pairs of salamander populations by leaving one male and one female together and later checking the females for the presence of sperm. Four mating combinations were tested for each pair of populations (A and B)—two *within* the same population (female A with male A and female B with male B) and two *between* populations (female A with male B and female B with male A).

Data from the Experiment The researchers used an index of reproductive isolation that ranged from a value of 0 (no isolation) to a value of 2 (full isolation). The proportion of successful matings for each mating combination was measured, with 100% success = 1 and no success = 0. The reproductive isolation value for two populations is the sum of the proportion of successful matings of each type within populations (AA + BB) minus the sum of the proportion of successful matings of each type between populations (AB + BA). The table provides distance and reproductive isolation data for 27 pairs of dusky salamander populations.

Interpret the Data

1. State the researchers' hypothesis, and identify the independent and dependent variables in this study. Explain why the researchers used four mating combinations for each pair of populations.

2. Calculate the value of the reproductive isolation index if (a) *all* of the matings within a population were successful, but *none* of the matings between populations were successful; (b) salamanders are equally successful in mating with members of their own population and members of another population.

3. Make a scatter plot to help you visualize any patterns that might indicate a relationship between the variables. Plot the independent variable on the *x*-axis and the dependent variable on the *y*-axis. (For additional information about graphs, see the Scientific Skills Review in Appendix F and the Study Area of MasteringBiology.)

4. Interpret your graph by (a) explaining in words any pattern indicating a possible relationship between the variables and (b) hypothesizing the possible cause of such a relationship.

(MB) A version of this Scientific Skills Exercise can be assigned in MasteringBiology.

Data from S. G. Tilley, A. Verrell, and S. J. Arnold, Correspondence between sexual isolation and allozyme differentiation: a test in the salamander *Desmognathus ochrophaeus, Proceedings of the National Academy of Sciences USA* 87:2715–2719 (1990).

Geographic Distance (km)	15	32	40	47	42	62	63	81	86	107	107	115	137	147
Reproductive Isolation Value	0.32	0.54	0.50	0.50	0.82	0.37	0.67	0.53	1.15	0.73	0.82	0.81	0.87	0.87
Distance (continued)	137	150	165	189	219	239	247	53	55	62	105	179	169	
Isolation (continued)	0.50	0.57	0.91	0.93	1.5	1.22	0.82	0.99	0.21	0.56	0.41	0.72	1.15	

their members remain in contact with each other? Although such contact (and the ongoing gene flow that results) makes sympatric speciation less common than allopatric speciation, sympatric speciation can occur if gene flow is reduced by such factors as polyploidy, sexual selection, and habitat differentiation. (Note that these factors can also promote allopatric speciation.)

Polyploidy

A species may originate from an accident during cell division that results in extra sets of chromosomes, a condition called **polyploidy**. Polyploid speciation occasionally occurs in animals; for example, the gray tree frog *Hyla versicolor* (see Figure 23.16) is thought to have originated in this way. However, polyploidy is far more common in plants. Botanists estimate that more than 80% of the plant species alive today are descended from ancestors that formed by polyploid speciation.

Two distinct forms of polyploidy have been observed in plant (and a few animal) populations. An **autopolyploid** (from the Greek *autos*, self) is an individual that has more than two chromosome sets that are all derived from a single species. In plants, for example, a failure of cell division could double a cell's chromosome number from the original number ($2n$) to a tetraploid number ($4n$).

A tetraploid can produce fertile tetraploid offspring by self-pollinating or by mating with other tetraploids. In addition, the tetraploids are reproductively isolated from $2n$ plants of the original population, because the triploid ($3n$) offspring of such unions have reduced fertility. Thus, in just one generation, autopolyploidy can generate reproductive isolation without any geographic separation.

A second form of polyploidy can occur when two different species interbreed and produce hybrid offspring. Most such hybrids are sterile because the set of chromosomes from one species cannot pair during meiosis with the set of chromosomes from the other species. However, an infertile hybrid may be able to propagate itself asexually (as many plants can do). In subsequent generations, various mechanisms can change a sterile hybrid into a fertile polyploid called an **allopolyploid** (**Figure 24.9**). The allopolyploids are fertile when mating with each other but cannot interbreed with either parent species; thus, they represent a new biological species.

▲ Autopolyploid speciation

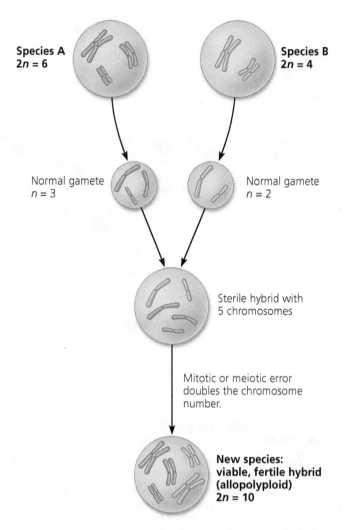

▲ **Figure 24.9 One mechanism for allopolyploid speciation in plants.** Most hybrids are sterile because their chromosomes are not homologous and cannot pair during meiosis. However, such a hybrid may be able to reproduce asexually. This diagram traces one mechanism that can produce fertile hybrids (allopolyploids) as new species. The new species has a diploid chromosome number equal to the sum of the diploid chromosome numbers of the two parent species.

Although it can be challenging to study speciation in the field, scientists have documented at least five new plant species that have originated by polyploid speciation since 1850. One of these examples involves the origin of a new species of goatsbeard plant (genus *Tragopogon*) in the Pacific Northwest. *Tragopogon* first arrived in the region when humans introduced three European species in the early 1900s: *T. pratensis, T. dubius,* and *T. porrifolius.* These three species are now common weeds in abandoned parking lots and other urban sites. In 1950, a new *Tragopogon* species was discovered near the Idaho-Washington border, a region where all three European species also were found. Genetic analyses revealed that this new species, *Tragopogon miscellus*, is a hybrid of two of the European species (**Figure 24.10**). Although the *T. miscellus* population grows mainly by reproduction of its own members, additional

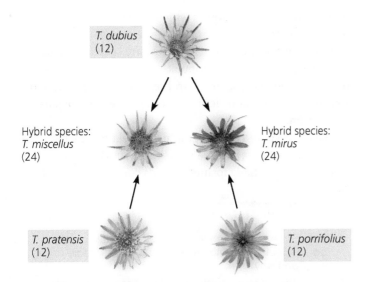

▲ **Figure 24.10 Allopolyploid speciation in *Tragopogon*.** The gray boxes indicate the three parent species. The diploid chromosome number of each species is shown in parentheses.

episodes of hybridization between the parent species continue to add new members to the *T. miscellus* population. Later, scientists discovered another new *Tragopogon* species, *T. mirus*—this one a hybrid of *T. dubius* and *T. porrifolius* (see Figure 24.10). The *Tragopogon* story is just one of several well-studied examples in which scientists have observed speciation in progress.

Many important agricultural crops—such as oats, cotton, potatoes, tobacco, and wheat—are polyploids. The wheat used for bread, *Triticum aestivum*, is an allohexaploid (six sets of chromosomes, two sets from each of three different species). The first of the polyploidy events that eventually led to modern wheat probably occurred about 8,000 years ago in the Middle East as a spontaneous hybrid of an early cultivated wheat species and a wild grass. Today, plant geneticists generate new polyploids in the laboratory by using chemicals that induce meiotic and mitotic errors. By harnessing the evolutionary process, researchers can produce new hybrid species with desired qualities, such as a hybrid that combines the high yield of wheat with the hardiness of rye.

Sexual Selection

There is evidence that sympatric speciation can also be driven by sexual selection. Clues to how this can occur have been found in cichlid fish from one of Earth's hot spots of animal speciation, East Africa's Lake Victoria. This lake was once home to as many as 600 species of cichlids. Genetic data indicate that these species originated within the last 100,000 years from a small number of colonizing species that arrived from other lakes and rivers. How did so many species—more than double the number of freshwater fish species known in all of Europe—originate within a single lake?

One hypothesis is that subgroups of the original cichlid populations adapted to different food sources and the resulting genetic divergence contributed to speciation in Lake Victoria. But sexual selection, in which (typically) females select males based on their appearance (see Concept 23.4), may also have been a factor. Researchers have studied two closely related sympatric species of cichlids that differ mainly in the coloration of breeding males: Breeding *Pundamilia pundamilia* males have a blue-tinged back, whereas breeding *Pundamilia nyererei* males have a red-tinged back (**Figure 24.11**). The studies' results suggest that mate choice based on male breeding coloration is the main reproductive barrier that normally keeps the gene pools of these two species separate.

▼ **Figure 24.11** | **Inquiry**

Does sexual selection in cichlids result in reproductive isolation?

Experiment Researchers placed males and females of *Pundamilia pundamilia* and *P. nyererei* together in two aquarium tanks, one with natural light and one with a monochromatic orange lamp. Under normal light, the two species are noticeably different in male breeding coloration; under monochromatic orange light, the two species are very similar in color. The researchers then observed the mate choices of the females in each tank.

Results Under normal light, females of each species strongly preferred males of their own species. But under orange light, females of each species responded indiscriminately to males of both species. The resulting hybrids were viable and fertile.

Conclusion The researchers concluded that mate choice by females based on male breeding coloration is the main reproductive barrier that normally keeps the gene pools of these two species separate. Since the species can still interbreed when this prezygotic behavioral barrier is breached in the laboratory, the genetic divergence between the species is likely to be small. This suggests that speciation in nature has occurred relatively recently.

Source: O. Seehausen and J. J. M. van Alphen, The effect of male coloration on female mate choice in closely related Lake Victoria cichlids (*Haplochromis nyererei* complex), *Behavioral Ecology and Sociobiology* 42:1–8 (1998).

WHAT IF? *Suppose that female cichlids living in the murky waters of a polluted lake could not distinguish colors well. In such waters, how might the gene pools of these species change over time?*

Habitat Differentiation

Sympatric speciation can also occur when a subpopulation exploits a habitat or resource not used by the parent population. Consider the North American apple maggot fly (*Rhagoletis pomonella*), a pest of apples. The fly's original habitat was the native hawthorn tree, but about 200 years ago, some populations colonized apple trees that had been introduced by European settlers. Apple maggot flies usually mate on or near their host plant. This results in a prezygotic barrier (habitat isolation) between populations that feed on apples and populations that feed on hawthorns. Furthermore, as apples mature more quickly than hawthorn fruit, natural selection has favored apple-feeding flies with rapid development. These apple-feeding populations now show temporal isolation from the hawthorn-feeding *R. pomonella*, providing a second prezygotic barrier to gene flow between the two populations. Researchers also have identified alleles that benefit the flies that use one host plant but harm the flies that use the other host plant. Natural selection operating on these alleles has provided a postzygotic barrier to reproduction,

▲ *R. pomonella* feeding on a hawthorn berry

further limiting gene flow. Altogether, although the two populations are still classified as subspecies rather than separate species, sympatric speciation appears to be well under way.

Allopatric and Sympatric Speciation: *A Review*

Now let's recap the processes by which new species form. In allopatric speciation, a new species forms in geographic isolation from its parent population. Geographic isolation severely restricts gene flow. Intrinsic barriers to reproduction with the parent population may then arise as a by-product of genetic changes that occur within the isolated population. Many different processes can produce such genetic changes, including natural selection under different environmental conditions, genetic drift, and sexual selection. Once formed, reproductive barriers that arise in allopatric populations can prevent interbreeding with the parent population even if the populations come back into contact.

Sympatric speciation, in contrast, requires the emergence of a reproductive barrier that isolates a subset of a population from the remainder of the population in the same area. Though rarer than allopatric speciation, sympatric speciation can occur when gene flow to and from the isolated subpopulation is blocked. This can occur as a result

of polyploidy, a condition in which an organism has extra sets of chromosomes. Sympatric speciation also can result from sexual selection. Finally, sympatric speciation can occur when a subset of a population becomes reproductively isolated because of natural selection that results from a switch to a habitat or food source not used by the parent population.

Having reviewed the geographic context in which species originate, we'll next explore in more detail what can happen when new or partially formed species come into contact.

CONCEPT CHECK 24.2

1. Summarize key differences between allopatric and sympatric speciation. Which type of speciation is more common, and why?

2. Describe two mechanisms that can decrease gene flow in sympatric populations, thereby making sympatric speciation more likely to occur.

3. **WHAT IF?** Is allopatric speciation more likely to occur on an island close to a mainland or on a more isolated island of the same size? Explain your prediction.

4. **MAKE CONNECTIONS** Review the process of meiosis in Figure 13.8. Describe how an error during meiosis could lead to polyploidy.

For suggested answers, see Appendix A.

CONCEPT 24.3

Hybrid zones reveal factors that cause reproductive isolation

What happens if species with incomplete reproductive barriers come into contact with one another? One possible outcome is the formation of a **hybrid zone**, a region in which members of different species meet and mate, producing at least some offspring of mixed ancestry. In this section, we'll explore hybrid zones and what they reveal about factors that cause the evolution of reproductive isolation.

Patterns Within Hybrid Zones

Some hybrid zones form as narrow bands, such as the one depicted in **Figure 24.12** for the yellow-bellied toad (*Bombina variegata*) and its close relative, the fire-bellied toad (*B. bombina*). This hybrid zone, represented by the red line on the map, extends for 4,000 km but is less than 10 km wide in most places. The hybrid zone occurs where the higher-altitude habitat of the yellow-bellied toad meets the lowland habitat of the fire-bellied toad. Across a given "slice" of the zone, the frequency of alleles specific to yellow-bellied toads typically decreases from close to 100% at the edge where only yellow-bellied toads are found, to 50% in the central portion of the zone, to 0% at the edge where only fire-bellied toads are found.

Fire-bellied toad, *Bombina bombina*: lives at lower altitudes

Hybrid zone (red line) occurs where the habitats of the two species meet.

Fire-bellied toad range

Hybrid zone

Yellow-bellied toad range

Yellow-bellied toad, *Bombina variegata*: lives at higher altitudes

© 1993 Oxford University Press, Inc.

▲ **Figure 24.12 A narrow hybrid zone for *Bombina* toads in Europe.** The graph shows the pattern of species-specific allele frequencies across the width of the zone near Krakow, Poland. Individuals with frequencies close to 1 are yellow-bellied toads, individuals with frequencies close to 0 are fire-bellied toads, and individuals with intermediate frequencies are considered hybrids.

? *Does the graph indicate that gene flow is spreading fire-bellied toad alleles into the range of the yellow-bellied toad? Explain.*

What causes such a pattern of allele frequencies across a hybrid zone? We can infer that there is an obstacle to gene flow—otherwise, alleles from one parent species would also be common in the gene pool of the other parent species. Are geographic barriers reducing gene flow? Not in this case, since the toads can move throughout the hybrid zone. A more important factor is that hybrid toads have increased rates of embryonic mortality and a variety of morphological abnormalities, including ribs that are fused to the spine and malformed tadpole mouthparts. Because the hybrids have poor survival and reproduction, they produce few viable offspring with members of the parent species. As a result, hybrid individuals rarely serve as a stepping-stone from which alleles are passed from one species to the other. Outside the hybrid zone, additional obstacles to gene flow may be provided by natural selection in the different environments in which the parent species live.

Hybrid zones typically are located wherever the habitats of the interbreeding species meet. Those regions often resemble a group of isolated patches scattered across the landscape—more like the complex pattern of spots on a Dalmatian than the continuous band shown in Figure 24.12. But regardless of whether they have complex or simple spatial patterns, hybrid zones form when two species lacking complete barriers to reproduction come into contact. Once formed, how does a hybrid zone change over time?

Hybrid Zones over Time

Studying a hybrid zone is like observing a naturally occurring experiment on speciation. Will the hybrids become reproductively isolated from their parents and form a new species, as occurred by polyploidy in the goatsbeard plant of the Pacific Northwest? If not, there are three possible outcomes for the hybrid zone over time: reinforcement of

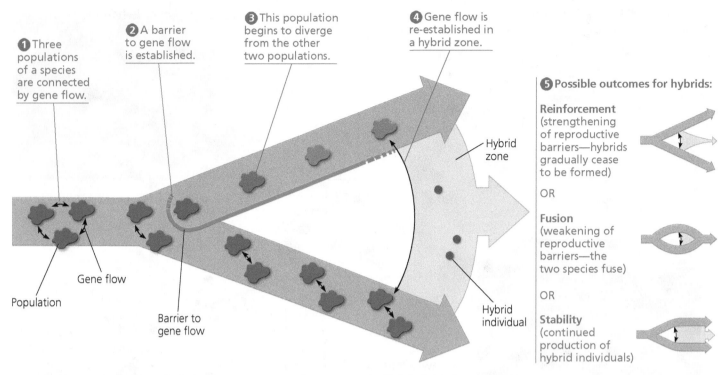

① Three populations of a species are connected by gene flow.

② A barrier to gene flow is established.

③ This population begins to diverge from the other two populations.

④ Gene flow is re-established in a hybrid zone.

Hybrid zone

Gene flow

Population

Barrier to gene flow

Hybrid individual

⑤ Possible outcomes for hybrids:

Reinforcement (strengthening of reproductive barriers—hybrids gradually cease to be formed)

OR

Fusion (weakening of reproductive barriers—the two species fuse)

OR

Stability (continued production of hybrid individuals)

▲ **Figure 24.13 Formation of a hybrid zone and possible outcomes for hybrids over time.** The thick colored arrows represent the passage of time.

WHAT IF? *Predict what might happen if gene flow were re-established at step 3 in this process.*

barriers, fusion of species, or stability (**Figure 24.13**). Let's examine what studies suggest about these possibilities.

Reinforcement: Strengthening Reproductive Barriers

Hybrids often are less fit than members of their parent species. In such cases, natural selection should strengthen prezygotic barriers to reproduction, reducing the formation of unfit hybrids. Because this process involves *reinforcing* reproductive barriers, it is called **reinforcement**. If reinforcement is occurring, a logical prediction is that barriers to reproduction between species should be stronger for sympatric populations than for allopatric populations.

As an example, we'll examine evidence for reinforcement in two species of European flycatcher, the pied flycatcher and the collared flycatcher. In allopatric populations of these birds, males of the two species closely resemble one another. But in sympatric populations, the males of the two species look very different: Male pied flycatchers are a dull brown, whereas male collared flycatchers have enlarged patches of white. Female pied and collared flycatchers do not select males of the other species when given a choice between males from sympatric populations, but they frequently do make mistakes when selecting between males from allopatric populations (**Figure 24.14**). Thus, barriers to reproduction are stronger in birds from sympatric populations than in birds from allopatric populations, as you would predict if reinforcement is occurring. Similar results have been

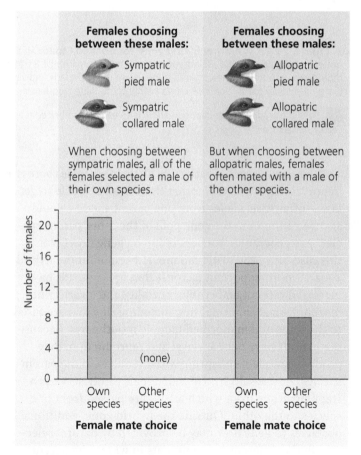

Females choosing between these males:
- Sympatric pied male
- Sympatric collared male

When choosing between sympatric males, all of the females selected a male of their own species.

Females choosing between these males:
- Allopatric pied male
- Allopatric collared male

But when choosing between allopatric males, females often mated with a male of the other species.

▲ **Figure 24.14 Reinforcement of barriers to reproduction in closely related species of European flycatchers.**

observed in a number of organisms, including fishes, insects, plants, and other birds.

Fusion: Weakening Reproductive Barriers

Next let's consider the case in which two species contact one another in a hybrid zone, but the barriers to reproduction are not strong. So much gene flow may occur that reproductive barriers weaken further and the gene pools of the two species become increasingly alike. In effect, the speciation process reverses, eventually causing the two hybridizing species to fuse into a single species.

Such a situation may be occurring among Lake Victoria cichlids. In the past 30 years, about 200 of the former 600 species of these cichlids have vanished. Some were driven to extinction by an introduced predator, the Nile perch. But many species not eaten by Nile perch also have disappeared— perhaps by species fusion. Many pairs of ecologically similar cichlid species are reproductively isolated because the females of one species prefer to mate with males of one color, while females of the other species prefer to mate with males of a different color (see Figure 24.11). Results from field and laboratory studies indicate that murky waters caused by pollution have hampered females in distinguishing males of their own species from males of closely related species. In some polluted waters, many hybrids have been produced, leading to fusion of the parent species' gene pools and a loss of species (Figure 24.15).

Pundamilia nyererei   *Pundamilia pundamilia*

Pundamilia "turbid water,"
hybrid offspring from a location
with turbid water

▲ **Figure 24.15 Fusion: The breakdown of reproductive barriers.** Increasingly cloudy water in Lake Victoria over the past 30 years may have weakened reproductive barriers between *P. nyererei* and *P. pundamilia*. In areas of cloudy water, the two species have hybridized extensively, causing their gene pools to fuse.

Stability: Continued Formation of Hybrid Individuals

Many hybrid zones are stable in the sense that hybrids continue to be produced. In some cases, this occurs because the hybrids survive or reproduce better than members of either parent species, at least in certain habitats or years. But stable hybrid zones have also been observed in cases where the hybrids are selected *against*—an unexpected result.

For example, hybrids continue to form in the *Bombina* hybrid zone even though they are strongly selected against. One explanation relates to the narrowness of the *Bombina* hybrid zone (see Figure 24.12). Evidence suggests that members of both parent species migrate into the zone from the parent populations located outside the zone, thus leading to the continued production of hybrids. If the hybrid zone were wider, this would be less likely to occur, since the center of the zone would receive little gene flow from distant parent populations located outside the hybrid zone.

Sometimes the outcomes in hybrid zones match our predictions (European flycatchers and cichlid fishes), and sometimes they don't (*Bombina*). But whether our predictions are upheld or not, events in hybrid zones can shed light on how barriers to reproduction between closely related species change over time. In the next section, we'll examine how interactions between hybridizing species can also provide a glimpse into the speed and genetic control of speciation.

CONCEPT CHECK 24.3

1. What are hybrid zones, and why can they be viewed as "natural laboratories" in which to study speciation?

2. **WHAT IF?** Consider two species that diverged while geographically separated but resumed contact before reproductive isolation was complete. Predict what would happen over time if the two species mated indiscriminately and (a) hybrid offspring survived and reproduced more poorly than offspring from intraspecific matings or (b) hybrid offspring survived and reproduced as well as offspring from intraspecific matings.

For suggested answers, see Appendix A.

CONCEPT 24.4

Speciation can occur rapidly or slowly and can result from changes in few or many genes

Darwin faced many questions when he began to ponder that "mystery of mysteries"—speciation. He found answers to some of those questions when he realized that evolution by natural selection helps explain both the diversity of life and the adaptations of organisms (see Concept 22.2). But biologists since Darwin have continued to ask fundamental questions about speciation. How long does it take for new species to form? And how many genes change when one species splits into two? Answers to these questions are also emerging.

The Time Course of Speciation

We can gather information about how long it takes new species to form from broad patterns in the fossil record and from studies that use morphological data (including fossils) or molecular data to assess the time interval between speciation events in particular groups of organisms.

Patterns in the Fossil Record

The fossil record includes many episodes in which new species appear suddenly in a geologic stratum, persist essentially unchanged through several strata, and then disappear. For example, there are dozens of species of marine invertebrates that make their debut in the fossil record with novel morphologies, but then change little for millions of years before becoming extinct. Paleontologists Niles Eldredge and Stephen Jay Gould coined the term **punctuated equilibria** to describe these periods of apparent stasis punctuated by sudden change (**Figure 24.16a**). Other species do not show a punctuated pattern; instead, they appear to have changed more gradually over long periods of time (**Figure 24.16b**).

What might punctuated and gradual patterns tell us about how long it takes new species to form? Suppose that a species survived for 5 million years, but most of the morphological changes that caused it to be designated a new species occurred during the first 50,000 years of its existence—just 1% of its total lifetime. Time periods this short (in geologic terms) often cannot be distinguished in fossil strata, in part because the rate of sediment accumulation may be too slow to separate layers this close in time. Thus, based on its fossils, the species would seem to have appeared suddenly and then lingered with little or no change before becoming extinct. Even though such a species may have originated more slowly than its fossils suggest (in this case taking up to 50,000 years), a punctuated pattern indicates that speciation occurred relatively rapidly. For species whose fossils changed much more gradually, we also cannot tell exactly when a new biological species formed, since information about reproductive isolation does not fossilize. However, it is likely that speciation in such groups occurred relatively slowly, perhaps taking millions of years.

Speciation Rates

The existence of fossils that display a punctuated pattern suggests that once the process of speciation begins, it can be completed relatively rapidly—a suggestion supported by a growing number of studies.

For example, rapid speciation appears to have produced the wild sunflower *Helianthus anomalus*. Genetic evidence indicates that this species originated by the hybridization of two other sunflower species, *H. annuus* and *H. petiolaris*. The hybrid species *H. anomalus* is ecologically distinct and reproductively isolated from both parent species (**Figure 24.17**). Unlike the outcome of allopolyploid speciation, in which there is a change in chromosome number after hybridization, in these sunflowers the two parent species and the hybrid all have the same number of chromosomes ($2n = 34$). How, then, did speciation occur? To study this question, researchers performed an experiment designed to mimic events in nature (**Figure 24.18**). Their results indicated that natural selection could produce extensive genetic changes in hybrid populations over short periods of time. These changes appear to have caused the hybrids to diverge reproductively from their parents and form a new species, *H. anomalus*.

The sunflower example, along with the apple maggot fly, Lake Victoria cichlid, and fruit fly examples discussed earlier, suggests that new species can arise rapidly *once divergence begins*. But what is the total length of time between speciation events? This interval consists of the time that elapses before populations of a newly formed species start to

(a) In a punctuated model, new species change most as they branch from a parent species and then change little for the rest of their existence.

Time

(b) In a gradual model, species diverge from one another more slowly and steadily over time.

▲ Figure 24.16 **Two models for the tempo of speciation.**

▲ **Figure 24.17 A hybrid sunflower species and its dry sand dune habitat.** The wild sunflower *Helianthus anomalus* originated via the hybridization of two other sunflowers, *H. annuus* and *H. petiolaris*, which live in nearby but moister environments.

diverge from one another plus the time it takes for speciation to be complete once divergence begins. It turns out that the total time between speciation events varies considerably. In a survey of data from 84 groups of plants and animals, speciation intervals ranged from 4,000 years (in cichlids of Lake Nabugabo, Uganda) to 40 million years (in some beetles). Overall, the time between speciation events averaged 6.5 million years and was rarely less than 500,000 years.

These data suggest that on average, millions of years may pass before a newly formed plant or animal species will itself give rise to another new species. As we'll see in Chapter 25, this finding has implications for how long it takes life on Earth to recover from mass extinction events. Moreover, the extreme variability in the time it takes new species to form indicates that organisms do not have an internal "speciation clock" causing them to produce new species at regular intervals. Instead, speciation begins only after gene flow between populations is interrupted, perhaps by changing environmental conditions or by unpredictable events, such as a storm that transports a few individuals to a new area. Furthermore, once gene flow is interrupted, the populations must diverge genetically to such an extent that they become reproductively isolated—all before other events cause gene flow to resume, possibly reversing the speciation process (see Figure 24.15).

Studying the Genetics of Speciation

Studies of ongoing speciation (as in hybrid zones) can reveal traits that cause reproductive isolation. By identifying the genes that control those traits, scientists can explore a fundamental question of evolutionary biology: How many genes influence the formation of new species?

In some cases, the evolution of reproductive isolation results from the effects of a single gene. For example, in Japanese snails of the genus *Euhadra*, a change in a single gene results in a mechanical barrier to reproduction. This gene controls the direction in which the shells spiral. When their shells spiral in different directions, the snails' genitalia

▼ **Figure 24.18** | Inquiry

How does hybridization lead to speciation in sunflowers?

Experiment Loren Rieseberg and his colleagues crossed the two parent sunflower species, *H. annuus* and *H. petiolaris*, to produce experimental hybrids in the laboratory (for each gamete, only two of the $n = 17$ chromosomes are shown).

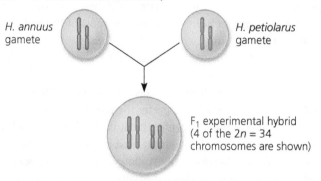

Note that in the first (F_1) generation, each chromosome of the experimental hybrids consisted entirely of DNA from one or the other parent species. The researchers then tested whether the F_1 and subsequent generations of experimental hybrids were fertile. They also used species-specific genetic markers to compare the chromosomes in the experimental hybrids with the chromosomes in the naturally occurring hybrid *H. anomalus*.

Results Although only 5% of the F_1 experimental hybrids were fertile, after just four more generations the hybrid fertility rose to more than 90%. The chromosomes of individuals from this fifth hybrid generation differed from those in the F_1 generation (see above) but were similar to those in *H. anomalus* individuals from natural populations:

▮ Comparison region containing *H. annuus*-specific marker
▮ Comparison region containing *H. petiolarus*-specific marker

Conclusion Over time, the chromosomes in the population of experimental hybrids became similar to the chromosomes of *H. anomalus* individuals from natural populations. This suggests that the observed rise in the fertility of the experimental hybrids may have occurred as selection eliminated regions of DNA from the parent species that were not compatible with one another. Overall, it appeared that the initial steps of the speciation process occurred rapidly and could be mimicked in a laboratory experiment.

Source: L. H. Rieseberg et al., Role of gene interactions in hybrid speciation: evidence from ancient and experimental hybrids, *Science* 272:741–745 (1996). Reprinted with permission from AAAS.

WHAT IF? *The increased fertility of the experimental hybrids could have resulted from natural selection for thriving under laboratory conditions. Evaluate this alternative explanation for the result.*

are oriented in a manner that prevents mating (Figure 24.3f shows a similar example). Recent genetic analyses have uncovered other single genes that cause reproductive isolation in fruit flies or mice.

A major barrier to reproduction between two closely related species of monkey flower, *Mimulus cardinalis* and *M. lewisii*, also appears to be influenced by a relatively small number of genes. These two species are isolated by several prezygotic and postzygotic barriers. Of these, one prezygotic barrier, pollinator choice, accounts for most of the isolation: In a hybrid zone between *M. cardinalis* and *M. lewisii*, nearly 98% of pollinator visits were restricted to one species or the other.

The two monkey flower species are visited by different pollinators: Hummingbirds prefer the red-flowered *M. cardinalis*, and bumblebees prefer the pink-flowered *M. lewisii*. Pollinator choice is affected by at least two loci in the monkey flowers, one of which, the "yellow upper," or *yup*, locus, influences flower color (**Figure 24.19**). By crossing the two parent species to produce F$_1$ hybrids and then performing repeated backcrosses of these F$_1$ hybrids to each parent species, researchers succeeded in transferring the *M. cardinalis* allele at this locus into *M. lewisii*, and vice versa. In a field experiment, *M. lewisii* plants with the *M. cardinalis yup* allele received 68-fold more visits from hummingbirds than did wild-type *M. lewisii*. Similarly, *M. cardinalis* plants with the *M. lewisii yup* allele received 74-fold more visits from bumblebees than did wild-type *M. cardinalis*. Thus, a mutation at a single locus can influence pollinator preference and hence contribute to reproductive isolation in monkey flowers.

In other organisms, the speciation process is influenced by larger numbers of genes and gene interactions. For example, hybrid sterility between two subspecies of the fruit fly *Drosophila pseudoobscura* results from gene interactions among at least four loci, and postzygotic isolation in the sunflower hybrid zone discussed earlier is influenced by at least 26 chromosome segments (and an unknown number of genes). Overall, studies suggest that few or many genes can influence the evolution of reproductive isolation and hence the emergence of a new species.

From Speciation to Macroevolution

As you've seen, speciation may begin with differences as small as the color on a cichlid's back. However, as speciation occurs again and again, such differences can accumulate and become more pronounced, eventually leading to the formation of new groups of organisms that differ greatly from their ancestors (as in the origin of whales from terrestrial mammals; see Figure 22.20). Moreover, as one group of organisms increases in size by producing many new species, another group of organisms may shrink, losing species to extinction. The cumulative effects of many such speciation and extinction events have helped shape the sweeping

(a) Typical *Mimulus lewisii*   **(b) *M. lewisii* with an *M. cardinalis* flower-color allele**

(c) Typical *Mimulus cardinalis*   **(d) *M. cardinalis* with an *M. lewisii* flower-color allele**

▲ **Figure 24.19 A locus that influences pollinator choice.** Pollinator preferences provide a strong barrier to reproduction between *Mimulus lewisii* and *M. cardinalis*. After transferring the *M. lewisii* allele for a flower-color locus into *M. cardinalis* and vice versa, researchers observed a shift in some pollinators' preferences.

WHAT IF? *If* M. cardinalis *individuals that had the* M. lewisii yup *allele were planted in an area that housed both monkey flower species, how might the production of hybrid offspring be affected?*

evolutionary changes that are documented in the fossil record. In the next chapter, we turn to such large-scale evolutionary changes as we begin our study of macroevolution.

CONCEPT CHECK **24.4**

1. Speciation can occur rapidly between diverging populations, yet the time between speciation events is often more than a million years. Explain this apparent contradiction.

2. Summarize evidence that the *yup* locus acts as a prezygotic barrier to reproduction in two species of monkey flowers. Do these results demonstrate that the *yup* locus alone controls barriers to reproduction between these species? Explain.

3. **MAKE CONNECTIONS** Compare Figure 13.11 with Figure 24.18. What cellular process could cause the hybrid chromosomes in Figure 24.18 to contain DNA from both parent species? Explain.

For suggested answers, see Appendix A.

SUMMARY OF KEY CONCEPTS

CONCEPT 24.1

The biological species concept emphasizes reproductive isolation (pp. 501–505)

- A biological **species** is a group of populations whose individuals may interbreed and produce viable, fertile offspring with each other but not with members of other species. The **biological species concept** emphasizes reproductive isolation through prezygotic and postzygotic barriers that separate gene pools.
- Although helpful in thinking about how speciation occurs, the biological species concept has limitations. For instance, it cannot be applied to organisms known only as fossils or to organisms that reproduce only asexually. Thus, scientists use other species concepts, such as the **morphological species concept**, in certain circumstances.

? *Explain the role of gene flow in the biological species concept.*

CONCEPT 24.2

Speciation can take place with or without geographic separation (pp. 505–510)

- In **allopatric speciation**, gene flow is reduced when two populations of one species become geographically separated from each other. One or both populations may undergo evolutionary change during the period of separation, resulting in the establishment of prezygotic or postzygotic barriers to reproduction.
- In **sympatric speciation**, a new species originates while remaining in the same geographic area as the parent species. Plant species (and, more rarely, animal species) have evolved sympatrically through polyploidy. Sympatric speciation can also result from sexual selection and habitat shifts.

Original population

Allopatric speciation   Sympatric speciation

? *Can factors that cause sympatric speciation also cause allopatric speciation? Explain.*

CONCEPT 24.3

Hybrid zones reveal factors that cause reproductive isolation (pp. 510–513)

- Many groups of organisms form **hybrid zones** in which members of different species meet and mate, producing at least some offspring of mixed ancestry.

- Many hybrid zones are *stable*, in that hybrid offspring continue to be produced over time. In others, **reinforcement** strengthens prezygotic barriers to reproduction, thus decreasing the formation of unfit hybrids. In still other hybrid zones, barriers to reproduction may weaken over time, resulting in the *fusion* of the species' gene pools (reversing the speciation process).

? *What factors can support the long-term stability of a hybrid zone if the parent species live in different environments?*

CONCEPT 24.4

Speciation can occur rapidly or slowly and can result from changes in few or many genes (pp. 513–516)

- New species can form rapidly once divergence begins—but it can take millions of years for that to happen. The time interval between speciation events varies considerably, from a few thousand years to tens of millions of years.
- New developments in genetics have enabled researchers to identify specific genes involved in some cases of speciation. Results show that speciation can be driven by few or many genes.

? *Is speciation something that happened only in the distant past, or are new species continuing to arise today? Explain.*

TEST YOUR UNDERSTANDING

LEVEL 1: KNOWLEDGE/COMPREHENSION

1. The *largest* unit within which gene flow can readily occur is a
   a. population.
   c. genus.
   b. species.
   d. hybrid.

2. Males of different species of the fruit fly *Drosophila* that live in the same parts of the Hawaiian Islands have different elaborate courtship rituals. These rituals involve fighting other males and making stylized movements that attract females. What type of reproductive isolation does this represent?
   a. habitat isolation
   b. temporal isolation
   c. behavioral isolation
   d. gametic isolation

3. According to the punctuated equilibria model,
   a. given enough time, most existing species will branch gradually into new species.
   b. most new species accumulate their unique features relatively rapidly as they come into existence, then change little for the rest of their duration as a species.
   c. most evolution occurs in sympatric populations.
   d. speciation is usually due to a single mutation.

LEVEL 2: APPLICATION/ANALYSIS

4. Bird guides once listed the myrtle warbler and Audubon's warbler as distinct species. Recently, these birds have been classified as eastern and western forms of a single species, the yellow-rumped warbler. Which of the following pieces of evidence, if true, would be cause for this reclassification?
   a. The two forms interbreed often in nature, and their offspring survive and reproduce well.
   b. The two forms live in similar habitats and have similar food requirements.
   c. The two forms have many genes in common.
   d. The two forms are very similar in appearance.

5. Which of the following factors would *not* contribute to allopatric speciation?
   a. The separated population is small, and genetic drift occurs.
   b. The isolated population is exposed to different selection pressures than the ancestral population.
   c. Different mutations begin to distinguish the gene pools of the separated populations.
   d. Gene flow between the two populations is extensive.

6. Plant species A has a diploid chromosome number of 12. Plant species B has a diploid number of 16. A new species, C, arises as an allopolyploid from A and B. The diploid number for species C would probably be
   a. 14.   b. 16.   c. 28.   d. 56.

LEVEL 3: SYNTHESIS/EVALUATION

7. Suppose that a group of male pied flycatchers migrated from a region where there were no collared flycatchers to a region where both species were present (see Figure 24.14). Assuming events like this are very rare, which of the following scenarios is *least* likely?
   a. The frequency of hybrid offspring would increase.
   b. Migrant pied males would produce fewer offspring than would resident pied males.
   c. Migrant males would mate with collared females more often than with pied females.
   d. The frequency of hybrid offspring would decrease.

8. **SCIENTIFIC INQUIRY**
   DRAW IT In this chapter, you read that bread wheat (*Triticum aestivum*) is an allohexaploid, containing two sets of chromosomes from each of three different parent species. Genetic analysis suggests that the three species pictured following this question each contributed chromosome sets to *T. aestivum*. (The capital letters here represent sets of chromosomes rather than individual genes, and the diploid chromosome number for each species is shown in parentheses.) Evidence also indicates that the first polyploidy event was a spontaneous hybridization of the early cultivated wheat species *T. monococcum* and a wild *Triticum* grass species. Based on this information, draw a diagram of one possible chain of events that could have produced the allohexaploid *T. aestivum*.

Ancestral species:

AA

Triticum monococcum (14)

BB

Wild *Triticum* (14)

DD

Wild *T. tauschii* (14)

Product:

AA BB DD

T. aestivum (bread wheat) (42)

9. **EVOLUTION CONNECTION**
   What is the biological basis for assigning all human populations to a single species? Can you think of a scenario by which a second human species could originate in the future?

10. **SCIENCE, TECHNOLOGY, AND SOCIETY**
    In the United States, the rare red wolf (*Canis lupus*) has been known to hybridize with coyotes (*Canis latrans*), which are much more numerous. Although red wolves and coyotes differ in terms of morphology, DNA, and behavior, genetic evidence suggests that living red wolf individuals are actually hybrids. Red wolves are designated as an endangered species and hence receive legal protection under the Endangered Species Act. Some people think that their endangered status should be withdrawn because the remaining red wolves are hybrids, not members of a "pure" species. Do you agree? Why or why not?

11. **WRITE ABOUT A THEME: INFORMATION**
    In sexually reproducing species, each individual begins life with DNA inherited from both parent organisms. In a short essay (100–150 words), apply this idea to what occurs when organisms of two species that have homologous chromosomes mate and produce (F_1) hybrid offspring. What percentage of the DNA in the F_1 hybrids' chromosomes comes from each parent species? As the hybrids mate and produce F_2 and later-generation hybrid offspring, describe how recombination and natural selection may affect whether the DNA in hybrid chromosomes is derived from one parent species or the other.

12. **SYNTHESIZE YOUR KNOWLEDGE**

Suppose that females of one population of strawberry poison dart frogs (*Dendrobates pumilio*) prefer to mate with males that have a bright red and black coloration. In a different population, the females prefer males with yellow skin. Propose a hypothesis to explain how such differences could have arisen in allopatric versus sympatric populations.

For selected answers, see Appendix A.

MasteringBiology®

Students Go to **MasteringBiology** for assignments, the eText, and the Study Area with practice tests, animations, and activities.

Instructors Go to **MasteringBiology** for automatically graded tutorials and questions that you can assign to your students, plus Instructor Resources.

25

The History of Life on Earth

KEY CONCEPTS

25.1 Conditions on early Earth made the origin of life possible

25.2 The fossil record documents the history of life

25.3 Key events in life's history include the origins of unicellular and multicellular organisms and the colonization of land

25.4 The rise and fall of groups of organisms reflect differences in speciation and extinction rates

25.5 Major changes in body form can result from changes in the sequences and regulation of developmental genes

25.6 Evolution is not goal oriented

◀ *Cryolophosaurus skull*

▲ **Figure 25.1 On what continent did these dinosaurs roam?**

Lost Worlds

Early Antarctic explorers encountered one of Earth's harshest, most barren environments, a land of extreme cold and almost no liquid water. Antarctic life is sparse and small—the largest fully terrestrial animal is a fly 5 mm long. But even as they struggled to survive, some of these explorers made an astonishing discovery: fossil evidence that life once thrived where it now barely exists. Fossils reveal that 500 million years ago, the ocean around Antarctica was warm and teeming with tropical invertebrates. Later, the continent was covered in forests for hundreds of millions of years. At various times, diverse animals stalked through these forests, including 3-m-tall predatory "terror birds" and giant dinosaurs such as the voracious *Cryolophosaurus* (**Figure 25.1**), a 7-m-long relative of *Tyrannosaurus rex*.

Fossils discovered in other parts of the world tell a similar story: Past organisms were very different from those presently living. The sweeping changes in life on Earth as revealed by fossils illustrate **macroevolution**, the broad pattern of evolution above the species level. Examples of macroevolutionary change include the emergence of terrestrial vertebrates through a series of speciation events, the impact of mass extinctions on biodiversity, and the origin of key adaptations such as flight.

Taken together, such changes provide a grand view of the evolutionary history of life. We'll begin by examining hypotheses regarding the origin of life. This is the most speculative topic of the entire unit, for no fossil evidence of that seminal

519

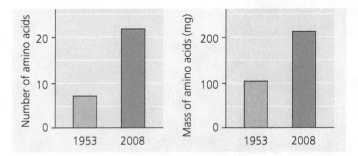

▲ **Figure 25.2 Amino acid synthesis in a simulated volcanic eruption.** In addition to his classic 1953 study, Miller also conducted an experiment simulating a volcanic eruption. In a 2008 reanalysis of those results, researchers found that far more amino acids were produced under simulated volcanic conditions than were produced in the conditions of the original 1953 experiment.

MAKE CONNECTIONS *How could more than 20 amino acids have been produced in the 2008 experiment? (See Concept 5.4.)*

CONCEPT 25.1

Conditions on early Earth made the origin of life possible

Direct evidence of life on early Earth comes from fossils of microorganisms that lived 3.5 billion years ago. But how did the first living cells appear? Observations and experiments in chemistry, geology, and physics have led scientists to propose one scenario that we'll examine here. They hypothesize that chemical and physical processes could have produced simple cells through a sequence of four main stages:

1. The abiotic (nonliving) synthesis of small organic molecules, such as amino acids and nitrogenous bases
2. The joining of these small molecules into macromolecules, such as proteins and nucleic acids
3. The packaging of these molecules into **protocells**, droplets with membranes that maintained an internal chemistry different from that of their surroundings
4. The origin of self-replicating molecules that eventually made inheritance possible

Though speculative, this scenario leads to predictions that can be tested in the laboratory. In this section, we'll examine some of the evidence for each stage.

Synthesis of Organic Compounds on Early Earth

Our planet formed 4.6 billion years ago, condensing from a vast cloud of dust and rocks that surrounded the young sun. For its first few hundred million years, Earth was bombarded by huge chunks of rock and ice left over from the formation of the solar system. The collisions generated so much heat that all of the available water was vaporized, preventing the formation of seas and lakes.

This massive bombardment ended about 4 billion years ago, setting the stage for the origin of life on our young planet. The first atmosphere had little oxygen and was probably thick with water vapor, along with various compounds released by volcanic eruptions, including nitrogen and its oxides, carbon dioxide, methane, ammonia, and hydrogen. As Earth cooled, the water vapor condensed into oceans, and much of the hydrogen escaped into space.

During the 1920s, Russian chemist A. I. Oparin and British scientist J. B. S. Haldane independently hypothesized that Earth's early atmosphere was a reducing (electron-adding) environment, in which organic compounds could have formed from simpler molecules. The energy for this synthesis could have come from lightning and UV radiation.

Haldane suggested that the early oceans were a solution of organic molecules, a "primitive soup" from which life arose.

In 1953, Stanley Miller, working with Harold Urey at the University of Chicago, tested the Oparin-Haldane hypothesis by creating laboratory conditions comparable to those that scientists at the time thought existed on early Earth (see Figure 4.2). His apparatus yielded a variety of amino acids found in organisms today, along with other organic compounds. Many laboratories have since repeated Miller's classic experiment using different recipes for the atmosphere, some of which also produced organic compounds.

However, some evidence suggests that the early atmosphere was made up primarily of nitrogen and carbon dioxide and was neither reducing nor oxidizing (electron removing). Recent Miller-Urey-type experiments using such "neutral" atmospheres have also produced organic molecules. In addition, small pockets of the early atmosphere, such as those near the openings of volcanoes, may have been reducing. Perhaps the first organic compounds formed near volcanoes. In a 2008 test of this hypothesis, researchers used modern equipment to reanalyze molecules that Miller had saved from one of his experiments. The 2008 study found that numerous amino acids had formed under conditions that simulated a volcanic eruption (**Figure 25.2**).

Another hypothesis is that organic compounds were first produced in deep-sea **hydrothermal vents**, areas on the seafloor where heated water and minerals gush from Earth's interior into the ocean. Some of these vents, known as "black smokers," release water so hot (300–400°C) that organic compounds formed there may have been unstable. But other deep-sea vents, called **alkaline vents**, release water that has a high pH (9–11) and is warm (40–90°C) rather than hot, an environment that may have been more suitable for the origin of life (**Figure 25.3**).

Studies related to the volcanic-atmosphere and alkaline-vent hypotheses show that the abiotic synthesis of organic molecules is possible under various conditions. Another

◀ **Figure 25.3 Did life originate in deep-sea alkaline vents?** The first organic compounds—and indeed, the first cells—may have arisen in warm alkaline vents similar to this one from the 40,000-year-old "Lost City" vent field in the mid-Atlantic Ocean. These vents contain hydrocarbons and are full of tiny pores (inset) lined with iron and other catalytic minerals. Early oceans were acidic, and so a pH gradient would have formed between the interior of the vents and the surrounding ocean water. Energy for the synthesis of organic compounds could have been harnessed from this pH gradient.

source of organic molecules may have been meteorites. For example, fragments of the Murchison meteorite, a 4.5-billion-year-old rock that landed in Australia in 1969, contain more than 80 amino acids, some in large amounts. These amino acids cannot be contaminants from Earth because they consist of an equal mix of D and L isomers (see Chapter 4). Organisms make and use only L isomers, with a few rare exceptions. Recent studies have shown that the Murchison meteorite also contained other key organic molecules, including lipids, simple sugars, and nitrogenous bases such as uracil.

Abiotic Synthesis of Macromolecules

The presence of small organic molecules, such as amino acids and nitrogenous bases, is not sufficient for the emergence of life as we know it. Every cell has many types of macromolecules, including enzymes and other proteins and the nucleic acids needed for self-replication. Could such macromolecules have formed on early Earth? A 2009 study demonstrated that one key step, the abiotic synthesis of RNA monomers, can occur spontaneously from simple precursor molecules. In addition, by dripping solutions of amino acids or RNA nucleotides onto hot sand, clay, or rock, researchers have produced polymers of these molecules. The polymers formed spontaneously, without the help of enzymes or ribosomes. Unlike proteins, the amino acid polymers are a complex mix of linked and cross-linked amino acids. Still, it is possible that such polymers acted as weak catalysts for a variety of chemical reactions on early Earth.

Protocells

All organisms must be able to carry out both reproduction and energy processing (metabolism). DNA molecules carry genetic information, including the instructions needed to replicate themselves accurately during reproduction. But DNA replication requires elaborate enzymatic machinery, along with an abundant supply of nucleotide building blocks provided by the cell's metabolism. This suggests that self-replicating molecules and a metabolism-like source of building blocks may have appeared together in early protocells. The necessary conditions may have been met in *vesicles*, fluid-filled compartments enclosed by a membrane-like structure. Recent experiments show that abiotically produced vesicles can exhibit certain properties of life, including simple reproduction and metabolism, as well as the maintenance of an internal chemical environment different from that of their surroundings (**Figure 25.4**).

For example, vesicles can form spontaneously when lipids or other organic molecules are added to water. When this occurs, the hydrophobic molecules in the mixture organize into a bilayer similar to the lipid bilayer of a plasma membrane. Adding substances such as *montmorillonite*, a soft mineral clay produced by the weathering of volcanic ash, greatly increases the rate of vesicle self-assembly (see Figure 25.4a). This clay, which is thought to have been common on early Earth, provides surfaces on which organic molecules become concentrated, increasing the likelihood that the molecules will react with each other and form vesicles. Abiotically produced vesicles can "reproduce" on their own (see Figure 25.4b), and

© 2003 AAAS

(a) Self-assembly. The presence of montmorillonite clay greatly increases the rate of vesicle self-assembly.

(b) Reproduction. Vesicles can divide on their own, as in this vesicle "giving birth" to smaller vesicles (LM).

(c) Absorption of RNA. This vesicle has incorporated montmorillonite clay particles coated with RNA (orange).

▲ **Figure 25.4 Features of abiotically produced vesicles.**

they can increase in size ("grow") without dilution of their contents. Vesicles also can absorb montmorillonite particles, including those on which RNA and other organic molecules have become attached (see Figure 25.4c). Finally, experiments have shown that some vesicles have a selectively permeable bilayer and can perform metabolic reactions using an external source of reagents—another important prerequisite for life.

Self-Replicating RNA

The first genetic material was most likely RNA, not DNA. RNA plays a central role in protein synthesis, but it can also function as an enzyme-like catalyst (see Chapter 17). Such RNA catalysts are called **ribozymes**. Some ribozymes can make complementary copies of short pieces of RNA, provided that they are supplied with nucleotide building blocks.

Natural selection on the molecular level has produced ribozymes capable of self-replication in the laboratory. How does this occur? Unlike double-stranded DNA, which takes the form of a uniform helix, single-stranded RNA molecules assume a variety of specific three-dimensional shapes mandated by their nucleotide sequences. In a particular environment, RNA molecules with certain nucleotide sequences may have shapes that enable them to replicate faster and with fewer errors than other sequences. The RNA molecule with the greatest ability to replicate itself will leave the most descendant molecules. Occasionally, a copying error will result in a molecule with a shape that is even more adept at self-replication than the ancestral sequence. Similar selection events may have occurred on early Earth. Thus, life as we know it may have been preceded by an "RNA world," in which small RNA molecules were able to replicate and to store genetic information about the vesicles that carried them.

A vesicle with self-replicating, catalytic RNA would differ from its many neighbors that lacked such molecules. If that vesicle could grow, split, and pass its RNA molecules to its daughters, the daughters would be protocells. Although the first such protocells likely carried only limited amounts of genetic information, specifying only a few properties, their inherited characteristics could have been acted on by natural selection. The most successful of the early protocells would have increased in number because they could exploit their resources effectively and pass their abilities on to subsequent generations.

Once RNA sequences that carried genetic information appeared in protocells, many additional changes would have been possible. For example, RNA could have provided the template on which DNA nucleotides were assembled. Double-stranded DNA is a more chemically stable repository for genetic information than is the more fragile RNA. DNA also can be replicated more accurately. Accurate replication was advantageous as genomes grew larger through gene duplication and other processes and as more properties of the protocells became coded in genetic information. Once DNA appeared, the stage was set for a blossoming of new forms of life—a change we see documented in the fossil record.

CONCEPT 25.2

The fossil record documents the history of life

Starting with the earliest traces of life, the fossil record opens a window into the world of long ago and provides glimpses of the evolution of life over billions of years. In this section, we'll examine fossils as a form of scientific evidence: how fossils form, how scientists date and interpret them, and what they can and cannot tell us about changes in the history of life.

The Fossil Record

Sedimentary rocks are the richest source of fossils. As a result, the fossil record is based primarily on the sequence in which fossils have accumulated in sedimentary rock layers, called *strata* (see Figure 22.3). Useful information is also provided by other types of fossils, such as insects preserved in amber (fossilized tree sap) and mammals frozen in ice.

The fossil record shows that there have been great changes in the kinds of organisms on Earth at different points in time **(Figure 25.5)**. Many past organisms were unlike organisms living today, and many organisms that once were common are now extinct. As we'll see later in this section, fossils also document how new groups of organisms arose from previously existing ones.

As substantial and significant as the fossil record is, keep in mind that it is an incomplete chronicle of evolutionary change. Many of Earth's organisms did not die in the right place at the right time to be preserved as fossils. Of those fossils that were formed, many were destroyed by later geologic processes, and only a fraction of the others have been discovered. As a result, the known fossil record is biased in favor of species that existed for a long time, were abundant and widespread in certain kinds of environments, and had hard shells, skeletons, or other parts that facilitated their

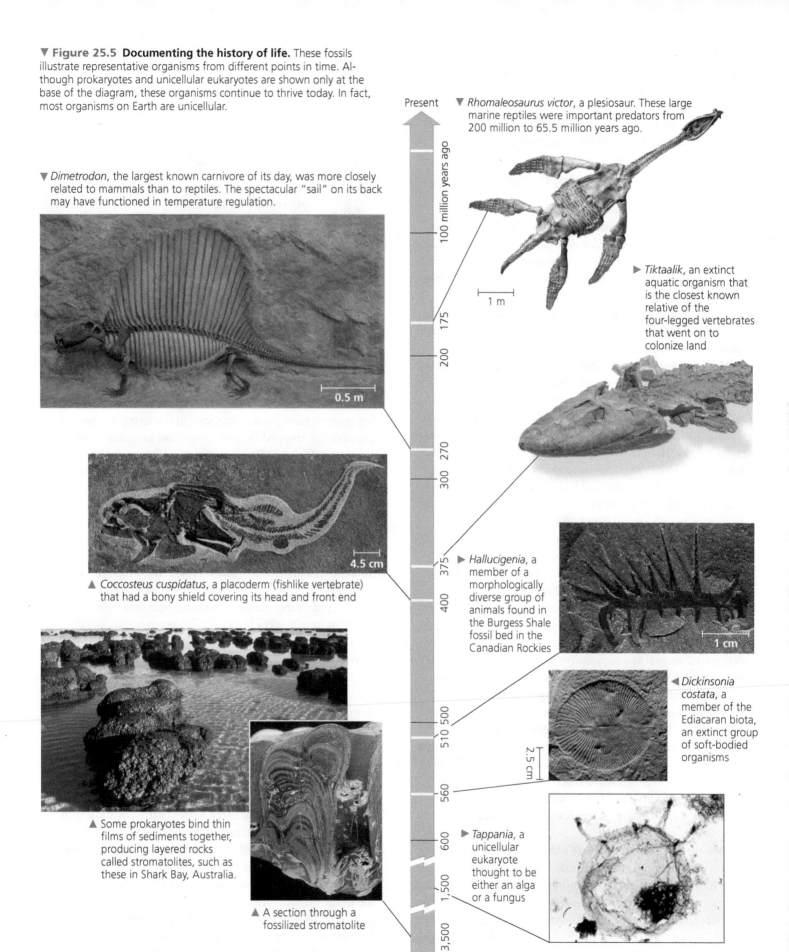

▼ **Figure 25.5 Documenting the history of life.** These fossils illustrate representative organisms from different points in time. Although prokaryotes and unicellular eukaryotes are shown only at the base of the diagram, these organisms continue to thrive today. In fact, most organisms on Earth are unicellular.

▼ *Dimetrodon*, the largest known carnivore of its day, was more closely related to mammals than to reptiles. The spectacular "sail" on its back may have functioned in temperature regulation.

0.5 m

Present

100 million years ago

175

200

270

300

375

400

500

510

560

600

1,500

3,500

▲ *Coccosteus cuspidatus*, a placoderm (fishlike vertebrate) that had a bony shield covering its head and front end

4.5 cm

▲ Some prokaryotes bind thin films of sediments together, producing layered rocks called stromatolites, such as these in Shark Bay, Australia.

▲ A section through a fossilized stromatolite

▼ *Rhomaleosaurus victor*, a plesiosaur. These large marine reptiles were important predators from 200 million to 65.5 million years ago.

1 m

▶ *Tiktaalik*, an extinct aquatic organism that is the closest known relative of the four-legged vertebrates that went on to colonize land

▶ *Hallucigenia*, a member of a morphologically diverse group of animals found in the Burgess Shale fossil bed in the Canadian Rockies

1 cm

◀ *Dickinsonia costata*, a member of the Ediacaran biota, an extinct group of soft-bodied organisms

2.5 cm

▶ *Tappania*, a unicellular eukaryote thought to be either an alga or a fungus fossilization. Even with its limitations, however, the fossil record is a remarkably detailed account of biological change over the vast scale of geologic time. Furthermore, as shown by the recently unearthed fossils of whale ancestors with hind limbs (see Figures 22.19 and 22.20), gaps in the fossil record continue to be filled by new discoveries.

How Rocks and Fossils Are Dated

Fossils are valuable data for reconstructing the history of life, but only if we can determine where they fit in that unfolding story. While the order of fossils in rock strata tells us the sequence in which the fossils were laid down—their relative ages—it does not tell us their actual (absolute) ages. Examining the relative positions of fossils is like peeling off layers of wallpaper in an old house. You can infer the sequence in which the layers were applied, but not the year each layer was added.

How can we determine the absolute age of a fossil? (Note that "absolute" does not mean errorless, but that an age is given in years rather than relative terms such as *before* and *after*.) One of the most common techniques is **radiometric dating**, which is based on the decay of radioactive isotopes (see Chapter 2). In this process, a radioactive "parent" isotope decays to a "daughter" isotope at a characteristic rate. The rate of decay is expressed by the **half-life**, the time required for 50% of the parent isotope to decay **(Figure 25.6)**. Each type of radioactive isotope has a characteristic half-life, which is not affected by temperature, pressure, or other environmental variables. For example, carbon-14 decays relatively quickly; its half-life is 5,730 years. Uranium-238 decays slowly; its half-life is 4.5 billion years.

Fossils contain isotopes of elements that accumulated in the organisms when they were alive. For example, a living organism contains the most common carbon isotope, carbon-12, as well as a radioactive isotope, carbon-14. When the organism dies, it stops accumulating carbon, and the amount of carbon-12 in its tissues does not change over time. However, the carbon-14 that it contains at the time of death slowly decays into another element, nitrogen-14. Thus, by measuring the ratio of carbon-14 to carbon-12 in a fossil, we can determine the fossil's age. This method works for fossils up to about 75,000 years old; fossils older than that contain too little carbon-14 to be detected with current techniques. Radioactive isotopes with longer half-lives are used to date older fossils.

Determining the age of these older fossils in sedimentary rocks is challenging. Organisms do not use radioisotopes with long half-lives, such as uranium-238, to build their bones or shells. In addition, the sedimentary rocks themselves tend to consist of sediments of differing ages. So while we may not be able to date these older fossils directly, an indirect method can be used to infer the age of fossils that are sandwiched between two layers of volcanic rock. As lava

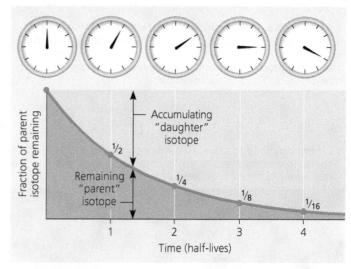

© Pearson Education, Inc.

▲ **Figure 25.6 Radiometric dating.** In this diagram, each division of the clock face represents a half-life.

DRAW IT *Relabel the x-axis of this graph in years to illustrate the radioactive decay of uranium-238 (half-life = 4.5 billion years).*

cools into volcanic rock, radioisotopes from the surrounding environment become trapped in the newly formed rock. Some of the trapped radioisotopes have long half-lives, allowing geologists to estimate the ages of ancient volcanic rocks. If two volcanic layers surrounding fossils are determined to be 525 million and 535 million years old, for example, then the fossils are roughly 530 million years old.

The Origin of New Groups of Organisms

Some fossils provide a detailed look at the origin of new groups of organisms. Such fossils are central to our understanding of evolution; they illustrate how new features arise and how long it takes for such changes to occur. We'll examine one such case here: the origin of mammals.

Along with amphibians and reptiles, mammals belong to the group of animals called *tetrapods* (from the Greek *tetra*, four, and *pod*, foot), named for having four limbs. Mammals have a number of unique anatomical features that fossilize readily, allowing scientists to trace their origin. For example, the lower jaw is composed of one bone (the dentary) in mammals but several bones in other tetrapods. In addition, the lower and upper jaws in mammals hinge between a different set of bones than in other tetrapods. Mammals also have a unique set of three bones that transmit sound in the middle ear, the hammer, anvil, and stirrup, whereas other tetrapods have only one such bone, the stirrup (see Chapter 34). Finally, the teeth of mammals are differentiated into incisors (for tearing), canines (for piercing), and the multi-pointed premolars and molars (for crushing and grinding). In contrast, the teeth of other tetrapods usually consist of a row of undifferentiated, single-pointed teeth.

As detailed in **Figure 25.7**, the fossil record shows that the unique features of mammalian jaws and teeth evolved

Exploring The Origin of Mammals

Over the course of 120 million years, mammals originated gradually from a group of tetrapods called synapsids. Shown here are a few of the many fossil organisms whose morphological features represent intermediate steps between living mammals and their synapsid ancestors. The evolutionary context of the origin of mammals is shown in the tree diagram at right (the dagger symbol † indicates extinct lineages).

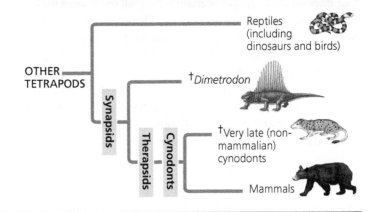

Key to skull bones

▨ Articular	▨ Dentary
▨ Quadrate	▨ Squamosal

Synapsid (300 mya)

Synapsids had multiple bones in the lower jaw and single-pointed teeth. The jaw hinge was formed by the articular and quadrate bones. Synapsids also had an opening called the temporal fenestra behind the eye socket. Powerful cheek muscles for closing the jaws probably passed through the temporal fenestra. Over time, this opening enlarged and moved in front of the hinge between the lower and upper jaws, thereby increasing the power and precision with which the jaws could be closed (much as moving a doorknob away from the hinge makes a door easier to close).

Therapsid (280 mya)

Later, a group of synapsids called therapsids appeared. Therapsids had large dentary bones, long faces, and the first examples of specialized teeth, large canines. These trends continued in a group of therapsids called cynodonts.

Early cynodont (260 mya)

In early cynodont therapsids, the dentary was the largest bone in the lower jaw, the temporal fenestra was large and positioned forward of the jaw hinge, and teeth with several cusps first appeared (not visible in the diagram). As in earlier synapsids, the jaw had an articular-quadrate hinge.

Later cynodont (220 mya)

Later cynodonts had teeth with complex cusp patterns and their lower and upper jaws hinged in two locations: They retained the original articular-quadrate hinge and formed a new, second hinge between the dentary and squamosal bones. (The temporal fenestra is not visible in this or the below cynodont skull at the angles shown.)

Very late cynodont (195 mya)

In some very late (non-mammalian) cynodonts and early mammals, the original articular-quadrate hinge was lost, leaving the dentary-squamosal hinge as the only hinge between the lower and upper jaws, as in living mammals. The articular and quadrate bones migrated into the ear region (not shown), where they functioned in transmitting sound. In the mammal lineage, these two bones later evolved into the familiar hammer (malleus) and anvil (incus) bones of the ear.

© 2001 AAAS

gradually over time, in a series of steps. As you study , bear in mind that it includes just a few examples of the fossil skulls that document the origin of mammals. If all the known fossils in the sequence were arranged by shape and placed side by side, their features would blend smoothly from one group to the next. Some of these fossils would reflect how the features of a group that dominates life today, the mammals, gradually arose in a previously existing group, the cynodonts. Others would reveal side branches on the tree of life—groups of organisms that thrived for millions of years but ultimately left no descendants that survive today.

CONCEPT CHECK 25.2

1. Your measurements indicate that a fossilized skull you unearthed has a carbon-14/carbon-12 ratio about $1/16$ that of the skulls of present-day animals. What is the approximate age of the fossilized skull?

2. Describe an example from the fossil record that shows how life has changed over time.

3. **WHAT IF?** Suppose researchers discover a fossil of an organism that lived 300 million years ago but had mammalian teeth and a mammalian jaw hinge. What inferences might you draw from this fossil about the origin of mammals and the evolution of novel skeletal structures? Explain.

For suggested answers, see Appendix A.

CONCEPT 25.3

Key events in life's history include the origins of unicellular and multicellular organisms and the colonization of land

The study of fossils has helped geologists establish a **geologic record**: a standard time scale that divides Earth's history into four eons and further subdivisions (Table 25.1). The first three eons—the Hadean, Archaean, and Proterozoic—together lasted about 4 billion years. The Phanerozoic eon, roughly the last half billion years, encompasses most of the time that animals have existed on Earth. It is divided into three eras: the Paleozoic, Mesozoic, and Cenozoic. Each era represents a distinct age in the history of Earth and its life. For example, the Mesozoic era is sometimes called the "age of reptiles" because of its abundance of reptilian fossils, including those of dinosaurs. The boundaries between the eras correspond to major extinction events seen in the fossil record, when many forms of life disappeared and were replaced by forms that evolved from the survivors.

As we've seen, the fossil record provides a sweeping overview of the history of life over geologic time. Here we will focus on a few major events in that history, returning to study the details in Unit Five.

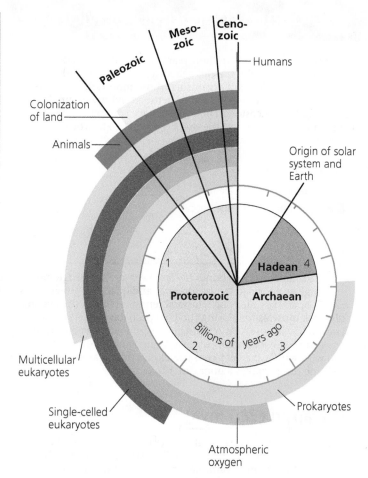

▲ **Figure 25.8 Clock analogy for some key events in Earth's history.** The clock ticks down from the origin of Earth 4.6 billion years ago to the present.

Figure 25.8 uses the analogy of a clock to place these events in the context of the geologic record. This clock will reappear at various points in this section as a quick visual reminder of when the events we are discussing took place.

The First Single-Celled Organisms

The earliest direct evidence of life, dating from 3.5 billion years ago, comes from fossilized stromatolites (see Figure 25.5). **Stromatolites** are layered rocks that form when certain prokaryotes bind thin films of sediment together. Present-day stromatolites are found in a few shallow marine bays. Stromatolites and other early prokaryotes were Earth's sole inhabitants for more than 1.5 billion years. As we will see, these prokaryotes transformed life on our planet.

Table 25.1 The Geologic Record

Relative Duration of Eons	Era	Period	Epoch	Age (Millions of Years Ago)	Some Important Events in the History of Life
Phanerozoic	Cenozoic	Quaternary	Holocene		Historical time
				0.01	
			Pleistocene		Ice ages; origin of genus *Homo*
				2.6	
		Neogene	Pliocene		Appearance of bipedal human ancestors
				5.3	
			Miocene		Continued radiation of mammals and angiosperms; earliest direct human ancestors
				23	
		Paleogene	Oligocene		Origins of many primate groups
				33.9	
			Eocene		Angiosperm dominance increases; continued radiation of most present-day mammalian orders
				55.8	
			Paleocene		Major radiation of mammals, birds, and pollinating insects
				65.5	
	Mesozoic	Cretaceous			Flowering plants (angiosperms) appear and diversify; many groups of organisms, including most dinosaurs, become extinct at end of period
				145.5	
		Jurassic			Gymnosperms continue as dominant plants; dinosaurs abundant and diverse
				199.6	
		Triassic			Cone-bearing plants (gymnosperms) dominate landscape; dinosaurs evolve and radiate; origin of mammals
				251	
	Paleozoic	Permian			Radiation of reptiles; origin of most present-day groups of insects; extinction of many marine and terrestrial organisms at end of period
				299	
		Carboniferous			Extensive forests of vascular plants form; first seed plants appear; origin of reptiles; amphibians dominant
				359	
		Devonian			Diversification of bony fishes; first tetrapods and insects appear
				416	
		Silurian			Diversification of early vascular plants
				444	
		Ordovician			Marine algae abundant; colonization of land by diverse fungi, plants, and animals
				488	
		Cambrian			Sudden increase in diversity of many animal phyla (Cambrian explosion)
				542	
Proterozoic		Ediacaran			Diverse algae and soft-bodied invertebrate animals appear
				635	
				1,800	Oldest fossils of eukaryotic cells appear
				2,500	
				2,700	Concentration of atmospheric oxygen begins to increase
Archaean				3,500	Oldest fossils of cells (prokaryotes) appear
				3,850	Oldest known rocks on Earth's surface
Hadean				Approx. 4,600	Origin of Earth

Photosynthesis and the Oxygen Revolution

Atmospheric oxygen

Most atmospheric oxygen gas (O_2) is of biological origin, produced during the water-splitting step of photosynthesis. When oxygenic photosynthesis first evolved, the free O_2 it produced probably dissolved in the surrounding water until it reached a high enough concentration to react with elements dissolved in water, including iron. This would have caused the iron to precipitate as iron oxide, which accumulated as sediments. These sediments were compressed into banded iron formations, red layers of rock containing iron oxide that are a source of iron ore today. Once all of the dissolved iron had precipitated, additional O_2 dissolved in the water until the seas and lakes became saturated with O_2. After this occurred, the O_2 finally began to "gas out" of the water and enter the atmosphere. This change left its mark in the rusting of iron-rich terrestrial rocks, a process that began about 2.7 billion years ago. This chronology implies that bacteria similar to today's cyanobacteria (oxygen-releasing, photosynthetic bacteria) originated before 2.7 billion years ago.

The amount of atmospheric O_2 increased gradually from about 2.7 to 2.4 billion years ago, but then shot up relatively rapidly to between 1% and 10% of its present level **(Figure 25.9)**. This "oxygen revolution" had an enormous impact on life. In certain of its chemical forms, oxygen attacks chemical bonds and can inhibit enzymes and damage cells. As a result, the rising concentration of atmospheric O_2 probably doomed many prokaryotic groups. Some species survived in habitats that remained anaerobic, where we find their descendants living today (see Chapter 27). Among other survivors, diverse adaptations to the changing atmosphere evolved, including cellular respiration, which uses O_2 in the process of harvesting the energy stored in organic molecules.

The rise in atmospheric O_2 levels left a huge imprint on the history of life. A few hundred million years later, another fundamental change occurred: the origin of the eukaryotic cell.

The First Eukaryotes

Single-celled eukaryotes

The oldest widely accepted fossils of eukaryotic organisms are 1.8 billion years old. Recall that eukaryotic cells have more complex organization than prokaryotic cells: Eukaryotic cells have a nuclear envelope, mitochondria, endoplasmic reticulum, and other internal structures that prokaryotes lack. Also, unlike prokaryotic cells, eukaryotic cells have a well-developed cytoskeleton, a feature that enables eukaryotic cells to change their shape and thereby surround and engulf other cells.

How did such eukaryotic features evolve from prokaryotic cells? Much evidence supports the **endosymbiont theory**, which posits that mitochondria and plastids (a general term for chloroplasts and related organelles) were formerly small prokaryotes that began living within larger cells. The term *endosymbiont* refers to a cell that lives within another cell, called the *host cell*. The prokaryotic ancestors of mitochondria and plastids probably entered the host cell as undigested prey or internal parasites. Though such a process may seem unlikely, scientists have directly observed cases in which endosymbionts that began as prey or parasites developed a mutually beneficial relationship with the host in as little as five years.

By whatever means the relationship began, we can hypothesize how the symbiosis could have become beneficial. For example, in a world that was becoming increasingly aerobic, a host that was itself an anaerobe would have benefited from endosymbionts that could make use of the oxygen. Over time, the host and endosymbionts would have become a single organism, its parts inseparable. Although all eukaryotes have mitochondria or remnants of these organelles, they do not all have plastids. Thus, the hypothesis of **serial endosymbiosis** supposes that mitochondria evolved before plastids through a sequence of endosymbiotic events **(Figure 25.10)**.

A great deal of evidence supports the endosymbiotic origin of mitochondria and plastids:

- The inner membranes of both organelles have enzymes and transport systems that are homologous to those found in the plasma membranes of living prokaryotes.

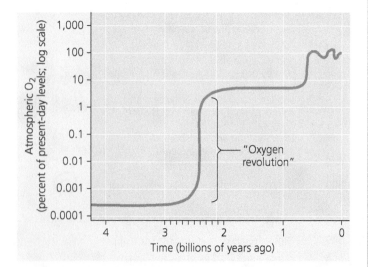

▲ **Figure 25.9 The rise of atmospheric oxygen.** Chemical analyses of ancient rocks have enabled this reconstruction of atmospheric oxygen levels during Earth's history.

- Mitochondria and plastids replicate by a splitting process that is similar to that of certain prokaryotes. In addition, each of these organelles contains circular DNA molecules that, like the chromosomes of bacteria, are not associated with histones or large amounts of other proteins.

- As might be expected of organelles descended from free-living organisms, mitochondria and plastids also have the cellular machinery (including ribosomes) needed to transcribe and translate their DNA into proteins.

- Finally, in terms of size, RNA sequences, and sensitivity to certain antibiotics, the ribosomes of mitochondria and plastids are more similar to prokaryotic ribosomes than they are to the cytoplasmic ribosomes of eukaryotic cells.

In Chapter 28, we'll return to origin of eukaryotes, focusing on what genomic data have revealed about the prokaryotic lineages that gave rise to the host and endosymbiont cells.

The Origin of Multicellularity

An orchestra can play a greater variety of musical compositions than a violin soloist can; the increased complexity of the orchestra makes more variations possible. Likewise, the appearance of structurally complex eukaryotic cells sparked the evolution of greater morphological diversity than was possible for the simpler prokaryotic cells. After the first eukaryotes appeared, a great range of unicellular forms evolved, giving rise to the diversity of single-celled eukaryotes that continue to flourish today. Another wave of diversification also occurred: Some single-celled eukaryotes gave rise to multicellular forms, whose descendants include a variety of algae, plants, fungi, and animals.

Early Multicellular Eukaryotes

The oldest known fossils of multicellular eukaryotes that can be resolved taxonomically are of relatively small red algae that lived 1.2 billion years ago; even older fossils, dating to 1.8 billion years ago, may also be of small, multicellular eukaryotes. Larger and more diverse multicellular eukaryotes do not appear in the fossil record until about 600 million years ago (see Figure 25.5). These fossils, referred to as the Ediacaran biota, were of soft-bodied organisms—some over 1 m long—that lived from 600 to 535 million years ago. The Ediacaran biota included both algae and animals, along with various organisms of unknown taxonomic affinity.

The rise of large eukaryotes in the Ediacaran period represents an enormous change in the history of life. Before that time, Earth was a microbial world: Its only inhabitants

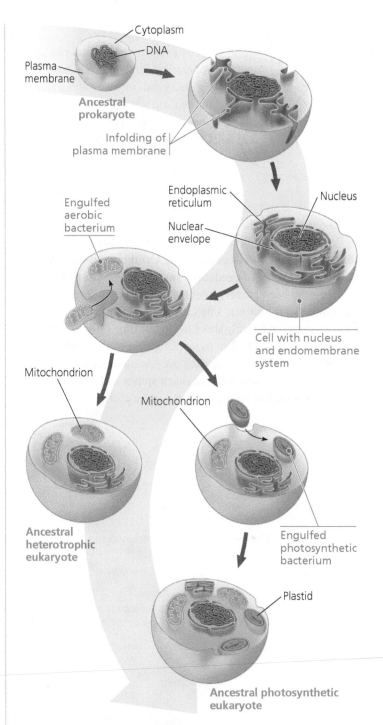

▲ **Figure 25.10 A hypothesis for the origin of eukaryotes through serial endosymbiosis.** The proposed ancestors of mitochondria were aerobic, heterotrophic prokaryotes (meaning that they used oxygen to metabolize organic molecules obtained from other organisms). The proposed ancestors of plastids were photosynthetic prokaryotes. In this figure, the arrows represent change over evolutionary time.

were single-celled prokaryotes and eukaryotes, along with an assortment of microscopic, multicellular eukaryotes. As the diversification of the Ediacaran biota came to a close about 535 million years ago, the stage was set for another, even more spectacular burst of evolutionary change.

The Cambrian Explosion

Many present-day animal phyla appear suddenly in fossils formed 535–525 million years ago, early in the Cambrian period. This phenomenon is referred to as the **Cambrian explosion**. Fossils of several animal groups—sponges, cnidarians (sea anemones and their relatives), and molluscs (snails, clams, and their relatives)—appear in even older rocks dating from the late Proterozoic (**Figure 25.11**).

Prior to the Cambrian explosion, all large animals were soft-bodied. The fossils of large pre-Cambrian animals reveal little evidence of predation. Instead, these animals appear to have been grazers (feeding on algae), filter feeders, or scavengers, not hunters. The Cambrian explosion changed all of that. In a relatively short period of time (10 million years), predators over 1 m in length emerged that had claws and other features for capturing prey; simultaneously, new defensive adaptations, such as sharp spines and heavy body armor, appeared in their prey (see Figure 25.5).

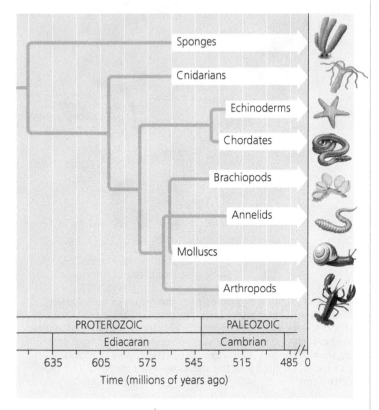

▲ **Figure 25.11 Appearance of selected animal groups.** The white bars indicate earliest appearances of these animal groups in the fossil record.

DRAW IT *Circle the branch point that represents the most recent common ancestor of chordates and annelids. What is a minimum estimate of that ancestor's age?*

Although the Cambrian explosion had an enormous impact on life on Earth, it appears that many animal phyla originated long before that time. Recent DNA analyses suggest that sponges, an early-diverging animal group, had evolved by 700 million years ago; such analyses also indicate that the common ancestor of arthropods, chordates, and other animal phyla that radiated during the Cambrian explosion lived 670 million years ago. Researchers have unearthed 710-million-year-old fossils containing steroids indicative of a particular group of sponges—a finding that supports the molecular data. In contrast, the oldest fossil assigned to an extant animal phylum is that of the mollusc *Kimberella*, which lived 560 million years ago. Overall, molecular and fossil data indicate that the Cambrian explosion had a "long fuse"—at least 25 million years long based on the age of *Kimberella* fossils, and over 100 million years long based on some DNA analyses. We'll explore factors that may have triggered the Cambrian explosion in Chapter 32.

The Colonization of Land

The colonization of land was another milestone in the history of life. There is fossil evidence that cyanobacteria and other photosynthetic prokaryotes coated damp terrestrial surfaces well over a billion years ago. However, larger forms of life, such as fungi, plants, and animals, did not begin to colonize land until about 500 million years ago. This gradual evolutionary venture out of aquatic environments was associated with adaptations that made it possible to reproduce on land and that helped prevent dehydration. For example, many land plants today have a vascular system for transporting materials internally and a waterproof coating of wax on their leaves that slows the loss of water to the air. Early signs of these adaptations were present 420 million years ago, at which time small plants (about 10 cm high) existed that had a vascular system but lacked true roots or leaves. By 40 million years later, plants had diversified greatly and included reeds and treelike plants with true roots and leaves.

Plants colonized land in the company of fungi. Even today, the roots of most plants are associated with fungi that aid in the absorption of water and minerals from the soil (see Chapter 31). These root fungi (or *mycorrhizae*), in turn, obtain their organic nutrients from the plants. Such mutually beneficial associations of plants and fungi are evident in some of the oldest fossilized plants, dating this relationship back to the early spread of life onto land (**Figure 25.12**).

Although many animal groups are now represented in terrestrial environments, the most widespread and diverse land

Zone of arbuscule-
containing cells

▲ **Figure 25.12 An ancient symbiosis.** This 405-million-year-old fossil stem (cross section) documents mycorrhizae in the early land plant *Aglaophyton major*. The inset shows an enlarged view of a cell containing a branched fungal structure called an arbuscule; the fossil arbuscule resembles those seen in plant cells today.

animals are arthropods (particularly insects and spiders) and tetrapods. Arthropods were among the first animals to colonize land, roughly 450 million years ago. The earliest tetrapods found in the fossil record lived about 365 million years ago and appear to have evolved from a group of lobe-finned fishes (see Chapter 34). Tetrapods include humans, although we are late arrivals on the scene. The human lineage diverged from other primates around 6–7 million years ago, and our species originated only about 195,000 years ago. If the clock of Earth's history were rescaled to represent an hour, humans appeared less than 0.2 second ago.

CONCEPT CHECK **25.3**

1. The first appearance of free oxygen in the atmosphere likely triggered a massive wave of extinctions among the prokaryotes of the time. Why?

2. What evidence supports the hypothesis that mitochondria preceded plastids in the evolution of eukaryotic cells?

3. **WHAT IF?** What would a fossil record of life today look like?

For suggested answers, see Appendix A.

CONCEPT 25.4

The rise and fall of groups of organisms reflect differences in speciation and extinction rates

From its beginnings, life on Earth has been marked by the rise and fall of groups of organisms. Anaerobic prokaryotes originated, flourished, and then declined as the oxygen content of the atmosphere rose. Billions of years later, the first tetrapods emerged from the sea, giving rise to several major

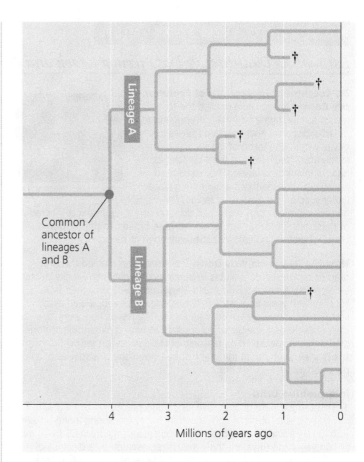

Millions of years ago

▲ **Figure 25.13 How speciation and extinction affect diversity.** The species diversity of an evolutionary lineage will increase when more new member species originate than are lost to extinction. In this hypothetical example, by 2 million years ago both lineage A and lineage B have given rise to four species, and no species have become extinct (denoted by a dagger symbol). By time 0, however, lineage A contains only one species while lineage B contains eight species.

INTERPRET THE DATA *Consider the period from 2 million years ago to time 0. For each lineage, determine how many speciation and extinction events occurred during that time.*

new groups of organisms. One of these, the amphibians, went on to dominate life on land for 100 million years, until other tetrapods (including dinosaurs and, later, mammals) replaced them as the dominant terrestrial vertebrates.

The rise and fall of these and other major groups of organisms have shaped the history of life. Narrowing our focus, we can also see that the rise or fall of any particular group is related to the speciation and extinction rates of its member species (**Figure 25.13**). Just as a population increases in size when there are more births than deaths, the rise of a group of organisms occurs when more new species are produced than are lost to extinction. The reverse occurs when a group is in decline. In the Scientific Skills Exercise, you will interpret data from the fossil record about changes in a group of snail species in the early Paleogene period. Such changes in the fates of groups of organisms have been influenced by large-scale processes such as plate tectonics, mass extinctions, and adaptive radiations.

Estimating Quantitative Data from a Graph and Developing Hypotheses

Do Ecological Factors Affect Evolutionary Rates? Researchers studied the fossil record to investigate whether differing modes of larval dispersal might explain species longevity within one taxon of marine snails, the family Volutidae. Some of the snail species had nonplanktonic larvae: They developed directly into adults without a swimming stage. Other species had planktonic larvae: They had a swimming stage and could disperse very long distances. The adults of these planktonic species tended to have broad geographic distributions, whereas nonplanktonic species tended to be more isolated.

How the Research Was Done The researchers studied the stratigraphic distribution of volutes in outcrops of sedimentary rocks located along North America's Gulf coast. These rocks, which formed from 65 to 37 million years ago, early in the Paleogene period, are an excellent source of well-preserved snail fossils. The researchers were able to classify each fossil species of volute snail as having planktonic or nonplanktonic larvae based on features of the earliest formed whorls of the snail's shell. Each bar in the graph shows how long one species of snail persisted in the fossil record.

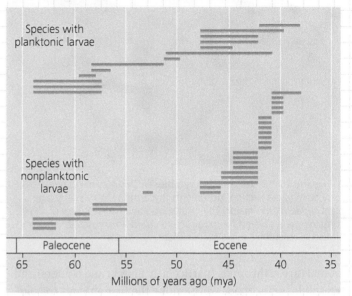

© 1978 AAAS

Interpret the Data

1. You can estimate quantitative data (fairly precisely) from a graph. The first step is to obtain a conversion factor by measuring along an axis that has a scale. In this case, 25 million years (my; from 65 to 40 million years ago (mya) on the *x*-axis) is represented by a distance of 7.0 cm. This yields a conversion factor (a ratio) of 25 my/7.0 cm = 3.6 my/cm. To estimate the time period represented by a horizontal bar on this graph, measure the length of that bar in centimeters and multiply that measurement by the conversion factor, 3.6 my/cm. For example, a bar that measures 1.1 cm on the graph represents a persistence time of 1.1 cm × 3.6 my/cm = 4 million years.

2. Calculate the mean (average) persistence times for species with planktonic larvae and species with nonplanktonic larvae.

3. Count the number of new species that form in each group beginning at 60 mya (the first three species in each group were present around 64 mya, the first time period sampled, so we don't know when those species first appear in the fossil record).

4. Propose a hypothesis to explain the differences in longevity of snail species with planktonic and nonplanktonic larvae.

(MB) A version of this Scientific Skills Exercise can be assigned in MasteringBiology.

Data from: T. A. Hansen, Larval dispersal and species longevity in Lower Tertiary gastropods, *Science* 199:885–887 (1978). Reprinted with permission from AAAS.

Plate Tectonics

If photographs of Earth were taken from space every 10,000 years and spliced together to make a movie, it would show something many of us find hard to imagine: The seemingly "rock solid" continents we live on move over time. Over the past 1.5 billion years, there have been three occasions (1.1 billion, 600 million, and 250 million years ago) when most of the landmasses of Earth came together to form a supercontinent, then later broke apart. Each time, this breakup yielded a different configuration of continents. Looking into the future, some geologists have estimated that the continents will come together again and form a new supercontinent roughly 250 million years from now.

According to the theory of **plate tectonics**, the continents are part of great plates of Earth's crust that essentially float on the hot, underlying portion of the mantle **(Figure 25.14)**. Movements in the mantle cause the plates to move over time in a process called *continental drift*. Geologists can measure the rate at which the plates are moving now, usually only a few centimeters per year. They can also infer the past locations of the continents using the magnetic signal recorded in rocks at the time of their formation. This method works because as a continent shifts its position over time, the direction of magnetic north recorded in its newly formed rocks also changes.

Earth's major tectonic plates are shown in **Figure 25.15**. Many important geologic processes, including the formation of mountains and islands, occur at plate boundaries. In some cases, two plates are moving away from each other, as are the North American and Eurasian plates, which are currently drifting apart at a rate of about 2 cm per year.

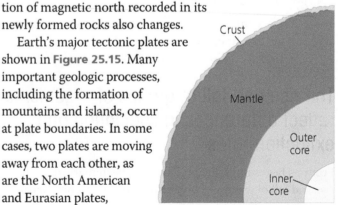

▲ **Figure 25.14 Cutaway view of Earth.** The thickness of the crust is exaggerated here.

In other cases, two plates are sliding past each other, forming regions where earthquakes are common. California's infamous San Andreas Fault is part of a border where two plates slide past each other. In still other cases, two plates collide, producing violent upheavals and forming new mountains along the plate boundaries. One spectacular example of this occurred 45 million years ago, when the Indian plate crashed into the Eurasian plate, starting the formation of the Himalayan mountains.

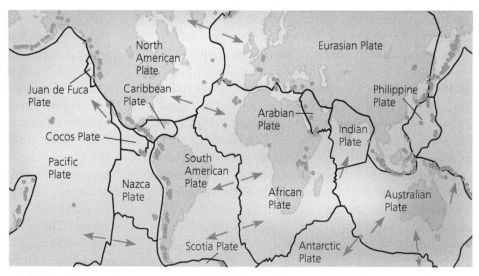

▲ **Figure 25.15 Earth's major tectonic plates.** The arrows indicate direction of movement. The reddish orange dots represent zones of violent tectonic activity.

Consequences of Continental Drift

Plate movements rearrange geography slowly, but their cumulative effects are dramatic. In addition to reshaping the physical features of our planet, continental drift also has a major impact on life on Earth.

One reason for this is that continental drift alters the habitats in which organisms live. Consider the changes shown in **Figure 25.16**. About 250 million years ago, plate movements brought previously separated landmasses together into a supercontinent named **Pangaea**. Ocean basins became deeper, which lowered sea levels and drained shallow coastal seas. At that time, as now, most marine species inhabited shallow waters, and the formation of Pangaea destroyed much of that habitat. Pangaea's interior was cold and dry, probably an even more severe environment than that of central Asia today. Overall, the formation of Pangaea greatly altered the physical environment and climate, which drove some species to extinction and provided new opportunities for groups of organisms that survived the crisis.

Organisms are also affected by the climate change that results when a continent shifts its location. The southern tip of Labrador, Canada, for example, once was located in the tropics but has moved 40° to the north over the last 200 million years. When faced with the changes in climate that such shifts in position entail, organisms adapt, move to a new location, or become extinct (this last outcome occurred for many organisms stranded on Antarctica).

Continental drift also promotes allopatric speciation on a grand scale. When supercontinents break apart, regions that once were connected become isolated. As the continents drifted apart over the last 200 million years, each became a separate evolutionary arena, with lineages of plants and animals that diverged from those on other continents.

Finally, continental drift can help explain puzzles about the geographic distribution of extinct organisms, such as why fossils of the same species of Permian freshwater reptiles have been discovered in both Brazil and the West African nation of Ghana. These two parts of the world, now separated by 3,000 km of ocean, were joined together when

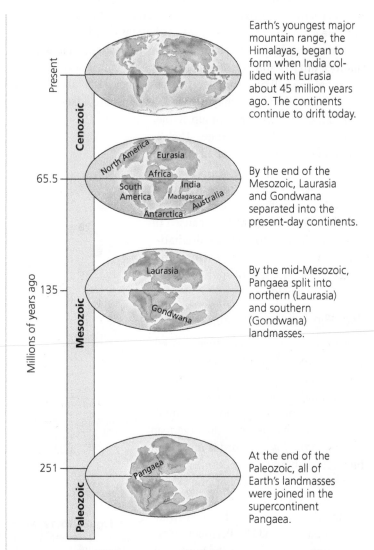

Earth's youngest major mountain range, the Himalayas, began to form when India collided with Eurasia about 45 million years ago. The continents continue to drift today.

By the end of the Mesozoic, Laurasia and Gondwana separated into the present-day continents.

By the mid-Mesozoic, Pangaea split into northern (Laurasia) and southern (Gondwana) landmasses.

At the end of the Paleozoic, all of Earth's landmasses were joined in the supercontinent Pangaea.

▲ **Figure 25.16 The history of continental drift during the Phanerozoic eon.**

? *Is the Australian plate's current direction of movement (see Figure 25.15) similar to the direction it traveled over the past 65 million years?*

these reptiles were living. Continental drift also explains much about the current distributions of organisms, such as why Australian fauna and flora contrast so sharply with those of the rest of the world. Marsupial mammals fill ecological roles in Australia analogous to those filled by eutherians (placental mammals) on other continents (see Figure 22.18). Fossil evidence suggests that marsupials originated in what is now Asia and reached Australia via South America and Antarctica while the continents were still joined. The subsequent breakup of the southern continents set Australia "afloat," like a giant raft of marsupials. In Australia, marsupials diversified, and the few eutherians that lived there became extinct; on other continents, most marsupials became extinct, and the eutherians diversified.

Mass Extinctions

The fossil record shows that the overwhelming majority of species that ever lived are now extinct. A species may become extinct for many reasons. Its habitat may have been destroyed, or its environment may have changed in a manner unfavorable to the species. For example, if ocean temperatures fall by even a few degrees, species that are otherwise well adapted may perish. Even if physical factors in the environment remain stable, biological factors may change—the origin of one species can spell doom for another.

Although extinction occurs regularly, at certain times disruptive changes to the global environment have caused the rate of extinction to increase dramatically. The result is a **mass extinction**, in which large numbers of species become extinct worldwide.

The "Big Five" Mass Extinction Events

Five mass extinctions are documented in the fossil record over the past 500 million years (Figure 25.17). These events are particularly well documented for the decimation of hard-bodied animals that lived in shallow seas, the organisms for which the fossil record is most complete. In each mass extinction, 50% or more of marine species became extinct.

Two mass extinctions—the Permian and the Cretaceous—have received the most attention. The Permian mass extinction, which defines the boundary between the Paleozoic and Mesozoic eras (251 million years ago), claimed about 96% of marine animal species and

drastically altered life in the ocean. Terrestrial life was also affected. For example, 8 out of 27 known orders of insects were wiped out. This mass extinction occurred in less than 500,000 years, possibly in just a few thousand years—an instant in the context of geologic time.

The Permian mass extinction occurred during the most extreme episode of volcanism in the past 500 million years. Geologic data indicate that 1.6 million km^2 (roughly half the size of western Europe) in Siberia was covered with lava hundreds of meters thick. The eruptions are thought to have produced enough carbon dioxide to warm the global climate by an estimated 6°C, harming many temperature-sensitive species. The rise in atmospheric CO_2 levels would also have led to ocean acidification, thereby reducing the availability of calcium carbonate, which is required by reef-building corals and many shell-building species (see Figure 3.11). The explosions would also have added nutrients such as phosphorous to ecosystems, stimulating the growth of microorganisms. Upon their deaths, these microorganisms would have provided food for bacterial decomposers. Bacteria use oxygen as they decompose the bodies of dead organisms, thus causing oxygen concentrations to drop. This would have harmed oxygen-breathers and promoted the growth of anaerobic bacteria that emit a poisonous metabolic by-product,

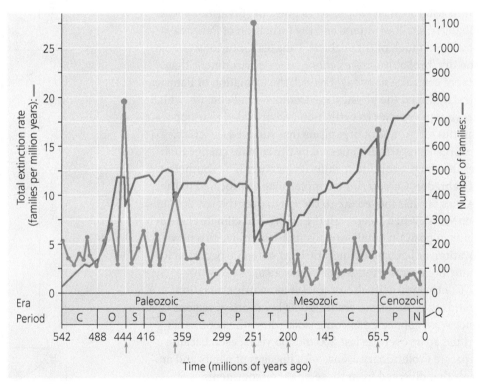

▲ Figure 25.17 **Mass extinction and the diversity of life.** The five generally recognized mass extinction events, indicated by red arrows, represent peaks in the extinction rate of marine animal families (red line and left vertical axis). These mass extinctions interrupted the overall increase in the number of marine animal families over time (blue line and right vertical axis).

INTERPRET THE DATA *96% of marine animal species became extinct in the Permian mass extinction. Explain why the blue curve shows only a 50% drop at that time.*

hydrogen sulfide (H_2S) gas. Overall, the volcanic eruptions appear to have triggered a series of catastrophic events that together resulted in the Permian mass extinction.

The Cretaceous mass extinction occurred 65.5 million years ago. This event extinguished more than half of all marine species and eliminated many families of terrestrial plants and animals, including all dinosaurs (except birds, which are members of the same group; see Chapter 34). One clue to a possible cause of the Cretaceous mass extinction is a thin layer of clay enriched in iridium that dates to the time of the mass extinction (about 65 million years ago). Iridium is an element that is very rare on Earth but common in many of the meteorites and other extraterrestrial objects that occasionally fall to Earth. As a result, researchers proposed that this clay is fallout from a huge cloud of debris that billowed into the atmosphere when an asteroid or large comet collided with Earth. This cloud would have blocked sunlight and severely disturbed the global climate for several months.

Is there evidence of such an asteroid or comet? Research has focused on the Chicxulub crater, a 65-million-year-old scar beneath sediments off the coast of Mexico (Figure 25.18).

▼ **Figure 25.18 A trauma for Cretaceous life.** Beneath the Caribbean Sea, the 65-million-year-old Chicxulub crater measures 180 km across. The horseshoe shape of the crater and the pattern of debris in sedimentary rocks indicate that an asteroid or comet struck at a low angle from the southeast. This drawing represents the impact and its immediate effect: a cloud of hot vapor and debris that could have killed many of the plants and animals in North America within hours.

The crater is the right size to have been caused by an object with a diameter of 10 km. Critical evaluation of this and other hypotheses for mass extinctions continues.

Is a Sixth Mass Extinction Under Way?

As you will read further in Chapter 56, human actions, such as habitat destruction, are modifying the global environment to such an extent that many species are threatened with extinction. More than a thousand species have become extinct in the last 400 years. Scientists estimate that this rate is 100 to 1,000 times the typical background rate seen in the fossil record. Is a sixth mass extinction now in progress?

This question is difficult to answer, in part because it is hard to document the total number of extinctions occurring today. Tropical rain forests, for example, harbor many undiscovered species. As a result, destroying tropical forest may drive species to extinction before we even learn of their existence. Such uncertainties make it hard to assess the full extent of the current extinction crisis. Even so, it is clear that losses to date have not reached those of the "big five" mass extinctions, in which large percentages of Earth's species became extinct. This does not in any way discount the seriousness of today's situation. Monitoring programs show that many species are declining at an alarming rate due to habitat loss, introduced species, overharvesting, and other factors. Recent studies on a variety of organisms, including lizards, pine trees, and polar bears, suggest that climate change may hasten some of these declines. The fossil record also highlights the potential importance of climate change: Over the last 500 million years, extinction rates have tended to increase when global temperatures were high (Figure 25.19).

© 2008 The Royal Society

▲ **Figure 25.19 Fossil extinctions and temperature.** Extinction rates increased when global temperatures were high. Temperatures were estimated using ratios of oxygen isotopes and converted to an index in which 0 is the overall average temperature.

Overall, the evidence suggests that unless dramatic actions are taken, a sixth, human-caused mass extinction is likely to occur within the next few centuries or millennia.

Consequences of Mass Extinctions

Mass extinctions have significant and long-term effects. By eliminating large numbers of species, a mass extinction can reduce a thriving and complex ecological community to a pale shadow of its former self. And once an evolutionary lineage disappears, it cannot reappear. The course of evolution is changed forever. Consider what would have happened if the early primates living 66 million years ago had died out in the Cretaceous mass extinction. Humans would not exist, and life on Earth would differ greatly from what it is today.

The fossil record shows that it typically takes 5–10 million years for the diversity of life to recover to previous levels after a mass extinction. In some cases, it has taken much longer than that: It took about 100 million years for the number of marine families to recover after the Permian mass extinction (see Figure 25.17). These data have sobering implications. If current trends continue and a sixth mass extinction occurs, it will take millions of years for life on Earth to recover.

Mass extinctions can also alter ecological communities by changing the types of organisms residing there. For example, after the Permian and Cretaceous mass extinctions, the percentage of marine organisms that were predators increased substantially (Figure 25.20). A rise in the number of predators can increase both the risks faced by prey and the competition among predators for food. In addition, mass extinctions can curtail lineages with novel and advantageous features. For example, in the late Triassic a group of gastropods (snails and their relatives) arose that could drill through the shells of bivalves (such as clams) and feed on the animals inside. Although shell drilling provided access to a new and abundant source of food, this newly formed group was wiped out during the mass extinction at the end of the Triassic (about 200 million years ago). Another 120 million years passed before another group of gastropods (the oyster drills) exhibited the ability to drill through shells. As their predecessors might have done if they had not originated at an unfortunate time, oyster drills have since diversified into many new species. Finally, by eliminating so many species, mass extinctions can pave the way for adaptive radiations, in which new groups of organisms proliferate.

Adaptive Radiations

The fossil record shows that the diversity of life has increased over the past 250 million years (see blue line in Figure 25.17). This increase has been fueled by **adaptive radiations**, periods of evolutionary change in which groups of organisms form many new species whose adaptations allow them to fill different ecological roles, or niches, in their communities. Large-scale adaptive radiations occurred after each of the big five mass extinctions, when survivors became adapted to the many vacant ecological niches. Adaptive radiations have also occurred in groups of organisms that possessed major evolutionary innovations, such as seeds or armored body coverings, or that colonized regions in which they faced little competition from other species.

Worldwide Adaptive Radiations

Fossil evidence indicates that mammals underwent a dramatic adaptive radiation after the extinction of terrestrial dinosaurs 65.5 million years ago (Figure 25.21). Although mammals originated about 180 million years ago, the mammal fossils older than 65.5 million years are mostly small and not morphologically diverse. Many species appear to have been nocturnal based on their large eye sockets, similar to those in living nocturnal mammals. A few early mammals were intermediate in size, such as *Repenomamus giganticus*, a 1-m-long predator that lived 130 million years ago—but none approached the size of many dinosaurs. Early mammals may have been restricted in size and diversity because they were eaten or outcompeted by the larger and more diverse dinosaurs. With the disappearance of the dinosaurs (except for birds), mammals expanded greatly in both diversity and size, filling the ecological roles once occupied by terrestrial dinosaurs.

The history of life has also been greatly altered by radiations in which groups of organisms increased in diversity as they came to play entirely new

▲ Figure 25.20 **Mass extinctions and ecology.** The Permian and Cretaceous mass extinctions (indicated by red arrows) altered the ecology of the oceans by increasing the percentage of marine genera that were predators.

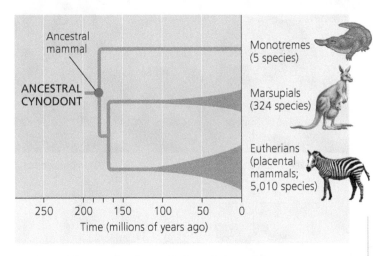

tetrapods. Each of these last three radiations was associated with major evolutionary innovations that facilitated life on land. The radiation of land plants, for example, was associated with key adaptations, such as stems that support plants against gravity and a waxy coat that protects leaves from water loss. Finally, organisms that arise in an adaptive radiation can serve as a new source of food for still other organisms. In fact, the diversification of land plants stimulated a series of adaptive radiations in insects that ate or pollinated plants, one reason that insects are the most diverse group of animals on Earth today.

Regional Adaptive Radiations

Striking adaptive radiations have also occurred over more limited geographic areas. Such radiations can be initiated when a few organisms make their way to a new, often distant location in which they face relatively little competition from other organisms. The Hawaiian archipelago is one of the world's great showcases of this type of adaptive radiation (**Figure 25.22**). Located about 3,500 km from the

ecological roles in their communities. Examples include the rise of photosynthetic prokaryotes, the evolution of large predators in the Cambrian explosion, and the radiations following the colonization of land by plants, insects, and

Close North American relative, the tarweed *Carlquistia muirii*

Dubautia laxa

Argyroxiphium sandwicense

KAUAI
5.1 million years

OAHU
3.7 million years

MOLOKAI

LANAI

MAUI

1.3 million years

Dubautia waialealae

HAWAII
0.4 million years

Dubautia scabra

Dubautia linearis

▲ Figure 25.22 **Adaptive radiation on the Hawaiian Islands.** Molecular analysis indicates that these remarkably varied Hawaiian plants, known collectively as the "silversword alliance," are all descended from an ancestral tarweed that arrived on the islands about 5 million years ago from North America. Members of the silversword alliance have since spread into different habitats and formed new species with strikingly different adaptations.

nearest continent, the volcanic islands are progressively older as one follows the chain toward the northwest; the youngest island, Hawaii, is less than a million years old and still has active volcanoes. Each island was born "naked" and was gradually populated by stray organisms that rode the ocean currents and winds either from far-distant land areas or from older islands of the archipelago itself. The physical diversity of each island, including immense variation in elevation and rainfall, provides many opportunities for evolutionary divergence by natural selection. Multiple invasions followed by speciation events have ignited an explosion of adaptive radiation in Hawaii. As a result, most of the thousands of species that inhabit the islands are found nowhere else on Earth.

CONCEPT CHECK 25.4

1. Explain the consequences of plate tectonics for life on Earth.

2. What factors promote adaptive radiations?

3. **WHAT IF?** Suppose that an invertebrate species was lost in a mass extinction caused by a sudden catastrophic event. Would the last appearance of this species in the fossil record necessarily be close to when the extinction actually occurred? Would the answer to this question differ depending on whether the species was common (abundant and widespread) or rare? Explain.

For suggested answers, see Appendix A.

CONCEPT 25.5

Major changes in body form can result from changes in the sequences and regulation of developmental genes

The fossil record tells us what the great changes in the history of life have been and when they occurred. Moreover, an understanding of plate tectonics, mass extinction, and adaptive radiation provides a picture of how those changes came about. But we can also seek to understand the intrinsic biological mechanisms that underlie changes seen in the fossil record. For this, we turn to genetic mechanisms of change, paying particular attention to genes that influence development.

Effects of Developmental Genes

As you read in Chapter 21, "evo-devo"—research at the interface between evolutionary biology and developmental biology—is illuminating how slight genetic differences can produce major morphological differences between species. In particular, large morphological differences can result from genes that alter the rate, timing, and spatial pattern of change in an organism's form as it develops from a zygote into an adult.

Chimpanzee infant   Chimpanzee adult

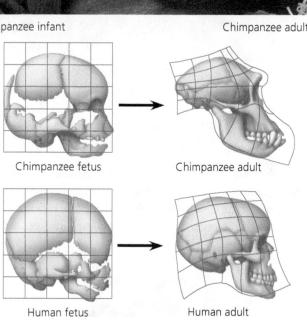

Chimpanzee fetus   Chimpanzee adult

Human fetus   Human adult

▲ **Figure 25.23 Relative skull growth rates.** In the human evolutionary lineage, mutations slowed the growth of the jaw relative to other parts of the skull. As a result, in humans the skull of an adult is more similar to the skull of an infant than is the case for chimpanzees..

Changes in Rate and Timing

Many striking evolutionary transformations are the result of **heterochrony** (from the Greek *hetero*, different, and *chronos*, time), an evolutionary change in the rate or timing of developmental events. For example, an organism's shape depends in part on the relative growth rates of different body parts during development. Changes to these rates can alter the adult form substantially, as seen in the contrasting shapes of human and chimpanzee skulls **(Figure 25.23)**. Other examples of the dramatic evolutionary effects of heterochrony include how increased growth rates of finger bones yielded the skeletal structure of wings in bats (see Figure 22.15) and how slowed growth of leg and pelvic bones led to the reduction and eventual loss of hind limbs in whales (see Figure 22.20).

Heterochrony can also alter the timing of reproductive development relative to the development of nonreproductive organs. If reproductive organ development accelerates compared to other organs, the sexually mature stage of a species may retain body features that were juvenile structures in an ancestral species, a condition called **paedomorphosis** (from the Greek *paedos*, of a child, and *morphosis*, formation). For example, most salamander species have

▲ **Figure 25.24 Paedomorphosis.** The adults of some species retain features that were juvenile in ancestors. This salamander is an axolotl, an aquatic species becomes a sexually mature adult while retaining certain larval (tadpole) characteristics, including gills.

aquatic larvae that undergo metamorphosis in becoming adults. But some species grow to adult size and become sexually mature while retaining gills and other larval features (Figure 25.24). Such an evolutionary alteration of developmental timing can produce animals that appear very different from their ancestors, even though the overall genetic change may be small. Indeed, recent evidence indicates that a change at a single locus was probably sufficient to bring about paedomorphosis in the axolotl salamander, although other genes may have contributed as well.

Changes in Spatial Pattern

Substantial evolutionary changes can also result from alterations in genes that control the spatial organization of body parts. For example, master regulatory genes called **homeotic genes** (described in Chapters 18 and 21) determine such basic features as where a pair of wings and legs will develop on a bird or how a plant's flower parts are arranged.

The products of one class of homeotic genes, the *Hox* genes, provide positional information in an animal embryo. This information prompts cells to develop into structures appropriate for a particular location. Changes in *Hox* genes or in how they are expressed can have a profound impact on morphology. For example, among crustaceans, a change in the location where two *Hox* genes (*Ubx* and *Scr*) are expressed correlates with the conversion of a swimming appendage to a feeding appendage. Similarly, when comparing plant species, changes to the expression of homeotic genes known as *MADS-box* genes can produce flowers that differ dramatically in form (see Chapter 35).

The Evolution of Development

The 560-million-year-old fossils of Ediacaran animals in Figure 25.5 suggest that a set of genes sufficient to produce complex animals existed at least 25 million years *before* the Cambrian explosion. If such genes have existed for so long, how can we explain the astonishing increases in diversity seen during and since the Cambrian explosion?

Adaptive evolution by natural selection provides one answer to this question. As we've seen throughout this unit, by sorting among differences in the sequences of protein-encoding genes, selection can improve adaptations rapidly. In addition, new genes (created by gene duplication events) can take on new metabolic and structural functions, as can existing genes that are regulated in new ways.

Examples in the previous section suggest that developmental genes may have been particularly important. Thus, we'll turn next to how new morphological forms can arise from changes in the nucleotide sequences or regulation of developmental genes.

Changes in Genes

New developmental genes arising after gene duplication events very likely facilitated the origin of novel morphological forms. But since other genetic changes also may have occurred at such times, it can be difficult to establish causal links between genetic and morphological changes that occurred in the past.

This difficulty was sidestepped in a study of developmental changes associated with the divergence of six-legged insects from crustacean-like ancestors that had more than six legs. In insects, such as *Drosophila*, the *Ubx* gene is expressed in the abdomen, while in crustaceans, such as *Artemia*, it is expressed in the main trunk of the body (Figure 25.25). When expressed, the *Ubx* gene suppresses leg formation in insects but not in crustaceans. To examine the workings of this gene, researchers cloned the *Ubx* gene from *Drosophila* and *Artemia*. Next, they genetically engineered fruit fly embryos to express either the *Drosophila Ubx* gene or the *Artemia Ubx* gene throughout their bodies. The *Drosophila* gene suppressed 100% of the limbs in the embryos, as expected, whereas the *Artemia* gene suppressed only 15%.

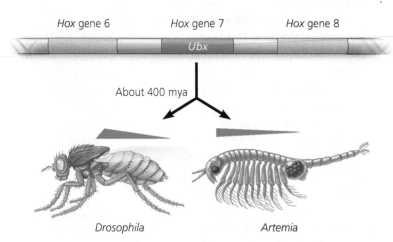

▲ **Figure 25.25 Origin of the insect body plan.** Expression of the *Hox* gene *Ubx* suppresses the formation of legs in fruit flies (*Drosophila*) but not in brine shrimp (*Artemia*), thus helping to build the insect body plan. Fruit fly and brine shrimp *Hox* genes have evolved independently for 400 million years. The green triangles indicate the relative amounts of *Ubx* expression in different body regions.

The researchers then sought to uncover key steps involved in the evolutionary transition from a crustacean *Ubx* gene to an insect *Ubx* gene. Their approach was to identify mutations that would cause the *Artemia Ubx* gene to suppress leg formation, thus making the crustacean gene act more like an insect *Ubx* gene. To do this, they constructed a series of "hybrid" *Ubx* genes, each of which contained known segments of the *Drosophila Ubx* gene and known segments of the *Artemia Ubx* gene. By inserting these hybrid genes into fruit fly embryos (one hybrid gene per embryo) and observing their effects on leg development, the researchers were able to pinpoint the exact amino acid changes responsible for the suppression of additional limbs in insects. In so doing, this study provided evidence linking a particular change in the nucleotide sequence of a developmental gene to a major evolutionary change: the origin of the six-legged insect body plan.

Changes in Gene Regulation

A change in the nucleotide sequence of a gene may affect its function wherever the gene is expressed, while changes in the regulation of gene expression can be limited to one cell type (see Chapter 18). Thus, a change in the regulation of a developmental gene may have fewer harmful side effects than a change to the sequence of the gene. This reasoning has prompted researchers to suggest that changes in the form of organisms may often be caused by mutations that affect the regulation of developmental genes—not their sequences.

This idea is supported by studies of a variety of species, including threespine stickleback fish. These fish live in the open ocean and in shallow, coastal waters. In western Canada, they also live in lakes formed when the coastline receded during the past 12,000 years. Marine stickleback fish have a pair of spines on their ventral (lower) surface, which deter some predators. These spines

▼ **Figure 25.26** | Inquiry

What causes the loss of spines in lake stickleback fish?

Experiment Marine populations of the threespine stickleback fish (*Gasterosteus aculeatus*) have a set of protective spines on their lower (ventral) surface; however, these spines have been lost or reduced in some lake populations of this fish. Working at Stanford University, Michael Shapiro, David Kingsley, and colleagues performed genetic crosses and found that most of the reduction in spine size resulted from the effects of a single developmental gene, *Pitx1*. The researchers then tested two hypotheses about how *Pitx1* causes this morphological change.

▲ **Threespine stickleback (*Gasterosteus aculeatus*)**

Hypothesis A: A change in the DNA sequence of *Pitx1* had caused spine reduction in lake populations. To test this idea, the team used DNA sequencing to compare the coding sequence of the *Pitx1* gene between marine and lake stickleback populations.

Hypothesis B: A change in the regulation of the expression of *Pitx1* had caused spine reduction. To test this idea, the researchers monitored where in the developing embryo the *Pitx1* gene was expressed. They conducted whole-body *in situ* hybridization experiments (see Chapter 20) using *Pitx1* DNA as a probe to detect *Pitx1* mRNA in the fish.

Results

Test of Hypothesis A:	Are there differences in the coding sequence of the *Pitx1* gene in marine and lake stickleback fish?	**Result: No** →	The 283 amino acids of the *Pitx1* protein are identical in marine and lake stickleback populations.
Test of Hypothesis B:	Are there any differences in the regulation of expression of *Pitx1*?	**Result: Yes** →	Red arrows (——▶) indicate regions of *Pitx1* gene expression in the photographs below. *Pitx1* is expressed in the ventral spine and mouth regions of developing marine stickleback fish but only in the mouth region of developing lake stickleback fish.

Marine stickleback embryo   **Lake stickleback embryo**

Close-up of mouth

Close-up of ventral surface

Conclusion The loss or reduction of ventral spines in lake populations of threespine stickleback fish appears to have resulted primarily from a change in the regulation of *Pitx1* gene expression, not from a change in the gene's sequence.

Source: M. D. Shapiro et al., Genetic and developmental basis of evolutionary pelvic reduction in three-spine sticklebacks, *Nature* 428:717–723 (2004).

WHAT IF? *Describe the set of results that would have led researchers to the conclusion that a change in the coding sequence of the* Pitx1 *gene was more important than a change in regulation of gene expression.*

are often reduced or absent in stickleback fish living in lakes that lack predatory fishes and that are also low in calcium. Spines may have been lost in such lakes because they are not advantageous in the absence of predators, and the limited calcium is needed for purposes other than constructing spines.

At the genetic level, the developmental gene *Pitx1* was known to influence whether stickleback fish have ventral spines. Was the reduction of spines in some lake populations due to changes in the *Pitx1* gene or to changes in how the gene is expressed (**Figure 25.26**)? The researchers' results indicate that the regulation of gene expression has changed, not the DNA sequence. Moreover, lake stickleback fish do express the *Pitx1* gene in tissues not related to the production of spines (for example, the mouth), illustrating how morphological change can be caused by altering the expression of a developmental gene in some parts of the body but not others. In a 2010 follow-up study, researchers showed that changes to the *Pel* enhancer, a noncoding DNA region that affects expression of the *Pitx1* gene, resulted in the reduction of ventral spines in lake sticklebacks.

CONCEPT CHECK 25.5

1. How can heterochrony cause the evolution of different body forms?

2. Why is it likely that *Hox* genes have played a major role in the evolution of novel morphological forms?

3. MAKE CONNECTIONS Given that changes in morphology are often caused by changes in the regulation of gene expression, predict whether noncoding DNA is likely to be affected by natural selection. See Concept 18.3 to review noncoding DNA and regulation of gene expression.

For suggested answers, see Appendix A.

CONCEPT 25.6

Evolution is not goal oriented

What does our study of macroevolution tell us about how evolution works? One lesson is that throughout the history of life, the origin of new species has been affected by both the small-scale factors described in Chapter 23 (such as natural selection operating in populations) and the large-scale factors described in this chapter (such as continental drift promoting bursts of speciation throughout the globe). Moreover, to paraphrase the Nobel Prize–winning geneticist François Jacob, evolution is like tinkering—a process in which new forms arise by the modification of existing structures or existing developmental genes. Over time, such tinkering has led to three key features of the natural world described in Chapter 22: the striking ways in which organisms are suited for life in their environments; the many shared characteristics of life; and the rich diversity of life.

Evolutionary Novelties

François Jacob's view of evolution harkens back to Darwin's concept of descent with modification. As new species form, novel and complex structures can arise as gradual modifications of ancestral structures. In many cases, complex structures have evolved in increments from simpler versions that performed the same basic function. For example, consider the human eye, an intricate organ constructed from numerous parts that work together in forming an image and transmitting it to the brain. How could the human eye have evolved in gradual increments? Some argue that if the eye needs all of its components to function, a partial eye could not have been of use to our ancestors.

The flaw in this argument, as Darwin himself noted, lies in the assumption that only complicated eyes are useful. In fact, many animals depend on eyes that are far less complex than our own. The simplest eyes that we know of are patches of light-sensitive photoreceptor cells. These simple eyes appear to have had a single evolutionary origin and are now found in a variety of animals, including small molluscs called limpets. Such eyes have no equipment for focusing images, but they do enable the animal to distinguish light from dark. Limpets cling more tightly to their rock when a shadow falls on them, a behavioral adaptation that reduces the risk of being eaten (**Figure 25.27**). Limpets have had a long evolutionary history, demonstrating that their "simple" eyes are quite adequate to support their survival and reproduction.

In the animal kingdom, complex eyes have evolved independently from such basic structures many times (**Figure 25.28**, on the next page). Some molluscs, such as squids and octopuses, have eyes as complex as those of humans and other vertebrates. Although complex mollusc eyes evolved independently of vertebrate eyes, both evolved from a simple cluster of photoreceptor cells present in a common ancestor. In each case, the complex eye evolved through a

▲ Figure 25.27 **Limpets (*Patella vulgata*), molluscs that can sense light and dark with a simple patch of photoreceptor cells.**

▼ **Figure 25.28** A range of eye complexity among molluscs.

(a) Patch of pigmented cells

Pigmented cells (photoreceptors)
Epithelium
Nerve fibers

The limpet *Patella* has a simple patch of photoreceptors.

(b) Eyecup

Pigmented cells
Nerve fibers

The slit shell mollusc *Pleurotomaria* has an eyecup.

(c) Pinhole camera-type eye

Epithelium
Fluid-filled cavity
Optic nerve
Pigmented layer (retina)

The *Nautilus* eye functions like a pinhole camera (an early type of camera lacking a lens).

(d) Eye with primitive lens

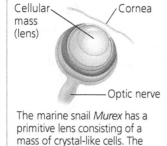

Cellular mass (lens)
Cornea
Optic nerve

The marine snail *Murex* has a primitive lens consisting of a mass of crystal-like cells. The cornea is a transparent region of tissue that protects the eye and helps focus light.

(e) Complex camera lens-type eye

Cornea
Lens
Retina
Optic nerve

The squid *Loligo* has a complex eye with features (cornea, lens, and retina) similar to those of vertebrate eyes. However, the squid eye evolved independently from vertebrate eyes.

series of steps that benefited the eyes' owners at every stage. Evidence of their independent evolution can be found in their structure: Vertebrate eyes detect light at the back layer of the retina and conduct nerve impulses toward the front, while complex mollusc eyes do the reverse.

Throughout their evolutionary history, eyes retained their basic function of vision. But evolutionary novelties can also arise when structures that originally played one role gradually acquire a different one. For example, as cynodonts gave rise to early mammals, bones that formerly comprised the jaw hinge (the articular and quadrate; see Figure 25.7) were incorporated into the ear region of mammals, where they eventually took on a new function: the transmission of sound (see Chapter 34). Structures that evolve in one context but become co-opted for another function are sometimes called *exaptations* to distinguish them from the adaptive origin of the original structure. Note that the concept of exaptation does not imply that a structure

somehow evolves in anticipation of future use. Natural selection cannot predict the future; it can only improve a structure in the context of its *current* utility. Novel features, such as the new jaw hinge and ear bones of early mammals, can arise gradually via a series of intermediate stages, each of which has some function in the organism's current context.

Evolutionary Trends

What else can we learn from patterns of macroevolution? Consider evolutionary "trends" observed in the fossil record. For instance, some evolutionary lineages exhibit a trend toward larger or smaller body size. An example is the evolution of the present-day horse (genus *Equus*), a descendant of the 55-million-year-old *Hyracotherium* (**Figure 25.29**). About the size of a large dog, *Hyracotherium* had four toes on its front feet, three toes on its hind feet, and teeth adapted for browsing on bushes and trees. In comparison, present-day horses are larger, have only one toe on each foot, and possess teeth modified for grazing on grasses.

Extracting a single evolutionary progression from the fossil record can be misleading, however; it is like describing a bush as growing toward a single point by tracing only the branches that lead to that twig. For example, by selecting certain species from the available fossils, it is possible to arrange a succession of animals intermediate between *Hyracotherium* and living horses that shows a trend toward large, single-toed species (follow the yellow highlighting in Figure 25.29). However, if we consider *all* fossil horses known today, this apparent trend vanishes. The genus *Equus* did not evolve in a straight line; it is the only surviving twig of an evolutionary tree that is so branched that it is more like a bush. *Equus* actually descended through a series of speciation episodes that included several adaptive radiations, not all of which led to large, one-toed, grazing horses. In fact, phylogenetic analyses suggest that all lineages that include grazers are closely related to *Parahippus*; the many other horse lineages, all of which are now extinct, remained multi-toed browsers for 35 million years.

Branching evolution *can* result in a real evolutionary trend even if some species counter the trend. One model of long-term trends views species as analogous to individuals: Speciation is their birth, extinction is their death, and new species that diverge from them are their offspring. In this model, just as populations of individual organisms undergo natural selection, species undergo *species selection*. The species that endure the longest and generate the most new offspring species determine the direction of major evolutionary trends. The species selection model suggests that "differential speciation success" plays a role in macroevolution similar to the role of differential reproductive success in microevolution. Evolutionary trends can also result directly from natural selection. For example, when horse ancestors invaded the grasslands that spread during the mid-Cenozoic,

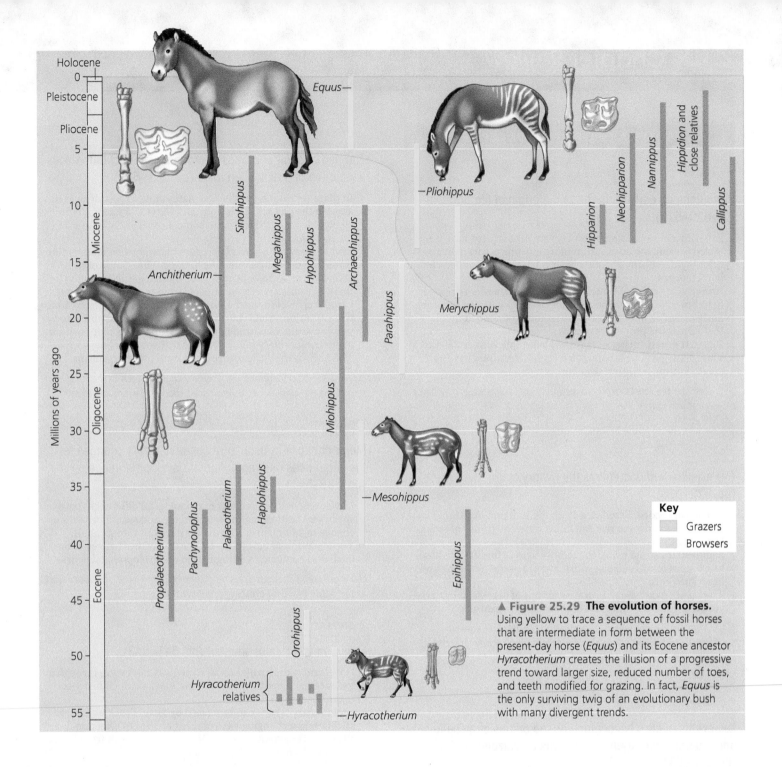

▲ **Figure 25.29 The evolution of horses.** Using yellow to trace a sequence of fossil horses that are intermediate in form between the present-day horse (*Equus*) and its Eocene ancestor *Hyracotherium* creates the illusion of a progressive trend toward larger size, reduced number of toes, and teeth modified for grazing. In fact, *Equus* is the only surviving twig of an evolutionary bush with many divergent trends.

Key
Grazers
Browsers

there was strong selection for grazers that could escape predators by running faster. This trend would not have occurred without open grasslands.

Whatever its cause, an evolutionary trend does not imply that there is some intrinsic drive toward a particular phenotype. Evolution is the result of the interactions between organisms and their current environments; if environmental conditions change, an evolutionary trend may cease or even reverse itself. The cumulative effect of these ongoing interactions between organisms and their environments is enormous: It is through them that the staggering diversity of life—Darwin's "endless forms most beautiful"—has arisen.

CONCEPT 25.1

Conditions on early Earth made the origin of life possible (pp. 520–522)

- Experiments simulating possible early atmospheres have produced organic molecules from inorganic precursors. Amino acids, lipids, sugars, and nitrogenous bases have also been found in meteorites.
- Amino acids and RNA nucleotides polymerize when dripped onto hot sand, clay, or rock. Organic compounds can spontaneously assemble into **protocells**, membrane-bounded droplets that have some properties of cells.
- The first genetic material may have self-replicating, catalytic RNA. Early protocells containing such RNA would have increased through natural selection.

? *Describe the roles that montmorillonite clay and vesicles may have played in the origin of life.*

CONCEPT 25.2

The fossil record documents the history of life (pp. 522–526)

- The **fossil record**, based largely on fossils found in sedimentary rocks, documents the rise and fall of different groups of organisms over time.
- Sedimentary strata reveal the relative ages of **fossils**. The absolute ages of fossils can be estimated by radiometric dating and other methods.
- The fossil record shows how new groups of organisms can arise via the gradual modification of preexisting organisms.

? *What are the challenges of estimating the absolute ages of old fossils? Explain how these challenges may be overcome in some circumstances.*

CONCEPT 25.3

Key events in life's history include the origins of unicellular and multicellular organisms and the colonization of land (pp. 526–531)

? *What is the "Cambrian explosion," and why is it significant?*

CONCEPT 25.4

The rise and fall of groups of organisms reflect differences in speciation and extinction rates (pp. 531–538)

- In **plate tectonics**, continental plates move gradually over time, altering the physical geography and climate of Earth. These changes lead to extinctions in some groups of organisms and bursts of speciation in others.
- Evolutionary history has been punctuated by five **mass extinctions** that radically altered the history of life. Some of these extinctions may have been caused by changes in continent positions, volcanic activity, or impacts from meteorites or comets.
- Large increases in the diversity of life have resulted from **adaptive radiations** that followed mass extinctions. Adaptive radiations have also occurred in groups of organisms that possessed major evolutionary innovations or that colonized new regions in which there was little competition from other organisms.

? *Explain how the broad evolutionary changes seen in the fossil record are the cumulative result of speciation and extinction events.*

CONCEPT 25.5

Major changes in body form can result from changes in the sequences and regulation of developmental genes (pp. 538–541)

- Developmental genes affect morphological differences between species by influencing the rate, timing, and spatial patterns of change in an organism's form as it develops into an adult.
- The evolution of new forms can be caused by changes in the nucleotide sequences or regulation of developmental genes.

? *How could changes in a single gene or DNA region ultimately lead to the origin of a new group of organisms?*

CONCEPT 25.6

Evolution is not goal oriented (pp. 541–543)

- Novel and complex biological structures can evolve through a series of incremental modifications, each of which benefits the organism that possesses it.
- Evolutionary trends can be caused by factors such as natural selection in a changing environment or species selection. Like all aspects of evolution, evolutionary trends result from interactions between organisms and their current environments.

? *Explain the reasoning behind the statement "Evolution is not goal oriented."*

TEST YOUR UNDERSTANDING

LEVEL 1: KNOWLEDGE/COMPREHENSION

1. Fossilized stromatolites
   a. formed around deep-sea vents.
   b. resemble structures formed by bacterial communities that are found today in some shallow marine bays.
   c. provide evidence that plants moved onto land in the company of fungi around 500 million years ago.
   d. contain the first undisputed fossils of eukaryotes and date from 1.8 billion years ago.

2. The oxygen revolution changed Earth's environment dramatically. Which of the following took advantage of the presence of free oxygen in the oceans and atmosphere?
   a. the evolution of cellular respiration, which used oxygen to help harvest energy from organic molecules
   b. the persistence of some animal groups in anaerobic habitats
   c. the evolution of photosynthetic pigments that protected early algae from the corrosive effects of oxygen
   d. the evolution of chloroplasts after early protists incorporated photosynthetic cyanobacteria

3. Which factor most likely caused animals and plants in India to differ greatly from species in nearby southeast Asia?
   a. The species became separated by convergent evolution.
   b. The climates of the two regions are similar.
   c. India is in the process of separating from the rest of Asia.
   d. India was a separate continent until 45 million years ago.

4. Adaptive radiations can be a direct consequence of three of the following four factors. Select the exception.
   a. vacant ecological niches
   b. genetic drift
   c. colonization of an isolated region that contains suitable habitat and few competitor species
   d. evolutionary innovation

5. Which of the following steps has *not* yet been accomplished by scientists studying the origin of life?
   a. synthesis of small RNA polymers by ribozymes
   b. formation of molecular aggregates with selectively permeable membranes
   c. formation of protocells that use DNA to direct the polymerization of amino acids
   d. abiotic synthesis of organic molecules

LEVEL 2: APPLICATION/ANALYSIS

6. A genetic change that caused a certain *Hox* gene to be expressed along the tip of a vertebrate limb bud instead of farther back helped make possible the evolution of the tetrapod limb. This type of change is illustrative of
   a. the influence of environment on development.
   b. paedomorphosis.
   c. a change in a developmental gene or in its regulation that altered the spatial organization of body parts.
   d. heterochrony.

7. A swim bladder is a gas-filled sac that helps fish maintain buoyancy. The evolution of the swim bladder from the air-breathing organ (a simple lung) of an ancestral fish is an example of
   a. exaptation.
   b. changes in *Hox* gene expression.
   c. paedomorphosis.
   d. adaptive radiation.

LEVEL 3: SYNTHESIS/EVALUATION

8. EVOLUTION CONNECTION
   Describe how gene flow, genetic drift, and natural selection all can influence macroevolution.

9. SCIENTIFIC INQUIRY
   Herbivory (plant eating) has evolved repeatedly in insects, typically from meat-eating or detritus-feeding ancestors (detritus is dead organic matter). Moths and butterflies, for example, eat plants, whereas their "sister group" (the insect group to which they are most closely related), the caddisflies, feed on animals, fungi, or detritus. As illustrated in the following phylogenetic tree, the combined moth/butterfly and caddisfly group shares a common ancestor with flies and fleas. Like caddisflies, flies and fleas are thought to have evolved from ancestors that did not eat plants.

There are 140,000 species of moths and butterflies and 7,000 species of caddisflies. State a hypothesis about the impact of herbivory on adaptive radiations in insects. How could this hypothesis be tested?

10. WRITE ABOUT A THEME: ORGANIZATION
    You have seen many examples of how form fits function at all levels of the biological hierarchy. However, we can imagine forms that would function better than some forms actually found in nature. For example, if the wings of a bird were not formed from its forelimbs, such a hypothetical bird could fly yet also hold objects with its forelimbs. In a short essay (100–150 words), use the concept of "evolution as tinkering" to explain why there are limits to the functionality of forms in nature.

11. SYNTHESIZE YOUR KNOWLEDGE

In 2010, the Soufriere Hills volcano on the Caribbean island of Montserrat erupted violently, spewing huge clouds of ash and gases into the sky. Explain how the volcanic eruptions at the end of the Permian period and the formation of Pangaea, both of which occurred about 251 million years ago, set in motion events that altered evolutionary history.

For suggested answers, see Appendix A.

MasteringBiology®

Students Go to **MasteringBiology** for assignments, the eText, and the Study Area with practice tests, animations, and activities.

Instructors Go to **MasteringBiology** for automatically graded tutorials and questions that you can assign to your students, plus Instructor Resources.

THE EVOLUTIONARY HISTORY OF BIOLOGICAL DIVERSITY

AN INTERVIEW WITH

Nicole King

Winner of a MacArthur Fellowship "genius" award, Nicole King is an Associate Professor of Genetics, Genomics, and Development at the University of California, Berkeley. Dr. King earned a B.S. in biology from Indiana University and a Ph.D. in biochemistry from Harvard University. Dr. King and her students are using an exciting mix of molecular genetic, developmental, and genomic approaches to reconstruct steps in a key event in the evolutionary history of life—how animals, which are multicellular, arose from their unicellular ancestors.

How did you first become interested in the history of life?

Growing up in Florida, my brother and I spent many hours exploring a creek near our home that was littered with fossilized sharks' teeth. We found tons of teeth, along with fossils of manta rays and other marine organisms. We could see that the land where we lived had once been covered by the ocean. Those fossils, combined with my love of being outdoors in nature, set the stage for my interest in the history of life. Also, my father is a historian. He took me on trips when he was working with Native American communities on reconstructing their oral histories. Just as you can learn about a human society today by studying its history, I became interested in what we can learn about animal biology by studying how animals first evolved.

> "Just as you can learn about a human society today by studying its history, I became interested in what we can learn about animal biology by studying how animals first evolved."

You're studying choanoflagellates in your lab. What are these organisms?

Choanoflagellates are single-celled organisms, although some also form simple colonies. Each cell has a flagellum that is surrounded at its base by projections that form a "collar." To me, the collar looks like a sieve or filter. The collar traps bacteria, which the cell then eats. Sponges, which are very simple animals, have cells that are almost indistinguishable from choanoflagellate cells. Thus, based on shape alone, the early indication was that choanoflagellates were related to animals. And now, with the benefit of genomics and other methods, the jury is in—choanoflagellates and animals are each other's closest relatives.

What can you learn about the origin of animals by studying choanoflagellates?

A key step in the origin of animals was the evolution of true multicellularity. This occurs when an organism's cells can't survive on their own—they have to be associated with other cells. My students and I discovered that choanoflagellates possess some of the genes necessary for multicellularity in animals. Previously, these genes were thought to be unique to animals. We've also been studying a particular species of choanoflagellate that can form simple colonies. By studying this organism in detail, we are learning how it transitions from a single cell to a colony—a change that can help us to answer the evolutionary question, "How does multicellularity evolve from organisms that are unicellular?"

What is a typical work day like for you, and what advice do you have for students?

Each day is different, but I always try to talk with people in my lab about their research. Sometimes they share an exciting new result, or they describe an experiment that is failing and we brainstorm about what might be going wrong. A few times, it turned out that an experiment was done correctly, but the results were very different from what we expected. It can be hard to determine what causes such unexpected results, but doing so can reveal features of an organism's biology that you had no idea existed! I'm really lucky, because I love what I do, and I have a diverse and talented group of scientists in my lab. They all are learning from each other, and I'm learning from them. Overall, I think the key to a happy and successful career is to do what you love.

 For an extended interview and video clip, go to the Study Area in MasteringBiology.

▲ Four choanoflagellate colonies.

26

Phylogeny and the Tree of Life

▲ **Figure 26.1 What kind of organism is this?**

Investigating the Tree of Life

Look closely at the organism in **Figure 26.1**. Although it resembles a snake, this animal is actually a legless lizard known as the eastern glass lizard (*Ophisaurus ventralis*). Why isn't this glass lizard considered a snake? More generally, how do biologists distinguish and categorize the millions of species on Earth?

An understanding of evolutionary relationships suggests one way to address these questions: We can decide in which category to place a species by comparing its traits with those of potential close relatives. For example, the eastern glass lizard does not have a highly mobile jaw, a large number of vertebrae, or a short tail located behind the anus, three traits shared by all snakes. These and other characteristics suggest that despite a superficial resemblance, the glass lizard is not a snake.

Snakes and lizards are part of the continuum of life extending from the earliest organisms to the great variety of species alive today. In this unit, we will survey this diversity and describe hypotheses regarding how it evolved. As we do so, our emphasis will shift from the *process* of evolution (the evolutionary mechanisms described in Unit Four) to its *pattern* (observations of evolution's products over time).

To set the stage for surveying life's diversity, in this chapter we consider how biologists trace **phylogeny**, the evolutionary history of a species or group of species. A phylogeny of lizards and snakes, for example, indicates that both the eastern glass lizard and snakes evolved from lizards with legs—but they evolved from

547

▲ Figure 26.2
Convergent evolution of limbless bodies.
A phylogeny based on DNA sequence data reveals that a legless body form evolved independently from legged ancestors in the lineages leading to the eastern glass lizard and to snakes.

Labels in figure: ANCESTRAL LIZARD (with limbs); No limbs; Geckos; Snakes; Iguanas; Monitor lizard; Eastern glass lizard; No limbs

different lineages of legged lizards (Figure 26.2). Thus, it appears that their legless conditions evolved independently. As we'll see, biologists reconstruct and interpret phylogenies like that in Figure 26.2 using **systematics**, a discipline focused on classifying organisms and determining their evolutionary relationships.

CONCEPT 26.1

Phylogenies show evolutionary relationships

Organisms share many characteristics because of common ancestry (see Chapter 22). As a result, we can learn a great deal about a species if we know its evolutionary history. For example, an organism is likely to share many of its genes, metabolic pathways, and structural proteins with its close relatives. We'll consider practical applications of such information later in this section, but first we'll examine how organisms are named and classified, the scientific discipline of **taxonomy**. We'll also look at how we can interpret and use diagrams that represent evolutionary history.

Binomial Nomenclature

Common names for organisms—such as monkey, finch, and lilac—convey meaning in casual usage, but they can also cause confusion. Each of these names, for example, refers to more than one species. Moreover, some common names do not accurately reflect the kind of organism they signify. Consider these three "fishes": jellyfish (a cnidarian), crayfish (a small lobsterlike crustacean), and silverfish (an insect). And of course, a given organism has different names in different languages.

To avoid ambiguity when communicating about their research, biologists refer to organisms by Latin scientific names. The two-part format of the scientific name, commonly called a **binomial**, was instituted in the 18th century by Carolus Linnaeus (see Chapter 22). The first part of a binomial is the name of the **genus** (plural, *genera*) to which the species belongs. The second part, called the specific epithet, is unique for each species within the genus. An example of a binomial is *Panthera pardus*, the scientific name for the large cat commonly called the leopard. Notice that the first letter of the genus is capitalized and the entire binomial is italicized. (Newly created scientific names are also "latinized": You can name an insect you discover after a friend, but you must add a Latin ending.) Many of the more than 11,000 binomials assigned by Linnaeus are still used today, including the optimistic name he gave our own species—*Homo sapiens*, meaning "wise man."

Hierarchical Classification

In addition to naming species, Linnaeus also grouped them into a hierarchy of increasingly inclusive categories. The first grouping is built into the binomial: Species that appear to be closely related are grouped into the same genus. For example, the leopard (*Panthera pardus*) belongs to a genus that also includes the African lion (*Panthera leo*), the tiger (*Panthera tigris*), and the jaguar (*Panthera onca*). Beyond genera, taxonomists employ progressively more comprehensive categories of classification. The taxonomic system named after Linnaeus, the Linnaean system, places related genera in the same **family**, families into **orders**, orders into **classes**, classes into **phyla** (singular, *phylum*), phyla into **kingdoms**, and, more recently, kingdoms into **domains** (Figure 26.3). The resulting biological classification of a particular organism is somewhat like a postal address identifying a person in a particular apartment, in a building with many apartments, on a street with many apartment buildings, in a city with many streets, and so on.

The named taxonomic unit at any level of the hierarchy is called a **taxon** (plural, *taxa*). In the leopard example, *Panthera* is a taxon at the genus level, and Mammalia is a taxon at the class level that includes all the many orders of mammals. Note that in the Linnaean system, taxa broader than the genus are not italicized, though they are capitalized.

Classifying species is a way to structure our human view of the world. We lump together various species of trees to which we give the common name of pines and distinguish them from other trees that we call firs. Taxonomists have decided that pines and firs are different enough to be placed in separate genera, yet similar enough to be grouped into the same family, Pinaceae. As with pines and firs, higher levels of classification are usually defined by particular characters chosen by taxonomists. However, characters that are useful for classifying one group of organisms may not be appropriate for other organisms. For this reason, the larger categories often are not comparable between lineages; that is, an

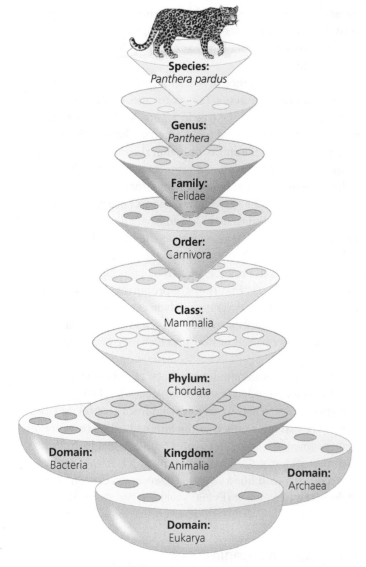

▲ **Figure 26.3 Linnaean classification.** At each level, or "rank," species are placed in groups within more inclusive groups.

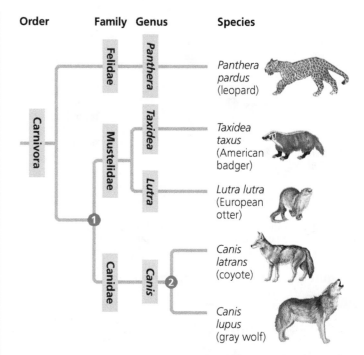

▲ **Figure 26.4 The connection between classification and phylogeny.** Hierarchical classification can reflect the branching patterns of phylogenetic trees. This tree traces possible evolutionary relationships between some of the taxa within order Carnivora, itself a branch of class Mammalia. The branch point ❶ represents the most recent common ancestor of all members of the weasel (Mustelidae) and dog (Canidae) families. The branch point ❷ represents the most recent common ancestor of coyotes and gray wolves.

❓ *What does this phylogenetic tree indicate about the evolutionary relationships between the leopard, badger, and wolf?*

order of snails does not exhibit the same degree of morphological or genetic diversity as an order of mammals. Furthermore, as we'll see, the placement of species into orders, classes, and so on, does not necessarily reflect evolutionary history.

Linking Classification and Phylogeny

The evolutionary history of a group of organisms can be represented in a branching diagram called a **phylogenetic tree**. As in **Figure 26.4**, the branching pattern often matches how taxonomists have classified groups of organisms nested within more inclusive groups. Sometimes, however, taxonomists have placed a species within a genus (or other group) to which it is *not* most closely related. One reason for such a mistake might be that over the course of evolution, a species has lost a key feature shared by its close relatives. If

DNA or other new evidence indicates that an organism has been misclassified, the organism may be reclassified to accurately reflect its evolutionary history. Another issue is that while the Linnaean system may distinguish groups, such as amphibians, mammals, reptiles, and other classes of vertebrates, it tells us nothing about these groups' evolutionary relationships to one another.

Such difficulties in aligning Linnaean classification with phylogeny have led some systematists to propose that classification be based entirely on evolutionary relationships. In such systems, names are only assigned to groups that include a common ancestor and all of its descendants. As a consequence of this approach, some commonly recognized groups would become part of other groups previously at the same level of the Linnaean system. For example, because birds evolved from a group of reptiles, Aves (the Linnaean class to which birds are assigned) would be considered a subgroup of Reptilia (also a class in the Linnaean system).

Regardless of how groups are named, a phylogenetic tree represents a hypothesis about evolutionary relationships. These relationships often are depicted as a series of dichotomies, or two-way **branch points**. Each branch point

Branch point: where lineages diverge

ANCESTRAL LINEAGE

Taxon A
Taxon B ⎱ Sister
Taxon C ⎰ taxa
Taxon D
Taxon E
Taxon F
Taxon G ⎱ Basal taxon

This branch point represents the common ancestor of taxa A–G.

This branch point forms a polytomy: an unresolved pattern of divergence.

▲ **Figure 26.5 How to read a phylogenetic tree.**

DRAW IT *Redraw this tree, rotating the branches around branch points* **2** *and* **4**. *Does your new version tell a different story about the evolutionary relationships between the taxa? Explain.*

represents the divergence of two evolutionary lineages from a common ancestor. In **Figure 26.5**, for example, branch point **3** represents the common ancestor of taxa A, B, and C. The position of branch point **4** to the right of **3** indicates that taxa B and C diverged after their shared lineage split from the lineage leading to taxon A. Note also that tree branches can be rotated around a branch point without changing their evolutionary relationships.

In Figure 26.5, taxa B and C are **sister taxa**, groups of organisms that share an immediate common ancestor (branch point **4**) and hence are each other's closest relatives. In addition, this tree, like most of the phylogenetic trees in this book, is **rooted**, which means that a branch point within the tree (often drawn farthest to the left) represents the most recent common ancestor of all taxa in the tree. The term **basal taxon** refers to a lineage that diverges early in the history of a group and hence, like taxon G in Figure 26.5, lies on a branch that originates near the common ancestor of the group. Finally, the lineage leading to taxa D–F includes a **polytomy**, a branch point from which more than two descendant groups emerge. A polytomy signifies that evolutionary relationships among the taxa are not yet clear.

What We Can and Cannot Learn from Phylogenetic Trees

Let's summarize three key points about phylogenetic trees. First, they are intended to show patterns of descent, not phenotypic similarity. Although closely related organisms often resemble one another due to their common ancestry, they may not if their lineages have evolved at different rates or faced very different environmental conditions. For

example, even though crocodiles are more closely related to birds than to lizards (see Figure 22.17), they look more like lizards because morphology has changed dramatically in the bird lineage.

Second, the sequence of branching in a tree does not necessarily indicate the actual (absolute) ages of the particular species. For example, the tree in Figure 26.4 does not indicate that the wolf evolved more recently than the European otter; rather, the tree shows only that the most recent common ancestor of the wolf and otter (branch point **1**) lived before the most recent common ancestor of the wolf and coyote (**2**). To indicate when wolves and otters evolved, the tree would need to include additional divergences in each evolutionary lineage, as well as the dates when those splits occurred. Generally, unless given specific information about what the branch lengths in a phylogenetic tree mean—for example, that they are proportional to time—we should interpret the diagram solely in terms of patterns of descent. No assumptions should be made about when particular species evolved or how much change occurred in each lineage.

Third, we should not assume that a taxon on a phylogenetic tree evolved from the taxon next to it. Figure 26.4 does not indicate that wolves evolved from coyotes or vice versa. We can infer only that the lineage leading to wolves and the lineage leading to coyotes both evolved from the common ancestor **2**. That ancestor, which is now extinct, was neither a wolf nor a coyote. However, its descendants include the two *extant* (living) species shown here, wolves and coyotes.

Applying Phylogenies

Understanding phylogeny can have practical applications. Consider maize (corn), which originated in the Americas and is now an important food crop worldwide. From a phylogeny of maize based on DNA data, researchers have been able to identify two species of wild grasses that may be maize's closest living relatives. These two close relatives may be useful as "reservoirs" of beneficial alleles that can be transferred to cultivated maize by cross-breeding or genetic engineering (see Chapter 20).

A different use of phylogenetic trees is to infer species identities by analyzing the relatedness of DNA sequences from different organisms. Researchers have used this approach to investigate whether "whale meat" had been harvested illegally from whale species protected under international law rather than from species that can be harvested legally **(Figure 26.6)**.

How do researchers construct trees like those we've considered here? In the next section, we'll begin to answer that question by examining the data used to determine phylogenies.

What is the species identity of food being sold as whale meat?

Experiment C. S. Baker and S. R. Palumbi purchased 13 samples of "whale meat" from Japanese fish markets. They sequenced part of the mitochondrial DNA (mtDNA) from each sample and compared their results with the comparable mtDNA sequence from known whale species. To infer the species identity of each sample, the team constructed a *gene tree*, a phylogenetic tree that shows patterns of relatedness among DNA sequences rather than among taxa.

Results Of the species in the resulting gene tree, only Minke whales caught in the Southern Hemisphere can be sold legally in Japan.

Minke
(Southern Hemisphere)
Unknowns #1a,
2, 3, 4, 5, 6, 7, 8

Minke
(North Atlantic)
Unknown #9

Humpback

Unknown #1b

Blue

Unknowns #10,
11, 12, 13

Fin

© 1994 AAAS

Conclusion This analysis indicated that mtDNA sequences of six of the unknown samples (in red) were most closely related to mtDNA sequences of whales that are not legal to harvest.

Source: C. S. Baker and S. R. Palumbi, Which whales are hunted? A molecular genetic approach to monitoring whaling, *Science* 265:1538–1539 (1994). Reprinted with permission from AAAS.

WHAT IF? *What different results would have indicated that the whale meat had* not *been harvested illegally?*

CONCEPT CHECK 26.1

1. Which levels of the classification in Figure 26.3 do humans share with leopards?
2. Which of the trees shown here depicts an evolutionary history different from the other two? Explain.

(a)   (b)   (c)

3. **WHAT IF?** Suppose new evidence indicates that taxon E in Figure 26.5 is the sister taxon of a group consisting of taxa D and F. Redraw the tree accordingly.

For suggested answers, see Appendix A.

Phylogenies are inferred from morphological and molecular data

To infer phylogeny, systematists must gather as much information as possible about the morphology, genes, and biochemistry of the relevant organisms. It is important to focus on features that result from common ancestry, because only such features reflect evolutionary relationships.

Morphological and Molecular Homologies

Recall that phenotypic and genetic similarities due to shared ancestry are called *homologies*. For example, the similarity in the number and arrangement of bones in the forelimbs of mammals is due to their descent from a common ancestor with the same bone structure; this is an example of a morphological homology (see Figure 22.15). In the same way, genes or other DNA sequences are homologous if they are descended from sequences carried by a common ancestor.

In general, organisms that share very similar morphologies or similar DNA sequences are likely to be more closely related than organisms with vastly different structures or sequences. In some cases, however, the morphological divergence between related species can be great and their genetic divergence small (or vice versa). Consider the Hawaiian silversword plants: some of these species are tall, twiggy trees, while others are dense, ground-hugging shrubs (see Figure 25.22). But despite these striking phenotypic differences, the silverswords' genes are very similar. Based on these small molecular divergences, scientists estimate that the silversword group began to diverge 5 million years ago. We'll discuss how scientists use molecular data to estimate such divergence times later in this chapter.

Sorting Homology from Analogy

A potential source of confusion in constructing a phylogeny is similarity between organisms that is due to convergent evolution—called **analogy**—rather than to shared ancestry (homology). Convergent evolution occurs when similar environmental pressures and natural selection produce similar (analogous) adaptations in organisms from different evolutionary lineages. For example, the two mole-like animals shown in **Figure 26.7**

Australian marsupial "mole"

North American eutherian mole

▲ **Figure 26.7 Convergent evolution in burrowers.** A long body, large front paws, small eyes, and a pad of thick skin that protects the nose all evolved independently in these species.

look very similar. However, their internal anatomy, physiology, and reproductive systems are very dissimilar. Indeed, genetic and fossil evidence indicate that the common ancestor of these moles lived 140 million years ago. This common ancestor and most of its descendents were not mole-like, but analogous characteristics evolved independently in these two mole lineages as they became adapted to similar lifestyles.

Distinguishing between homology and analogy is critical in reconstructing phylogenies. To see why, consider bats and birds, both of which have adaptations that enable flight. This superficial resemblance might imply that bats are more closely related to birds than they are to cats, which cannot fly. But a closer examination reveals that a bat's wing is more similar to the forelimbs of cats and other mammals than to a bird's wing. Bats and birds descended from a common tetrapod ancestor that lived about 320 million years ago. This common ancestor could not fly. Thus, although the underlying skeletal systems of bats and birds are homologous, their *wings* are not. Flight is enabled in different ways—stretched membranes in the bat wing versus feathers in the bird wing. Fossil evidence also documents that bat wings and bird wings arose independently from the forelimbs of different tetrapod ancestors. Thus, with respect to flight, a bat's wing is *analogous*, not homologous, to a bird's wing. Analogous structures that arose independently are also called **homoplasies** (from the Greek, meaning "to mold in the same way").

Besides corroborative similarities and fossil evidence, another clue to distinguishing between homology and analogy is the complexity of the characters being compared. The more elements that are similar in two complex structures, the more likely it is that they evolved from a common ancestor. For instance, the skulls of an adult human and an adult chimpanzee both consist of many bones fused together. The compositions of the skulls match almost perfectly, bone for bone. It is highly improbable that such complex structures, matching in so many details, have separate origins. More likely, the genes involved in the development of both skulls were inherited from a common ancestor. The same argument applies to comparisons at the gene level. Genes are sequences of thousands of nucleotides, each of which represents an inherited character in the form of one of the four DNA bases: A (adenine), G (guanine), C (cytosine), or T (thymine). If genes in two organisms share many portions of their nucleotide sequences, it is likely that the genes are homologous.

Evaluating Molecular Homologies

Comparing DNA molecules often poses technical challenges for researchers. The first step after sequencing the molecules is to align comparable sequences from the species being studied. If the species are very closely related, the sequences probably differ at only one or a few sites. In contrast, comparable nucleic acid sequences in distantly related

species usually have different bases at many sites and may have different lengths. This is because insertions and deletions accumulate over long periods of time.

Suppose, for example, that certain noncoding DNA sequences near a particular gene are very similar in two species, except that the first base of the sequence has been deleted in one of the species. The effect is that the remaining sequence shifts back one notch. A comparison of the two sequences that does not take this deletion into account would overlook what in fact is a very good match. To address such problems, researchers have developed computer programs that estimate the best way to align comparable DNA segments of differing lengths (Figure 26.8).

Such molecular comparisons reveal that many base substitutions and other differences have accumulated in the comparable genes of an Australian mole and a North American mole. The many differences indicate that their lineages have diverged greatly since their common ancestor; thus, we say that the living species are not closely related. In contrast, the high degree of gene sequence similarity among the silversword plants indicates that they are all very closely related, in spite of their considerable morphological differences.

Just as with morphological characters, it is necessary to distinguish homology from analogy in evaluating molecular similarities for evolutionary studies. Two sequences that

1 These homologous DNA sequences are identical as species 1 and species 2 begin to diverge from their common ancestor.

1 CCATCAGAGTCC
2 CCATCAGAGTCC

2 Deletion and insertion mutations shift what had been matching sequences in the two species.

Deletion
1 CCATCAGAGTCC
2 CCATCAGAGTCC
GTA Insertion

3 Of the regions of the species 2 sequence that match the species 1 sequence, those shaded orange no longer align because of these mutations.

1 CCATCAAGTCC
2 CCATGTACAGAGTCC

4 The matching regions realign after a computer program adds gaps in sequence 1.

1 CCAT___CA_AGTCC
2 CCATGTACAGAGTCC

▲ **Figure 26.8 Aligning segments of DNA.** Systematists search for similar sequences along DNA segments from two species (only one DNA strand is shown for each species). In this example, 11 of the original 12 bases have not changed since the species diverged. Hence, those portions of the sequences still align once the length is adjusted.

ACGGATAGTCCACTAGGCACTA
TCACCGACAGGTCTTTGACTAG

▲ Figure 26.9 **A molecular homoplasy.**

resemble each other at many points along their length most likely are homologous (see Figure 26.8). But in organisms that do not appear to be closely related, the bases that their otherwise very different sequences happen to share may simply be coincidental matches, called molecular homoplasies. For example, if the two DNA sequences in **Figure 26.9** were from distantly related organisms, the fact that they share 23% of their bases would be coincidental. Statistical tools have been developed to determine whether DNA sequences that share more than 25% of their bases do so because they are homologous.

CONCEPT CHECK 26.2

1. Decide whether each of the following pairs of structures more likely represents analogy or homology, and explain your reasoning: (a) a porcupine's quills and a cactus's spines; (b) a cat's paw and a human's hand; (c) an owl's wing and a hornet's wing.

2. **WHAT IF?** Suppose that two species, A and B, have similar appearances but very divergent gene sequences, while species B and C have very different appearances but similar gene sequences. Which pair of species is more likely to be closely related: A and B or B and C? Explain.

For suggested answers, see Appendix A.

Shared characters are used to construct phylogenetic trees

As we've discussed, a key step in reconstructing phylogenies is to distinguish homologous features from analogous ones (since only homology reflects evolutionary history). We must also choose a method of inferring phylogeny from these homologous characters. A widely used set of methods is known as cladistics.

Cladistics

In the approach to systematics called **cladistics**, common ancestry is the primary criterion used to classify organisms. Using this methodology, biologists attempt to place species into groups called **clades**, each of which includes an ancestral species and all of its descendants **(Figure 26.10a)**. Clades, like taxonomic categories of the Linnaean system, are nested within larger clades. In Figure 26.4, for example, the cat group (Felidae) represents a clade within a larger clade (Carnivora) that also includes the dog group (Canidae).

However, a taxon is equivalent to a clade only if it is **monophyletic** (from the Greek, meaning "single tribe"), signifying that it consists of an ancestral species and all of its descendants (see Figure 26.10a). Contrast this with a **paraphyletic** ("beside the tribe") group, which consists of an ancestral species and some, but not all, of its descendants **(Figure 26.10b)**, or a **polyphyletic** ("many tribes") group, which includes distantly related species but does not include their most recent common ancestor **(Figure 26.10c)**.

▼ Figure 26.10 **Monophyletic, paraphyletic, and polyphyletic groups.**

(a) Monophyletic group (clade)	(b) Paraphyletic group	(c) Polyphyletic group

 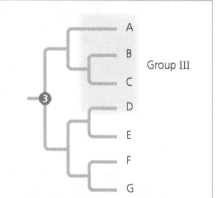

Group I, consisting of three species (A, B, C) and their common ancestor ❶, is a monophyletic group (clade), meaning that it consists of an ancestral species and *all* of its descendants.

Group II is paraphyletic, meaning that it consists of an ancestral species ❷ and some of its descendants (species D, E, F) but not all of them (missing species G).

Group III, consisting of four species (A, B, C, D), is polyphyletic, meaning that the common ancestor ❸ of its members is *not* part of the group.

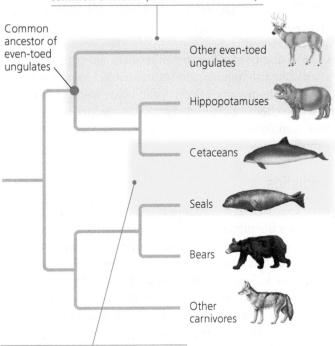

This group is paraphyletic because it does not include all the descendants of the common ancestor (it excludes cetaceans).

Common ancestor of even-toed ungulates

Other even-toed ungulates

Hippopotamuses

Cetaceans

Seals

Bears

Other carnivores

This group is polyphyletic because it does not include the most recent common ancestor of its members.

▲ **Figure 26.11 Examples of a paraphyletic and a polyphyletic group.**

? *Circle the branch point that represents the most recent common ancestor of cetaceans and seals. Explain why that ancestor would not be part of a cetacean–seal group defined by their similar body forms.*

Note that in a paraphyletic group, the most recent common ancestor of all members of the group *is* part of the group, whereas in a polyphyletic group the most recent common ancestor *is not* part of the group. For example, a group consisting of even-toed ungulates (hippopotamuses, deer, and their relatives) and their common ancestor is paraphyletic because it includes the common ancestor but excludes cetaceans (whales, dolphins, and porpoises), which descended from that ancestor **(Figure 26.11)**. In contrast, a group consisting of seals and cetaceans (based on their similar body forms) would be polyphyletic because it does not include the common ancestor of seals and cetaceans. Biologists avoid defining such polyphyletic groups; if new evidence indicates that an existing group is polyphyletic, organisms in that group are reclassified.

Shared Ancestral and Shared Derived Characters

As a result of descent with modification, organisms have characteristics they share with their ancestors, and they also have characteristics that differ from those of their ancestors. For example, all mammals have backbones, but a backbone does not distinguish mammals from other vertebrates because *all* vertebrates have backbones. The backbone predates the branching of mammals from other vertebrates. Thus for mammals, the backbone is a **shared ancestral character**, a character that originated in an ancestor of the taxon. In contrast, hair is a character shared by all mammals but *not* found in their ancestors. Thus, in mammals, hair is considered a **shared derived character**, an evolutionary novelty unique to a clade.

	TAXA					
CHARACTERS	Lancelet (outgroup)	Lamprey	Bass	Frog	Turtle	Leopard
Vertebral column (backbone)	0	1	1	1	1	1
Hinged jaws	0	0	1	1	1	1
Four walking legs	0	0	0	1	1	1
Amnion	0	0	0	0	1	1
Hair	0	0	0	0	0	1

(a) Character table. A 0 indicates that a character is absent; a 1 indicates that a character is present.

(b) Phylogenetic tree. Analyzing the distribution of these derived characters can provide insight into vertebrate phylogeny.

▲ **Figure 26.12 Constructing a phylogenetic tree.** The characters used here include the amnion, a membrane that encloses the embryo inside a fluid-filled sac (see Figure 34.25).

DRAW IT *In (b), circle the most inclusive clade for which a hinged jaw is a shared ancestral character.*

Note that it is a relative matter whether a character is considered ancestral or derived. A backbone can also qualify as a shared derived character, but only at a deeper branch point that distinguishes all vertebrates from other animals.

Inferring Phylogenies Using Derived Characters

Shared derived characters are unique to particular clades. Because all features of organisms arose at some point in the history of life, it should be possible to determine the clade in which each shared derived character first appeared and to use that information to infer evolutionary relationships.

To see how this analysis is done, consider the set of characters shown in **Figure 26.12a** for each of five vertebrates— a leopard, turtle, frog, bass, and lamprey (a jawless aquatic vertebrate). As a basis of comparison, we need to select an outgroup. An **outgroup** is a species or group of species from an evolutionary lineage that is known to have diverged before the lineage that includes the species we are studying (the **ingroup**). A suitable outgroup can be determined based on evidence from morphology, paleontology, embryonic development, and gene sequences. An appropriate outgroup for our example is the lancelet, a small animal that lives in mudflats and (like vertebrates) is a member of the more inclusive group called the chordates. Unlike the vertebrates, however, the lancelet does not have a backbone.

By comparing members of the ingroup with each other and with the outgroup, we can determine which characters were derived at the various branch points of vertebrate evolution. For example, *all* of the vertebrates in the ingroup have backbones: This character was present in the ancestral vertebrate, but not in the outgroup. Now note that hinged jaws are a character absent in lampreys but present in other members of the ingroup; this character helps us to identify an early branch point in the vertebrate clade. Proceeding in this way, we can translate the data in our table of characters into a phylogenetic tree that groups all the ingroup taxa into a hierarchy based on their shared derived characters (**Figure 26.12b**).

Phylogenetic Trees with Proportional Branch Lengths

In the phylogenetic trees we have presented so far, the lengths of the tree's branches do not indicate the degree of evolutionary change in each lineage. Furthermore, the chronology represented by the branching pattern of the tree is relative (earlier versus later) rather than absolute (how many millions of years ago). But in some tree diagrams, branch lengths are proportional to amount of evolutionary change or to the times at which particular events occurred.

In **Figure 26.13**, for example, the branch length of the phylogenetic tree reflects the number of changes that have taken place in a particular DNA sequence in that lineage. Note that the total length of the horizontal lines from the base of the tree to the mouse is less than that of the line leading to the outgroup species, the fruit fly *Drosophila*. This implies that in the time since the mouse and fly diverged from a common ancestor, more genetic changes have occurred in the *Drosophila* lineage than in the mouse lineage.

Even though the branches of a phylogenetic tree may have different lengths, among organisms alive today, all the different lineages that descend from a common ancestor have survived for the same number of years. To take an extreme example, humans and bacteria had a common ancestor that lived over 3 billion years ago. Fossils and genetic evidence indicate that this ancestor was a single-celled prokaryote. Even though bacteria have apparently changed

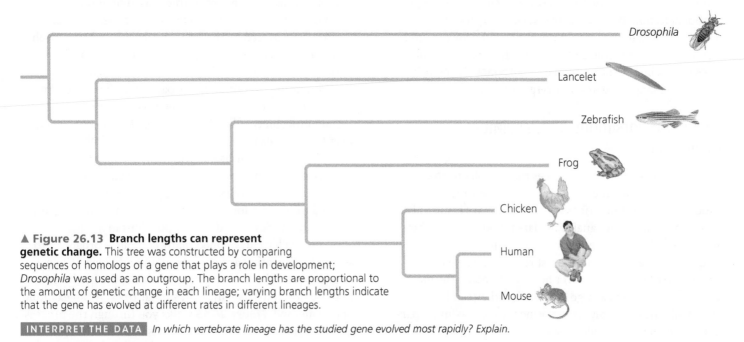

▲ **Figure 26.13 Branch lengths can represent genetic change.** This tree was constructed by comparing sequences of homologs of a gene that plays a role in development; *Drosophila* was used as an outgroup. The branch lengths are proportional to the amount of genetic change in each lineage; varying branch lengths indicate that the gene has evolved at different rates in different lineages.

INTERPRET THE DATA *In which vertebrate lineage has the studied gene evolved most rapidly? Explain.*

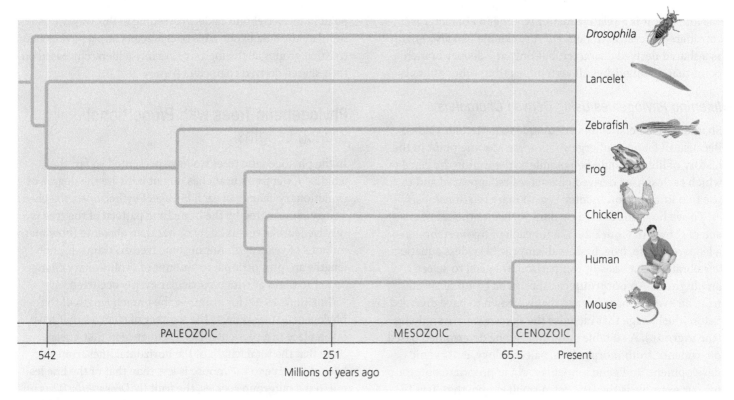

▲ **Figure 26.14 Branch lengths can indicate time.** This tree is based on the same molecular data as the tree in Figure 26.13, but here the branch points are mapped to dates based on fossil evidence. Thus, the branch lengths are proportional to time. Each lineage has the same total length from the base of the tree to the branch tip, indicating that all the lineages have diverged from the common ancestor for equal amounts of time.

little in their morphology since that common ancestor, there have nonetheless been 3 billion years of evolution in the bacterial lineage, just as there have been 3 billion years of evolution in the lineage that ultimately gave rise to humans.

These equal spans of chronological time can be represented in a phylogenetic tree whose branch lengths are proportional to time (**Figure 26.14**). Such a tree draws on fossil data to place branch points in the context of geologic time. Additionally, it is possible to combine these two types of trees by labeling branch points with information about rates of genetic change or dates of divergence.

Maximum Parsimony and Maximum Likelihood

As the database of DNA sequences that enables us to study more species grows, the difficulty of building the phylogenetic tree that best describes their evolutionary history also grows. What if you are analyzing data for 50 species? There are 3×10^{76} different ways to arrange 50 species into a tree! And which tree in this huge forest reflects the true phylogeny? Systematists can never be sure of finding the most accurate tree in such a large data set, but they can narrow the possibilities by applying the principles of maximum parsimony and maximum likelihood.

According to the principle of **maximum parsimony**, we should first investigate the simplest explanation that is consistent with the facts. (The parsimony principle is also called "Occam's razor" after William of Occam, a 14th-century English philosopher who advocated this minimalist problem-solving approach of "shaving away" unnecessary complications.) In the case of trees based on morphology, the most parsimonious tree requires the fewest evolutionary events, as measured by the origin of shared derived morphological characters. For phylogenies based on DNA, the most parsimonious tree requires the fewest base changes.

A **maximum likelihood** approach identifies the tree most likely to have produced a given set of DNA data, based on certain probability rules about how DNA sequences change over time. For example, the underlying probability rules could be based on the assumption that all nucleotide substitutions are equally likely. However, if evidence suggests that this assumption is not correct, more complex rules could be devised to account for different rates of change among different nucleotides or at different positions in a gene.

Scientists have developed many computer programs to search for trees that are parsimonious and likely. When a large amount of accurate data is available, the methods used in these programs usually yield similar trees. As an example of one method, **Figure 26.15** walks you through the process of identifying the most parsimonious molecular tree for a

Applying Parsimony to a Problem in Molecular Systematics

Application In considering possible phylogenies for a group of species, systematists compare molecular data for the species. An efficient way to begin is by identifying the most parsimonious hypothesis—the one that requires the fewest evolutionary events (molecular changes) to have occurred.

Technique Follow the numbered steps as we apply the principle of parsimony to a hypothetical phylogenetic problem involving three closely related bird species.

Species I   Species II   Species III

1 First, draw the three possible phylogenies for the species. (Although only 3 trees are possible when ordering 3 species, the number of possible trees increases rapidly with the number of species: There are 15 trees for 4 species and 34,459,425 trees for 10 species.)

Three phylogenetic hypotheses:

2 Tabulate the molecular data for the species. In this simplified example, the data represent a DNA sequence consisting of just four nucleotide bases. Data from several outgroup species (not shown) were used to infer the ancestral DNA sequence.

	Site			
	1	2	3	4
Species I	C	T	A	T
Species II	C	T	T	C
Species III	A	G	A	C
Ancestral sequence	A	G	T	T

3 Now focus on site 1 in the DNA sequence. In the tree on the left, a single base-change event, represented by the purple hatchmark on the branch leading to species I and II (and labeled 1/C, indicating a change at site 1 to nucleotide C), is sufficient to account for the site 1 data. In the other two trees, two base-change events are necessary.

4 Continuing the comparison of bases at sites 2, 3, and 4 reveals that each of the three trees requires a total of five additional base-change events (purple hatchmarks).

Results To identify the most parsimonious tree, we total all of the base-change events noted in steps 3 and 4. We conclude that the first tree is the most parsimonious of the three possible phylogenies. (In a real example, many more sites would be analyzed. Hence, the trees would often differ by more than one base-change event.)

6 events   7 events   7 events

three-species problem. Computer programs use the principle of parsimony to estimate phylogenies in a similar way: They examine large numbers of possible trees and identify those that require the fewest evolutionary changes.

Phylogenetic Trees as Hypotheses

This is a good place to reiterate that any phylogenetic tree represents a hypothesis about how the organisms in the tree are related to one another. The best hypothesis is the one that best fits all the available data. A phylogenetic hypothesis may be modified when new evidence compels systematists to revise their trees. Indeed, while many older phylogenetic hypotheses have been supported by new morphological and molecular data, others have been changed or rejected.

Thinking of phylogenies as hypotheses also allows us to use them in a powerful way: We can make and test predictions based on the assumption that a particular phylogeny—our hypothesis—is correct. For example, in an approach known as *phylogenetic bracketing*, we can predict (by parsimony) that features shared by two groups of closely related organisms are present in their common ancestor and all of its descendants unless independent data indicate otherwise. (Note that "prediction" can refer to unknown past events as well as to evolutionary changes yet to occur.)

This approach has been used to make novel predictions about dinosaurs. For example, there is evidence that birds descended from the theropods, a group of bipedal saurischian dinosaurs. As seen in **Figure 26.16**, the closest living relatives of birds are crocodiles. Birds and crocodiles share numerous features: They have four-chambered hearts, they "sing" to defend territories and attract mates (although a crocodile's "song" is more like a bellow), and they build nests. Both birds and crocodiles also care for their eggs by *brooding*, a behavior in which a parent warms the eggs with its body. Birds brood by sitting on their eggs, whereas crocodiles cover their eggs with their neck. Reasoning that any feature shared by birds and crocodiles is likely to have been present in their common ancestor (denoted by the blue dot in Figure 26.16) and *all* of its descendants, biologists predicted that dinosaurs had four-chambered hearts, sang, built nests, and exhibited brooding.

Internal organs, such as the heart, rarely fossilize, and it is, of course, difficult to test whether dinosaurs sang to defend territories and attract mates. However, fossilized dinosaur eggs and nests have provided evidence supporting the prediction of brooding in dinosaurs. First, a fossil embryo of an *Oviraptor* dinosaur was found, still inside its egg. This egg was identical to those found in another fossil, one that showed an *Oviraptor* crouching over a group of eggs in a posture similar to that seen in brooding birds today **(Figure 26.17)**. Researchers suggested that the *Oviraptor* dinosaur preserved in this second fossil died while incubating or protecting its eggs. The broader conclusion that emerged from this work—that dinosaurs built nests and exhibited brooding—has since been strengthened by additional fossil discoveries that show that other species of dinosaurs built nests and sat on their eggs. Finally, by supporting predictions based on the phylogenetic hypothesis shown in Figure 26.16, fossil discoveries of nests and brooding in dinosaurs provide independent data that suggest that the hypothesis is correct.

Front limb

Hind limb

(a) Fossil remains of *Oviraptor* and eggs. The orientation of the bones, which surround and cover the eggs, suggests that the dinosaur died while incubating or protecting its eggs.

Eggs

(b) Artist's reconstruction of the dinosaur's posture based on the fossil findings.

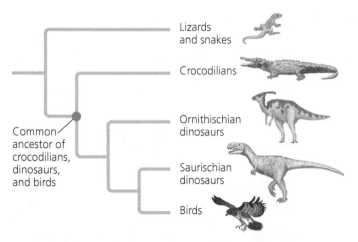

Lizards and snakes

Crocodilians

Ornithischian dinosaurs

Saurischian dinosaurs

Birds

Common ancestor of crocodilians, dinosaurs, and birds

▲ **Figure 26.16 A phylogenetic tree of birds and their close relatives.**

? *What is the most basal taxon represented in this tree?*

▲ **Figure 26.17 Fossil support for a phylogenetic prediction: Dinosaurs built nests and brooded their eggs.**

1. To distinguish a particular clade of mammals within the larger clade that corresponds to class Mammalia, would hair be a useful character? Why or why not?

2. The most parsimonious tree of evolutionary relationships can be inaccurate. How can this occur?

3. **WHAT IF?** Draw a phylogenetic tree that includes the relationships from Figure 25.7 and Figure 26.16. Traditionally, all the taxa shown besides birds and mammals were classified as reptiles. Would a cladistic approach support that classification? Explain.

For suggested answers, see Appendix A.

CONCEPT 26.4

An organism's evolutionary history is documented in its genome

As you have seen in this chapter, molecular systematics—using comparisons of nucleic acids or other molecules to deduce relatedness—can reveal phylogenetic relationships that cannot be determined by nonmolecular methods such as comparative anatomy. For example, molecular systematics helps us uncover evolutionary relationships between groups that have little common ground for morphological comparison, such as animals and fungi. And molecular methods allow us to reconstruct phylogenies among groups of present-day organisms for which the fossil record is poor or lacking entirely.

Different genes can evolve at different rates, even in the same evolutionary lineage. As a result, molecular trees can represent short or long periods of time, depending on which genes are used. For example, the DNA that codes for ribosomal RNA (rRNA) changes relatively slowly. Therefore, comparisons of DNA sequences in these genes are useful for investigating relationships between taxa that diverged hundreds of millions of years ago. Studies of rRNA sequences indicate, for instance, that fungi are more closely related to animals than to plants. In contrast, mitochondrial DNA (mtDNA) evolves relatively rapidly and can be used to explore recent evolutionary events. One research team has traced the relationships among Native American groups through their mtDNA sequences. The molecular findings corroborate other evidence that the Pima of Arizona, the Maya of Mexico, and the Yanomami of Venezuela are closely related, probably descending from the first of three waves of immigrants that crossed the Bering Land Bridge from Asia to the Americas about 15,000 years ago.

Gene Duplications and Gene Families

What do molecular data reveal about the evolutionary history of genome change? Consider gene duplication, which plays a particularly important role in evolution because it increases the number of genes in the genome, providing more opportunities for further evolutionary changes. Molecular techniques now allow us to trace the phylogenies of gene duplications. These molecular phylogenies must account for repeated duplications that have resulted in *gene families*, groups of related genes within an organism's genome (see Figure 21.11).

Accounting for such duplications leads us to distinguish two types of homologous genes **(Figure 26.18)**: orthologous genes and paralogous genes. In **orthologous genes** (from the Greek *orthos*, exact), the homology is the result of a

▼ **Figure 26.18 Two types of homologous genes.** Colored bands mark regions of the genes where differences in base sequences have accumulated.

(a) Formation of orthologous genes: a product of speciation

Ancestral gene

Ancestral species

Speciation with divergence of gene

Orthologous genes

Species A   **Species B**

(b) Formation of paralogous genes: within a species

Ancestral gene

Species C

Gene duplication and divergence

Paralogous genes

Species C after many generations

speciation event and hence occurs between genes found in different species (see Figure 26.18a). For example, the genes that code for cytochrome *c* (a protein that functions in electron transport chains) in humans and dogs are orthologous. In **paralogous genes** (from the Greek *para*, in parallel), the homology results from gene duplication; hence, multiple copies of these genes have diverged from one another within a species (see Figure 26.18b). In Chapter 23, you encountered the example of olfactory receptor genes, which have undergone many gene duplications in vertebrates; humans have 350 of these paralogous genes, while mice have 1,000.

Note that orthologous genes can only diverge after speciation has taken place, that is, after the genes are found in separate gene pools. For example, although the cytochrome *c* genes in humans and dogs serve the same function, the gene's sequence in humans has diverged from that in dogs in the time since these species last shared a common ancestor. Paralogous genes, on the other hand, can diverge within a species because they are present in more than one copy in the genome. The paralogous genes that make up the olfactory receptor gene family in humans have diverged from each other during our long evolutionary history. They now specify proteins that confer sensitivity to a wide variety of molecules, ranging from food odors to sex pheromones.

Genome Evolution

Now that we can compare the entire genomes of different organisms, including our own, two patterns have emerged. First, lineages that diverged long ago often share many orthologous genes. For example, though the human and mouse lineages diverged about 65 million years ago, 99% of the genes of humans and mice are orthologous. And 50% of human genes are orthologous with those of yeast, despite 1 billion years of divergent evolution. Such commonalities explain why disparate organisms nevertheless share many biochemical and developmental pathways. As a result of these shared pathways, the functioning of genes linked to diseases in humans can often be investigated by studying yeast and other organisms distantly related to humans.

Second, the number of genes a species has doesn't seem to increase through duplication at the same rate as perceived phenotypic complexity. Humans have only about four times as many genes as yeast, a single-celled eukaryote, even though—unlike yeast—we have a large, complex brain and a body with more than 200 different types of tissues. Evidence is emerging that many human genes are more versatile than those of yeast: A single human gene can encode multiple proteins that perform different tasks in various body tissues. Unraveling the mechanisms that cause this genomic versatility and phenotypic variation is an exciting challenge.

CONCEPT 26.5

Molecular clocks help track evolutionary time

One goal of evolutionary biology is to understand the relationships among all organisms, including those for which there is no fossil record. However, if we attempt to determine the timing of phylogenies that extend beyond the fossil record, we must rely on an important assumption about how change occurs at the molecular level.

Molecular Clocks

We stated earlier that researchers have estimated that the common ancestor of Hawaiian silversword plants lived about 5 million years ago. How did they make this estimate? They relied on the concept of a **molecular clock**, an approach for measuring the absolute time of evolutionary change based on the observation that some genes and other regions of genomes appear to evolve at constant rates. An assumption underlying the molecular clock is that the number of nucleotide substitutions in orthologous genes is proportional to the time that has elapsed since the genes branched from their common ancestor (divergence time). In the case of paralogous genes, the number of substitutions is proportional to the time since the ancestral gene was duplicated.

We can calibrate the molecular clock of a gene that has a reliable average rate of evolution by graphing the number of genetic differences—for example, nucleotide, codon, or amino acid differences—against the dates of evolutionary branch points that are known from the fossil record (Figure 26.19). The average rates of genetic change inferred from such graphs can then be used to estimate the dates of events that cannot be discerned from the fossil record, such as the origin of the silverswords discussed earlier.

Of course, no gene marks time with complete precision. In fact, some portions of the genome appear to have evolved

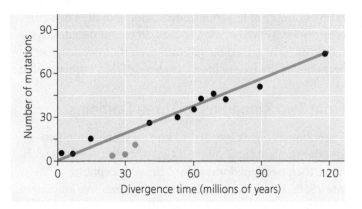

▲ **Figure 26.19 A molecular clock for mammals.** The number of accumulated mutations in seven proteins has increased over time in a consistent manner for most mammal species. The three green data points represent primate species, whose proteins appear to have evolved more slowly than those of other mammals. The divergence time for each data point was based on fossil evidence.

INTERPRET THE DATA *Use the graph to estimate the divergence time for a mammal with a total of 30 mutations in the seven proteins.*

in irregular bursts that are not at all clocklike. And even those genes that seem to act as reliable molecular clocks are accurate only in the statistical sense of showing a fairly smooth *average* rate of change. Over time, there may still be deviations from that average rate. Furthermore, the same gene may evolve at different rates in different groups of organisms. Finally, when comparing genes that are clocklike, the rate of the clock may vary greatly from one gene to another; some genes evolve a million times faster than others.

Differences in Clock Speed

What causes such differences in the speed at which clocklike genes evolve? The answer stems from the fact that some mutations are selectively neutral—neither beneficial nor detrimental. Of course, many new mutations are harmful and are removed quickly by selection. But if most of the rest are neutral and have little or no effect on fitness, then the rate of evolution of those neutral mutations should indeed be regular, like a clock. Differences in the clock rate for different genes are a function of how important a gene is. If the exact sequence of amino acids that a gene specifies is essential to survival, most of the mutational changes will be harmful and only a few will be neutral. As a result, such genes change only slowly. But if the exact sequence of amino acids is less critical, fewer of the new mutations will be harmful and more will be neutral. Such genes change more quickly.

Potential Problems with Molecular Clocks

In fact, molecular clocks do not run as smoothly as would be expected if the underlying mutations were selectively neutral. Many irregularities are likely to be the result of natural selection in which certain DNA changes are favored over

others. Indeed, evidence suggests that almost half the amino acid differences in proteins of two *Drosophila* species, *D. simulans* and *D. yakuba*, are not neutral but have resulted from natural selection. But because the direction of natural selection may change repeatedly over long periods of time (and hence may average out), some genes experiencing selection can nevertheless serve as approximate markers of elapsed time.

Another question arises when researchers attempt to extend molecular clocks beyond the time span documented by the fossil record. Although some fossils are more than 3 billion years old, these are very rare. An abundant fossil record extends back only about 550 million years, but molecular clocks have been used to date evolutionary divergences that occurred a billion or more years ago. These estimates assume that the clocks have been constant for all that time. Such estimates are highly uncertain.

In some cases, problems may be avoided by calibrating molecular clocks with data on the rates at which genes have evolved in different taxa. In other cases, problems may be avoided by using many genes rather than the common approach of using just one or a few genes. By using many genes, fluctuations in evolutionary rate due to natural selection or other factors that vary over time may average out. For example, one group of researchers constructed molecular clocks of vertebrate evolution from published sequence data for 658 nuclear genes. Despite the broad period of time covered (nearly 600 million years) and the fact that natural selection probably affected some of these genes, their estimates of divergence times agreed closely with fossil-based estimates. As this example suggests, if used with care, molecular clocks can aid our understanding of evolutionary relationships.

Applying a Molecular Clock: Dating the Origin of HIV

Researchers have used a molecular clock to date the origin of HIV infection in humans. Phylogenetic analysis shows that HIV, the virus that causes AIDS, is descended from viruses that infect chimpanzees and other primates. (Most of these viruses do not cause AIDS-like diseases in their native hosts.) When did HIV jump to humans? There is no simple answer, because the virus has spread to humans more than once. The multiple origins of HIV are reflected in the variety of strains (genetic types) of the virus. HIV's genetic material is made of RNA, and like other RNA viruses, it evolves quickly.

The most widespread strain in humans is HIV-1 M. To pinpoint the earliest HIV-1 M infection, researchers compared samples of the virus from various times during the epidemic, including a sample from 1959. A comparison of gene sequences showed that the virus has evolved in a clocklike

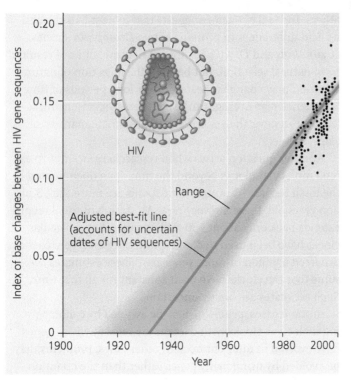

© 2000 AAAS

▲ **Figure 26.20 Dating the origin of HIV-1 M.** The black data points are based on DNA sequences of an HIV gene in patients' blood samples. (The dates when these individual HIV gene sequences arose are not certain because a person can harbor the virus for years before symptoms occur.) Projecting the gene's rate of change backward in time suggests that the virus originated in the 1930s.

fashion (**Figure 26.20**). Extrapolating backward in time using the molecular clock indicates that the HIV-1 M strain first spread to humans around 1930. A later study, which dated the origin of HIV using a more advanced molecular clock approach than that covered in this book, estimated that the HIV-1 M strain first spread to humans around 1910.

CONCEPT CHECK 26.5

1. What is a molecular clock? What assumption underlies the use of a molecular clock?

2. **MAKE CONNECTIONS** Review Concept 17.5. Then explain how numerous base changes could occur in an organism's DNA yet have no effect on its fitness.

3. **WHAT IF?** Suppose a molecular clock dates the divergence of two taxa at 80 million years ago, but new fossil evidence shows that the taxa diverged at least 120 million years ago. Explain how this could happen.

For suggested answers, see Appendix A.

CONCEPT 26.6

Our understanding of the tree of life continues to change based on new data

The discovery that the glass lizard in Figure 26.1 evolved from a different lineage of legless lizards than did snakes

is one example of how our understanding of life's diversity is informed by systematics. Indeed, in recent decades, systematists have gained insight into even the very deepest branches of the tree of life by analyzing DNA sequence data.

From Two Kingdoms to Three Domains

Taxonomists once classified all known species into two kingdoms: plants and animals. Classification schemes with more than two kingdoms gained broad acceptance in the late 1960s, when many biologists recognized five kingdoms: Monera (prokaryotes), Protista (a diverse kingdom consisting mostly of unicellular organisms), Plantae, Fungi, and Animalia. This system highlighted the two fundamentally different types of cells, prokaryotic and eukaryotic, and set the prokaryotes apart from all eukaryotes by placing them in their own kingdom, Monera.

However, phylogenies based on genetic data soon began to reveal a problem with this system: Some prokaryotes differ as much from each other as they do from eukaryotes. Such difficulties have led biologists to adopt a three-domain system. The three domains—Bacteria, Archaea, and Eukarya—are a taxonomic level higher than the kingdom level. The validity of these domains is supported by many studies, including a recent study that analyzed nearly 100 completely sequenced genomes.

The domain Bacteria contains most of the currently known prokaryotes, while the domain Archaea consists of a diverse group of prokaryotic organisms that inhabit a wide variety of environments. The domain Eukarya consists of all the organisms that have cells containing true nuclei. This domain includes many groups of single-celled organisms as well as multicellular plants, fungi, and animals. **Figure 26.21** represents one possible phylogenetic tree for the three domains and some of the many lineages they encompass.

The three-domain system highlights the fact that much of the history of life has been about single-celled organisms. The two prokaryotic domains consist entirely of single-celled organisms, and even in Eukarya, only the branches labeled in blue type (land plants, fungi, and animals) are dominated by multicellular organisms. Of the five kingdoms previously recognized by taxonomists, most biologists continue to recognize Plantae, Fungi, and Animalia, but not Monera and Protista. The kingdom Monera is obsolete because it would have members in two different domains. The kingdom Protista has also crumbled because it includes members that are more closely related to plants, fungi, or animals than to other protists (see Chapter 28).

The Important Role of Horizontal Gene Transfer

In the phylogeny shown in Figure 26.21, the first major split in the history of life occurred when bacteria diverged from

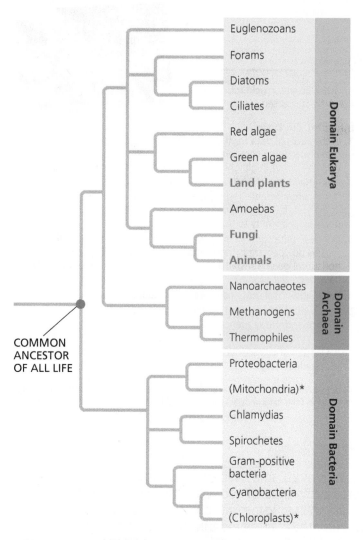

Euglenozoans

Forams

Diatoms

Ciliates

Red algae

Green algae

Land plants

Amoebas

Fungi

Animals

Domain Eukarya

Nanoarchaeotes

Methanogens

Thermophiles

Domain Archaea

Proteobacteria

(Mitochondria)*

Chlamydias

Spirochetes

Gram-positive bacteria

Cyanobacteria

(Chloroplasts)*

Domain Bacteria

COMMON ANCESTOR OF ALL LIFE

▲ **Figure 26.21 The three domains of life.** This phylogenetic tree is based on sequence data for rRNA and other genes. For simplicity, only some of the major branches in each domain are shown. Lineages within Eukarya that are dominated by multicellular organisms (land plants, fungi, and animals) are in blue type, while the two lineages denoted by an asterisk are based on DNA from cellular organelles. All other lineages consist solely or mainly of single-celled organisms.

MAKE CONNECTIONS *After reviewing endosymbiont theory (see Figure 6.16), explain the specific positions of the mitochondrion and chloroplast lineages on this tree.*

other organisms. If this tree is correct, eukaryotes and archaea are more closely related to each other than either is to bacteria.

This reconstruction of the tree of life is based in part on sequence comparisons of rRNA genes, which code for the RNA components of ribosomes. However, some other genes reveal a different set of relationships. For example, researchers have found that many of the genes that influence metabolism in yeast (a unicellular eukaryote) are more similar to genes in the domain Bacteria than they are to genes in the domain Archaea—a finding that suggests that the eukaryotes may share a more recent common ancestor with bacteria than with archaea.

What causes trees based on data from different genes to yield such different results? Comparisons of complete genomes from the three domains show that there have been substantial movements of genes between organisms in the different domains. These took place through **horizontal gene transfer**, a process in which genes are transferred from one genome to another through mechanisms such as exchange of transposable elements and plasmids, viral infection (see Chapter 19), and perhaps fusions of organisms (as when a host and its endosymbiont become a single organism). Recent research reinforces the view that horizontal gene transfer is important. For example, a 2008 analysis indicated that, on average, 80% of the genes in 181 prokaryotic genomes had moved between species at some point during the course of evolution. Because phylogenetic trees are based on the assumption that genes are passed vertically from one generation to the next, the occurrence of such horizontal transfer events helps to explain why trees built using different genes can give inconsistent results.

Horizontal gene transfer can also occur between eukaryotes. For example, over 200 cases of the horizontal transfer of transposons have been reported in eukaryotes, including humans and other primates, plants, birds, and the gecko shown in **Figure 26.22**. Nuclear genes have also been transferred horizontally from one eukaryote to another. The Scientific Skills Exercise describes one such example, giving you the opportunity to interpret data on the transfer of a pigment gene to an aphid from another species.

Overall, horizontal gene transfer has played a key role throughout the evolutionary history of life and it continues to occur today. Some biologists have argued that horizontal gene transfer was so common that the early history of life should be represented not as a dichotomously branching tree like that in Figure 26.21, but rather as a tangled network

▼ **Figure 26.22 A recipient of transferred genes: the Mediterranean house gecko (*Hemidactylus turcicus*).** Recent genetic evidence indicates that this gecko is one of 17 reptile species that acquired the transposon *SPIN* as a result of horizontal gene transfer. The transposon may have been transferred from one species to another by the feeding activities of blood-sucking insects.

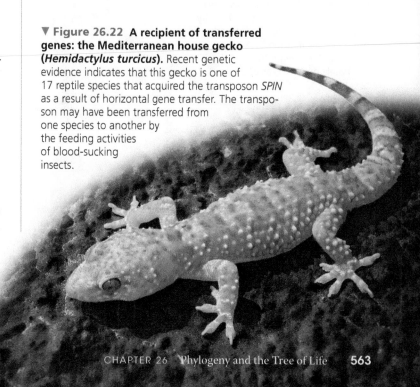

Using Protein Sequence Data to Test an Evolutionary Hypothesis

Did Aphids Acquire Their Ability to Make Carotenoids Through Horizontal Gene Transfer? Carotenoids are colored molecules that have diverse functions in many organisms, such as photosynthesis in plants and light detection in animals. Plants and many microorganisms can synthesize carotenoids from scratch, but animals generally cannot (they must obtain carotenoids from their diet). One exception is the pea aphid *Acyrthosiphon pisum*, a small plant-dwelling insect whose genome includes a full set of genes for the enzymes needed to make carotenoids. Because other animals lack these genes, it is unlikely that aphids inherited them from a single-celled common ancestor shared with microorganisms and plants. So where did they come from? Evolutionary biologists hypothesize that an aphid ancestor acquired these genes by horizontal gene transfer from distantly related organisms.

How the Experiment Was Done Scientists obtained the DNA sequences for the carotenoid-biosynthesis genes from several species, including aphids, fungi, bacteria, and plants. A computer "translated" these sequences into amino acid sequences of the encoded polypeptides and aligned the amino acid sequences. This allowed the team to compare the corresponding polypeptides in the different organisms.

Data from the Experiment The sequences below show the first 60 amino acids of one polypeptide of the carotenoid-biosynthesis enzymes in the plant *Arabidopsis thaliana* (bottom) and the corresponding amino acids in five nonplant species, using the one-letter abbreviations for the amino acids (see Figure 5.14). A hyphen (-) indicates that a species lacks

a particular amino acid found in the *Arabidopsis* sequence.

Interpret the Data

1. In the rows of data for the organisms being compared with the aphid, highlight the amino acids that are identical to the corresponding amino acids in the aphid.
2. Which organism has the most amino acids in common with the aphid? Rank the partial polypeptides from the other four organisms in degree of similarity to that of the aphid.
3. Do these data support the hypothesis that aphids acquired the gene for this polypeptide by horizontal gene transfer? Why or why not? If horizontal gene transfer did occur, what type of organism is likely to have been the source?
4. What additional sequence data would support your hypothesis?
5. How would you account for the similarities between the aphid sequence and the sequences for the bacteria and plant?

(MB) A version of this Scientific Skills Exercise can be assigned in MasteringBiology.

Data from Nancy A. Moran, Yale University. See N. A. Moran and T. Jarvik, Lateral transfer of genes from fungi underlies carotenoid production in aphids, *Science* 328:624–627 (2010).

Organism	Alignment of Amino Acid Sequences
Acyrthosiphon (aphid)	IKIIIGSGV GGTAAAARLS KKGFQVEVYE KNSYNGGRCS IIR-HNGHRF DQGPSL--YL
Ustilago (fungus)	KKVVIIGAGA GGTALAARLG RRGYSVTVLE KNSFGGGRCS LIH-HDGHRW DQGPSL--YL
Gibberella (fungus)	KSVIVIGAGV GGVSTAARLA KAGFKVTILE KNDFTGGRCS LIH-NDGHRF DQGPSL--LL
Staphylococcus (bacterium)	MKIAVIGAGV TGLAAAARIA SQGHEVTIFE KNNNVGGRMN QLK-KDGFTF DMGPTI--VM
Pantoea (bacterium)	KRTFVIGAGF GGLALAIRLQ AAGIATTVLE QHDKPGGRAY VWQ-DQGFTF DAGPTV--IT
Arabidopsis (plant)	WDAVVIGGGH NGLTAAAYLA RGGLSVAVLE RRHVIGGAAV TEEIVPGFKF SRCSYLQGLL

▶ **Figure 26.23 A tangled web of life.** Horizontal gene transfer may have been so common in the early history of life that the base of a "tree of life" might be more accurately portrayed as a tangled web.

© 1999 AAAS

of connected branches (**Figure 26.23**). Although scientists continue to debate whether early steps in the history of life are best represented as a tree or a tangled web, in recent decades there have been many exciting discoveries about evolutionary events that occurred over time. We'll explore such discoveries in the rest of this unit's chapters, beginning with Earth's earliest inhabitants, the prokaryotes.

CONCEPT CHECK 26.6

1. Why is the kingdom Monera no longer considered a valid taxon?
2. Explain why phylogenies based on different genes can yield different branching patterns for the tree of all life.
3. **WHAT IF?** Draw the three possible dichotomously branching trees showing evolutionary relationships for the domains Bacteria, Archaea, and Eukarya. Two of these trees have been supported by genetic data. Is it likely that the third tree might also receive such support? Explain your answer.

For suggested answers, see Appendix A.

SUMMARY OF KEY CONCEPTS

CONCEPT 26.1

Phylogenies show evolutionary relationships (pp. 548–551)

- Linnaeus's **binomial** classification system gives organisms two-part names: a **genus** plus a specific epithet.
- In the Linnaean system, species are grouped in increasingly broad taxa: Related genera are placed in the same family, families in orders, orders in classes, classes in phyla, phyla in kingdoms, and (more recently) kingdoms in domains.
- Systematists depict evolutionary relationships as branching **phylogenetic trees**. Many systematists propose that classification be based entirely on evolutionary relationships.

- Unless branch lengths are proportional to time or genetic change, a phylogenetic tree indicates only patterns of descent.
- Much information can be learned about a species from its evolutionary history; hence, phylogenies are useful in a wide range of applications.

? *Humans and chimpanzees are sister species. Explain what that means.*

CONCEPT 26.2

Phylogenies are inferred from morphological and molecular data (pp. 551–553)

- Organisms with similar morphologies or DNA sequences are likely to be more closely related than organisms with very different structures and genetic sequences.
- To infer phylogeny, **homology** (similarity due to shared ancestry) must be distinguished from **analogy** (similarity due to convergent evolution).
- Computer programs are used to align comparable DNA sequences and to distinguish molecular homologies from coincidental matches between taxa that diverged long ago.

? *Why is it necessary to distinguish homology from analogy to infer phylogeny?*

CONCEPT 26.3

Shared characters are used to construct phylogenetic trees (pp. 553–559)

- A **clade** is a monophyletic grouping that includes an ancestral species and all of its descendants.

- Clades can be distinguished by their **shared derived characters**.

- Among phylogenies, the most parsimonious tree is the one that requires the fewest evolutionary changes. The most likely tree is the one based on the most likely pattern of changes.
- Well-supported phylogenetic hypotheses are consistent with a wide range of data.

? *Explain the logic of using shared derived characters to infer phylogeny.*

CONCEPT 26.4

An organism's evolutionary history is documented in its genome (pp. 559–560)

- **Orthologous genes** are homologous genes found in different species as a result of speciation. **Paralogous genes** are homologous genes within a species that result from gene duplication; such genes can diverge and potentially take on new functions.
- Distantly related species often have many orthologous genes. The small variation in gene number in organisms of varying complexity suggests that genes are versatile and may have multiple functions.

? *When reconstructing phylogenies, is it better to compare orthologous or paralogous genes? Explain.*

CONCEPT 26.5

Molecular clocks help track evolutionary time (pp. 560–562)

- Some regions of DNA change at a rate consistent enough to serve as a **molecular clock**, in which the amount of genetic change is used to estimate the date of past evolutionary events. Other DNA regions change in a less predictable way.
- Molecular clock analyses suggest that the most common strain of HIV jumped from primates to humans in the early 1900s.

? *Describe some assumptions and limitations of molecular clocks.*

CONCEPT 26.6

Our understanding of the tree of life continues to change based on new data (pp. 562–564)

- Past classification systems have given way to the current view of the tree of life, which consists of three great **domains**: Bacteria, Archaea, and Eukarya.

- Phylogenies based in part on rRNA genes suggest that eukaryotes are most closely related to archaea, while data from some other genes suggest a closer relationship to bacteria.
- Genetic analyses indicate that extensive horizontal gene transfer has occurred throughout the evolutionary history of life.

? *Why was the five-kingdom system abandoned for a three-domain system?*

TEST YOUR UNDERSTANDING

LEVEL 1: KNOWLEDGE/COMPREHENSION

1. In a comparison of birds and mammals, the condition of having four limbs is
   a. a shared ancestral character.
   b. a shared derived character.
   c. a character useful for distinguishing birds from mammals.
   d. an example of analogy rather than homology.

2. To apply parsimony to constructing a phylogenetic tree,
   a. choose the tree that assumes all evolutionary changes are equally probable.
   b. choose the tree in which the branch points are based on as many shared derived characters as possible.
   c. choose the tree that represents the fewest evolutionary changes, in either DNA sequences or morphology.
   d. choose the tree with the fewest branch points.

LEVEL 2: APPLICATION/ANALYSIS

3. In Figure 26.4, which similarly inclusive taxon descended from the same common ancestor as Canidae?
   a. Felidae   c. Carnivora
   b. Mustelidae   d. *Lutra*

4. Three living species X, Y, and Z share a common ancestor T, as do extinct species U and V. A grouping that consists of species T, X, Y, and Z (but not U or V) makes up
   a. a monophyletic taxon.
   b. an ingroup, with species U as the outgroup.
   c. a paraphyletic group.
   d. a polyphyletic group.

5. Based on the tree below, which statement is *not* correct?

   a. The salamander lineage is a basal taxon.
   b. Salamanders are a sister group to the group containing lizards, goats, and humans.
   c. Salamanders are as closely related to goats as to humans.
   d. Lizards are more closely related to salamanders than to humans.

6. If you were using cladistics to build a phylogenetic tree of cats, which of the following would be the best outgroup?
   a. wolf   c. lion
   b. domestic cat   d. leopard

7. The relative lengths of the frog and mouse branches in the phylogenetic tree in Figure 26.13 indicate that
   a. frogs evolved before mice.
   b. mice evolved before frogs.
   c. the homolog has evolved more rapidly in mice.
   d. the homolog has evolved more slowly in mice.

LEVEL 3: SYNTHESIS/EVALUATION

8. **EVOLUTION CONNECTION**
   Darwin suggested looking at a species' close relatives to learn what its ancestors may have been like. How does his suggestion anticipate recent methods, such as phylogenetic bracketing and the use of outgroups in cladistic analysis?

9. **SCIENTIFIC INQUIRY**
   DRAW IT (a) Draw a phylogenetic tree based on characters 1–5 in the table below. Place hatch marks on the tree to indicate the origin(s) of characters 1–6. (b) Assume that tuna and dolphins are sister species and redraw the phylogenetic tree accordingly. Use hatch marks to indicate the origin(s) of characters 1–6. (c) How many evolutionary changes are required in each tree? Which tree is most parsimonious?

Character	Lancelet (outgroup)	Lamprey	Tuna	Salamander	Turtle	Leopard	Dolphin
(1) Backbone	0	1	1	1	1	1	1
(2) Hinged jaw	0	0	1	1	1	1	1
(3) Four limbs	0	0	0	1	1	1	1*
(4) Amnion	0	0	0	0	1	1	1
(5) Milk	0	0	0	0	0	1	1
(6) Dorsal fin	0	0	1	0	0	0	1

*Although adult dolphins have only two obvious limbs (their flippers), as embryos they have two hind-limb buds, for a total of four limbs.

10. **WRITE ABOUT A THEME: INFORMATION**
    In a short essay (100–150 words), explain how genetic information—along with an understanding of the process of descent with modification—enables scientists to reconstruct phylogenies that extend hundreds of millions of years back in time.

11. **SYNTHESIZE YOUR KNOWLEDGE**

This West Indian manatee (*Trichechus manatus*) is an aquatic mammal. Like amphibians and reptiles, mammals are tetrapods (vertebrates with four limbs). Explain why manatees are considered tetrapods even though they lack hind limbs, and suggest traits that manatees likely share with leopards and other mammals (see Figure 26.12b). How might early members of the manatee lineage have differed from today's manatees?

For selected answers, see Appendix A.

MasteringBiology®

Students Go to **MasteringBiology** for assignments, the eText, and the Study Area with practice tests, animations, and activities.

Instructors Go to **MasteringBiology** for automatically graded tutorials and questions that you can assign to your students, plus Instructor Resources.

27

Bacteria and Archaea

▲ **Figure 27.1 Why is this lake's water pink?**

Masters of Adaptation

At certain times of year, the Laguna Salada de Torrevieja in Spain (the "Salty Lagoon") appears pink **(Figure 27.1)**, a sign of waters many times saltier than seawater. Yet despite these harsh conditions, the dramatic color is caused not by minerals or other nonliving sources, but by living things. What organisms can live in such an inhospitable environment, and how do they do it?

The pink color in the Laguna Salada de Torrevieja comes from trillions of prokaryotes in the domains Archaea and Bacteria, including archaea in the genus *Halobacterium*. These archaea have red membrane pigments, some of which capture light energy that is used to drive ATP synthesis. *Halobacterium* species are among the most salt-tolerant organisms on Earth; they thrive in salinities that dehydrate and kill other cells. A *Halobacterium* cell compensates for water lost through osmosis by pumping potassium ions (K^+) into the cell until the ionic concentration inside the cell matches the concentration outside.

Like *Halobacterium*, many other prokaryotes can tolerate extreme conditions. Examples include *Deinococcus radiodurans*, which can survive 3 million rads of radiation (3,000 times the dose fatal to humans), and *Picrophilus oshimae*, which can grow at a pH of 0.03 (acidic enough to dissolve metal). Other prokaryotes live

567

in environments that are too cold or too hot for most other organisms, and some have even been found living in rocks 3.2 km (2 miles) below Earth's surface.

Prokaryotic species are also very well adapted to more "normal" habitats—the lands and waters in which most other species are found. Their ability to adapt to a broad range of habitats helps explain why prokaryotes are the most abundant organisms on Earth: Indeed, the number of prokaryotes in a handful of fertile soil is greater than the number of people who have ever lived. In this chapter, we'll examine the adaptations, diversity, and enormous ecological impact of these remarkable organisms.

CONCEPT 27.1

Structural and functional adaptations contribute to prokaryotic success

The first organisms to inhabit Earth were prokaryotes that lived 3.5 billion years ago (see Chapter 25). Throughout their long evolutionary history, prokaryotic populations have been (and continue to be) subjected to natural selection in all kinds of environments, resulting in their enormous diversity today.

We'll begin by describing prokaryotes. Most prokaryotes are unicellular, although the cells of some species remain attached to each other after cell division. Prokaryotic cells typically have diameters of 0.5–5 μm, much smaller than the 10–100 μm diameter of many eukaryotic cells. (One notable exception, *Thiomargarita namibiensis*, can be as large as 750 μm in diameter—bigger than the dot on this i.) Prokaryotic cells have a variety of shapes (**Figure 27.2**). Finally, although they are unicellular and small, prokaryotes are well organized, achieving all of an organism's life functions within a single cell.

Cell-Surface Structures

A key feature of nearly all prokaryotic cells is the cell wall, which maintains cell shape, protects the cell, and prevents it from bursting in a hypotonic environment (see Figure 7.12). In a hypertonic environment, most prokaryotes lose water and shrink away from their wall (plasmolyze). Such water losses can inhibit cell reproduction. Thus, salt can be used to preserve foods because it causes food-spoiling prokaryotes to lose water, preventing them from rapidly multiplying.

The cell walls of prokaryotes differ in structure from those of eukaryotes. In eukaryotes that have cell walls, such as plants and fungi, the walls are usually made of cellulose or chitin (see Concept 5.2). In contrast, most bacterial cell walls contain **peptidoglycan**, a polymer composed of modified sugars cross-linked by short polypeptides. This molecular fabric encloses the entire bacterium and anchors other

(a) Spherical   (b) Rod-shaped   (c) Spiral

▲ **Figure 27.2 The most common shapes of prokaryotes.** **(a)** Cocci (singular, *coccus*) are spherical prokaryotes. They occur singly, in pairs (diplococci), in chains of many cells (streptococci), and in clusters resembling bunches of grapes (staphylococci). **(b)** Bacilli (singular, *bacillus*) are rod-shaped prokaryotes. They are usually solitary, but in some forms the rods are arranged in chains (streptobacilli). **(c)** Spiral prokaryotes include spirilla, which range from comma-like shapes to loose coils, and spirochetes (shown here), which are corkscrew-shaped (colorized SEMs).

molecules that extend from its surface. Archaeal cell walls contain a variety of polysaccharides and proteins but lack peptidoglycan.

Using a technique called the **Gram stain**, developed by the 19th-century Danish physician Hans Christian Gram, scientists can categorize many bacterial species according to differences in cell wall composition. To do this, samples are first stained with crystal violet dye and iodine, then rinsed in alcohol, and finally stained with a red dye such as safranin. The structure of a bacterium's cell wall determines the staining response (**Figure 27.3**). **Gram-positive** bacteria have simpler walls with a relatively large amount of peptidoglycan. **Gram-negative** bacteria have less peptidoglycan and are structurally more complex, with an outer membrane that contains lipopolysaccharides (carbohydrates bonded to lipids).

Gram staining is a valuable tool in medicine for quickly determining if a patient's infection is due to gram-negative or to gram-positive bacteria. This information has treatment implications. The lipid portions of the lipopolysaccharides in the walls of many gram-negative bacteria are toxic, causing fever or shock. Furthermore, the outer membrane of a gram-negative bacterium helps protect it from the body's defenses. Gram-negative bacteria also tend to be more resistant than gram-positive species to antibiotics because the outer membrane impedes entry of the drugs. However, certain gram-positive species have virulent strains that are resistant to one or more antibiotics. (Figure 22.14 discusses

(a) Gram-positive bacteria

Gram-positive bacteria

Cell wall { Peptido-glycan layer

Plasma membrane {

10 µm

Gram-positive bacteria have a thick wall made of peptidoglycan. The crystal violet enters the cell, where it forms a complex with the iodine in the stain. Too large to pass through the thick cell wall, this complex is not removed by the alcohol rinse. Result: The crystal violet masks the red safranin dye.

(b) Gram-negative bacteria

Gram-negative bacteria

Carbohydrate portion of lipopolysaccharide

Cell wall { Outer membrane { Peptido-glycan layer

Plasma membrane {

Gram-negative bacteria have a thin layer of peptidoglycan, which is located between the plasma membrane and an outer membrane. The crystal violet–iodine complex can pass through this thin cell wall and hence is removed by the alcohol rinse. Result: The safranin dye stains the cell pink or red.

one example: methicillin-resistant *Staphylococcus aureus*, or MRSA, which can cause lethal skin infections.)

The effectiveness of certain antibiotics, such as penicillin, derives from their inhibition of peptidoglycan cross-linking. The resulting cell wall may not be functional, particularly in gram-positive bacteria. Such drugs destroy many species of pathogenic bacteria without adversely affecting human cells, which do not have peptidoglycan.

The cell wall of many prokaryotes is surrounded by a sticky layer of polysaccharide or protein. This layer is called a **capsule** if it is dense and well-defined (**Figure 27.4**) or a

slime layer if it is not as well organized. Both kinds of sticky outer layers enable prokaryotes to adhere to their substrate or to other individuals in a colony. Some capsules and slime layers protect against dehydration, and some shield pathogenic prokaryotes from attacks by their host's immune system.

In another way of withstanding harsh conditions, certain bacteria develop resistant cells called **endospores** when they lack an essential nutrient (**Figure 27.5**). The original cell produces a copy of its chromosome and surrounds that copy with a tough multilayered structure, forming the endospore.

Bacterial cell wall

Bacterial capsule

Tonsil cell

200 nm

▲ **Figure 27.4 Capsule.** The polysaccharide capsule around this *Streptococcus* bacterium enables the prokaryote to attach to cells in the respiratory tract—in this colorized TEM, a tonsil cell.

Endospore

Coat

0.3 µm

▲ **Figure 27.5 An endospore.** *Bacillus anthracis*, the bacterium that causes the disease anthrax, produces endospores (TEM). An endospore's protective, multilayered coat helps it survive in the soil for years.

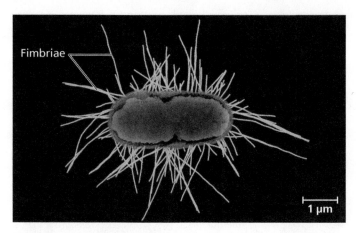

▲ **Figure 27.6 Fimbriae.** These numerous protein-containing appendages enable some prokaryotes to attach to surfaces or to other cells (colorized TEM).

Water is removed from the endospore, and its metabolism halts. The original cell then lyses, releasing the endospore. Most endospores are so durable that they can survive in boiling water; killing them requires heating lab equipment to 121°C under high pressure. In less hostile environments, endospores can remain dormant but viable for centuries, able to rehydrate and resume metabolism when their environment improves.

Finally, some prokaryotes stick to their substrate or to one another by means of hairlike appendages called **fimbriae** (singular, *fimbria*) (**Figure 27.6**). For example, the bacterium that causes gonorrhea, *Neisseria gonorrhoeae*, uses fimbriae to fasten itself to the mucous membranes of its host. Fimbriae are usually shorter and more numerous than **pili** (singular, *pilus*), appendages that pull two cells together prior to DNA transfer from one cell to the other (see Figure 27.12); pili are sometimes referred to as *sex pili*.

Motility

About half of all prokaryotes are capable of **taxis**, a directed movement toward or away from a stimulus (from the Greek *taxis*, to arrange). For example, prokaryotes that exhibit *chemotaxis* change their movement pattern in response to chemicals. They may move *toward* nutrients or oxygen (positive chemotaxis) or *away from* a toxic substance (negative chemotaxis). Some species can move at velocities exceeding 50 µm/sec—up to 50 times their body length per second. For perspective, consider that a person 1.7 m tall moving that fast would be running 306 km (190 miles) per hour!

Of the various structures that enable prokaryotes to move, the most common are flagella (**Figure 27.7**). Flagella (singular, *flagellum*) may be scattered over the entire surface of the cell or concentrated at one or both ends. Prokaryotic flagella differ greatly from eukaryotic flagella: They are one-tenth the width and typically are not covered by an extension of the plasma membrane (see Figure 6.24). The flagella of prokaryotes and eukaryotes also differ in their molecular composition and their mechanism of propulsion. Among prokaryotes, bacterial and archaeal flagella are similar in size and propulsion mechanism, but they are composed of entirely different and unrelated proteins. Overall, these structural and molecular comparisons indicate that the flagella of bacteria, archaea, and eukaryotes arose independently. Since current evidence shows that the flagella of organisms in the three domains perform similar functions but are not related by common descent, they are described as analogous, not homologous, structures.

Evolutionary Origins of Bacterial Flagella

The bacterial flagellum shown in **Figure 27.7** has three main parts (the motor, hook, and filament) that are themselves composed of 42 different kinds of proteins. How could such a complex structure evolve? In fact, much evidence indicates that bacterial flagella originated as simpler structures that were modified in a stepwise fashion over time. As in the case of the human eye (see Concept 25.6), biologists asked whether a less complex version of the flagellum could still benefit its owner. Analyses of hundreds of bacterial genomes indicate that

Flagellum

Filament

Hook

20 nm

Motor

Cell wall

Plasma membrane

Rod

Peptidoglycan layer

▲ **Figure 27.7 A prokaryotic flagellum.** The motor of a prokaryotic flagellum consists of a system of rings embedded in the cell wall and plasma membrane (TEM). The electron transport chain pumps protons out of the cell. The diffusion of protons back into the cell provides the force that turns a curved hook and thereby causes the attached filament to rotate and propel the cell. (This diagram shows flagellar structures characteristic of gram-negative bacteria.)

only half of the flagellum's protein components appear to be necessary for it to function; the others are inessential or not encoded in the genomes of some species. Of the 21 proteins required by all species studied to date, 19 are modified versions of proteins that perform other tasks in bacteria. For example, a set of 10 proteins in the motor are homologous to 10 similar proteins in a secretory system found in bacteria. (A secretory system is a protein complex that enables a cell to secrete certain macromolecules.) Two other proteins in the motor are homologous to proteins that function in ion transport. The proteins that comprise the rod, hook, and filament are all related to each other and are descended from an ancestral protein that formed a pilus-like tube. These findings suggest that the bacterial flagellum evolved as other proteins were added to an ancestral secretory system. This is an example of *exaptation*, the process in which existing structures take on new functions through descent with modification.

Internal Organization and DNA

The cells of prokaryotes are simpler than those of eukaryotes in both their internal structure and the physical arrangement of their DNA (see Figure 6.5). Prokaryotic cells lack the complex compartmentalization associated with the membrane-enclosed organelles found in eukaryotic cells. However, some prokaryotic cells do have specialized membranes that perform metabolic functions (Figure 27.8). These membranes are usually infoldings of the plasma membrane. Recent discoveries also indicate that some prokaryotes can store metabolic by-products in simple compartments that are made out of proteins; these compartments do not have a membrane.

The genome of a prokaryote is structurally different from a eukaryotic genome and in most cases has considerably less

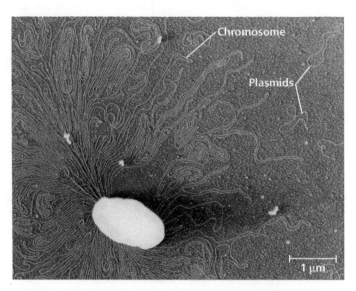

▲ **Figure 27.9 A prokaryotic chromosome and plasmids.** The thin, tangled loops surrounding this ruptured *E. coli* cell are parts of the cell's large, circular chromosome (colorized TEM). Three of the cell's plasmids, the much smaller rings of DNA, are also shown.

DNA. Prokaryotes generally have circular chromosomes (Figure 27.9), whereas eukaryotes have linear chromosomes. In addition, in prokaryotes the chromosome is associated with many fewer proteins than are the chromosomes of eukaryotes. Also unlike eukaryotes, prokaryotes lack a nucleus; their chromosome is located in the **nucleoid**, a region of cytoplasm that is not enclosed by a membrane. In addition to its single chromosome, a typical prokaryotic cell may also have much smaller rings of independently replicating DNA molecules called **plasmids** (see Figure 27.9), most carrying only a few genes.

Although DNA replication, transcription, and translation are fundamentally similar processes in prokaryotes and eukaryotes, some of the details are different (see Chapter 17). For example, prokaryotic ribosomes are slightly smaller than eukaryotic ribosomes and differ in their protein and RNA content. These differences allow certain antibiotics, such as erythromycin and tetracycline, to bind to ribosomes and block protein synthesis in prokaryotes but not in eukaryotes. As a result, people can use these antibiotics to kill or inhibit the growth of bacteria without harming themselves.

Reproduction

Many prokaryotes can reproduce quickly in favorable environments. By *binary fission* (see Figure 12.12), a single prokaryotic cell divides into 2 cells, which then divide into 4, 8, 16, and so on. Under optimal conditions, many prokaryotes can divide every 1–3 hours; some species can produce a new generation in only 20 minutes. At this rate, a single prokaryotic cell could give rise to a colony outweighing Earth in only two days!

(a) Aerobic prokaryote   **(b) Photosynthetic prokaryote**

▲ **Figure 27.8 Specialized membranes of prokaryotes.**
(a) Infoldings of the plasma membrane, reminiscent of the cristae of mitochondria, function in cellular respiration in some aerobic prokaryotes (TEM). **(b)** Photosynthetic prokaryotes called cyanobacteria have thylakoid membranes, much like those in chloroplasts (TEM).

In reality, of course, this does not occur. The cells eventually exhaust their nutrient supply, poison themselves with metabolic wastes, face competition from other microorganisms, or are consumed by other organisms. Still, the fact that many prokaryotic species can divide after short periods of time draws attention to three key features of their biology: *They are small, they reproduce by binary fission, and they often have short generation times.* As a result, prokaryotic populations can consist of many trillions of individuals—far more than populations of multicellular eukaryotes, such as plants or animals.

CONCEPT CHECK 27.1

1. Identify and explain two adaptations that enable prokaryotes to survive in environments too harsh for other organisms.
2. Contrast the cellular and DNA structures of prokaryotes and eukaryotes.
3. **MAKE CONNECTIONS** Suggest a hypothesis to explain why the thylakoid membranes of chloroplasts resemble those of cyanobacteria. Refer to Figures 6.18 and 26.21.

For suggested answers, see Appendix A.

CONCEPT 27.2

Rapid reproduction, mutation, and genetic recombination promote genetic diversity in prokaryotes

As we discussed in Unit Four, evolution cannot occur without genetic variation. The diverse adaptations exhibited by prokaryotes suggest that their populations must have considerable genetic variation—and they do. In this section, we'll examine three factors that give rise to high levels of genetic diversity in prokaryotes: rapid reproduction, mutation, and genetic recombination.

Rapid Reproduction and Mutation

In sexually reproducing species, the generation of a novel allele by a new mutation is rare for any particular gene. Instead, most of the genetic variation in sexual populations results from the way existing alleles are arranged in new combinations during meiosis and fertilization (see Chapter 13). Prokaryotes do not reproduce sexually, so at first glance their extensive genetic variation may seem puzzling. But in many species, this variation can result from a combination of rapid reproduction and mutation.

Consider the bacterium *Escherichia coli* as it reproduces by binary fission in a human intestine, one of its natural environments. After repeated rounds of division, most of the

offspring cells are genetically identical to the original parent cell. However, if errors occur during DNA replication, some of the offspring cells may differ genetically. The probability of such a mutation occurring in a given *E. coli* gene is about one in 10 million (1×10^{-7}) per cell division. But among the 2×10^{10} new *E. coli* cells that arise each day in a person's intestine,

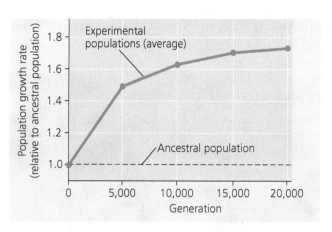

▼ Figure 27.10 **Inquiry**

Can prokaryotes evolve rapidly in response to environmental change?

Experiment Vaughn Cooper and Richard Lenski tested the ability of *E. coli* populations to adapt to a new environment. They established 12 populations, each founded by a single cell from an *E. coli* strain, and followed these populations for 20,000 generations (3,000 days). To maintain a continual supply of resources, each day the researchers performed a *serial transfer*: They transferred 0.1 mL of each population to a new tube containing 9.9 mL of fresh growth medium. The growth medium used throughout the experiment provided a challenging environment that contained only low levels of glucose and other resources needed for growth.

Samples were periodically removed from the 12 populations and grown in competition with the common ancestral strain in the experimental (low-glucose) environment.

Daily serial transfer
0.1 mL (population sample)
Old tube (discarded after transfer)
New tube (9.9 mL growth medium)

Results The fitness of the experimental populations, as measured by the growth rate of each population, increased rapidly for the first 5,000 generations (2 years) and more slowly for the next 15,000 generations. The graph shows the averages for the 12 populations.

Conclusion Populations of *E. coli* continued to accumulate beneficial mutations for 20,000 generations, allowing rapid evolution of increased population growth rates in their new environment.

Source: V. S. Cooper and R. E. Lenski, The population genetics of ecological specialization in evolving *Escherichia coli* populations, *Nature* 407:736–739 (2000).

WHAT IF? *Suggest possible functions of the genes whose sequence or expression was altered as the experimental populations evolved in the low-glucose environment.*

there will be approximately $(2 \times 10^{10}) \times (1 \times 10^{-7}) = 2{,}000$ bacteria that have a mutation in that gene. The total number of mutations when all 4,300 *E. coli* genes are considered is about $4{,}300 \times 2{,}000 = 9$ million per day per human host.

The key point is that new mutations, though rare on a per gene basis, can increase genetic diversity quickly in species with short generation times and large populations. This diversity, in turn, can lead to rapid evolution: Individuals that are genetically better equipped for their environment tend to survive and reproduce at higher rates than other individuals (Figure 27.10). The ability of prokaryotes to adapt rapidly to new conditions highlights the point that although the structure of their cells is simpler than that of eukaryotic cells, prokaryotes are not "primitive" or "inferior" in an evolutionary sense. They are, in fact, highly evolved: For 3.5 billion years, prokaryotic populations have responded successfully to many types of environmental challenges.

Genetic Recombination

Although new mutations are a major source of variation in prokaryotic populations, additional diversity arises from *genetic recombination*, the combining of DNA from two sources. In eukaryotes, the sexual processes of meiosis and fertilization combine DNA from two individuals in a single zygote. But meiosis and fertilization do not occur in prokaryotes. Instead, three other mechanisms—transformation, transduction, and conjugation—can bring together prokaryotic DNA from different individuals (that is, different cells). When the individuals are members of different species, this movement of genes from one organism to another is called *horizontal gene transfer*. Although scientists have found evidence that each of these mechanisms can transfer DNA within and between species in both domain Bacteria and domain Archaea, to date most of our knowledge comes from research on bacteria.

Transformation and Transduction

In **transformation**, the genotype and possibly phenotype of a prokaryotic cell are altered by the uptake of foreign DNA from its surroundings. For example, a harmless strain of *Streptococcus pneumoniae* can be transformed into pneumonia-causing cells if the cells are exposed to DNA from a pathogenic strain (see Concept 16.1). This transformation occurs when a nonpathogenic cell takes up a piece of DNA carrying the allele for pathogenicity and replaces its own allele with the foreign allele, an exchange of homologous DNA segments. The cell is now a recombinant: Its chromosome contains DNA derived from two different cells.

For many years after transformation was discovered in laboratory cultures, most biologists thought the process to be too rare and haphazard to play an important role in natural bacterial populations. But researchers have since learned that many bacteria have cell-surface proteins that recognize DNA from closely related species and transport it into the cell. Once inside the cell, the foreign DNA can be incorporated into the genome by homologous DNA exchange.

In **transduction**, phages (from "bacteriophages," the viruses that infect bacteria) carry prokaryotic genes from one host cell to another. In most cases, transduction results from accidents that occur during the phage replicative cycle (Figure 27.11). A virus that carries prokaryotic DNA may not be able to replicate because it lacks some or all of its own genetic material. However, the virus can attach to another prokaryotic cell (a recipient) and inject prokaryotic DNA acquired from the first cell (the donor). If some of this DNA is then incorporated into the recipient cell's chromosome by crossing over, a recombinant cell is formed.

❶ A phage infects a bacterial cell that carries the A^+ and B^+ alleles on its chromosome (brown). This bacterium will be the "donor" cell.

Phage DNA

$A^+ B^+$

Donor cell

❷ The phage DNA is replicated, and the cell makes many copies of the proteins encoded by its genes. Meanwhile, certain phage proteins halt the synthesis of proteins encoded by the host cell's DNA, and the host cell's DNA may be fragmented, as shown here.

A^+ B^+

❸ As new phage particles assemble, a fragment of bacterial DNA carrying the A^+ allele happens to be packaged in a phage capsid.

A^+

❹ The phage carrying the A^+ allele from the donor cell infects a recipient cell with alleles A^- and B^-. Crossing over at two sites (dotted lines) allows donor DNA (brown) to be incorporated into recipient DNA (green).

Crossing over

A^+

A^- B^-

Recipient cell

Recombinant cell

❺ The genotype of the resulting recombinant cell (A^+B^-) differs from the genotypes of both the donor (A^+B^+) and the recipient (A^-B^-).

A^+ B^-

▲ **Figure 27.11 Transduction.** Phages may carry pieces of a bacterial chromosome from one cell (the donor) to another (the recipient). If crossing over occurs after the transfer, genes from the donor may be incorporated into the recipient's genome.

❓ *Under what circumstances would a transduction event result in horizontal gene transfer?*

▲ **Figure 27.12 Bacterial conjugation.** The *E. coli* donor cell (left) extends a pilus that attaches to a recipient cell, a key first step in the transfer of DNA. The pilus is a flexible tube of protein subunits (TEM).

▼ **Figure 27.13 Conjugation and recombination in *E. coli*.** The DNA replication that accompanies transfer of an F plasmid or part of an Hfr bacterial chromosome is called *rolling circle replication*. In effect, the intact circular parental DNA strand "rolls" as its other strand peels off and a new complementary strand is synthesized.

Conjugation and Plasmids

In a process called **conjugation**, DNA is transferred between two prokaryotic cells (usually of the same species) that are temporarily joined. In bacteria, the DNA transfer is always one-way: One cell donates the DNA, and the other receives it. We'll focus here on the mechanism used by *E. coli*.

First, a pilus of the donor cell attaches to the recipient **(Figure 27.12)**. The pilus then retracts, pulling the two cells together, like a grappling hook. The next step is thought to be the formation of a temporary "mating bridge" structure between the two cells, through which the donor may transfer DNA to the recipient. However, the mechanism by which DNA transfer occurs is unclear; indeed, recent evidence indicates that DNA may pass directly through the hollow pilus.

The ability to form pili and donate DNA during conjugation results from the presence of a particular piece of DNA called the **F factor** (F for *fertility*). The F factor of *E. coli* consists of about 25 genes, most required for the production of pili. As shown in **Figure 27.13**, the F factor can

① A cell carrying an F plasmid (an F⁺ cell) forms a mating bridge with an F⁻ cell. One strand of the plasmid's DNA breaks at the point marked by the arrowhead.

② Using the unbroken strand as a template, the cell synthesizes a new strand (light blue). Meanwhile, the broken strand peels off (red arrow), and one end enters the F⁻ cell. There synthesis of its complementary strand begins.

③ DNA replication continues in both the donor and recipient cells, as the transferred plasmid strand moves farther into the recipient cell.

④ Once DNA transfer and synthesis are completed, the plasmid in the recipient cell circularizes. The recipient cell is now a recombinant F⁺ cell.

(a) Conjugation and transfer of an F plasmid

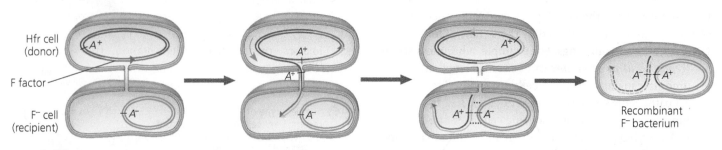

① In an Hfr cell, the F factor (dark blue) is integrated into the bacterial chromosome. Since an Hfr cell has all of the F factor genes, it can form a mating bridge with an F⁻ cell and transfer DNA.

② A single strand of the F factor breaks and begins to move through the bridge. DNA replication occurs in both donor and recipient cells, resulting in double-stranded DNA (daughter strands shown in lighter color).

③ The mating bridge usually breaks before the entire chromosome is transferred. Crossing over at two sites (dotted lines) can result in the exchange of homologous genes between the transferred DNA (brown) and the recipient's chromosome (green).

④ Cellular enzymes degrade any linear DNA not incorporated into the chromosome. The recipient cell, with a new combination of genes but no F factor, is now a recombinant F⁻ cell.

(b) Conjugation and transfer of part of an Hfr bacterial chromosome, resulting in recombination

exist either as a plasmid or as a segment of DNA within the bacterial chromosome.

The F Factor as a Plasmid The F factor in its plasmid form is called the **F plasmid**. Cells containing the F plasmid, designated F$^+$ cells, function as DNA donors during conjugation (**Figure 27.13a**). Cells lacking the F factor, designated F$^-$, function as DNA recipients during conjugation. The F$^+$ condition is transferable in the sense that an F$^+$ cell converts an F$^-$ cell to F$^+$ if a copy of the entire F plasmid is transferred.

The F Factor in the Chromosome Chromosomal genes can be transferred during conjugation when the donor cell's F factor is integrated into the chromosome. A cell with the F factor built into its chromosome is called an *Hfr cell* (for *high frequency of recombination*). Like an F$^+$ cell, an Hfr cell functions as a donor during conjugation with an F$^-$ cell (**Figure 27.13b**). When chromosomal DNA from an Hfr cell enters an F$^-$ cell, homologous regions of the Hfr and F$^-$ chromosomes may align, allowing segments of their DNA to be exchanged. As a result, the recipient cell becomes a recombinant bacterium that has genes derived from the chromosomes of two different cells—a new genetic variant on which evolution can act.

R Plasmids and Antibiotic Resistance During the 1950s in Japan, physicians started noticing that some hospital patients with bacterial dysentery, which produces severe diarrhea, did not respond to antibiotics that had been effective in the past. Apparently, resistance to these antibiotics had evolved in some strains of *Shigella*, the bacterium that causes the disease.

Eventually, researchers began to identify the specific genes that confer antibiotic resistance in *Shigella* and other pathogenic bacteria. Sometimes, mutation in a chromosomal gene of the pathogen can confer resistance. For example, a mutation in one gene may make it less likely that the pathogen will transport a particular antibiotic into its cell. Mutation in a different gene may alter the intracellular target protein for an antibiotic molecule, reducing its inhibitory effect. In other cases, bacteria have "resistance genes," which code for enzymes that specifically destroy or otherwise hinder the effectiveness of certain antibiotics, such as tetracycline or ampicillin. Such resistance genes are often carried by plasmids known as **R plasmids** (R for *resistance*).

Exposing a bacterial population to a specific antibiotic will kill antibiotic-sensitive bacteria but not those that happen to have R plasmids with genes that counter the antibiotic. Under these circumstances, we would predict that natural selection would cause the fraction of the bacterial population carrying genes for antibiotic resistance to increase, and that is exactly what happens. The medical consequences are also predictable: Resistant strains of pathogens are becoming more common, making the treatment of certain bacterial infections more difficult. The problem is compounded by the fact that many R plasmids, like F plasmids, have genes that encode pili and enable DNA transfer from one bacterial cell to another by conjugation. Making the problem still worse, some R plasmids carry as many as ten genes for resistance to that many antibiotics.

CONCEPT CHECK 27.2

1. Although rare on a per gene basis, new mutations can add considerable genetic variation to prokaryotic populations in each generation. Explain how this occurs.

2. Distinguish between the three mechanisms of transferring DNA from one bacterial cell to another.

3. In a rapidly changing environment, which bacterial population would likely be more successful, one that includes individuals capable of conjugation or one that does not? Explain.

4. **WHAT IF?** If a nonpathogenic bacterium were to acquire resistance to antibiotics, could this strain pose a health risk to people? In general, how does DNA transfer among bacteria affect the spread of resistance genes?

For suggested answers, see Appendix A.

CONCEPT 27.3

Diverse nutritional and metabolic adaptations have evolved in prokaryotes

The extensive genetic variation found in prokaryotes is reflected in their diverse nutritional adaptations. Like all organisms, prokaryotes can be categorized by how they obtain energy and the carbon used in building the organic molecules that make up cells. Every type of nutrition observed in eukaryotes is represented among prokaryotes, along with some nutritional modes unique to prokaryotes. In fact, prokaryotes have an astounding range of metabolic adaptations, much broader than that found in eukaryotes.

Organisms that obtain energy from light are called *phototrophs*, and those that obtain energy from chemicals are called *chemotrophs*. Organisms that need only CO_2 or related compounds as a carbon source are called *autotrophs*. In contrast, *heterotrophs* require at least one organic nutrient, such as glucose, to make other organic compounds. Combining possible energy sources and carbon sources results in four major modes of nutrition, summarized in **Table 27.1** on the next page.

The Role of Oxygen in Metabolism

Prokaryotic metabolism also varies with respect to oxygen (O_2). **Obligate aerobes** must use O_2 for cellular respiration (see Chapter 9) and cannot grow without it. **Obligate anaerobes**, on the other hand, are poisoned by O_2. Some obligate anaerobes live exclusively by fermentation; others extract chemical energy by **anaerobic respiration**, in which substances other than O_2, such as nitrate ions (NO_3^-) or

Table 27.1 Major Nutritional Modes

Mode	Energy Source	Carbon Source	Types of Organisms
AUTOTROPH			
Photoautotroph	Light	CO_2, HCO_3^-, or related compound	Photosynthetic prokaryotes (for example, cyanobacteria); plants; certain protists (for example, algae)
Chemoautotroph	Inorganic chemicals (such as H_2S, NH_3, or Fe^{2+})	CO_2, HCO_3^-, or related compound	Unique to certain prokaryotes (for example, *Sulfolobus*)
HETEROTROPH			
Photoheterotroph	Light	Organic compounds	Unique to certain aquatic and salt-loving prokaryotes (for example, *Rhodobacter*, *Chloroflexus*)
Chemoheterotroph	Organic compounds	Organic compounds	Many prokaryotes (for example, *Clostridium*) and protists; fungi; animals; some plants

sulfate ions (SO_4^{2-}), accept electrons at the "downhill" end of electron transport chains. **Facultative anaerobes** use O_2 if it is present but can also carry out fermentation or anaerobic respiration in an anaerobic environment.

Nitrogen Metabolism

Nitrogen is essential for the production of amino acids and nucleic acids in all organisms. Whereas eukaryotes can obtain nitrogen from a limited group of nitrogen compounds, prokaryotes can metabolize nitrogen in many forms. For example, some cyanobacteria and some methanogens (a group of archaea) convert atmospheric nitrogen (N_2) to ammonia (NH_3), a process called **nitrogen fixation**. The cells can then incorporate this "fixed" nitrogen into amino acids and other organic molecules. In terms of nutrition, nitrogen-fixing cyanobacteria are some of the most self-sufficient organisms, since they need only light, CO_2, N_2, water, and some minerals to grow.

Nitrogen fixation has a large impact on other organisms. For example, nitrogen-fixing prokaryotes can increase the nitrogen available to plants, which cannot use atmospheric nitrogen but can use the nitrogen compounds that the prokaryotes produce from ammonia. Concept 55.4 discusses this and other essential roles that prokaryotes play in the nitrogen cycles of ecosystems.

Metabolic Cooperation

Cooperation between prokaryotic cells allows them to use environmental resources they could not use as individual cells. In some cases, this cooperation takes place between specialized cells of a filament. For instance, the cyanobacterium *Anabaena* has genes that encode proteins for photosynthesis and for nitrogen fixation, but a single cell cannot carry out both processes at the same time. The reason is that photosynthesis produces O_2, which inactivates the enzymes involved in nitrogen fixation. Instead of living as isolated cells, *Anabaena* forms filamentous chains **(Figure 27.14)**. Most cells in a filament carry out only photosynthesis, while a few specialized cells called **heterocysts** (sometimes called *heterocytes*) carry out only nitrogen fixation. Each heterocyst is surrounded by a thickened cell wall that restricts entry of O_2 produced by neighboring photosynthetic cells. Intercellular connections allow heterocysts to transport fixed nitrogen to neighboring cells and to receive carbohydrates.

Metabolic cooperation between different prokaryotic species often occurs in surface-coating colonies known as **biofilms**. Cells in a biofilm secrete signaling molecules that recruit nearby cells, causing the colonies to grow. The cells also produce polysaccharides and proteins that stick the cells to the substrate and to one another; these polysaccharides and proteins form the capsule or slime layer mentioned earlier in the chapter. Channels in the biofilm allow nutrients to reach cells in the interior and wastes to be expelled. Biofilms are common in nature, but they can cause problems by contaminating industrial products and medical equipment and contributing to tooth decay and more serious health problems. Altogether, damage caused by biofilms costs billions of dollars annually.

In another example of cooperation between prokaryotes, sulfate-consuming bacteria coexist with methane-consuming archaea in ball-shaped aggregates on the ocean floor. The bacteria appear to use the archaea's waste products, such as organic compounds and hydrogen. In turn, the bacteria produce sulfur compounds that the archaea use as oxidizing agents when they consume methane in the absence of

▲ **Figure 27.14 Metabolic cooperation in a prokaryote.** In the filamentous freshwater cyanobacterium *Anabaena*, heterocysts fix nitrogen, while the other cells carry out photosynthesis (LM).

oxygen. This partnership has global ramifications: Each year, these archaea consume an estimated 300 billion kg of methane, a major greenhouse gas (see Concept 56.4).

CONCEPT 27.4

Prokaryotes have radiated into a diverse set of lineages

Since their origin 3.5 billion years ago, prokaryotic populations have radiated extensively as a wide range of structural and metabolic adaptations have evolved in them. Collectively, these adaptations have enabled prokaryotes to inhabit every environment known to support life—if there are organisms in a particular place, some of those organisms are prokaryotes. In recent decades, advances in genomics are beginning to reveal the extent of prokaryotic diversity.

An Overview of Prokaryotic Diversity

In the 1970s, microbiologists began using small-subunit ribosomal RNA as a marker for evolutionary relationships. Their results indicated that many prokaryotes once classified as bacteria are actually more closely related to eukaryotes and belong in a domain of their own: Archaea. Microbiologists have since analyzed larger amounts of genetic data—including more than 1,700 entire genomes—and have concluded that a few traditional taxonomic groups, such as cyanobacteria, are monophyletic. However, other traditional groups, such as gram-negative bacteria, are scattered throughout several lineages. **Figure 27.15** shows one phylogenetic hypothesis for some of the major taxa of prokaryotes based on molecular systematics.

One lesson from studying prokaryotic phylogeny is that the genetic diversity of prokaryotes is immense. When researchers began to sequence the genes of prokaryotes, they could investigate only the small fraction of species that could be cultured in the laboratory. In the 1980s, researchers began using the polymerase chain reaction (PCR; see Figure 20.8) to analyze the genes of prokaryotes collected from the environment (such as from soil or water samples). Such "genetic prospecting" is now widely used; in fact, today entire prokaryotic genomes can be obtained from environmental samples

▲ **Figure 27.15 A simplified phylogeny of prokaryotes.** This phylogenetic tree based on molecular data shows one of several debated hypotheses of the relationships between the major prokaryotic groups discussed in this chapter. Within Archaea, the placement of the korarchaeotes and nanoarchaeotes remains unclear.

? *Which domain is the sister group of Archaea?*

using *metagenomics* (see Chapter 21). Each year these techniques add new branches to the tree of life. While only about 10,500 prokaryotic species worldwide have been assigned scientific names, a single handful of soil could contain 10,000 prokaryotic species by some estimates. Taking full stock of this diversity will require many years of research.

Another important lesson from molecular systematics is that horizontal gene transfer has played a key role in the evolution of prokaryotes. Over hundreds of millions of years, prokaryotes have acquired genes from even distantly related species, and they continue to do so today. As a result, significant portions of the genomes of many prokaryotes are actually mosaics of genes imported from other species. For example, a 2011 study of 329 sequenced bacterial genomes found that an average of 75% of the genes in each genome had been transferred horizontally at some point in their evolutionary history. As we saw in Chapter 26, such gene transfers can make it difficult to determine phylogenetic relationships. Still, it is clear that for billions of years, the prokaryotes have evolved in two separate lineages, the bacteria and the archaea (see Figure 27.15).

Bacteria

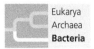

As surveyed in **Figure 27.16**, bacteria include the vast majority of prokaryotic species familiar to most people, from the

Exploring Selected Major Groups of Bacteria

Proteobacteria

This large and diverse clade of gram-negative bacteria includes photo-autotrophs, chemoautotrophs, and heterotrophs. Some proteobacteria are anaerobic, while others are aerobic. Molecular systematists currently recognize five subgroups of proteobacteria; the phylogenetic tree at right shows their relationships based on molecular data.

Alpha
Beta
Gamma } Proteobacteria
Delta
Epsilon

Subgroup: Alpha Proteobacteria

Many of the species in this subgroup are closely associated with eukaryotic hosts. For example, *Rhizobium* species live in nodules within the roots of legumes (plants of the pea/bean family), where the bacteria convert atmospheric N_2 to compounds the host plant can use to make proteins. Species in the genus *Agrobacterium* produce tumors in plants; genetic engineers use these bacteria to carry foreign DNA into the genomes of crop plants. Scientists hypothesize that mitochondria evolved from aerobic alpha proteobacteria through endosymbiosis.

Rhizobium (arrows) inside a root cell of a legume (TEM)

2.5 µm

Subgroup: Beta Proteobacteria

This nutritionally diverse subgroup includes *Nitrosomonas*, a genus of soil bacteria that play an important role in nitrogen recycling by oxidizing ammonium (NH_4^+), producing nitrite (NO_2^-) as a waste product. Other members of this subgroup include a wide range of aquatic species, such as the photoheterotroph *Rubrivivax*, along with pathogens such as the species that causes gonorrhea, *Neisseria gonorrhoeae*.

Nitrosomonas (colorized TEM)

1 µm

Subgroup: Gamma Proteobacteria

This subgroup's autotrophic members include sulfur bacteria such as *Thiomargarita namibiensis*, which obtain energy by oxidizing H_2S, producing sulfur as a waste product (the small globules in the photograph at right). Some heterotrophic gamma proteobacteria are pathogens; for example, *Legionella* causes Legionnaires' disease, *Salmonella* is responsible for some cases of food poisoning, and *Vibrio cholerae* causes cholera. *Escherichia coli*, a common resident of the intestines of humans and other mammals, normally is not pathogenic.

Thiomargarita namibiensis containing sulfur wastes (LM)

200 µm

Subgroup: Delta Proteobacteria

This subgroup includes the slime-secreting myxobacteria. When the soil dries out or food is scarce, the cells congregate into a fruiting body that releases resistant "myxospores." These cells found new colonies in favorable environments. Another group of delta proteobacteria, the bdellovibrios, attack other bacteria, charging at up to 100 µm/sec (comparable to a human running 240 km/hr). The attack begins when a bdellovibrio attaches to specific molecules found on the outer covering of some bacterial species. The bdellovibrio then drills into its prey by using digestive enzymes and spinning at 100 revolutions per second.

Fruiting bodies of *Chondromyces crocatus,* a myxobacterium (SEM)

300 µm

Subgroup: Epsilon Proteobacteria

Most species in this subgroup are pathogenic to humans or other animals. Epsilon proteobacteria include *Campylobacter*, which causes blood poisoning and intestinal inflammation, and *Helicobacter pylori*, which causes stomach ulcers.

Helicobacter pylori (colorized TEM)

2 µm

Chlamydias

These parasites can survive only within animal cells, depending on their hosts for resources as basic as ATP. The gram-negative walls of chlamydias are unusual in that they lack peptidoglycan. One species, *Chlamydia trachomatis*, is the most common cause of blindness in the world and also causes nongonococcal urethritis, the most common sexually transmitted disease in the United States.

Chlamydia (arrows) inside an animal cell (colorized TEM)

2.5 μm

Spirochetes

These gram-negative heterotrophs spiral through their environment by means of rotating, internal, flagellum-like filaments. Many spirochetes are free-living, but others are notorious pathogenic parasites: *Treponema pallidum* causes syphilis, and *Borrelia burgdorferi* causes Lyme disease (see Figure 27.20).

Leptospira, a spirochete (colorized TEM)

5 μm

Cyanobacteria

These gram-negative photoautotrophs are the only prokaryotes with plantlike, oxygen-generating photosynthesis. (In fact, chloroplasts likely evolved from an endosymbiotic cyanobacterium.) Both solitary and filamentous cyanobacteria are abundant components of freshwater and marine *phytoplankton*, the collection of photosynthetic organisms that drift near the water's surface. Some filaments have cells specialized for nitrogen fixation, the process that incorporates atmospheric N_2 into inorganic compounds that can be used in the synthesis of amino acids and other organic molecules (see Figure 27.14).

Oscillatoria, a filamentous cyanobacterium

40 μm

Gram-Positive Bacteria

Gram-positive bacteria rival the proteobacteria in diversity. Species in one subgroup, the actinomycetes (from the Greek *mykes*, fungus, for which these bacteria were once mistaken), form colonies containing branched chains of cells. Two species of actinomycetes cause tuberculosis and leprosy. However, most actinomycetes are free-living species that help decompose the organic matter in soil; their secretions are partly responsible for the "earthy" odor of rich soil. Soil-dwelling species in the genus *Streptomyces* (top) are cultured by pharmaceutical companies as a source of many antibiotics, including streptomycin.

Gram-positive bacteria include many solitary species, such as *Bacillus anthracis* (see Figure 27.5), which causes anthrax, and *Clostridium botulinum*, which causes botulism. The various species of *Staphylococcus* and *Streptococcus* are also gram-positive bacteria.

Mycoplasmas (bottom) are the only bacteria known to lack cell walls. They are also the tiniest known cells, with diameters as small as 0.1 μm, only about five times as large as a ribosome. Mycoplasmas have small genomes—*Mycoplasma genitalium* has only 517 genes, for example. Many mycoplasmas are free-living soil bacteria, but others are pathogens.

Streptomyces, the source of many antibiotics (SEM)

5 μm

Hundreds of mycoplasmas covering a human fibroblast cell (colorized SEM)

2 μm

pathogenic species that cause strep throat and tuberculosis to the beneficial species used to make Swiss cheese and yogurt. Every major mode of nutrition and metabolism is represented among bacteria, and even a small taxonomic group of bacteria may contain species exhibiting many different nutritional modes. As we'll see, the diverse nutritional and metabolic capabilities of bacteria—and archaea—are behind the great impact these organisms have on Earth and its life.

Archaea

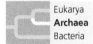

Archaea share certain traits with bacteria and other traits with eukaryotes (Table 27.2). However, archaea also have many unique characteristics, as we would expect in a taxon that has followed a separate evolutionary path for so long.

The first prokaryotes assigned to domain Archaea live in environments so extreme that few other organisms can survive there. Such organisms are called **extremophiles**, meaning "lovers" of extreme conditions (from the Greek *philos*, lover), and include extreme halophiles and extreme thermophiles.

Extreme halophiles (from the Greek *halo*, salt) live in highly saline environments, such as the Great Salt Lake in Utah, the Dead Sea in Israel, and the Spanish lake shown in

▲ **Figure 27.17 Extreme thermophiles.** Orange and yellow colonies of thermophilic prokaryotes grow in the hot water of Yellowstone National Park's Grand Prismatic Spring.

MAKE CONNECTIONS *How might the enzymes of thermophiles differ from those of other organisms? (Review enzymes in Concept 8.4.)*

Figure 27.1. Some species merely tolerate salinity, while others require an environment that is several times saltier than seawater (which has a salinity of 3.5%). For example, the proteins and cell wall of *Halobacterium* have unusual features that improve function in extremely salty environments but render these organisms incapable of survival if the salinity drops below 9%.

Extreme thermophiles (from the Greek *thermos*, hot) thrive in very hot environments (**Figure 27.17**). For example, archaea in the genus *Sulfolobus* live in sulfur-rich volcanic springs as hot as 90°C. At temperatures this high, the cells of most organisms die because their DNA does not remain in a double helix and many of their proteins denature. *Sulfolobus* and other extreme thermophiles avoid this fate because they have structural and biochemical adaptations that make their DNA and proteins stable at high temperatures. One extreme thermophile that lives near deep-sea hot springs called *hydrothermal vents* is informally known as "strain 121," since it can reproduce even at 121°C. Another extreme thermophile, *Pyrococcus furiosus*, is used in biotechnology as a source of DNA polymerase for the PCR technique (see Figure 20.8).

Many other archaea live in more moderate environments. Consider the **methanogens**, archaea that release methane as a by-product of their unique ways of obtaining energy. Many methanogens use CO_2 to oxidize H_2, a process that produces both energy and methane waste. Among the strictest of anaerobes, methanogens are poisoned by O_2. Although some methanogens live in extreme environments, such as under kilometers of ice in Greenland, others live in swamps and marshes where other microorganisms have consumed all the O_2. The "marsh gas" found in such environments is the

Table 27.2	A Comparison of the Three Domains of Life		
	DOMAIN		
CHARACTERISTIC	**Bacteria**	**Archaea**	**Eukarya**
Nuclear envelope	Absent	Absent	Present
Membrane-enclosed organelles	Absent	Absent	Present
Peptidoglycan in cell wall	Present	Absent	Absent
Membrane lipids	Unbranched hydrocarbons	Some branched hydrocarbons	Unbranched hydrocarbons
RNA polymerase	One kind	Several kinds	Several kinds
Initiator amino acid for protein synthesis	Formyl-methionine	Methionine	Methionine
Introns in genes	Very rare	Present in some genes	Present in many genes
Response to the antibiotics streptomycin and chloramphenicol	Growth usually inhibited	Growth not inhibited	Growth not inhibited
Histones associated with DNA	Absent	Present in some species	Present
Circular chromosome	Present	Present	Absent
Growth at temperatures > 100°C	No	Some species	No

methane released by these archaea. Other species inhabit the anaerobic guts of cattle, termites, and other herbivores, playing an essential role in the nutrition of these animals. Methanogens are also useful to humans as decomposers in sewage treatment facilities.

Many extreme halophiles and all known methanogens are archaea in the clade Euryarchaeota (from the Greek *eurys*, broad, a reference to their wide habitat range). The euryarchaeotes also include some extreme thermophiles, though most thermophilic species belong to a second clade, Crenarchaeota (*cren* means "spring," such as a hydrothermal spring). Recent metagenomic studies have identified many species of euryarchaeotes and crenarchaeotes that are not extremophiles. These archaea exist in habitats ranging from farm soils to lake sediments to the surface of the open ocean.

New findings continue to inform our understanding of archaeal phylogeny. In 1996, researchers sampling a hot spring in Yellowstone National Park discovered archaea that do not appear to belong to either Euryarchaeota or Crenarchaeota. They placed these archaea in a new clade, Korarchaeota (from the Greek *koron*, young man). In 2002, researchers exploring hydrothermal vents off the coast of Iceland discovered archaeal cells only 0.4 μm in diameter attached to a much larger crenarchaeote. The genome of the smaller archaean is one of the smallest known of any organism, containing only 500,000 base pairs. Genetic analysis indicates that this prokaryote belongs to a fourth archaeal clade, Nanoarchaeota (from the Greek *nanos*, dwarf). Within a year after this clade was named, three other DNA sequences from nanoarchaeote species were isolated: one from Yellowstone's hot springs, one from hot springs in Siberia, and one from a hydrothermal vent in the Pacific. As metagenomic prospecting continues, the tree in Figure 27.15 may well undergo further changes.

CONCEPT CHECK 27.4

1. Explain how molecular systematics and metagenomics have contributed to our understanding of the phylogeny and evolution of prokaryotes.

2. **WHAT IF?** What would the discovery of a bacterial species that is a methanogen imply about the evolution of the methane-producing pathway?

For suggested answers, see Appendix A.

CONCEPT 27.5

Prokaryotes play crucial roles in the biosphere

If people were to disappear from the planet tomorrow, life on Earth would change for many species, but few would be

driven to extinction. In contrast, prokaryotes are so important to the biosphere that if they were to disappear, the prospects of survival for many other species would be dim.

Chemical Recycling

The atoms that make up the organic molecules in all living things were at one time part of inorganic substances in the soil, air, and water. Sooner or later, those atoms will return there. Ecosystems depend on the continual recycling of chemical elements between the living and nonliving components of the environment, and prokaryotes play a major role in this process. For example, chemoheterotrophic prokaryotes function as **decomposers**, breaking down dead organisms as well as waste products and thereby unlocking supplies of carbon, nitrogen, and other elements. Without the actions of prokaryotes and other decomposers such as fungi, life as we know it would cease. (See Concept 55.4 for a detailed discussion of chemical cycles.)

Prokaryotes also convert some molecules to forms that can be taken up by other organisms. Cyanobacteria and other autotrophic prokaryotes use CO_2 to make organic compounds such as sugars, which are then passed up through food chains. Cyanobacteria also produce atmospheric O_2, and a variety of prokaryotes fix atmospheric nitrogen (N_2) into forms that other organisms can use to make the building blocks of proteins and nucleic acids. Under some conditions, prokaryotes can increase the availability of nutrients that plants require for growth, such as nitrogen, phosphorus, and potassium **(Figure 27.18)**. Prokaryotes

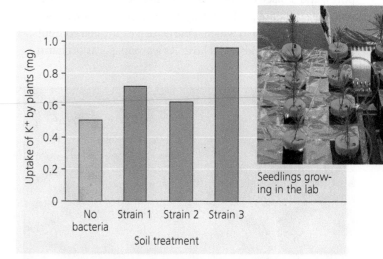

Seedlings growing in the lab

▲ **Figure 27.18 Impact of bacteria on soil nutrient availability.** Pine seedlings grown in sterile soils to which one of three strains of the bacterium *Burkholderia glathei* had been added absorbed more potassium (K^+) than did seedlings grown in soil without any bacteria. Other results (not shown) demonstrated that strain 3 increased the amount of K^+ released from mineral crystals to the soil.

WHAT IF? *Estimate the average uptake of K^+ for seedlings in soils with bacteria. What would you expect this average to be if bacteria had no effect on nutrient availability?*

can also *decrease* the availability of key plant nutrients; this occurs when prokaryotes "immobilize" nutrients by using them to synthesize molecules that remain within their cells. Thus, prokaryotes can have complex effects on soil nutrient concentrations. In marine environments, an archaean from the clade Crenarchaeota can perform nitrification, a key step in the nitrogen cycle (see Figure 55.14). Crenarchaeotes dominate the oceans by numbers, comprising an estimated 10^{28} cells. The sheer abundance of these organisms suggests that they may have a large impact on the global nitrogen cycle; scientists are investigating this possibility.

Ecological Interactions

Prokaryotes play a central role in many ecological interactions. Consider **symbiosis** (from a Greek word meaning "living together"), an ecological relationship in which two species live in close contact with each other. Prokaryotes often form symbiotic associations with much larger organisms. In general, the larger organism in a symbiotic relationship is known as the **host**, and the smaller is known as the **symbiont**. There are many cases in which a prokaryote and its host participate in **mutualism**, an ecological interaction between two species in which both benefit (Figure 27.19). Other interactions take the form of **commensalism**, an ecological relationship in which one species benefits while the other is not harmed or helped in any significant way. For example, more than 150 bacterial species live on the surface of your body, covering portions of your skin with up to 10 million cells per square centimeter. Some of these species are commensalists: You provide them with food, such as the oils that exude from your pores, and a place to live, while they neither harm nor benefit you. Finally, some prokaryotes engage in **parasitism**, an ecological relationship in which a **parasite** eats the cell contents, tissues, or body fluids of its host. As a group, parasites harm

but usually do not kill their host, at least not immediately (unlike a predator). Parasites that cause disease are known as **pathogens**, many of which are prokaryotic. (We'll discuss mutualism, commensalism, and parasitism in greater detail in Chapter 54.)

The very existence of an ecosystem can depend on prokaryotes. For example, consider the diverse ecological communities found at hydrothermal vents. These communities are densely populated by many different kinds of animals, including worms, clams, crabs, and fishes. But since sunlight does not penetrate to the deep ocean floor, the community does not include photosynthetic organisms. Instead, the energy that supports the community is derived from the metabolic activities of chemoautotrophic bacteria. These bacteria harvest chemical energy from compounds such as hydrogen sulfide (H_2S) that are released from the vent. An active hydrothermal vent may support hundreds of eukaryotic species, but when the vent stops releasing chemicals, the chemoautotrophic bacteria cannot survive. As a result, the entire vent community collapses.

CONCEPT CHECK 27.5

1. Explain how prokaryotes, though small, can be considered giants in their collective impact on Earth and its life.
2. MAKE CONNECTIONS Review photosynthesis in Figure 10.6. Then summarize the main steps by which cyanobacteria produce O_2 and use CO_2 to make organic compounds.

For suggested answers, see Appendix A.

CONCEPT 27.6

Prokaryotes have both beneficial and harmful impacts on humans

Although the best-known prokaryotes tend to be the bacteria that cause human illness, these pathogens represent only a small fraction of prokaryotic species. Many other prokaryotes have positive interactions with people, and some play essential roles in agriculture and industry.

Mutualistic Bacteria

As is true for many other eukaryotes, human well-being can depend on mutualistic prokaryotes. For example, our intestines are home to an estimated 500–1,000 species of bacteria; their cells outnumber all human cells in the body by a factor of ten. Different species live in different portions of the intestines, and they vary in their ability to process different foods. Many of these species are mutualists, digesting food that our own intestines cannot break down. For example, the genome of one of these gut mutualists, *Bacteroides thetaiotaomicron*,

▲ **Figure 27.19 Mutualism: bacterial "headlights."** The glowing oval below the eye of the flashlight fish (*Photoblepharon palpebratus*) is an organ harboring bioluminescent bacteria. The fish uses the light to attract prey and to signal potential mates. The bacteria receive nutrients from the fish.

includes a large array of genes involved in synthesizing carbohydrates, vitamins, and other nutrients needed by humans. Signals from the bacterium activate human genes that build the network of intestinal blood vessels necessary to absorb nutrient molecules. Other signals induce human cells to produce antimicrobial compounds to which *B. thetaiotaomicron* is not susceptible. This action may reduce the population sizes of other, competing species, thus potentially benefiting both *B. thetaiotaomicron* and its human host.

Pathogenic Bacteria

All the pathogenic prokaryotes known to date are bacteria, and they deserve their negative reputation. Bacteria cause about half of all human diseases. For example, more than 1 million people die each year of the lung disease tuberculosis, caused by *Mycobacterium tuberculosis*. And another 2 million people die each year from diarrheal diseases caused by various bacteria.

Some bacterial diseases are transmitted by other species, such as fleas or ticks. In the United States, the most widespread pest-carried disease is Lyme disease, which infects 15,000 to 20,000 people each year (**Figure 27.20**). Caused by a bacterium carried by ticks that live on deer and field mice, Lyme disease can result in debilitating arthritis, heart disease, nervous disorders, and death if untreated.

Pathogenic prokaryotes usually cause illness by producing poisons, which are classified as exotoxins or endotoxins. **Exotoxins** are proteins secreted by certain bacteria and other organisms. Cholera, a dangerous diarrheal disease, is caused by an exotoxin secreted by the proteobacterium *Vibrio cholerae*. The exotoxin stimulates intestinal cells to release chloride ions into the gut, and water follows by osmosis. In another example, the potentially fatal disease botulism is caused by botulinum toxin, an exotoxin secreted by the gram-positive bacterium *Clostridium botulinum* as it

ferments various foods, including improperly canned meat, seafood, and vegetables. Like other exotoxins, the botulinum toxin can produce disease even if the bacteria that manufacture it are no longer present when the food is eaten. Another species in the same genus, *C. difficile*, produces exotoxins that cause severe diarrhea, resulting in more than 12,000 deaths per year in the United States alone.

Endotoxins are lipopolysaccharide components of the outer membrane of gram-negative bacteria. In contrast to exotoxins, endotoxins are released only when the bacteria die and their cell walls break down. Endotoxin-producing bacteria include species in the genus *Salmonella*, such as *Salmonella typhi*, which causes typhoid fever. You might have heard of food poisoning caused by other *Salmonella* species that can be found in poultry and some fruits and vegetables.

Since the 19th century, improved sanitation systems in the industrialized world have greatly reduced the threat of pathogenic bacteria. Antibiotics have saved a great many lives and reduced the incidence of disease. However, resistance to antibiotics is currently evolving in many bacterial strains. As you read earlier, the rapid reproduction of bacteria enables cells carrying resistance genes to quickly give rise to large populations as a result of natural selection, and these genes can also spread to other species by horizontal gene transfer.

Horizontal gene transfer can also spread genes associated with virulence, turning normally harmless bacteria into potent pathogens. *E. coli*, for instance, is ordinarily a harmless symbiont in the human intestines, but pathogenic strains that cause bloody diarrhea have emerged. One of the most dangerous strains, O157:H7, is a global threat; in the United States alone, there are 75,000 cases of O157:H7 infection per year, often from contaminated beef or produce. In 2001, scientists sequenced the genome of O157:H7 and compared it with the genome of a harmless strain of *E. coli* called K-12. They discovered that 1,387 out of the 5,416 genes in O157:H7 have no counterpart in K-12. Many of these 1,387 genes are found in chromosomal regions that include phage DNA. This suggests that at least some of the 1,387 genes were incorporated into the genome of O157:H7 through phage-mediated horizontal gene transfer (transduction). Some of the genes found only in O157:H7 are associated with virulence, including genes that code for adhesive fimbriae that enable O157:H7 to attach itself to the intestinal wall and extract nutrients.

Prokaryotes in Research and Technology

On a positive note, we reap many benefits from the metabolic capabilities of both bacteria and archaea. For example, people have long used bacteria to convert milk to cheese and yogurt. In recent years, our greater understanding of

▲ **Figure 27.20 Lyme disease.** Ticks in the genus *Ixodes* spread the disease by transmitting the spirochete *Borrelia burgdorferi* (colorized SEM). A rash may develop at the site of the tick's bite; the rash may be large and ring-shaped (as shown) or much less distinctive.

prokaryotes has led to an explosion of new applications in biotechnology; two examples are the use of *E. coli* in gene cloning (see Figure 20.2) and the use of *Agrobacterium tumefaciens* in producing transgenic plants (see Figure 35.25). Naturally occurring soil bacteria may have potential for combating diseases that affect crop plants; in the Scientific Skills Exercise, you can interpret data from an experiment studying the effect of these bacteria.

Bacteria may soon figure prominently in another major industry: plastics. Globally, each year about 350 billion pounds of plastic are produced from petroleum and used to make toys, storage containers, soft drink bottles, and many other items. These products degrade slowly, creating environmental problems. Bacteria can now be used to make natural plastics (Figure 27.21). For example, some bacteria synthesize a type of polymer known as PHA

▶ **Figure 27.22 Bioremediation of an oil spill.** Spraying fertilizer stimulates the growth of native bacteria that metabolize oil, increasing the breakdown process up to fivefold.

(polyhydroxyalkanoate), which they use to store chemical energy. The PHA can be extracted, formed into pellets, and used to make durable, yet biodegradable, plastics.

Another way to harness prokaryotes is in **bioremediation**, the use of organisms to remove pollutants from soil, air, or water. For example, anaerobic bacteria and archaea decompose the organic matter in sewage, converting it to material that can be used as landfill or fertilizer after chemical sterilization. Other bioremediation applications include cleaning up oil spills (Figure 27.22) and precipitating radioactive material (such as uranium) out of groundwater.

Through genetic engineering, we can now modify bacteria to produce vitamins, antibiotics, hormones, and

◀ **Figure 27.21 Bacteria synthesizing and storing PHA, a component of biodegradeable plastics.**

SCIENTIFIC SKILLS EXERCISE

Making a Bar Graph and Interpreting Data

Do Soil Microorganisms Protect Against Crop Disease? The soil layer surrounding plant roots, called the *rhizosphere*, is a complex community in which archaea, bacteria, fungi, and plants interact with one another. When crop plants are attacked by fungal or bacterial pathogens, in some cases soil from the rhizosphere protects plants from future attacks. Such protective soil is called disease-suppressive soil. Plants grown in disease-suppressive soils appear to be less vulnerable to pathogen attack. In this exercise, you'll interpret data from an experiment studying whether microorganisms were responsible for the protective effects of disease-suppressive soils.

How the Experiment Was Done The researchers obtained disease-suppressive soil from 25 random sites in an agricultural field in the Netherlands in which sugar beet crops had previously been attacked by *Rhizoctonia solani*, a fungal pathogen that also afflicts potatoes and rice. The researchers collected other soil samples from the grassy margins of the field where sugar beets had not been grown. The researchers predicted that these soil samples from the margins would not offer protection against pathogens.

The researchers then planted and raised sugar beets in greenhouses, using five different soil treatments. Each soil treatment was applied to four pots, and each pot contained eight plants. The pots were inoculated with *R. solani*. After 20 days, the percentage of infected sugar beet seedlings was determined for each pot and then averaged for each soil treatment.

Data from the Experiment

Soil Treatment	Average Percentage of Seedlings Afflicted with Fungal Disease
Disease-suppressive soil	3.0
Soil from margin of field	62
Soil from margin of field + 10% disease-suppressive soil	39
Disease-suppressive soil heated to 50°C for 1 hour	31
Disease-suppressive soil heated to 80°C for 1 hour	70

Interpret the Data

1. What hypothesis were the researchers testing in this study? What is the independent variable in this study? What is the dependent variable?

2. What is the total number of pots used in this experiment, and how many plants received each soil treatment? Explain why multiple pots and plants were used for each treatment.

3. Use the data in the table to create a bar graph. Then, in words, describe and compare the results for the five soil treatments.

4. The researchers stated, "Collectively, these results indicated that disease suppressiveness [of soil] toward *Rhizoctonia solani* was microbiological in nature." Is this statement supported by the results shown in the graph? Explain.

(MB) A version of this Scientific Skills Exercise can be assigned in MasteringBiology.

Data from R. Mendes et al. Deciphering the rhizosphere for disease-suppressive bacteria, *Science* 332:1097–1100 (2011).

other products (see Chapter 20). Researchers are seeking to reduce fossil fuel use by engineering bacteria that can produce ethanol from various forms of biomass, including agricultural waste, switch-grass, municipal waste (such as paper products that are not recycled), and corn **(Figure 27.23)**.

The usefulness of prokaryotes largely derives from their diverse forms

▶ **Figure 27.23 Fuel production.** Researchers are developing bacteria that produce ethanol (E-85) fuel from renewable plant products.

of nutrition and metabolism. All this metabolic versatility evolved prior to the appearance of the structural novelties that heralded the evolution of eukaryotic organisms, to which we devote the remainder of this unit.

CONCEPT CHECK 27.6

1. Identify at least two ways that prokaryotes have affected you positively today.
2. A pathogenic bacterium's toxin causes symptoms that increase the bacterium's chance of spreading from host to host. Does this information indicate whether the poison is an exotoxin or endotoxin? Explain.
3. **WHAT IF?** How might a sudden and dramatic change in your diet affect the diversity of prokaryotic species that live in your digestive tract?

For suggested answers, see Appendix A.

27 Chapter Review

SUMMARY OF KEY CONCEPTS

CONCEPT 27.1

Structural and functional adaptations contribute to prokaryotic success (pp. 568–572)

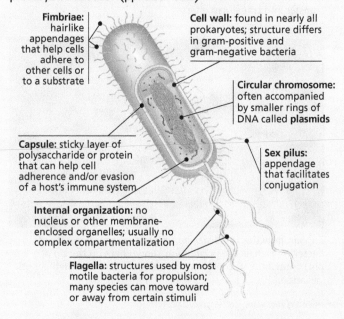

Fimbriae: hairlike appendages that help cells adhere to other cells or to a substrate

Cell wall: found in nearly all prokaryotes; structure differs in gram-positive and gram-negative bacteria

Circular chromosome: often accompanied by smaller rings of DNA called **plasmids**

Capsule: sticky layer of polysaccharide or protein that can help cell adherence and/or evasion of a host's immune system

Sex pilus: appendage that facilitates conjugation

Internal organization: no nucleus or other membrane-enclosed organelles; usually no complex compartmentalization

Flagella: structures used by most motile bacteria for propulsion; many species can move toward or away from certain stimuli

- Many prokaryotic species can reproduce quickly by binary fission, leading to the formation of populations containing enormous numbers of individuals. Some form endospores, which can remain viable in harsh conditions for centuries.

  ? *Describe features of prokaryotes that enable them to thrive in a wide range of different environments.*

CONCEPT 27.2

Rapid reproduction, mutation, and genetic recombination promote genetic diversity in prokaryotes (pp. 572–575)

- Because prokaryotes can often proliferate rapidly, mutations can quickly increase a population's genetic variation. As a result, prokaryotic populations often can evolve in short periods of time in response to changing conditions.
- Genetic diversity in prokaryotes also can arise by recombination of the DNA from two different cells (via transformation, transduction, or conjugation). By transferring advantageous alleles, such as ones for antibiotic resistance, genetic recombination can promote adaptive evolution in prokaryotic populations.

  ? *Mutations are rare and prokaryotes reproduce asexually, yet their populations can have high genetic diversity. Explain how this can occur.*

CONCEPT 27.3

Diverse nutritional and metabolic adaptations have evolved in prokaryotes (pp. 575–577)

- Nutritional diversity is much greater in prokaryotes than in eukaryotes. As a group, prokaryotes perform all four modes of nutrition: photoautotrophy, chemoautotrophy, photoheterotrophy, and chemoheterotrophy.
- Among prokaryotes, **obligate aerobes** require O_2, **obligate anaerobes** are poisoned by O_2, and **facultative anaerobes** can survive with or without O_2.
- Unlike eukaryotes, prokaryotes can metabolize nitrogen in many different forms. Some can convert atmospheric nitrogen to ammonia, a process called **nitrogen fixation**.
- Prokaryotic cells and even species may cooperate metabolically. In *Anabaena*, photosynthetic cells and nitrogen-fixing cells exchange metabolic products. Metabolic cooperation also occurs in surface-coating **biofilms** that include different species.

  ? *Describe the range of prokaryotic metabolic adaptations.*

CONCEPT 27.4

Prokaryotes have radiated into a diverse set of lineages (pp. 577–581)

- Molecular systematics is helping biologists classify prokaryotes and identify new clades.
- Diverse nutritional types are scattered among the major groups of bacteria. The two largest groups are the proteobacteria and gram-positive bacteria.
- Some archaea, such as extreme thermophiles and extreme halophiles, live in extreme environments. Other archaea live in moderate environments such as soils and lakes.

? *How have molecular data informed prokaryotic phylogeny?*

CONCEPT 27.5

Prokaryotes play crucial roles in the biosphere (pp. 581–582)

- Decomposition by heterotrophic prokaryotes and the synthetic activities of autotrophic and nitrogen-fixing prokaryotes contribute to the recycling of elements in ecosystems.
- Many prokaryotes have a symbiotic relationship with a host; the relationships between prokaryotes and their hosts range from mutalism to commensalism to parasitism.

? *In what ways are prokaryotes key to the survival of many species?*

CONCEPT 27.6

Prokaryotes have both beneficial and harmful impacts on humans (pp. 582–585)

- People depend on mutualistic prokaryotes, including hundreds of species that live in our intestines and help digest food.
- Pathogenic bacteria typically cause disease by releasing **exotoxins** or **endotoxins**. Horizontal gene transfer can spread genes associated with virulence to harmless species or strains.
- Prokaryotes can be used in bioremediation, production of biodegradable plastics, and the synthesis of vitamins, antibiotics, and other products.

? *Describe beneficial and harmful impacts of prokaryotes on humans.*

TEST YOUR UNDERSTANDING

LEVEL 1: KNOWLEDGE/COMPREHENSION

1. Genetic variation in bacterial populations cannot result from
   a. transduction.
   b. conjugation.
   c. mutation.
   d. meiosis.

2. Photoautotrophs use
   a. light as an energy source and CO_2 as a carbon source.
   b. light as an energy source and methane as a carbon source.
   c. N_2 as an energy source and CO_2 as a carbon source.
   d. CO_2 as both an energy source and a carbon source.

3. Which of the following statements is *not* true?
   a. Archaea and bacteria have different membrane lipids.
   b. The cell walls of archaea lack peptidoglycan.
   c. Only bacteria have histones associated with DNA.
   d. Only some archaea use CO_2 to oxidize H_2, releasing methane.

4. Which of the following involves metabolic cooperation among prokaryotic cells?
   a. binary fission
   b. endospore formation
   c. biofilms
   d. photoautotrophy

5. Bacteria perform the following ecological roles. Which role typically does *not* involve symbiosis?
   a. skin commensalist
   b. decomposer
   c. gut mutualist
   d. pathogen

6. Plantlike photosynthesis that releases O_2 occurs in
   a. cyanobacteria.
   b. gram-positive bacteria.
   c. archaea.
   d. chemoautotrophic bacteria.

LEVEL 2: APPLICATION/ANALYSIS

7. EVOLUTION CONNECTION
   In patients with nonresistant strains of the tuberculosis bacterium, antibiotics can relieve symptoms in a few weeks. However, it takes much longer to halt the infection, and patients may discontinue treatment while bacteria are still present. How might this result in the evolution of drug-resistant pathogens?

LEVEL 3: SYNTHESIS/EVALUATION

8. SCIENTIFIC INQUIRY
   INTERPRET THE DATA The nitrogen-fixing bacterium *Rhizobium* infects the roots of some plant species, forming a mutualism in which the bacterium provides nitrogen, and the plant provides carbohydrates. Scientists measured the 12-week growth of one such plant species (*Acacia irrorata*) when infected by six different *Rhizobium* strains. (a) Graph the data. (b) Interpret your graph.

Rhizobium strain	1	2	3	4	5	6
Plant mass (g)	0.91	0.06	1.56	1.72	0.14	1.03

Source: J. J. Burdon et al., Variation in the effectiveness of symbiotic associations between native rhizobia and temperate Australian *Acacia*: within species interactions, *Journal of Applied Ecology* 36:398–408 (1999).

Note: Without *Rhizobium*, after 12 weeks, *Acacia* plants have a mass of about 0.1 g.

9. WRITE ABOUT A THEME: ENERGY
   In a short essay (about 100–150 words), discuss how prokaryotes and other members of hydrothermal vent communities transfer and transform energy.

10. SYNTHESIZE YOUR KNOWLEDGE

Explain how the small size and rapid reproduction rate of bacteria (such as the population shown here on the tip of a pin) contribute to their large population sizes and high genetic variation.

For selected answers, see Appendix A.

MasteringBiology®

Students Go to **MasteringBiology** for assignments, the eText, and the Study Area with practice tests, animations, and activities.

Instructors Go to **MasteringBiology** for automatically graded tutorials and questions that you can assign to your students, plus Instructor Resources.

47

Animal Development

1 mm

KEY CONCEPTS

47.1 Fertilization and cleavage initiate embryonic development

47.2 Morphogenesis in animals involves specific changes in cell shape, position, and survival

47.3 Cytoplasmic determinants and inductive signals contribute to cell fate specification

▲ **Figure 47.1 How did a single cell develop into this intricately detailed embryo?**

A Body-Building Plan

The 7-week-old human embryo in **Figure 47.1** has already achieved a remarkable number of milestones in its development. Its heart—the red spot in the center—is beating, and a digestive tract traverses the length of its body. Its brain is forming (at the upper left in the photo), while the blocks of tissue that will give rise to the vertebrae are lined up along its back.

By combining molecular genetics with classical embryology, developmental biologists have learned a great deal about the transformation of a fertilized egg into an adult. Examining embryos from a range of species, such as the chick embryo shown at the left, biologists have long noted common features of early stages, as evident by comparing the human and chick embryos shown on this page. More recently, researchers have demonstrated that specific patterns of gene expression in a developing embryo direct cells to adopt distinct fates. Furthermore, even animals that display widely differing body plans share many basic mechanisms of development and often use a common set of regulatory genes. For example, the gene that specifies heart location in a human embryo (such as the one in Figure 47.1) has a close counterpart with a nearly identical function in the fruit fly *Drosophila melanogaster*. Researchers dubbed the fly gene *tinman*. Why? Embryos in which this gene is defective lack a heart, much like the Tin Man in *The Wizard of Oz*.

In studying development, biologists frequently make use of **model organisms**, species chosen for the ease with which they can be studied in the laboratory. *Drosophila melanogaster*, for example, is a useful model organism: Its life cycle is short, and mutants can be readily identified and studied (see Chapters 15 and 18). In this chapter, we will concentrate on four other model organisms: the sea urchin, the frog, the chick, and the nematode (roundworm). We will also explore some aspects of human embryonic development. Even though humans are not model organisms, we are, of course, intensely interested in our own species.

Development occurs at many points in the life cycle of an animal **(Figure 47.2)**. In a frog, for example, a major developmental period is metamorphosis, when the larva (tadpole) undergoes sweeping changes in anatomy in becoming an adult. Development occurs in the adult too, as when stem cells in the gonads produce sperm and eggs (gametes). In this chapter, our focus is on embryonic development.

Across a range of animal species, embryonic development involves common stages that occur in a set order. The first is fertilization, the fusion of sperm and egg. Development proceeds with the cleavage stage, during which a series of cell divisions divide, or cleave, the embryo into many cells. These cleavage divisions, which typically are rapid and lack accompanying cell growth, generate a hollow ball of cells called a blastula. Next, the blastula folds in on itself, rearranging into a multilayered embryo, the gastrula, in a process called gastrulation. During organogenesis, the last major stage of embryonic development, local changes in cell shape and large-scale changes in cell location generate the rudimentary organs from which adult structures grow.

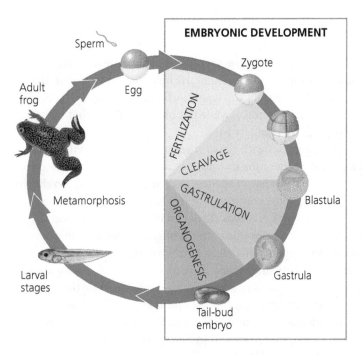

▲ **Figure 47.2 Developmental events in the life cycle of a frog.**

Our exploration of embryonic development will begin with a description of the basic stages common to most animals. We will then look at some of the cellular mechanisms that generate body form. Finally, we will consider how a cell becomes committed to a particular specialized role.

CONCEPT 47.1

Fertilization and cleavage initiate embryonic development

In considering the initiation of embryonic development, we'll begin with the events surrounding **fertilization**, the formation of a diploid zygote from a haploid egg and sperm.

Fertilization

Molecules and events at the egg surface play a crucial role in each step of fertilization. First, sperm dissolve or penetrate any protective layer surrounding the egg to reach the plasma membrane. Next, molecules on the sperm surface bind to receptors on the egg surface, helping ensure that fertilization involves a sperm and egg of the same species. Finally, changes at the surface of the egg prevent *polyspermy*, a condition in which multiple sperm nuclei enter the egg, fatally disrupting development.

The cell surface events that take place during fertilization have been studied most extensively in sea urchins, members of the phylum Echinodermata (see Figure 33.45). Sea urchin gametes are easy to collect, and fertilization is external. As a result, researchers can observe fertilization and subsequent development simply by combining eggs and sperm in seawater in the laboratory. Furthermore, fertilization in sea urchins provides a good general model for the same process in vertebrates.

The Acrosomal Reaction

When sea urchins release their gametes into the water, the jelly coat that surrounds the egg exudes soluble molecules that attract the sperm, which swim toward the egg. As soon as a sperm head contacts the jelly coat of an egg, molecules in the jelly coat trigger the **acrosomal reaction** in the sperm. As detailed in **Figure 47.3**, this reaction begins with the discharge of hydrolytic enzymes from the **acrosome**, a specialized vesicle at the tip of the sperm. These enzymes partially digest the jelly coat, enabling a sperm structure called the *acrosomal process* to elongate and penetrate the coat. Protein molecules on the tip of the extended acrosomal process bind to specific receptor proteins that jut out from the plasma membrane of the egg. This "lock-and-key" recognition is especially important for sea urchins and other species with external fertilization because the water into

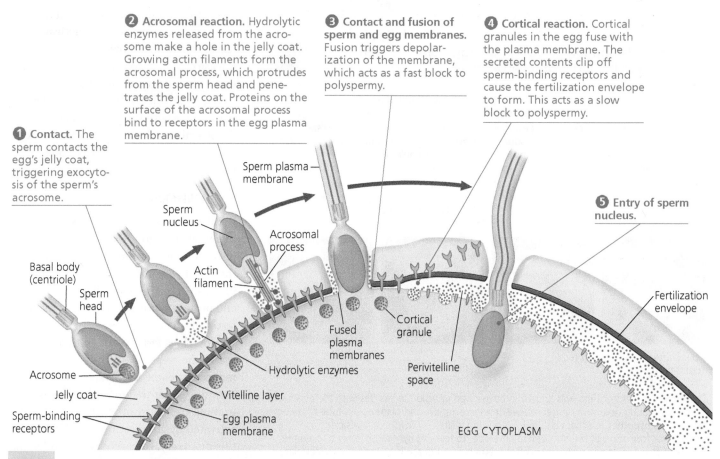

① Contact. The sperm contacts the egg's jelly coat, triggering exocytosis of the sperm's acrosome.

② Acrosomal reaction. Hydrolytic enzymes released from the acrosome make a hole in the jelly coat. Growing actin filaments form the acrosomal process, which protrudes from the sperm head and penetrates the jelly coat. Proteins on the surface of the acrosomal process bind to receptors in the egg plasma membrane.

③ Contact and fusion of sperm and egg membranes. Fusion triggers depolarization of the membrane, which acts as a fast block to polyspermy.

④ Cortical reaction. Cortical granules in the egg fuse with the plasma membrane. The secreted contents clip off sperm-binding receptors and cause the fertilization envelope to form. This acts as a slow block to polyspermy.

⑤ Entry of sperm nucleus.

Sperm plasma membrane

Sperm nucleus

Acrosomal process

Actin filament

Basal body (centriole)

Sperm head

Fertilization envelope

Fused plasma membranes

Cortical granule

Acrosome

Perivitelline space

Jelly coat

Hydrolytic enzymes

Sperm-binding receptors

Vitelline layer

Egg plasma membrane

EGG CYTOPLASM

▲ **Figure 47.3 The acrosomal and cortical reactions during sea urchin fertilization.** The events following contact of a single sperm and egg ensure that the nucleus of only one sperm enters the egg cytoplasm.

The icon above is a simplified drawing of an adult sea urchin. Throughout the chapter, this icon and others representing an adult frog, chicken, nematode, and human indicate the animals whose embryos are featured in certain figures.

which sperm and eggs are released may contain gametes of other species.

The recognition event between the sperm and egg triggers fusion of their plasma membranes. The sperm nucleus then enters the egg cytoplasm as ion channels open in the egg's plasma membrane. Sodium ions diffuse into the egg and cause *depolarization*, a decrease in the membrane potential, the charge difference across the plasma membrane (see Chapter 7). The depolarization occurs within about 1–3 seconds after a sperm binds to an egg. By preventing additional sperm from fusing with the egg's plasma membrane, this depolarization acts as the **fast block to polyspermy**.

The Cortical Reaction

Although membrane depolarization in sea urchins lasts for only a minute or so, there is a longer-lasting change that prevents polyspermy. This **slow block to polyspermy** is established by vesicles that lie just beneath the egg plasma membrane, in the rim of cytoplasm known as the cortex.

Within seconds after a sperm binds to the egg, these vesicles, called cortical granules, fuse with the egg plasma membrane (see Figure 47.3, step 4). Contents of the cortical granules are released into the space between the plasma membrane and the surrounding vitelline layer, a structure formed by the egg's extracellular matrix. Enzymes and other macromolecules from the granules then trigger a *cortical reaction*, which lifts the vitelline layer away from the egg and hardens the layer into a protective fertilization envelope. Additional enzymes clip off and release the external portions of the remaining receptor proteins, along with any attached sperm.

Formation of the fertilization envelope requires a high concentration of calcium ions (Ca^{2+}) in the egg. Does a change in the Ca^{2+} concentration trigger the cortical reaction? To answer this question, researchers used a calcium-sensitive dye to assess how Ca^{2+} is distributed in the egg before and during fertilization. As described in **Figure 47.4**, they found that Ca^{2+} spread across the egg in a wave that correlated with the appearance of the fertilization envelope.

▼ Figure 47.4 Inquiry

Does the distribution of Ca²⁺ in an egg correlate with formation of the fertilization envelope?

Experiment During fertilization, fusion of cortical granules with the egg plasma membrane causes the fertilization envelope to rise and spread around the egg from the point of sperm binding. To produce this series of images, investigators mixed sea urchin eggs with sperm, waited for 10 to 60 seconds, and then added a chemical fixative, freezing cellular structures in place. The researchers then took photomicrographs of each sample. When these images are ordered according to the time of fixation, they illustrate the stages in fertilization membrane formation for a single egg.

Fertilization envelope

10 sec after fertilization   25 sec   35 sec   1 min   500 µm

Calcium ion (Ca²⁺) signaling was known to be involved in fusion of vesicles with the plasma membrane during neurotransmitter release, insulin secretion, and plant pollen tube formation. Researchers hypothesized that calcium ion signaling is similarly involved in vesicle fusion required for formation of the fertilization envelope. To test this hypothesis, they tracked the release of free Ca²⁺ in sea urchin eggs after sperm binding to see if calcium release correlated with formation of the fertilization envelope. A fluorescent dye that glows when it binds free Ca²⁺ was injected into unfertilized eggs. The scientists then added sea urchin sperm and observed the eggs with a fluorescence microscope as fertilization took place, producing the results shown here.

Results A rise in cytosolic Ca²⁺ concentration began on the side of the egg where the sperm had entered and spread in a wave to the other side of the egg. Soon after the wave passed, the fertilization envelope rose.

Spreading wave of Ca²⁺

Point of sperm nucleus entry

1 sec before fertilization   10 sec after fertilization   20 sec   30 sec   500 µm

Conclusion The researchers concluded that Ca²⁺ release is correlated with the cortical reaction and formation of the fertilization envelope, supporting their hypothesis that an increase in Ca²⁺ levels triggers cortical granule fusion.

Sources: R. Steinhardt et al., Intracellular calcium release at fertilization in the sea urchin egg, *Developmental Biology* 58:185–197 (1977). M. Hafner et al., Wave of free calcium at fertilization in the sea urchin egg visualized with Fura-2, *Cell Motility and the Cytoskeleton* 9:271–277 (1988).

(MB) See the related Experimental Inquiry Tutorial in MasteringBiology.

WHAT IF? *Suppose you were given a chemical compound that could enter the egg and bind to Ca²⁺, blocking its function. How would you use this compound to further test the hypothesis that a rise in Ca²⁺ level triggers cortical granule fusion?*

Further studies demonstrated that the binding of sperm to the egg activates a signal transduction pathway that triggers release of Ca²⁺ into the cytosol from the endoplasmic reticulum. The resulting increase in Ca²⁺ levels causes cortical granules to fuse with the plasma membrane. A cortical reaction triggered by Ca²⁺ also occurs in vertebrates such as fishes and mammals.

Egg Activation

Fertilization initiates and speeds up metabolic reactions that trigger the onset of embryonic development, "activating" the egg. There is, for example, a marked increase in the rates of cellular respiration and protein synthesis in the egg following fertilization.

How does fertilization initiate the metabolic steps that activate the egg? A major clue came from experiments demonstrating that the unfertilized eggs of sea urchins and many other species can be activated by an injection of Ca²⁺. Based on this discovery, researchers concluded that the rise in Ca²⁺ concentration that causes the cortical reaction also causes egg activation. Subsequent experiments revealed that artificial activation is possible even if the nucleus has been removed from the egg. This further finding indicates that the proteins and mRNAs required for activation are already present in the cytoplasm of the unfertilized egg.

Not until about 20 minutes after the sperm nucleus enters the sea urchin egg do the sperm and egg nuclei fuse. DNA synthesis then begins. The first cell division, which occurs after about 90 minutes, marks the end of the fertilization stage.

Fertilization in other species shares many features with the process in sea urchins. However, there are differences, such as the stage of meiosis the egg has reached by the time it is fertilized. Sea urchin eggs have already completed meiosis when they are released from the female. In other species, eggs are arrested at a specific stage of meiosis and do not complete the meiotic divisions until a sperm head enters. Human eggs, for example, are arrested at metaphase of meiosis II prior to sperm entry (see Figure 46.11).

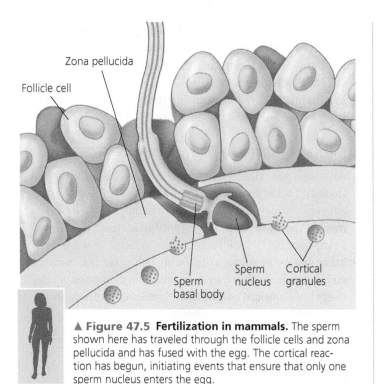

Zona pellucida

Follicle cell

Sperm basal body

Sperm nucleus

Cortical granules

▲ **Figure 47.5 Fertilization in mammals.** The sperm shown here has traveled through the follicle cells and zona pellucida and has fused with the egg. The cortical reaction has begun, initiating events that ensure that only one sperm nucleus enters the egg.

Fertilization in Mammals

Unlike sea urchins and most other marine invertebrates, terrestrial animals, including mammals, fertilize eggs internally. Support cells of the developing follicle surround the mammalian egg before and after ovulation. As shown in **Figure 47.5**, a sperm must travel through this layer of follicle cells before it reaches the **zona pellucida**, the extracellular matrix of the egg. There, the binding of a sperm to a sperm receptor induces an acrosomal reaction, facilitating sperm entry.

As in sea urchin fertilization, sperm binding triggers a cortical reaction, the release of enzymes from cortical granules to the outside of the cell. These enzymes catalyze changes in the zona pellucida, which then functions as the slow block to polyspermy. (No fast block to polyspermy has been identified in mammals.)

Overall, the process of fertilization is much slower in mammals than in sea urchins: The first cell division occurs within 12–36 hours after sperm binding in mammals, compared with about 90 minutes in sea urchins. This cell division marks the end of fertilization and the beginning of the next stage of development, cleavage.

Cleavage

Once fertilization is complete, the zygotes of many animal species undergo a succession of rapid cell divisions that characterize the **cleavage** stage of early development. During cleavage, the cell cycle consists primarily of the S (DNA synthesis) and M (mitosis) phases. The G_1 and G_2 (gap) phases are essentially skipped, and little or no protein synthesis occurs (see Figure 12.6 for a review of the cell cycle). As a result, there is no increase in mass. Instead, cleavage partitions the cytoplasm of the large fertilized egg into many smaller cells called **blastomeres**. The first five to seven cleavage divisions produce a hollow ball of cells, the **blastula**, surrounding a fluid-filled cavity called the **blastocoel** (Figure 47.6).

The pattern of cleavage divisions differs among species. In some cases, as in sand dollars and sea urchins, the division pattern is uniform across the embryo (see Figure 47.6). In others, including frogs, the pattern is asymmetric, with regions of the embryo differing in both the number and size of newly formed cells.

50 μm

(a) Fertilized egg. Shown here is the zygote shortly before the first cleavage division, surrounded by the fertilization envelope.

(b) Four-cell stage. Remnants of the mitotic spindle can be seen between the two pairs of cells that have just completed the second cleavage division.

(c) Early blastula. After further cleavage divisions, the embryo is a multicellular ball that is still surrounded by the fertilization envelope. The blastocoel has begun to form in the center.

(d) Later blastula. A single layer of cells surrounds a large blastocoel. (Although not visible here, the fertilization envelope is still present at this stage.)

▲ **Figure 47.6 Cleavage in an echinoderm embryo.** Cleavage is a series of mitotic cell divisions that transform the fertilized egg into a blastula, a hollow ball composed of cells called blastomeres. These light micrographs show the cleavage stages of a sand dollar embryo, which are virtually identical to those of a sea urchin.

Cleavage Pattern in Frogs

In frogs (and many other animals), cleavage is asymmetric **(Figure 47.7)**, reflecting the asymmetric distribution of **yolk** (stored nutrients) across the egg. Yolk is often concentrated toward one pole, called the **vegetal pole**, and away from the opposite or **animal pole**. As a result, the two halves of the egg, called the animal and vegetal hemispheres, differ in color. As we will see shortly, the yolk greatly affects the pattern of cleavage.

When an animal cell divides, an indentation called a *cleavage furrow* forms in the cell surface as cytokinesis divides the cell in half. As shown in Figure 47.7, the first two cleavage furrows in the frog embryo form parallel to the line (or meridian) connecting the two poles. During these divisions, the main effect of yolk is to slow completion of cytokinesis. As a result, the first cleavage furrow is still dividing the yolky cytoplasm in the vegetal hemisphere when the second cell division begins. Eventually, four blastomeres of equal size extend from the animal pole to the vegetal pole.

During the third division, the yolk begins to affect the relative size of cells produced in the two hemispheres. This division is equatorial (perpendicular to the line connecting the poles) and produces an eight-celled embryo. However, as each of the four blastomeres begins this division, yolk near the vegetal pole displaces the mitotic apparatus toward the animal pole. This in turn displaces the cleavage furrow from the egg equator toward the animal pole, yielding smaller blastomeres in the animal hemisphere than in the vegetal hemisphere. The displacing effect of the yolk persists in subsequent divisions, causing the blastocoel to form entirely in the animal hemisphere (see Figure 47.7).

Cleavage Patterns in Other Animals

Although yolk affects where division occurs in the eggs of frogs and other amphibians, the cleavage furrow still passes entirely through the egg. Cleavage in amphibian development is therefore said to be **holoblastic** (from the Greek *holos*, complete). Holoblastic cleavage is also seen in many other groups of animals, including echinoderms, mammals, and annelids. In those animals whose eggs contain a relatively little amount of yolk, the blastocoel forms centrally and the blastomeres are often of similar size, particularly during the first few divisions of cleavage (see Figure 47.6). This is the case for humans.

Yolk is most plentiful and has its most pronounced effect on cleavage in the eggs of birds, other reptiles, many fishes, and insects. In these animals, the volume of yolk is so great that cleavage furrows cannot pass through it, and only the region of the egg lacking yolk undergoes cleavage. This incomplete cleavage of a yolk-rich egg is said to be **meroblastic** (from the Greek *meros*, partial).

▶ **Figure 47.7 Cleavage in a frog embryo.** The cleavage planes in the first and second divisions extend from the animal pole to the vegetal pole, but the third cleavage is perpendicular to the polar axis. In some species, the first division bisects the gray crescent, a lighter-colored region that appears opposite the site of sperm entry.

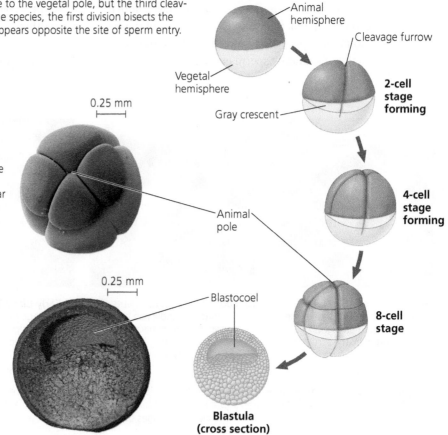

8-cell stage (viewed from the animal pole). The large amount of yolk displaces the third cleavage toward the animal pole, forming two tiers of cells. The four cells near the animal pole (closer, in this view) are smaller than the other four cells (colorized SEM).

0.25 mm

Blastula (at least 128 cells). As cleavage continues, a fluid-filled cavity, the blastocoel, forms within the embryo. Because of unequal cell division, the blastocoel is located in the animal hemisphere. Both the drawing and the micrograph (assembled from fluorescence images) show cross sections of a blastula with about 4,000 cells.

0.25 mm

Interpreting a Change in Slope

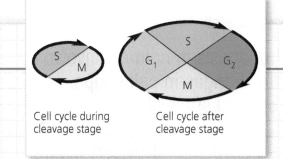

Cell cycle during cleavage stage

Cell cycle after cleavage stage

What Causes the End of Cleavage in a Frog Embryo? During cleavage in a frog embryo, as in many other animals, the cell cycle consists mainly of the S (DNA synthesis) and M (mitosis) phases, and there are no G_1 and G_2 phases. However, after the 12th cell division, G_1 and G_2 phases appear, and the cells grow, producing proteins and cytoplasmic organelles. These and other changes in activity mark the end of cleavage. But what triggers the change in the cell cycle?

How the Experiments Were Done Researchers tested the hypothesis that a mechanism for counting cell divisions determines when cleavage ends. They allowed frog embryos to take up radioactively labeled nucleosides, in one experiment labeling thymidine to measure DNA synthesis and in another experiment labeling uridine to measure RNA synthesis. They then repeated these two experiments in the presence of a toxin that prevents cell division by blocking cleavage furrow formation and cytokinesis.

Data from the Experiments

	Nucleic Acid Synthesis (on scale of 0–100)										
DNA Toxin added	35	48	54	71	83	85	88	87	100	96	
DNA No toxin	10	24	28	31	47	49	49	53	55	55	55
RNA Toxin added			0		6		25	27			33
RNA No toxin			0		3		14	22			27
Time Point (every 35 min)	1	2	3	4	5	6	7	8	9	10	11

Interpret the Data

1. How were the researchers able to independently measure DNA synthesis and RNA synthesis?

2. Use the data in the table to create a graph showing DNA synthesis and RNA synthesis with and without the toxin that prevents cell division. Note that time point 5 corresponds to cell division 12. For the DNA data, draw a straight line to represent the general trend for time points 1–5 and another straight line for time points 5 and later. For RNA, connect each data point with the next. Describe the changes in synthesis that occur at the end of cleavage.

3. The researchers hypothesized that the toxin increases diffusion of thymidine into the embryos. Explain their logic.

4. Do the data support the hypothesis that the timing of the end of cleavage depends on counting cell divisions? Explain.

5. In a separate experiment, researchers disrupted the block to polyspermy, generating embryos with 7 to 10 sperm nuclei. At the end of cleavage, these embryos had the same nucleus-to-cytoplasm ratio as the wild-type embryos, but cleavage ended at the 10th cell division rather than the 12th cell division. What do these results indicate about the timing of the end of cleavage?

(MB) A version of this Scientific Skills Exercise can be assigned in MasteringBiology.

Data from J. Newport and M. Kirschner, A major developmental transition in early *Xenopus* embryos: I. Characterization and timing of cellular changes at the midblastula stage, *Cell* 30:675–686 (1982).

For chickens and other birds, the part of the egg that we commonly call the yolk is actually the entire egg cell. Cell divisions are limited to a small whitish area at the animal pole. These divisions produce a cap of cells that sort into upper and lower layers. The cavity between these two layers is the avian version of the blastocoel.

In *Drosophila* and most other insects, yolk is found throughout the egg. Early in development, multiple rounds of mitosis occur without cytokinesis. In other words, no cell membranes form around the early nuclei. The first several hundred nuclei spread throughout the yolk and later migrate to the outer edge of the embryo. After several more rounds of mitosis, a plasma membrane forms around each nucleus, and the embryo, now the equivalent of a blastula, consists of a single layer of about 6,000 cells surrounding a mass of yolk (see Figure 18.22).

Regulation of Cleavage

The single nucleus in a newly fertilized egg has too little DNA to produce the amount of messenger RNA required to meet the cell's need for new proteins. Instead, initial

development is carried out by RNA and proteins deposited in the egg during oogenesis. After cleavage, the egg cytoplasm has been divided among the many blastomeres, each with its own nucleus. Because each blastomere is much smaller than the entire egg, its nucleus can make enough RNA to program the cell's metabolism and further development.

Given that the number of cleavage divisions varies among animals, what mechanism determines the end of the cleavage stage? The Scientific Skills Exercise explores one of the landmark studies that addressed this question.

CONCEPT CHECK 47.1

1. How does the fertilization envelope form in sea urchins? What is its function?

2. **WHAT IF?** Predict what would happen if Ca^{2+} was injected into an unfertilized sea urchin egg.

3. **MAKE CONNECTIONS** Thinking about cell cycle control, would you expect MPF activity to remain steady during cleavage (see Figure 12.16)? Explain your logic.

For suggested answers, see Appendix A.

CONCEPT 47.2

Morphogenesis in animals involves specific changes in cell shape, position, and survival

After cleavage, the rate of cell division slows considerably as the normal cell cycle is restored. The last two stages of embryonic development are responsible for **morphogenesis**, the cellular and tissue-based processes by which the animal body takes shape. During **gastrulation**, a set of cells at or near the surface of the blastula moves to an interior location, cell layers are established, and a primitive digestive tube is formed. Further transformation occurs during **organogenesis**, the formation of organs. We will discuss these two stages in turn, focusing in each case on the development of a few model organisms.

Gastrulation

Gastrulation is a dramatic reorganization of the hollow blastula into a two-layered or three-layered embryo called a **gastrula**. The cell layers produced are collectively called the embryonic **germ layers** (from the Latin *germen*, to sprout or germinate). In the late gastrula, **ectoderm** forms the outer layer and **endoderm** lines the embryonic digestive compartment or tract. In cnidarians and a few other radially symmetrical animals, only these two germ layers form during gastrulation. Such animals are called diploblasts (see Chapter 32). In contrast, vertebrates and other animals with bilateral symmetry are triploblasts, in which a third germ layer, the **mesoderm**, forms between the ectoderm and the endoderm.

Gastrulation in Sea Urchins

As illustrated in **Figure 47.8**, gastrulation in the sea urchin involves cell migration as well as *invagination*, the infolding of a sheet of cells into the embryo. Extensive rearrangement of cells transforms the shallow depression into a deeper, narrower, blind-ended tube called the **archenteron**. The open end of the archenteron, which will become the anus, is called the **blastopore**. A second opening,

which will become the mouth, forms later. Sea urchins and other animals in which the mouth develops from the second opening of the embryo are called *deuterostomes* (from the Greek, meaning "second mouth"). All chordates, including ourselves and other vertebrates, fall in this grouping (see Chapter 32). In contrast, mollusks, annelids, and arthropods are *protostomes*, animals in which the mouth develops from the first opening formed during gastrulation.

Gastrulation in Frogs

Each germ layer contributes to a distinct set of structures in the adult animal, as shown for vertebrates in **Figure 47.9**. Some organs and many organ systems of the adult derive from more than one germ layer. For example, the adrenal glands have both ectodermal and mesoderm tissue, and many other endocrine glands contain endodermal tissue.

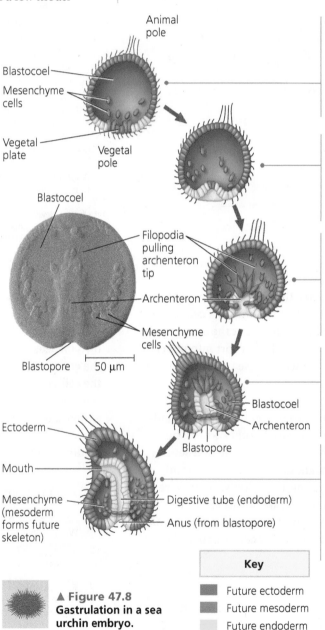

❶ A group of *mesenchyme* cells migrates from the vegetal pole of the blastula into the blastocoel. Some of these cells will eventually secrete calcium carbonate and form a simple internal skeleton.

❷ Cells at the vegetal plate flatten slightly, causing the vegetal pole of the embryo to buckle inward. This infolding of a sheet of cells is called *invagination*.

❸ Endoderm cells form the archenteron, the future digestive tube. New mesenchyme cells at the tip of the archenteron send out thin extensions (filopodia) toward the blastocoel wall (left, LM).

❹ The filopodia contract, dragging the archenteron across the blastocoel. The open end of the archenteron, which will become the anus, is called the blastospore.

❺ Fusion of the archenteron with the blastocoel wall forms the digestive tube, which now has a mouth and an anus. The gastrula has three germ layers and is covered with cilia, which will function in feeding and movement.

▲ **Figure 47.8 Gastrulation in a sea urchin embryo.**

Key
- Future ectoderm
- Future mesoderm
- Future endoderm

Figure labels: Animal pole, Blastocoel, Mesenchyme cells, Vegetal plate, Vegetal pole, Blastocoel, Filopodia pulling archenteron tip, Archenteron, Mesenchyme cells, Blastopore, 50 µm, Blastocoel, Archenteron, Blastopore, Ectoderm, Mouth, Mesenchyme (mesoderm forms future skeleton), Digestive tube (endoderm), Anus (from blastopore)

1044 UNIT SEVEN Animal Form and Function

Frogs and other bilaterally sym-metrical animals have a dorsal (top) side and a ventral (bottom) side, a left side and a right side, and an anterior (front) end and a posterior (back) end. The cell movements that begin gastrulation occur on the dorsal side of the blastula, opposite where the sperm entered the egg (Figure 47.10). As in the sea urchin, the frog's anus develops from the blas-topore, and the mouth eventually breaks through at the opposite end of the archenteron.

▼ **Figure 47.9 Major derivatives of the three embryonic germ layers in vertebrates.**

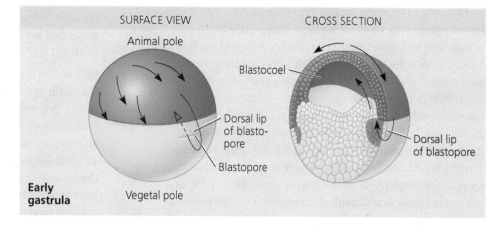

ECTODERM (outer layer of embryo)	MESODERM (middle layer of embryo)	ENDODERM (inner layer of embryo)
• Epidermis of skin and its derivatives (including sweat glands, hair follicles) • Nervous and sensory systems • Pituitary gland, adrenal medulla • Jaws and teeth • Germ cells	• Skeletal and muscular systems • Circulatory and lymphatic systems • Excretory and reproductive systems (except germ cells) • Dermis of skin • Adrenal cortex	• Epithelial lining of digestive tract and associated organs (liver, pancreas) • Epithelial lining of respiratory, excretory, and reproductive tracts and ducts • Thymus, thyroid, and parathyroid glands

▼ **Figure 47.10 Gastrulation in a frog embryo.** In the frog blastula, the blastocoel is displaced toward the animal pole and is surrounded by a wall several cells thick.

1 Gastrulation begins when cells on the dorsal side invaginate to form a small indented crease, the blastopore. The part above the crease is called the **dorsal lip**. As the blastopore is forming, a sheet of cells begins to spread out of the animal hemisphere, rolls inward over the dorsal lip (involution), and moves into the interior (shown by the dashed arrow). In the interior, these cells will form endoderm and mesoderm, with the endodermal layer on the inside. Meanwhile, cells at the animal pole change shape and begin spreading over the outer surface.

2 The blastopore extends around both sides of the embryo as more cells invaginate. When the ends meet, the blastopore forms a circle that becomes smaller as ectoderm spreads downward over the surface. Internally, continued involution expands the endoderm and mesoderm; an archenteron forms and grows as the blastocoel shrinks and eventually disappears.

3 Late in gastrulation, the cells remaining on the surface make up the ectoderm. The endoderm is the innermost layer, and the mesoderm lies between the ectoderm and endoderm. The circular blastopore surrounds a plug of yolk-filled cells.

Key	
■	Future ectoderm
■	Future mesoderm
□	Future endoderm

SURFACE VIEW · CROSS SECTION

Animal pole · Blastocoel · Dorsal lip of blasto-pore · Blastopore · Dorsal lip of blastopore

Early gastrula · Vegetal pole

Blastocoel shrinking · Archenteron · Blastopore · Blastopore

Blastocoel remnant · Ectoderm · Mesoderm · Endoderm · Archenteron · Blastopore

Late gastrula · Blastopore · Yolk plug

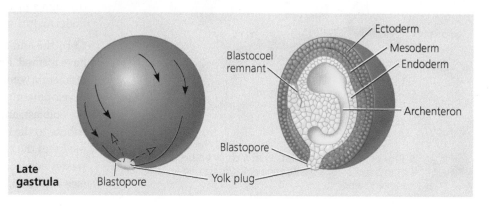

Gastrulation in Chicks

The starting point for gastrulation in chicks is an embryo consisting of upper and lower layers—known as the *epiblast* and *hypoblast*—lying atop a yolk mass. All the cells that will form the embryo come from the epiblast. During gastrulation, some epiblast cells move toward the midline of the blastoderm, detach, and move inward toward the yolk (Figure 47.11). The pileup of cells moving inward at the blastoderm's midline produces a thickening called the **primitive streak**. Some of these cells move downward and form endoderm, pushing aside the hypoblast cells, while others migrate laterally (sideways) and form mesoderm. The cells left behind on the surface of the embryo at the end of gastrulation will become ectoderm. The hypoblast cells later segregate from the endoderm and eventually form part of the sac that surrounds the yolk and also part of the stalk that connects the yolk mass to the embryo.

Over the course of chick gastrulation, the primitive streak lengthens and narrows. This shape change results from a movement and sorting of cells called convergent extension. We'll explore the mechanism of this process shortly, when we examine how form and shape arise in development.

Although different terms describe gastrulation in different vertebrate species, the rearrangements and movements of cells exhibit a number of fundamental similarities. In particular, the primitive streak, shown in Figure 47.11 for the chick embryo, is the counterpart of the blastopore lip, shown in Figure 47.10 for the frog embryo. Formation of a primitive streak is also central to human embryo gastrulation, our next topic.

▲ **Figure 47.11 Gastrulation in a chick embryo.** This is a cross section of a gastrulating embryo, looking toward the anterior end.

Gastrulation in Humans

Unlike the large, yolky eggs of many vertebrates, human eggs are quite small, storing little in the way of food reserves. Fertilization takes place in the oviduct, and development begins while the embryo completes its journey down the oviduct to the uterus (see Figure 46.15).

Figure 47.12 outlines development of the human embryo, starting about 6 days after fertilization. This depiction is largely based on observations of embryos from other mammals, such as the mouse, and of very early human embryos following *in vitro* fertilization.

❶ At the end of cleavage, the embryo has more than 100 cells arranged around a central cavity and has reached the uterus. At this stage, the embryo is called a **blastocyst**, the mammalian version of a blastula. Clustered at one end of the blastocyst cavity is a group of cells called the **inner cell mass**, which will develop into the embryo proper. It is the cells of the very early blastocyst stage that are the source of embryonic stem cell lines (see Concept 20.3).

❷ Embryo implantation is initiated by the **trophoblast**, the outer epithelium of the blastocyst. Enzymes secreted by the trophoblast during implantation break down molecules of the endometrium, the lining of the uterus, allowing invasion by the blastocyst. The trophoblast also extends finger-like projections that cause capillaries in the endometrium to spill out blood that can be captured by trophoblast tissues. Around the time the embryo undergoes implantation, the inner cell mass of the blastocyst forms a flat disk with an inner layer of cells, the *epiblast*, and an outer layer, the *hypoblast*. As is true for a bird embryo, the human embryo develops almost entirely from epiblast cells.

❸ Following implantation, the trophoblast continues to expand into the endometrium, and four new membranes appear. Although these **extraembryonic membranes** arise from the embryo, they enclose specialized structures located outside the embryo. As implantation is completed, gastrulation begins. Some epiblast cells remain as ectoderm on the surface, while others move inward through a primitive streak and form mesoderm and endoderm, just as in the chick (see Figure 47.11).

❹ By the end of gastrulation, the embryonic germ layers have formed. Extraembryonic mesoderm and four distinct extraembryonic membranes now surround the embryo. As development proceeds, cells of the invading trophoblast, the epiblast, and the adjacent endometrial tissue all contribute to the formation of the placenta. This vital organ mediates the exchange of nutrients, gases, and nitrogenous wastes between the developing embryo and the mother (see Figure 46.16).

① Blastocyst reaches uterus.

- Endometrial epithelium (uterine lining)
- Inner cell mass
- Trophoblast
- Blastocoel

Uterus

② Blastocyst implants (7 days after fertilization).

- Maternal blood vessel
- Expanding region of trophoblast
- Epiblast
- Hypoblast
- Trophoblast

③ Extraembryonic membranes start to form (10–11 days), and gastrulation begins (13 days).

- Expanding region of trophoblast
- Amniotic cavity
- Epiblast
- Hypoblast
- Yolk sac (from hypoblast)
- Extraembryonic mesoderm cells (from epiblast)
- Chorion (from trophoblast)

④ Gastrulation has produced a three-layered embryo with four extraembryonic membranes: the amnion, chorion, yolk sac, and allantois.

- Amnion
- Chorion
- Ectoderm
- Mesoderm
- Endoderm
- Yolk sac
- Extraembryonic mesoderm
- Allantois

▲ **Figure 47.12 Four stages in the early embryonic development of a human.** The names of the tissues that develop into the embryo proper are printed in blue.

Developmental Adaptations of Amniotes

EVOLUTION Mammals and reptiles (including birds) form four extraembryonic membranes: the chorion, allantois, amnion, and yolk sac (**Figure 47.13**; see also Figure 34.25). In all these groups, such membranes provide a "life-support system" for further embryonic development. Why did this adaptation appear in the evolutionary history of reptiles and mammals,

- Chorion
- Allantois
- Amnion
- Yolk sac

▲ **Figure 47.13 The four extraembryonic membranes in the shelled egg of a reptile.**

but not other vertebrates, such as fishes and amphibians? We can formulate a reasonable hypothesis by considering a few basic facts about embryonic development. All vertebrate embryos require an aqueous environment for their development. The embryos of fishes and amphibians usually develop in the surrounding sea or pond and need no specialized water-filled enclosure. However, the extensive colonization of land by vertebrates was possible only after the evolution of structures that would allow reproduction in dry environments. Two such structures exist today: (1) the shelled egg of birds and other reptiles as well as a few mammals (the monotremes) and (2) the uterus of marsupial and eutherian mammals. Inside the shell or uterus, the embryos of these animals are surrounded by fluid within a sac formed by one of the extraembryonic membranes, the amnion. Mammals and reptiles, including birds, are therefore called **amniotes** (see Concept 34.5).

For the most part, the extraembryonic membranes have similar functions in mammals and reptiles, consistent with a common evolutionary origin. The chorion is the site of gas exchange, and the fluid within the amnion physically protects the developing embryo. (This amniotic fluid is released from the vagina when a pregnant woman's "water breaks" before childbirth.) The allantois, which disposes of wastes in the reptilian egg, is incorporated into the umbilical cord in mammals. There it forms blood vessels that transport oxygen and nutrients from the placenta to the embryo and rid the embryo of carbon dioxide and nitrogenous wastes. The fourth extraembryonic membrane, the yolk sac, encloses yolk in the eggs of reptiles. In mammals it is a site of early formation of blood cells, which later migrate into the embryo proper. Thus, the extraembryonic membranes common to reptiles and mammals exhibit adaptations specific to development within a shelled egg or a uterus.

After gastrulation is complete and any extraembryonic membranes are formed, the next stage of embryonic development begins: organogenesis, the formation of organs.

Organogenesis

During organogenesis, regions of the three embryonic germ layers develop into the rudiments of organs. Often, cells from two or three germ layers participate in formation of a single organ, with interactions between cells of different germ layers helping to specify cell fates. Adoption of particular developmental fates may in turn cause cells to change shape or, in certain circumstances, migrate to another location in the body. To see how these processes contribute to organogenesis, we'll consider *neurulation*, the early steps in the formation of the brain and spinal cord in vertebrates.

Neurulation

Neurulation begins as cells from the dorsal mesoderm form the **notochord**, a rod that extends along the dorsal side of the chordate embryo, as seen for the frog in **Figure 47.14a**.

Signaling molecules secreted by these mesodermal cells and other tissues cause the ectoderm above the notochord to become the *neural plate*. Formation of the neural plate is thus an example of **induction**, a process in which a group of cells or tissues influences the development of another group through close-range interactions (see Figure 18.17b).

After the neural plate is formed, its cells change shape, curving the structure inward. In this way, the neural plate rolls itself into the **neural tube**, which runs along the anterior-posterior axis of the embryo **(Figure 47.14b)**. The neural tube will become the brain in the head and the spinal cord along the rest of the body. In contrast, the notochord disappears before birth, although parts persist as the inner portions of the disks in the adult spine. (These are the disks that can herniate or rupture, causing back pain.)

Neurulation, like other stages of development, is sometimes imperfect. In humans, an error in neural tube

(a) Neural plate formation. By this stage, the notochord has developed from dorsal mesoderm, and the dorsal ectoderm has thickened, forming the neural plate, in response to signals from other embryonic tissues. The neural folds are the two ridges that form the lateral edges of the neural plate. These folds are visible in the micrograph (LM) of a whole embryo.

(b) Neural tube formation. Infolding and pinching off of the neural plate generates the neural tube. Note the neural crest cells, which will migrate and form nerves, teeth, and other structures.

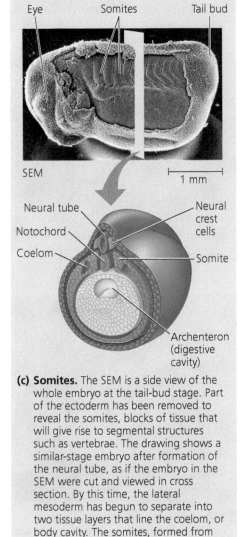

(c) Somites. The SEM is a side view of the whole embryo at the tail-bud stage. Part of the ectoderm has been removed to reveal the somites, blocks of tissue that will give rise to segmental structures such as vertebrae. The drawing shows a similar-stage embryo after formation of the neural tube, as if the embryo in the SEM were cut and viewed in cross section. By this time, the lateral mesoderm has begun to separate into two tissue layers that line the coelom, or body cavity. The somites, formed from mesoderm, flank the notochord.

 ▲ **Figure 47.14 Neurulation in a frog embryo.**

formation results in *spina bifida*, the most common disabling birth defect in the United States. In spina bifida, a portion of the neural tube fails to develop or close properly, leaving an opening in the spinal column and causing nerve damage. Although the opening can be surgically repaired shortly after birth, the nerve damage is permanent, resulting in varying degrees of leg paralysis.

Cell Migration in Organogenesis

Although organogenesis requires local cellular interactions and activities, some cells undergo long-range migration. For example, two sets of cells that develop near the neural tube of vertebrate embryos migrate in the body before assuming their developmental fate. The first set is a band of cells called the **neural crest**, which develops along the borders where the neural tube pinches off from the ectoderm (see Figure 47.14b). Neural crest cells subsequently migrate to many parts of the embryo, forming a variety of tissues that include peripheral nerves as well as parts of the teeth and skull bones.

A second set of migratory cells is formed when groups of cells located in strips of mesoderm lateral to the notochord separate into blocks called **somites** (Figure 47.14c). The somites are arranged serially on both sides along the length of the notochord. Somites play a significant role in organizing the segmented structure of the vertebrate body. Parts of the somites dissociate into mesenchyme cells, which migrate individually to new locations. Some of these cells form the vertebrae. Somite cells that become mesenchymal also form the muscles associated with the vertebral column and the ribs.

By contributing to formation of vertebrae, ribs, and associated muscles, serially repeating structures of the embryo (somites) form repeated structures in the adult. Chordates, including ourselves, are thus segmented, although in the adult form the segmentation is much less obvious than in shrimp and many other segmented invertebrates.

Organogenesis in Chicks and Insects

Early organogenesis in the chick is quite similar to that in the frog. For example, the borders of the chick blastoderm fold downward and come together, pinching the embryo into a three-layered tube joined under the middle of the body to the yolk **(Figure 47.15a)**. By the time the chick embryo is 3 days old, rudiments of the major organs, including the brain, eyes, and heart, are readily apparent **(Figure 47.15b)**.

In invertebrates, organogenesis is somewhat different, which is not surprising, given that their body plans diverge significantly from those of vertebrates. In insects, for example, tissues of the nervous system form on the ventral side of the insect embryo rather than the dorsal side, as in vertebrates. The mechanism, however, is quite similar to vertebrate neurulation: Ectoderm along the anterior-posterior axis rolls into a tube inside the embryo. Furthermore, the molecular signaling pathways that bring about the events in different locations in the two groups are remarkably similar, underscoring a shared evolutionary history. Likewise, formation of other organs in invertebrates involves many of the same cellular activities observed in vertebrates: inductive interactions, cell shape changes, and cell migration.

As we have seen in our consideration of gastrulation and organogenesis, changes in cell shape and location are essential to early development. We turn now to an exploration of how these changes take place.

► **Figure 47.15 Organogenesis in a chick embryo.**

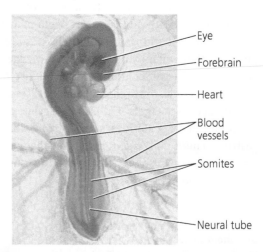

(a) Early organogenesis. The archenteron forms when lateral folds pinch the embryo away from the yolk. The embryo remains open to the yolk, attached by the yolk stalk, about midway along its length, as shown in this cross section. The notochord, neural tube, and somites subsequently develop much as they do in the frog. The germ layers lateral to the embryo itself form extraembryonic membranes.

(b) Late organogenesis. Rudiments of most major organs have already formed in this chick embryo, which is 3 days old and about 2–3 mm long. The extraembryonic membranes eventually are supplied by blood vessels extending from the embryo; several major blood vessels are seen here in this light micrograph (LM).

Mechanisms of Morphogenesis

Morphogenesis is a major stage of development in both animals and plants, but only in animals does it involve the *movement* of cells. The rigid cell wall that surrounds plant cells prevents complex movements like those that occur during gastrulation and organogenesis. In animals, movement of parts of a cell can bring about changes in cell shape or enable a cell to migrate from one place to another within the embryo. One set of cellular components essential to these events is the collection of microtubules and microfilaments that make up the cytoskeleton (see Table 6.1).

The Cytoskeleton in Morphogenesis

Reorganization of the cytoskeleton is a major force in changing cell shape during development. As an example, let's return to the topic of neurulation. At the onset of neural tube formation, microtubules oriented from dorsal to ventral in a sheet of ectodermal cells help lengthen the cells along that axis **(Figure 47.16)**. At the dorsal end of each cell is a bundle of actin filaments (microfilaments) oriented crosswise. These actin filaments contract, giving the cells a wedge shape that bends the ectoderm layer inward. Similar changes in cell shape occur at the hinge regions where the neural tube is pinching off from the ectoderm. However, the generation of wedge-shaped cells is not limited to neurulation or even to vertebrates. In *Drosophila* gastrulation, for instance, the formation of wedge-shaped cells along the ventral surface is responsible for invagination of a tube of cells that form the mesoderm.

The cytoskeleton also directs a morphogenetic movement called **convergent extension**, a rearrangement that causes a sheet of cells to become narrower (converge) while it becomes longer (extends). It's as if a crowd of people waiting to enter a theater for a concert begin to form a single-file line. The cells elongate, with their ends pointing in the direction they will move, and they then wedge between each other to form fewer columns of cells **(Figure 47.17)**. This is how, for example, the archenteron elongates in the sea urchin embryo (see Figure 47.8). Convergent extension is also important in other settings, such as involution in the frog gastrula. There, convergent extension changes the gastrulating embryo from a spherical shape to the rounded rectangular shape seen in Figure 47.14c.

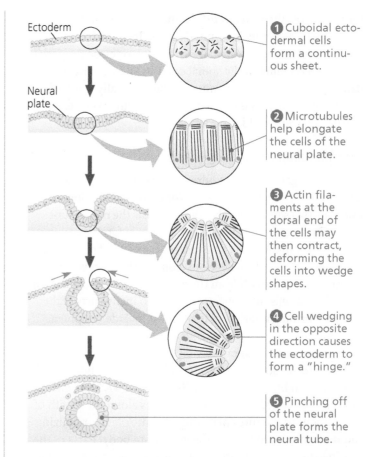

▲ **Figure 47.16 Change in cell shape during morphogenesis.** Reorganization of the cytoskeleton is associated with morphogenetic changes in embryonic tissues, as shown here for the formation of the neural tube in vertebrates.

① Cuboidal ectodermal cells form a continuous sheet.

② Microtubules help elongate the cells of the neural plate.

③ Actin filaments at the dorsal end of the cells may then contract, deforming the cells into wedge shapes.

④ Cell wedging in the opposite direction causes the ectoderm to form a "hinge."

⑤ Pinching off of the neural plate forms the neural tube.

The cytoskeleton is responsible not only for cell shape changes but also for cell migration. During organogenesis in vertebrates, cells from the neural crest and from somites migrate to locations throughout the embryo. Cells "crawl" within the embryo by using cytoskeletal fibers to extend and retract cellular protrusions. This type of motility is akin to amoeboid movement (see Figure 6.26b). Transmembrane glycoproteins called *cell adhesion molecules* play a key role in cell migration by promoting interaction between pairs of cells. Cell migration also involves the *extracellular matrix (ECM)*, the meshwork of secreted glycoproteins and other macromolecules lying outside the plasma membranes of cells (see Figure 6.28).

▶ **Figure 47.17 Convergent extension of a sheet of cells.** In this simplified diagram, the cells elongate coordinately in a particular direction and crawl between each other (convergence) as the sheet becomes longer and narrower (extension).

Convergence
Cells elongate and crawl between each other.

Extension
The sheet of cells becomes longer and narrower.

The ECM helps to guide cells in many types of movements, such as migration of individual cells and shape changes of cell sheets. Cells that line migration pathways regulate movement of migrating cells by secreting specific molecules into the ECM. For these reasons, there is a substantial effort underway to generate an artificial ECM that can serve as a scaffold for the repair or replacement of damaged tissues or organs. One promising approach involves the use of nanofiber fabrication to produce materials that mimic the essential properties of the natural ECM.

Programmed Cell Death

Just as certain cells of the embryo are programmed to change shape or location, others are programmed to die. A type of *programmed cell death* called **apoptosis** is in fact a common feature of animal development. At various times in development, individual cells, sets of cells, or whole tissues cease to develop, die, and are engulfed by neighboring cells. In some cases, a structure functions in a larval or other immature form of the organism and then is eliminated during later development. One familiar example is provided by the cells in the tail of a tadpole, which undergo apoptosis during frog metamorphosis (see Figure 45.22).

In both nervous and immune system development, large numbers of cells undergo apoptosis. In the vertebrate nervous system, for instance, many more neurons are produced during development than exist in the adult. In general, neurons survive if they make functional connections with other neurons and die if they do not (see Concept 49.4). In the adaptive immune system, cells that are self-reactive are often eliminated by apoptosis, as are effector cells that arise after encountering a pathogen but are no longer required after the infection has been eliminated.

Some cells that undergo apoptosis don't seem to have any function in the developing embryo. Why do such cells form? The answer can be found by considering the evolution of amphibians, birds, and mammals. When these groups began to diverge during evolution, the developmental program for making a vertebrate body was already in place. The differences in present-day body forms arose through modification of that common developmental program (which is why the early embryos of all vertebrates look so similar). As these groups evolved, many structures produced by the ancestral program that no longer offered a selective advantage were targeted for cell death. For example, the shared developmental program generates webbing between the embryonic digits, but in many birds and mammals, including humans, the webbing is eliminated by apoptosis (see Figure 11.21).

As you have seen, cell behavior and the molecular mechanisms underlying it are crucial to the morphogenesis of the embryo. In the next section, you'll learn that a shared set of cellular and genetic processes ensure that the various types of cells end up in the right places in each embryo.

CONCEPT CHECK 47.2

1. In the frog embryo, convergent extension elongates the notochord. Explain how the words *convergent* and *extension* apply to this process.

2. **WHAT IF?** Predict what would happen if, just before neural tube formation, you treated frog embryos with a drug that enters all the cells of the embryo and blocks the function of microfilaments.

3. **MAKE CONNECTIONS** Unlike some other types of birth defects, neural tube defects are largely preventable. Explain (see Figure 41.4).

For suggested answers, see Appendix A.

CONCEPT 47.3

Cytoplasmic determinants and inductive signals contribute to cell fate specification

During embryonic development, cells arise by division, take up particular locations in the body, and become specialized in structure and function. Where a cell resides, how it appears, and what it does define its development fate. Developmental biologists use the terms **determination** to refer to the process by which a cell or group of cells becomes committed to a particular fate and **differentiation** to refer to the resulting specialization in structure and function. You may find it a useful analogy to think about determination being equivalent to declaring a major in college and differentiation being comparable to taking the courses required by your major.

Every diploid cell formed during an animal's development has the same genome. With the exception of certain mature immune cells, the collection of genes present in a given cell is the same throughout the cell's life. How, then, do cells acquire different fates? As discussed in Concept 18.4, particular tissues, and often cells within a tissue, differ from one another by expressing distinct sets of genes from their shared genome.

A major focus of developmental biology is to uncover the mechanisms that direct the differences in gene expression underlying developmental fates. As one step toward this goal, scientists often seek to trace tissues and cell types back to their origins in the early embryo.

Fate Mapping

One way to trace the ancestry of embryonic cells is direct observation through the microscope. Such studies produced the first **fate maps**, diagrams showing the structures arising from each region of an embryo. In the 1920s, German embryologist Walther Vogt used this approach to

(a) Fate map of a frog embryo. The fates of groups of cells in a frog blastula (left) were determined in part by marking different regions of the blastula surface with nontoxic dyes of various colors. The embryos were sectioned at later stages of development, such as the neural tube stage shown on the right, and the locations of the dyed cells determined. The two embryonic stages shown here represent the result of numerous such experiments.

(b) Cell lineage analysis in a tunicate. In lineage analysis, an individual blastomere is injected with a dye during cleavage, as indicated in the drawings of 64-cell embryos of a tunicate, an invertebrate chordate (top). The dark regions in the light micrographs of larvae (bottom) correspond to the cells that developed from the two different blastomeres indicated in the drawings.

▲ **Figure 47.18 Fate mapping for two chordates.**

determine where groups of cells from the blastula end up in the gastrula (**Figure 47.18a**). Later researchers developed techniques that allowed them to mark an individual blastomere during cleavage and then follow the marker as it was distributed to all the mitotic descendants of that cell (**Figure 47.18b**).

A much more comprehensive approach to fate mapping has been carried out on the soil-dwelling nematode *Caenorhabditis elegans*. This roundworm is about 1 mm long, has a simple, transparent body with only a few types of cells, and develops into a mature adult hermaphrodite in only 3½ days in the laboratory. These attributes allowed Sydney Brenner, Robert Horvitz, and John Sulston to determine the complete developmental history, or *lineage*, of every cell in *C. elegans*. They found that every adult hermaphrodite has exactly 959 somatic cells, which arise from the fertilized egg in virtually the same way for every individual. Careful microscopic observations of worms at all stages of development, coupled with experiments in which particular cells or groups of cells were destroyed by a laser beam or through mutations, resulted in the cell lineage diagram shown in **Figure 47.19**. Using this cell lineage

▲ **Figure 47.19 Cell lineage in *Caenorhabditis elegans*.** The *C. elegans* embryo is transparent, making it possible for researchers to trace the lineage of every cell, from the zygote to the adult worm (LM). The diagram shows a detailed lineage only for the intestine, which is derived exclusively from one of the first four cells formed from the zygote.

INTERPRET THE DATA *The pattern of divisions that produces cells of the* C. elegans *intestine is always the same. Is the number of divisions that gives rise to a mature cell always the same?*

diagram, you can identify all of the progeny of a single cell, just as you would use a family history to trace the descendants of one great-great-grandparent.

As an example of a particular cell fate let's consider *germ cells*, the specialized cells that give rise to eggs or sperm. In all animals studied, complexes of RNA and protein are involved in the specification of germ cell fate. In *C. elegans*, such complexes, called *P granules*, can be detected in four cells of the newly hatched larva (Figure 47.20) and, later, in the cells of the adult gonad that produce sperm or eggs.

Tracing the position of the P granules provides a dramatic illustration of cell fate specification during development. As shown in Figure 47.21 ❶ and ❷, the P granules are distributed throughout the newly fertilized egg but move to the posterior end of the zygote before the first cleavage division. ❸ As a result, only the posterior of the two cells formed by the first division contains P granules. ❹ The P granules continue to be asymmetrically partitioned during subsequent divisions. Thus, the P granules act as cytoplasmic determinants (see Concept 18.4), fixing germ cell fate at the earliest stage of *C. elegans* development.

Fate mapping in *C. elegans* paved the way for major discoveries about programmed cell death. Lineage analysis demonstrated that exactly 131 cells die during normal *C. elegans* development. In the 1980s, researchers found that a mutation inactivating a single gene allows all 131 cells to live. Further research revealed that this gene is part of a pathway that controls and carries out apoptosis in a wide range of animals, including humans. In 2002, Brenner, Horvitz, and Sulston shared a Nobel Prize for their use of the *C. elegans* fate map in studies of programmed cell death and organogenesis.

Having established fate maps for early development, scientists were positioned to answer questions about underlying mechanisms, such as how the basic axes of the embryo are established, a process known as axis formation.

▲ **Figure 47.20 Determination of germ cell fate in *C. elegans*.** Labeling with a fluorescent antibody that is specific for a *C. elegans* P granule protein (green) reveals the incorporation of P granules into four cells of the newly hatched larva (two of the four cells are visible in this view).

⊢ 20 μm ⊣

❶ Newly fertilized egg

❷ Zygote prior to first division

❸ Two-cell embryo

▶ **Figure 47.21 Partitioning of P granules during *C. elegans* development.** The differential interference contrast micrographs (left) highlight the boundaries of nuclei and cells through the first two cell divisions. The fluorescence micrographs (right) show identically staged embryos labeled with a fluorescent antibody specific for a P granule protein.

❹ Four-cell embryo

Axis Formation

A body plan with bilateral symmetry is found across a range of animals, including nematodes, echinoderms, and vertebrates (see Chapter 32). As shown for a frog tadpole in **Figure 47.22a**, this body plan exhibits asymmetry along the dorsal-ventral and anterior-posterior axes. The right-left axis is largely symmetrical, as the two sides are roughly mirror images. When and how are the three axes established?

In the frog, the future position of the anterior-posterior axis is determined during oogenesis. Asymmetry in the egg is apparent in the formation of two distinct hemispheres: Dark melanin granules are embedded in the cortex of the animal hemisphere, whereas a yellow yolk fills the vegetal hemisphere. This animal-vegetal asymmetry dictates where the anterior-posterior axis forms in the embryo. Note, however, that the anterior-posterior and animal-vegetal axes are not the same; that is, the head of the embryo does not coincide with the animal pole.

Surprisingly, the dorsal-ventral axis of the frog embryo is determined at random. Once the sperm and egg fuse, the egg surface—the plasma membrane and associated cortex—rotates with respect to the inner cytoplasm, a movement called *cortical rotation*. From the perspective of the animal pole, this rotation is always toward the point of sperm entry, wherever in the animal hemisphere it occurs **(Figure 47.22b)**.

How does cortical rotation establish the dorsal-ventral axis? Cortical rotation allows molecules in one portion of the vegetal cortex to interact with molecules in the inner cytoplasm of the animal hemisphere. These inductive interactions activate regulatory proteins in specific portions of the vegetal cortex, leading to expression of different sets of genes in dorsal and ventral regions of the embryo.

In chicks, gravity is apparently involved in establishing the anterior-posterior axis as the egg travels down the hen's oviduct before being laid. Later, pH differences between the two sides of the blastoderm cells establish the dorsal-ventral axis. If the pH is artificially reversed above and below the blastoderm, the cells' fates will be reversed: The side facing the egg white will become the ventral part of the embryo, whereas the side facing the yolk will become the dorsal part.

In mammals, no polarity is obvious until after cleavage. However, the results of recent experiments suggest that the orientation of the egg and sperm nuclei before they fuse influences the location of the first cleavage plane and thus may play a role in establishing the embryonic axes. In insects, morphogen gradients establish both the anterior-posterior and dorsal-ventral axes (see Chapter 18).

Once the anterior-posterior and dorsal-ventral axes are established, the position of the left-right axis is fixed. Nevertheless, specific molecular mechanisms must establish which side is left and which is right. In vertebrates, there are marked left-right differences in the location of internal organs as well as in the organization and structure of the heart and brain.

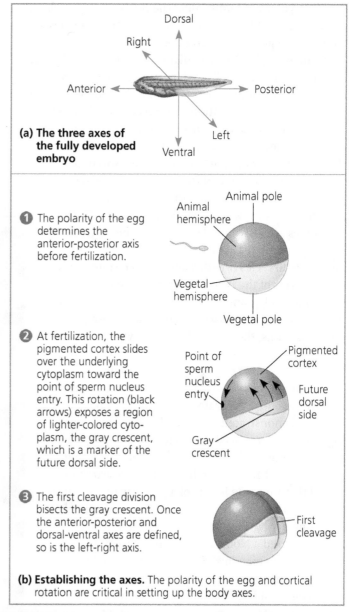

(a) The three axes of the fully developed embryo

❶ The polarity of the egg determines the anterior-posterior axis before fertilization.

Animal pole
Animal hemisphere
Vegetal hemisphere
Vegetal pole

❷ At fertilization, the pigmented cortex slides over the underlying cytoplasm toward the point of sperm nucleus entry. This rotation (black arrows) exposes a region of lighter-colored cytoplasm, the gray crescent, which is a marker of the future dorsal side.

Point of sperm nucleus entry
Pigmented cortex
Future dorsal side
Gray crescent

❸ The first cleavage division bisects the gray crescent. Once the anterior-posterior and dorsal-ventral axes are defined, so is the left-right axis.

First cleavage

(b) Establishing the axes. The polarity of the egg and cortical rotation are critical in setting up the body axes.

▲ **Figure 47.22 The body axes and their establishment in an amphibian.** All three axes are established before the zygote begins to undergo cleavage.

WHAT IF? *When researchers allowed normal cortical rotation to occur, and then forced the opposite rotation, the result was a two-headed embryo. How might you explain this finding, thinking about how cortical rotation influences body axis formation?*

Recent research has revealed that cilia are involved in setting up this left-right asymmetry. We will discuss this and other developmental roles of cilia at the end of this chapter.

Restricting Developmental Potential

Earlier we described determination in terms of commitment to a particular cell fate. The fertilized egg gives rise to all cell fates. How long during development do cells retain this ability? The German zoologist Hans Spemann addressed this question in 1938. By manipulating embryos to perturb normal development and then examining cell fate after the manipulation, he was able to assay a cell's *developmental potential*, the range of structures to which it can give rise (Figure 47.23). The work of Spemann and others demonstrated that the first two blastomeres of the frog embryo are **totipotent**, meaning that they can each develop into all the different cell types of that species.

In mammals, embryonic cells remain totipotent through the eight-cell stage, much longer than in many other animals. Recent work, however, indicates that the very early cells (even the first two) are not actually equivalent in a normal embryo.

Rather, their totipotency when isolated likely means that the cells can regulate their fate in response to their embryonic environment. Once the 16-cell stage is reached, mammalian cells are determined to form the trophoblast or the inner cell mass. Although the cells have a limited developmental potential from this point onward, their nuclei remain totipotent, as demonstrated in transplantation and cloning experiments (see Figures 20.16 and 20.17).

The totipotency of cells early in human embryogenesis is the reason why you or a classmate may have an identical twin. Identical (monozygotic) twins result when cells or groups of cells from a single embryo become separated. If the separation occurs before the trophoblast and inner cell mass become differentiated, two embryos grow, each with its own chorion and amnion. This is the case for about a third of identical twins. For the rest, the two embryos that develop share a chorion and, in very rare cases where separation is particularly late, an amnion as well.

Regardless of how uniform or varied early embryonic cells are in a particular species, the progressive restriction of developmental potential is a general feature of development in all animals. In general, the tissue-specific fates of cells are fixed in a late gastrula, but not always so in an early gastrula. For example, if the dorsal ectoderm of an early amphibian gastrula is experimentally replaced with ectoderm from some other location in the same gastrula, the transplanted tissue forms a neural plate. But if the same experiment is performed on a late-stage gastrula, the transplanted ectoderm does not respond to its new environment and does not form a neural plate.

▼ **Figure 47.23**   Inquiry

How does distribution of the gray crescent affect the developmental potential of the first two daughter cells?

Experiment Hans Spemann, at the University of Freiburg-im-Breisgau, in Germany, carried out the following experiment in 1938 to test whether substances were located asymmetrically in the gray crescent.

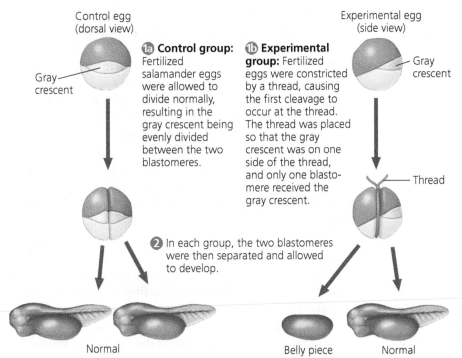

Control egg (dorsal view)

Gray crescent

1a Control group: Fertilized salamander eggs were allowed to divide normally, resulting in the gray crescent being evenly divided between the two blastomeres.

1b Experimental group: Fertilized eggs were constricted by a thread, causing the first cleavage to occur at the thread. The thread was placed so that the gray crescent was on one side of the thread, and only one blastomere received the gray crescent.

Experimental egg (side view)

Gray crescent

Thread

2 In each group, the two blastomeres were then separated and allowed to develop.

Normal   Normal   Belly piece   Normal

Results Blastomeres that received half or all of the material in the gray crescent developed into normal embryos, but a blastomere that received none of the gray crescent gave rise to an abnormal embryo without dorsal structures. Spemann called it a "belly piece."

Conclusion The developmental potential of the two blastomeres normally formed during the first cleavage division depends on their acquisition of cytoplasmic determinants localized in the gray crescent.

Source: H. Spemann, Embryonic Development and Induction, Yale University Press, New Haven, CT (1938).

WHAT IF? *In a similar experiment 40 years earlier, embryologist Hans Roux allowed the first cleavage to occur and then used a needle to kill just one blastomere. The embryo that developed from the remaining blastomere (plus remnants of the dead cell) was abnormal, resembling a half-embryo. How might the presence of molecules in the dead cell explain why Roux's result differed from the control result in Spemann's experiment?*

Cell Fate Determination and Pattern Formation by Inductive Signals

As embryonic development continues, cells influence each other's fates by induction. At the molecular level, the response to an inductive signal is usually to switch on a set of genes that make the receiving cells differentiate into a specific cell type or tissue. Here we will examine examples of this important developmental process in organizing the basic body plan of an embryo and in directing development of a vertebrate limb.

The "Organizer" of Spemann and Mangold

Before his studies of totipotency in the fertilized frog egg, Spemann had investigated cell fate determination during gastrulation. In these experiments, he and his student Hilde Mangold transplanted tissues between early gastrulas. In their most famous such experiment, summarized in **Figure 47.24**, they made a remarkable discovery. Not only

▼ **Figure 47.24** | Inquiry

Can the dorsal lip of the blastopore induce cells in another part of the amphibian embryo to change their developmental fate?

Experiment In 1924, Hans Spemann and Hilde Mangold, at the University of Freiburg-im-Breisgau in Germany, investigated the inductive ability of the dorsal lip. Using newts, they transplanted a piece of the dorsal lip from a pigmented gastrula to the ventral side of a nonpigmented gastrula; cross sections are shown here.

Dorsal lip of blastopore

Pigmented gastrula (donor embryo)

Nonpigmented gastrula (recipient embryo)

Results The recipient embryo formed a second notochord and neural tube in the region of the transplant, and eventually most of a second embryo developed. In the interior of the double embryo, secondary structures were formed partly from recipient tissue.

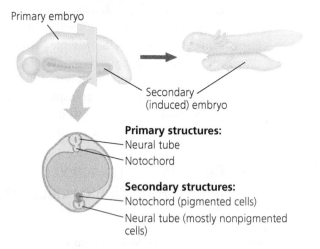

Primary embryo

Secondary (induced) embryo

Primary structures:
- Neural tube
- Notochord

Secondary structures:
- Notochord (pigmented cells)
- Neural tube (mostly nonpigmented cells)

Conclusion The transplanted dorsal lip was able to induce cells in a different region of the recipient to form structures different from their normal fate. In effect, the transplanted dorsal lip "organized" the later development of an entire extra embryo.

Source: H. Spemann and H. Mangold, Induction of embryonic primordia by implantation of organizers from a different species, Trans. V. Hamburger (1924). Reprinted in *International Journal of Developmental Biology* 45:13–38 (2001).

WHAT IF? *Because the transplant caused the recipient tissue to become something it would not have otherwise, a signal must have passed from the dorsal lip. If you identified a protein candidate for the signaling molecule, how would injecting it into ventral cells of a gastrula test its function?*

did a transplanted dorsal lip of the blastopore continue to be a blastopore lip, but it also triggered gastrulation of the surrounding tissue. They concluded that the dorsal lip of the blastopore in the early gastrula functions as an "organizer" of the embryo's body plan, inducing changes in surrounding tissue that direct formation of the notochord, the neural tube, and other organs.

Nearly a century later, developmental biologists are still studying the basis of induction by what is now called *Spemann's organizer*. An important clue has come from studies of a growth factor called bone morphogenetic protein 4 (BMP-4). One major function of the organizer seems to be to inactivate BMP-4 on the dorsal side of the embryo. Inactivation of BMP-4 allows cells on the dorsal side to make dorsal structures, such as the notochord and neural tube. Proteins related to BMP-4 and its inhibitors are found as well in invertebrates such as the fruit fly, where they also function in regulating the dorsal-ventral axis.

Formation of the Vertebrate Limb

Inductive signals play a major role in **pattern formation**, the process governing the arrangement of organs and tissues in their characteristic places in three-dimensional space. The molecular cues that control pattern formation, called **positional information**, tell a cell where it is with respect to the animal's body axes and help to determine how the cell and its descendants will respond to molecular signaling.

In Chapter 18, we discussed pattern formation in the development of *Drosophila*. For the study of pattern formation in vertebrates, a classic model system has been limb development in the chick. The wings and legs of chicks, like all vertebrate limbs, begin as limb buds, bumps of mesodermal tissue covered by a layer of ectoderm (**Figure 47.25a**). Each component of a chick limb, such as a specific bone or muscle, develops with a precise location and orientation relative to three axes: proximal-distal (shoulder to fingertip), anterior-posterior (thumb to little finger), and dorsal-ventral (knuckle to palm), as shown in **Figure 47.25b**.

Two regions in a limb bud have profound effects on its development. One such region is the **apical ectodermal ridge (AER)**, a thickened area of ectoderm at the tip of the bud (see Figure 47.25a). Surgically removing the AER blocks outgrowth of the limb along the proximal-distal axis. Why? The AER secretes a protein signal called fibroblast growth factor (FGF) that promotes limb-bud outgrowth. If the AER is replaced with beads soaked with FGF, a nearly normal limb develops.

The second major limb-bud regulatory region is the **zone of polarizing activity (ZPA)**, a specialized block of mesodermal tissue (see Figure 47.25a). The ZPA regulates development along the anterior-posterior axis of the limb. Cells nearest the ZPA form posterior structures, such as the most posterior of the chick's digits (equivalent to our little finger);

cells farthest from the ZPA form anterior structures, including the most anterior digit (like our thumb). This model is based on several lines of experiments, including the tissue transplantations outlined in **Figure 47.26**.

Like the AER, the ZPA influences development by secreting a protein signal. The signal secreted by the ZPA is called Sonic hedgehog, named after both a video game character and a similar protein in *Drosophila* that also regulates

development. Implanting cells genetically engineered to produce Sonic hedgehog into the anterior region of a normal limb bud causes formation of a mirror-image limb—just as if a ZPA had been grafted there. Furthermore, experiments with mice reveal that production of Sonic hedgehog in part of the limb bud where it is normally absent can result in extra toes.

The AER and ZPA regulate the axes of a limb bud, but what determines whether the bud develops into a forelimb or hind limb? That information is provided by spatial

(a) Organizer regions.
Vertebrate limbs develop from protrusions called limb buds, each consisting of mesoderm cells covered by a layer of ectoderm. Two regions in each limb bud, the apical ectodermal ridge (AER, shown in this SEM) and the zone of polarizing activity (ZPA), play key roles as organizers in limb pattern formation.

50 µm

Apical ectodermal ridge (AER)

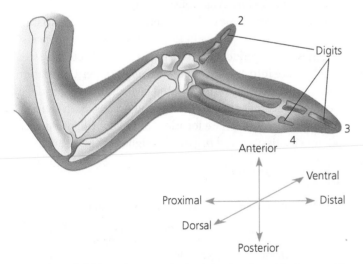

(b) Wing of chick embryo. As the bud develops into a limb, a specific pattern of tissues emerges. In the chick wing, for example, the digits are always present in the arrangement shown here. Pattern formation requires each embryonic cell to receive some kind of positional information indicating location along the three axes of the limb. The AER and ZPA secrete molecules that help provide this information. (Numbers are assigned to the digits based on a convention established for vertebrate limbs. The chicken wing has only four digits; the first digit points backward and is not shown in the diagram.)

▲ **Figure 47.25 Vertebrate limb development.**

▼ **Figure 47.26** | Inquiry

What role does the zone of polarizing activity (ZPA) play in limb pattern formation in vertebrates?

Experiment In 1985, researchers were eager to investigate the nature of the zone of polarizing activity. They transplanted ZPA tissue from a donor chick embryo under the ectoderm in the anterior margin of a limb bud in another chick (the host).

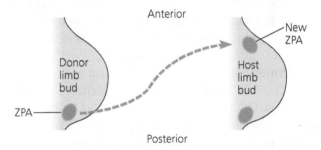

Results The host limb bud developed extra digits from host tissue in a mirror-image arrangement to the normal digits, which also formed (compare with Figure 47.24b, which shows a normal chick wing).

Conclusion The mirror-image duplication observed in this experiment suggests that ZPA cells secrete a signal that diffuses from its source and conveys positional information indicating "posterior." As the distance from the ZPA increases, the signal concentration decreases, and hence more anterior digits develop.

Source: L. S. Honig and D. Summerbell, Maps of strength of positional signaling activity in the developing chick wing bud, *Journal of Embryology and Experimental Morphology* 87:163–174 (1985).

WHAT IF? *Suppose you learned that the ZPA forms after the AER, leading you to develop the hypothesis that the AER is necessary for formation of the ZPA. If you removed the AER and looked for expression of Sonic hedgehog, how would that test your hypothesis?*

patterns of *Hox* genes, which specify different developmental fates in particular body regions (see Figure 21.18).

BMP-4, FGF, hedgehog, and Hox proteins are examples of a much larger set of molecules that govern cell fates in animals. Having mapped out many of the basic functions of these molecules in embryonic development, researchers are now addressing their role in organogenesis, focusing in particular on the development of the brain.

Cilia and Cell Fate

For many years, biologists studying organogenesis largely ignored the cellular organelles known as cilia. That is no longer the case. There is now good evidence that cilia are essential for specifying cell fate in human embryos.

Like other mammals, humans have stationary and motile cilia (see Figure 6.24). Stationary primary cilia, or *monocilia*, jut from the surface of nearly all cells, one per cell. In contrast, motile cilia are restricted to cells that propel fluid over their surface, such as the epithelial cells of airways, and on sperm (as flagella that propel sperm movement). Both stationary and motile cilia play vital roles in development.

Genetic studies provided vital clues to the developmental role of monocilia. In 2003, researchers discovered that certain mutations disrupting development of the mouse nervous system affect genes that function in the assembly of monocilia. Other geneticists found that mutations responsible for a severe kidney disease in mice alter a gene important for the transport of materials up and down monocilia. In addition, mutations in humans that block the function of monocilia were linked to cystic kidney disease.

Given that monocilia are stationary, how do they function in development? The answer is that monocilia act as antennae on the cell surface, receiving signals from multiple signaling proteins, including Sonic hedgehog. Mechanisms that regulate the set of receptor proteins that are present tune the cilium to particular signals. When the monocilia are defective, signaling is disrupted.

Insight into the role of motile cilia in development grew from the identification of Kartagener's syndrome, a particular set of medical conditions that often appear together. These conditions include male infertility due to immotile sperm and infections of the nasal sinuses and bronchi in both males and females. However, by far the most intriguing feature of Kartagener's syndrome is *situs inversus*, a reversal of the normal left-right asymmetry of the organs in the chest and abdomen (**Figure 47.27**). The heart, for example, is on the right side rather than the left. (By itself, situs inversus causes no significant medical problems.)

Scientists studying Kartagener's syndrome came to realize that all of the associated conditions result from a defect that makes cilia immotile. Without motility, sperm tails cannot beat and airway cells cannot sweep mucus and microbes

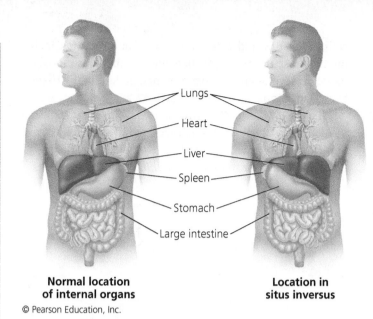

| Normal location of internal organs | Location in situs inversus |

© Pearson Education, Inc.

▲ **Figure 47.27 Situs inversus, a reversal of normal left-right asymmetry in the chest and abdomen.**

out of the airway. But what causes situs inversus in these individuals? The current model proposes that ciliary motion in a particular part of the embryo is essential for normal development. Evidence indicates that movement of the cilia generates a leftward fluid flow, breaking the symmetry between left and right sides. Without that flow, asymmetry along the left-right axis arises randomly, and half of the affected embryos develop situs inversus.

If we step back from the specification of particular cell fates to consider development as a whole, we see a sequence of events marked by cycles of signaling and differentiation. Initial cell asymmetries allow different types of cells to influence each other, resulting in the expression of specific sets of genes. The products of these genes then direct cells to differentiate into specific types. Through pattern formation and morphogenesis, differentiated cells ultimately produce a complex arrangement of tissues and organs, each functioning in its appropriate location and in coordination with other cells, tissues, and organs throughout the organism.

CONCEPT CHECK 47.3

1. How do axis formation and pattern formation differ?

2. **MAKE CONNECTIONS** How does a morphogen gradient differ from cytoplasmic determinants and inductive interactions with regard to the set of cells it affects (see Concept 18.4)?

3. **WHAT IF?** If the ventral cells of an early frog gastrula are experimentally induced to express large amounts of a protein that inhibits BMP-4, could a second embryo develop? Explain.

4. **WHAT IF?** If you removed the ZPA from a limb bud and then placed a bead soaked in Sonic hedgehog in the middle of the bud, what would be the most likely result?

For suggested answers, see Appendix A.

CONCEPT 47.1

Fertilization and cleavage initiate embryonic development (pp. 1038–1043)

- **Fertilization** forms a diploid zygote and initiates embryonic development. The **acrosomal reaction** releases hydrolytic enzymes from the sperm head that digest material surrounding the egg.

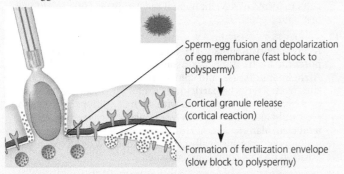

Sperm-egg fusion and depolarization of egg membrane (fast block to polyspermy)

Cortical granule release (cortical reaction)

Formation of fertilization envelope (slow block to polyspermy)

In mammalian fertilization, the cortical reaction modifies the zona pellucida as a **slow block to polyspermy**.

- Fertilization is followed by **cleavage**, a period of rapid cell division without growth, producing a large number of cells called **blastomeres**. The amount and distribution of **yolk** strongly influence the pattern of cleavage. The midblastula transition marks the end of cleavage, which in many species generates a **blastula** containing a fluid-filled cavity, the **blastocoel**.

2-cell stage forming

Animal pole

8-cell stage

Vegetal pole

Blastocoel

Blastula

? *What cell-surface event would likely fail if a sperm contacted an egg of another species?*

CONCEPT 47.2

Morphogenesis in animals involves specific changes in cell shape, position, and survival (pp. 1044–1051)

- **Gastrulation** converts the blastula to a **gastrula**, which has a primitive digestive cavity and three **germ layers: ectoderm** (blue), which forms the outer layer of the embryo, **mesoderm** (red), which forms the middle layer, and **endoderm** (yellow), which gives rise to the innermost tissues.

- Gastrulation and organogenesis in mammals resemble the processes in birds and other reptiles. After fertilization and early cleavage in the oviduct, the **blastocyst** implants in the uterus. The **trophoblast** initiates formation of the fetal portion of the placenta, and the embryo proper develops from a cell layer, the epiblast, within the blastocyst.
- The embryos of birds, other reptiles, and mammals develop within a fluid-filled sac that is contained within a shell or the uterus. In these organisms, the three germ layers produce four **extraembryonic membranes**: the amnion, chorion, yolk sac, and allantois.
- The organs of the animal body develop from specific portions of the three embryonic germ layers. Early events in **organogenesis** in vertebrates include neurulation: formation of the **notochord** by cells of the dorsal mesoderm and development of the **neural tube** from infolding of the ectodermal neural plate.

Neural tube   Notochord

Coelom

Neural tube

Notochord

Coelom

- Cytoskeletal rearrangements cause changes in the shape of cells that underlie cell movements in gastrulation and organogenesis, including invaginations and **convergent extension**. The cytoskeleton is also involved in cell migration, which relies on cell adhesion molecules and the extracellular matrix to help cells reach specific destinations. Migratory cells arise both from the neural crest and from somites.

? *How does the neural tube form? How do neural crest cells arise?*

CONCEPT 47.3

Cytoplasmic determinants and inductive signals contribute to cell fate specification (pp. 1051–1058)

- Experimentally derived **fate maps** of embryos show that specific regions of the zygote or blastula develop into specific parts of older embryos. The complete cell lineage has been worked out for *C. elegans*, revealing that programmed cell death contributes to animal development. In all species, the developmental potential of cells becomes progressively more limited as embryonic development proceeds.
- Cells in a developing embryo receive and respond to **positional information** that varies with location. This information is often in the form of signaling molecules secreted by cells in specific regions of the embryo, such as the dorsal lip of the blastopore in the amphibian gastrula and the **apical ectodermal ridge** and **zone of polarizing activity** of the vertebrate limb bud.

? *Suppose you found two classes of mouse mutations, one that affected limb development only and one that affected both limb and kidney development. Which class would be more likely to alter the function of monocilia? Explain.*

LEVEL 1: KNOWLEDGE/COMPREHENSION

1. The cortical reaction of sea urchin eggs functions directly in
   a. the formation of a fertilization envelope.
   b. the production of a fast block to polyspermy.
   c. the generation of an electrical impulse by the egg.
   d. the fusion of egg and sperm nuclei.

2. Which of the following is common to the development of both birds and mammals?
   a. holoblastic cleavage
   b. epiblast and hypoblast
   c. trophoblast
   d. gray crescent

3. The archenteron develops into
   a. the mesoderm.
   b. the endoderm.
   c. the placenta.
   d. the lumen of the digestive tract.

4. What structural adaptation in chickens allows them to lay their eggs in arid environments rather than in water?
   a. extraembryonic membranes
   b. yolk
   c. cleavage
   d. gastrulation

LEVEL 2: APPLICATION/ANALYSIS

5. If an egg cell were treated with EDTA, a chemical that binds calcium and magnesium ions,
   a. the acrosomal reaction would be blocked.
   b. the fusion of sperm and egg nuclei would be blocked.
   c. the fast block to polyspermy would not occur.
   d. the fertilization envelope would not form.

6. In humans, identical twins are possible because
   a. extraembryonic cells interact with the zygote nucleus.
   b. convergent extension occurs.
   c. early blastomeres can form a complete embryo if isolated.
   d. the gray crescent divides the dorsal-ventral axis into new cells.

7. Cells transplanted from the neural tube of a frog embryo to the ventral part of another embryo develop into nervous system tissues. This result indicates that the transplanted cells were
   a. totipotent.
   b. determined.
   c. differentiated.
   d. mesenchymal.

8. **DRAW IT** Each blue sphere in the figure below represents a cell in a cell lineage. Draw two modified versions of the cell lineage so that each version produces three cells. Use apoptosis in one of the versions, marking any dead cells with an X.

LEVEL 3: SYNTHESIS/EVALUATION

9. **EVOLUTION CONNECTION**
   Evolution in insects and vertebrates has involved the repeated duplication of body segments, followed by fusion of some segments and specialization of their structure and function. What parts of vertebrate anatomy reflect the vertebrate segmentation pattern?

10. **SCIENTIFIC INQUIRY**
    The "snout" of a frog tadpole bears a sucker. A salamander tadpole has a mustache-shaped structure called a balancer in the same area. Suppose that you perform an experiment in which you transplant ectoderm from the side of a young salamander embryo to the snout of a frog embryo. The tadpole that develops has a balancer. When you transplant ectoderm from the side of a slightly older salamander embryo to the snout of a frog embryo, the frog tadpole ends up with a patch of salamander skin on its snout. Suggest a hypothesis to explain these results in terms of developmental mechanisms. How might you test your hypothesis?

11. **SCIENCE, TECHNOLOGY, AND SOCIETY**
    Many scientists think that fetal tissue transplants offer great potential for treating Parkinson's disease, epilepsy, diabetes, Alzheimer's disease, and spinal cord injuries. Why might tissues from a fetus be particularly useful for replacing diseased or damaged cells in patients with such conditions? Some people would allow only tissues from miscarriages to be used in fetal transplant research. However, most researchers prefer to use tissues from surgically aborted fetuses. Why? Explain your position on this controversial issue.

12. **WRITE ABOUT A THEME: ORGANIZATION**
    In a short essay (100–150 words), describe how the emergent properties of the cells of the gastrula direct embryonic development.

13. SYNTHESIZE YOUR KNOWLEDGE

Occasionally, two-headed animals are born, such as this turtle. Thinking about the occurrence of identical twins and the property of totipotency, explain how this might occur.

For selected answers, see Appendix A.

MasteringBiology®

Students Go to **MasteringBiology** for assignments, the eText, and the Study Area with practice tests, animations, and activities.

Instructors Go to **MasteringBiology** for automatically graded tutorials and questions that you can assign to your students, plus Instructor Resources.

6 ECOLOGY

Monica Turner

As a biology undergraduate at Fordham University in New York, Monica Turner dreamed of becoming either a veterinarian or a forest ranger. A summer internship in Yellowstone National Park steered her toward forest ecology and ultimately changed her life. After graduating *summa cum laude*, Turner obtained her Ph.D. in ecology from the University of Georgia and became a pioneer in the field of landscape ecology. A member of the U.S. National Academy of Sciences, Turner is the Eugene P. Odum Professor of Ecology at the University of Wisconsin, Madison, where she has taught since 1994.

What was it about your first summer in Yellowstone that made you want to be an ecologist?

I had never been out of the eastern United States. So basically take a kid who's going to college in the Bronx, and put them in Yellowstone for a summer, and that's what made the difference. I loved being out of doors. I enjoyed natural history and helping with research. I decided I didn't want to spend my career in a clinical setting.

> "It's so important that we understand the world around us and see the changes that are happening globally and regionally."

You've spent much of your career working in landscape ecology. What is landscape ecology?

Landscape ecology focuses on the causes and consequences of spatial patterning in the environment. Landscape ecologists think about how patches of habitats, and the organisms and processes occurring in them, are arranged and connected. Imagine looking out of an airplane and seeing a mosaic of forest and agricultural patches below you. Across these many patches, you have nutrients flowing, organisms migrating, diseases spreading, and disturbances occurring. How the patches are shaped and arranged makes a world of difference.

You had another transformative moment in Yellowstone that shaped your research. Describe what you saw.

This is one time in my career where I can point to a single event that shaped the direction of my work. I was interested in disturbances because they change landscapes so quickly. In the summer of 1988 fires were burning all over Yellowstone. People thought that the fires had just gone through and burned everything. From a helicopter, I saw instead that the fires had left a mosaic of burned and unburned patches. It was an unparalleled natural experiment. Since then, I've worked to understand what the consequences of fire mosaics and other disturbances are for ecosystems and for species recovery. Despite the extent of the fires, the Yellowstone ecosystem recovered much more quickly than any of us expected. It was incredibly resilient.

How important is it for students to become interested in ecology today?

It's so important that we understand the world around us and see the changes that are happening globally and regionally. We're observing long-term changes in climate. We're seeing disturbances that are becoming larger and more severe. They're happening faster than I think many people had appreciated. We're also learning a lot about ecosystem services, the values and benefits that we gain from nature. Students see changes in the world around them and appreciate ecology as a result. To foster this appreciation, anything that gets young people out to experience nature—whatever nature is around them locally—is a good thing. Having students take a breadth of biology classes as undergraduates is also important. Students need classes in ecology as well as in cell biology and genetics, so that they're not closing off options before they really even know what the breadth of biology is.

◀ Recovery after the 1988 fires in Yellowstone.

MB° For an extended interview and video clip, go to the Study Area in MasteringBiology.

52

An Introduction to Ecology and the Biosphere

▲ Figure 52.1 What limits the distribution of this tiny frog?

Discovering Ecology

Kneeling by a stream in Papua New Guinea in 2008, Cornell University undergraduate Michael Grundler heard a series of clicks. He first thought that the sounds must be coming from a nearby cricket. Turning to look, however, he saw instead a tiny frog inflating its vocal sac to call for a mate. Grundler would later learn that he had just discovered the first of two new frog species from the area, *Paedophryne swiftorum* and *Paedophryne amauensis* (Figure 52.1). The entire *Paedophryne* genus is known only from the Papuan Peninsula in eastern New Guinea. Adult frogs of both species are typically only 8 mm (0.3 inch) long and may be the smallest adult vertebrates on Earth.

What environmental factors limit the geographic distribution of *Paedophryne* frogs? How do variations in their food supply or interactions with other species, such as pathogens, affect the size of their population? Questions like these are the subject of **ecology** (from the Greek *oikos*, home, and *logos*, study), the scientific study of the interactions between organisms and the environment. The interactions studied by ecologists can be organized into a hierarchy that ranges in scale from single organisms to the planet (Figure 52.2).

Exploring The Scope of Ecological Research

Ecologists work at different levels of the biological hierarchy, from individual organisms to the planet. Here we present a sample research question for each level of the hierarchy.

Global Ecology

The **biosphere** is the global ecosystem—the sum of all the planet's ecosystems and landscapes. **Global ecology** examines how the regional exchange of energy and materials influences the functioning and distribution of organisms across the biosphere.

◄ How does ocean circulation affect the global distribution of crustaceans?

Landscape Ecology

A **landscape** (or seascape) is a mosaic of connected ecosystems. Research in **landscape ecology** focuses on the factors controlling exchanges of energy, materials, and organisms across multiple ecosystems.

◄ To what extent do the trees lining a river serve as corridors of dispersal for animals?

Ecosystem Ecology

An **ecosystem** is the community of organisms in an area and the physical factors with which those organisms interact. **Ecosystem ecology** emphasizes energy flow and chemical cycling between organisms and the environment.

◄ What factors control photosynthetic productivity in a temperate grassland ecosystem?

Community Ecology

A **community** is a group of populations of different species in an area. **Community ecology** examines how species interactions, such as predation and competition, affect community structure and organization.

◄ What factors influence the diversity of species that make up a forest?

Population Ecology

A **population** is a group of individuals of the same species living in an area. **Population ecology** analyzes factors that affect population size and how and why it changes through time.

◄ What environmental factors affect the reproductive rate of flamingos?

Organismal Ecology

Organismal ecology, which includes the subdisciplines of physiological, evolutionary, and behavioral ecology, is concerned with how an organism's structure, physiology, and behavior meet the challenges posed by its environment.

◄ How do hammerhead sharks select a mate?

Exploring Global Climate Patterns

Latitudinal Variation in Sunlight Intensity

Earth's curved shape causes latitudinal variation in the intensity of sunlight. Because sunlight strikes the **tropics** (those regions that lie between 23.5° north latitude and 23.5° south latitude) most directly, more heat and light per unit of surface area are delivered there. At higher latitudes, sunlight strikes Earth at an oblique angle, and thus the light energy is more diffuse on Earth's surface.

Atmosphere
90°N (North Pole)
Low angle of incoming sunlight
23.5°N (Tropic of Cancer)
Sun overhead at equinoxes
0° (Equator)
23.5°S (Tropic of Capricorn)
Low angle of incoming sunlight
90°S (South Pole)

Global Air Circulation and Precipitation Patterns

Intense solar radiation near the equator initiates a global pattern of air circulation and precipitation. High temperatures in the tropics evaporate water from Earth's surface and cause warm, wet air masses to rise (blue arrows) and flow toward the poles. As the rising air masses cool, they release much of their water content, creating abundant precipitation in tropical regions. The high-altitude air masses, now dry, descend (tan arrows) toward Earth around 30° north and south, absorbing moisture from the land and creating an arid climate conducive to the development of the deserts that are common at those latitudes. Some of the descending air then flows toward the poles. At latitudes around 60° north and south, the air masses again rise and release abundant precipitation (though less than in the tropics). Some of the cold, dry rising air then flows to the poles, where it descends and flows back toward the equator, absorbing moisture and creating the comparatively rainless and bitterly cold climates of the polar regions.

30°N
ARID ZONE
Descending dry air absorbs moisture.
Ascending moist air releases moisture.
0°

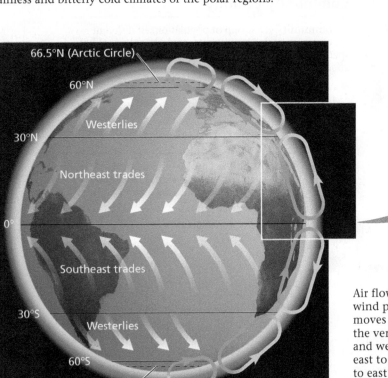

66.5°N (Arctic Circle)
60°N
Westerlies
30°N
Northeast trades
0°
Southeast trades
30°S
Westerlies
60°S
66.5°S (Antarctic Circle)

Air flowing close to Earth's surface creates predictable global wind patterns. As Earth rotates on its axis, land near the equator moves faster than that at the poles, deflecting the winds from the vertical paths shown above and creating the more easterly and westerly flows shown at left. Cooling trade winds blow from east to west in the tropics; prevailing westerlies blow from west to east in the temperate zones, defined as the regions between the Tropic of Cancer and the Arctic Circle and between the Tropic of Capricorn and the Antarctic Circle.

Ecology is a rigorous experimental science that requires a breadth of biological knowledge. Ecologists observe nature, generate hypotheses, manipulate environmental variables, and observe outcomes. In this chapter, we'll first consider how Earth's climate and other factors determine the location of major life zones on land and in the oceans. We'll then examine how ecologists investigate what controls the distribution of species. The next four chapters focus on population, community, ecosystem, and global ecology, as we explore how ecologists apply biological knowledge to predict the global consequences of human activities and to conserve Earth's biodiversity.

CONCEPT 52.1

Earth's climate varies by latitude and season and is changing rapidly

The most significant influence on the distribution of organisms on land and in the oceans is **climate**, the long-term prevailing weather conditions in a given area. Four physical factors—temperature, precipitation, sunlight, and wind—are particularly important components of climate. In this section, we'll describe climate patterns at two scales: **macroclimate**, patterns on the global, regional, and landscape level, and **microclimate**, very fine, localized patterns, such as those encountered by the community of organisms that live in the microhabitat beneath a fallen log. First, let's examine Earth's macroclimate.

Global Climate Patterns

Global climate patterns are determined largely by the input of solar energy and Earth's movement in space. The sun warms the atmosphere, land, and water. This warming establishes the temperature variations, cycles of air and water movement, and evaporation of water that cause dramatic latitudinal variations in climate. **Figure 52.3** summarizes Earth's climate patterns and how they are formed.

Regional and Local Effects on Climate

Climate patterns include seasonal variation and can be modified by other factors, such as large bodies of water and mountain ranges. We will examine each of these factors in more detail.

Seasonality

As described in **Figure 52.4**, Earth's tilted axis of rotation and its annual passage around the sun cause strong seasonal cycles in middle to high latitudes. In addition to these global

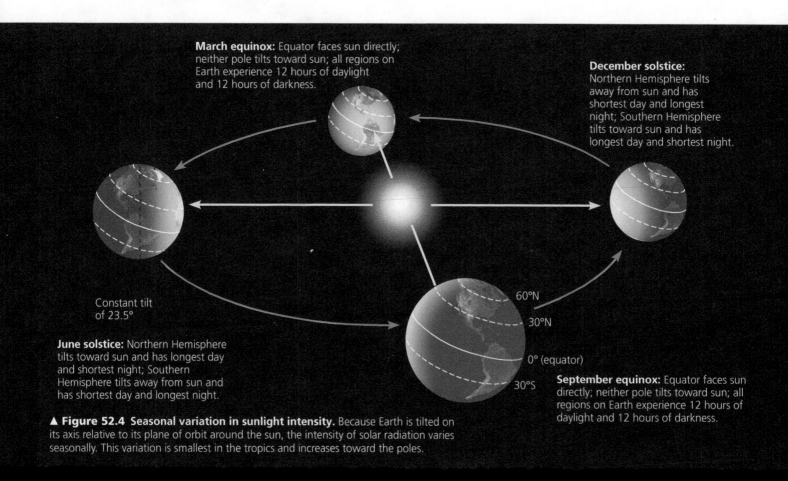

March equinox: Equator faces sun directly; neither pole tilts toward sun; all regions on Earth experience 12 hours of daylight and 12 hours of darkness.

December solstice: Northern Hemisphere tilts away from sun and has shortest day and longest night; Southern Hemisphere tilts toward sun and has longest day and shortest night.

June solstice: Northern Hemisphere tilts toward sun and has longest day and shortest night; Southern Hemisphere tilts away from sun and has shortest day and longest night.

Constant tilt of 23.5°

60°N
30°N
0° (equator)
30°S

September equinox: Equator faces sun directly; neither pole tilts toward sun; all regions on Earth experience 12 hours of daylight and 12 hours of darkness.

▲ **Figure 52.4 Seasonal variation in sunlight intensity.** Because Earth is tilted on its axis relative to its plane of orbit around the sun, the intensity of solar radiation varies seasonally. This variation is smallest in the tropics and increases toward the poles.

changes in day length, solar radiation, and temperature, the changing angle of the sun over the course of the year affects local environments. For example, the belts of wet and dry air on either side of the equator move slightly northward and southward with the changing angle of the sun, producing marked wet and dry seasons around 20° north and 20° south latitude, where many tropical deciduous forests grow. In addition, seasonal changes in wind patterns alter ocean currents, sometimes causing the upwelling of cold water from deep ocean layers. This nutrient-rich water stimulates the growth of surface-dwelling phytoplankton and the organisms that feed on them. These upwelling zones make up only a few percent of ocean area but are responsible for more than a quarter of fish caught globally.

Bodies of Water

Ocean currents influence climate along the coasts of continents by heating or cooling overlying air masses that pass across the land. Coastal regions are also generally wetter than inland areas at the same latitude. The cool, misty climate produced by the cold California Current that flows southward along western North America supports a coniferous rain forest ecosystem along much of the continent's

Pacific coast and large redwood groves farther south. Conversely, the west coast of northern Europe has a mild climate because the Gulf Stream carries warm water from the equator to the North Atlantic (**Figure 52.5**). As a result, northwestern Europe is warmer during winter than southeastern Canada, which is farther south but is cooled by the Labrador Current flowing south from the coast of Greenland.

Because of the high specific heat of water (see Concept 3.2), oceans and large lakes tend to moderate the climate of nearby land. During a hot day, when land is warmer than the water, air over the land heats up and rises, drawing a cool breeze from the water across the land (**Figure 52.6**). In contrast, because temperatures drop more quickly over land than over water at night, air over the now warmer water rises, drawing cooler air from the land back out over the water and replacing it with warmer air from offshore. This local moderation of climate can be limited to the coast itself, however. In regions such as southern California and southwestern Australia, cool, dry ocean breezes in summer are warmed when they contact the land, absorbing moisture and creating a hot, arid climate just a few kilometers inland (see Figure 3.5). This climate pattern also occurs around the Mediterranean Sea, which gives it the name *Mediterranean climate.*

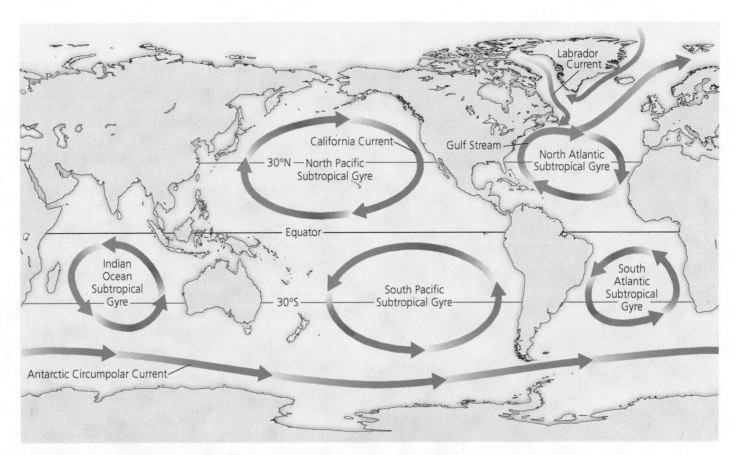

▲ **Figure 52.5 Global circulation of surface water in the oceans.** Water is warmed at the equator and flows north and south toward the poles, where it cools. Note the similarities between the direction of water circulation in the gyres and the direction of the trade winds in Figure 52.3.

▼ **Figure 52.6 How large bodies of water and mountains affect climate.** This figure illustrates what can happen on a hot summer day.

1 Cool air flows inland from the water, moderating temperatures near the shore.

2 Air that encounters mountains flows upward, cools at higher altitudes, and releases water as precipitation.

Leeward side of mountains

3 Less moisture is left in the air reaching the leeward side, which therefore has little precipitation. This rain shadow can create a desert on the back side of the mountain range.

Mountain range

Ocean

Mountains

Like large bodies of water, mountains influence air flow over land. When warm, moist air approaches a mountain, the air rises and cools, releasing moisture on the windward side of the peak (see Figure 52.6). On the leeward side, cooler, dry air descends, absorbing moisture and producing a "rain shadow." This leeward rain shadow determines where many deserts are found, including the Great Basin and the Mojave Desert of western North America and the Gobi Desert of Asia.

Mountains also affect the amount of sunlight reaching an area and thus the local temperature and rainfall. South-facing slopes in the Northern Hemisphere receive more sunlight than north-facing slopes and are therefore warmer and drier. These physical differences influence species distributions locally. In many mountains of western North America, spruce and other conifers grow on the cooler north-facing slopes, but shrubby, drought-resistant plants inhabit the south-facing slopes. In addition, every 1,000-m increase in elevation produces an average temperature drop of 6°C, equivalent to that produced by an 880-km increase in latitude. This is one reason that high-elevation communities at one latitude can be similar to those at lower elevations much farther from the equator.

Microclimate

Many features in the environment influence microclimate by casting shade, altering evaporation from soil, or changing wind patterns. Forest trees often moderate the microclimate below them. Cleared areas therefore typically experience greater temperature extremes than the forest interior because of greater solar radiation and wind currents that arise from the rapid heating and cooling of open land. Within a forest, low-lying ground is usually wetter than higher ground and tends to be occupied by different tree species. A log or large stone can shelter organisms such as salamanders, worms, and insects, buffering them from the extremes of temperature and moisture.

Every environment on Earth is characterized by a mosaic of small-scale differences in chemical and physical attributes, such as temperature, light, water, and nutrients. These **abiotic**, or nonliving, factors influence the distribution and abundance of organisms. Later in this chapter, we'll also examine how all of the **biotic**, or living, factors—the other organisms that are part of an individual's environment—similarly influence the distribution and abundance of life on Earth.

Global Climate Change

Because climatic variables affect the geographic ranges of most plants and animals, any large-scale change in Earth's climate profoundly affects the biosphere. In fact, such a large-scale climate "experiment" is already under way, a topic we'll examine in more detail in Concept 56.4. The burning of fossil fuels and deforestation are increasing the concentrations of carbon dioxide and other greenhouse gases in the atmosphere. As a result, Earth has warmed an average of 0.8°C (1.4°F) since 1900 and is projected to warm 1–6°C (2–11°F) more by the year 2100.

One way to predict the possible effects of future climate change on geographic ranges is to look back at the changes that have occurred in temperate regions since the last ice age ended. Until about 16,000 years ago, continental glaciers covered much of North America and Eurasia. As the climate warmed and the glaciers retreated, tree distributions expanded northward. A detailed record of these changes is captured in fossil pollen deposited in lakes and ponds. If researchers can determine the climatic limits of current distributions of organisms, they can make predictions about how those distributions may change with continued climatic warming.

▲ American beech

▲ Sugar maple

A question when applying this approach to plants is whether seeds can disperse quickly enough as climate changes. Fossil pollen shows that species with winged seeds that disperse relatively far from a parent tree, such as the sugar maple (*Acer saccharum*), expanded rapidly northward after the last ice age ended. In contrast, the northward range expansion of the American beech (*Fagus grandifolia*), whose seeds lack wings, was delayed for thousands of years compared with the shift in suitable habitat.

Will plants and other species be able to keep up with the much more rapid warming projected for this century? Ecologists have attempted to answer this question for the American beech. Their models predict that the northern limit of the beech's range may move 700–900 km northward in the next century, and its southern range limit will shift even more. The current and predicted geographic ranges of this species under two different climate-change scenarios are illustrated in **Figure 52.7**. If these predictions are even approximately correct, the beech's range must shift 7–9 km northward per year to keep pace with the warming climate. However, since the end of the last ice age, the beech has moved at a rate of only 0.2 km per year. Without human help in moving to new habitats, species such as the American beech may have much smaller ranges or even become extinct.

Changes in the distributions of species are already evident in many well-studied groups of terrestrial, marine, and freshwater organisms, consistent with the signature of a

(a) Current range
© 1989 AAAS

(b) 4.5°C warming over next century

(c) 6.5°C warming over next century

▲ **Figure 52.7** Current range and predicted ranges for the American beech under two climate-change scenarios.

[?] *The predicted range in each scenario is based on climate factors alone. What other factors might alter the distribution of this species?*

warmer world. For example, 22 of 35 European butterfly species studied have shifted their ranges farther north by 35–240 km in recent decades. Other research shows that a Pacific diatom species, *Neodenticula seminae*, recently has colonized the Atlantic Ocean for the first time in 800,000 years. As Arctic sea ice has receded in the past decade, the increased flow of water from the Pacific has swept these diatoms around Canada and into the Atlantic, where they quickly became established. In the next section, we'll continue to examine the importance of climate in determining species distributions around the world.

CONCEPT CHECK 52.1

1. Explain how the sun's unequal heating of Earth's surface leads to the development of deserts around 30° north and south of the equator.

2. What are some of the differences in microclimate between an unplanted agricultural field and a nearby stream corridor with trees?

3. **WHAT IF?** Changes in Earth's climate at the end of the last ice age happened gradually, taking centuries to thousands of years. If the current global warming happens very quickly, as predicted, how may this rapid climate change affect the evolution of long-lived trees compared with that of annual plants, which have much shorter generation times?

4. **MAKE CONNECTIONS** Focusing just on the effects of temperature, would you expect the global distribution of C_4 plants to expand or contract as Earth becomes warmer? Why? (See Concept 10.4.)

For suggested answers, see Appendix A.

CONCEPT 52.2

The structure and distribution of terrestrial biomes are controlled by climate and disturbance

Throughout this book, you have seen many examples of how climate and other factors influence where individual species are found (see Figure 30.7, for instance). We turn now to the role of climate in determining the nature and location of Earth's **biomes**, major life zones characterized by vegetation type in terrestrial biomes or by the physical environment in aquatic biomes.

Climate and Terrestrial Biomes

Because climate has a strong influence on the distribution of plant species, it is a major factor in determining the locations of terrestrial biomes **(Figure 52.8)**. One way to highlight the importance of climate on the distribution of biomes is to construct a **climograph**, a plot of the annual mean temperature and precipitation in a particular region.

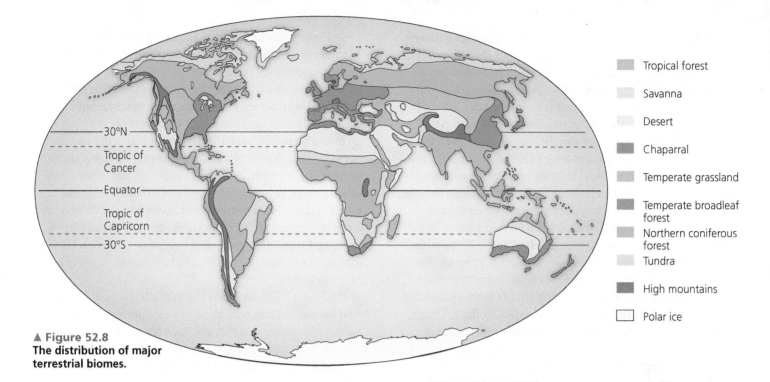

▲ **Figure 52.8**
The distribution of major terrestrial biomes.

Tropical forest

Savanna

Desert

Chaparral

Temperate grassland

Temperate broadleaf forest

Northern coniferous forest

Tundra

High mountains

Polar ice

Figure 52.9 is a climograph for some of the biomes found in North America. Notice, for instance, that the range of precipitation in northern coniferous and temperate forests is similar but that temperate forests are generally warmer. Grasslands are typically drier than either kind of forest, and deserts are drier still.

Factors other than mean temperature and precipitation also play a role in determining where biomes exist. Some areas in North America with a particular combination of temperature and precipitation support a temperate broadleaf forest, but other areas with similar values for these variables support a coniferous forest (see the overlap in Figure 52.9). How might we explain this variation? One thing to remember is that the climograph is based on annual *averages*. Often, however, the pattern of climatic variation is as important as the average climate. Some areas may receive regular precipitation throughout the year, whereas other areas may have distinct wet and dry seasons.

General Features of Terrestrial Biomes

Most terrestrial biomes are named for major physical or climatic features and for their predominant vegetation. Temperate grasslands, for instance, are generally found in middle latitudes, where the climate is more moderate than in the tropics or polar regions, and are dominated by various grass species (see Figure 52.8). Each biome is also characterized by microorganisms, fungi, and animals adapted to that particular environment. Temperate grasslands are usually more likely than temperate forests to be populated by large grazing mammals and to have arbuscular mycorrhizal fungi (see Figure 37.13).

▲ **Figure 52.9 A climograph for some major types of biomes in North America.** The areas plotted here encompass the ranges of annual mean temperature and precipitation in the biomes.

INTERPRET THE DATA *Some arctic tundra ecosystems receive as little rainfall as deserts but have much more dense vegetation. What climatic factor might explain this difference? Explain.*

Although Figure 52.8 shows distinct boundaries between the biomes, terrestrial biomes usually grade into neighboring biomes, sometimes over large areas. The area of intergradation, called an **ecotone**, may be wide or narrow.

Vertical layering of vegetation is an important feature of terrestrial biomes. In many forests, the layers from top to bottom consist of the upper **canopy**, the low-tree layer, the shrub understory, the ground layer of herbaceous plants, the forest floor (litter layer), and the root layer. Nonforest biomes have similar, though usually less pronounced, layers. Layering of vegetation provides many different habitats for animals, which sometimes exist in well-defined feeding groups, from the insectivorous birds and bats that feed above canopies to the small mammals, numerous worms, and arthropods that search for food in the litter and root layers below.

The species composition of each kind of biome varies from one location to another. For instance, in the northern coniferous forest (taiga) of North America, red spruce is common in the east but does not occur in most other areas, where black spruce and white spruce are abundant. As **Figure 52.10** shows, cacti living in deserts of North and South America appear very similar to plants called euphorbs found in African deserts. But since cacti and euphorbs belong to different evolutionary lineages, their similarities are due to convergent evolution (see Figure 22.18).

Disturbance and Terrestrial Biomes

Biomes are dynamic, and disturbance rather than stability tends to be the rule. In ecological terms, **disturbance** is an event such as a storm, fire, or human activity that changes a community, removing organisms from it and altering resource availability. Frequent fires can kill woody plants and keep a savanna from becoming the woodland that climate alone would support. Hurricanes and other storms create openings for new species in many tropical and temperate forests and can alter forest composition. After Hurricane Katrina struck the Gulf Coast of the United States in 2005,

mixed swamp forests in the area shifted toward a dominance of baldcypress (*Taxodium distichum*) and water tupelo (*Nyssa aquatica*) because these species are less susceptible to wind damage than other tree species found there. As a result of disturbances, biomes are often patchy, containing several different communities in a single area.

In many biomes, even the dominant plants depend on periodic disturbance. Natural wildfires are an integral component of grasslands, savannas, chaparral, and many coniferous forests. Before agricultural and urban development, much of the southeastern United States was dominated by a single conifer species, the longleaf pine. Without periodic burning, broadleaf trees tended to replace the pines. Forest managers now use fire as a tool to help maintain many coniferous forests.

Figure 52.11 summarizes the major features of terrestrial biomes. As you read about the characteristics of each biome, remember that humans have altered much of Earth's surface, replacing natural communities with urban and agricultural ones. The central United States, for example, is classified as grassland and once contained extensive areas of tallgrass prairie. Very little of the original prairie remains today, however, having been converted to agriculture.

CONCEPT CHECK **52.2**

1. **INTERPRET THE DATA** Based on the climograph in Figure 52.9, what mainly differentiates temperate grassland from temperate broadleaf forest?

2. Identify the natural biome in which you live, and summarize its abiotic and biotic characteristics. Do these reflect your actual surroundings? Explain.

3. **WHAT IF?** If global warming increases average temperatures on Earth by 4°C in this century, predict which biome is most likely to replace tundra in some locations as a result. Explain your answer.

For suggested answers, see Appendix A.

▼ **Figure 52.10 Convergent evolution in a cactus and a euphorb.** Cacti in the genus *Cereus* are found in the Americas; *Euphorbia canariensis*, a euphorb, is native to the Canary Islands, off the northwest coast of Africa.

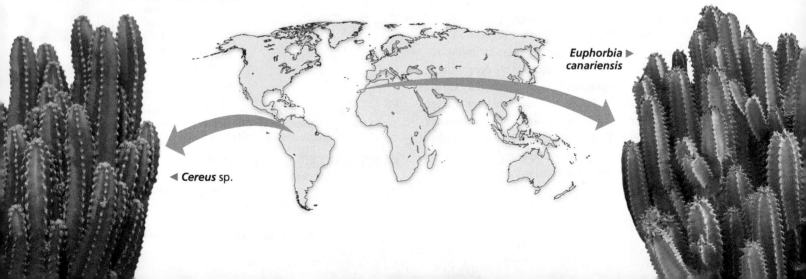

◄ *Cereus* sp.

Euphorbia canariensis ►

Exploring Terrestrial Biomes

Tropical Forest

Distribution Tropical forest occurs in equatorial and subequatorial regions.

Precipitation In **tropical rain forests**, rainfall is relatively constant, about 200–400 cm annually. In **tropical dry forests**, precipitation is highly seasonal, about 150–200 cm annually, with a six- to seven-month dry season.

Temperature High year-round, averaging 25–29°C with little seasonal variation.

Plants Tropical forests are vertically layered, and competition for light is intense. Layers in rain forests include trees that grow above a closed canopy, the canopy trees, one or two layers of subcanopy trees, and layers of shrubs and herbs (small, nonwoody plants). There are generally fewer layers in tropical dry forests. Broadleaf evergreen trees are dominant in tropical rain forests, whereas many tropical dry forest trees drop their leaves during the dry season. Epiphytes such as bromeliads and orchids generally cover tropical forest trees but are less abundant in dry forests. Thorny shrubs and succulent plants are common in some tropical dry forests.

Animals Earth's tropical forests are home to millions of species, including an estimated 5–30 million still undescribed species of insects, spiders, and other arthropods. In fact, animal diversity is higher in tropical forests than in any other terrestrial biome. The animals, including amphibians, birds and other reptiles, mammals, and arthropods, are adapted to the vertically layered environment and are often inconspicuous.

Human Impact Humans long ago established thriving communities in tropical forests. Rapid population growth leading to agriculture and development is now destroying many tropical forests.

A tropical rain forest in Costa Rica

Desert

Distribution **Deserts** occur in bands near 30° north and south latitude or at other latitudes in the interior of continents (for instance, the Gobi Desert of north-central Asia).

Precipitation Precipitation is low and highly variable, generally less than 30 cm per year.

Temperature Temperature is variable seasonally and daily. Maximum air temperature in hot deserts may exceed 50°C; in cold deserts air temperature may fall below –30°C.

Plants Desert landscapes are dominated by low, widely scattered vegetation; the proportion of bare ground is high compared with other terrestrial biomes. The plants include succulents such as cacti or euphorbs, deeply rooted shrubs, and herbs that grow during the infrequent moist periods. Desert plant adaptations include tolerance of heat and dessication, water storage, and reduced leaf surface area. Physical defenses, such as spines, and chemical defenses, such as toxins in the leaves of shrubs, are common. Many of the plants exhibit C_4 or CAM photosynthesis.

Animals Common desert animals include snakes and lizards, scorpions, ants, beetles, migratory and resident birds, and seed-eating rodents. Many species are nocturnal. Water conservation is a common adaptation, with some species surviving solely on water obtained from breaking down carbohydrates in seeds.

Human Impact Long-distance transport of water and deep groundwater wells have allowed humans to maintain substantial populations in deserts. Urbanization and conversion to irrigated agriculture have reduced the natural biodiversity of some deserts.

Organ Pipe Cactus National Monument, Arizona

Savanna

Distribution Savanna occurs in equatorial and subequatorial regions.

Precipitation Seasonal rainfall averages 30–50 cm per year. The dry season can last up to eight or nine months.

Temperature The **savanna** is warm year-round, averaging 24–29°C, but with somewhat more seasonal variation than in tropical forests.

Plants The scattered trees found at different densities in the savanna often are thorny and have small leaves, an apparent adaptation to the relatively dry conditions. Fires are common in the dry season, and the dominant plant species are fire-adapted and tolerant of seasonal drought. Grasses and small nonwoody plants called forbs, which make up most of the ground cover, grow rapidly in response to seasonal rains and are tolerant of grazing by large mammals and other herbivores.

A savanna in Kenya

Animals Large plant-eating mammals, such as wilde-beests and zebras, and predators, including lions and hyenas, are common inhabitants. However, the dominant herbivores are actually insects, especially termites. During seasonal droughts, grazing mammals often migrate to parts of the savanna with more forage and scattered watering holes.

Human Impact There is evidence that the earliest humans lived in savannas. Fires set by humans may help maintain this biome, though overly frequent fires reduce tree regeneration by killing the seedlings and saplings. Cattle ranching and overhunting have led to declines in large-mammal populations.

Chaparral

Distribution This biome occurs in midlatitude coastal regions on several continents, and its many names reflect its far-flung distribution: **chaparral** in North America, *matorral* in Spain and Chile, *garigue* and *maquis* in southern France, and *fynbos* in South Africa.

Precipitation Precipitation is highly seasonal, with rainy winters and dry summers. Annual precipitation generally falls within the range of 30–50 cm.

Temperature Fall, winter, and spring are cool, with average temperatures in the range of 10–12°C. Average summer tempera-ture can reach 30°C, and daytime maximum temperature can exceed 40°C.

Plants Chaparral is dominated by shrubs and small trees, along with many kinds of grasses and herbs. Plant diversity is high, with many species confined to a specific, relatively small geographic area. Adaptations of the woody plants to drought include their tough evergreen leaves, which reduce water loss. Adaptations to fire are also promi-nent. Some of the shrubs produce seeds that will germinate only after a hot fire; food reserves stored in their fire-resistant roots enable them to resprout quickly and use nutrients released by the fire.

Animals Native mammals include browsers, such as deer and goats, that feed on twigs and buds of woody vegetation, and a high diversity of small mammals. Chaparral areas also support many species of amphib-ians, birds and other reptiles, and insects.

Human Impact Chaparral areas have been heavily settled and reduced through conversion to agriculture and urbanization. Humans contribute to the fires that sweep across the chaparral.

An area of chaparral in California

Temperate Grassland

Distribution The veldts of South Africa, the *puszta* of Hungary, the pampas of Argentina and Uruguay, the steppes of Russia, and the plains and prairies of central North America are examples of **temperate grasslands**.

Precipitation Precipitation is often highly seasonal, with relatively dry winters and wet summers. Annual precipitation generally averages between 30 and 100 cm. Periodic drought is common.

Temperature Winters are generally cold, with average temperatures falling below –10°C. Summers, with average temperatures often approaching 30°C, are hot.

Plants The dominant plants are grasses and forbs, which vary in height from a few centimeters to 2 m in tallgrass prairie. Many grassland plants have adaptations that help them survive periodic, protracted droughts and fire. For example, grasses can sprout quickly following fire. Grazing by large mammals helps prevent establishment of woody shrubs and trees.

A grassland in Mongolia

Animals Native mammals include large grazers such as bison and wild horses. Temperate grasslands are also inhabited by a wide variety of burrowing mammals, such as prairie dogs in North America.

Human Impact Deep, fertile soils make temperate grasslands ideal places for agriculture, especially for growing grains. As a consequence, most grassland in North America and much of Eurasia has been converted to farmland. In some drier grasslands, cattle and other grazers have turned parts of the biome into desert.

Northern Coniferous Forest

Distribution Extending in a broad band across northern North America and Eurasia to the edge of the arctic tundra, the **northern coniferous forest**, or *taiga*, is the largest terrestrial biome on Earth.

Precipitation Annual precipitation generally ranges from 30 to 70 cm, and periodic droughts are common. However, some coastal coniferous forests of the U.S. Pacific Northwest are temperate rain forests that may receive over 300 cm of annual precipitation.

Temperature Winters are usually cold; summers may be hot. Some areas of coniferous forest in Siberia typically range in temperature from –50°C in winter to over 20°C in summer.

Plants Northern coniferous forests are dominated by cone-bearing trees, such as pine, spruce, fir, and hemlock, some of which depend on fire to regenerate. The conical shape of many conifers prevents too much snow from accumulating and breaking their branches, and their needle- or scale-like leaves reduce water loss. The diversity of plants in the shrub and herb layers of these forests is lower than in temperate broadleaf forests.

Animals While many migratory birds nest in northern coniferous forests, other species reside there year-round. The mammals of this biome, which include moose, brown bears, and Siberian tigers, are diverse. Periodic outbreaks of insects that feed on the dominant trees can kill vast tracts of trees.

Human Impact Although they have not been heavily settled by human populations, northern coniferous forests are being logged at an alarming rate, and the old-growth stands of these trees may soon disappear.

A coniferous forest in Norway

Temperate Broadleaf Forest

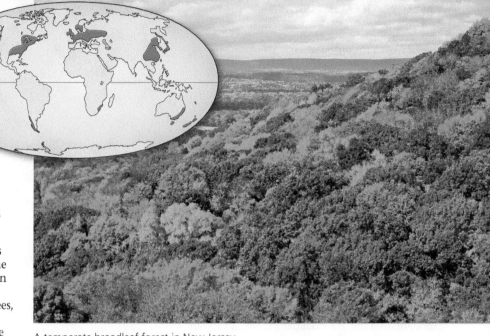

Distribution Temperate broadleaf forest is found mainly at midlatitudes in the Northern Hemisphere, with smaller areas in Chile, South Africa, Australia, and New Zealand.

Precipitation Precipitation can average from about 70 to over 200 cm annually. Significant amounts fall during all seasons, including summer rain and, in some forests, winter snow.

Temperature Winter temperatures average 0°C. Summers, with temperatures up to 35°C, are hot and humid.

Plants A mature **temperate broadleaf forest** has distinct vertical layers, including a closed canopy, one or two strata of understory trees, a shrub layer, and an herb layer. There are few epiphytes. The dominant plants in the Northern Hemisphere are deciduous trees, which drop their leaves before winter, when low temperatures would reduce photosynthesis and make water uptake from frozen soil difficult. In Australia, evergreen eucalyptus trees dominate these forests.

Animals In the Northern Hemisphere, many mammals hibernate in winter, while many bird species migrate to warmer climates. Mammals, birds, and insects make use of all the vertical layers of the forest.

A temperate broadleaf forest in New Jersey

Human Impact Temperate broadleaf forest has been heavily settled on all continents. Logging and land clearing for agriculture and urban development cleared virtually all the original deciduous forests in North America. However, owing to their capacity for recovery, these forests are returning over much of their former range.

Tundra

Distribution **Tundra** covers expansive areas of the Arctic, amounting to 20% of Earth's land surface. High winds and low temperatures produce similar plant communities, called *alpine tundra*, on very high mountaintops at all latitudes, including the tropics.

Precipitation Precipitation averages from 20 to 60 cm annually in arctic tundra but may exceed 100 cm in alpine tundra.

Temperature Winters are cold, with averages in some areas below –30°C. Summer temperatures generally average less than 10°C.

Plants The vegetation of tundra is mostly herbaceous, consisting of a mixture of mosses, grasses, and forbs, along with some dwarf shrubs and trees and lichens. A permanently frozen layer of soil called permafrost restricts the growth of plant roots.

Animals Large grazing musk oxen are resident, while caribou and reindeer are migratory. Predators include bears, wolves, and foxes. Many bird species migrate to the tundra for summer nesting.

Human Impact Tundra is sparsely settled but has become the focus of significant mineral and oil extraction in recent years.

Dovrefjell National Park, Norway, in autumn

CONCEPT 52.3

Aquatic biomes are diverse and dynamic systems that cover most of Earth

Unlike terrestrial biomes, aquatic biomes are characterized primarily by their physical environment. They also show far less latitudinal variation, with all types found across the globe. Ecologists distinguish between freshwater and marine biomes on the basis of physical and chemical differences. Marine biomes generally have salt concentrations that average 3%, whereas freshwater biomes are usually characterized by a salt concentration of less than 0.1%.

The oceans make up the largest marine biome, covering about 75% of Earth's surface. Because of their vast size, they greatly impact the biosphere. Water evaporated from the oceans provides most of the planet's rainfall, and ocean temperatures have a major effect on global climate and wind patterns (see Figure 52.3). Marine algae and photosynthetic bacteria also supply much of the world's oxygen and consume large amounts of atmospheric carbon dioxide.

Freshwater biomes are closely linked to the soils and biotic components of the surrounding terrestrial biome. The particular characteristics of a freshwater biome are also influenced by the patterns and speed of water flow and the climate to which the biome is exposed.

Zonation in Aquatic Biomes

Many aquatic biomes are physically and chemically stratified (layered), vertically and horizontally, as illustrated for both a lake and a marine environment in **Figure 52.12**. Light is absorbed by the water itself and by photosynthetic organisms, so its intensity decreases rapidly with depth. Ecologists distinguish between the upper **photic zone**, where there is sufficient light for photosynthesis, and the lower **aphotic zone**, where little light penetrates. The photic and aphotic zones together make up the **pelagic zone**. Deep in the aphotic zone lies the **abyssal zone**, the part of the ocean 2,000–6,000 m below the surface. At the bottom of all of these aquatic zones, deep or shallow, is the **benthic zone**. Made up of sand and organic and inorganic sediments, the benthic zone is occupied by communities of organisms collectively called the **benthos**. A major source of food for many benthic species is dead organic matter called **detritus**, which "rains" down from the productive surface waters of the photic zone.

Thermal energy from sunlight warms surface waters to whatever depth the sunlight penetrates, but the deeper waters remain quite cold. In the ocean and in most lakes, a narrow layer of abrupt temperature change called a **thermocline**

▼ Figure 52.12 Zonation in aquatic environments.

(a) Zonation in a lake

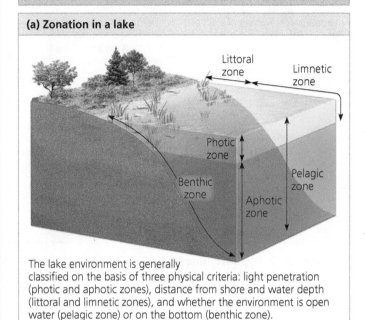

The lake environment is generally classified on the basis of three physical criteria: light penetration (photic and aphotic zones), distance from shore and water depth (littoral and limnetic zones), and whether the environment is open water (pelagic zone) or on the bottom (benthic zone).

(b) Marine zonation

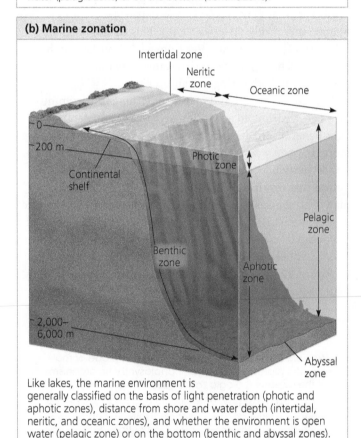

Like lakes, the marine environment is generally classified on the basis of light penetration (photic and aphotic zones), distance from shore and water depth (intertidal, neritic, and oceanic zones), and whether the environment is open water (pelagic zone) or on the bottom (benthic and abyssal zones).

separates the more uniformly warm upper layer from more uniformly cold deeper waters. Lakes tend to be particularly layered with respect to temperature, especially during summer and winter, but many temperate lakes undergo a semiannual mixing of their waters as a result of changing

1 In winter, the coldest water in the lake (0°C) lies just below the surface ice; water becomes progressively warmer at deeper levels of the lake, typically 4°C at the bottom.

2 In spring, the surface water warms to 4°C and mixes with the layers below, eliminating thermal stratification. Spring winds help mix the water, bringing oxygen to the bottom and nutrients to the surface.

3 In summer, the lake regains a distinctive thermal profile, with warm surface water separated from cold bottom water by a narrow vertical zone of abrupt temperature change, called a thermocline.

4 In autumn, as surface water cools rapidly, it sinks beneath the underlying layers, remixing the water until the surface begins to freeze and the winter temperature profile is reestablished.

Winter

Spring

Summer

Autumn

▲ **Figure 52.13 Seasonal turnover in lakes with winter ice cover.** Seasonal turnover causes the lake waters to be well oxygenated at all depths in spring and autumn; in winter and summer, when the lake is stratified by temperature, the oxygen concentration decreases with depth.

temperature profiles **(Figure 52.13)**. This **turnover**, as it is called, sends oxygenated water from a lake's surface to the bottom and brings nutrient-rich water from the bottom to the surface in both spring and autumn.

In both freshwater and marine environments, communities are distributed according to water depth, degree of light penetration, distance from shore, and whether they are found in open water or near the bottom. Marine communities, in particular, illustrate the limitations on species distribution that result from these abiotic factors. Plankton and many fish species occur in the relatively shallow photic zone (see Figure 52.12b). Because water absorbs light so well and the ocean is so deep, most of the ocean volume is dark (the aphotic zone) and harbors relatively little life.

Figure 52.14 explores the main characteristics of Earth's major aquatic biomes.

CONCEPT CHECK 52.3

1. Why are phytoplankton, and not benthic algae or rooted aquatic plants, the dominant photosynthetic organisms of the oceanic pelagic zone? (See Figure 52.14.)

2. **MAKE CONNECTIONS** Many organisms living in estuaries experience freshwater and saltwater conditions each day with the rising and falling of tides. Explain how these changing conditions challenge the survival of these organisms (see Concept 44.1).

3. **WHAT IF?** Water leaving a reservoir behind a dam is often taken from deep layers of the reservoir. Would you expect fish found in a river below a dam in summer to be species that prefer colder or warmer water than fish found in an undammed river? Explain.

For suggested answers, see Appendix A.

CONCEPT 52.4

Interactions between organisms and the environment limit the distribution of species

So far in this chapter we've examined Earth's climate and the characteristics of terrestrial and aquatic biomes. We've also introduced the range of biological levels at which ecologists work (see Figure 52.2). In this section, we will examine how ecologists determine what factors control the distribution of species, such as the *Paedophryne* frog shown in Figure 52.1.

Species distributions are a consequence of both ecological and evolutionary interactions through time. The differential survival and reproduction of individuals that lead to evolution occur in *ecological time*, the minute-to-minute time frame of interactions between organisms and the environment. Through natural selection, organisms adapt to their environment over the time frame of many generations, in *evolutionary time*. One example of how events in ecological time have led to evolution is the selection for beak depth in Galápagos finches (see Figures 23.1 and 23.2). On the island of Daphne Major, finches with larger, deeper beaks were better able to survive during a drought because they could eat the large, hard seeds that were available. Finches with shallower beaks, which required smaller, softer seeds that were in short supply, were less likely to survive and reproduce. Because beak depth is hereditary in this species, the generation of finches born after the drought had beaks that were deeper than those of previous generations.

Exploring Aquatic Biomes

Lakes

Physical Environment Standing bodies of water range from ponds a few square meters in area to lakes covering thousands of square kilometers. Light decreases with depth, creating stratification. Temperate lakes may have a seasonal thermocline; tropical lowland lakes have a thermocline year-round.

Chemical Environment The salinity, oxygen concentration, and nutrient content differ greatly among lakes and can vary with season. **Oligotrophic lakes** are nutrient-poor and generally oxygen-rich; **eutrophic lakes** are nutrient-rich and often depleted of oxygen in the deepest zone in summer and if covered with ice in winter. The amount of decomposable organic matter in bottom sediments is low in oligotrophic lakes and high in eutrophic lakes; high rates of decomposition in deeper layers of eutrophic lakes cause periodic oxygen depletion.

Geologic Features Oligotrophic lakes may become more eutrophic over time as runoff adds sediments and nutrients. They tend to have less surface area relative to their depth than eutrophic lakes.

Photosynthetic Organisms Rooted and floating aquatic plants in lakes live in the

An oligotrophic lake in Jasper National Park, Alberta

littoral zone, the shallow, well-lit waters close to shore. Farther from shore, where water is too deep to support rooted aquatic plants, the **limnetic zone** is inhabited by a variety of phytoplankton, including cyanobacteria.

Heterotrophs In the limnetic zone, small drifting heterotrophs, or zooplankton, graze on the phytoplankton. The benthic zone is inhabited by assorted invertebrates whose species composition depends partly on oxygen levels. Fishes live in all zones with sufficient oxygen.

A eutrophic lake in the Okavango Delta, Botswana

Human Impact Runoff from fertilized land and dumping of wastes lead to nutrient enrichment, which can produce algal blooms, oxygen depletion, and fish kills.

Wetlands

Physical Environment A **wetland** is a habitat that is inundated by water at least some of the time and that supports plants adapted to water-saturated soil. Some wetlands are inundated at all times, whereas others flood infrequently.

Chemical Environment Because of high organic production by plants and decomposition by microbes and other organisms, both the water and the soils are periodically low in dissolved oxygen. Wetlands have a high capacity to filter dissolved nutrients and chemical pollutants.

Geologic Features *Basin wetlands* develop in shallow basins, ranging from upland depressions to filled-in lakes and ponds. *Riverine wetlands* develop along shallow and periodically flooded banks of rivers and streams. *Fringe wetlands* occur along the coasts of large lakes and seas, where water flows back and forth because of rising lake levels or tidal action. Thus, fringe wetlands include both freshwater and marine biomes.

Photosynthetic Organisms Wetlands are among the most productive biomes on Earth. Their water-saturated soils favor the growth of plants such as floating pond lilies and emergent cattails, many sedges, bald cypress, and black spruce, which have adaptations enabling them to grow in water or in soil that is periodically anaerobic owing to the presence of unaerated water. Woody plants dominate the vegetation of swamps, while bogs are dominated by sphagnum mosses.

Heterotrophs Wetlands are home to a diverse community of invertebrates, birds, and many other organisms. Herbivores, from crustaceans and aquatic insect larvae to muskrats, consume algae, detritus, and plants. Carnivores are also varied and may include dragonflies, otters, frogs, alligators, and herons.

Human Impact Wetlands help purify water and reduce peak flooding. Draining and filling have destroyed up to 90% of wetlands.

A basin wetland in the United Kingdom

Streams and Rivers

Physical Environment The most prominent physical characteristic of streams and rivers is the speed and volume of their flow. Headwater streams are generally cold, clear, turbulent, and swift. Farther downstream, where numerous tributaries may have joined, forming a river, the water is generally warmer and more turbid because of suspended sediment. Streams and rivers are stratified into vertical zones.

Chemical Environment The salt and nutrient content of streams and rivers increases from the headwaters to the mouth. Headwaters are generally rich in oxygen. Downstream water may also contain substantial oxygen, except where there has been organic enrichment. A large fraction of the organic matter in rivers consists of dissolved or highly fragmented material that is carried by the current from forested streams.

Geologic Features Headwater stream channels are often narrow, have a rocky bottom, and alternate between shallow sections and deeper pools. The downstream stretches of rivers are generally wide and meandering. River bottoms are often silty from sediments deposited over long periods of time.

A headwater stream in Washington

Photosynthetic Organisms Headwater streams that flow through grasslands or deserts may be rich in phytoplankton or rooted aquatic plants.

Heterotrophs A great diversity of fishes and invertebrates inhabit unpolluted rivers and streams, distributed according to, and throughout, the vertical zones. In streams flowing through temperate or tropical forests, organic matter from terrestrial vegetation is the primary source of food for aquatic consumers.

The Loire river in France, far from its headwaters

Human Impact Municipal, agricultural, and industrial pollution degrade water quality and kill aquatic organisms. Damming and flood control impair the natural functioning of stream and river ecosystems and threaten migratory species such as salmon.

Estuaries

Physical Environment An **estuary** is a transition area between river and sea. Seawater flows up the estuary channel during a rising tide and flows back down during the falling tide. Often, higher-density seawater occupies the bottom of the channel and mixes little with the lower-density river water at the surface.

Chemical Environment Salinity varies spatially within estuaries, from nearly that of fresh water to that of seawater. Salinity also varies with the rise and fall of the tides. Nutrients from the river make estuaries, like wetlands, among the most productive biomes.

Geologic Features Estuarine flow patterns combined with the sediments carried by river and tidal waters create a complex network of tidal channels, islands, natural levees, and mudflats.

Photosynthetic Organisms Saltmarsh grasses and algae, including phytoplankton, are the major producers in estuaries.

Heterotrophs Estuaries support an abundance of worms, oysters, crabs, and many fish species that humans consume. Many marine invertebrates and fishes use estuaries as a breeding ground or migrate through them to freshwater habitats upstream. Estuaries are also crucial feeding areas for waterfowl and some marine mammals.

Human Impact Filling, dredging, and pollution from upstream have disrupted estuaries worldwide.

An estuary in southern Spain

Intertidal Zones

Physical Environment An **intertidal zone** is periodically submerged and exposed by the tides, twice daily on most marine shores. Upper zones experience longer exposures to air and greater variations in temperature and salinity. Changes in physical conditions from the upper to the lower intertidal zones limit the distributions of many organisms to particular strata, as shown in the photograph.

Chemical Environment Oxygen and nutrient levels are generally high and are renewed with each turn of the tides. Geologic Features The substrates of intertidal zones, which are generally either rocky or sandy, select for particular behavior and anatomy among intertidal organisms. The configuration of bays or coastlines influences the magnitude of tides and the relative exposure of intertidal organisms to wave action.

Photosynthetic Organisms A high diversity and biomass of attached marine algae inhabit rocky intertidal zones, especially in the lower zone. Sandy

intertidal zones exposed to vigorous wave action generally lack attached plants or algae, while sandy intertidal zones in protected bays or lagoons often support rich beds of seagrass and algae.

Heterotrophs Many of the animals in rocky intertidal environments have structural adaptations that enable them to attach to the hard substrate. The composition, density, and diversity of animals change markedly from the upper to the lower intertidal zones. Many of the animals in sandy or muddy intertidal zones, such as worms, clams, and predatory crustaceans, bury themselves and feed as the tides bring sources of food. Other common animals are sponges, sea anemones, echinoderms, and small fishes.

Human Impact Oil pollution has disrupted many intertidal areas. The construction of rock walls and barriers to reduce erosion from waves and storm surges has disrupted this zone in some locations.

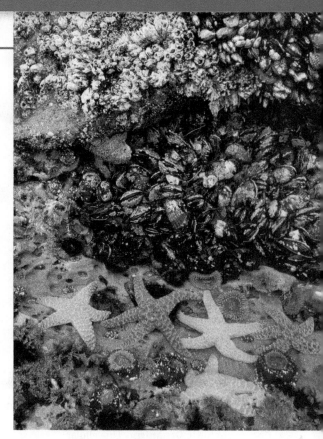

A rocky intertidal zone on the Oregon coast

Oceanic Pelagic Zone

Physical Environment The **oceanic pelagic zone** is a vast realm of open blue water, constantly mixed by wind driven oceanic currents. Because of higher water clarity, the photic zone extends to greater depths than in coastal marine waters.

Chemical Environment Oxygen levels are generally high. Nutrient concentrations are generally lower than in coastal waters. Because they are thermally stratified year-round, some tropical areas of the oceanic pelagic zone have lower nutrient concentrations than temperate oceans. Turnover between fall and spring renews nutrients in the photic zones of temperate and high-latitude ocean areas.

Geologic Features This biome covers approximately 70% of Earth's surface and has an average depth of nearly 4,000 m. The deepest point in the ocean is more than 10,000 m beneath the surface.

Photosynthetic Organisms The dominant photosynthetic organisms are phytoplankton, including photosynthetic bacteria, that drift with the oceanic currents. Spring turnover renews nutrients in temperate

oceans producing a surge of phytoplankton growth. Because of the large extent of this biome, photosynthetic plankton account for about half of the photosynthetic activity on Earth.

Heterotrophs The most abundant heterotrophs in this biome are zooplankton. These protists, worms, copepods, shrimp-like krill,

jellies, and small larvae of invertebrates and fishes graze on photosynthetic plankton. The oceanic pelagic zone also includes numerous free-swimming animals, such as large squids, fishes, sea turtles, and marine mammals.

Human Impact Overfishing has depleted fish stocks in all Earth's oceans, which have also been polluted by waste dumping.

Open ocean near Iceland

Coral Reefs

Physical Environment **Coral reefs** are formed largely from the calcium carbonate skeletons of corals. Shallow reef-building corals live in the photic zone of relatively stable tropical marine environments with high water clarity, primarily near islands and along the edge of some continents. They are sensitive to temperatures below about 18–20°C and above 30°C. Deep-sea coral reefs, found between 200 and 1,500 m deep, are less known than their shallow counterparts but harbor as much diversity as many shallow reefs do.

Chemical Environment Corals require high oxygen levels and are excluded by high inputs of fresh water and nutrients.

Geologic Features Corals require a solid substrate for attachment. A typical coral reef begins as a *fringing reef* on a young, high island, forming an offshore *barrier reef* later in the history of the island and becoming a *coral atoll* as the older island submerges.

A coral reef in the Red Sea

Photosynthetic Organisms Unicellular algae live within the tissues of the corals, forming a mutualistic relationship that provides the corals with organic molecules. Diverse multicellular red and green algae growing on the reef also contribute substantial amounts of photosynthesis.

Heterotrophs Corals, a diverse group of cnidarians, are themselves the predominant animals on coral reefs. However, fish and invertebrate diversity is exceptionally high. Overall animal diversity on coral reefs rivals that of tropical forests.

Human Impact Collecting of coral skeletons and overfishing have reduced populations of corals and reef fishes. Global warming and pollution may be contributing to large-scale coral death. Development of coastal mangroves for aquaculture has also reduced spawning grounds for many species of reef fishes.

Marine Benthic Zone

Physical Environment The **marine benthic zone** consists of the seafloor below the surface waters of the coastal, or **neritic**, zone and the offshore, pelagic zone. Except for shallow, near-coastal areas, the marine benthic zone receives no sunlight. Water temperature declines with depth, while pressure increases. As a result, organisms in the very deep benthic, or abyssal, zone are adapted to continuous cold (about 3°C) and very high water pressure.

Chemical Environment Except in areas of organic enrichment, oxygen is usually present at sufficient concentrations to support diverse animal life.

Geologic Features Soft sediments cover most of the benthic zone. However, there are areas of rocky substrate on reefs, submarine mountains, and new oceanic crust.

Autotrophs Photosynthetic organisms, mainly seaweeds and filamentous algae, are limited to shallow benthic areas with sufficient light to support them. Unique assemblages of organisms, such as those shown in the photo, are found near

deep-sea hydrothermal vents on mid-ocean ridges. In these dark, hot environments, the food producers are chemoautotrophic prokaryotes that obtain energy by oxidizing H_2S formed by a reaction of the hot water with dissolved sulfate (SO_4^{2-}).

Heterotrophs Neritic benthic communities include numerous invertebrates and fishes. Beyond the photic zone, most consumers depend entirely on organic matter raining down from above. Among the animals of the deep-sea hydrothermal vent communities are giant tube worms (pictured at left), some more than 1 m long. They are nourished by chemoautotrophic prokaryotes that live as symbionts within their bodies. Many other invertebrates, including arthropods and echinoderms, are also abundant around the hydrothermal vents.

Human Impact Overfishing has decimated important benthic fish populations, such as the cod of the Grand Banks off Newfoundland. Dumping of organic wastes has created oxygen-deprived benthic areas.

A deep-sea hydrothermal vent community

Biologists have long recognized global and regional patterns in the distribution of organisms (see the discussion of biogeography in Concept 22.3). Ecologists ask not only *where* species occur, but also *why* species occur where they do: What factors determine their distribution? In seeking to answer this question, ecologists focus on both biotic and abiotic factors.

Both kinds of factors often affect the distribution of a species, as we can see for the saguaro (*Carnegiea gigantea*). Saguaro cacti are found almost exclusively in the Sonoran Desert of the southwestern United States and northwestern Mexico (Figure 52.15). To the north, their range is limited by an abiotic factor: temperature. Saguaros tolerate freezing temperatures only briefly, typically for less than a day, and generally cannot survive at temperatures below −4°C (25°F). For the same reason, saguaros are rarely found at elevations above 1,200 m (4,000 feet).

Additional factors must be taken into account to fully explain the distribution of saguaros, however, including why they are missing from the western portion of the Sonoran Desert. Water availability is important because seedling survival typically requires consecutive years of moist conditions, something that may occur only a few times each century. Biotic factors almost certainly influence their distribution as well. Mice and grazers such as goats eat the seedlings, and bats pollinate the large, white flowers that open at night. Saguaros are also vulnerable to a deadly bacterial disease. Thus, for the saguaro, as for most other species, ecologists need to consider multiple factors and alternative hypotheses when attempting to explain the distribution of a species.

To see how ecologists might arrive at such an explanation, let's work our way through the series of questions in the flowchart in Figure 52.16.

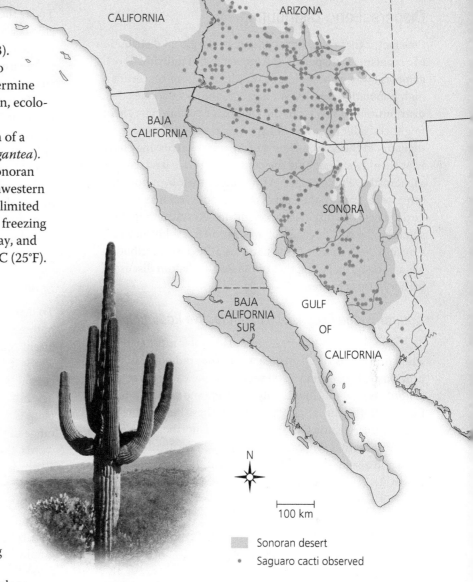

▲ **Figure 52.15 Distribution of the saguaro in North America.** Freezing temperatures strongly limit where saguaros are found, but other abiotic and biotic factors are also important.

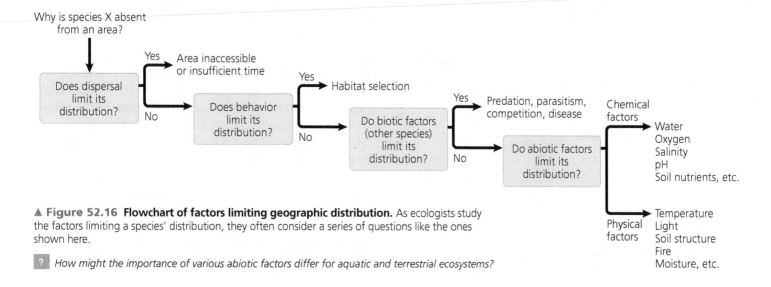

▲ **Figure 52.16 Flowchart of factors limiting geographic distribution.** As ecologists study the factors limiting a species' distribution, they often consider a series of questions like the ones shown here.

? *How might the importance of various abiotic factors differ for aquatic and terrestrial ecosystems?*

Dispersal and Distribution

One factor that contributes greatly to the global distribution of organisms is **dispersal**, the movement of individuals or gametes away from their area of origin or from centers of high population density. A biogeographer who studies the distributions of species in the context of evolutionary theory might consider dispersal in hypothesizing why there are no saguaros in the Sahara Desert of Africa: A barrier may have kept them from reaching the continent. While land-bound saguaros have not reached Africa under their own power, other organisms that disperse more readily, such as some birds, have. The dispersal of organisms is critical to understanding the role of geographic isolation in evolution (see Concept 24.2) as well as the patterns of species distribution we see today, including that of the Pacific diatom discussed earlier in this chapter.

Natural Range Expansions and Adaptive Radiation

EVOLUTION The importance of dispersal is most evident when organisms reach an area where they did not exist previously. For instance, 200 years ago, the cattle egret (*Bubulcus ibis*) was found only in Africa and southwestern Europe. But in the late 1800s, some of these birds managed to cross the Atlantic Ocean and colonize northeastern South America. From there, cattle egrets gradually spread southward and also northward through Central America and into North America, reaching Florida by 1960 (**Figure 52.17**).

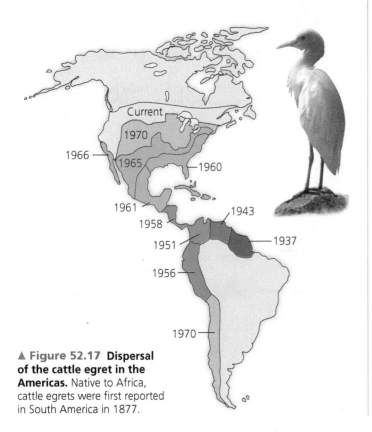

▲ **Figure 52.17 Dispersal of the cattle egret in the Americas.** Native to Africa, cattle egrets were first reported in South America in 1877.

Today they have breeding populations as far west as the Pacific coast of the United States and as far north as southern Canada.

In rare cases, such long-distance dispersal can lead to adaptive radiation, the rapid evolution of an ancestral species into new species that fill many ecological niches (see Concept 25.4). The incredible diversity of Hawaiian silverswords is an example of adaptive radiation that was possible only with the long-distance dispersal of an ancestral tarweed from North America (see Figure 25.22).

Natural range expansions clearly show the influence of dispersal on distribution. However, opportunities to observe such dispersal directly are rare, so ecologists often turn to experimental methods to better understand the role of dispersal in limiting the distribution of species.

Species Transplants

To determine if dispersal is a key factor limiting the distribution of a species, ecologists may observe the results of intentional or accidental transplants of the species to areas where it was previously absent. For a transplant to be successful, some of the organisms must not only survive in the new area but also reproduce there sustainably. If a transplant is successful, then we can conclude that the *potential* range of the species is larger than its *actual* range; in other words, the species *could* live in certain areas where it currently does not.

Species introduced to new geographic locations often disrupt the communities and ecosystems to which they have been introduced and can spread quickly (see Concept 56.1). Consequently, ecologists rarely move species to new geographic regions. Instead, they document the outcome when a species has been transplanted for other purposes, such as to introduce game animals or predators of pest species, or when a species has been accidentally transplanted or released outside its normal range.

Behavior and Habitat Selection

As transplant experiments show, some organisms do not occupy all of their potential range, even though they may be physically able to disperse into the unoccupied areas. To follow our line of questioning from Figure 52.16, does behavior play a role in limiting distribution in such cases? When individuals seem to avoid certain habitats, even when the habitats are suitable, the organism's distribution may be limited by habitat selection behavior.

Although habitat selection is one of the least understood of all ecological processes, some instances in insects have been closely studied. Female insects often deposit eggs only in response to a very narrow set of stimuli, which may restrict distribution of the insects to certain host plants. Larvae of the European corn borer, for example, can feed on a wide variety of plants but are found almost exclusively on corn (maize) because egg-laying females are attracted by odors produced by the plant. Habitat selection behavior clearly restricts this insect to geographic locations where corn is found.

Biotic Factors

If behavior does not limit the distribution of a species, our next question is whether biotic factors—other species—are responsible. Often, negative interactions with predators (organisms that kill their prey) or herbivores (organisms that eat plants or algae) restrict the ability of a species to survive and reproduce. **Figure 52.18** describes a specific case of an herbivore, a sea urchin, limiting the distribution of a food species. In certain marine ecosystems, there is often an inverse relationship between the abundance of sea urchins and seaweeds (multicellular algae, such as kelp). Where urchins that graze on seaweeds and other algae are common, large stands of seaweeds do not become established. As described in Figure 52.18, Australian researchers have tested the hypothesis that sea urchins are a biotic factor limiting seaweed distribution. When sea urchins were removed from experimental plots, seaweed cover increased dramatically, showing that urchins limited the distribution of seaweeds.

In addition to predation and herbivory, the presence or absence of pollinators, food resources, parasites, pathogens, and competing organisms can act as a biotic limitation on species distribution. Such biotic limitations are common in nature.

▼ **Figure 52.18** | Inquiry

Does feeding by sea urchins limit seaweed distribution?

Experiment W. J. Fletcher, of the University of Sydney, Australia, reasoned that if sea urchins are a limiting biotic factor in a particular ecosystem, then more seaweeds should invade an area from which sea urchins have been removed. To isolate the effect of sea urchins from that of a seaweed-eating mollusc, the limpet, he removed only urchins, only limpets, or both from study areas adjacent to a control site.

▼ Limpet

▲ Sea urchin

Results Fletcher observed a large difference in seaweed growth between areas with and without sea urchins.

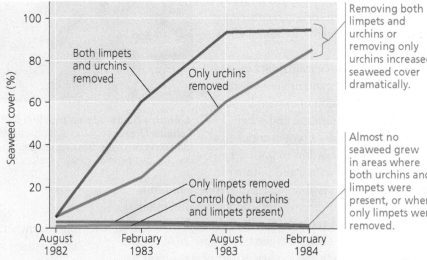

Removing both limpets and urchins or removing only urchins increased seaweed cover dramatically.

Almost no seaweed grew in areas where both urchins and limpets were present, or where only limpets were removed.

Both limpets and urchins removed

Only urchins removed

Only limpets removed

Control (both urchins and limpets present)

Conclusion Removing both limpets and urchins resulted in the greatest increase in seaweed cover, indicating that both species have some influence on seaweed distribution. But since removing only urchins greatly increased seaweed growth whereas removing only limpets had little effect, Fletcher concluded that sea urchins have a much greater effect than limpets in limiting seaweed distribution.

Source: W. J. Fletcher, Interactions among subtidal Australian sea urchins, gastropods, and algae: effects of experimental removals, *Ecological Monographs* 57:89–109 (1987).

INTERPRET THE DATA *Seaweed cover increased the most when both urchins and limpets were removed. How might you explain this result?*

Abiotic Factors

The last question in the flowchart in Figure 52.16 considers whether abiotic factors, such as temperature, water, oxygen, salinity, sunlight, or soil, might be limiting a species' distribution. If the physical conditions at a site do not allow a species to survive and reproduce, then the species will not be found there. Throughout this discussion, keep in mind that most abiotic factors vary substantially in space and time. Daily and annual fluctuations of abiotic factors may either blur or accentuate regional distinctions. Furthermore, organisms can avoid some stressful conditions temporarily through behaviors such as dormancy or hibernation (see Concept 40.4).

Temperature

Environmental temperature is an important factor in the distribution of organisms because of its effect on biological processes. Cells may rupture if the water they contain freezes (at temperatures below 0°C), and the proteins of most organisms denature at temperatures above 45°C. Most organisms function best within a specific range of environmental temperature. Temperatures outside that range may force some animals to expend energy regulating their internal temperature, as mammals and birds do (see Figure 40.17). Extraordinary adaptations enable certain organisms, such as thermophilic prokaryotes (see Figure 27.17), to live outside the temperature range habitable by other life.

Water and Oxygen

The dramatic variation in water availability among habitats is another important factor in species distribution. Species living at the seashore or in tidal wetlands can desiccate (dry out) as the tide recedes. Terrestrial organisms face a nearly constant threat of desiccation, and the distribution of terrestrial species reflects their ability to obtain and conserve water. Many amphibians, such as the *Paedophryne* frog in Figure 52.1, are particularly vulnerable to drying because they use their moist, delicate skin for gas exchange. Desert organisms exhibit a variety of adaptations for acquiring and conserving water in dry environments, as described in Chapter 44.

Water affects oxygen availability in aquatic environments and in flooded soils, where the slow diffusion of oxygen in water can limit cellular respiration and other physiological processes. Oxygen concentrations can be particularly low in both deep ocean and deep lake waters and sediments where organic matter is abundant. Flooded wetland soils may also have low oxygen content. Mangroves and other trees have specialized roots that project above the water and help the root system obtain oxygen (see Figure 35.4). Unlike many flooded wetlands, the surface waters of streams and rivers tend to be well oxygenated because of rapid exchange of gases with the atmosphere.

Salinity

The salt concentration of water in the environment affects the water balance of organisms through osmosis (see Figure 7.12). Most aquatic organisms are restricted to either freshwater or saltwater habitats by their limited ability to osmoregulate (see Concept 44.1). Although most terrestrial organisms can excrete excess salts from specialized glands or in feces or urine, high-salinity habitats typically have few species of plants or animals. In the Scientific Skills Exercise, you can interpret data from an experiment that investigated the influence of salinity on plant distributions.

Salmon that migrate between freshwater streams and the ocean use both behavioral and physiological mechanisms to osmoregulate. They balance their salt content by adjusting the amount of water they drink and by switching their gills from taking up salt in fresh water to excreting salt in the ocean.

Sunlight

Sunlight provides the energy that drives most ecosystems, and too little sunlight can limit the distribution of

▲ **Figure 52.19 Alpine tree line in Banff National Park, Canada.** Organisms living at high elevations are exposed not only to high levels of ultraviolet radiation but also to freezing temperatures, moisture deficits, and strong winds. Above the tree line, the combination of such factors restricts the growth and survival of trees.

photosynthetic species. In forests, shading by leaves makes competition for light especially intense, particularly for seedlings growing on the forest floor. In aquatic environments, every meter of water depth absorbs about 45% of the red light and about 2% of the blue light passing through it. As a result, most photosynthesis occurs relatively near the water surface.

Too much light can also limit the survival of organisms. In some ecosystems, such as deserts, high light levels can increase temperature stress if animals and plants are unable to avoid the light or to cool themselves through evaporation (see Figure 40.12). At high elevations, the sun's rays are more likely to damage DNA and proteins because the atmosphere is thinner, absorbing less ultraviolet (UV) radiation. Damage from UV radiation, combined with other abiotic stresses, prevents trees from surviving above a certain elevation, resulting in the appearance of a tree line on mountain slopes (**Figure 52.19**).

Rocks and Soil

In terrestrial environments, the pH, mineral composition, and physical structure of rocks and soil limit the distribution of plants and thus of the animals that feed on them, contributing to the patchiness of terrestrial ecosystems. The pH of soil can limit the distribution of organisms directly, through extreme acidic or basic conditions (see Figure 54.12), or

SCIENTIFIC SKILLS EXERCISE

Making a Bar Graph and a Line Graph to Interpret Data

How Do Salinity and Competition Affect the Distribution of Plants in an Estuary? Many ecologists begin their research by observing the distributions of organisms in the field. For example, field observations show that *Spartina patens* (salt marsh hay) is a dominant plant in salt marshes and *Typha angustifolia* (cattail) is a dominant plant in freshwater marshes. In this exercise, you will graph and interpret data from an experiment that examined the influence of an abiotic factor, salinity, and a biotic factor, competition, on the growth of these two species.

How the Experiment Was Done In a field experiment, researchers planted *S. patens* and *T. angustifolia* in salt marshes and freshwater marshes with and without neighboring plants. After two growing seasons (one and a half years), they measured the biomass of each species in each treatment. The researchers also grew both species in a greenhouse at six salinity levels and measured the biomass at each level after eight weeks.

Data from the Field Experiment Data are averages of 16 replicate samples.

▲ *Spartina patens*

▲ *Typha angustifolia*

	Average Biomass (g/100 cm²)			
	Spartina patens		**Typha angustifolia**	
	Salt Marshes	Freshwater Marshes	Salt Marshes	Freshwater Marshes
With neighbors	8	3	0	18
Without neighbors	10	20	0	33

Data from the Greenhouse Experiment

Salinity (parts per thousand)	0	20	40	60	80	100
% maximum biomass (*Spartina patens*)	77	40	29	17	9	0
% maximum biomass (*Typha angustifolia*)	80	20	10	0	0	0

Interpret the Data

1. Make a bar graph of the data from the field experiment. (For additional information about graphs, see the Scientific Skills Review in Appendix F and in the Study Area in MasteringBiology.) What do these data indicate about the salinity tolerances of *S. patens* and *T. angustifolia*?

2. What do the data from the field experiment indicate about the effect of competition on the growth of these two species? Which species was limited more by competition?

3. Make a line graph of the data from the greenhouse experiment. Decide which values constitute the dependent and independent variables, and use these values to set up the axes of your graph.

4. (a) In the field, *S. patens* is typically absent from freshwater marshes. Based on the data, does this appear to be due to salinity or competition? Explain your answer. (b) *T. angustifolia* does not grow in salt marshes. Does this appear to be due to salinity or competition? Explain your answer.

(MB) A version of this Scientific Skills Exercise can be assigned in MasteringBiology.

Data from C. M. Crain et al., Physical and biotic drivers of plant distribution across estuarine salinity gradients, *Ecology* 85:2539–2549 (2004).

---

indirectly, by affecting the solubility of toxins and nutrients. Soil phosphorus, for instance, is relatively insoluble in basic soils and precipitates into forms unavailable to plants.

In a river, the composition of rocks and soil that make up the substrate (riverbed) can affect water chemistry, which in turn influences the resident organisms. In freshwater and marine environments, the structure of the substrate determines the organisms that can attach to it or burrow into it.

Throughout this chapter, you have seen how the distributions of biomes and organisms depend on abiotic and biotic factors. In the next chapter, we'll continue to work our way through the hierarchy outlined in Figure 52.2, focusing on how abiotic and biotic factors influence the ecology of populations.

CONCEPT CHECK 52.4

1. Give examples of human actions that could expand a species' distribution by changing its (a) dispersal or (b) biotic interactions.

2. **WHAT IF?** You suspect that deer are restricting the distribution of a tree species by preferentially eating the seedlings of the tree. How might you test this hypothesis?

3. **MAKE CONNECTIONS** Hawaiian silverswords underwent a remarkable adaptive radiation after their ancestor reached Hawaii, while the islands were still young (see Figure 25.22). Would you expect the cattle egret to undergo a similar adaptive radiation in the Americas (see Figure 52.17)? Explain.

For suggested answers, see Appendix A.

CONCEPT 52.1

Earth's climate varies by latitude and season and is changing rapidly (pp. 1161–1164)

- Global **climate** patterns are largely determined by the input of solar energy and Earth's revolution around the sun.
- The changing angle of the sun over the year, bodies of water, and mountains exert seasonal, regional, and local effects on **macroclimate**.
- Fine-scale differences in **abiotic** (nonliving) factors, such as sunlight and temperature, determine **microclimate**.
- Increasing greenhouse gas concentrations in the air are warming Earth and altering the distributions of many species. Some species will not be able to shift their ranges quickly enough to reach suitable habitat in the future.

? *Suppose global air circulation suddenly reversed, with most air ascending at 30° north and south latitude and descending at the equator. At what latitude would you most likely find deserts in this scenario?*

CONCEPT 52.2

The structure and distribution of terrestrial biomes are controlled by climate and disturbance (pp. 1164–1170)

- **Climographs** show that temperature and precipitation are correlated with **biomes**. Because other factors also play roles in biome location, biomes overlap.
- Terrestrial biomes are often named for major physical or climatic factors and for their predominant vegetation. Vertical layering is an important feature of terrestrial biomes.
- **Disturbance**, both natural and human-induced, influences the type of vegetation found in biomes. Humans have altered much of Earth's surface, replacing the natural terrestrial communities described and depicted in Figure 52.11 with urban and agricultural ones.
- The pattern of climatic variation is as important as the average climate in determining where biomes occur.

? *In what ways are disturbances important for savanna ecosystems and the plants in them?*

CONCEPT 52.3

Aquatic biomes are diverse and dynamic systems that cover most of Earth (pp. 1171–1172)

- Aquatic biomes are characterized primarily by their physical environment rather than by climate and are often layered with regard to light penetration, temperature, and community structure. Marine biomes have a higher salt concentration than freshwater biomes.
- In the ocean and in most lakes, an abrupt temperature change called a **thermocline** separates a more uniformly warm upper layer from more uniformly cold deeper waters.
- Many temperate lakes undergo a **turnover** or mixing of water in spring and fall that sends deep, nutrient-rich water to the surface and shallow, oxygen-rich water to deeper layers.

? *In which aquatic biomes might you find an aphotic zone?*

CONCEPT 52.4

Interactions between organisms and the environment limit the distribution of species (pp. 1172–1181)

- Ecologists want to know not only *where* species occur but also *why* those species occur where they do.

? *If you were an ecologist studying the chemical and physical limits to the distributions of species, how might you rearrange the flowchart preceding this question?*

LEVEL 1: KNOWLEDGE/COMPREHENSION

1. Which of the following areas of study focuses on the exchange of energy, organisms, and materials between ecosystems?
   a. organismal ecology
   b. landscape ecology
   c. ecosystem ecology
   d. community ecology

2. Which lake zone would be absent in a very shallow lake?
   a. benthic zone
   b. aphotic zone
   c. pelagic zone
   d. littoral zone

3. Which of the following is true with respect to oligotrophic lakes and eutrophic lakes?
   a. Oligotrophic lakes are more subject to oxygen depletion.
   b. Rates of photosynthesis are lower in eutrophic lakes.
   c. Eutrophic lakes are richer in nutrients.
   d. Sediments in oligotrophic lakes contain larger amounts of decomposable organic matter.

LEVEL 2: APPLICATION/ANALYSIS

4. Which of the following is characteristic of most terrestrial biomes?
   a. a distribution predicted almost entirely by rock and soil patterns
   b. clear boundaries between adjacent biomes
   c. vegetation demonstrating vertical layering
   d. cold winter months

5. The oceans affect the biosphere in all of the following ways *except*
   a. producing a substantial amount of the biosphere's oxygen.
   b. removing carbon dioxide from the atmosphere.
   c. moderating the climate of terrestrial biomes.
   d. regulating the pH of freshwater biomes and terrestrial groundwater.

6. Which statement about dispersal is *false*?
   a. Dispersal is a common component of the life cycles of plants and animals.
   b. Colonization of devastated areas after floods or volcanic eruptions depends on dispersal.
   c. Dispersal occurs only on an evolutionary time scale.
   d. The ability to disperse can expand the geographic distribution of a species.

7. When climbing a mountain, we can observe transitions in biological communities that are analogous to the changes
   a. in biomes at different latitudes.
   b. in different depths in the ocean.
   c. in a community through different seasons.
   d. in an ecosystem as it evolves over time.

8. Suppose that the number of bird species is determined mainly by the number of vertical strata found in the environment. If so, in which of the following biomes would you find the greatest number of bird species?
   a. tropical rain forest
   b. savanna
   c. desert
   d. temperate broadleaf forest

LEVEL 3: SYNTHESIS/EVALUATION

9. **WHAT IF?** If the direction of Earth's rotation reversed, the most predictable effect would be
   a. a big change in the length of the year.
   b. winds blowing from west to east along the equator.
   c. a loss of seasonal variation at high latitudes.
   d. the elimination of ocean currents.

10. **INTERPRET THE DATA** After examining Figure 52.18, you decide to study feeding relationships among sea otters, sea urchins, and kelp. You know that sea otters prey on sea urchins and that urchins eat kelp. At four coastal sites, you measure kelp abundance. Then you spend one day at each site and mark whether otters are present or absent every 5 minutes during the day. Make a graph that shows how otter density depends on kelp abundance, using the data below. Then formulate a hypothesis to explain the pattern you observed.

Site	Kelp Abundance (% cover)	Otter Density (# sightings per day)
1	75	98
2	15	18
3	60	85
4	25	36

11. **EVOLUTION CONNECTION**
    Discuss how the concept of time applies to ecological situations and evolutionary changes. Do ecological time and evolutionary time ever overlap? If so, what are some examples?

12. **SCIENTIFIC INQUIRY**
    Jens Clausen and colleagues, at the Carnegie Institution of Washington, studied how the size of yarrow plants (*Achillea lanulosa*) growing on the slopes of the Sierra Nevada varied with elevation. They found that plants from low elevations were generally taller than plants from high elevations, as shown in the diagram.

Seed collection sites

Source: J. Clausen et al., Experimental studies on the nature of species. III. Environmental responses of climatic races of *Achillea*, Carnegie Institution of Washington Publication No. 581 (1948).

Clausen and colleagues proposed two hypotheses to explain this variation within a species: (1) There are genetic differences between populations of plants found at different elevations. (2) The species has developmental flexibility and can assume tall or short growth forms, depending on local abiotic factors. If you had seeds from yarrow plants found at low and high elevations, what experiments would you perform to test these hypotheses?

13. **WRITE ABOUT A THEME: INTERACTIONS**
    Global warming is occurring rapidly in Arctic marine and terrestrial ecosystems, including tundra and northern coniferous forests. In such locations, reflective white snow and ice cover are melting quickly and extensively, uncovering darker-colored ocean water, plants, and rocks. In a short essay (100–150 words), explain how this process might represent a positive-feedback loop (see Concept 40.2).

14. **SYNTHESIZE YOUR KNOWLEDGE**

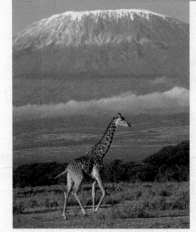

If you were to hike up Mount Kilimanjaro in Tanzania, you would pass through several habitats, including savanna at the base, forest on the slopes, and alpine tundra near the top. Explain how such diverse habitats can be found at one location near the equator.

For selected answers, see Appendix A.

MasteringBiology®

Students Go to **MasteringBiology** for assignments, the eText, and the Study Area with practice tests, animations, and activities.

Instructors Go to **MasteringBiology** for automatically graded tutorials and questions that you can assign to your students, plus Instructor Resources.

53

Population Ecology

▲ **Figure 53.1 What causes the survival of turtle hatchlings to vary each year?**

Turtle Tracks

Each year in Florida, thousands of loggerhead turtle (*Caretta caretta*) hatchlings break out of their eggshells, dig up through the sand, and crawl down the beach for their first journey to the ocean **(Figure 53.1)**. Several factors determine how many turtles will hatch and reach the water. The number of females returning to lay eggs each year varies by a factor of 20. Nest predation by raccoons also varies greatly, ranging from less than 10% in some years to almost 100% in others. Those hatchlings that do manage to dig to the surface can become disoriented by lights and wander away from the ocean or be eaten by birds or crabs before they reach the water.

Why does offspring survival for turtles and other species fluctuate greatly from year to year? To answer this question, we turn to the field of population ecology, the study of populations in relation to their environment. Population ecology explores how biotic and abiotic factors influence the density, distribution, size, and age structure of populations.

Populations evolve as natural selection acts on heritable variations among individuals, changing the frequencies of alleles and traits over time (see Chapter 23). Evolution remains a central theme as we now view populations in the context of ecology.

In this chapter, we will first examine some of the structural and dynamic aspects of populations. We will then explore the tools and models ecologists use to analyze populations and the factors that can regulate the abundance of organisms. Finally, we will apply these basic concepts as we examine recent trends in the size and makeup of the human population.

CONCEPT 53.1

Biological processes influence population density, dispersion, and demographics

A **population** is a group of individuals of a single species living in the same general area. Members of a population rely on the same resources, are influenced by similar environmental factors, and are likely to interact and breed with one another.

Populations are often described by their boundaries and size (the number of individuals living within those boundaries). Ecologists usually begin investigating a population by defining boundaries appropriate to the organism under study and to the questions being asked. A population's boundaries may be natural ones, as in the case of an island or a lake, or they may be arbitrarily defined by an investigator—for example, a specific county in Minnesota for a study of oak trees.

Density and Dispersion

The **density** of a population is the number of individuals per unit area or volume: the number of oak trees per square kilometer in the Minnesota county or the number of *Escherichia coli* bacteria per milliliter in a test tube. **Dispersion** is the pattern of spacing among individuals within the boundaries of the population.

Density: A Dynamic Perspective

In rare cases, population size and density can be determined by counting all individuals within the boundaries of the population. We could count all the sea stars in a tide pool, for instance. Large mammals that live in herds, such as elephants, can sometimes be counted accurately from airplanes. In most cases, however, it is impractical or impossible to count all individuals in a population. Instead, ecologists use various sampling techniques to estimate densities and total population sizes. They might count the number of oak trees in several randomly located 100 × 100 m plots, calculate the average density in the plots, and then extend the estimate to the population size in the entire area. Such estimates are most accurate when there are many sample plots

and when the habitat is fairly homogeneous. In other cases, instead of counting single organisms, population ecologists estimate density from an indicator of population size, such as the number of nests, burrows, tracks, or fecal droppings. Ecologists also use the **mark-recapture method** to estimate the size of wildlife populations (Figure 53.2).

Births

Births and immigration add individuals to a population.

Immigration

Deaths

Deaths and emigration remove individuals from a population.

Emigration

▲ Figure 53.3 **Population dynamics.**

Density is not a static property but changes as individuals are added to or removed from a population (**Figure 53.3**). Additions occur through birth (which we define here to include all forms of reproduction) and **immigration**, the influx of new individuals from other areas. The factors that remove individuals from a population are death (mortality) and **emigration**, the movement of individuals out of a population and into other locations.

While birth and death rates influence the density of all populations, immigration and emigration also alter the density of many populations. Studies of a population of Hector's dolphins (see Figure 53.2) in New Zealand showed that immigration was approximately 15% of the total population size each year. Emigration of dolphins in the area tends to occur during the winter season when the animals move farther from shore. Both immigration and emigration represent important biological exchanges among populations through time.

Patterns of Dispersion

Within a population's geographic range, local densities may differ substantially, creating contrasting patterns of dispersion. Differences in local density are among the most important characteristics for a population ecologist to study, since they provide insight into the environmental associations and social interactions of individuals in the population.

The most common pattern of dispersion is *clumped*, in which individuals are aggregated in patches. Plants and fungi are often clumped where soil conditions and other environmental factors favor germination and growth. Mushrooms, for instance, may be clumped within and on top of a rotting log. Insects and salamanders may be clumped under the same log because of the higher humidity there. Clumping of animals may also be associated with mating behavior. Sea stars group together in tide pools,

where food is readily available and where they can breed successfully (**Figure 53.4a**). Forming groups may also increase the effectiveness of predation or defense; for example, a wolf pack is more likely than a single wolf to subdue a moose, and a flock of birds is more likely than a single bird to warn of a potential attack.

A *uniform*, or evenly spaced, pattern of dispersion may result from direct interactions between individuals in the population. Some plants secrete chemicals that inhibit the germination and growth of nearby individuals that could compete for resources. Animals often exhibit uniform dispersion as a result of antagonistic social interactions, such as **territoriality**—the defense of a bounded physical space against encroachment by other individuals (**Figure 53.4b**). Uniform patterns are rarer than clumped patterns.

In *random* dispersion (unpredictable spacing), the position of each individual in a population is independent of other individuals. This pattern occurs in the absence of strong attractions or repulsions among individuals or where key physical or chemical factors are relatively constant across the study area. Plants established by windblown seeds, such as dandelions, may be randomly distributed in a fairly uniform habitat (**Figure 53.4c**).

Demographics

The factors that influence population density and dispersion patterns—the ecological needs of a species, structure of the environment, and interactions among individuals within the population—also influence other characteristics of populations. **Demography** is the study of the vital statistics of populations and how they change over time. Of particular interest to demographers are birth rates and death rates. A useful way to summarize some of the vital statistics of a population is to make a life table.

▼ **Figure 53.4 Patterns of dispersion within a population's geographic range.**

(a) Clumped	(b) Uniform	(c) Random

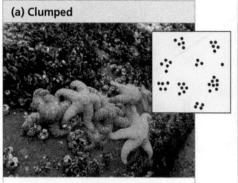

Sea stars group together where food is abundant.

Nesting albatrosses exhibit uniform spacing, maintained by aggressive interactions between neighbors.

Dandelions grow from windblown seeds that land at random and later germinate.

WHAT IF? *Patterns of dispersion can depend on scale. How might the penguin dispersion look from an airplane over the ocean?*

Life Tables

About a century ago, when life insurance first became available, insurance companies began to estimate how long, on average, people of a given age could be expected to live. To do this, demographers developed **life tables**, age-specific summaries of the survival pattern of a population. Population ecologists adapted this approach to the study of populations in general. The best way to construct a life table is to follow the fate of a **cohort**, a group of individuals of the same age, from birth until all of the individuals are dead. To build the life table, we need to determine the number of individuals that die in each age-group and to calculate the proportion of the cohort surviving from one age class to the next. Studies of a population of Belding's ground squirrels produced the life table in **Table 53.1**. The table reveals many things about the population. For instance, the third and eighth columns list, respectively, the proportions of females and males in the cohort that are still alive at each age. A comparison of the fifth and tenth columns reveals that males have higher death rates than females.

Table 53.1 Life Table for Belding's Ground Squirrels (*Spermophilus beldingi*) at Tioga Pass, in the Sierra Nevada of California*

	FEMALES					MALES				
Age (years)	Number Alive at Start of Year	Proportion Alive at Start of Year	Number of Deaths During Year	Death Rate[†]	Average Additional Life Expectancy (years)	Number Alive at Start of Year	Proportion Alive at Start of Year	Number of Deaths During Year	Death Rate[†]	Average Additional Life Expectancy (years)
0–1	337	1.000	207	0.61	1.33	349	1.000	227	0.65	1.07
1–2	252[‡]	0.386	125	0.50	1.56	248[‡]	0.350	140	0.56	1.12
2–3	127	0.197	60	0.47	1.60	108	0.152	74	0.69	0.93
3–4	67	0.106	32	0.48	1.59	34	0.048	23	0.68	0.89
4–5	35	0.054	16	0.46	1.59	11	0.015	9	0.82	0.68
5–6	19	0.029	10	0.53	1.50	2	0.003	2	1.00	0.50
6–7	9	0.014	4	0.44	1.61	0				
7–8	5	0.008	1	0.20	1.50					
8–9	4	0.006	3	0.75	0.75					
9–10	1	0.002	1	1.00	0.50					

Source: P. W. Sherman and M. L. Morton, Demography of Belding's ground squirrel, *Ecology* 65:1617–1628 (1984).

*Females and males have different mortality schedules, so they are tallied separately.

[†]The death rate is the proportion of individuals dying during the specific time interval.

[‡]Includes 122 females and 126 males first captured as 1-year-olds and therefore not included in the count of squirrels age 0–1.

► Researchers working with a Belding's ground squirrel

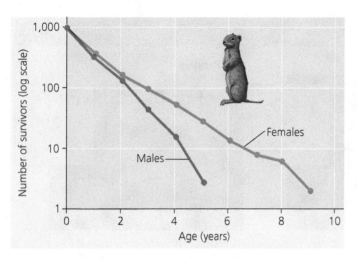

▲ **Figure 53.5 Survivorship curves for male and female Belding's ground squirrels.** The logarithmic scale on the *y*-axis allows the number of survivors to be visible across the entire range (2–1,000 individuals) on the graph.

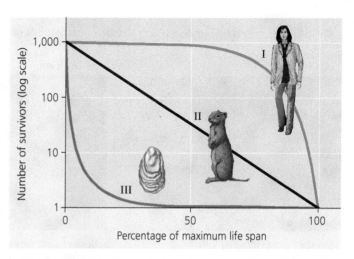

▲ **Figure 53.6 Idealized survivorship curves: Types I, II, and III.** The *y*-axis is logarithmic and the *x*-axis is on a relative scale, so that species with widely varying life spans can be presented together on the same graph.

Survivorship Curves

A graphic method of representing some of the data in a life table is a **survivorship curve**, a plot of the proportion or numbers in a cohort still alive at each age. As an example, let's use the data for Belding's ground squirrels in Table 53.1 to draw a survivorship curve for this population. Generally, a survivorship curve begins with a cohort of a convenient size—say, 1,000 individuals. To obtain the other points in the curve for the Belding's ground squirrel population, we multiply the proportion alive at the start of each year (the third and eighth columns of Table 53.1) by 1,000 (the hypothetical beginning cohort). The result is the number alive at the start of each year. Plotting these numbers versus age for female and male Belding's ground squirrels yields **Figure 53.5**. The relatively straight lines of the plots indicate relatively constant rates of death; however, male Belding's ground squirrels have a lower survival rate than females.

Figure 53.5 represents just one of many patterns of survivorship exhibited by natural populations. Though diverse, survivorship curves can be classified into three general types **(Figure 53.6)**. A Type I curve is flat at the start, reflecting low death rates during early and middle life, and then drops steeply as death rates increase among older age-groups. Many large mammals, including humans, that produce few offspring but provide them with good care exhibit this kind of curve. In contrast, a Type III curve drops sharply at the start, reflecting very high death rates for the young, but flattens out as death rates decline for those few individuals that survive the early period of die-off. This type of curve is usually associated with organisms that produce very large numbers of offspring but provide little or no care, such as long-lived plants, many fishes, and most marine invertebrates. An oyster, for example, may release millions of eggs, but most larvae hatched from fertilized eggs die from predation or other causes. Those few offspring that survive long

enough to attach to a suitable substrate and begin growing a hard shell tend to survive for a relatively long time. Type II curves are intermediate, with a constant death rate over the organism's life span. This kind of survivorship occurs in Belding's ground squirrels (see Figure 53.5) and some other rodents, invertebrates, lizards, and annual plants.

Many species fall somewhere between these basic types of survivorship or show more complex patterns. In birds, mortality is often high among the youngest individuals (as in a Type III curve) but fairly constant among adults (as in a Type II curve). Some invertebrates, such as crabs, may show a "stair-stepped" curve, with brief periods of increased mortality during molts, followed by periods of lower mortality when their protective exoskeleton is hard.

In populations not experiencing immigration or emigration, survivorship is one of the two key factors determining changes in population size. The other key factor determining population trends is reproductive rate.

Reproductive Rates

Demographers who study sexually reproducing species generally ignore the males and concentrate on the females in a population because only females produce offspring. Therefore, demographers view populations in terms of females giving rise to new females. The simplest way to describe the reproductive pattern of a population is to ask how reproductive output varies with the number of females and their ages.

Estimating the number of breeding females is one important step in determining reproductive rates for a population or species. Ecologists use many approaches to do this, including direct counts and the mark-recapture method (see Figure 53.2). Increasingly, they also use molecular tools. Scientists working in the state of Georgia collected skin samples from 198 female loggerhead turtles between 2005 and 2009. From these samples, they amplified nuclear short tandem repeats at 14 loci using the polymerase chain reaction (PCR) and produced a genetic profile for each female (Figure 53.7). They then extracted DNA from an eggshell from each turtle nest on the beaches they studied and, using their database of genetic profiles, matched the nest to a specific female. This approach allowed them to determine how many of the 198 females were breeding without having to disturb the females during egg laying.

The age of reproductive females is another important variable for estimating reproductive rates. A **reproductive table**, or fertility schedule, is an age-specific summary of the reproductive rates in a population. It is constructed by measuring the reproductive output of a cohort from birth until death. For a sexual species, the reproductive table tallies the number of female offspring produced by each age-group. **Table 53.2** illustrates a reproductive table for Belding's ground squirrels. Reproductive output for sexual organisms such as birds and mammals is the product of the proportion of females of a given age that are breeding and the number of female offspring of those breeding females. Multiplying

Table 53.2	Reproductive Table for Belding's Ground Squirrels at Tioga Pass			
Age (years)	Proportion of Females Weaning a Litter	Mean Size of Litters (Males + Females)	Mean Number of Females in a Litter	Average Number of Female Offspring*
0–1	0.00	0.00	0.00	0.00
1–2	0.65	3.30	1.65	1.07
2–3	0.92	4.05	2.03	1.87
3–4	0.90	4.90	2.45	2.21
4–5	0.95	5.45	2.73	2.59
5–6	1.00	4.15	2.08	2.08
6–7	1.00	3.40	1.70	1.70
7–8	1.00	3.85	1.93	1.93
8–9	1.00	3.85	1.93	1.93
9–10	1.00	3.15	1.58	1.58

Source: P. W. Sherman and M. L. Morton, Demography of Belding's ground squirrel, *Ecology* 65:1617–1628 (1984).

*The average number of female offspring is the proportion weaning a litter multiplied by the mean number of females in a litter.

Part 1: Developing the Database:

Skin samples are collected from female loggerhead turtles.

In a lab, DNA is extracted from each skin sample, and short tandem repeats at 14 loci are amplified by PCR.

A genetic profile is determined for each turtle and stored in a database.

Breeding female #108   Breeding female #109

Part 2: Comparing Samples to the Database:

An eggshell is collected from a loggerhead turtle nest.

In a lab, DNA is extracted from the eggshell, and short tandem repeats at 14 loci are amplified by PCR.

A genetic profile is determined for each eggshell sample.

Eggshell sample #74

The genetic profile of the eggshell is compared with an established database containing genetic profiles of adult female loggerhead turtles.

A match identifies the female that laid the eggs in the nest.

▲ **Figure 53.7 Using genetic profiles from loggerhead turtle eggshells to identify the eggs' mother.**

? *Which breeding female laid the eggs in the nest that eggshell sample #74 was taken from?*

these numbers gives the average number of female offspring for each female in a given age-group (the last column in Table 53.2). For Belding's ground squirrels, which begin to reproduce at age 1 year, reproductive output rises to a peak at 4 years of age and then falls off in older females.

Reproductive tables vary considerably by species. Squirrels, for example, have a litter of two to six young once a year for less than a decade, whereas oak trees drop thousands of acorns each year for tens or hundreds of years. Mussels and other invertebrates may release millions of eggs and sperm in a spawning cycle. However, a high reproductive rate will not lead to rapid population growth unless conditions are near ideal for the growth and survival of offspring, as you'll learn in the next section.

CONCEPT CHECK 53.1

1. DRAW IT Each female of a particular fish species produces millions of eggs per year. Draw and label the most likely survivorship curve for this species, and explain your choice.

2. WHAT IF? As noted in Figure 53.2, an important assumption of the mark-recapture method is that marked individuals have the same probability of being captured as unmarked individuals. Describe a situation where this assumption might not be valid, and explain how the estimate of population size would be affected.

3. MAKE CONNECTIONS A male stickleback fish attacks other males that invade its nesting territory (see Figure 51.2a). Predict the likely pattern of dispersion for male sticklebacks, and explain your reasoning.

For suggested answers, see Appendix A.

CONCEPT 53.2

The exponential model describes population growth in an idealized, unlimited environment

Populations of all species have the potential to expand greatly when resources are abundant. To appreciate the potential for population increase, consider a bacterium that can reproduce by fission every 20 minutes under ideal laboratory conditions. There would be two bacteria after 20 minutes, four after 40 minutes, and eight after 60 minutes. If reproduction continued at this rate for a day and a half without mortality, there would be enough bacteria to form a layer 30 cm deep over the entire globe. Unlimited growth does not occur for long in nature, where individuals typically have access to fewer resources as a population grows. Nonetheless, ecologists study population growth in ideal, unlimited environments to reveal how fast populations are capable of growing and the conditions under which rapid growth might actually occur.

Per Capita Rate of Increase

Imagine a population consisting of a few individuals living in an ideal, unlimited environment. Under these conditions, there are no external limits on the abilities of individuals to harvest energy, grow, and reproduce. The population will increase in size with every birth and with the immigration of individuals from other populations, and it will decrease in size with every death and with the emigration of individuals out of the population. We can thus define a change in population size during a fixed time interval with the following verbal equation:

$$\begin{matrix} \text{Change in} \\ \text{population} \\ \text{size} \end{matrix} = \text{Births} + \begin{matrix} \text{Immigrants} \\ \text{entering} \\ \text{population} \end{matrix} - \text{Deaths} - \begin{matrix} \text{Emigrants} \\ \text{leaving} \\ \text{population} \end{matrix}$$

For now, we will simplify the equation by ignoring the effects of immigration and emigration.

We can use mathematical notation to express this simplified relationship more concisely. If N represents population size and t represents time, then ΔN is the change in population size and Δt is the time interval (appropriate to the life span or generation time of the species) over which we are evaluating population growth. (The Greek letter delta, Δ, indicates change, such as change in time.) Using B for the number of births in the population during the time interval and D for the number of deaths, we can rewrite the verbal equation:

$$\frac{\Delta N}{\Delta t} = B - D$$

Next, we can convert this simple model to one in which births and deaths are expressed as the average number of births and deaths per individual (per capita) during the specified time interval. The *per capita birth rate* is the number of offspring produced per unit time by an average member of the population. If, for example, there are 34 births per year in a population of 1,000 individuals, then the annual per capita birth rate is 34/1,000, or 0.034. If we know the annual per capita birth rate (symbolized by b), we can use the formula $B = bN$ to calculate the expected number of births per year in a population of any size. For example, if the annual per capita birth rate is 0.034 and the population size is 500,

$$B = bN = 0.034 \times 500 = 17 \text{ per year}$$

Similarly, the *per capita death rate* (symbolized by m, for mortality) allows us to calculate the expected number of deaths per unit time in a population of any size, using the formula $D = mN$. If $m = 0.016$ per year, we would expect 16 deaths per year in a population of 1,000 individuals. For natural populations or those in the laboratory, the per capita birth and death rates can be calculated from estimates of population size and data in life tables and reproductive tables (for example, Tables 53.1 and 53.2).

Now we can revise the population growth equation again, this time using per capita birth and death rates rather than the numbers of births and deaths:

$$\frac{\Delta N}{\Delta t} = bN - mN$$

One final simplification is in order. Population ecologists are most interested in the *difference* between the per capita birth rate and the per capita death rate. This difference is the *per capita rate of increase*, or *r*:

$$r = b - m$$

The value of *r* indicates whether a given population is growing (*r* > 0) or declining (*r* < 0). **Zero population growth (ZPG)** occurs when the per capita birth and death rates are equal (*r* = 0). Births and deaths still occur in such a population, of course, but they balance each other exactly.

Using the per capita rate of increase, we can now rewrite the equation for change in population size as

$$\frac{\Delta N}{\Delta t} = rN$$

Remember that this equation is for a discrete, or fixed, time interval (often one year, as in the previous example) and does not include immigration or emigration. Most ecologists prefer to use differential calculus to express population growth *instantaneously*, as growth rate at a particular instant in time:

$$\frac{dN}{dt} = r_{inst}N$$

In this case r_{inst} is simply the instantaneous per capita rate of increase. If you have not yet studied calculus, don't be intimidated by the last equation; it is similar to the previous one, except that the time intervals Δt are very short and are expressed in the equation as *dt*. In fact, as Δt becomes shorter, the discrete *r* approaches the instantaneous r_{inst} in value.

Exponential Growth

Earlier we described a population whose members all have access to abundant food and are free to reproduce at their physiological capacity. Population increase under these conditions, called **exponential population growth**, occurs when r_{inst} is greater than zero and is constant at each instant in time. Under ideal conditions, the per capita rate of increase may assume the maximum rate for the species, denoted as r_{max}. The general equation for exponential growth is

$$\frac{dN}{dt} = r_{inst}N$$

The size of a population that is growing exponentially increases at a constant rate, resulting eventually in a J-shaped growth curve when population size is plotted over time **(Figure 53.8)**. Although the maximum *rate* of increase is constant, the population accumulates more new individuals per unit of time when it is large than when it is small; thus,

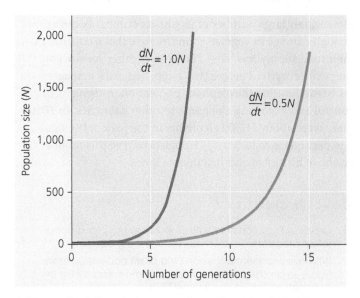

▲ **Figure 53.8 Population growth predicted by the exponential model.** This graph compares growth in two populations with different values of r_{inst}. Increasing the value of r_{inst} from 0.5 to 1.0 increases the rate of rise in population size over time, as reflected by the relative slopes of the curves at any given population size.

the curves in Figure 53.8 get progressively steeper over time. This occurs because population growth depends on *N* as well as r_{inst}, and larger populations experience more births (and deaths) than small ones growing at the same per capita rate. It is also clear from Figure 53.8 that a population with a higher maximum rate of increase (*dN/dt* = 1.0*N*) will grow faster than one with a lower rate of increase (*dN/dt* = 0.5*N*).

The J-shaped curve of exponential growth is characteristic of some populations that are introduced into a new environment or whose numbers have been drastically reduced by a catastrophic event and are rebounding. For example, the population of elephants in Kruger National Park, South Africa, grew exponentially for approximately 60 years after they were first protected from hunting **(Figure 53.9)**. The

▲ **Figure 53.9 Exponential growth in the African elephant population of Kruger National Park, South Africa.**

increasingly large number of elephants eventually caused enough damage to vegetation in the park that a collapse in their food supply was likely. To protect other species and the park ecosystem before that happened, park managers began limiting the elephant population by using birth control and exporting elephants to other countries. In 2010 there were about 11,500 elephants in the park, more than one per square mile. Many ecologists believe this number to be above historical and sustainable levels.

CONCEPT CHECK 53.2

1. Explain why a constant rate of increase (r_{inst}) for a population produces a growth curve that is J-shaped.

2. Where is exponential growth by a plant population more likely—in an area where a forest was destroyed by fire or in a mature, undisturbed forest? Why?

3. **WHAT IF?** In 2011, the United States had a population of 311 million people. If there were 14 births and 8 deaths per 1,000 people, what was the country's net population growth that year (ignoring immigration and emigration)? What would you need to know to determine whether the population of the United States is currently experiencing exponential growth?

For suggested answers, see Appendix A.

CONCEPT 53.3

The logistic model describes how a population grows more slowly as it nears its carrying capacity

The exponential growth model assumes that resources remain abundant, which is rarely the case in the real world. As population density increases, each individual has access to fewer resources. Ultimately, there is a limit to the number of individuals that can occupy a habitat. Ecologists define the **carrying capacity**, symbolized by K, as the maximum population size that a particular environment can sustain. Carrying capacity varies over space and time with the abundance of limiting resources. Energy, shelter, refuge from predators, nutrient availability, water, and suitable nesting sites can all be limiting factors. For example, the carrying capacity for bats may be high in a habitat with abundant flying insects and roosting sites but lower where there is abundant food but fewer suitable shelters.

Crowding and resource limitation can have a profound effect on population growth rate. If individuals cannot obtain sufficient resources to reproduce, the per capita birth rate (b) will decline. If they cannot consume enough energy to maintain themselves or if disease or parasitism increases with density, the per capita death rate (m) may increase. A decrease in b or an increase in m results in a lower per capita rate of increase (r).

The Logistic Growth Model

We can modify our mathematical model to include changes in growth rate as N increases. In the **logistic population growth** model, the per capita rate of increase approaches zero as the population size nears the carrying capacity.

To construct the logistic model, we start with the exponential population growth model and add an expression that reduces the per capita rate of increase as N increases. If the maximum sustainable population size (carrying capacity) is K, then $K - N$ is the number of additional individuals the environment can support, and $(K - N)/K$ is the fraction of K that is still available for population growth. By multiplying the exponential rate of increase $r_{inst}N$ by $(K - N)/K$, we modify the change in population size as N increases:

$$\frac{dN}{dt} = r_{inst}N\frac{(K - N)}{K}$$

When N is small compared to K, the term $(K - N)/K$ is close to 1, and the per capita rate of increase, $r_{inst}(K - N)/K$, approaches the maximum rate of increase. But when N is large and resources are limiting, then $(K - N)/K$ is close to 0, and the per capita rate of increase is small. When N equals K, the population stops growing. Table 53.3 shows calculations of population growth rate for a hypothetical population growing according to the logistic model, with $r_{inst} = 1.0$ per individual per year. Notice that the overall population growth rate is highest, +375 individuals per year, when the population size is 750, or half the carrying capacity. At a population size of 750, the per capita rate of increase remains relatively high (one-half the maximum rate), but there are more reproducing individuals (N) in the population than at lower population sizes.

As shown in Figure 53.10, the logistic model of population growth produces a sigmoid (S-shaped) growth curve when N is plotted over time (the red line). New individuals

Table 53.3 Logistic Growth of a Hypothetical Population ($K = 1,500$)

Population Size (N)	Maximum Rate of Increase (r_{inst})	$\frac{(K - N)}{K}$	Per Capita Rate of Increase: $r_{inst}\frac{(K - N)}{K}$	Population Growth Rate:* $r_{inst}N\frac{(K - N)}{K}$
25	1.0	0.98	0.98	+25
100	1.0	0.93	0.93	+93
250	1.0	0.83	0.83	+208
500	1.0	0.67	0.67	+333
750	1.0	0.50	0.50	+375
1,000	1.0	0.33	0.33	+333
1,500	1.0	0.00	0.00	0

*Rounded to the nearest whole number.

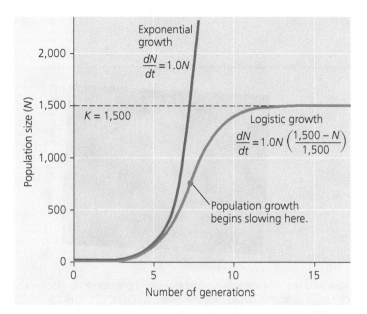

▲ **Figure 53.10 Population growth predicted by the logistic model.** The rate of population growth decreases as population size (N) approaches the carrying capacity (K) of the environment. The red line shows logistic growth in a population where $r_{inst} = 1.0$ and $K = 1,500$ individuals. For comparison, the blue line illustrates a population continuing to grow exponentially with the same r_{inst}.

are added to the population most rapidly at intermediate population sizes, when there is not only a breeding population of substantial size, but also lots of available space and other resources in the environment. The population growth rate decreases dramatically as N approaches K.

Note that we haven't said anything yet about *why* the population growth rate decreases as N approaches K. For a population's growth rate to decrease, the birth rate *b* must decrease, the death rate *m* must increase, or both. Later

in the chapter, we'll consider some of the factors affecting these rates, including the presence of disease, predation, and limited amounts of food and other resources. In the Scientific Skills Exercise, you can model what happens to a population if N becomes *greater* than K.

The Logistic Model and Real Populations

The growth of laboratory populations of some small animals, such as beetles and crustaceans, and of some microorganisms, such as bacteria, *Paramecium*, and yeasts, fits an S-shaped curve fairly well under conditions of limited resources (Figure 53.11a). These populations are grown in a constant environment lacking predators and competing species that may reduce growth of the populations, conditions that rarely occur in nature.

Some of the basic assumptions built into the logistic model clearly do not apply to all populations. The logistic model assumes that populations adjust instantaneously to growth and approach carrying capacity smoothly. In reality, there is often a delay before the negative effects of an increasing population are realized. If food becomes limiting for a population, for instance, reproduction will decline eventually, but females may use their energy reserves to continue reproducing for a short time. This may cause the population to overshoot its carrying capacity temporarily, as shown for the water fleas in Figure 53.11b. If the population then drops below carrying capacity, there will be a delay in population growth until the increased number of offspring are actually born. Still other populations fluctuate greatly, making it difficult even to define carrying capacity. We will examine some possible reasons for such fluctuations later in the chapter.

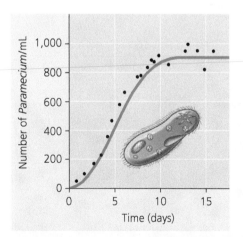

(a) A *Paramecium* population in the lab. The growth (black dots) of *Paramecium aurelia* in a small culture closely approximates logistic growth (red curve) if the researcher maintains a constant environment.

(b) A *Daphnia* population in the lab. The growth (black dots) of a population of water fleas (*Daphnia*) in a small laboratory culture does not correspond well to the logistic model (red curve). This population overshoots the carrying capacity of its artificial environment before it settles down to an approximately stable population size.

◄ **Figure 53.11 How well do these populations fit the logistic growth model?**

Using the Logistic Equation to Model Population Growth

What Happens to the Size of a Population When It Overshoots Its Carrying Capacity? In the logistic population growth model, the per capita rate of population increase approaches zero as the population size (N) approaches the carrying capacity (K). Under some conditions, however, a population in the laboratory or the field can overshoot K, at least temporarily. If food becomes limiting to a population, for instance, there may be a delay before reproduction declines, and N may briefly exceed K. In this exercise, you will use the logistic equation to model the growth of the hypothetical population in Table 53.3 when $N > K$.

▶ *Daphnia*

Interpret the Data

1. Assuming that $r_{inst} = 1.0$ and $K = 1,500$, calculate the population growth rate for four cases where population size (N) is greater than carrying capacity (K): $N = 1,510, 1,600, 1,750,$ and $2,000$ individuals. To do this, first write the equation for population growth rate given in Table 53.3. Plug in the values for each of the four cases, starting with $N = 1,510$, and solve the equation for each one. Which population size has the highest growth rate?

2. If r_{inst} is doubled, predict how the population growth rates will change for the four population sizes given in question 1. Now calculate the population growth rate for the same four cases, this time assuming that $r_{inst} = 2.0$ (and with K still $= 1,500$).

3. Now let's see how the growth of a real-world population of *Daphnia* corresponds to this model. At what times in Figure 53.11b is the *Daphnia* population changing in ways that correspond to the values you calculated? Hypothesize why the population drops below the carrying capacity briefly late in the experiment.

(MB) A version of this Scientific Skills Exercise can be assigned in MasteringBiology.

In addition to the assumption that populations adjust instantaneously to growth, the logistic model is based on another assumption—that regardless of population density, each individual added to a population has the same negative effect on population growth rate. However, some populations show an *Allee effect* (named after W. C. Allee, of the University of Chicago, who first described it), in which individuals may have a more difficult time surviving or reproducing if the population size is too small. For example, a single plant may be damaged by excessive wind if it is standing alone, but it would be protected in a clump of individuals.

The logistic model is a useful starting point for thinking about how populations grow and for constructing more complex models. The model is also important in conservation biology for predicting how rapidly a particular population might increase in numbers after it has been reduced to a small size and for estimating sustainable harvest rates for wildlife populations. Conservation biologists can use the model to estimate the critical size below which populations of certain organisms, such as the northern subspecies of the white rhinoceros (*Ceratotherium simum*), may become extinct **(Figure 53.12)**.

▶ **Figure 53.12 White rhinoceros mother and calf.** The two animals pictured here are members of the southern subspecies, which has a population of more than 20,000 individuals. The northern subspecies is critically endangered, with a population of fewer than 10 known individuals.

CONCEPT CHECK 53.3

1. Explain why a population that fits the logistic growth model increases more rapidly at intermediate size than at relatively small and large sizes.

2. **WHAT IF?** Given the latitudinal differences in sunlight intensity (see Figure 52.3), how might you expect the carrying capacity of plant species found at the equator to compare with that of plant species found at high latitudes?

3. **MAKE CONNECTIONS** Many viruses are pathogens of animals and plants (see Concept 19.3). How might the presence of pathogens alter the carrying capacity of a population? Explain.

For suggested answers, see Appendix A.

CONCEPT 53.4

Life history traits are products of natural selection

EVOLUTION Natural selection favors traits that improve an organism's chances of survival and reproductive success. In every species, there are trade-offs between survival and reproductive traits such as frequency of reproduction, number of offspring (number of seeds produced by plants; litter or clutch size for animals), and investment in parental care. The traits that affect an organism's schedule of reproduction and survival make up its **life history**. Life history traits of an organism are evolutionary outcomes reflected in its development, physiology, and behavior.

Evolution and Life History Diversity

The fundamental idea that evolution accounts for the diversity of life is manifest in a broad range of life histories found in nature. A life history entails three main variables: when reproduction begins (the age at first reproduction or age at maturity), how often the organism reproduces, and how many offspring are produced per reproductive episode. A typical loggerhead turtle is about 30 years old when it first crawls onto a beach to lay eggs (see Figure 53.1). In contrast, the coho salmon (*Oncorhynchus kisutch*) is often only three or four years old when it spawns.

The coho salmon is one example of many organisms that undergo a "one-shot" pattern of big-bang reproduction, or **semelparity** (from the Latin *semel*, once, and *parere*, to beget). It hatches in the headwaters of a freshwater stream and then migrates to the Pacific Ocean, where it typically requires a few years to mature. The salmon eventually returns to the same stream to spawn, producing thousands of eggs in a single reproductive opportunity before it dies. Semelparity also occurs in some plants, such as the agave, or "century plant" **(Figure 53.13a)**. Agaves generally grow in arid climates with unpredictable rainfall and poor soils. An agave grows for years, accumulating nutrients in its tissues, until there is an unusually wet year. It then sends up a large flowering stalk, produces seeds, and dies. This life history is an adaptation to the agave's harsh desert environment.

In contrast to semelparity is **iteroparity** (from the Latin *iterare*, to repeat), or repeated reproduction. For example, a female loggerhead turtle produces four clutches totaling approximately 300 eggs in a year. It then typically waits two to three years before laying more eggs; presumably, the turtles lack sufficient resources to produce that many eggs every year. A mature turtle may lay eggs for 30 years after the first

▶ **Figure 53.13 Semelparity and iteroparity. (a)** An agave (*Agave americana*) is an example of semelparity, or big-bang reproduction. The leaves of the plant are visible at the base of the giant flowering stalk, which is produced only at the end of the agave's life. **(b)** Organisms that reproduce repeatedly, like humans, undergo iteroparity. Such organisms tend to have fewer, larger offspring and take better care of them.

(a) Semelparity, one-time reproducer

(b) Iteroparity, repeat reproducer

clutch. In iteroparity, organisms tend to produce relatively few but large offspring each time they reproduce, and they provide for the offspring better **(Figure 53.13b)**.

What factors contribute to the evolution of semelparity versus iteroparity? Two factors appear to be especially important: the survival rate of the offspring and the likelihood that the adult will survive to reproduce again. Where the survival rate of offspring is low, typically in highly variable or unpredictable environments, semelparity is often favored. Adults are also less likely to survive in such environments, so producing large numbers of offspring should increase the probability that at least some of those offspring will survive. Iteroparity is favored in more dependable environments, where adults are more likely to survive to breed again and where competition for resources may be intense. In this case, a few relatively large, well-provisioned offspring should have a better chance of surviving until they can reproduce.

Nature abounds with life histories that are intermediate between the two extremes of semelparity and iteroparity. Oak trees and sea urchins, for example, can live a long time but repeatedly produce relatively large numbers of offspring.

"Trade-offs" and Life Histories

No organism could produce as many offspring as a semelparous species and provision them as well as an iteroparous species. There is a trade-off between reproduction and

Figure 53.14 Inquiry

How does caring for offspring affect parental survival in kestrels?

Experiment Cor Dijkstra and colleagues in the Netherlands studied the effects of parental caregiving in Eurasian kestrels over five years. The researchers transferred chicks among nests to produce reduced broods (three or four chicks), normal broods (five or six), and enlarged broods (seven or eight). They then measured the percentage of male and female parent birds that survived the following winter. (Both males and females provide care for chicks.)

Results

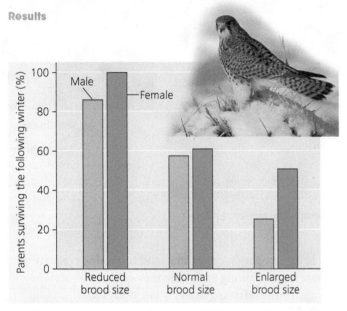

Conclusion The lower survival rates of kestrels with larger broods indicate that caring for more offspring negatively affects survival of the parents.

Source: C. Dijkstra et al., Brood size manipulations in the kestrel (*Falco tinnunculus*): effects on offspring and parent survival, *Journal of Animal Ecology* 59:269–285 (1990).

INTERPRET THE DATA *The males of some bird species provide no parental care. If this were true for the Eurasian kestrel, how would the experimental results differ from those shown above?*

survival. **Figure 53.14** describes a study of Eurasian kestrels that demonstrated a survival cost to parents that care for a large number of young. In another study, in Scotland, researchers found that female red deer that reproduced in a given summer were more likely to die the next winter than were females that did not reproduce.

Selective pressures influence the trade-off between the number and size of offspring. Plants and animals whose young are more likely to die often produce many small offspring. Plants that colonize disturbed environments, for example, usually produce many small seeds, only a few of which may reach a suitable habitat. Small size may also increase the chance of seedling establishment by enabling the seeds to be carried longer distances to a broader range of habitats (**Figure 53.15a**). Animals that suffer high predation

rates, such as quail, sardines, and mice, also tend to produce many offspring.

In other organisms, extra investment on the part of the parent greatly increases the offspring's chances of survival. Walnut and Brazil nut trees produce large seeds packed with nutrients that help the seedlings become established (**Figure 53.15b**). Primates generally bear only one or two offspring at a time; parental care and an extended period of learning in the first several years of life are very important to offspring fitness. Such provisioning and extra care can be especially important in habitats with high population densities.

Ecologists have attempted to connect differences in favored traits at different population densities with the logistic growth model discussed in Concept 53.3. Selection for traits that are sensitive to population density and are favored at high densities is known as *K*-**selection**, or density-dependent selection. In contrast, selection for traits that maximize reproductive success in uncrowded environments (low densities) is called *r*-**selection**, or density-independent selection. These names follow from the variables of the logistic equation. *K*-selection is said to operate in populations living at a

(a) Dandelions grow quickly and release a large number of tiny fruits, each containing a single seed. Producing numerous seeds ensures that at least some will grow into plants that eventually produce seeds themselves.

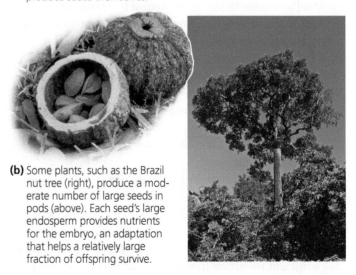

(b) Some plants, such as the Brazil nut tree (right), produce a moderate number of large seeds in pods (above). Each seed's large endosperm provides nutrients for the embryo, an adaptation that helps a relatively large fraction of offspring survive.

▲ **Figure 53.15 Variation in the size of seed crops in plants.**

density near the limit imposed by their resources (the carrying capacity, K), where competition among individuals is stronger. Mature trees growing in an old-growth forest are an example of K-selected organisms. In contrast, r-selection is said to maximize r, the per capita rate of increase, and occurs in environments in which population densities are well below carrying capacity or individuals face little competition. Such conditions are often found in disturbed habitats. Weeds growing in an abandoned agricultural field are an example of r-selected organisms.

The concepts of K- and r-selection represent two extremes in a range of actual life histories. The framework of K- and r-selection, grounded in the idea of carrying capacity, has helped ecologists to propose alternative hypotheses of life history evolution. They have also forced ecologists to address the important question we alluded to earlier: *Why does population growth rate decrease as population size approaches carrying capacity?* Answering this question is the focus of the next section.

CONCEPT CHECK 53.4

1. Consider two rivers: One is spring fed and has a constant water volume and temperature year-round; the other drains a desert landscape and floods and dries out at unpredictable intervals. Which river would you predict is more likely to support many species of iteroparous animals? Why?

2. In the fish called the peacock wrasse (*Symphodus tinca*), females disperse some of their eggs widely and lay other eggs in a nest. Only the latter receive parental care. Explain the trade-offs in reproduction that this behavior illustrates.

3. **WHAT IF?** Mice that experience stress such as a food shortage will sometimes abandon their young. Explain how this behavior might have evolved in the context of reproductive trade-offs and life history.

For suggested answers, see Appendix A.

CONCEPT 53.5

Many factors that regulate population growth are density dependent

What environmental factors keep populations from growing indefinitely? Why are some populations fairly stable in size, while others are not?

Population regulation is an area of ecology that has many practical applications. Farmers may want to reduce the abundance of insect pests or stop the growth of an invasive weed that is spreading rapidly. Conservation ecologists need to know what environmental factors create favorable feeding or breeding habitats for endangered species, such as the white rhinoceros and the whooping crane. Management programs based on population-regulating factors have helped prevent the extinction of many endangered species.

Population Change and Population Density

To understand why a population stops growing, ecologists study how the rates of birth, death, immigration, and emigration change as population density rises. If immigration and emigration offset each other, then a population grows when the birth rate exceeds the death rate and declines when the death rate exceeds the birth rate.

Similar to the case of r-selection, a birth rate or death rate that does *not* change with population density is said to be **density independent**. In a classic study of population regulation, Andrew Watkinson and John Harper, of the University of Wales, found that the mortality of dune fescue grass (*Vulpia fasciculata*) is mainly due to physical factors that kill similar proportions of a local population, regardless of its density. For example, drought stress that arises when the roots of the grass are uncovered by shifting sands is a density-independent factor. In contrast, a death rate that increases with population density or a birth rate that falls with rising density is said to be **density dependent**, a situation similar to K-selection. Watkinson and Harper found that reproduction by dune fescue declines as population density increases, in part because water or nutrients become more scarce. Thus, the key factors regulating birth rate in this population are density dependent, while death rate is largely regulated by density-independent factors. **Figure 53.16** shows how the combination of density-dependent reproduction and density-independent mortality can stop population growth, leading to an equilibrium population density in species such as dune fescue.

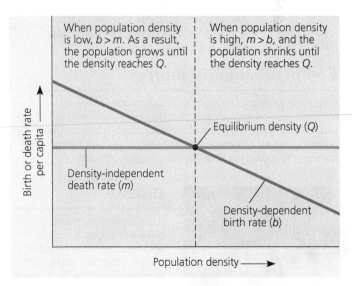

When population density is low, $b > m$. As a result, the population grows until the density reaches Q.

When population density is high, $m > b$, and the population shrinks until the density reaches Q.

Equilibrium density (Q)

Density-independent death rate (m)

Density-dependent birth rate (b)

Birth or death rate per capita

Population density

▲ **Figure 53.16 Determining equilibrium for population density.** This simple model considers only birth and death rates. (Immigration and emigration rates are assumed to be either zero or equal.) In this example, the birth rate changes with population density, while the death rate is constant. At the equilibrium density (Q), the birth and death rates are equal.

DRAW IT *Redraw this figure for the case where the birth and death rates are both density dependent, as occurs for many species.*

Mechanisms of Density-Dependent Population Regulation

The principle of feedback regulation applies to population dynamics. Without some type of negative feedback between population density and the rates of birth and death, a population would never stop growing. That feedback is provided by density-dependent regulation, which halts population growth through mechanisms that reduce birth rates or increase death rates. For example, proportional mortality of the kelp perch (*Brachyistius frenatus*) rose as its density increased. Without sufficient kelp to hide in, the perch was vulnerable to predation by a second fish species, the kelp bass (*Paralabrax clathratus*). Proportionally more of the perch were eaten as perch density increased, a result consistent with density-dependent regulation (Figure 53.17). Mechanisms of density-dependent population regulation are described in Figure 53.18.

These various examples of population regulation by negative feedback show how increased densities cause population growth rates to decline by affecting reproduction, growth, and survival. But though negative feedback helps explain why populations stop growing, it does not address why some populations fluctuate dramatically while others remain relatively stable. That is the topic we address next.

Kelp perch (prey)   Kelp bass (predator)

▲ Figure 53.17 **Density-dependent regulation by predation.** As the density of kelp perch increased, predation by kelp bass increased, resulting in a higher proportion of kelp perch deaths.

Population Dynamics

All populations show some fluctuation in size. Such population fluctuations from year to year or place to place, called **population dynamics**, are influenced by many factors and in turn affect other species. For example, fluctuations in fish populations influence seasonal harvests of commercially

▼ Figure 53.18

Exploring Mechanisms of Density-Dependent Regulation

As population density increases, many density-dependent mechanisms slow or stop population growth by decreasing birth rates or increasing death rates.

Competition for Resources

Increasing population density intensifies competition for nutrients and other resources, reducing reproductive rates. Farmers minimize the effect of resource competition on the growth of wheat (*Triticum aestivum*) and other crops by applying fertilizers to reduce nutrient limitations on crop yield.

Disease

If the transmission rate of a disease increases as a population becomes more crowded, then the disease's impact is density dependent. In humans, the respiratory diseases influenza (flu) and tuberculosis are spread through the air when an infected person sneezes or coughs. Both diseases strike a greater percentage of people in densely populated cities than in rural areas.

Predation

Predation can be an important cause of density-dependent mortality if a predator captures more food as the population density of the prey increases. As a prey population builds up, predators may also feed preferentially on that species. Population increases in the collared lemming (*Dicrostonyx groenlandicus*) lead to density-dependent predation by several predators, including the snowy owl (*Bubo scandiacus*).

important species. The study of population dynamics focuses on the complex interactions between biotic and abiotic factors that cause variation in population sizes.

Stability and Fluctuation

Populations of large mammals were once thought to remain relatively stable, but long-term studies have challenged that idea. For instance, the moose population on Isle Royale in Lake Superior has fluctuated substantially since around 1900. At that time, moose from the Ontario mainland 25 km away colonized the island, likely by swimming to it or by walking across the lake when it was frozen over. Wolves, which rely on moose for most of their food, reached the island around 1950 by walking across the frozen lake. The lake has not frozen over in recent years, and both populations appear to have been isolated from immigration and emigration since then. Despite this isolation, the moose population experienced two major increases and collapses during the last 50 years (**Figure 53.19**).

What factors cause the size of the moose population to change so dramatically? Harsh weather, particularly cold, wet winters, can weaken moose and reduce food availability, decreasing the population size. When moose numbers are low and the weather is mild, food is readily available and the population grows quickly. Conversely, when moose

▲ **Figure 53.19 Fluctuations in moose and wolf populations on Isle Royale, 1959–2011.**

ANIMATION **BioFlix** Visit the Study Area in **MasteringBiology** for the BioFlix® 3-D Animation on Population Ecology. BioFlix Tutorials can also be assigned in MasteringBiology.

numbers are high, factors such as predation and an increase in the density of ticks and other parasites cause the population to shrink. The effects of some of these factors can be seen in Figure 53.19. The first major collapse coincided with a peak in the numbers of wolves from 1975 to 1980.

Territoriality

Territoriality can limit population density when space becomes the resource for which individuals compete. Cheetahs (*Acinonyx jubatus*) use a chemical marker in urine to warn other cheetahs of their territorial boundaries. The presence of surplus, or nonbreeding, individuals is a good indication that territoriality is restricting population growth.

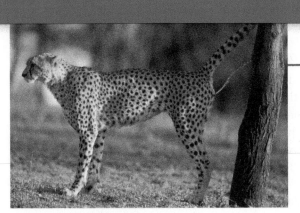

Intrinsic Factors

Intrinsic physiological factors can regulate population size. Reproductive rates of white-footed mice (*Peromyscus leucopus*) in a field enclosure can drop even when food and shelter are abundant. This drop in reproduction at high population density is associated with aggressive interactions and hormonal changes that delay sexual maturation and depress the immune system.

Toxic Wastes

Yeasts, such as the brewer's yeast *Saccharomyces cerevisiae*, are used to convert carbohydrates to ethanol in winemaking. The ethanol that accumulates in the wine is toxic to yeasts and contributes to density-dependent regulation of yeast population size. The alcohol content of wine is usually less than 13% because that is the maximum concentration of ethanol that most wine-producing yeast cells can tolerate.

5 μm

The second major collapse, around 1995, coincided with harsh winter weather, which increased the energy needs of the moose and made it harder for them to find food under the deep snow.

Population Cycles: *Scientific Inquiry*

While many populations fluctuate at unpredictable intervals, others undergo regular boom-and-bust cycles. Some small herbivorous mammals, such as voles and lemmings, tend to have 3- to 4-year cycles, and some birds, such as ruffed grouse and ptarmigans, have 9- to 11-year cycles.

One striking example of population cycles is the roughly 10-year cycling of snowshoe hares (*Lepus americanus*) and lynx (*Lynx canadensis*) in the far northern forests of Canada and Alaska. Lynx are predators that feed predominantly on snowshoe hares, so lynx numbers might be expected to rise and fall with the numbers of hares (**Figure 53.20**). But why do hare numbers rise and fall in approximately 10-year cycles? Two main hypotheses have been proposed. First, the cycles may be caused by food shortage during winter. Hares eat the terminal twigs of small shrubs such as willow and birch in winter, although why this food supply might cycle in 10-year intervals is uncertain. Second, the cycles may be due to predator-prey interactions. Many predators other than lynx eat hares, and they may overexploit their prey.

▲ **Figure 53.20 Population cycles in the snowshoe hare and lynx.** Population counts are based on the number of pelts sold by trappers to the Hudson Bay Company.

INTERPRET THE DATA *What do you observe about the relative timing of the peaks in lynx numbers and hare numbers? What might explain this observation?*

Let's consider the evidence for the two hypotheses. If hare cycles are due to winter food shortage, then they should stop if extra food is provided to a field population. Researchers conducted such experiments in the Yukon for 20 years—over two hare cycles. They found that hare populations in the areas with extra food increased about threefold in density but continued to cycle in the same way as the unfed control populations. Therefore, food supplies alone do not cause the hare cycles shown in Figure 53.20, so we can reject the first hypothesis.

To study the effects of predation, ecologists used radio collars to track individual hares to determine why they died. Predators, including lynx, coyotes, hawks, and owls, killed 95% of the hares in such studies. None of the hares appeared to have died of starvation. These data support the second hypothesis. When ecologists set up electric fences to exclude predators from certain areas, the collapse in survival that normally occurs in the decline phase of the cycle was nearly eliminated. Overexploitation by predators thus seems to be an essential part of snowshoe hare cycles; without predators, it is unlikely that hare populations would cycle in northern Canada.

The availability of prey is the major factor influencing population changes for predators such as lynx, great-horned owls, and weasels, each of which depends heavily on a single prey species. When prey become scarce, predators often turn on one another. Coyotes kill both foxes and lynx, and great-horned owls kill smaller birds of prey as well as weasels, accelerating the collapse of the predator populations. Long-term experimental studies help to unravel the causes of such population cycles.

Immigration, Emigration, and Metapopulations

So far, our discussion of population dynamics has focused mainly on the contributions of births and deaths. However, immigration and emigration also influence populations. When a population becomes crowded and resource competition increases (see Figure 53.17), emigration often increases.

Immigration and emigration are particularly important when a number of local populations are linked, forming a **metapopulation**. Local populations in a metapopulation can be thought of as occupying discrete patches of suitable habitat in a sea of otherwise unsuitable habitat. Such patches vary in size, quality, and isolation from other patches, factors that influence how many individuals move among the populations. If one population becomes extinct, the patch it occupied may be recolonized by immigrants from another population.

The Glanville fritillary (*Melitaea cinxia*) illustrates the movement of individuals between populations. This butterfly is found in about 500 meadows across the Åland Islands of Finland, but its potential habitat in the islands is much larger, approximately 4,000 suitable patches. New populations of the butterfly regularly appear and existing

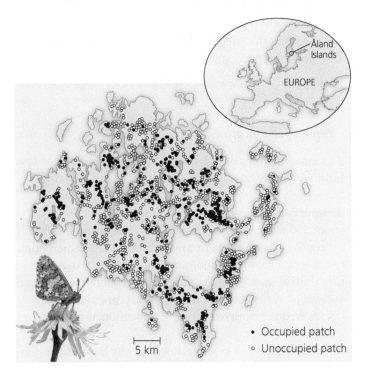

▲ **Figure 53.21 The Glanville fritillary: a metapopulation.** On the Åland Islands, local populations of this butterfly (filled circles) are found in only a fraction of the suitable habitat patches at any given time. Individuals can move between local populations and colonize unoccupied patches (open circles).

• Occupied patch
◦ Unoccupied patch

5 km

populations become extinct, constantly shifting the locations of the 500 colonized patches **(Figure 53.21)**. The species persists in a balance of extinctions and recolonizations.

An individual's ability to move between populations depends on a number of factors, including its genetic makeup. One gene with apparently strong fitness effects on movement in the Glanville fritillary is *Pgi*, which codes for the enzyme phosphoglucoisomerase. This enzyme catalyzes the second step of glycolysis (see Figure 9.9), and its activity correlates with the rate of CO_2 production from respiration by the butterflies. Ecologists studied butterflies known to be heterozygous or homozygous for a single nucleotide polymorphism in *Pgi*. They tracked the movements of individual butterflies using radar and transponders attached to the butterflies that emit an identifying signal. Butterfly movements ranged widely, from 10 m to 4 km, in two-hour periods. Heterozygous individuals flew more than twice as far in the morning and at lower ambient temperatures than homozygous individuals. The results indicated a fitness advantage to the heterozygous genotype in low temperatures and a greater likelihood of heterozygotes colonizing new locations in the metapopulation.

The metapopulation concept underscores the significance of immigration and emigration in the butterfly populations. It also helps ecologists understand population dynamics and gene flow in patchy habitats, providing a framework for the conservation of species living in a network of habitat fragments and reserves.

CONCEPT CHECK 53.5

1. Describe three attributes of habitat patches that could affect population density and rates of immigration and emigration.
2. **WHAT IF?** Suppose you were studying a species that has a population cycle of about ten years. How long would you need to study the species to determine if its population size were declining? Explain.
3. **MAKE CONNECTIONS** Negative feedback is a process that regulates biological systems (see Concept 40.2). Explain how the density-dependent birth rate of dune fescue grass exemplifies negative feedback.

For suggested answers, see Appendix A.

CONCEPT 53.6

The human population is no longer growing exponentially but is still increasing rapidly

In the last few centuries, the human population has grown at an unprecedented rate, more like the elephant population in Kruger National Park (see Figure 53.9) than the fluctuating populations we considered in Concept 53.5. No population can grow indefinitely, however. In this section of the chapter, we'll apply the concepts of population dynamics to the specific case of the human population.

The Global Human Population

The exponential growth model in Figure 53.8 approximates the explosive growth of the human population over the last four centuries **(Figure 53.22)**. The human population

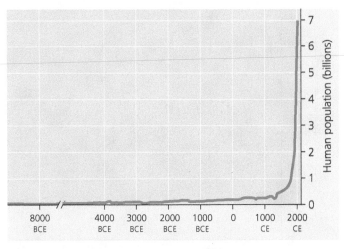

▲ **Figure 53.22 Human population growth (data as of 2012).** The global human population has grown almost continuously throughout history, but it skyrocketed after the Industrial Revolution. Though it is not apparent at this scale, the rate of population growth has slowed in recent decades, mainly as a result of decreased birth rates throughout the world.

increased relatively slowly until about 1650, at which time approximately 500 million people inhabited Earth. Our population doubled to 1 billion within the next two centuries, doubled again to 2 billion by 1930, and doubled still again by 1975 to more than 4 billion. The global population is now more than 7 billion people and is increasing by about 78 million each year. Currently the population grows by more than 200,000 people each day, the equivalent of adding a city the size of Amarillo, Texas. At this rate, it takes only about four years to add the equivalent of another United States to the world population. Ecologists predict a population of 8.1–10.6 billion people on Earth by the year 2050.

Though the global population is still growing, the *rate* of growth began to slow during the 1960s (Figure 53.23). The annual rate of increase in the global population peaked at 2.2% in 1962 but was only 1.1% in 2011. Current models project a growth rate of 0.5% by 2050, which would add 45 million more people per year if the population climbs to a projected 9 billion. The reduction in annual growth rate already observed is the result of fundamental changes in population dynamics due to diseases, including AIDS, and to voluntary population control.

Regional Patterns of Population Change

We have described changes in the global population, but population dynamics vary widely from region to region. In a stable regional population, birth rate equals death rate

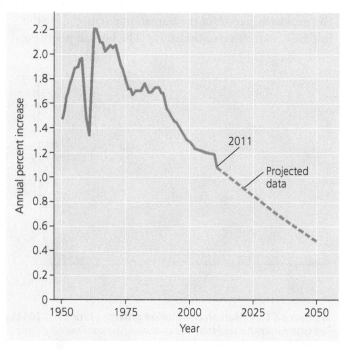

▲ **Figure 53.23 Annual percent increase in the global human population (data as of 2011).** The sharp dip in the 1960s is due mainly to a famine in China in which about 60 million people died.

(disregarding the effects of immigration and emigration). Two possible configurations for a stable population are

Zero population growth = High birth rate − High death rate

or

Zero population growth = Low birth rate − Low death rate

The movement from high birth and death rates toward low birth and death rates, which tends to accompany industrialization and improved living conditions, is called the **demographic transition**. In Sweden, this transition took about 150 years, from 1810 to 1975, when birth rates finally approached death rates. In Mexico, where the human population is still growing rapidly, the transition is projected to take until at least 2050. Demographic transition is associated with an increase in the quality of health care and sanitation as well as improved access to education, especially for women.

After 1950, death rates declined rapidly in most developing countries, but birth rates have declined more variably. Birth rates have fallen most dramatically in China. In 1970, the Chinese birth rate predicted an average of 5.9 children per woman per lifetime (total fertility rate); by 2011, largely because of the government's strict one-child policy, the total fertility rate was 1.6 children. In some countries of Africa, the transition to lower birth rates has also been rapid, though birth rates remain high in most of sub-Saharan Africa. In India, birth rates have fallen more slowly.

How do such variable birth rates affect the growth of the world's population? In industrialized nations, populations are near equilibrium, with reproductive rates near the replacement level (total fertility rate = 2.1 children per female). In many industrialized countries, including Canada, Germany, Japan, and the United Kingdom, total reproductive rates are in fact *below* the replacement level. These populations will eventually decline if there is no immigration and if the birth rate does not change. In fact, the population is already declining in many eastern and central European countries. Most of the current global population growth (1.1% per year) is concentrated in less industrialized countries, where about 80% of the world's people now live.

A unique feature of human population growth is our ability to control family sizes through planning and voluntary contraception. Reduced family size is the key to the demographic transition. Social change and the rising educational and career aspirations of women in many cultures encourage women to delay marriage and postpone reproduction. Delayed reproduction helps to decrease population growth rates and to move a society toward zero population growth under conditions of low birth rates and low death rates. However, there is a great deal of disagreement as to how much support should be provided for global family planning efforts.

Age Structure

Another important demographic variable in present and future growth trends is a country's **age structure**, the relative number of individuals of each age in the population. Age structure is commonly graphed as "pyramids" like those in **Figure 53.24**. For Afghanistan, the pyramid is bottom-heavy, skewed toward young individuals who will grow up and perhaps sustain the explosive growth with their own reproduction. The age structure for the United States is relatively even until the older, postreproductive ages. Although the current total reproductive rate in the United States is 2.1 children per woman—approximately replacement rate—the population is projected to grow slowly through 2050 as a result of immigration. For Italy, the pyramid has a small base, indicating that individuals younger than reproductive age are relatively underrepresented in the population. This situation contributes to the projection of a population decrease in Italy.

Age-structure diagrams not only predict a population's growth trends but also can illuminate social conditions. Based on the diagrams in Figure 53.24, we can predict that employment and education opportunities will continue to be a problem for Afghanistan in the foreseeable future. In the United States and Italy, a decreasing proportion of younger working-age people will soon be supporting an increasing population of retired "boomers." This demographic feature has made the future of Social Security and Medicare a major political issue in the United States. Understanding age structures can help us plan for the future.

Infant Mortality and Life Expectancy

Infant mortality, the number of infant deaths per 1,000 live births, and *life expectancy at birth*, the predicted average length of life at birth, vary widely in different countries. In 2011, for example, the infant mortality rate was 149 (14.9%) in Afghanistan but only 2.8 (0.28%) in Japan. Life expectancy at birth was only 48 years in Afghanistan but 82 years in Japan. These differences reflect the quality of life faced by children at birth and influence the reproductive choices parents make. If infant mortality is high, then parents are likely to have more children to ensure that some reach adulthood.

Although global life expectancy has been increasing since about 1950, it has recently dropped in a number of regions, including countries of the former Soviet Union and in sub-Saharan Africa. In these regions, social upheaval, decaying infrastructure, and infectious diseases such as AIDS and tuberculosis are reducing life expectancy. In the African country of Angola, life expectancy in 2011 was 43 years, about half of that in Japan, Sweden, Italy, and Spain.

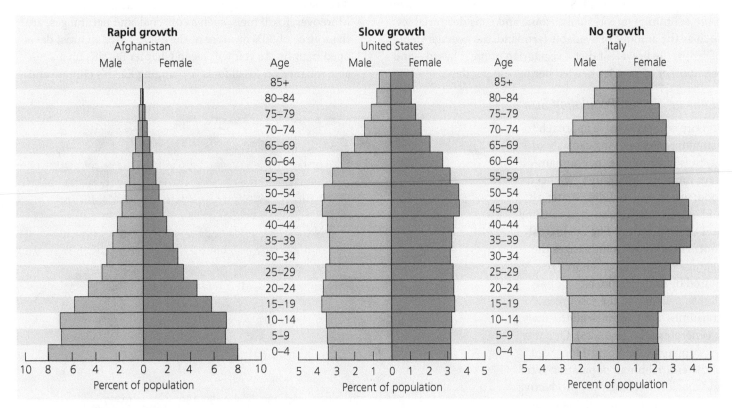

▲ **Figure 53.24 Age-structure pyramids for the human population of three countries (data as of 2010).** The annual growth rate was approximately 2.6% in Afghanistan, 1.0% in the United States, and 0.0% in Italy.

Global Carrying Capacity

No ecological question is more important than the future size of the human population. The projected worldwide population size depends on assumptions about future changes in birth and death rates. As we noted earlier, population ecologists project a global population of approximately 8.1–10.6 billion people in 2050. In other words, an estimated 1–4 billion people will be added to the population in the next four decades because of the momentum of population growth. But just how many humans can the biosphere support? Will the world be overpopulated in 2050? Is it *already* overpopulated?

Estimates of Carrying Capacity

For over three centuries, scientists have attempted to estimate the human carrying capacity of Earth. The first known estimate, 13.4 billion people, was made in 1679 by Anton van Leeuwenhoek, the discoverer of protists (see Chapter 28). Since then, estimates have varied from less than 1 billion to more than 1,000 billion (1 trillion).

Carrying capacity is difficult to estimate, and scientists use different methods to produce their estimates. Some current researchers use curves like that produced by the logistic equation (see Figure 53.10) to predict the future maximum of the human population. Others generalize from existing "maximum" population density and multiply this number by the area of habitable land. Still others base their estimates on a single limiting factor, such as food, and consider variables such as the amount of available farmland, the average yield of crops, the prevalent diet—vegetarian or meat based—and the number of calories needed per person per day.

Limits on Human Population Size

A more comprehensive approach to estimating the carrying capacity of Earth is to recognize that humans have multiple constraints: We need food, water, fuel, building materials, and other resources, such as clothing and transportation. The **ecological footprint** concept summarizes the aggregate land and water area required by each person, city, or nation to produce all the resources it consumes and to absorb all the waste it generates (Figure 53.25). One way to estimate the ecological footprint of the entire human population is to add up all the ecologically productive land on the planet and divide by the population. This calculation yields approximately 2 hectares (ha) per

▲ **Figure 53.25 Ecological footprint.** The resources we use and the waste we produce determine our ecological footprint. Technology castoffs, such as these circuit boards, contribute to our ecological footprint.

person (1 ha = 2.47 acres). Reserving some land for parks and conservation means reducing this allotment to 1.7 ha per person—the benchmark for comparing actual ecological footprints. Anyone who consumes resources that require more than 1.7 ha to produce is said to be using an unsustainable share of Earth's resources. A typical ecological footprint for a person in the United States is about 10 ha.

Ecologists sometimes calculate ecological footprints using other currencies besides land area, such as energy use. Average energy use differs greatly for a person in developed and developing nations (Figure 53.26). A typical person in the United States, Canada, or Norway consumes roughly 30 times the energy that a person in central Africa does. Moreover, fossil fuels, such as oil, coal, and natural gas, are the source of 80% or more of the energy used in most developed nations. As you will see in Chapter 56, this unsustainable reliance on fossil fuels is changing Earth's climate and

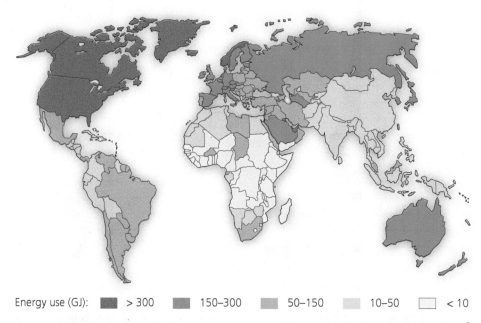

Energy use (GJ):   ■ > 300   ■ 150–300   ■ 50–150   ■ 10–50   □ < 10

▲ **Figure 53.26 Annual per capita energy use around the world.** A gigajoule (GJ) equals 10^9 J. For comparison, leaving a 100-watt lightbulb on continuously for one year would use 3.15 GJ.

increasing the amount of waste that each of us produces. Ultimately, the combination of resource use per person and population density determines our global ecological footprint.

We can only speculate about Earth's ultimate carrying capacity for the human population and about what factors will eventually limit our growth. Perhaps food will be the main limiting factor. Malnutrition and famine are common in some regions, but they result mainly from the unequal distribution of food rather than from inadequate production. So far, technological improvements in agriculture have allowed food supplies to keep up with global population growth.

The demands of many populations have already far exceeded the local and even regional supplies of one renewable resource—fresh water. More than 1 billion people do not have access to sufficient water to meet their basic sanitation needs. The human population may also be limited by the capacity of the environment to absorb its wastes. If so, then Earth's current human occupants could lower the planet's long-term carrying capacity for future generations.

Technology has substantially increased Earth's carrying capacity, but no population can grow indefinitely. After reading this chapter, you should realize that there is no single carrying capacity. How many people our planet can sustain depends on the quality of life each of us enjoys and the distribution of wealth across people and nations, topics of great concern and political debate. We can decide whether zero population growth will be attained through social changes based on human choices or, instead, through increased mortality due to resource limitation, plagues, war, and environmental degradation.

CONCEPT CHECK 53.6

1. How does a human population's age structure affect its growth rate?
2. How has the growth of Earth's human population changed in recent decades? In your answer, discuss growth rate and the number of people added each year.
3. **WHAT IF?** What choices can you make to influence your own ecological footprint?

For suggested answers, see Appendix A.

53 Chapter Review

SUMMARY OF KEY CONCEPTS

CONCEPT 53.1

Biological processes influence population density, dispersion, and demographics (pp. 1185–1190)

- Population **density**—the number of individuals per unit area or volume—reflects the interplay of births, deaths, immigration, and emigration. Environmental and social factors influence the **dispersion** of individuals.

Patterns of dispersion

| Clumped | Uniform | Random |

- Populations increase from births and **immigration** and decrease from deaths and **emigration**. **Life tables**, **survivorship curves**, and **reproductive tables** summarize specific trends in **demography**.

? *Gray whales* (Eschrichtius robustus) *gather each winter near Baja California to give birth. How might such behavior make it easier for ecologists to estimate birth and death rates for the species?*

CONCEPT 53.2

The exponential model describes population growth in an idealized, unlimited environment (pp. 1190–1192)

- If immigration and emigration are ignored, a population's growth rate (the per capita rate of increase) equals its birth rate minus its death rate.
- The **exponential growth** equation $dN/dt = r_{inst}N$ represents a population's growth when resources are relatively abundant, where r_{inst} is the instantaneous per capita rate of increase and N is the number of individuals in the population.

? *Suppose one population has an* r_{inst} *that is twice as large as the* r_{inst} *of another population. What is the maximum size that both populations will reach over time, based on the exponential model?*

CONCEPT 53.3

The logistic model describes how a population grows more slowly as it nears its carrying capacity (pp. 1192–1194)

- Exponential growth cannot be sustained for long in any population. A more realistic population model limits growth by incorporating **carrying capacity** (K), the maximum population size the environment can support.
- According to the **logistic growth** equation $dN/dt = r_{inst}N$ $(K - N)/K$, growth levels off as population size approaches the carrying capacity.

- The logistic model fits few real populations perfectly, but it is useful for estimating possible growth.

? *As an ecologist who manages a wildlife preserve, you want to increase the preserve's carrying capacity for a particular endangered species. How might you go about accomplishing this?*

CONCEPT 53.4

Life history traits are products of natural selection (pp. 1195–1197)

- **Life history** traits are evolutionary outcomes reflected in the development, physiology, and behavior of organisms.
- Big-bang, or **semelparous**, organisms reproduce once and die. **Iteroparous** organisms produce offspring repeatedly.
- Life history traits such as brood size, age at maturity, and parental caregiving represent trade-offs between conflicting demands for time, energy, and nutrients. Two hypothetical life history patterns are **K-selection**, or density-dependent selection, and **r-selection**, or density-independent selection.

? *What two factors likely contribute to the evolution of semelparity versus iteroparity?*

CONCEPT 53.5

Many factors that regulate population growth are density dependent (pp. 1197–1201)

- In **density-dependent** population regulation, death rates rise and birth rates fall with increasing density. In **density-independent** population regulation, birth and death rates do not vary with density.
- Density-dependent changes in birth and death rates curb population increase through negative feedback and can eventually stabilize a population near its carrying capacity. Density-dependent limiting factors include intraspecific competition for limited food or space, increased predation, disease, intrinsic physiological factors, and buildup of toxic substances.
- Because changing environmental conditions periodically disrupt them, all populations exhibit some size fluctuations. Many populations undergo regular boom-and-bust cycles that are

influenced by complex interactions between biotic and abiotic factors. A **metapopulation** is a group of populations linked by immigration and emigration.

? *Give an example of one biotic and one abiotic factor that contribute to yearly fluctuations in the size of the human population.*

CONCEPT 53.6

The human population is no longer growing exponentially but is still increasing rapidly (pp. 1201–1205)

- Since about 1650, the global human population has grown exponentially, but within the last 50 years, the rate of growth has fallen by half. Differences in **age structure** show that while some nations' populations are growing rapidly, those of others are stable or declining in size. Infant mortality rates and life expectancy at birth vary widely in different countries.
- **Ecological footprint** is the aggregate land and water area needed to produce all the resources a person or group of people consume and to absorb all of their wastes. It is one measure of how close we are to the carrying capacity of Earth, which is uncertain. With a world population of more than 7 billion people, we are already using many resources in an unsustainable manner.

? *How are humans different from other species in the ability to "choose" a carrying capacity for their environment?*

TEST YOUR UNDERSTANDING

LEVEL 1: KNOWLEDGE/COMPREHENSION

1. Population ecologists follow the fate of same-age cohorts to
   a. determine a population's carrying capacity.
   b. determine the birth rate and death rate of each group in a population.
   c. determine if a population is regulated by density-dependent processes.
   d. determine the factors that regulate the size of a population.

2. A population's carrying capacity
   a. may change as environmental conditions change.
   b. can be accurately calculated using the logistic growth model.
   c. increases as the per capita growth rate (r) decreases.
   d. can never be exceeded.

3. Scientific study of the population cycles of the snowshoe hare and its predator, the lynx, has revealed that
   a. predation is the dominant factor affecting prey population cycling.
   b. hares and lynx are so mutually dependent that each species cannot survive without the other.
   c. both hare and lynx populations are regulated mainly by abiotic factors.
   d. the hare population is r-selected and the lynx population is K-selected.

4. Analyzing ecological footprints reveals that
   a. Earth's carrying capacity would increase if per capita meat consumption increased.
   b. current demand by industrialized countries for resources is much smaller than the ecological footprint of those countries.
   c. it is not possible for technological improvements to increase Earth's carrying capacity for humans.
   d. the ecological footprint of the United States is large because per capita resource use is high.

5. Based on current growth rates, Earth's human population in 2015 will be closest to
   a. 2 million.   c. 7 billion.
   b. 4 billion.   d. 10 billion.

LEVEL 2: APPLICATION/ANALYSIS

6. The observation that members of a population are uniformly distributed suggests that
   a. resources are distributed unevenly.
   b. the members of the population are competing for access to a resource.
   c. the members of the population are neither attracted to nor repelled by one another.
   d. the density of the population is low.

7. According to the logistic growth equation

$$\frac{dN}{dt} = r_{inst}N\frac{(K-N)}{K}$$

   a. the number of individuals added per unit time is greatest when N is close to zero.
   b. the per capita growth rate (r) increases as N approaches K.
   c. population growth is zero when N equals K.
   d. the population grows exponentially when K is small.

8. Which pair of terms most accurately describes life history traits for a stable population of wolves?
   a. semelparous; r-selected
   b. semelparous; K-selected
   c. iteroparous; r-selected
   d. iteroparous; K-selected

9. During exponential growth, a population always
   a. has a constant, instantaneous per capita growth rate.
   b. quickly reaches its carrying capacity.
   c. cycles through time.
   d. loses some individuals to emigration.

10. Which of the following statements about human population in industrialized countries is *incorrect*?
    a. Life history is r-selected.
    b. Average family size is relatively small.
    c. The population has undergone the demographic transition.
    d. The survivorship curve is Type I.

LEVEL 3: SYNTHESIS/EVALUATION

11. **INTERPRET THE DATA** To estimate which age cohort in a population of females produces the most female offspring, you need information about the number of offspring produced per capita within that cohort and the number of individuals alive in the cohort. Make this estimate for Belding's ground squirrels by multiplying the number of females alive at the start of the year (column 2 in Table 53.1) by the average number of female offspring produced per female (column 5 in Table 53.2). Draw a bar graph with female age in years on the *x*-axis (0–1, 1–2, and so on) and total number of female offspring produced for each age cohort on the *y*-axis. Which cohort of female Belding's ground squirrels produces the most female young?

12. EVOLUTION CONNECTION
    Write a paragraph contrasting the conditions that favor the evolution of semelparous (one-time) reproduction versus iteroparous (repeated) reproduction.

13. SCIENTIFIC INQUIRY
    You are testing the hypothesis that increased population density of a particular plant species increases the rate at which a pathogenic fungus infects the plant. Because the fungus causes visible scars on the leaves, you can easily determine whether a plant is infected. Design an experiment to test your hypothesis. Describe your experimental and control groups, how you would collect data, and what results you would see if your hypothesis is correct.

14. SCIENCE, TECHNOLOGY, AND SOCIETY
    Many people regard the rapid population growth of less industrialized countries as our most serious environmental problem. Others think that the population growth in industrialized countries, though smaller, is actually a greater environmental threat. What problems result from population growth in (a) less industrialized countries and (b) industrialized nations? Which do you think is a greater threat, and why?

15. WRITE ABOUT A THEME: INTERACTIONS
    In a short essay (100–150 words), identify the factor or factors in Figure 53.18 that you think may ultimately be most important for density-dependent population regulation in humans, and explain your reasoning.

16. SYNTHESIZE YOUR KNOWLEDGE

Locusts (grasshoppers in the family Acrididae) undergo cyclic population outbreaks. Of the mechanisms of density-dependent regulation shown in Figure 53.18, choose the two that you think most apply to locust swarms, and explain why.

For selected answers, see Appendix A.

MasteringBiology®

Students Go to **MasteringBiology** for assignments, the eText, and the Study Area with practice tests, animations, and activities.

Instructors Go to **MasteringBiology** for automatically graded tutorials and questions that you can assign to your students, plus Instructor Resources.

54

Community Ecology

▲ **Figure 54.1 Which species benefits from this interaction?**

Communities in Motion

Deep in the Lembeh Strait of Indonesia, a carrier crab scuttles across the ocean floor holding a large sea urchin on its back **(Figure 54.1)**. When a predatory fish arrives, the crab quickly settles into the sediments and puts its living shield to use. The fish darts in and tries to bite the crab. In response, the crab tilts the spiny sea urchin toward whichever side the fish attacks. The fish eventually gives up and swims away. Carrier crabs use many organisms to protect themselves, including jellies (lower left).

The crab in Figure 54.1 clearly benefits from having the sea urchin on its back. But how does the sea urchin fare in this relationship? Its association with the crab might harm it, help it, or have no effect on its survival and reproduction. Additional observations or experiments would be needed before ecologists could answer this question.

In Chapter 53, you learned how individuals within a population can affect other individuals of the same species. This chapter will examine ecological interactions between populations of different species. A group of populations of different species living close enough to interact is called a biological **community**. Ecologists define the boundaries of a particular community to fit their research questions: They might study the community of decomposers and other organisms living on a rotting log, the benthic community in Lake Superior, or the community of trees and shrubs in Sequoia National Park in California.

We begin this chapter by exploring the kinds of interactions that occur between species in a community, such as the crab and sea urchin in Figure 54.1. We'll then consider several of the factors that are most significant in structuring a community—in determining how many species there are, which particular species are present, and the relative abundance of these species. Finally, we'll apply some of the principles of community ecology to the study of human disease.

CONCEPT 54.1

Community interactions are classified by whether they help, harm, or have no effect on the species involved

Some key relationships in the life of an organism are its interactions with individuals of other species in the community. These **interspecific interactions** include competition, predation, herbivory, symbiosis (including parasitism, mutualism, and commensalism), and facilitation. In this section, we'll define and describe each of these interactions, recognizing that ecologists do not always agree on the precise boundaries of each type of interaction.

We'll use the symbols + and − to indicate how each interspecific interaction affects the survival and reproduction of the two species engaged in the interaction. For example, predation is a +/− interaction, with a positive effect on the survival and reproduction of the predator population and a negative effect on that of the prey population. Mutualism is a +/+ interaction because the survival and reproduction of both species are increased in the presence of the other. A 0 indicates that a population is not affected by the interaction in any known way.

Historically, most ecological research has focused on interactions that have a negative effect on at least one species, such as competition and predation. However, positive interactions are ubiquitous, and their contributions to community structure are the subject of considerable study today.

Competition

Interspecific competition is a −/− interaction that occurs when individuals of different species compete for a resource that limits their growth and survival. Weeds growing in a garden compete with garden plants for soil nutrients and water. Grasshoppers and bison in the Great Plains compete for the grass they both eat. Lynx and foxes in the northern forests of Alaska and Canada compete for prey such as snowshoe hares. In contrast, some resources, such as oxygen, are rarely in short supply on land; most terrestrial species use this resource but do not usually compete for it.

Competitive Exclusion

What happens in a community when two species compete for limited resources? In 1934, Russian ecologist G. F. Gause studied this question using laboratory experiments with two closely related species of ciliated protists, *Paramecium aurelia* and *Paramecium caudatum*. He cultured the species under stable conditions, adding a constant amount of food each day. When Gause grew the two species separately, each population increased rapidly and then leveled off at the apparent carrying capacity of the culture (see Figure 53.11a for an illustration of the logistic growth of *P. aurelia*). But when Gause grew the two species together, *P. caudatum* became extinct in the culture. Gause inferred that *P. aurelia* had a competitive edge in obtaining food. He concluded that two species competing for the same limiting resources cannot coexist permanently in the same place. In the absence of disturbance, one species will use the resources more efficiently and reproduce more rapidly than the other. Even a slight reproductive advantage will eventually lead to local elimination of the inferior competitor, an outcome called **competitive exclusion**.

Paramecium caudatum

25 μm

Ecological Niches and Natural Selection

EVOLUTION The sum of a species' use of the biotic and abiotic resources in its environment is called its **ecological niche**. American ecologist Eugene Odum used the following analogy to explain the niche concept: If an organism's habitat is its "address," the niche is the organism's "profession." The niche of a tropical tree lizard, for instance, includes the temperature range it tolerates, the size of branches on which it perches, the time of day when it is active, and the sizes and kinds of insects it eats. Such factors define the lizard's niche, or ecological role—how it fits into an ecosystem.

We can use the niche concept to restate the principle of competitive exclusion: Two species cannot coexist permanently in a community if their niches are identical. However, ecologically similar species *can* coexist in a community if one or more significant differences in their niches arise through time. Evolution by natural selection can result in one of the species using a different set of resources or similar resources at different times of the day or year. The differentiation of niches that enables similar species

A. distichus perches on fence posts and other sunny surfaces.

A. insolitus usually perches on shady branches.

A. ricordi

A. insolitus
A. christophei

A. aliniger
A. distichus

A. cybotes
A. etheridgei

▲ **Figure 54.2 Resource partitioning among Dominican Republic lizards.** Seven species of *Anolis* lizards live in close proximity, and all feed on insects and other small arthropods. However, competition for food is reduced because each lizard species has a different preferred perch, thus occupying a distinct niche.

to coexist in a community is called **resource partitioning** (**Figure 54.2**).

As a result of competition, a species' *fundamental niche*, which is the niche potentially occupied by that species, is often different from its *realized niche*, the portion of its fundamental niche that it actually occupies. Ecologists can identify the fundamental niche of a species by testing the range of conditions in which it grows and reproduces in the absence of competitors. They can also test whether a potential competitor limits a species' realized niche by removing the competitor and seeing if the first species expands into the newly available space. The classic experiment depicted in **Figure 54.3** clearly showed that competition between two barnacle species kept one species from occupying part of its fundamental niche.

Species can partition their niches not just in space, as lizards and barnacles do, but in time as well. The common spiny mouse (*Acomys cahirinus*) and the golden spiny mouse (*A. russatus*) live in rocky habitats of the Middle East and Africa, sharing similar microhabitats and food sources. Where they coexist, *A. cahirinus* is nocturnal (active at night), while *A. russatus* is diurnal (active during the day). Surprisingly, laboratory research showed that *A. russatus* is naturally nocturnal. To be active during the day, it must override its biological clock in the presence of *A. cahirinus*. When researchers in Israel removed all *A. cahirinus*

◀ **The golden spiny mouse**
(*Acomys russatus*)

▼ **Figure 54.3** Inquiry

Can a species' niche be influenced by interspecific competition?

Experiment Ecologist Joseph Connell studied two barnacle species—*Chthamalus stellatus* and *Balanus balanoides*—that have a stratified distribution on rocks along the coast of Scotland. *Chthamalus* is usually found higher on the rocks than *Balanus*. To determine whether the distribution of *Chthamalus* is the result of interspecific competition with *Balanus*, Connell removed *Balanus* from the rocks at several sites.

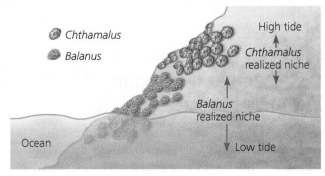

Chthamalus

Balanus

High tide

Chthamalus realized niche

Balanus realized niche

Ocean

Low tide

Results *Chthamalus* spread into the region formerly occupied by *Balanus*.

High tide

Chthamalus fundamental niche

Ocean

Low tide

Conclusion Interspecific competition makes the realized niche of *Chthamalus* much smaller than its fundamental niche.

Source: J. H. Connell, The influence of interspecific competition and other factors on the distribution of the barnacle Chthamalus stellatus, Ecology *42:710–723 (1961).*

(MB) A related Experimental Inquiry Tutorial can be assigned in MasteringBiology.

WHAT IF? *Other observations showed that* Balanus *cannot survive high on the rocks because it dries out during low tides. How would* Balanus's *realized niche compare with its fundamental niche?*

individuals from a site in the species' natural habitat, *A. russatus* individuals at that site became nocturnal, consistent with the laboratory results. This change in behavior suggests that competition exists between the species and that partitioning of their active time helps them coexist.

Character Displacement

Closely related species whose populations are sometimes allopatric (geographically separate; see Chapter 24) and sometimes sympatric (geographically overlapping) provide more evidence for the importance of competition in structuring communities. In some cases, the allopatric populations

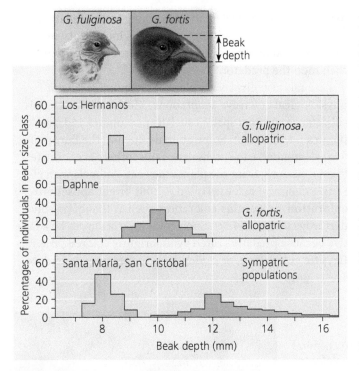

Figure 54.4 Character displacement: indirect evidence of past competition.

▲ Figure 54.4 **Character displacement: indirect evidence of past competition.** Allopatric populations of *Geospiza fuliginosa* and *Geospiza fortis* on Los Hermanos and Daphne Islands have similar beak morphologies (top two graphs) and presumably eat similarly sized seeds. However, where the two species are sympatric on Santa María and San Cristóbal, *G. fuliginosa* has a shallower, smaller beak and *G. fortis* a deeper, larger one (bottom graph), adaptations that favor eating different-sized seeds.

INTERPRET THE DATA *If the beak length of* G. fortis *is typically 12% longer than the beak depth, what is the predicted beak length of* G. fortis *individuals with the smallest beak depths observed on Santa María and San Cristóbal Islands?*

of such species are morphologically similar and use similar resources. By contrast, sympatric populations, which would potentially compete for resources, show differences in body structures and in the resources they use. This tendency for characteristics to diverge more in sympatric than in allopatric populations of two species is called **character displacement**, as shown for Galápagos finches in **Figure 54.4.**

Predation

Predation refers to a +/− interaction between species in which one species, the predator, kills and eats the other, the prey. Though the term *predation* generally elicits such images as a lion attacking and eating an antelope, it applies to a wide range of interactions. An animal that kills a plant by eating the plant's tissues can also be considered a predator. Because eating and avoiding being eaten are prerequisite to reproductive success, the adaptations of both predators and prey tend to be refined through natural selection. In the Scientific Skills Exercise, you can interpret data from an investigation of a specific predator-prey interaction.

Making a Bar Graph and a Scatter Plot

Can a Native Predator Species Adapt Rapidly to an Introduced Prey Species? Cane toads (*Bufo marinus*), shown above, were introduced to Australia in 1935 in a failed attempt to control an insect pest. Since then, the toads have spread across northeastern Australia, with a population of over 200 million today. Cane toads have glands that produce a toxin that is poisonous to snakes and other potential predators of the toads. In this exercise, you will graph and interpret data from a two-part experiment conducted to determine whether native Australian predators have developed resistance to the cane toad toxin.

How the Experiment Was Done In part 1, researchers collected 12 black snakes (*Pseudechis porphyriacus*) from areas where cane toads had existed for 40–60 years and another 12 from areas free of cane toads. They offered the snakes either a freshly killed native frog (*Limnodynastes peronii*, a species the snakes commonly eat) or a freshly killed cane toad from which the toxin gland had been removed (making the toad nonpoisonous). In part 2, researchers collected snakes from areas where cane toads had been present for 5–60 years. To assess how cane toad toxin affected the physiological activity of these snakes, they injected small amounts of the toxin into the snakes' stomachs and measured the snakes' swimming speed in a small pool.

Data from the Experiment, Part 1

Type of Prey Offered	% of Snakes That Ate Prey Offered in Each Area	
	Cane Toads Present in Area for 40–60 Years	No Cane Toads in Area
Native frog	100	100
Cane toad	0	50

Data from the Experiment, Part 2

Time Since First Exposure to Cane Toads (years)	5	10	10	20	50	60	60	60	60	60
% Reduction in Swimming Speed	52	19	30	30	5	5	9	11	12	22

Interpret the Data

1. Make a bar graph of the data in part 1. (For additional information about graphs, see the Scientific Skills Review in Appendix F and in the Study Area in Mastering Biology.)

2. What do the data represented in the graph suggest about the effects of cane toads on the predatory behavior of black snakes in areas where the toads are and are not currently found?

3. Suppose an enzyme that deactivates the cane toad toxin evolves in black snakes living in areas with cane toads. If the researchers repeated part 1 of this study, predict how the results would change.

4. Identify the dependent and independent variables in part 2 and make a scatter plot. What conclusion would you draw about whether exposure to cane toads is having a selective effect on black snakes? Explain.

5. Explain why a bar graph is appropriate for presenting the data in part 1 and a scatter plot is appropriate for the data in part 2.

(MB) A version of this Scientific Skills Exercise can be assigned in MasteringBiology.

Data from B. L. Phillips and R. Shine, An invasive species induces rapid adaptive change in a native predator: cane toads and black snakes in Australia, *Proceedings of the Royal Society B* 273:1545–1550 (2006).

Many important feeding adaptations of predators are obvious and familiar. Most predators have acute senses that enable them to find and identify potential prey. Rattlesnakes and other pit vipers, for example, find their prey with a pair of heat-sensing organs located between their eyes and nostrils (see Figure 50.7a). Owls have characteristically large eyes that help them see prey at night. Many predators also have adaptations such as claws, fangs, or poison that help them catch and subdue their food. Predators that pursue their prey are generally fast and agile, whereas those that lie in ambush are often disguised in their environments.

Just as predators possess adaptations for capturing prey, potential prey animals have adaptations that help them avoid being eaten. Some common behavioral defenses are hiding, fleeing, and forming herds or schools. Active self-defense is less common, though some large grazing mammals vigorously defend their young from predators such as lions. Other behavioral defenses include alarm calls that summon many individuals of the prey species, which then mob the predator.

Animals also display a variety of morphological and physiological defensive adaptations. Mechanical or chemical defenses protect species such as porcupines and skunks (**Figure 54.5a** and **b**). Some animals, such as the European fire salamander, can synthesize toxins; others accumulate toxins passively from the plants they eat. Animals with effective chemical defenses often exhibit bright **aposematic coloration**, or warning coloration, such as that of poison dart frogs (**Figure 54.5c**). Such coloration seems to be adaptive because predators often avoid brightly colored prey. **Cryptic coloration**, or camouflage, makes prey difficult to see (**Figure 54.5d**).

▼ **Figure 54.5 Examples of defensive adaptations in animals.**

(a) Mechanical defense

▶ Porcupine

(b) Chemical defense

▶ Skunk

(c) Aposematic coloration: warning coloration

◀ Poison dart frog

(d) Cryptic coloration: camouflage

◀ Canyon tree frog

(e) Batesian mimicry: A harmless species mimics a harmful one.

▲ Venomous green parrot snake

◀ Nonvenomous hawkmoth larva

(f) Müllerian mimicry: Two unpalatable species mimic each other.

◀ Yellow jacket

◀ Cuckoo bee

Some prey species are protected by their resemblance to other species. In **Batesian mimicry**, a palatable or harmless species mimics an unpalatable or harmful one. The larva of the hawkmoth *Hemeroplanes ornatus* puffs up its head and thorax when disturbed, looking like the head of a small venomous snake **(Figure 54.5e)**. In this case, the mimicry even involves behavior; the larva weaves its head back and forth and hisses like a snake. In **Müllerian mimicry**, two or more unpalatable species, such as the cuckoo bee and yellow jacket, resemble each other **(Figure 54.5f)**. Presumably, the more unpalatable prey there are, the more quickly predators learn to avoid prey with that particular appearance. In an example of convergent evolution, unpalatable animals in several different taxa have similar patterns of coloration: Black and yellow or red stripes characterize unpalatable animals as diverse as yellow jackets and coral snakes.

Many predators also use mimicry. The mimic octopus (*Thaumoctopus mimicus*), discovered in 1998, can take on the appearance and movement of more than a dozen marine animals, including crabs, sea stars, sea snakes, fish, and stingrays **(Figure 54.6)**. It uses its mimicry to approach prey—for example, imitating a crab to approach another crab and eat it. It also uses its mimicry to scare predators. When attacked by a damselfish, the octopus quickly mimics a banded sea snake, a known predator of the damselfish.

(a) Mimicking a sea snake

(b) Mimicking a flounder

(c) Mimicking a stingray

▲ **Figure 54.6 The mimic octopus. (a)** After hiding six of its tentacles in a hole in the seafloor, the octopus waves its other two tentacles to mimic a sea snake. **(b)** Flattening its body and arranging its arms to trail behind, the octopus mimics a flounder (a flat fish). **(c)** It can mimic a stingray by flattening most of its tentacles alongside its body while allowing one tentacle to extend behind.

Herbivory

Ecologists use the term **herbivory** to refer to a +/− interaction in which an organism eats parts of a plant or alga. While large mammalian herbivores such as cattle, sheep, and water buffalo may be most familiar, most herbivores are actually invertebrates, such as grasshoppers, caterpillars, and beetles. In the ocean, herbivores include sea urchins, some tropical fishes, and certain mammals **(Figure 54.7)**.

Like predators, herbivores have many specialized adaptations. Many herbivorous insects have chemical sensors on their feet that enable them to distinguish between plants based on their toxicity or nutritional value. Some mammalian herbivores, such as goats, use their sense of smell to examine plants, rejecting some and eating others. They may also eat just a specific part of a plant, such as the flowers. Many herbivores also have specialized teeth or digestive systems adapted for processing vegetation (see Chapter 41).

Unlike prey animals, plants cannot run away to avoid being eaten. Instead, a plant's arsenal against herbivores may feature chemical toxins or structures such as spines and thorns. Among the plant compounds that serve as chemical defenses are the poison strychnine, produced by the tropical vine *Strychnos toxifera*; nicotine, from the tobacco plant; and tannins, from a variety of plant species. Compounds that are not toxic to humans but may be distasteful to many herbivores are responsible for the familiar flavors of cinnamon, cloves, and peppermint. Certain plants produce chemicals that cause abnormal development in some insects that eat them. For more examples of how plants defend themselves, see Figure 39.27, "Make Connections: Levels of Plant Defenses Against Herbivores."

▲ **Figure 54.7 A West Indian manatee (*Trichechus manatus*) in Florida.** This mammalian herbivore is grazing on *Hydrilla*, an introduced plant species.

Symbiosis

When individuals of two or more species live in direct and intimate contact with one another, their relationship is called **symbiosis**. In this book, we define symbiosis to include all such interactions, whether they are harmful, helpful, or neutral. Some biologists define symbiosis more narrowly as a synonym for mutualism, an interaction in which both species benefit.

Parasitism

Parasitism is a +/− symbiotic interaction in which one organism, the **parasite**, derives its nourishment from another organism, its **host**, which is harmed in the process. Parasites that live within the body of their host, such as tapeworms, are called **endoparasites**; parasites that feed on the external surface of a host, such as ticks and lice, are called **ectoparasites**. In one particular type of parasitism, parasitoid insects—usually small wasps—lay eggs on or in living hosts. The larvae then feed on the body of the host, eventually killing it. Some ecologists have estimated that at least one-third of all species on Earth are parasites.

Many parasites have complex life cycles involving multiple hosts. The blood fluke, which currently infects approximately 200 million people around the world, requires two hosts at different times in its development: humans and freshwater snails (see Figure 33.11). Some parasites change the behavior of their current host in ways that increase the likelihood that the parasite will reach its next host. For instance, crustaceans that are parasitized by acanthocephalan (spiny-headed) worms leave protective cover and move into the open, where they are more likely to be eaten by the birds that are the second host in the worm's life cycle.

Parasites can significantly affect the survival, reproduction, and density of their host population, either directly or indirectly. For example, ticks that live as ectoparasites on moose weaken their hosts by withdrawing blood and causing hair breakage and loss. In their weakened condition, the moose have a greater chance of dying from cold stress or predation by wolves (see Figure 53.19).

Mutualism

Mutualistic symbiosis, or **mutualism**, is an interspecific interaction that benefits both species (+/+). We have described many mutualisms in previous chapters: nitrogen fixation by bacteria in the root nodules of legumes; cellulose digestion by microorganisms in the alimentary canals of termites and ruminant mammals; nutrient exchange between fungi and plant roots in mycorrhizae; and photosynthesis by unicellular algae in corals. The interaction between termites and the microorganisms in their digestive system is an example of *obligate mutualism*, in which at least one species has lost the ability to survive on its own. In *facultative mutualism*, as

(a) Certain species of acacia trees in Central and South America have hollow thorns that house stinging ants of the genus *Pseudomyrmex*. The ants feed on nectar produced by the tree and on protein-rich swellings along the bases of leaves.

(b) The acacia benefits because the pugnacious ants, which attack anything that touches the tree, remove fungal spores, small herbivores, and debris. They also clip vegetation that grows close to the acacia.

▲ **Figure 54.8 Mutualism between acacia trees and ants.**

in the acacia-ant example shown in **Figure 54.8**, both species can survive alone.

Mutualisms typically involve the coevolution of related adaptations in both species, with changes in either species likely to affect the survival and reproduction of the other. For example, most flowering plants have adaptations such as nectar or fruit that attract animals that pollinate flowers or disperse seeds (see Concept 38.1). In turn, many animals have adaptations that help them find and consume nectar.

Commensalism

An interaction between species that benefits one of the species but neither harms nor helps the other (+/0) is called **commensalism**. Commensal interactions are difficult to document in nature because any close association between species likely affects both species, even if only slightly. For

▲ **Figure 54.9 A possible example of commensalism between cattle egrets and African buffalo.**

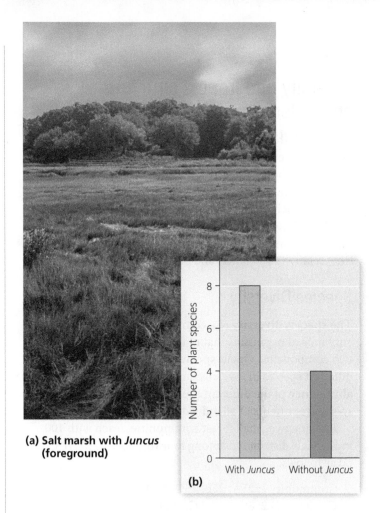

(a) Salt marsh with *Juncus* (foreground)

(b)

▲ **Figure 54.10 Facilitation by black rush (*Juncus gerardii*) in New England salt marshes.** Black rush increases the number of plant species that can live in the upper middle zone of the marsh.

instance, "hitchhiking" species, such as algae that live on the shells of aquatic turtles or barnacles that attach to whales, are sometimes considered commensal. The hitchhikers gain a place to grow while having seemingly little effect on their ride. However, they may reduce the hosts' efficiency of movement in searching for food or escaping from predators. Conversely, the hitchhikers may help camouflage the hosts.

Some commensal associations involve one species obtaining food that is inadvertently exposed by another. Cowbirds and cattle egrets feed on insects flushed out of the grass by grazing bison, cattle, horses, and other herbivores. Because the birds increase their feeding rates when following the herbivores, they clearly benefit from the association. Much of the time, the herbivores may be unaffected by the birds **(Figure 54.9)**. However, they, too, may sometimes benefit; the birds occasionally remove and eat ticks and other ecto-parasites from the herbivores or may warn the herbivores of a predator's approach.

Facilitation

Species can have positive effects (+/+ or 0/+) on the survival and reproduction of other species without necessarily living in the direct and intimate contact of a symbiosis. This type of interaction, called **facilitation**, is particularly common in plant ecology. For instance, the black rush *Juncus gerardii* makes the soil more hospitable for other plant species in some zones of New England salt marshes **(Figure 54.10a)**. *Juncus* helps prevent salt buildup in the soil by shading the soil surface, which reduces evaporation. *Juncus* also prevents the salt marsh soils from becoming oxygen depleted as it transports oxygen to its belowground tissues. In one study, when *Juncus* was removed from areas in the upper middle intertidal zone, those areas supported 50% fewer plant species **(Figure 54.10b)**.

All five types of interactions that we have discussed so far—competition, predation, herbivory, symbiosis, and facilitation—strongly influence the structure of communities. You'll see other examples of these interactions throughout this chapter.

CONCEPT CHECK 54.1

1. Explain how interspecific competition, predation, and mutualism differ in their effects on the interacting populations of two species.

2. According to the principle of competitive exclusion, what outcome is expected when two species with identical niches compete for a resource? Why?

3. **MAKE CONNECTIONS** Figure 24.13 illustrates the formation of and possible outcomes for a hybrid zone over time. Imagine that two finch species colonize a new island and are capable of hybridizing. The island contains two plant species, one with large seeds and one with small seeds, growing in isolated habitats. If the two finch species specialize in eating different plant species, would reproductive barriers be reinforced, weakened, or unchanged in this hybrid zone? Explain.

For suggested answers, see Appendix A.

CONCEPT 54.2

Diversity and trophic structure characterize biological communities

Along with the specific interactions described in the previous section, communities are also characterized by more general attributes, including how diverse they are and the feeding relationships of their species. In this section, you'll read why such ecological attributes are important. You'll also learn how a few species sometimes exert strong control on a community's structure, particularly on the composition, relative abundance, and diversity of its species.

Species Diversity

The **species diversity** of a community—the variety of different kinds of organisms that make up the community—has two components. One is **species richness**, the number of different species in the community. The other is the **relative abundance** of the different species, the proportion each species represents of all individuals in the community.

Imagine two small forest communities, each with 100 individuals distributed among four tree species (A, B, C, and D) as follows:

Community 1: 25A, 25B, 25C, 25D
Community 2: 80A, 5B, 5C, 10D

The species richness is the same for both communities because they both contain four species of trees, but the relative abundance is very different **(Figure 54.11)**. You would easily notice the four types of trees in community 1, but you might see only the abundant species A in the second forest. Most observers would intuitively describe community 1 as the more diverse of the two communities.

Ecologists use many tools to compare the diversity of communities across time and space. They often calculate indexes of diversity based on species richness and relative abundance. One widely used index is **Shannon diversity** (H):

$$H = -(p_A \ln p_A + p_B \ln p_B + p_C \ln p_C + \ldots)$$

where A, B, C . . . are the species in the community, p is the relative abundance of each species, and ln is the natural logarithm. A higher value of H indicates a more diverse community. Let's use this equation to calculate the Shannon diversity index of the two communities in Figure 54.11. For community 1, $p = 0.25$ for each species, so

$$H = -4(0.25 \ln 0.25) = 1.39.$$

For community 2,

$$H = -[0.8 \ln 0.8 + 2(0.05 \ln 0.05) + 0.1 \ln 0.1] = 0.71.$$

These calculations confirm our intuitive description of community 1 as more diverse.

Community 1
A: 25% B: 25% C: 25% D: 25%

Community 2
A: 80% B: 5% C: 5% D: 10%

▲ **Figure 54.11 Which forest is more diverse?** Ecologists would say that community 1 has greater species diversity, a measure that includes both species richness and relative abundance.

Determining the number and relative abundance of species in a community can be challenging. Because most species in a community are relatively rare, it may be hard to obtain a sample size large enough to be representative. It can also be difficult to identify the species in the community. If an unknown organism cannot be identified on the basis of morphology alone, it is useful to compare all or part of its genome to a reference database of DNA sequences from known organisms. For example, although the two samples of algae shown at right might appear to be two different species, comparing their sequences of a short standardized section of DNA (a *DNA "barcode"*) to a reference database showed that they belong to the same species. More and more, researchers are using DNA sequencing for species identification as it becomes cheaper and as DNA sequences from more organisms are placed in comparative databases.

It is also difficult to census the highly mobile or less visible members of communities, such as microorganisms, deep-sea creatures, and nocturnal species. The small size of microorganisms makes them particularly difficult to sample, so ecologists now use molecular tools to help determine microbial diversity **(Figure 54.12)**. Despite the challenges, measuring species diversity is essential for understanding community structure and for conserving diversity (as you'll read in Chapter 56).

▼ Figure 54.12 Research Method

Determining Microbial Diversity Using Molecular Tools

Application Ecologists are increasingly using molecular techniques to determine microbial diversity and richness in environmental samples. One such technique produces a DNA profile for microbial taxa based on sequence variations in the DNA that encodes the small subunit of ribosomal RNA. Noah Fierer and Rob Jackson, of Duke University, used this method to compare the diversity of soil bacteria in 98 habitats across North and South America to help identify environmental variables associated with high bacterial diversity.

Technique Researchers first extract and purify DNA from the microbial community in each sample. They use the polymerase chain reaction (PCR; see Figure 20.8) to amplify the ribosomal DNA and label the

DNA with a fluorescent dye. Restriction enzymes then cut the amplified, labeled DNA into fragments of different lengths, which are separated by gel electrophoresis. (A gel is shown on the left; see also Figures 20.6 and 20.7.) The number and abundance of these fragments characterize the DNA profile of the sample. Based on their analysis, Fierer and Jackson calculated the Shannon diversity (H) of each sample. They then looked for a correlation between H and several environmental variables, including vegetation type, mean annual temperature and rainfall, and acidity and quality of the soil at each site.

Results The diversity of bacterial communities in soils across North and South America was related almost exclusively to soil pH, with the Shannon diversity being highest in neutral soils and lowest in acidic soils. Amazonian rain forests, which have extremely high plant and animal diversity, had the most acidic soils and the lowest bacterial diversity of the samples tested.

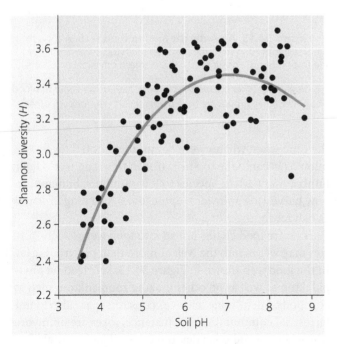

Source: N. Fierer and R. B. Jackson, The diversity and biogeography of soil bacterial communities, *Proceedings of the National Academy of Sciences USA* 103:626–631 (2006).

▶ **Figure 54.13**
Study plots at the Cedar Creek Ecosystem Science Reserve, University of Minnesota, site of long-term experiments on manipulating plant diversity.

Diversity and Community Stability

In addition to measuring species diversity, ecologists manipulate diversity in experimental communities in nature and in the laboratory. They do this to examine the potential benefits of diversity, including increased productivity and stability of biological communities.

Researchers at the Cedar Creek Ecosystem Science Reserve, in Minnesota, have been manipulating plant diversity in experimental communities for more than two decades **(Figure 54.13)**. Higher-diversity communities generally are more productive and are better able to withstand and recover from environmental stresses, such as droughts. More diverse communities are also more stable year to year in their productivity. In one decade-long experiment, for instance, researchers at Cedar Creek created 168 plots, each containing 1, 2, 4, 8, or 16 perennial grassland species. The most diverse plots consistently produced more **biomass** (the total mass of all organisms in a habitat) than the single-species plots each year.

Higher-diversity communities are often more resistant to **invasive species**, which are organisms that become established outside their native range. Scientists working in Long Island Sound, off the coast of Connecticut, created communities of different levels of diversity consisting of sessile marine invertebrates, including tunicates (see Figure 34.5). They then examined how vulnerable these experimental communities were to invasion by an exotic tunicate. They found that the exotic tunicate was four times more likely to survive in lower-diversity communities than in higher-diversity ones. The researchers concluded that relatively diverse communities captured more of the resources available in the system, leaving fewer resources for the invader and decreasing its survival.

Trophic Structure

Experiments like the ones just described often examine the importance of diversity within one trophic level. The structure and dynamics of a community also depend on the feeding relationships between organisms—the **trophic structure** of the community. The transfer of food energy up the trophic levels from its source in plants and other autotrophs (primary producers) through herbivores (primary

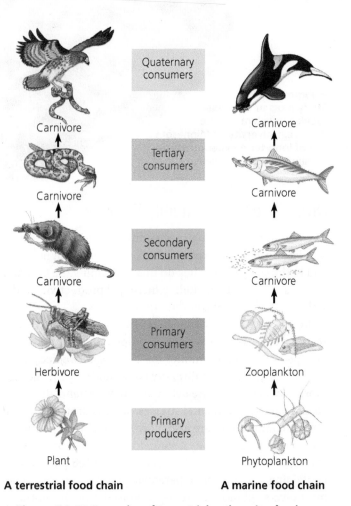

A terrestrial food chain   A marine food chain

▲ **Figure 54.14 Examples of terrestrial and marine food chains.** The arrows trace energy and nutrients that pass through the trophic levels of a community when organisms feed on one another. Decomposers, which "feed" on organisms from all trophic levels, are not shown here.

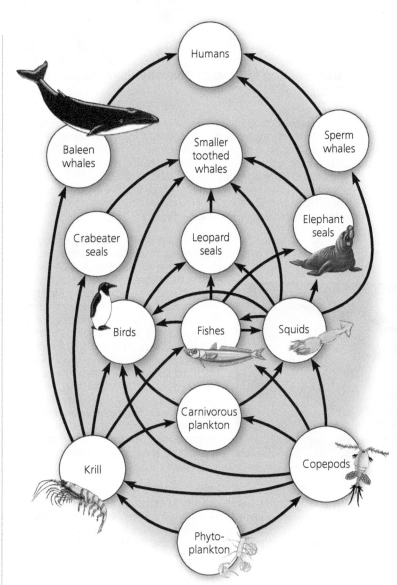

▲ **Figure 54.15 An Antarctic marine food web.** Arrows follow the transfer of food from the producers (phytoplankton) up through the trophic levels. For simplicity, this diagram omits decomposers.

[?] *How many other organism types does each group eat in this food web? Which two groups are both predator and prey for each other?*

consumers) to carnivores (secondary, tertiary, and quaternary consumers) and eventually to decomposers is referred to as a **food chain** (Figure 54.14).

Food Webs

In the 1920s, Oxford University biologist Charles Elton recognized that food chains are not isolated units but are linked together in **food webs**. Ecologists diagram the trophic relationships of a community using arrows that link species according to who eats whom. In an Antarctic pelagic community, for example, the primary producers are phytoplankton, which serve as food for the dominant grazing zooplankton, especially krill and copepods, both of which are crustaceans (Figure 54.15). These zooplankton species are in turn eaten by various carnivores, including other plankton, penguins, seals, fishes, and baleen whales. Squids, which are carnivores that feed on fish and zooplankton, are another important link in these food webs, as they are in turn eaten by seals and toothed whales. During

the time when whales were commonly hunted for food, humans became the top predator in this food web. Having hunted many whale species to low numbers, humans are now harvesting at lower trophic levels, catching krill as well as fish for food.

How are food chains linked into food webs? A given species may weave into the web at more than one trophic level. In the food web shown in Figure 54.15, krill feed on phytoplankton as well as on other grazing zooplankton, such as copepods. Such "nonexclusive" consumers are also found in terrestrial communities. For instance, foxes are omnivores whose diet includes berries and other plant materials, herbivores such as mice, and other predators, such as weasels. Humans are among the most versatile of omnivores.

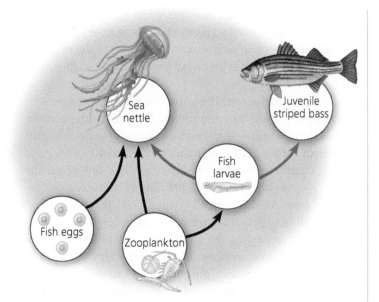

▲ **Figure 54.16 Partial food web for Chesapeake Bay estuary.** The sea nettle (*Chrysaora quinquecirrha*) and juvenile striped bass (*Morone saxatilis*) are the main predators of fish larvae (bay anchovy and several other species). Note that sea nettles are secondary consumers (black arrows) when they eat zooplankton, but tertiary consumers (red arrows) when they eat fish larvae, which are themselves secondary consumers of zooplankton.

Complicated food webs can be simplified in two ways for easier study. First, species with similar trophic relationships in a given community can be grouped into broad functional groups. In Figure 54.15, more than 100 phytoplankton species are grouped as the primary producers in the food web. A second way to simplify a food web for closer study is to isolate a portion of the web that interacts very little with the rest of the community. **Figure 54.16** illustrates a partial food web for sea nettles (a type of cnidarian) and juvenile striped bass in Chesapeake Bay estuary on the Atlantic coast of the United States.

Limits on Food Chain Length

Each food chain within a food web is usually only a few links long. In the Antarctic web of Figure 54.15, there are rarely more than seven links from the producers to any top-level predator, and most chains in this web have fewer links. In fact, most food webs studied to date have chains consisting of five or fewer links.

Why are food chains relatively short? The most common explanation, the **energetic hypothesis**, suggests that the length of a food chain is limited by the inefficiency of energy transfer along the chain. Only about 10% of the energy stored in the organic matter of each trophic level is converted to organic matter at the next trophic level (see Chapter 55). Thus, a producer level consisting of 100 kg of plant material can support about 10 kg of herbivore biomass and 1 kg of carnivore biomass. The energetic hypothesis predicts

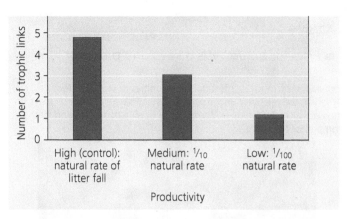

▲ **Figure 54.17 Test of the energetic hypothesis for the restriction of food chain length.** Researchers manipulated the productivity of tree-hole communities in Queensland, Australia, by providing leaf litter input at three levels. Reducing energy input reduced food chain length, a result consistent with the energetic hypothesis.

that food chains should be relatively longer in habitats of higher photosynthetic production, since the amount of energy stored in primary producers is greater than in habitats with lower photosynthetic production.

Ecologists tested the energetic hypothesis using tree-hole communities in tropical forests as experimental models. Many trees have small branch scars that rot, forming holes in the tree trunk. The holes hold water and provide a habitat for tiny communities consisting of microorganisms and insects that feed on leaf litter, as well as predatory insects. **Figure 54.17** shows the results of experiments in which researchers manipulated productivity by varying the amount of leaf litter in tree holes. As predicted by the energetic hypothesis, holes with the most leaf litter, and hence the greatest total food supply at the producer level, supported the longest food chains.

Another factor that may limit food chain length is that carnivores in a food chain tend to be larger at successive trophic levels. The size of a carnivore and its feeding mechanism put some upper limit on the size of food it can take into its mouth. And except in a few cases, large carnivores cannot live on very small food items because they cannot obtain enough food in a given time to meet their metabolic needs. Among the exceptions are baleen whales, huge filter feeders with adaptations that enable them to consume enormous quantities of krill and other small organisms (see Figure 41.6).

Species with a Large Impact

Certain species have an especially large impact on the structure of entire communities because they are highly abundant or play a pivotal role in community dynamics. The impact of these species occurs through trophic interactions and their influence on the physical environment.

▼ Figure 54.18   Inquiry

Is *Pisaster ochraceus* a keystone predator?

Experiment In rocky intertidal communities of western North America, the relatively uncommon sea star *Pisaster ochraceus* preys on mussels such as *Mytilus californianus*, a dominant species and strong competitor for space.

Robert Paine, of the University of Washington, removed *Pisaster* from an area in the intertidal zone and examined the effect on species richness.

Results In the absence of *Pisaster*, species richness declined as mussels monopolized the rock face and eliminated most other invertebrates and algae. In a control area where *Pisaster* was not removed, species richness changed very little.

Conclusion *Pisaster* acts as a keystone species, exerting an influence on the community that is not reflected in its abundance.

Source: R. T. Paine, Food web complexity and species diversity, *American Naturalist* 100:65–75 (1966).

WHAT IF? *Suppose that an invasive fungus killed most individuals of* Mytilus *at these sites. Predict how species richness would be affected if* Pisaster *were then removed.*

Dominant species in a community are the species that are the most abundant or that collectively have the highest biomass. There is no single explanation for why a species becomes dominant. One hypothesis suggests that dominant species are competitively superior in exploiting limited resources such as water or nutrients. Another hypothesis is that dominant species are most successful at avoiding predation or the impact of disease. The latter idea could explain the high biomass attained in some environments by invasive species. Such species may not face the natural predators or parasites that would otherwise hold their populations in check.

One way to discover the impact of a dominant species is to remove it from the community. The American chestnut was a dominant tree in deciduous forests of eastern North America before 1910, making up more than 40% of mature trees. Then humans accidentally introduced the fungal disease chestnut blight to New York City via nursery stock imported from Asia. Between 1910 and 1950, this fungus killed almost all of the chestnut trees in eastern North America. In this case, removing the dominant species had a relatively small impact on some species but severe effects on others. Oaks, hickories, beeches, and red maples that were already present in the forest increased in abundance and replaced the chestnuts. No mammals or birds seemed to have been harmed by the loss of the chestnut, but seven species of moths and butterflies that fed on the tree became extinct.

In contrast to dominant species, **keystone species** are not usually abundant in a community. They exert strong control on community structure not by numerical might but by their pivotal ecological roles, or niches. **Figure 54.18** highlights the importance of a keystone species, a sea star, in maintaining the diversity of an intertidal community.

Other organisms exert their influence on a community not through trophic interactions but by changing their physical environment. Species that dramatically alter their environment are called **ecosystem engineers** or, to avoid implying conscious intent, "foundation species." A familiar ecosystem engineer is the beaver (**Figure 54.19**). The effects of ecosystem engineers on other species can be positive or negative, depending on the needs of the other species.

▲ **Figure 54.19 Beavers as ecosystem engineers.** By felling trees, building dams, and creating ponds, beavers can transform large areas of forest into flooded wetlands.

1220   UNIT EIGHT   Ecology

Bottom-Up and Top-Down Controls

Simplified models based on relationships between adjacent trophic levels are useful for describing community organization. Let's consider the three possible relationships between plants (*V* for vegetation) and herbivores (*H*):

$$V \rightarrow H \quad V \leftarrow H \quad V \leftrightarrow H$$

The arrows indicate that a change in the biomass of one trophic level causes a change in the other trophic level. $V \rightarrow H$ means that an increase in vegetation will increase the numbers or biomass of herbivores, but not vice versa. In this situation, herbivores are limited by vegetation, but vegetation is not limited by herbivory. In contrast, $V \leftarrow H$ means that an increase in herbivore biomass will decrease the abundance of vegetation, but not vice versa. A double-headed arrow indicates that each trophic level is sensitive to changes in the biomass of the other.

Two models of community organization are common: the bottom-up model and the top-down model. The $V \rightarrow H$ linkage suggests a **bottom-up model**, which postulates a unidirectional influence from lower to higher trophic levels. In this case, the presence or absence of mineral nutrients (*N*) controls plant (*V*) numbers, which control herbivore (*H*) numbers, which in turn control predator (*P*) numbers. The simplified bottom-up model is thus $N \rightarrow V \rightarrow H \rightarrow P$. To change the community structure of a bottom-up community, you need to alter biomass at the lower trophic levels, allowing those changes to propagate up through the food web. If you add mineral nutrients to stimulate plant growth, then the higher trophic levels should also increase in biomass. If you change predator abundance, however, the effect should not extend down to the lower trophic levels.

In contrast, the **top-down model** postulates the opposite: Predation mainly controls community organization because predators limit herbivores, herbivores limit plants, and plants limit nutrient levels through nutrient uptake. The simplified top-down model, $N \leftarrow V \leftarrow H \leftarrow P$, is also called the *trophic cascade model*. In a lake community with four trophic levels, the model predicts that removing the top carnivores will increase the abundance of primary carnivores, in turn decreasing the number of herbivores, increasing phytoplankton abundance, and decreasing concentrations of mineral nutrients. The effects thus move down the trophic structure as alternating +/− effects.

Ecologists have applied the top-down model to improve water quality in polluted lakes. This approach, called **biomanipulation**, attempts to prevent algal blooms and eutrophication by altering the density of higher-level consumers instead of using chemical treatments. In lakes with three trophic levels, removing fish should improve water quality by increasing zooplankton density, thereby decreasing algal populations. In lakes with four trophic levels,

adding top predators should have the same effect. We can summarize the scenario of three trophic levels with the following diagram:

	Polluted State	Restored State
Fish	Abundant	Rare
Zooplankton	Rare	Abundant
Algae	Abundant	Rare

Ecologists in Finland used biomanipulation to help purify Lake Vesijärvi, a large lake that was polluted with city sewage and industrial wastewater until 1976. After pollution controls reduced these inputs, the water quality of the lake began to improve. By 1986, however, massive blooms of cyanobacteria started to occur in the lake. These blooms coincided with an increase in the population of roach, a fish species that eats zooplankton, which otherwise keep the cyanobacteria and algae in check. To reverse these changes, ecologists removed nearly a million kilograms of fish from the lake between 1989 and 1993, reducing roach abundance by about 80%. At the same time, they added a fourth trophic level by stocking the lake with pike perch, a predatory fish that eats roach. The water became clear, and the last cyanobacterial bloom was in 1989. Ecologists continue to monitor the lake for evidence of cyanobacterial blooms and low oxygen availability, but the lake has remained clear, even though roach removal ended in 1993.

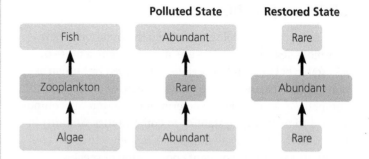

▼ Lake Vesijärvi, Finland

As these examples show, communities vary in their degree of bottom-up and top-down control. To manage agricultural landscapes, parks, reservoirs, and fisheries, we need to understand each particular community's dynamics.

CONCEPT CHECK 54.2

1. What two components contribute to species diversity? Explain how two communities with the same number of species can differ in species diversity.

2. How is a food chain different from a food web?

3. **WHAT IF?** Consider a grassland with five trophic levels: grasses, mice, snakes, raccoons, and bobcats. If you released additional bobcats into the grassland, how would grass biomass change if the bottom-up model applied? If the top-down model applied?

For suggested answers, see Appendix A.

CONCEPT 54.3

Disturbance influences species diversity and composition

Decades ago, most ecologists favored the traditional view that biological communities are at equilibrium, a more or less stable balance, unless seriously disturbed by human activities. The "balance of nature" view focused on interspecific competition as a key factor determining community composition and maintaining stability in communities. *Stability* in this context refers to a community's tendency to reach and maintain a relatively constant composition of species.

One of the earliest proponents of this view, F. E. Clements, of the Carnegie Institution of Washington, argued in the early 1900s that the community of plants at a site had only one stable equilibrium, a *climax community* controlled solely by climate. According to Clements, biotic interactions caused the species in the community to function as an integrated unit—in effect, as a superorganism. His argument was based on the observation that certain species of plants are consistently found together, such as the oaks, maples, birches, and beeches in deciduous forests of the northeastern United States.

Other ecologists questioned whether most communities were at equilibrium or functioned as integrated units. A. G. Tansley, of Oxford University, challenged the concept of a climax community, arguing that differences in soils, topography, and other factors created many potential communities that were stable within a region. H. A. Gleason, of the University of Chicago, saw communities not as superorganisms but more as chance assemblages of species found together because they happen to have similar abiotic requirements—for example, for temperature, rainfall, and soil type. Gleason and other ecologists also realized that disturbance keeps many communities from reaching a state of equilibrium in species diversity or composition. A **disturbance** is an event, such as a storm, fire, flood, drought, or human activity, that changes a community by removing organisms from it or altering resource availability.

This recent emphasis on change has produced the **nonequilibrium model**, which describes most communities as constantly changing after disturbance. Even relatively stable communities can be rapidly transformed into nonequilibrium communities. Let's examine some of the ways that disturbances influence community structure and composition.

Characterizing Disturbance

The types of disturbances and their frequency and severity vary among communities. Storms disturb almost all communities, even those in the oceans through the action of waves.

Fire is a significant disturbance; in fact, chaparral and some grassland biomes require regular burning to maintain their structure and species composition. Many streams and ponds are disturbed by spring flooding and seasonal drying. A high level of disturbance is generally the result of frequent *and* intense disturbance, while low disturbance levels can result from either a low frequency or low intensity of disturbance.

The **intermediate disturbance hypothesis** states that moderate levels of disturbance foster greater species diversity than do high or low levels of disturbance. High levels of disturbance reduce diversity by creating environmental stresses that exceed the tolerances of many species or by disturbing the community so often that slow-growing or slow-colonizing species are excluded. At the other extreme, low levels of disturbance can reduce species diversity by allowing competitively dominant species to exclude less competitive ones. Meanwhile, intermediate levels of disturbance can foster greater species diversity by opening up habitats for occupation by less competitive species. Such intermediate disturbance levels rarely create conditions so severe that they exceed the environmental tolerances or recovery rates of potential community members.

The intermediate disturbance hypothesis is supported by many terrestrial and aquatic studies. In one study, ecologists in New Zealand compared the richness of invertebrates living in the beds of streams exposed to different frequencies and intensities of flooding (**Figure 54.20**). When floods occurred either very frequently or rarely, invertebrate richness was low. Frequent floods made it difficult for some species to become established in the streambed, while rare floods resulted in species being displaced by superior competitors. Invertebrate richness peaked in streams that had an intermediate frequency or intensity of flooding, as predicted by the hypothesis.

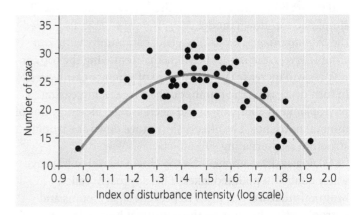

▲ **Figure 54.20 Testing the intermediate disturbance hypothesis.** Researchers identified the taxa (species or genera) of invertebrates at two locations in each of 27 New Zealand streams. They assessed the intensity of flooding at each location using an index of streambed disturbance. The number of invertebrate taxa peaked where the intensity of flooding was at intermediate levels.

(a) **Soon after fire.** The fire has left a patchy landscape. Note the unburned trees in the far distance.

(b) **One year after fire.** The community has begun to recover. Herbaceous plants, different from those in the former forest, cover the ground.

▲ **Figure 54.21 Recovery following a large-scale disturbance.** The 1988 Yellowstone National Park fires burned large areas of forests dominated by lodgepole pines.

Although moderate levels of disturbance appear to maximize species diversity, small and large disturbances often have important effects on community structure. Small-scale disturbances can create patches of different habitats across a landscape, which help maintain diversity in a community. Large-scale disturbances are also a natural part of many communities. Much of Yellowstone National Park, for example, is dominated by lodgepole pine, a tree species that requires the rejuvenating influence of periodic fires. Lodgepole pine cones remain closed until exposed to intense heat. When a forest fire burns the trees, the cones open and the seeds are released. The new generation of lodgepole pines can then thrive on nutrients released from the burned trees and in the sunlight that is no longer blocked by taller trees.

In the summer of 1988, extensive areas of Yellowstone burned during a severe drought. Monica Turner (see the Unit 8 interview before Chapter 52) and other ecologists showed that many burned areas in the park were already covered with new vegetation just one year later, suggesting that the species in this community are adapted to rapid recovery after fire (Figure 54.21). In fact, large-scale fires have periodically swept through the lodgepole pine forests of Yellowstone and other northern areas for thousands of years. In contrast, more southerly pine forests were historically affected by frequent but low-intensity fires. In these forests, a century of human intervention to suppress small fires has allowed an unnatural buildup of fuels in some places and elevated the risk of large, severe fires to which the species are not adapted.

Studies of the Yellowstone forest community and many others indicate that they are nonequilibrium communities, changing continually because of natural disturbances and the internal processes of growth and reproduction.

Mounting evidence suggests that nonequilibrium conditions are in fact the norm for most communities.

Ecological Succession

Changes in the composition and structure of terrestrial communities are most apparent after some severe disturbance, such as a volcanic eruption or a glacier, strips away all the existing vegetation. The disturbed area may be colonized by a variety of species, which are gradually replaced by other species, which are in turn replaced by still other species—a process called **ecological succession**. When this process begins in a virtually lifeless area where soil has not yet formed, such as on a new volcanic island or on the rubble (moraine) left by a retreating glacier, it is called **primary succession**.

During primary succession, the only life-forms initially present are often prokaryotes and protists. Lichens and mosses, which grow from windblown spores, are commonly the first macroscopic photosynthesizers to colonize such areas. Soil develops gradually as rocks weather and organic matter accumulates from the decomposed remains of the early colonizers. Once soil is present, the lichens and mosses are usually overgrown by grasses, shrubs, and trees that sprout from seeds blown in from nearby areas or carried in by animals. Eventually, an area is colonized by plants that become the community's dominant form of vegetation. Producing such a community through primary succession may take hundreds or thousands of years.

Early-arriving species and later-arriving ones may be linked by one of three key processes. The early arrivals may *facilitate* the appearance of the later species by making the environment more favorable—for example, by increasing

1 Pioneer stage

2 *Dryas* stage

4 Spruce stage

3 Alder stage

1941
1907
1860
Glacier
Bay
Alaska
1760

0 5 10 15
Kilometers

▲ **Figure 54.22 Glacial retreat and primary succession at Glacier Bay, Alaska.** The different shades of blue on the map show retreat of the glacier since 1760, based on historical descriptions.

the fertility of the soil. Alternatively, the early species may *inhibit* establishment of the later species, so that successful colonization by later species occurs in spite of, rather than because of, the activities of the early species. Finally, the early species may be completely independent of the later species, which *tolerate* conditions created early in succession but are neither helped nor hindered by early species.

Ecologists have conducted some of the most extensive research on primary succession at Glacier Bay in southeastern Alaska, where glaciers have retreated more than 100 km since 1760 **(Figure 54.22)**. By studying the communities at different distances from the mouth of the bay, ecologists can examine different stages in succession. **1** The exposed glacial moraine is colonized first by pioneering species that include liverworts, mosses, fireweed, scattered *Dryas* (a mat-forming shrub), and willows. **2** After about three decades, *Dryas* dominates the plant community. **3** A few decades later, the area is invaded by alder, which forms dense thickets up to 9 m tall. **4** In the next two centuries, these alder stands are overgrown first by Sitka spruce and later by western hemlock and mountain hemlock. In areas of poor drainage, the forest floor of this spruce-hemlock forest is invaded by sphagnum moss, which holds water and acidifies the soil,

eventually killing the trees. Thus, by about 300 years after glacial retreat, the vegetation consists of sphagnum bogs on the poorly drained flat areas and spruce-hemlock forest on the well-drained slopes.

Succession on glacial moraines is related to changes in soil nutrients and other environmental factors caused by transitions in the vegetation. Because the bare soil after glacial retreat is low in nitrogen content, almost all the pioneer plant species begin succession with poor growth and yellow leaves due to limited nitrogen supply. The exceptions are *Dryas* and alder, which have symbiotic bacteria that fix atmospheric nitrogen (see Chapter 37). Soil nitrogen content increases quickly during the alder stage of succession and keeps increasing during the spruce stage **(Figure 54.23)**. By altering soil properties, pioneer plant species can facilitate colonization by new plant species during succession.

In contrast to primary succession, **secondary succession** occurs when an existing community has been cleared by some disturbance that leaves the soil intact, as in Yellowstone following the 1988 fires (see Figure 54.21). Following the disturbance, the area may return to something like its original state. For instance, in a forested area that has been cleared for farming and later abandoned, the earliest plants

▲ Figure 54.23 Changes in soil nitrogen content during succession at Glacier Bay.

MAKE CONNECTIONS *Figures 37.10 and 37.11 illustrate two types of atmospheric nitrogen fixation by prokaryotes. At the earliest stages of primary succession, before any plants are present at a site, which type of nitrogen fixation would occur, and why?*

After ► trawling

▲ Figure 54.24 Disturbance of the ocean floor by trawling. These photos show the seafloor off northwestern Australia before (top) and after (bottom) deep-sea trawlers have passed.

to recolonize are often herbaceous species that grow from windblown or animal-borne seeds. If the area has not been burned or heavily grazed, woody shrubs may in time replace most of the herbaceous species, and forest trees may eventually replace most of the shrubs.

Human Disturbance

Ecological succession is a response to disturbance of the environment, and the strongest disturbances today are human activities. Agricultural development has disrupted what were once the vast grasslands of the North American prairie. Tropical rain forests are quickly disappearing as a result of clear-cutting for lumber, cattle grazing, and farmland. Centuries of overgrazing and agricultural disturbance have contributed to famine in parts of Africa by turning seasonal grasslands into vast barren areas.

Humans disturb marine ecosystems as well as terrestrial ones. The effects of ocean trawling, where boats drag weighted nets across the seafloor, are similar to those of clear-cutting a forest or plowing a field (**Figure 54.24**). The trawls scrape and scour corals and other life on the seafloor. In a typical year, ships trawl an area about the size of South America, 150 times larger than the area of forests that are clear-cut annually.

Because disturbance by human activities is often severe, it reduces species diversity in many communities. In Chapter 56, we'll take a closer look at how human-caused disturbance is affecting the diversity of life.

CONCEPT CHECK 54.3

1. Why do high and low levels of disturbance usually reduce species diversity? Why does an intermediate level of disturbance promote species diversity?

2. During succession, how might the early species facilitate the arrival of other species?

3. **WHAT IF?** Most prairies experience regular fires, typically every few years. If these disturbances were relatively modest, how would the species diversity of a prairie likely be affected if no burning occurred for 100 years? Explain your answer.

For suggested answers, see Appendix A.

CONCEPT 54.4

Biogeographic factors affect community diversity

So far, we have examined relatively small-scale or local factors that influence the diversity of communities, including the effects of species interactions, dominant species, and many types of disturbances. Ecologists also recognize that large-scale biogeographic factors contribute to the tremendous range of diversity observed in biological communities. The contributions of two biogeographic factors in particular—the latitude of a community and the area it occupies—have been investigated for more than a century.

Latitudinal Gradients

In the 1850s, both Charles Darwin and Alfred Wallace pointed out that plant and animal life was generally more abundant and diverse in the tropics than in other parts of the globe. Since that time, many researchers have confirmed this observation. One study found that a 6.6-hectare (1 ha = 10,000 m²) plot in tropical Malaysia contained 711 tree species, while a 2-ha plot of deciduous forest in Michigan typically contained just 10 to 15 tree species. Many groups of animals show similar latitudinal gradients. For instance, there are more than 200 species of ants in Brazil but only 7 in Alaska.

The two key factors in latitudinal gradients of species richness are probably evolutionary history and climate. Over the course of evolutionary time, species richness may increase in a community as more speciation events occur (see Chapter 24). Tropical communities are generally older than temperate or polar communities, which have repeatedly "started over" after major disturbances from glaciations. Also, the growing season in tropical forests is about five times as long as in the tundra communities of high latitudes. In effect, biological time runs about five times as fast in the tropics as near the poles, so intervals between speciation events are shorter in the tropics.

Climate is the other key factor in latitudinal gradients of richness and diversity. In terrestrial communities, the two main climatic factors correlated with diversity are sunlight and precipitation, both of which are relatively abundant in the tropics. These factors can be considered together by measuring a community's rate of **evapotranspiration**, the evaporation of water from soil and plants. Evapotranspiration, a function of solar radiation, temperature, and water availability, is much higher in hot areas with abundant rainfall than in areas with low temperatures or low precipitation. *Potential evapotranspiration*, a measure of potential water loss that assumes that water is readily available, is determined by the amount of solar radiation and temperature and is highest in regions where both are plentiful. The species richness of plants and animals correlates with both measures, as shown for vertebrates and potential evapotranspiration in **Figure 54.25**.

Area Effects

In 1807, naturalist and explorer Alexander von Humboldt described one of the first patterns of species richness to be recognized, the **species-area curve**: All other factors being equal, the larger the geographic area of a community, the more species it has, in part because larger areas offer a greater diversity of habitats and microhabitats. In conservation biology, developing species-area curves for key taxa in a community helps ecologists predict how the loss of a given area of habitat will affect the community's diversity.

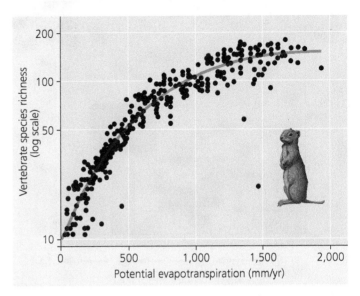

▲ **Figure 54.25 Energy, water, and species richness.** Vertebrate species richness in North America increases most predictably with potential evapotranspiration, expressed as rainfall equivalents (mm/yr).

The first, and still widely used, mathematical description of the species-area relationship was proposed a century ago:

$$S = cA^z$$

where S is the number of species found in a habitat, c is a constant, and A is the area of the habitat. The exponent z tells you how many more species should be found in a habitat as its area increases. In a log-log plot of S versus A, z is the slope of the line through the data points. A value of $z = 1$ would indicate a linear relationship between species number and area, meaning that ten times as many species would be found in a habitat that has ten times the area.

In the 1960s, Robert MacArthur and E. O. Wilson tested the predictions of the species-area relationship by examining the number of animals and plants on different island chains. As one example, in the Sunda Islands of Malaysia, they found that the number of bird species increased with island size, with a value of $z = 0.4$ (**Figure 54.26**). These and other studies have shown that z is usually between 0.2 and 0.4.

Although the slopes of different species-area curves vary, the basic concept of diversity increasing with increasing area applies in many situations, from surveys of ant diversity in New Guinea to studies of plant species richness on islands of different sizes.

Island Equilibrium Model

Because of their isolation and limited size, islands provide excellent opportunities for studying the biogeographic factors that affect the species diversity of communities. By "islands," we mean not only oceanic islands, but also habitat

▼ Figure 54.26 Inquiry

How does species richness relate to area?

Field Study Ecologists Robert MacArthur and E. O. Wilson studied the number of bird species on the Sunda Islands of Malaysia in relation to the area of the different islands.

Results

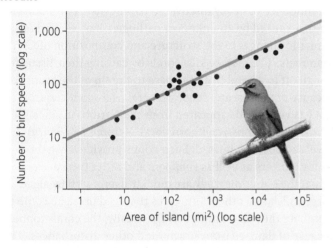

Conclusion Bird species richness increases with island size. The slope of the best-fit line through the data points (the parameter z) is about 0.4.

Source: R. H. MacArthur and E. O. Wilson, An equilibrium theory of insular zoogeography, *Evolution* 17:373–387 (1963).

WHAT IF? *Four islands in this study, ranging in area from about 100 to 800 square miles, each contained about 100 bird species. What does such variation tell you about the simple assumptions of the island equilibrium model?*

---

islands on land, such as lakes, mountain peaks separated by lowlands, or habitat fragments—any patch surrounded by an environment not suitable for the "island" species. While studying the species-area relationship, MacArthur and Wilson developed a general model of island biogeography, identifying the key determinants of species diversity on an island with a given set of physical characteristics.

Consider a newly formed oceanic island that receives colonizing species from a distant mainland. Two factors that determine the number of species on the island are the rate at which new species immigrate to the island and the rate at which species become extinct on the island. At any given time, an island's immigration and extinction rates are affected by the number of species already present. As the number of species on the island increases, the immigration rate of new species decreases, because any individual reaching the island is less likely to represent a species that is not already present. At the same time, as more species inhabit an island, extinction rates on the island increase because of the greater likelihood of competitive exclusion.

▲ **Figure 54.27 A mangrove island in the Florida Keys.** Like this one, most of the islands that Simberloff studied were small, consisting of one or a few mangrove trees. Their small size made it possible for Simberloff to cover each island with a tent to contain the fumigant he used in his experiment.

Two physical features of the island further affect immigration and extinction rates: its size and its distance from the mainland. Small islands generally have lower immigration rates because potential colonizers are less likely to reach a small island than a large one. Small islands also have higher extinction rates because they generally contain fewer resources, have less diverse habitats, and have smaller population sizes. Distance from the mainland is also important; a closer island generally has a higher immigration rate and a lower extinction rate than one farther away. Arriving colonists help sustain the presence of a species on a near island and prevent its extinction.

MacArthur and Wilson's model is called the *island equilibrium model* because an equilibrium will eventually be reached where the rate of species immigration equals the rate of species extinction. The number of species at this equilibrium point is correlated with the island's size and distance from the mainland. Like any ecological equilibrium, this species equilibrium is dynamic; immigration and extinction continue, and the exact species composition may change over time.

MacArthur and Wilson's studies of the diversity of animals and plants on many island chains support the prediction that species richness increases with island size, in keeping with the island equilibrium model (see Figure 54.26). Species counts also fit the prediction that the number of species decreases with increasing remoteness of the island.

In 1967, Dan Simberloff, then a graduate student with E. O. Wilson, tested the island equilibrium model in an experiment on six small mangrove islands in the Florida Keys **(Figure 54.27)**. He first painstakingly identified and counted all of the arthropod species on each island. As predicted by the model, he found more species on islands that were larger and closer to the mainland. He then fumigated four of the islands with methyl bromide to kill all of the arthropods. Within a year or two, the arthropod species richness on these islands increased to near their pre-fumigation values. The island closest to the mainland recovered first, while the island farthest from the mainland was the slowest to recover.

Over long periods, disturbances such as storms, adaptive evolutionary changes, and speciation generally alter the species composition and community structure on islands. Nonetheless, the island equilibrium model is widely applied in ecology. Conservation biologists in particular use it when designing habitat reserves or establishing a starting point for predicting the effects of habitat loss on species diversity.

CONCEPT CHECK 54.4

1. Describe two hypotheses that explain why species diversity is greater in tropical regions than in temperate and polar regions.

2. Describe how an island's size and distance from the mainland affect the island's species richness.

3. **WHAT IF?** Based on MacArthur and Wilson's island equilibrium model, how would you expect the richness of birds on islands to compare with the richness of snakes and lizards? Explain.

For suggested answers, see Appendix A.

CONCEPT 54.5

Pathogens alter community structure locally and globally

Now that we have examined several important factors that structure biological communities, we'll finish the chapter by examining community interactions involving **pathogens**— disease-causing microorganisms, viruses, viroids, or prions. (Viroids and prions are infectious RNA molecules and proteins, respectively; see Chapter 19.) Scientists have only recently come to appreciate how universal the effects of pathogens are in structuring ecological communities.

Pathogens produce especially clear effects when they are introduced into new habitats, as in the case of chestnut blight and the fungus that causes it (see Concept 54.2). A pathogen can be particularly virulent in a new habitat because new host populations have not had a chance to become resistant to the pathogen through natural selection. The invasive chestnut blight fungus had far stronger effects on the American chestnut, for instance, than it had on Asian chestnut species in the fungus's native habitat. Humans are similarly vulnerable to the effects of emerging diseases spread by our increasingly global economy. Ecologists are applying ecological knowledge to help track and control the pathogens that cause such diseases.

Pathogens and Community Structure

In spite of the potential of pathogens to limit populations, pathogens have until recently been the subject of relatively few ecological studies. This imbalance is now being addressed as events highlight the ecological importance of disease.

Coral reef communities are increasingly susceptible to the influence of newly discovered pathogens. White-band disease, caused by an unknown pathogen, has resulted in dramatic changes in the structure and composition of Caribbean reefs. The disease kills corals by causing their tissue to slough off in a band from the base to the tip of the branches. Because of the disease, staghorn coral (*Acropora cervicornis*) has virtually disappeared from the Caribbean since the 1980s. Populations of elkhorn coral (*Acropora palmata*) have also been decimated. Such corals provide key habitat for lobsters as well as snappers and other fish species. When the corals die, they are quickly overgrown by algae. Surgeonfish and other herbivores that feed on algae come to dominate the fish community. Eventually, the corals topple because of damage from storms and other disturbances. The complex, three-dimensional structure of the reef disappears, and diversity plummets.

Pathogens also influence community structure in terrestrial ecosystems. In the forests and savannas of California, trees of several species are dying from sudden oak death (SOD). This recently discovered disease is caused by the fungus-like protist *Phytophthora ramorum* (see Chapter 28). SOD was first described in California in 1995, when hikers noticed trees dying around San Francisco Bay. By 2012, it had spread more than 1,000 km, from the central California coast to southern Oregon, and killed more than a million oaks and other trees. The loss of the oaks has led to the decreased abundance of at least five bird species, including the acorn woodpecker and the oak titmouse, that rely on oaks for food and habitat.

Human activities are transporting pathogens around the world at unprecedented rates. Genetic analyses using simple sequence DNA (see Chapter 21) suggest that *P. ramorum* likely came to North America from Europe through the horticulture trade. Similarly, the pathogens that cause human diseases are spread by our global economy. H1N1, the virus that causes "swine flu" in humans, was first detected in Veracruz, Mexico, in early 2009. It quickly spread around the world when infected individuals flew on airplanes to other countries. By 2011, the world's first flu pandemic in 40 years had killed more than 18,000 people.

Community Ecology and Zoonotic Diseases

Three-quarters of emerging human diseases and many of the most devastating diseases are caused by **zoonotic**

pathogens—those that are transferred to humans from other animals, either through direct contact with an infected animal or by means of an intermediate species, called a **vector**. The vectors that spread zoonotic diseases are often parasites, including ticks, lice, and mosquitoes.

Identifying the community of hosts and vectors for a pathogen can help prevent illnesses such as Lyme disease, which is spread by ticks. For years, scientists thought that the primary host for the Lyme pathogen was the white-footed mouse. When researchers vaccinated mice against Lyme disease and released them into the wild, however, the number of infected ticks hardly changed. This prompted biologists to look for other hosts for the Lyme pathogen. They first trapped individuals of 11 potential host species in the field and measured the density of larval ticks on the animals **(Figure 54.28)**. They found that each host species transmitted to the ticks a unique set of alleles of a gene that encodes a protein on the pathogen's outer surface. The researchers then collected ticks in the field that were no longer attached to any host and used the genetic database to identify their former hosts. Surprisingly, two inconspicuous shrew species were the source for more than half the ticks collected in the field. Identifying the dominant hosts for a pathogen provides information that may be used to control the hosts most responsible for spreading diseases.

Ecologists also use their knowledge of community interactions to track the spread of zoonotic diseases. One example, avian flu, is caused by highly contagious viruses transmitted through the saliva and feces of birds (see Chapter 19). Most of these viruses affect wild birds mildly, but

▲ **Figure 54.28 Identifying Lyme disease host species.** A student researcher collects ticks from a white-footed mouse. Genetic analysis of the ticks from a variety of hosts enables scientists to identify the former hosts of other ticks collected in the field.

MAKE CONNECTIONS *Concept 23.1 describes genetic variation between populations. How might genetic variation between shrew populations in different locations affect the results of the Lyme disease study described in the text?*

▲ **Figure 54.29 Tracking avian flu.** Graduate student Travis Booms, of Boise State University, bands a young gyrfalcon as part of a project to monitor the spread of avian flu.

they often cause stronger symptoms in domesticated birds, the most common source of human infections. Since 2003, one particular viral strain, called H5N1, has killed hundreds of millions of poultry and more than 300 people.

Control programs that quarantine domestic birds or monitor their transport may be ineffective if avian flu spreads naturally through the movements of wild birds. From 2003 to 2006, the H5N1 strain spread rapidly from southeast Asia into Europe and Africa, but by 2012 it had not appeared in Australia or the Americas. The most likely place for infected wild birds to enter the Americas is Alaska, the entry point for ducks, geese, and shorebirds that migrate across the Bering Sea from Asia every year. Ecologists are studying the spread of the virus by trapping and testing migrating and resident birds in Alaska **(Figure 54.29)**. These ecological detectives are trying to catch the first wave of the disease entering North America.

Community ecology provides the foundation for understanding the life cycles of pathogens and their interactions with hosts. Pathogen interactions are also greatly influenced by changes in the physical environment. To control pathogens and the diseases they cause, scientists need an ecosystem perspective—an intimate knowledge of how the pathogens interact with other species and with all aspects of their environment. Ecosystems are the subject of Chapter 55.

CONCEPT CHECK 54.5

1. What are pathogens?

2. **WHAT IF?** Rabies, a viral disease in mammals, is not currently found in the British Isles. If you were in charge of disease control there, what practical approaches might you employ to keep the rabies virus from reaching these islands?

For suggested answers, see Appendix A.

CONCEPT 54.1

Community interactions are classified by whether they help, harm, or have no effect on the species involved (pp. 1209–1215)

- A variety of **interspecific interactions** affect the survival and reproduction of the species that engage in them. These interactions include interspecific competition, predation, herbivory, symbiosis, and facilitation.
- Competitive exclusion states that two species competing for the same resource cannot coexist permanently in the same place. **Resource partitioning** is the differentiation of **ecological niches** that enables species to coexist in a community.

Interspecific Interaction	Description
Interspecific competition (–/–)	Two or more species compete for a resource that is in short supply.
Predation (+/–)	One species, the predator, kills and eats the other, the prey. Predation has led to diverse adaptations, including mimicry.
Herbivory (+/–)	An herbivore eats part of a plant or alga.
Symbiosis	Individuals of two or more species live in close contact with one another. Symbiosis includes parasitism, mutualism, and commensalism.
Parasitism (+/–)	The **parasite** derives its nourishment from a second organism, its **host**, which is harmed.
Mutualism (+/+)	Both species benefit from the interaction.
Commensalism (+/0)	One species benefits from the interaction, while the other is unaffected by it.
Facilitation (+/+ or 0/+)	Species have positive effects on the survival and reproduction of other species without the intimate contact of a symbiosis.

? *Give an example of a pair of species that exhibit each interaction listed in the table above.*

CONCEPT 54.2

Diversity and trophic structure characterize biological communities (pp. 1216–1221)

- **Species diversity** measures the number of species in a community—its **species richness**—and their **relative abundance**.
- More diverse communities typically produce more **biomass** and show less year-to-year variation in growth than less diverse communities and are more resistant to invasion by exotic species.
- **Trophic structure** is a key factor in community dynamics. **Food chains** link the trophic levels from producers to top carnivores. Branching food chains and complex trophic interactions form **food webs**.

- **Dominant species** are the most abundant species in a community. **Keystone species** are usually less abundant species that exert a disproportionate influence on community structure.
- The **bottom-up model** proposes a unidirectional influence from lower to higher trophic levels, in which nutrients and other abiotic factors primarily determine community structure. **The top-down model** proposes that control of each trophic level comes from the trophic level above, with the result that predators control herbivores, which in turn control primary producers.

? *Based on indexes such as Shannon diversity, is a community of higher species richness always more diverse than a community of lower species richness? Explain.*

CONCEPT 54.3

Disturbance influences species diversity and composition (pp. 1222–1225)

- Increasing evidence suggests that **disturbance** and lack of equilibrium, rather than stability and equilibrium, are the norm for most communities. According to the **intermediate disturbance hypothesis**, moderate levels of disturbance can foster higher species diversity than can low or high levels of disturbance.
- **Ecological succession** is the sequence of community and ecosystem changes after a disturbance. **Primary succession** occurs where no soil exists when succession begins; **secondary succession** begins in an area where soil remains after a disturbance.

? *Is the disturbance pictured in Figure 54.24 more likely to initiate primary or secondary succession? Explain.*

CONCEPT 54.4

Biogeographic factors affect community diversity (pp. 1225–1228)

- Species richness generally declines along a latitudinal gradient from the tropics to the poles. The greater age of tropical environments may account for their greater species richness.
- Species richness is directly related to a community's geographic size, a principle formalized in the **species-area curve**.
- Species richness on islands depends on island size and distance from the mainland. The island equilibrium model maintains that species richness on an ecological island reaches an equilibrium where new immigrations are balanced by extinctions.

? *How have periods of glaciation influenced latitudinal patterns of diversity?*

CONCEPT 54.5

Pathogens alter community structure locally and globally (pp. 1228–1229)

- Recent work has highlighted the role that **pathogens** play in structuring terrestrial and marine communities.
- **Zoonotic pathogens** are transferred from other animals to humans and cause the largest class of emerging human diseases. Community ecology provides the framework for identifying key species interactions associated with such pathogens and for helping us track and control their spread.

? *In what way can a **vector** of a zoonotic pathogen differ from a host of the pathogen?*

LEVEL 1: KNOWLEDGE/COMPREHENSION

1. The feeding relationships among the species in a community determine the community's
   a. secondary succession.
   b. ecological niche.
   c. species richness.
   d. trophic structure.

2. The principle of competitive exclusion states that
   a. two species cannot coexist in the same habitat.
   b. competition between two species always causes extinction or emigration of one species.
   c. two species that have exactly the same niche cannot coexist in a community.
   d. two species will stop reproducing until one species leaves the habitat.

3. Based on the intermediate disturbance hypothesis, a community's species diversity is increased by
   a. frequent massive disturbance.
   b. stable conditions with no disturbance.
   c. moderate levels of disturbance.
   d. human intervention to eliminate disturbance.

4. According to the island equilibrium model, species richness would be greatest on an island that is
   a. large and remote.
   b. small and remote.
   c. large and close to a mainland.
   d. small and close to a mainland.

LEVEL 2: APPLICATION/ANALYSIS

5. Predators that are keystone species can maintain species diversity in a community if they
   a. competitively exclude other predators.
   b. prey on the community's dominant species.
   c. reduce the number of disruptions in the community.
   d. prey only on the least abundant species in the community.

6. Food chains are sometimes short because
   a. only a single species of herbivore feeds on each plant species.
   b. local extinction of a species causes extinction of the other species in its food chain.
   c. most of the energy in a trophic level is lost as energy passes to the next higher level.
   d. most producers are inedible.

7. Which of the following could qualify as a top-down control on a grassland community?
   a. limitation of plant biomass by rainfall amount
   b. influence of temperature on competition among plants
   c. influence of soil nutrients on the abundance of grasses versus wildflowers
   d. effect of grazing intensity by bison on plant species diversity

8. The most plausible hypothesis to explain why species richness is higher in tropical than in temperate regions is that
   a. tropical communities are younger.
   b. tropical regions generally have more available water and higher levels of solar radiation.
   c. higher temperatures cause more rapid speciation.
   d. diversity increases as evapotranspiration decreases.

9. Community 1 contains 100 individuals distributed among four species: 5A, 5B, 85C, and 5D. Community 2 contains 100 individuals distributed among three species: 30A, 40B, and 30C. Calculate the Shannon diversity (H) for each community. Which community is more diverse?

LEVEL 3: SYNTHESIS/EVALUATION

10. **DRAW IT** An important species in the Chesapeake Bay estuary (see Figure 54.16) is the blue crab (*Callinectes sapidus*). It is an omnivore, eating eelgrass and other primary producers as well as clams. It is also a cannibal. In turn, the crabs are eaten by humans and by the endangered Kemp's Ridley sea turtle. Based on this information, draw a food web that includes the blue crab. Assuming that the top-down model holds for this system, what would happen to the abundance of eelgrass if humans stopped eating blue crabs?

11. **EVOLUTION CONNECTION**
    Explain why adaptations of particular organisms to interspecific competition may not necessarily represent instances of character displacement. What would a researcher have to demonstrate about two competing species to make a convincing case for character displacement?

12. **SCIENTIFIC INQUIRY**
    An ecologist studying desert plants performed the following experiment. She staked out two identical plots, containing sagebrush plants and small annual wildflowers. She found the same five wildflower species in roughly equal numbers on both plots. She then enclosed one plot with a fence to keep out kangaroo rats, the most common grain-eaters of the area. After two years, four of the wildflower species were no longer present in the fenced plot, but one species had become much more abundant. The control plot had not changed in species diversity. Using the principles of community ecology, propose a hypothesis to explain her results. What additional evidence would support your hypothesis?

13. **WRITE ABOUT A THEME: INTERACTIONS**
    In Batesian mimicry, a palatable species gains protection by mimicking an unpalatable one. Imagine that individuals of a palatable, brightly colored fly species are blown to three remote islands. The first island has no predators of that species; the second has predators but no similarly colored, unpalatable species; and the third has both predators and a similarly colored, unpalatable species. In a short essay (100–150 words), predict what might happen to the coloration of the palatable species on each island through evolutionary time if coloration is a genetically controlled trait. Explain your predictions.

14.

Describe two types of interspecific interactions that you can observe in this photo. What morphological adaptation can be seen in the species that is at the highest trophic level in this scene?

For selected answers, see Appendix A.

MasteringBiology®

Students Go to **MasteringBiology** for assignments, the eText, and the Study Area with practice tests, animations, and activities.

Instructors Go to **MasteringBiology** for automatically graded tutorials and questions that you can assign to your students, plus Instructor Resources.

55

Ecosystems and Restoration Ecology

▲ **Figure 55.1 How can a fox transform a grassland into tundra?**

Transformed to Tundra

The arctic fox (*Vulpes lagopus*) is a predator native to arctic regions of North America, Europe, and Asia **(Figure 55.1)**. Valued for its fur, it was introduced onto hundreds of islands between Alaska and Russia a century ago in an effort to establish populations that could be easily harvested. The introduction had a surprising effect—it transformed many habitats on the islands from grassland to tundra. How did this remarkable change come about? The foxes fed on seabirds, decreasing their density almost 100-fold compared to that on fox-free islands. Fewer seabirds meant less bird guano, the primary source of nutrients for plants on the islands. The reduction in nutrient availability in turn favored slower-growing forbs and shrubs typical of tundra instead of grasses and sedges, which require more nutrients. To test this explanation, researchers added fertilizer to plots of tundra on one of the fox-infested islands in 2001. Three years later, the fertilized plots had turned back into grassland.

Each of these islands and the community of organisms on it make up an **ecosystem**,

◀ An island ecosystem

▼ A desert spring ecosystem

▲ **Figure 55.2 Ecosystems at different scales.**

the sum of all the organisms living in a given area and the abiotic factors with which they interact. An ecosystem can encompass a vast area, such as a lake, forest, or island, or a microcosm, such as the space under a fallen log or a desert spring (**Figure 55.2**). As with populations and communities, the boundaries of ecosystems are not always discrete. Many ecologists view the entire biosphere as a global ecosystem, a composite of all the local ecosystems on Earth.

Regardless of an ecosystem's size, two key ecosystem processes cannot be fully described by population or community phenomena: energy flow and chemical cycling. Energy enters most ecosystems as sunlight. It is converted to chemical energy by autotrophs, passed to heterotrophs in the organic compounds of food, and dissipated as heat. Chemical elements, such as carbon and nitrogen, are cycled among abiotic and biotic components of the ecosystem. Photosynthetic and chemosynthetic organisms take up these elements in inorganic form from the air, soil, and water and incorporate them into their biomass, some of which is consumed by animals. The elements are returned in inorganic form to the environment by the metabolism of plants and animals and by organisms such as bacteria and fungi that break down organic wastes and dead organisms.

Both energy and matter are transformed in ecosystems through photosynthesis and feeding relationships. But unlike matter, energy cannot be recycled. An ecosystem must be powered by a continuous influx of energy from an external source—in most cases, the sun. Energy flows through ecosystems, whereas matter cycles within and through them.

Resources critical to human survival and welfare, ranging from the food we eat to the oxygen we breathe, are products of ecosystem processes. In this chapter, we'll explore the dynamics of energy flow and chemical cycling, emphasizing the results of ecosystem experiments. One way to study ecosystem processes is to alter environmental factors, such as temperature or the abundance of nutrients, and measure how ecosystems respond. We'll also consider some of the impacts of human activities on energy flow and chemical cycling. Finally, we'll explore the growing science of restoration ecology, which focuses on returning degraded ecosystems to a more natural state.

CONCEPT 55.1

Physical laws govern energy flow and chemical cycling in ecosystems

Cells transform energy and matter, subject to the laws of thermodynamics (see Concept 8.1). Cell biologists study these transformations within organelles and cells and measure the amounts of energy and matter that cross the cells' boundaries. Ecosystem ecologists do the same thing, except in their case the "cell" is a complete ecosystem. By studying the dynamics of populations (see Chapter 53) and by grouping the species in a community into trophic levels of feeding relationships (see Chapter 54), ecologists can follow the transformations of energy in an ecosystem and map the movements of chemical elements.

Conservation of Energy

Because ecosystem ecologists study the interactions of organisms with the physical environment, many ecosystem approaches are based on laws of physics and chemistry. The first law of thermodynamics states that energy cannot be created or destroyed but only transferred or transformed (see Concept 8.1). Plants and other photosynthetic organisms convert solar energy to chemical energy, but the total amount of energy does not change: The amount of energy stored in organic molecules must equal the total solar energy intercepted by the plant minus the amounts reflected and dissipated as heat. Ecosystem ecologists often measure transfers within and across ecosystems, in part to understand how many organisms a habitat can support and the amount of food humans can harvest from a site.

One implication of the second law of thermodynamics, which states that every exchange of energy increases the entropy of the universe, is that energy conversions are inefficient. Some energy is always lost as heat (see Concept 8.1). We can measure the efficiency of ecological energy conversions just as we measure the efficiency of lightbulbs and car engines. Because energy flowing through ecosystems is ultimately dissipated into space as heat, most ecosystems would vanish if the sun were not continuously providing energy to Earth.

Conservation of Mass

Matter, like energy, cannot be created or destroyed. This **law of conservation of mass** is as important for ecosystems as the laws of thermodynamics are. Because mass is conserved, we can determine how much of a chemical element cycles within an ecosystem or is gained or lost by that ecosystem over time.

Unlike energy, chemical elements are continually recycled within ecosystems. A carbon atom in CO_2 is released from the soil by a decomposer, taken up by a grass through photosynthesis, consumed by a grazing animal, and returned to the soil in the animal's waste. Measurement and analysis of chemical cycling are important in ecosystem ecology.

Although most elements are not gained or lost on a global scale, they can be gained by or lost from a particular ecosystem. In a forest, most mineral nutrients—the essential elements that plants obtain from soil—typically enter as dust or as solutes dissolved in rainwater or leached from rocks in the ground. Nitrogen is also supplied through the biological process of nitrogen fixation (see Figure 37.10). In terms of losses, some elements return to the atmosphere as gases, and others are carried out of the ecosystem by moving water or by wind. Like organisms, ecosystems are open systems, absorbing energy and mass and releasing heat and waste products.

In nature, most gains and losses to ecosystems are small compared to the amounts recycled within them. Still, the balance between inputs and outputs determines whether an ecosystem is a source or a sink for a given element. If a mineral nutrient's outputs exceed its inputs, it will eventually limit production in that system. Human activities often change the balance of inputs and outputs considerably, as we'll see later in this chapter and in Chapter 56.

Energy, Mass, and Trophic Levels

Ecologists group species into trophic levels based on their main source of nutrition and energy (see Concept 54.2). The trophic level that ultimately supports all others consists of autotrophs, also called the **primary producers** of the ecosystem. Most autotrophs are photosynthetic organisms that use light energy to synthesize sugars and other organic compounds, which they use as fuel for cellular respiration and as building material for growth. The most common autotrophs are plants, algae, and photosynthetic prokaryotes, although chemosynthetic prokaryotes are the primary producers in ecosystems such as deep-sea hydrothermal vents (see Figure 52.14) and places deep under the ground or ice.

Organisms in trophic levels above the primary producers are heterotrophs, which depend directly or indirectly on the outputs of primary producers for their source of energy. Herbivores, which eat plants and other primary producers,

▼ Fungi decomposing a dead tree

▲ Rod-shaped and spherical bacteria in compost (colorized SEM)

▲ **Figure 55.3** Detritivores.

are **primary consumers**. Carnivores that eat herbivores are **secondary consumers**, and carnivores that eat other carnivores are **tertiary consumers**.

Another group of heterotrophs is the **detritivores**, or **decomposers**, terms used synonymously in this text to refer to consumers that get their energy from detritus. **Detritus** is nonliving organic material, such as the remains of dead organisms, feces, fallen leaves, and wood. Many detritivores are in turn eaten by secondary and tertiary consumers. Two important groups of detritivores are prokaryotes and fungi (**Figure 55.3**). These organisms secrete enzymes that digest organic material; they then absorb the breakdown products, linking the consumers and primary producers in an ecosystem. In a forest, for instance, birds eat earthworms that have been feeding on leaf litter and its associated prokaryotes and fungi.

Detritivores also play a critical role in recycling chemical elements to primary producers. They convert organic matter from all trophic levels to inorganic compounds usable by primary producers, closing the loop of an ecosystem's chemical cycling. Producers recycle these elements into organic compounds. If decomposition stopped, life would cease as detritus piled up and the supply of ingredients needed to synthesize organic matter was exhausted. **Figure 55.4** summarizes the trophic relationships in an ecosystem.

CONCEPT CHECK **55.1**

1. Why is the transfer of energy in an ecosystem referred to as energy flow, not energy cycling?

2. **WHAT IF?** You are studying nitrogen cycling on the Serengeti Plain in Africa. During your experiment, a herd of migrating wildebeests grazes through your study plot. What would you need to know to measure their effect on nitrogen balance in the plot?

3. **MAKE CONNECTIONS** How does the second law of thermodynamics explain why an ecosystem's energy supply must be continually replenished (see Concept 8.1)?

For suggested answers, see Appendix A.

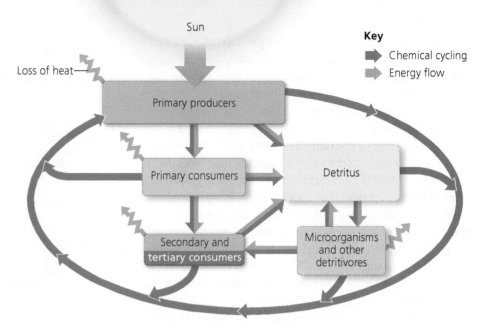

▶ **Figure 55.4 An overview of energy and nutrient dynamics in an ecosystem.** Energy enters, flows through, and exits an ecosystem, whereas chemical nutrients cycle primarily within it. In this generalized scheme, energy (dark orange arrows) enters from the sun as radiation, moves as chemical energy transfers through the food web, and exits as heat radiated into space. Most transfers of nutrients (blue arrows) through the trophic levels lead eventually to detritus; the nutrients then cycle back to the primary producers.

Energy and other limiting factors control primary production in ecosystems

The theme of energy transfer underlies all biological interactions (see Concept 1.1). In most ecosystems, the amount of light energy converted to chemical energy—in the form of organic compounds—by autotrophs during a given time period is the ecosystem's **primary production**. These photosynthetic products are the starting point for most studies of ecosystem metabolism and energy flow. In ecosystems where the primary producers are chemoautotrophs, the initial energy input is chemical, and the initial products are the organic compounds synthesized by the microorganisms.

Ecosystem Energy Budgets

In most ecosystems, primary producers use light energy to synthesize energy-rich organic molecules, and consumers acquire their organic fuels secondhand (or even third- or fourthhand) through food webs (see Figure 54.15). Therefore, the total amount of photosynthetic production sets the spending limit for the entire ecosystem's energy budget.

The Global Energy Budget

Each day, Earth's atmosphere is bombarded by about 10^{22} joules of solar radiation (1 J = 0.239 cal). This is enough energy to supply the demands of the entire human population for approximately 20 years at 2010 energy consumption levels. The intensity of the solar energy striking Earth varies with latitude, with the tropics receiving the greatest input (see Figure 52.3). Most incoming solar radiation is absorbed, scattered, or reflected by clouds and dust in the atmosphere. The amount of solar radiation that ultimately reaches Earth's surface limits the possible photosynthetic output of ecosystems. Only a small fraction of the sunlight that reaches Earth's surface is actually used in photosynthesis. Much of the radiation strikes materials that don't photosynthesize, such as ice and soil. Of the radiation that does reach photosynthetic organisms, only certain wavelengths are absorbed by photosynthetic pigments (see Figure 10.9); the rest is transmitted, reflected, or lost as heat. As a result, only about 1% of the visible light that strikes photosynthetic organisms is converted to chemical energy. Nevertheless, Earth's primary producers create about 150 billion metric tons (1.50×10^{14} kg) of organic material each year.

Gross and Net Production

Total primary production in an ecosystem is known as that ecosystem's **gross primary production (GPP)**—the amount of energy from light (or chemicals, in chemoautotrophic systems) converted to the chemical energy of organic molecules per unit time. Not all of this production is stored as organic material in the primary producers because they use some of the molecules as fuel in their own cellular respiration. **Net primary production (NPP)** is equal to gross primary production minus the energy used by the primary producers for their "autotrophic respiration" (R_a):

$$NPP = GPP - R_a$$

On average, NPP is about one-half of GPP. To ecologists, NPP is the key measurement because it represents the storage of chemical energy that will be available to consumers in the ecosystem.

Net primary production can be expressed as energy per unit area per unit time [$J/(m^2 \cdot yr)$] or as biomass (mass of vegetation) added per unit area per unit time [$g/(m^2 \cdot yr)$]. (Note that biomass is usually expressed in terms of the dry mass of organic material.) An ecosystem's NPP should not be confused with the total biomass of photosynthetic autotrophs present, a measure called the *standing crop*. The net primary production is the amount of *new* biomass added in a given period of time. Although a forest has a large standing crop, its NPP may actually be less than that of some grasslands; grasslands do not accumulate as much biomass as forests because animals consume the plants rapidly and because grasses and herbs decompose more quickly than trees do.

Satellites provide a powerful tool for studying global patterns of primary production (**Figure 55.5**). Images produced from satellite data show that different ecosystems vary considerably in their NPP. Tropical rain forests are among the most productive terrestrial ecosystems and contribute a large portion of the planet's NPP. Estuaries and coral reefs also have very high NPP, but their contribution to the global total is smaller because these ecosystems cover only about one-tenth the area covered by tropical rain forests. In contrast, while the open oceans are relatively unproductive (**Figure 55.6**), their vast size means that together they contribute as much global NPP as terrestrial systems do.

Whereas NPP can be stated as the amount of new biomass added in a given period of time, **net ecosystem production (NEP)** is a measure of the *total biomass accumulation* during that time. Net ecosystem production is defined as gross primary production minus the total respiration of all organisms in the system (R_T)—not just primary producers, as for the calculation of NPP, but decomposers and other heterotrophs as well:

$$NEP = GPP - R_T$$

NEP is useful to ecologists because its value determines whether an ecosystem is gaining or losing carbon over time. A forest may have a positive NPP but still lose carbon if heterotrophs release it as CO_2 more quickly than primary producers incorporate it into organic compounds.

The most common way to estimate NEP is to measure the net flux (flow) of CO_2 or O_2 entering or leaving the ecosystem. If more CO_2 enters than leaves, the system is storing carbon. Because O_2 release is directly coupled to photosynthesis and respiration (see Figure 9.2), a system that is giving

▼ **Figure 55.5**

Research Method

Determining Primary Production with Satellites

Application Because chlorophyll captures visible light (see Figure 10.9), photosynthetic organisms absorb more light at visible wavelengths (about 380–750 nm) than at near-infrared wavelengths (750–1,100 nm). Scientists use this difference in absorption to estimate the rate of photosynthesis in different regions of the globe using satellites.

Technique Most satellites determine what they "see" by comparing the ratios of wavelengths reflected back to them. Vegetation reflects much more near-infrared radiation than visible radiation, producing a reflectance pattern very different from that of snow, clouds, soil, and liquid water.

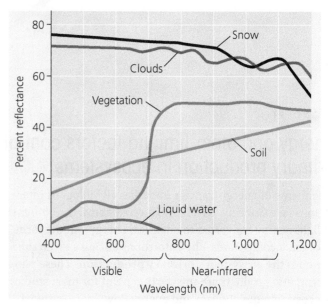

Results Scientists use the satellite data to help produce maps of primary production like the one in Figure 55.6.

off O_2 is also storing carbon. On land, ecologists typically measure only the net flux of CO_2 from ecosystems because detecting small changes in O_2 flux in a large atmospheric O_2 pool is difficult.

Recent research has revealed surprisingly high NEP in some of the nutrient-poor waters that cover much of the

▶ **Figure 55.6 Global net primary production.** The map is based on satellite-collected data, such as amount of sunlight absorbed by vegetation. Note that tropical land areas have the highest rates of production (yellow and red on the map).

? *Does this map accurately reflect the importance of some highly productive habitats, such as wetlands, coral reefs, and coastal zones? Explain.*

Net primary production [kg carbon/(m²· yr)]

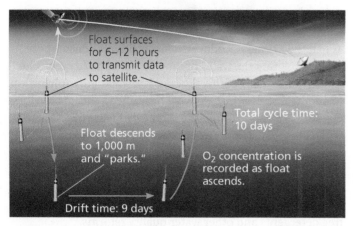

▲ **Figure 55.7 Ocean production revealed.** Oxygen sensors deployed on floats record and transmit data that can be used to calculate net ecosystem production (NEP).

MAKE CONNECTIONS *Consider the role of photosynthetic protists as producers in aquatic ecosystems. (Review the discussion in Concept 28.6.) What factors in addition to light availability are likely to limit primary production in the oceans?*

open ocean. In 2008, scientists measured NEP in the Pacific Ocean using high-resolution oxygen sensors (**Figure 55.7**). As the floats drifted with the current, they repeatedly moved between the ocean surface and a depth of 1,000 m, recording the O_2 concentration in the water as they ascended. The researchers estimated an average NEP of 25 g C/(m^2·yr) over the three-year study, suggesting that phytoplankton in extensive regions of the oceans are more productive than previously thought. Studies like this are giving ecologists a new understanding of Earth's carbon cycle and marine production.

What limits production in ecosystems? To ask this question another way, what factors could we change to increase production for a given ecosystem? We'll address this question first for aquatic ecosystems.

Primary Production in Aquatic Ecosystems

In aquatic (marine and freshwater) ecosystems, both light and nutrients are important in controlling primary production.

Light Limitation

Because solar radiation drives photosynthesis, you would expect light to be a key variable in controlling primary production in oceans. Indeed, the depth of light penetration affects primary production throughout the photic zone of an ocean or lake (see Figure 52.12). About half of the solar radiation is absorbed in the first 15 m of water. Even in "clear" water, only 5–10% of the radiation may reach a depth of 75 m.

If light were the main variable limiting primary production in the ocean, you would expect production to increase along a gradient from the poles toward the equator, which

receives the greatest intensity of light. However, you can see in Figure 55.6 that there is no such gradient. Another factor must strongly influence primary production in the ocean.

Nutrient Limitation

More than light, nutrients limit primary production in most oceans and lakes. A **limiting nutrient** is the element that must be added for production to increase. The nutrient most often limiting marine production is either nitrogen or phosphorus. Concentrations of these nutrients are typically low in the photic zone because they are rapidly taken up by phytoplankton and because detritus tends to sink.

As detailed in **Figure 55.8**, nutrient enrichment experiments confirmed that nitrogen was limiting phytoplankton

▼ **Figure 55.8** | **Inquiry**

Which nutrient limits phytoplankton production along the coast of Long Island?

Experiment Pollution from duck farms concentrated near Moriches Bay adds both nitrogen and phosphorus to the coastal water off Long Island, New York. To determine which nutrient limits phytoplankton growth in this area, John Ryther and William Dunstan, of the Woods Hole Oceanographic Institution, cultured the phytoplankton *Nannochloris atomus* with water collected from several sites, identified as A–G. They added either ammonium (NH_4^+) or phosphate (PO_4^{3-}) to some of the cultures.

Results The addition of ammonium caused heavy phytoplankton growth in the cultures, but the addition of phosphate did not.

Conclusion The researchers concluded that nitrogen is the nutrient that limits phytoplankton growth in this ecosystem because adding phosphorus, which was already in rich supply, did not increase *Nannochloris* growth, whereas adding nitrogen increased phytoplankton density dramatically.

Source: J. H. Ryther and W. M. Dunstan, Nitrogen, phosphorus, and eutrophication in the coastal marine environment, *Science* 171:1008–1013 (1971). © 1971 by AAAS. Reprinted with permission.

WHAT IF? *How would you expect the results of this experiment to change if new duck farms substantially increased the amount of pollution in the water? Explain your reasoning.*

growth off the south shore of Long Island, New York. One practical application of this work is in preventing algal "blooms" caused by excess nitrogen runoff that fertilizes the phytoplankton. Prior to this research, phosphate contamination was thought to cause many such blooms in the ocean, but eliminating phosphates alone may not help unless nitrogen pollution is also controlled.

The macronutrients nitrogen and phosphorus are not the only nutrients that limit aquatic production. Several large areas of the ocean have low phytoplankton densities despite relatively high nitrogen concentrations. The Sargasso Sea, a subtropical region of the Atlantic Ocean, has some of the clearest water in the world because of its low phytoplankton density. Nutrient enrichment experiments have revealed that the availability of the micronutrient iron limits primary production there (Table 55.1). Windblown dust from land supplies most of the iron to the oceans but is relatively scarce in this and certain other regions compared to the oceans as a whole.

Areas of upwelling, where deep, nutrient-rich waters circulate to the ocean surface, have exceptionally high primary production. This fact supports the hypothesis that nutrient availability determines marine primary production. Because upwelling stimulates growth of the phytoplankton that form the base of marine food webs, upwelling areas typically host highly productive, diverse ecosystems and are prime fishing locations. The largest areas of upwelling occur in the Southern Ocean (also called the Antarctic Ocean), along the equator, and in the coastal waters off Peru, California, and parts of western Africa.

In freshwater lakes, nutrient limitation is also common. During the 1970s, scientists showed that the sewage and fertilizer runoff from farms and lawns adds considerable nutrients to lakes, promoting the growth of primary producers. When the primary producers die, detritivores decompose them, depleting the water of much or all of its oxygen. The ecological impacts of this process, known as **eutrophication** (from the Greek *eutrophos*, well nourished), include the loss of many fish species from the lakes (see Figure 52.14).

To control eutrophication, scientists need to know which nutrient is responsible. While nitrogen rarely limits primary production in lakes, whole-lake experiments showed that phosphorus availability limited cyanobacterial growth. This and other ecological research led to the use of phosphate-free detergents and other water quality reforms.

Primary Production in Terrestrial Ecosystems

At regional and global scales, temperature and moisture are the main factors controlling primary production in terrestrial ecosystems. Tropical rain forests, with their warm, wet conditions that promote plant growth, are the most productive terrestrial ecosystems (see Figure 55.6). In contrast, low-productivity systems are generally hot and dry, like many deserts, or cold and dry, like arctic tundra. Between these extremes lie the temperate forest and grassland ecosystems, with moderate climates and intermediate productivity.

The climate variables of moisture and temperature are very useful for predicting NPP in terrestrial ecosystems. Primary production is greater in wetter ecosystems, as shown for the plot of NPP and annual precipitation in Figure 55.9. Along with mean annual precipitation, a second useful predictor is *evapotranspiration*, the total amount of water transpired by plants and evaporated from a landscape. Evapotranspiration increases with the temperature and amount of solar energy available to drive evaporation and transpiration.

Table 55.1	Nutrient Enrichment Experiment for Sargasso Sea Samples
Nutrients Added to Experimental Culture	**Relative Uptake of ^{14}C by Cultures***
None (controls)	1.00
Nitrogen (N) + phosphorus (P) only	1.10
N + P + metals excluding iron (Fe)	1.08
N + P + metals including Fe	12.90
N + P + Fe	12.00

*^{14}C uptake by cultures measures primary production.

Source: D. W. Menzel and J. H. Ryther, Nutrients limiting the production of phytoplankton in the Sargasso Sea, with special reference to iron, *Deep Sea Research* 7:276–281 (1961).

INTERPRET THE DATA *The element molybdenum (Mo) is another micronutrient that can limit primary production in the oceans. If the researchers found the following results for additions of Mo, what would you conclude about its relative importance for growth?*

N + P + Mo	*6.0*
N + P + Fe + Mo	*72.0*

▲ Figure 55.9 **A global relationship between net primary production and mean annual precipitation for terrestrial ecosystems.**

Nutrient Limitations and Adaptations That Reduce Them

EVOLUTION Soil nutrients also limit primary production in terrestrial ecosystems. As in aquatic systems, nitrogen and phosphorus are the nutrients that most commonly limit terrestrial production. Globally, nitrogen limits plant growth most. Phosphorus limitations are common in older soils where phosphate molecules have been leached away by water, such as in many tropical ecosystems. Phosphorus availability is also often low in soils of deserts and other ecosystems with a basic pH, where some phosphorus precipitates and becomes unavailable to plants. Adding a nonlimiting nutrient, even one that is scarce, will not stimulate production. Conversely, adding more of the limiting nutrient will increase production until some other nutrient becomes limiting.

▲ Root nodules containing nitrogen-fixing bacteria

Various adaptations have evolved in plants that can increase their uptake of limiting nutrients. One important adaptation is the symbiosis between plant roots and nitrogen-fixing bacteria (see Figure 37.11 and the photo on the left). Another is the mycorrhizal association between plant roots and fungi that supply phosphorus and other limiting elements to plants (see Figure 37.13). Plant roots also have hairs and other anatomical features that increase the area of the soil that roots contact (see Figure 35.3). Many plants release enzymes and other substances into the soil that increase the availability of limiting nutrients; such substances include phosphatases, which cleave a phosphate group from larger molecules, and chelating agents that make micronutrients such as iron more soluble in the soil.

Studies relating nutrients to terrestrial primary production have practical applications in agriculture. Farmers maximize their crop yields by using fertilizers with the right balance of nutrients for the local soil and type of crop. This knowledge of limiting nutrients helps feed billions of people.

CONCEPT CHECK 55.2

1. Why is only a small portion of the solar energy that strikes Earth's atmosphere stored by primary producers?
2. How can ecologists experimentally determine the factor that limits primary production in an ecosystem?
3. **MAKE CONNECTIONS** Explain how nitrogen and phosphorus, the nutrients that most often limit primary production, are necessary for the Calvin cycle to function in photosynthesis (see Concept 10.3).

For suggested answers, see Appendix A.

Energy transfer between trophic levels is typically only 10% efficient

The amount of chemical energy in consumers' food that is converted to their own new biomass during a given period is called the **secondary production** of the ecosystem. Consider the transfer of organic matter from primary producers to herbivores, the primary consumers. In most ecosystems, herbivores eat only a small fraction of plant material produced; globally, they consume only about one-sixth of total plant production. Moreover, they cannot digest all the plant material that they *do* eat, as anyone who has walked through a dairy farm will attest. Most of an ecosystem's production is eventually consumed by detritivores. Let's analyze the process of energy transfer and cycling more closely.

Production Efficiency

First we'll examine secondary production in one organism—a caterpillar. When a caterpillar feeds on a leaf, only about 33 J out of 200 J, or one-sixth of the potential energy in the leaf, is used for secondary production, or growth **(Figure 55.10)**. The caterpillar stores some of the remaining energy in organic compounds that will be used for cellular respiration and passes the rest in its feces. The energy in the feces remains in the ecosystem temporarily, but most of it is lost as heat after the feces are consumed by detritivores. The energy used for the caterpillar's respiration is also eventually lost from the ecosystem as heat. This is why energy is said to flow through, not cycle within, ecosystems. Only the chemical energy stored

Plant material eaten by caterpillar

200 J

Feces

100 J

Not assimilated

33 J

Growth (new biomass; secondary production)

67 J

Cellular respiration

Assimilated

▲ **Figure 55.10 Energy partitioning within a link of the food chain.**

INTERPRET THE DATA *What percentage of the energy in the caterpillar's food is actually used for secondary production (growth)?*

by herbivores as biomass, through growth or the production of offspring, is available as food to secondary consumers.

We can measure the efficiency of animals as energy transformers using the following equation:

$$\text{Production efficiency} = \frac{\text{Net secondary production} \times 100\%}{\text{Assimilation of primary production}}$$

Net secondary production is the energy stored in biomass represented by growth and reproduction. Assimilation consists of the total energy taken in, not including losses in feces, used for growth, reproduction, and respiration. **Production efficiency**, therefore, is the percentage of energy stored in assimilated food that is *not* used for respiration. For the caterpillar in Figure 55.10, production efficiency is 33%; 67 J of the 100 J of assimilated energy is used for respiration. (The 100 J of energy lost as undigested material in feces does not count toward assimilation.) Birds and mammals typically have low production efficiencies, in the range of 1–3%, because they use so much energy in maintaining a constant, high body temperature. Fishes, which are mainly ectothermic (see Concept 40.3), have production efficiencies around 10%. Insects and microorganisms are even more efficient, with production efficiencies averaging 40% or more.

Trophic Efficiency and Ecological Pyramids

Let's scale up now from the production efficiencies of individual consumers to the flow of energy through trophic levels.

Trophic efficiency is the percentage of production transferred from one trophic level to the next. Trophic efficiencies must always be less than production efficiencies because they take into account not only the energy lost through respiration and contained in feces, but also the energy in organic material in a lower trophic level that is not consumed by the next trophic level. Trophic efficiencies are generally only about 10% and range from approximately 5% to 20% in different ecosystems. In other words, 90% of the energy available at one trophic level typically is *not* transferred to the next. This loss is multiplied over the length of a food chain. If 10% of available energy is transferred from primary producers to primary consumers, such as caterpillars, and 10% of that energy is transferred to secondary consumers (carnivores), then only 1% of net primary production is available to secondary consumers (10% of 10%). In the Scientific Skills Exercise, you can calculate trophic efficiency and other measures of energy flow in a salt marsh ecosystem.

SCIENTIFIC SKILLS EXERCISE

Interpreting Quantitative Data in a Table

How Efficient Is Energy Transfer in a Salt Marsh Ecosystem? In a classic experiment, John Teal studied the flow of energy through the producers, consumers, and detritivores in a salt marsh. In this exercise, you will use the data from this study to calculate some measures of energy transfer between trophic levels in this ecosystem.

How the Study Was Done Teal measured the amount of solar radiation entering a salt marsh in Georgia over a year. He also measured the aboveground biomass of the dominant primary producers, which were grasses, as well as the biomass of the dominant consumers, including insects, spiders, and crabs, and of the detritus that flowed out of the marsh to the surrounding coastal waters. To determine the amount of

energy in each unit of biomass, he dried the biomass, burned it in a calorimeter, and measured the amount of heat produced.

Data from the Study

Form of Energy	kcal/(m^2 · yr)
Solar radiation	600,000
Gross grass production	34,580
Net grass production	6,585
Gross insect production	305
Net insect production	81
Detritus leaving marsh	3,671

Interpret the Data

1. What proportion of the solar energy that reaches the marsh is incorporated into gross primary production? Into net primary production? (A proportion is the same as a percentage divided by 100. Both measures are useful for comparing relative efficiencies across different ecosystems.)

2. How much energy is lost by primary producers as respiration in this ecosystem? How much is lost as respiration by the insect population?

3. If all of the detritus leaving the marsh is plant material, what proportion of all net primary production leaves the marsh as detritus each year?

(MB) A version of this Scientific Skills Exercise can be assigned in MasteringBiology.

Data from J. M. Teal, Energy flow in the salt marsh ecosystem of Georgia, *Ecology* 43:614–624 (1962).

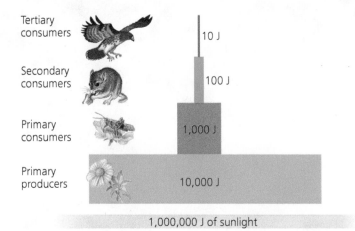

Tertiary consumers — 10 J

Secondary consumers — 100 J

Primary consumers — 1,000 J

Primary producers — 10,000 J

1,000,000 J of sunlight

▲ **Figure 55.11 An idealized pyramid of net production.** This example assumes a trophic efficiency of 10% for each link in the food chain. Notice that primary producers convert only about 1% of the energy available to them to net primary production.

Trophic level	Dry mass (g/m²)
Tertiary consumers	1.5
Secondary consumers	11
Primary consumers	37
Primary producers	809

(a) Most biomass pyramids show a sharp decrease in biomass at successively higher trophic levels, as illustrated by data from a Florida bog.

Trophic level	Dry mass (g/m²)
Primary consumers (zooplankton)	21
Primary producers (phytoplankton)	4

(b) In some aquatic ecosystems, such as the English Channel, a small standing crop of primary producers (phytoplankton) supports a larger standing crop of primary consumers (zooplankton).

▲ **Figure 55.12 Pyramids of biomass (standing crop).** Numbers denote the dry mass of all organisms at each trophic level.

The progressive loss of energy along a food chain severely limits the abundance of top-level carnivores that an ecosystem can support. Only about 0.1% of the chemical energy fixed by photosynthesis can flow all the way through a food web to a tertiary consumer, such as a snake or a shark. This explains why most food webs include only about four or five trophic levels (see Figure 54.14).

The loss of energy with each transfer in a food chain can be represented by a *pyramid of net production*, in which the trophic levels are arranged in tiers **(Figure 55.11)**. The width of each tier is proportional to the net production, expressed in joules, of each trophic level. The highest level, which represents top-level predators, contains relatively few individuals. The small population size typical of top predator species is one reason they tend to be vulnerable to extinction (and to the evolutionary consequences of small population size, discussed in Chapter 23).

One important ecological consequence of low trophic efficiencies is represented in a *biomass pyramid*, in which each tier represents the standing crop (the total dry mass of all organisms) in one trophic level. Most biomass pyramids narrow sharply from primary producers at the base to top-level carnivores at the apex because energy transfers between trophic levels are so inefficient **(Figure 55.12a)**. Certain aquatic ecosystems, however, have inverted biomass pyramids: Primary consumers outweigh the producers **(Figure 55.12b)**. Such inverted biomass pyramids occur because the producers—phytoplankton—grow, reproduce, and are consumed so quickly by the zooplankton that they never develop a large population size, or standing crop. In other words, the phytoplankton have a short **turnover time**, which means they have a small standing crop compared to their production:

$$\text{Turnover time} = \frac{\text{Standing crop (g/m}^2)}{\text{Production [g/(m}^2 \cdot \text{day)]}}$$

Because the phytoplankton continually replace their biomass at such a rapid rate, they can support a biomass of zooplankton bigger than their own biomass. Nevertheless, because phytoplankton have much higher production than zooplankton, the pyramid of *production* for this ecosystem is still bottom-heavy, like the one in Figure 55.11.

Figure 55.13 illustrates energy transfer, nutrient cycling, and other key processes for an Arctic tundra ecosystem. Note the conceptual similarities between this figure and Figure 10.23 (The Working Cell). The scale of the two figures is different, but the physical laws and biological rules that govern life apply equally to both systems.

In the next section, we'll look at how the transfer of nutrients and energy through food webs is part of a larger picture of chemical cycling in ecosystems.

CONCEPT CHECK 55.3

1. If an insect that eats plant seeds containing 100 J of energy uses 30 J of that energy for respiration and excretes 50 J in its feces, what is the insect's net secondary production? What is its production efficiency?

2. Tobacco leaves contain nicotine, a poisonous compound that is energetically expensive for the plant to make. What advantage might the plant gain by using some of its resources to produce nicotine?

3. **WHAT IF?** Detritivores are consumers that obtain their energy from detritus. How many joules of energy are potentially available to detritivores in the ecosystem represented in Figure 55.11?

For suggested answers, see Appendix A.

▼ Figure 55.13

MAKE CONNECTIONS

The Working Ecosystem

This Arctic tundra ecosystem teems with life in the short two-month growing season each summer. In ecosystems, organisms interact with each other and with the environment around them in diverse ways, including those illustrated here.

Populations Are Dynamic (Chapter 53)

1 Populations change in size through births and deaths and through immigration and emigration. Caribou migrate across the tundra to give birth at their calving grounds each year. *See Figure 53.3.*

2 Snow geese and many other species migrate to the Arctic each spring for the abundant food found there in summer. *See Concept 51.1.*

3 Birth and death rates influence the density of all populations. Death in the tundra comes from many causes, including predation, competition for resources, and lack of food in winter. *See Figure 53.18.*

1 Caribou

2 Snow geese

5 Herbivory

Arctic fox

3

4

Predation

Snow goose

Species Interact in Diverse Ways (Chapter 54)

4 In predation, an individual of one species kills and eats another. *See Concept 54.1.*

5 In herbivory, an individual of one species eats part of a plant or other primary producer, such as a caribou eating a lichen. *See Concept 54.1.*

6 In symbiosis, two or more species live in direct contact. For example, a lichen is a symbiosis between a fungus and an alga or cyanobacterium. *See Concept 54.1 and Figures 31.22 and 31.23.*

7 In competition, individuals seek to acquire the same limiting resources. For example, snow geese and caribou both eat cottongrass. *See Concept 54.1.*

1242

Organisms Transfer Energy and Matter in Ecosystems (Chapter 55)

8 Primary producers convert the energy in sunlight to chemical energy through photosynthesis. Their growth is often limited by abiotic factors such as low temperatures, scarce soil nutrients, and lack of light in winter. *See Figures 10.6, 52.11, and 55.4.*

9 Food chains are typically short in the tundra because primary production is lower than in most other ecosystems. *See Figure 54.14.*

10 When one organism eats another, the transfer of energy from one trophic level to the next is usually less than 10%. *See Figure 55.11.*

11 Detritivores recycle chemical elements back to primary producers. *See Figures 55.3 and 55.4.*

12 Chemical elements such as carbon and nitrogen move in cycles between the physical environment and organisms. *See Figure 55.14.*

Nitrogen cycle
N_2
Carbon cycle
CO_2

Denitrification
Cellular respiration
Photosynthesis
Organisms   N fixation

12

Secondary consumers (wolves)

9

10

Primary consumers (caribou)

Primary producers (plants and lichens)

Chemical elements

Detritivores (soil fungi and prokaryotes)

11

7 Competition

8

6 Symbiosis
Algal cell
Fungal hyphae
Lichen

MAKE CONNECTIONS *Lichens are important primary producers in the tundra and can comprise more than half the diet of caribou in winter. Why might you predict that lichens would be more abundant in tundra ecosystems than in most other ecosystems around the world? (See Concept 31.5.)*

ANIMATION *BioFlix* For animations of the tundra ecosystem, visit the Study Area in **MasteringBiology** for the BioFlix® 3-D Animations on Population Ecology (Chapter 53) and The Carbon Cycle (Chapter 55). BioFlix Tutorials can also be assigned in MasteringBiology.

1243

Biological and geochemical processes cycle nutrients and water in ecosystems

Although most ecosystems receive abundant solar energy, chemical elements are available only in limited amounts. Life therefore depends on the recycling of essential chemical elements. Much of an organism's chemical stock is replaced continuously as nutrients are assimilated and waste products are released. When the organism dies, the atoms in its body are returned to the atmosphere, water, or soil by decomposers. Decomposition replenishes the pools of inorganic nutrients that plants and other autotrophs use to build new organic matter. Because nutrient cycles involve both biotic and abiotic components, they are called **biogeochemical cycles**.

Biogeochemical Cycles

An element's specific route through a biogeochemical cycle depends on the element and the trophic structure of the ecosystem. For convenience, we can recognize two general categories of biogeochemical cycles: global and local. Gaseous forms of carbon, oxygen, sulfur, and nitrogen occur in the atmosphere, and cycles of these elements are essentially global. For example, some of the carbon and oxygen atoms a plant acquires from the air as CO_2 may have been released into the atmosphere by the respiration of an organism in a distant locale. Other elements, including phosphorus, potassium, and calcium, are too heavy to occur as gases at Earth's surface, although they are transported in dust. In terrestrial ecosystems, these elements cycle more locally, absorbed from the soil by plant roots and eventually returned to the soil by decomposers. In aquatic systems, however, they cycle more broadly as dissolved forms carried in currents.

Figure 55.14 provides a detailed look at the cycling of water, carbon, nitrogen, and phosphorus. When you study each cycle, consider which steps are driven primarily by biological processes. For the carbon cycle, for instance, plants, animals, and other organisms control most of the key steps, including photosynthesis and decomposition. For the water cycle, however, purely physical processes control many key steps, such as evaporation from the oceans.

▼ **Figure 55.14**

Exploring Water and Nutrient Cycling

Examine each cycle closely, considering the major reservoirs of water, carbon, nitrogen, and phosphorus and the processes that drive each cycle. The widths of the arrows in the diagrams approximately reflect the relative contribution of each process to the movement of water or a nutrient in the biosphere.

The Water Cycle

Biological importance   Water is essential to all organisms, and its availability influences the rates of ecosystem processes, particularly primary production and decomposition in terrestrial ecosystems.

Forms available to life   All organisms can exchange water directly with their environment. Liquid water is the primary physical phase in which water is used, though some organisms can harvest water vapor. Freezing of soil water can limit water availability to terrestrial plants.

Reservoirs   The oceans contain 97% of the water in the biosphere. Approximately 2% is bound in glaciers and polar ice caps, and the remaining 1% is in lakes, rivers, and groundwater. A negligible amount is in the atmosphere.

Key processes   The main processes driving the water cycle are evaporation of liquid water by solar energy, condensation of water vapor into clouds, and precipitation. Transpiration by terrestrial plants also moves large volumes of water into the atmosphere. Surface and groundwater flow returns water to the oceans, completing the water cycle.

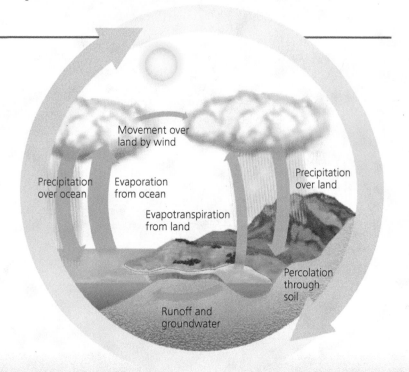

Movement over land by wind

Precipitation over ocean

Evaporation from ocean

Evapotranspiration from land

Precipitation over land

Percolation through soil

Runoff and groundwater

The Carbon Cycle

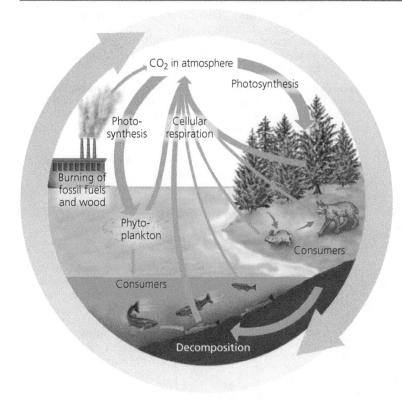

Biological importance
Carbon forms the framework of the organic molecules essential to all organisms.

Forms available to life
Photosynthetic organisms utilize CO_2 during photosynthesis and convert the carbon to organic forms that are used by consumers, including animals, fungi, and heterotrophic protists and prokaryotes. All organisms can return carbon directly to their environment as CO_2 through respiration.

Reservoirs
The major reservoirs of carbon include fossil fuels, soils, the sediments of aquatic ecosystems, the oceans (dissolved carbon compounds), plant and animal biomass, and the atmosphere (CO_2). The largest reservoir is sedimentary rocks such as limestone; however, this pool turns over very slowly.

Key processes
Photosynthesis by plants and phytoplankton removes substantial amounts of atmospheric CO_2 each year. This quantity is approximately equaled by CO_2 added to the atmosphere through cellular respiration by producers and consumers. The burning of fossil fuels and wood is adding significant amounts of additional CO_2 to the atmosphere. Over geologic time, volcanoes are also a substantial source of CO_2.

ANIMATION **BioFlix** Visit the Study Area in **MasteringBiology** for the BioFlix® 3-D Animation on The Carbon Cycle. BioFlix Tutorials can also be assigned in MasteringBiology.

The Phosphorus Cycle

Biological importance
Organisms require phosphorus as a major constituent of nucleic acids, phospholipids, and ATP and other energy-storing molecules and as a mineral constituent of bones and teeth.

Forms available to life
The most biologically important inorganic form of phosphorus is phosphate (PO_4^{3-}), which plants absorb and use in the synthesis of organic compounds.

Reservoirs
The largest accumulations of phosphorus are in sedimentary rocks of marine origin. There are also large quantities of phosphorus in soil, in the oceans (in dissolved form), and in organisms. Because soil particles bind PO_4^{3-}, the recycling of phosphorus tends to be quite localized in ecosystems.

Key processes
Weathering of rocks gradually adds PO_4^{3-} to soil; some leaches into groundwater and surface water and may eventually reach the sea. Phosphate taken up by producers and incorporated into biological molecules may be eaten by consumers. Phosphate is returned to soil or water by either decomposition of biomass or excretion by consumers. Because there are no significant phosphorus-containing gases, only relatively small amounts of phosphorus move through the atmosphere, usually in the forms of dust and sea spray.

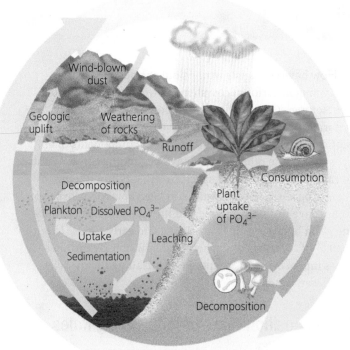

Continued on next page

The Nitrogen Cycle

Biological importance Nitrogen is part of amino acids, proteins, and nucleic acids and is often a limiting plant nutrient.

Forms available to life Plants can assimilate (use) two inorganic forms of nitrogen—ammonium (NH_4^+) and nitrate (NO_3^-)—and some organic forms, such as amino acids. Various bacteria can use all of these forms as well as nitrite (NO_2^-). Animals can use only organic forms of nitrogen.

Reservoirs The main reservoir of nitrogen is the atmosphere, which is 78% free nitrogen gas (N_2). The other reservoirs of inorganic and organic nitrogen compounds are soils and the sediments of lakes, rivers, and oceans; surface water and groundwater; and the biomass of living organisms.

Key processes The major pathway for nitrogen to enter an ecosystem is via nitrogen fixation, the conversion of N_2 to forms that can be used to synthesize organic nitrogen compounds. Certain bacteria, as well as lightning and volcanic activity, fix nitrogen naturally (see Figures 37.10–37.12). Nitrogen inputs from human activities now outpace natural inputs on land. Two major contributors are industrially produced fertilizers and legume crops that fix nitrogen via bacteria in their root nodules. Other bacteria in soil convert nitrogen to different forms. Some bacteria carry out denitrification, the reduction of nitrate to nitrogen gases. Human activities also release large quantities of reactive nitrogen gases, such as nitrogen oxides, to the atmosphere.

How have ecologists worked out the details of chemical cycling in various ecosystems? Two common methods use isotopes. One method is to follow the movement of naturally occurring, nonradioactive isotopes through the biotic (organic) and abiotic (inorganic) components of an ecosystem. The other method involves adding tiny amounts of radioactive isotopes of specific elements and tracing their progress. Scientists have also been able to make use of radioactive carbon (^{14}C) released into the atmosphere during atom bomb testing in the 1950s and early 1960s. This "spike" of ^{14}C can reveal where and how quickly carbon flows into ecosystem components, including plants, soils, and ocean water.

Decomposition and Nutrient Cycling Rates

The diagrams in Figure 55.14 illustrate the essential role that decomposers (detritivores) play in recycling carbon, nitrogen, and phosphorus. The rates at which these nutrients cycle in different ecosystems vary considerably, mostly as a result of differences in rates of decomposition.

Decomposition is controlled by the same factors that limit primary production in aquatic and terrestrial ecosystems (see Concept 55.2). These factors include temperature, moisture, and nutrient availability. Decomposers usually grow faster and decompose material more quickly in warmer ecosystems (**Figure 55.15**). In tropical rain forests, most organic material decomposes in a few months to a few years, whereas in temperate forests, decomposition takes four to six years, on average. The difference is largely the result of the higher temperatures and more abundant precipitation in tropical rain forests.

Because decomposition in a tropical rain forest is rapid, relatively little organic material accumulates as leaf litter on the forest floor; about 75% of the nutrients in the ecosystem are present in the woody trunks of trees, and only about 10% is contained in the soil. Thus, the relatively low concentrations of some nutrients in the soil of tropical rain

How does temperature affect litter decomposition in an ecosystem?

Experiment Researchers with the Canadian Forest Service placed identical samples of organic material—litter—on the ground in 21 sites across Canada (marked by letters on the map below). Three years later, they returned to see how much of each sample had decomposed.

Ecosystem type
- Arctic
- Subarctic
- Boreal
- Temperate
- Grassland
- Mountain

Results The mass of litter decreased four times faster in the warmest ecosystem than in the coldest ecosystem.

Conclusion Decomposition rate increases with temperature across much of Canada.

Source: T. R. Moore et al., Litter decomposition rates in Canadian forests, *Global Change Biology* 5:75–82 (1999).

WHAT IF? *What factors other than temperature might also have varied across these 21 sites? How might this variation have affected the interpretation of the results?*

forests result from a short cycling time, not from a lack of these elements in the ecosystem. In temperate forests, where decomposition is much slower, the soil may contain as much as 50% of all the organic material in the ecosystem.

The nutrients that are present in temperate forest detritus and soil may remain there for years before plants assimilate them.

Decomposition on land is also slower when conditions are either too dry for decomposers to thrive or too wet to supply them with enough oxygen. Ecosystems that are both cold and wet, such as peatlands, store large amounts of organic matter (see Figure 29.9a). Decomposers grow poorly there, and net primary production greatly exceeds the rate of decomposition.

In aquatic ecosystems, decomposition in anaerobic muds can take 50 years or longer. Bottom sediments are comparable to the detritus layer in terrestrial ecosystems, but algae and aquatic plants usually assimilate nutrients directly from the water. Thus, the sediments often constitute a nutrient sink, and aquatic ecosystems are very productive only when there is exchange between the bottom layers of water and surface waters (as occurs in the upwelling regions described earlier).

Case Study: Nutrient Cycling in the Hubbard Brook Experimental Forest

Since 1963, ecologist Gene Likens and colleagues have been studying nutrient cycling at the Hubbard Brook Experimental Forest in the White Mountains of New Hampshire. Their research site is a deciduous forest that grows in six small valleys, each drained by a single creek. Impenetrable bedrock underlies the soil of the forest.

The research team first determined the mineral budget for each of six valleys by measuring the input and outflow of several key nutrients. They collected rainfall at several sites to measure the amount of water and dissolved minerals added to the ecosystem. To monitor the loss of water and minerals, they constructed a small concrete dam with a V-shaped spillway across the creek at the bottom of each valley. They found that about 60% of the water added to the ecosystem as rainfall and snow exits through the stream, and the remaining 40% is lost by evapotranspiration.

Preliminary studies confirmed that internal cycling conserved most of the mineral nutrients in the system. For example, only about 0.3% more calcium (Ca^{2+}) leaves a valley via its creek than is added by rainwater, and this small net loss is probably replaced by chemical decomposition of the bedrock. During most years, the forest even registers small net gains of a few mineral nutrients, including nitrogen.

(a) One watershed was clear-cut to study the effects of the loss of vegetation on drainage and nutrient cycling. All of the cut plant material was left in place to decompose.

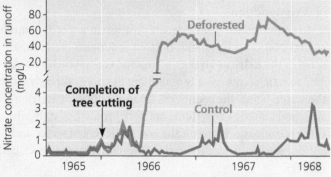

(b) The concentration of nitrate in runoff from the deforested watershed was 60 times greater than in a control (unlogged) watershed.

▶ **Figure 55.16 Nutrient cycling in the Hubbard Brook Experimental Forest: an example of long-term ecological research.**

(MB) *A related Experimental Inquiry Tutorial can be assigned in MasteringBiology.*

Experimental deforestation of a watershed dramatically increased the flow of water and minerals leaving the watershed (**Figure 55.16a**). Over three years, water runoff from the newly deforested watershed was 30–40% greater than in a control watershed, apparently because there were no plants to absorb and transpire water from the soil. Most remarkable was the loss of nitrate, whose concentration in the creek increased 60-fold, reaching levels considered unsafe for drinking water (**Figure 55.16b**). The Hubbard Brook deforestation study showed that the amount of nutrients leaving an intact forest ecosystem is controlled mainly by the plants. Retaining nutrients in ecosystems helps to maintain the productivity of the systems and avoid problems, such as algal "blooms," caused by excess nutrient runoff.

CONCEPT CHECK 55.4

1. **DRAW IT** For each of the four biogeochemical cycles in Figure 55.14, draw a simple diagram that shows one possible path for an atom of that chemical from abiotic to biotic reservoirs and back.

2. Why does deforestation of a watershed increase the concentration of nitrates in streams draining the watershed?

3. **WHAT IF?** Why is nutrient availability in a tropical rain forest particularly vulnerable to logging?

For suggested answers, see Appendix A.

Restoration ecologists return degraded ecosystems to a more natural state

Ecosystems can recover naturally from most disturbances (including the experimental deforestation at Hubbard Brook) through the stages of ecological succession (see Chapter 54). Sometimes that recovery takes centuries, though, particularly when humans have degraded the environment. Tropical areas that are cleared for farming may quickly become unproductive because of nutrient losses. Mining activities may last for several decades, and the lands are often abandoned in a degraded state. Ecosystems can also be damaged by salts that build up in soils from irrigation and by toxic chemicals or oil spills. Biologists increasingly are called on to help restore and repair damaged ecosystems.

Restoration ecologists seek to initiate or speed up the recovery of degraded ecosystems. One of the basic assumptions is that environmental damage is at least partly reversible. This optimistic view must be balanced by a second assumption—that ecosystems are not infinitely resilient. Restoration ecologists therefore work to identify and manipulate the processes that most limit recovery of ecosystems from disturbances. Where disturbance is so severe that restoring all of a habitat is impractical, ecologists try to reclaim as much of a habitat or ecological process as possible, within the limits of the time and money available to them.

In extreme cases, the physical structure of an ecosystem may need to be restored before biological restoration can occur. If a stream was straightened to channel water quickly through a suburb, ecologists may reconstruct a meandering channel to slow down the flow of water eroding the stream bank. To restore an open-pit mine, engineers may grade the site with heavy equipment to reestablish a gentle slope, spreading topsoil when the slope is in place (**Figure 55.17**).

◀ In 1991, before restoration

▶ In 2000, near the completion of restoration

▲ **Figure 55.17 A gravel and clay mine site in New Jersey before and after restoration.**

Once physical reconstruction of the ecosystem is complete—or when it is not needed—biological restoration is the next step. Two key strategies in biological restoration are bioremediation and biological augmentation.

Bioremediation

Using organisms—usually prokaryotes, fungi, or plants—to detoxify polluted ecosystems is known as **bioremediation** (see Chapter 27). Some plants and lichens adapted to soils containing heavy metals can accumulate high concentrations of toxic metals such as lead and cadmium in their tissues. Restoration ecologists can introduce such species to sites polluted by mining and other human activities and then harvest these organisms to remove the metals from the ecosystem. For instance, researchers in the United Kingdom have discovered a lichen species that grows on soil polluted with uranium dust left over from mining. The lichen concentrates uranium in a dark pigment, making it useful as a biological monitor and potentially as a remediator.

Ecologists already use the abilities of many prokaryotes to carry out bioremediation of soils and water. Scientists have sequenced the genomes of at least ten prokaryotic species specifically for their bioremediation potential. One of the species, the bacterium *Shewanella oneidensis*, appears particularly promising. It can metabolize a dozen or more elements under aerobic and anaerobic conditions. In doing so, it converts soluble forms of uranium, chromium, and nitrogen to insoluble forms that are less likely to leach into streams or groundwater. Researchers at Oak Ridge National Laboratory, in Tennessee, stimulated the growth of *Shewanella* and other uranium-reducing bacteria by adding ethanol to groundwater contaminated with uranium; the bacteria can use ethanol as an energy source. In just five months, the concentration of soluble uranium in the ecosystem dropped by 80% **(Figure 55.18)**.

Biological Augmentation

In contrast to bioremediation, which is a strategy for removing harmful substances from an ecosystem, **biological augmentation** uses organisms to *add* essential materials to a degraded ecosystem. To augment ecosystem processes, restoration ecologists need to determine which factors, such as chemical nutrients, have been lost from a system and are limiting its recovery.

Encouraging the growth of plants that thrive in nutrient-poor soils often speeds up succession and ecosystem recovery. In alpine ecosystems of the western United States, nitrogen-fixing plants such as lupines are often planted to raise nitrogen concentrations in soils disturbed by mining and other activities. Once these nitrogen-fixing plants become established, other native species are better able to obtain enough soil nitrogen to survive. In other systems where the soil has been severely disturbed or where topsoil

▲ **Figure 55.18 Bioremediation of groundwater contaminated with uranium at Oak Ridge National Laboratory, Tennessee.** Wastes containing uranium were dumped in four unlined pits for more than 30 years, contaminating soils and groundwater. After ethanol was added, microbial activity decreased the concentration of soluble uranium in groundwater near the pits.

is missing entirely, plant roots may lack the mycorrhizal symbionts that help them meet their nutritional needs (see Chapter 31). Ecologists restoring a tallgrass prairie in Minnesota recognized this limitation and enhanced the recovery of native species by adding mycorrhizal symbionts to the soil they seeded.

Restoring the physical structure and plant community of an ecosystem does not always ensure that animal species will recolonize a site and persist there. Because animals provide critical ecosystem services, including pollination and seed dispersal, restoration ecologists sometimes help wildlife reach and use restored ecosystems. They might release animals at a site or establish habitat corridors that connect a restored site to places where the animals are found. They sometimes establish artificial perches for birds to use at the site. These and other efforts can increase the biodiversity of restored ecosystems and help the community persist.

The long-term objective of restoration is to return an ecosystem as much as possible to its predisturbance state. **Figure 55.19** identifies several ambitious and successful restoration projects around the world. The great number of such projects and the dedication of the people engaged in them suggest that restoration ecology will continue to grow as a discipline for many years.

CONCEPT CHECK **55.5**

1. Identify the main goal of restoration ecology.

2. **WHAT IF?** In what way is the Kissimmee River project a more complete ecological restoration than the Maungatautari project (see Figure 55.19)?

For suggested answers, see Appendix A.

The examples highlighted on these pages are just a few of the many restoration ecology projects taking place around the world. The color-coded squares on the map indicate the locations of the projects.

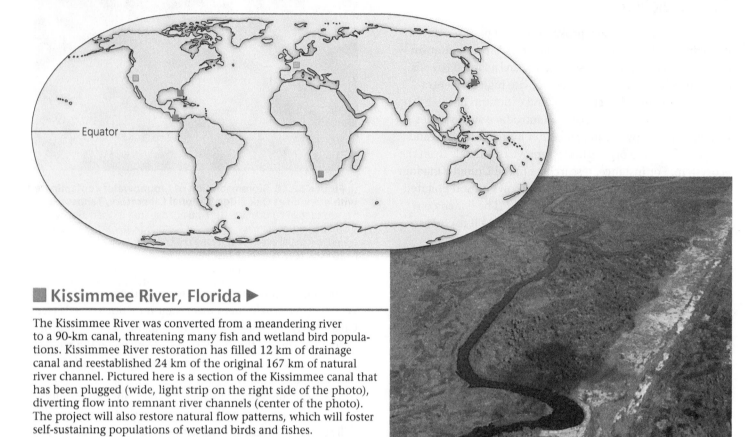

Equator

■ Kissimmee River, Florida ▶

The Kissimmee River was converted from a meandering river to a 90-km canal, threatening many fish and wetland bird populations. Kissimmee River restoration has filled 12 km of drainage canal and reestablished 24 km of the original 167 km of natural river channel. Pictured here is a section of the Kissimmee canal that has been plugged (wide, light strip on the right side of the photo), diverting flow into remnant river channels (center of the photo). The project will also restore natural flow patterns, which will foster self-sustaining populations of wetland birds and fishes.

◀ Truckee River, Nevada ■

Damming and water diversions during the 20th century reduced flow in the Truckee River, leading to declines in riparian (riverside) forests. Restoration ecologists worked with water managers to ensure that sufficient water would be released during the short season of seed release by the native cottonwood and willow trees for seedlings to become established. Nine years of controlled-flow release led to the result shown here: a dramatic recovery of cottonwood-willow riparian forest.

■ Tropical dry forest, Costa Rica ▶

Clearing for agriculture, mainly for livestock grazing, eliminated approximately 98% of tropical dry forest in Central America and Mexico. Reversing this trend, tropical dry forest restoration in Costa Rica has used domestic livestock to disperse the seeds of native trees into open grasslands. The photo shows one of the first trees (right center), dispersed as seed by livestock, to colonize former pastureland. This project is a model for joining restoration ecology with the local economy and educational institutions.

▲ Rhine River, Europe ▢

Centuries of dredging and channeling for navigation (see the barges in the wide, main channel on the right side of the photo) have straightened the once-meandering Rhine River and disconnected it from its floodplain and associated wetlands. The countries along the Rhine, particularly France, Germany, Luxembourg, the Netherlands, and Switzerland, are cooperating to reconnect the river to side channels, such as the one shown on the left side of the photo. Such side channels increase the diversity of habitats available to aquatic organisms, improve water quality, and provide flood protection.

▲ Coastal Japan ▣

Seaweed and seagrass beds are important nursery grounds for a wide variety of fishes and shellfish. Once extensive but now reduced by development, these beds are being restored in the coastal areas of Japan. Techniques include constructing suitable seafloor habitat, transplanting from natural beds using artificial substrates, and hand seeding (shown in this photograph).

▲ Succulent Karoo, South Africa ▣

In this desert region of southern Africa, as in many arid regions, overgrazing by livestock has damaged vast areas. Private landowners and government agencies in South Africa are restoring large areas of this unique region, revegetating the land and employing more sustainable resource management. The photo shows a small sample of the exceptional plant diversity of the Succulent Karoo; its 5,000 plant species include the highest diversity of succulent plants in the world.

▲ Maungatautari, New Zealand ▢

Weasels, rats, pigs, and other introduced species pose a serious threat to New Zealand's native plants and animals, including kiwis, a group of flightless, ground-dwelling bird species. The goal of the Maungatautari restoration project is to exclude all exotic mammals from a 3,400-ha reserve located on a forested volcanic cone. A specialized fence around the reserve eliminates the need to continue setting traps and using poisons that can harm native wildlife. In 2006, a pair of critically endangered takahe (a species of flightless rail) were released into the reserve in hopes of reestablishing a breeding population of this colorful bird on New Zealand's North Island.

CONCEPT 55.1

Physical laws govern energy flow and chemical cycling in ecosystems (pp. 1233–1234)

- An **ecosystem** consists of all the organisms in a community and all the abiotic factors with which they interact. The laws of physics and chemistry apply to ecosystems, particularly regarding the conservation of energy. Energy is conserved but degraded to heat during ecosystem processes.
- Chemical elements enter and leave an ecosystem and cycle within it, subject to the **law of conservation of mass**. Inputs and outputs are generally small compared to recycled amounts, but their balance determines whether the ecosystem gains or loses an element over time.

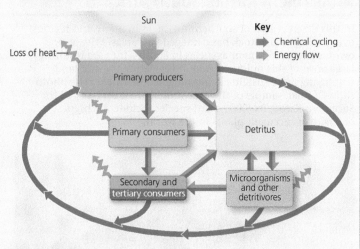

? Considering the second law of thermodynamics, would you expect the typical biomass of primary producers in an ecosystem to be greater than or less than the biomass of secondary producers in the system? Explain your reasoning.

CONCEPT 55.2

Energy and other limiting factors control primary production in ecosystems (pp. 1235–1239)

- **Primary production** sets the spending limit for the global energy budget. **Gross primary production** is the total energy assimilated by an ecosystem in a given period. **Net primary production**, the energy accumulated in autotroph biomass, equals gross primary production minus the energy used by the primary producers for respiration. **Net ecosystem production** is the total biomass accumulation of an ecosystem, defined as the difference between gross primary production and total ecosystem respiration.
- In aquatic ecosystems, light and nutrients limit primary production. In terrestrial ecosystems, climatic factors such as temperature and moisture affect primary production at large scales, but a soil nutrient is often the limiting factor locally.

? If you know NPP, what additional variable do you need to know to estimate NEP? Why might measuring this variable be difficult, for instance, in a sample of ocean water?

CONCEPT 55.3

Energy transfer between trophic levels is typically only 10% efficient (pp. 1239–1243)

- The amount of energy available to each trophic level is determined by the net primary production and the **production efficiency**, the efficiency with which food energy is converted to biomass at each link in the food chain.
- The percentage of energy transferred from one trophic level to the next, called **trophic efficiency**, is typically 10%. Pyramids of net production and biomass reflect low trophic efficiency.

? Why would runners have a lower production efficiency when running a long-distance race than when they are sedentary?

CONCEPT 55.4

Biological and geochemical processes cycle nutrients and water in ecosystems (pp. 1244–1248)

- Water moves in a global cycle driven by solar energy. The carbon cycle primarily reflects the reciprocal processes of photosynthesis and cellular respiration. Nitrogen enters ecosystems through atmospheric deposition and nitrogen fixation by prokaryotes.
- The proportion of a nutrient in a particular form and its cycling in that form vary among ecosystems, largely because of differences in the rate of decomposition.
- Nutrient cycling is strongly regulated by vegetation. The Hubbard Brook case study showed that logging increases water runoff and can cause large losses of minerals.

? If decomposers usually grow faster and decompose material more quickly in warmer ecosystems, why is decomposition in hot deserts so slow?

CONCEPT 55.5

Restoration ecologists return degraded ecosystems to a more natural state (pp. 1248–1251)

- Restoration ecologists harness organisms to detoxify polluted ecosystems through the process of **bioremediation**.
- In **biological augmentation**, ecologists use organisms to add essential materials to ecosystems.

? In preparing a site for surface mining and later restoration, why would engineers separate the topsoil from the deeper soil, rather than removing all soil at once and mixing it in a single pile?

LEVEL 1: KNOWLEDGE/COMPREHENSION

1. Which of the following organisms is *incorrectly* paired with its trophic level?
   a. cyanobacterium—primary producer
   b. grasshopper—primary consumer
   c. zooplankton—primary producer
   d. fungus—detritivore

2. Which of these ecosystems has the *lowest* net primary production per square meter?
   a. a salt marsh
   b. an open ocean
   c. a coral reef
   d. a tropical rain forest

3. The discipline that applies ecological principles to returning degraded ecosystems to a more natural state is known as
   a. restoration ecology.
   b. thermodynamics.
   c. eutrophication.
   d. biogeochemistry.

LEVEL 2: APPLICATION/ANALYSIS

4. Nitrifying bacteria participate in the nitrogen cycle mainly by
   a. converting nitrogen gas to ammonia.
   b. releasing ammonium from organic compounds, thus returning it to the soil.
   c. converting ammonium to nitrate, which plants absorb.
   d. incorporating nitrogen into amino acids and organic compounds.

5. Which of the following has the greatest effect on the rate of chemical cycling in an ecosystem?
   a. the rate of decomposition in the ecosystem
   b. the production efficiency of the ecosystem's consumers
   c. the trophic efficiency of the ecosystem
   d. the location of the nutrient reservoirs in the ecosystem

6. The Hubbard Brook watershed deforestation experiment yielded all of the following results *except*:
   a. Most minerals were recycled within a forest ecosystem.
   b. Calcium levels remained high in the soil of deforested areas.
   c. Deforestation increased water runoff.
   d. The nitrate concentration in waters draining the deforested area became dangerously high.

7. Which of the following would be considered an example of bioremediation?
   a. adding nitrogen-fixing microorganisms to a degraded ecosystem to increase nitrogen availability
   b. using a bulldozer to regrade a strip mine
   c. reconfiguring the channel of a river
   d. adding seeds of a chromium-accumulating plant to soil contaminated by chromium

8. If you applied a fungicide to a cornfield, what would you expect to happen to the rate of decomposition and net ecosystem production (NEP)?
   a. Both decomposition rate and NEP would decrease.
   b. Neither would change.
   c. Decomposition rate would increase and NEP would decrease.
   d. Decomposition rate would decrease and NEP would increase.

LEVEL 3: SYNTHESIS/EVALUATION

9. **INTERPRET THE DATA** (a) Draw a simplified global water cycle showing ocean, land, atmosphere, and runoff from the land to the ocean. Add these annual water fluxes to your drawing: ocean evaporation, 425 km^3; ocean evaporation that returns to the ocean as precipitation, 385 km^3; ocean evaporation that falls as precipitation on land, 40 km^3; evapotranspiration from plants and soil that falls as precipitation on land, 70 km^3; runoff to the oceans, 40 km^3. (b) What is the ratio of ocean evaporation that falls as precipitation on land compared with runoff from land to the oceans? (c) How would this ratio change during an ice age, and why?

10. **EVOLUTION CONNECTION**
    Some biologists have suggested that ecosystems are emergent, "living" systems capable of evolving. One manifestation of this idea is environmentalist James Lovelock's Gaia hypothesis, which views Earth itself as a living, homeostatic entity—a kind of superorganism. If ecosystems are capable of evolving, would this be a form of Darwinian evolution? Why or why not?

11. **SCIENTIFIC INQUIRY**
    Using two neighboring ponds in a forest as your study site, design a controlled experiment to measure the effect of falling leaves on net primary production in a pond.

12. **WRITE ABOUT A THEME: ENERGY AND MATTER**
    Decomposition typically occurs quickly in moist tropical forests. However, waterlogging in the soil of some moist tropical forests results over time in a buildup of organic matter called "peat." In a short essay (100–150 words), discuss the relationship of net primary production, net ecosystem production, and decomposition for such an ecosystem. Are NPP and NEP likely to be positive? What do you think would happen to NEP if a landowner drained the water from a tropical peatland, exposing the organic matter to air?

13. **SYNTHESIZE YOUR KNOWLEDGE**

This dung beetle (genus *Scarabaeus*) is burying a ball of dung it has collected from a large mammalian herbivore in Kenya. Explain why this process is important for the cycling of nutrients and for primary production.

For selected answers, see Appendix A.

MasteringBiology®

Students Go to **MasteringBiology** for assignments, the eText, and the Study Area with practice tests, animations, and activities.

Instructors Go to **MasteringBiology** for automatically graded tutorials and questions that you can assign to your students, plus Instructor Resources.

56

Conservation Biology and Global Change

▲ **Figure 56.1 What will be the fate of this newly described lizard species?**

Psychedelic Treasure

Scurrying across a rocky outcrop, a lizard stops abruptly in a patch of sunlight. A conservation biologist senses the motion and turns to find a gecko splashed with rainbow colors, its bright orange legs and tail blending into a striking blue body, its head splotched with yellow and green. The psychedelic rock gecko (*Cnemaspis psychedelica*) was discovered in 2009 during an expedition to the Greater Mekong region of southeast Asia **(Figure 56.1)**. Its known habitat is restricted to Hon Khoai, an island occupying just 8 km² (3 square miles) in southern Vietnam. Other new species found during the same series of expeditions include the Elvis monkey (*Rhinopithecus strykeri*, shown in the lower left in an illustration), which sports a hairdo like that of Elvis Presley. Between 2000 and 2010, biologists identified more than a thousand new species in the Greater Mekong region alone.

To date, scientists have described and formally named about 1.8 million species of organisms. Some biologists think that about 10 million more species currently exist; others estimate the number to be as high as 100 million. Some of the greatest concentrations of species are found in the

▲ Figure 56.2 **Tropical deforestation in Vietnam.**

tropics. Unfortunately, tropical forests are being cleared at an alarming rate to make room for and support a burgeoning human population. Rates of deforestation in Vietnam are among the very highest in the world **(Figure 56.2)**. What will become of the psychedelic rock gecko and other newly discovered species if such activities continue unchecked?

Throughout the biosphere, human activities are altering trophic structures, energy flow, chemical cycling, and natural disturbance—ecosystem processes on which we and all other species depend (see Chapter 55). We have physically altered nearly half of Earth's land surface, and we use over half of all accessible surface fresh water. In the oceans, stocks of most major fisheries are shrinking because of overharvesting. By some estimates, we may be pushing more species toward extinction than the large asteroid that triggered the mass extinctions at the close of the Cretaceous period 65.5 million years ago (see Figure 25.18).

Biology is the science of life. Thus, it is fitting that this chapter applies a global perspective to the changes happening across Earth, focusing in detail on a discipline that seeks to preserve life. **Conservation biology** integrates ecology, physiology, molecular biology, genetics, and evolutionary biology to conserve biological diversity at all levels. Efforts to sustain ecosystem processes and stem the loss of biodiversity also connect the life sciences with the social sciences, economics, and humanities.

In this chapter, we'll take a closer look at the biodiversity crisis and examine some of the conservation strategies being adopted to slow the rate of species loss. We'll also examine how human activities are altering the environment through climate change, ozone depletion, and other global processes. Finally, we'll consider how decisions about long-term conservation priorities could affect life on Earth.

CONCEPT 56.1

Human activities threaten Earth's biodiversity

Extinction is a natural phenomenon that has been occurring since life first evolved; it is the high *rate* of extinction that is responsible for today's biodiversity crisis (see Concept 25.4). Because we can only estimate the number of species currently existing, we cannot determine the exact rate of species loss. However, we do know that the extinction rate is high and that human activities threaten Earth's biodiversity at all levels.

Three Levels of Biodiversity

Biodiversity—short for biological diversity—can be considered at three main levels: genetic diversity, species diversity, and ecosystem diversity **(Figure 56.3)**.

Genetic diversity in a vole population

Species diversity in a coastal redwood ecosystem

Community and ecosystem diversity across the landscape of an entire region

▲ Figure 56.3 **Three levels of biodiversity.** The oversized chromosomes in the top diagram symbolize the genetic variation within the population.

CHAPTER 56 Conservation Biology and Global Change **1255**

Genetic Diversity

Genetic diversity comprises not only the individual genetic variation *within* a population, but also the genetic variation *between* populations that is often associated with adaptations to local conditions (see Chapter 23). If one population becomes extinct, then a species may have lost some of the genetic diversity that makes microevolution possible. This erosion of genetic diversity in turn reduces the adaptive potential of the species.

Species Diversity

Public awareness of the biodiversity crisis centers on species diversity—the variety of species in an ecosystem or across the biosphere (see Chapter 54). As more species are lost to extinction, species diversity decreases. The U.S. Endangered Species Act defines an **endangered species** as one that is "in danger of extinction throughout all or a significant portion of its range." **Threatened species** are those considered likely to become endangered in the near future. The following are just a few statistics that illustrate the problem of species loss:

- According to the International Union for Conservation of Nature and Natural Resources (IUCN), 12% of the 10,000 known species of birds and 21% of the 5,500 known species of mammals are threatened.
- A survey by the Center for Plant Conservation showed that of the nearly 20,000 known plant species in the United States, 200 have become extinct since such records have been kept, and 730 are endangered or threatened.
- In North America, at least 123 freshwater animal species have become extinct since 1900, and hundreds more species are threatened. The extinction rate for North American freshwater fauna is about five times as high as that for terrestrial animals.

Extinction of species may also be local; for example, a species may be lost in one river system but survive in an adjacent one. Global extinction of a species means that it is lost from *all* the ecosystems in which it lived, leaving them permanently impoverished **(Figure 56.4)**.

Ecosystem Diversity

The variety of the biosphere's ecosystems is a third level of biological diversity. Because of the many interactions between populations of different species in an ecosystem, the local extinction of one species can have a negative impact on other species in the ecosystem (see Figure 54.18). For instance, bats called "flying foxes" are important pollinators and seed dispersers in the Pacific Islands, where they are increasingly hunted as a luxury food **(Figure 56.5)**. Conservation biologists fear that the extinction of flying foxes would also harm the native plants of the Samoan Islands, where four-fifths of the tree species depend on flying foxes for pollination or seed dispersal.

Philippine eagle

Yangtze River dolphin

▲ **Figure 56.4 A hundred heartbeats from extinction.** These are two members of what Harvard biologist E. O. Wilson calls the Hundred Heartbeat Club, species with fewer than 100 individuals remaining on Earth. The Yangtze River dolphin is likely to be extinct, but a few individuals were reportedly sighted in 2007.

> **?** *To document that a species has actually become extinct, what factors would you need to consider?*

Some ecosystems have already been heavily affected by humans, and others are being altered at a rapid pace. Since European colonization, more than half of the wetlands in the contiguous United States have been drained and converted to agricultural and other uses. In California, Arizona, and New Mexico, roughly 90% of native riparian (streamside) communities have been affected by overgrazing, flood control, water diversions, lowering of water tables, and invasion by non-native plants.

▲ **Figure 56.5 The endangered Marianas "flying fox" bat (*Pteropus mariannus*), an important pollinator.**

Biodiversity and Human Welfare

Why should we care about the loss of biodiversity? One reason is what Harvard biologist E. O. Wilson calls *biophilia*, our sense of connection to nature and all life. The belief that other species are entitled to life is a pervasive theme of many religions and the basis of a moral argument that we should protect biodiversity. There is also a concern for future human generations. Paraphrasing an old proverb, G. H. Brundtland, a former prime minister of Norway, said: "We must consider our planet to be on loan from our children, rather than being a gift from our ancestors." In addition to such philosophical and moral justifications, species and genetic diversity bring us many practical benefits.

Benefits of Species and Genetic Diversity

Many species that are threatened could potentially provide medicines, food, and fibers for human use, making biodiversity a crucial natural resource. Products from aspirin to antibiotics were derived originally from natural sources. In food production, if we lose wild populations of plants closely related to agricultural species, we lose genetic resources that could be used to improve crop qualities, such as disease resistance. For instance, plant breeders responded to devastating outbreaks of the grassy stunt virus in rice (*Oryza sativa*) by screening 7,000 populations of this species and its close relatives for resistance to the virus. One population of a single relative, Indian rice (*Oryza nivara*), was found to be resistant to the virus, and scientists succeeded in breeding the resistance trait into commercial rice varieties. Today, the original disease-resistant population has apparently become extinct in the wild.

In the United States, about 25% of the prescriptions dispensed from pharmacies contain substances originally derived from plants. In the 1970s, researchers discovered that the rosy periwinkle, which grows on the island of Madagascar, off the coast of Africa, contains alkaloids that inhibit cancer cell growth **(Figure 56.6)**. This discovery led to

treatments for two deadly forms of cancer, Hodgkin's lymphoma and childhood leukemia, resulting in remission in most cases. Madagascar is also home to five other species of periwinkles, one of which is approaching extinction. Losing these species would mean the loss of any possible medicinal benefits they might offer.

Each species lost means the loss of unique genes, some of which may code for enormously useful proteins. The enzyme Taq polymerase was first extracted from a bacterium, *Thermus aquaticus*, found in hot springs at Yellowstone National Park. This enzyme is essential for the polymerase chain reaction (PCR) because it is stable at the high temperatures required for automated PCR (see Figure 20.8). DNA from many other species of prokaryotes, living in a variety of environments, is used in the mass production of proteins for new medicines, foods, petroleum substitutes, other industrial chemicals, and other products. However, because millions of species may become extinct before we discover them, we stand to lose the valuable genetic potential held in their unique libraries of genes.

Ecosystem Services

The benefits that individual species provide to humans are substantial, but saving individual species is only part of the reason for preserving ecosystems. Humans evolved in Earth's ecosystems, and we rely on these systems and their inhabitants for our survival. **Ecosystem services** encompass all the processes through which natural ecosystems help sustain human life. Ecosystems purify our air and water. They detoxify and decompose our wastes and reduce the impacts of extreme weather and flooding. The organisms in ecosystems pollinate our crops, control pests, and create and preserve our soils. Moreover, these diverse services are provided for free.

Perhaps because we don't attach a monetary value to the services of natural ecosystems, we generally undervalue them. In 1997, ecologist Robert Costanza and his colleagues estimated the value of Earth's ecosystem services at $33 trillion per year, nearly twice the gross national product of all the countries on Earth at the time ($18 trillion). It may be more realistic to do the accounting on a smaller scale. In 1996, New York City invested more than $1 billion to buy land and restore habitat in the Catskill Mountains, the source of much of the city's fresh water. This investment was spurred by increasing pollution of the water by sewage, pesticides, and fertilizers. By harnessing ecosystem services to purify its water naturally, the city saved $8 billion it would have otherwise spent to build a new water treatment plant and $300 million a year to run the plant.

There is growing evidence that the functioning of ecosystems, and hence their capacity to perform services, is linked to biodiversity. As human activities reduce biodiversity, we are reducing the capacity of the planet's ecosystems to perform processes critical to our own survival.

▶ **Figure 56.6**
The rosy periwinkle (*Catharanthus roseus*), a plant that saves lives.

Threats to Biodiversity

Many different human activities threaten biodiversity on local, regional, and global scales. The threats posed by these activities are of four major types: habitat loss, introduced species, overharvesting, and global change.

Habitat Loss

Human alteration of habitat is the single greatest threat to biodiversity throughout the biosphere. Habitat loss has been brought about by factors such as agriculture, urban development, forestry, mining, and pollution. As discussed later in this chapter, global climate change is already altering habitats today and will have an even larger effect later this century. When no alternative habitat is available or a species is unable to move, habitat loss may mean extinction. The IUCN implicates destruction of habitat for 73% of the species that have become extinct, endangered, vulnerable, or rare in the last few hundred years.

Habitat loss and fragmentation may occur over immense regions. Approximately 98% of the tropical dry forests of Central America and Mexico have been cut down. The clearing of tropical rain forest in the state of Veracruz, Mexico, mostly for cattle ranching, has resulted in the loss of more than 90% of the original forest, leaving relatively small, isolated patches of forest. Other natural habitats have also been fragmented by human activities (Figure 56.7).

In almost all cases, habitat fragmentation leads to species loss because the smaller populations in habitat fragments have a higher probability of local extinction. Prairie covered about 800,000 hectares of southern Wisconsin when Europeans first arrived in North America but occupies only 800 hectares today; most of the original prairie in this area is now used to grow crops. Plant diversity surveys of 54 Wisconsin prairie remnants conducted in 1948–1954 and 1987–1988 showed that the remnants lost 8–60% of their plant species in the time between the two surveys.

▲ **Figure 56.7 Habitat fragmentation in the foothills of Los Angeles.** Development in the valleys may confine the organisms that inhabit the narrow strips of hillside.

Habitat loss is also a major threat to aquatic biodiversity. About 70% of coral reefs, among Earth's most species-rich aquatic communities, have been damaged by human activities. At the current rate of destruction, 40–50% of the reefs, home to one-third of marine fish species, could disappear in the next 30 to 40 years. Freshwater habitats are also being lost, often as a result of the dams, reservoirs, channel modification, and flow regulation now affecting most of the world's rivers. For example, the more than 30 dams and locks built along the Mobile River basin in the southeastern United States changed river depth and flow. While providing the benefits of hydroelectric power and increased ship traffic, these dams and locks also helped drive more than 40 species of mussels and snails to extinction.

Introduced Species

Introduced species, also called exotic species, are those that humans move intentionally or accidentally from the species' native locations to new geographic regions. Human travel by ship and airplane has accelerated the transplant of species. Free from the predators, parasites, and pathogens that limit their populations in their native habitats, such transplanted species may spread rapidly through a new region.

Some introduced species disrupt their new community, often by preying on native organisms or outcompeting native organisms for resources. The brown tree snake was accidentally introduced to the island of Guam from other parts of the South Pacific after World War II, as a "stowaway" in military cargo. Since then, 12 species of birds and 6 species of lizards that the snakes ate have become extinct on Guam. The devastating zebra mussel, a filter-feeding mollusc, was introduced into the Great Lakes of North America in 1988, most likely in the ballast water of ships arriving from Europe. Zebra mussels form dense colonies and have disrupted freshwater ecosystems, threatening native aquatic species. They have also clogged water intake structures, causing billions of dollars in damage to domestic and industrial water supplies.

Humans have deliberately introduced many species with good intentions but disastrous effects. An Asian plant called kudzu, which the U.S. Department of Agriculture once introduced in the southern United States to help control erosion, has taken over large areas of the landscape there (Figure 56.8). The European starling was brought intentionally into New York's Central Park in 1890 by a citizens' group intent on introducing all the plants and animals mentioned in Shakespeare's plays. It quickly spread across North America, where its population now exceeds 100 million, displacing many native songbirds.

Introduced species are a worldwide problem, contributing to approximately 40% of the extinctions recorded since 1750 and costing billions of dollars each year in damage and control efforts. There are more than 50,000 introduced species in the United States alone.

▲ **Figure 56.8 Kudzu, an introduced species, thriving in South Carolina.**

Overharvesting

The term *overharvesting* refers generally to the harvesting of wild organisms at rates exceeding the ability of their populations to rebound. Species with restricted habitats, such as small islands, are particularly vulnerable to overharvesting. One such species was the great auk, a large, flightless seabird found on islands in the North Atlantic Ocean. By the 1840s, humans had hunted the great auk to extinction to satisfy demand for its feathers, eggs, and meat.

Also susceptible to overharvesting are large organisms with low reproductive rates, such as elephants, whales, and rhinoceroses. The decline of Earth's largest terrestrial animals, the African elephants, is a classic example of the impact of overhunting. Largely because of the trade in ivory, elephant populations have been declining in most of Africa for the last 50 years. An international ban on the sale of new ivory resulted in increased poaching (illegal hunting), so the ban had little effect in much of central and eastern Africa. Only in South Africa, where once-decimated herds have been well protected for nearly a century, have elephant populations been stable or increasing (see Figure 53.9).

Conservation biologists increasingly use the tools of molecular genetics to track the origins of tissues harvested from endangered species. Researchers at the University of Washington constructed a DNA reference map for the African elephant (*Loxodonta africana*) using DNA isolated from elephant dung. By comparing this reference map with DNA isolated from ivory harvested legally or by poachers, they can determine to within a few hundred kilometers where the elephants were killed (Figure 56.9). Such work in Zambia suggested that poaching rates were 30 times higher than previously estimated, leading to improved anti-poaching efforts by the Zambian government. Similarly, biologists using phylogenetic analyses of mitochondrial DNA (mtDNA) showed that some whale meat sold in Japanese fish markets came from illegally harvested species, including fin and humpback whales, which are endangered (see Figure 26.6).

▲ **Figure 56.9 Ecological forensics and elephant poaching.** These severed tusks were part of an illegal shipment of ivory intercepted on its way from Africa to Singapore in 2002. DNA-based evidence showed that the thousands of elephants killed for the tusks came from a relatively narrow east-west band centered in Zambia rather than from across Africa.

MAKE CONNECTIONS *The text and Figure 26.6 describe another example in which conservation biologists used DNA analyses to compare harvested samples of whale meat with a reference DNA database. How are these examples similar, and how are they different? What limitations might there be to using such forensic methods in other suspected cases of poaching?*

Many commercially important fish populations, once thought to be inexhaustible, have been decimated by overfishing. Demands for protein-rich food from an increasing human population, coupled with new harvesting technologies, such as long-line fishing and modern trawlers, have reduced these fish populations to levels that cannot sustain further exploitation. Until the past few decades, the North Atlantic bluefin tuna was considered a sport fish of little commercial value—just a few cents per pound for use in cat food. In the 1980s, however, wholesalers began airfreighting fresh, iced bluefin to Japan for sushi and sashimi. In that market, the fish now brings up to $100 per pound (Figure 56.10). With increased harvesting spurred by such high prices, it took just ten years to reduce the western North Atlantic bluefin population to less than 20% of its 1980 size.

▲ **Figure 56.10 Overharvesting.** North Atlantic bluefin tuna are auctioned in a Japanese fish market.

Global Change

The fourth threat to biodiversity, global change, alters the fabric of Earth's ecosystems at regional to global scales. Global change includes alterations in climate, atmospheric chemistry, and broad ecological systems that reduce the capacity of Earth to sustain life.

One of the first types of global change to cause concern was *acid precipitation*, which is rain, snow, sleet, or fog with a pH less than 5.2. The burning of wood and fossil fuels releases oxides of sulfur and nitrogen that react with water in air, forming sulfuric and nitric acids. The acids eventually fall to Earth's surface, harming some aquatic and terrestrial organisms.

In the 1960s, ecologists determined that lake-dwelling organisms in eastern Canada were dying because of air pollution from factories in the Midwestern United States. Newly hatched lake trout, for instance, die when the pH drops below 5.4. Lakes and streams in southern Norway and Sweden were losing fish because of pollution generated in Great Britain and central Europe. By 1980, the pH of precipitation in large areas of North America and Europe averaged 4.0–4.5 and sometimes dropped as low as 3.0. (To review pH, see Concept 3.3.)

Environmental regulations and new technologies have enabled many countries to reduce sulfur dioxide emissions in recent decades. In the United States, sulfur dioxide emissions decreased more than 40% between 1993 and 2008, gradually reducing the acidity of precipitation **(Figure 56.11)**. However, ecologists estimate that it will take decades for aquatic ecosystems to recover. Meanwhile, emissions of nitrogen oxides are increasing in the United States, and emissions of sulfur dioxide and acid precipitation continue to damage forests in central and eastern Europe.

We'll explore the importance of global change for Earth's biodiversity in more detail in Concept 56.4, where we examine such factors as climate change and ozone depletion.

Can Extinct Species Be Resurrected?

To the best of our knowledge, extinction has always been forever. Some scientists are nevertheless trying to use cloning to resurrect species that have become extinct. Resurrecting species is at least theoretically possible because of recent progress in cloning living animals. The most famous case of cloning resulted in the birth of "Dolly" the lamb in 1997 (see Figure 20.17). To create Dolly, Scottish researchers took an egg cell from an adult sheep, removed its nucleus, fused the egg cell with a mammary cell from another sheep, and implanted the fused cell into a surrogate mother.

Spanish researchers used a similar approach on the Pyrenean ibex (*Capra pyrenaica pyrenaica*), one of four subspecies of wild goat endemic to Spain and other countries of the Iberian Peninsula. In 1999, researchers removed a small skin sample from the ear of the last living individual, a female, and froze it. When that individual died a year later, its subspecies became extinct. Using cells from the frozen tissue, the scientists then attempted to resurrect the ibex. Out of hundreds of fused cells and approximately 60 embryos implanted into surrogate mothers (either another species of ibex or a domestic goat), one individual ibex was born in 2009. Sadly, it lived for only 7 minutes before succumbing to lung defects similar to those observed in other cloned animals, including sheep. Nonetheless, this research demonstrated that species recovery may be possible in cases where frozen tissue is available.

Tissue from an extinct species need not be new to be used in cloning. A team of Russian and Japanese scientists is trying to revive the extinct woolly mammoth (*Mammuthus primigenius*) using well-preserved bone marrow from the thigh of a mammoth frozen in Arctic ice **(Figure 56.12)**. Will they succeed? No one knows yet, but eventually someone likely will, with this species and with others. In fact, scientists are already banking frozen tissues from many endangered species so that cells will be available for cloning if those species become extinct. Other scientists are examining whether they can obtain viable cells from museum specimens, such as pelts or feathers. And, of course, some are trying to isolate ancient DNA in soft tissue from dinosaur fossils. Thus far, such attempts have failed.

The quest to resurrect extinct species raises a host of ethical questions. Should scientists be free to resurrect any species for which viable cells or DNA are available? If not, who will decide which species are off-limits? What rules should be put in place before resurrection occurs? Should

▲ **Figure 56.11 Changes in the pH of precipitation at the Hubbard Brook Experimental Forest, New Hampshire.**

MAKE CONNECTIONS *Describe the relationship between pH and acidity. (See Concept 3.3.) Overall, is the precipitation in this forest becoming more acidic or less acidic?*

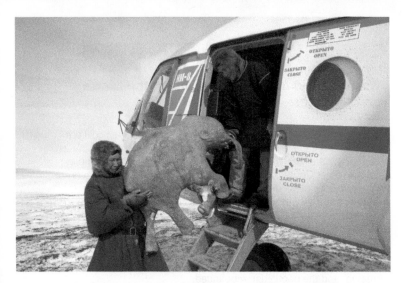

▲ **Figure 56.12 Collecting a frozen woolly mammoth.** Such specimens are being used in an attempt to resurrect the species through biotechnology.

the species eventually be restored to the wild? Note that, for the Pyrenean ibex, frozen tissue exists for only one female. No males of that subspecies may ever exist again.

Although resurrecting species now seems possible, we still need to preserve species across Earth. For many reasons, including the issue of genetic diversity discussed in Concept 56.2, preservation remains the scientifically and ethically prudent course of action.

CONCEPT CHECK 56.1

1. Explain why it is too narrow to define the biodiversity crisis as simply a loss of species.

2. Identify the four main threats to biodiversity and explain how each damages diversity.

3. **WHAT IF?** Imagine two populations of a fish species, one in the Mediterranean Sea and one in the Caribbean Sea. Now imagine two scenarios: (1) The populations breed separately, and (2) adults of both populations migrate yearly to the North Atlantic to interbreed. Which scenario would result in a greater loss of genetic diversity if the Mediterranean population were harvested to extinction? Explain your answer.

For suggested answers, see Appendix A.

CONCEPT 56.2

Population conservation focuses on population size, genetic diversity, and critical habitat

Biologists who work on conservation at the population and species levels use two main approaches. One approach focuses on populations that are small and hence often vulnerable. The other emphasizes populations that are declining rapidly, even if they are not yet small.

Small-Population Approach

Small populations are particularly vulnerable to overharvesting, habitat loss, and the other threats to biodiversity that you read about in Concept 56.1. After such factors have reduced a population's size to a small number of individuals, the small size itself can push the population to extinction. Conservation biologists who adopt the small-population approach study the various processes that cause extinctions once population sizes have been reduced.

The Extinction Vortex: Evolutionary Implications of Small Population Size

EVOLUTION   A small population is vulnerable to inbreeding and genetic drift, which draw the population down an **extinction vortex** toward smaller and smaller population size until no individuals survive **(Figure 56.13)**. A key factor driving the extinction vortex is the loss of the genetic variation that enables evolutionary responses to environmental change, such as the appearance of new strains of pathogens. Both inbreeding and genetic drift can cause a loss of genetic variation (see Chapter 23), and their effects become more harmful as a population shrinks. Inbreeding often reduces fitness because offspring are more likely to be homozygous for harmful recessive traits.

Not all small populations are doomed by low genetic diversity, and low genetic variability does not automatically lead to permanently small populations. For instance, overhunting of northern elephant seals in the 1890s reduced the species to only 20 individuals—clearly a bottleneck with reduced genetic variation. Since that time, however, the northern elephant seal populations have rebounded to about 150,000 individuals today, though their genetic variation remains relatively low. Thus, low genetic diversity does not always impede population growth.

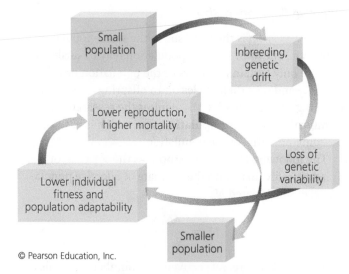

© Pearson Education, Inc.

▲ **Figure 56.13 Processes driving an extinction vortex.**

Case Study: *The Greater Prairie Chicken and the Extinction Vortex*

When Europeans arrived in North America, the greater prairie chicken (*Tympanuchus cupido*) was common from New England to Virginia and across the western prairies of the continent. Land cultivation for agriculture fragmented the populations of this species, and its abundance decreased rapidly (see Figure 23.11). Illinois had millions of greater prairie chickens in the 19th century but fewer than 50 by 1993. Researchers found that the decline in the Illinois population was associated with a decrease in fertility. As a test of the extinction vortex hypothesis, scientists increased genetic variation by importing 271 birds from larger populations elsewhere (Figure 56.14). The Illinois population rebounded, confirming that it had been on its way to extinction until rescued by the transfusion of genetic variation.

Minimum Viable Population Size

How small does a population have to be before it starts down an extinction vortex? The answer depends on the type of organism and other factors. Large predators that feed high on the food chain usually require extensive individual ranges, resulting in low population densities. Therefore, not all rare species concern conservation biologists. All populations, however, require some minimum size to remain viable.

The minimal population size at which a species is able to sustain its numbers is known as the **minimum viable population (MVP)**. MVP is usually estimated for a given species using computer models that integrate many factors. The calculation may include, for instance, an estimate of how many individuals in a small population are likely to be killed by a natural catastrophe such as a storm. Once in the extinction vortex, two or three consecutive years of bad weather could finish off a population that is already below its MVP.

Effective Population Size

Genetic variation is the key issue in the small-population approach. The *total* size of a population may be misleading because only certain members of the population breed successfully and pass their alleles on to offspring. Therefore, a meaningful estimate of MVP requires the researcher to determine the **effective population size**, which is based on the breeding potential of the population.

The following formula incorporates the sex ratio of breeding individuals into the estimate of effective population size, abbreviated N_e:

$$N_e = \frac{4N_f N_m}{N_f + N_m}$$

where N_f and N_m are, respectively, the number of females and the number of males that successfully breed. If we apply

---

▼ Figure 56.14 | Inquiry

What caused the drastic decline of the Illinois greater prairie chicken population?

Experiment Researchers had observed that the population collapse of the greater prairie chicken was mirrored in a reduction in fertility, as measured by the hatching rate of eggs. Comparison of DNA samples from the Jasper County, Illinois, population with DNA from feathers in museum specimens showed that genetic variation had declined in the study population (see Figure 23.11). In 1992, Ronald Westemeier, Jeffrey Brawn, and colleagues began translocating prairie chickens from Minnesota, Kansas, and Nebraska in an attempt to increase genetic variation.

Results After translocation (black arrow), the viability of eggs rapidly increased, and the population rebounded.

(a) Population dynamics

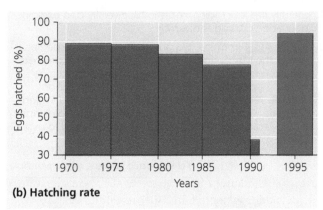

(b) Hatching rate

Conclusion Reduced genetic variation had started the Jasper County population of prairie chickens down the extinction vortex.

Source: R. L. Westemeier et al., Tracking the long-term decline and recovery of an isolated population, *Science* 282:1695–1698 (1998). © 1998 by AAAS. Reprinted with permission.

Inquiry in Action Read and analyze the original paper in *Inquiry in Action: Interpreting Scientific Papers.*

WHAT IF? *Given the success of using transplanted birds as a tool for increasing the percentage of hatched eggs in Illinois, why wouldn't you transplant additional birds immediately to Illinois?*

---

this formula to an idealized population whose total size is 1,000 individuals, N_e will also be 1,000 if every individual breeds and the sex ratio is 500 females to 500 males. In this case, $N_e = (4 \times 500 \times 500)/(500 + 500) = 1,000$. Any deviation from these conditions (not all individuals breed or there is not a 1:1 sex ratio) reduces N_e. For instance, if the total population size is 1,000 but only 400 females and 400 males breed, then $N_e = (4 \times 400 \times 400)/(400 + 400) = 800$, or 80% of the total population size. Numerous life history traits can influence N_e. Alternative formulas for estimating N_e take into account factors such as family size, age at maturation, genetic relatedness among population members, the effects of gene flow between geographically separated populations, and population fluctuations.

In actual study populations, N_e is always some fraction of the total population. Thus, simply determining the total number of individuals in a small population does not provide a good measure of whether the population is large enough to avoid extinction. Whenever possible, conservation programs attempt to sustain total population sizes that include at least the minimum viable number of *reproductively active* individuals. The conservation goal of sustaining effective population size (N_e) above MVP stems from the concern that populations retain enough genetic diversity to adapt as their environment changes.

The MVP of a population is often used in population viability analysis. The objective of this analysis is to predict a population's chances for survival, usually expressed as a specific probability of survival, such as a 95% chance, over a particular time interval, perhaps 100 years. Such modeling approaches allow conservation biologists to explore the potential consequences of alternative management plans.

Case Study: *Analysis of Grizzly Bear Populations*

One of the first population viability analyses was conducted in 1978 by Mark Shaffer, of Duke University, as part of a long-term study of grizzly bears in Yellowstone National Park and its surrounding areas (Figure 56.15). A threatened species in the United States, the grizzly bear (*Ursus arctos horribilis*) is currently found in only 4 of the 48 contiguous states. Its populations in those states have been drastically reduced and fragmented. In 1800, an estimated 100,000 grizzlies ranged over about 500 million hectares of habitat, while today only about 1,000 individuals in six relatively isolated populations range over less than 5 million hectares.

Shaffer attempted to determine viable sizes for the Yellowstone grizzly population. Using life history data obtained for individual Yellowstone bears over a 12-year period, he simulated the effects of environmental factors on survival and reproduction. His models predicted that, given a suitable habitat, a Yellowstone grizzly bear population of 70–90 individuals would have about a 95% chance of surviving for 100 years. A slightly larger population of only 100 bears

▲ **Figure 56.15 Long-term monitoring of a grizzly bear population.** The ecologist is fitting this tranquilized bear with a radio collar so that the bear's movements can be compared with those of other grizzlies in the Yellowstone National Park population.

would have a 95% chance of surviving for twice as long, about 200 years.

How does the actual size of the Yellowstone grizzly population compare with Shaffer's predicted MVP? A current estimate puts the total grizzly bear population in the greater Yellowstone ecosystem at about 500 individuals. The relationship of this estimate to the effective population size (N_e) depends on several factors. Usually, only a few dominant males breed, and it may be difficult for them to locate females, since individuals inhabit such large areas. Moreover, females may reproduce only when there is abundant food. As a result, N_e is only about 25% of the total population size, or about 125 bears.

Because small populations tend to lose genetic variation over time, a number of research teams have analyzed proteins, mtDNA, and short tandem repeats (see Chapter 21) to assess genetic variability in the Yellowstone grizzly bear population. All results to date indicate that the Yellowstone population has less genetic variability than other grizzly bear populations in North America.

How might conservation biologists increase the effective size and genetic variation of the Yellowstone grizzly bear population? Migration between isolated populations of grizzlies could increase both effective and total population sizes. Computer models predict that introducing only two unrelated bears each decade into a population of 100 individuals would reduce the loss of genetic variation by about half. For the grizzly bear, and probably for many other species with small populations, finding ways to promote dispersal among populations may be one of the most urgent conservation needs.

This case study and that of the greater prairie chicken bridge small-population models and practical applications in conservation. Next, we look at an alternative approach to understanding the biology of extinction.

Declining-Population Approach

The declining-population approach focuses on threatened and endangered populations that show a downward trend, even if the population is far above its minimum viable population. The distinction between a declining population, which may not be small, and a small population, which may not be declining, is less important than the different priorities of the two approaches. The small-population approach emphasizes smallness itself as an ultimate cause of a population's extinction, especially through the loss of genetic diversity. In contrast, the declining-population approach emphasizes the environmental factors that caused a population decline in the first place. If, for instance, an area is deforested, then species that depend on trees will decline in abundance and become locally extinct, whether or not they retain genetic variation.

Steps for Analysis and Intervention

The declining-population approach requires that researchers carefully evaluate the causes of a decline before taking steps to correct it. If an invasive species such as the brown tree snake in Guam is harming a native bird species, then managers need to reduce or eliminate the invader to restore vulnerable populations of the bird. Although most situations are more complex, we can use the following steps for analyzing declining populations:

1. Confirm, using population data, that the species was more widely distributed or more abundant in the past compared to its current population level.
2. Study the natural history of this and related species, including reviewing the research literature, to determine the species' environmental needs.
3. Develop hypotheses for all possible causes of the decline, including human activities and natural events, and list the predictions of each hypothesis.
4. Because many factors may be correlated with the decline, test the most likely hypothesis first. For example, remove the suspected cause of decline to see if the experimental population rebounds compared to a control population.
5. Apply the results of the diagnosis to manage the threatened species and monitor its recovery.

The following case study is one example of how the declining-population approach has been applied to the conservation of an endangered species.

Case Study: *Decline of the Red-cockaded Woodpecker*

The red-cockaded woodpecker (*Picoides borealis*) is found only in the southeastern United States. It requires mature pine forests, preferably ones dominated by the longleaf pine, for its habitat. Most woodpeckers nest in dead trees, but the red-cockaded woodpecker drills its nest holes in mature, living pine trees. It also drills small holes around the entrance to its nest cavity, which causes resin from the tree to ooze down the trunk. The resin seems to repel predators, such as corn snakes, that eat bird eggs and nestlings.

Another critical habitat factor for the red-cockaded woodpecker is that the undergrowth of plants around the pine trunks must be low (Figure 56.16a). Breeding birds tend to abandon nests when vegetation among the pines is thick and higher than about 4.5 m (Figure 56.16b). Apparently, the birds need a clear flight path between their home

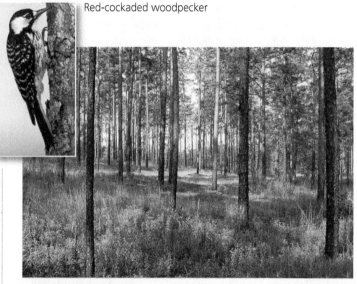

Red-cockaded woodpecker

(a) Forests that can sustain red-cockaded woodpeckers have low undergrowth.

(b) Forests that cannot sustain red-cockaded woodpeckers have high, dense undergrowth that interferes with the woodpeckers' access to feeding grounds.

▲ Figure 56.16 **A habitat requirement of the red-cockaded woodpecker.**

? *How is habitat disturbance absolutely necessary for the long-term survival of the woodpecker?*

trees and the neighboring feeding grounds. Periodic fires have historically swept through longleaf pine forests, keeping the undergrowth low.

One factor leading to decline of the red-cockaded woodpecker has been the destruction or fragmentation of suitable habitats by logging and agriculture. By recognizing key habitat factors, protecting some longleaf pine forests, and using controlled fires to reduce forest undergrowth, conservation managers have helped restore habitat that can support viable populations.

Sometimes conservation managers also help species colonize restored habitats. Because red-cockaded woodpeckers take months to excavate nesting cavities, researchers performed an experiment to see whether providing cavities for the birds would make them more likely to use a site. The researchers constructed cavities in pine trees at 20 sites. The results were dramatic. Cavities in 18 of the 20 sites were colonized by red-cockaded woodpeckers, and new breeding groups formed only in those sites. Based on this experiment, conservationists initiated a habitat maintenance program that included controlled burning and excavation of new nesting cavities, enabling this endangered species to begin to recover.

Weighing Conflicting Demands

Determining population numbers and habitat needs is only part of a strategy to save species. Scientists also need to weigh a species' needs against other conflicting demands. Conservation biology often highlights the relationship between science, technology, and society. For example, an ongoing, sometimes bitter debate in the western United States pits habitat preservation for wolf, grizzly bear, and bull trout populations against job opportunities in the grazing and resource extraction industries. Programs that restocked wolves in Yellowstone National Park remain controversial for people concerned about human safety and for many ranchers concerned with potential loss of livestock outside the park.

Large, high-profile vertebrates are not always the focal point in such conflicts, but habitat use is almost always the issue. Should work proceed on a new highway bridge if it destroys the only remaining habitat of a species of freshwater mussel? If you were the owner of a coffee plantation growing varieties that thrive in bright sunlight, would you be willing to change to shade-tolerant varieties that produce less coffee per hectare but can grow beneath trees that support large numbers of songbirds?

Another important consideration is the ecological role of a species. Because we cannot save every endangered species, we must determine which species are most important for conserving biodiversity as a whole. Identifying keystone species and finding ways to sustain their populations can

be central to maintaining communities and ecosystems. In most situations, conservation biologists must also look beyond single species and consider the whole community and ecosystem as an important unit of biodiversity.

CONCEPT CHECK 56.2

1. How does the reduced genetic diversity of small populations make them more vulnerable to extinction?

2. If there were 100 greater prairie chickens in a population, and 30 females and 10 males bred, what would be the effective population size (N_e)?

3. **WHAT IF?** In 2005, at least ten grizzly bears in the greater Yellowstone ecosystem were killed through contact with people. Three things caused most of these deaths: collisions with automobiles, hunters (of other animals) shooting when charged by a female grizzly bear with cubs nearby, and conservation managers killing bears that attacked livestock repeatedly. If you were a conservation manager, what steps might you take to minimize such encounters in Yellowstone?

For suggested answers, see Appendix A.

CONCEPT 56.3

Landscape and regional conservation help sustain biodiversity

Although conservation efforts historically focused on saving individual species, efforts today often seek to sustain the biodiversity of entire communities, ecosystems, and landscapes. Such a broad view requires applying not just the principles of community, ecosystem, and landscape ecology but aspects of human population dynamics and economics as well. The goals of landscape ecology (see Figure 52.2) include projecting future patterns of landscape use and making biodiversity conservation part of land-use planning.

Landscape Structure and Biodiversity

The biodiversity of a given landscape is in large part a function of the structure of the landscape. Understanding landscape structure is critically important in conservation because many species use more than one kind of ecosystem, and many live on the borders between ecosystems.

Fragmentation and Edges

The boundaries, or *edges*, between ecosystems—such as between a lake and the surrounding forest or between cropland and suburban housing tracts—are defining features of landscapes. An edge has its own set of physical conditions, which differ from those on either side of it. The soil surface of an edge between a forest patch and a burned area receives more sunlight and is usually hotter and drier than the forest

▲ **Figure 56.17 Edges in Yellowstone National Park.**

? *What edges between ecosystems do you see in this photo?*

interior, but it is cooler and wetter than the soil surface in the burned area. The photo of Yellowstone National Park in **Figure 56.17** shows several edges between ecosystems.

Some organisms thrive in edge communities because they gain resources from both adjacent areas. The ruffed grouse (*Bonasa umbellus*) is a bird that needs forest habitat for nesting, winter food, and shelter, but it also needs forest openings with dense shrubs and herbs for summer food.

Ecosystems in which edges arise from human alterations often have reduced biodiversity and a preponderance of edge-adapted species. For example, white-tailed deer (*Odocoileus virginianus*) thrive in edge habitats, where they can browse on woody shrubs; deer populations often expand when forests are logged and more edges are generated. The brown-headed cowbird (*Molothrus ater*) is an edge-adapted species that lays its eggs in the nests of other birds, often migratory songbirds. Cowbirds need forests, where they can parasitize the nests of other birds, and open fields, where they forage on seeds and insects. Consequently, their populations are growing where forests are being cut and fragmented, creating more edge habitat and open land. Increasing cowbird parasitism and habitat loss are correlated with declining populations of several of the cowbird's host species.

The influence of fragmentation on the structure of communities has been explored since 1979 in the long-term Biological Dynamics of Forest Fragments Project. Located in the heart of the Amazon River basin, the study area consists of isolated fragments of tropical rain forest separated from surrounding continuous forest by distances of 80–1,000 m (**Figure 56.18**). Numerous researchers working on this project have clearly documented the effects of this fragmentation on organisms ranging from bryophytes to beetles to birds. They have consistently found that species adapted to forest interiors show the greatest declines when patches are

▲ **Figure 56.18 Amazon rain forest fragments created as part of the Biological Dynamics of Forest Fragments Project.**

the smallest, suggesting that landscapes dominated by small fragments will support fewer species.

Corridors That Connect Habitat Fragments

In fragmented habitats, the presence of a **movement corridor**, a narrow strip or series of small clumps of habitat connecting otherwise isolated patches, can be extremely important for conserving biodiversity. Riparian habitats often serve as corridors, and in some nations, government policy prohibits altering these habitats. In areas of heavy human use, artificial corridors are sometimes constructed. Bridges or tunnels, for instance, can reduce the number of animals killed trying to cross highways (**Figure 56.19**).

Movement corridors can also promote dispersal and reduce inbreeding in declining populations. Corridors have been shown to increase the exchange of individuals among populations of many organisms, including butterflies, voles,

▲ **Figure 56.19 An artificial corridor.** This bridge in Banff National Park, Canada, helps animals cross a human-created barrier.

and aquatic plants. Corridors are especially important to species that migrate between different habitats seasonally. However, a corridor can also be harmful—for example, by allowing the spread of disease. In a 2003 study, a scientist at the University of Zaragoza, Spain, showed that habitat corridors facilitate the movement of disease-carrying ticks among forest patches in northern Spain. All the effects of corridors are not yet understood, and their impact is an area of active research in conservation biology.

Establishing Protected Areas

Conservation biologists are applying their understanding of landscape dynamics in establishing protected areas to slow biodiversity loss. Currently, governments have set aside about 7% of the world's land in various forms of reserves. Choosing where to place nature reserves and how to design them poses many challenges. Should the reserve be managed to minimize the risks of fire and predation to a threatened species? Or should the reserve be left as natural as possible, with such processes as fires ignited by lightning allowed to play out on their own? This is just one of the debates that arise among people who share an interest in the health of national parks and other protected areas.

Preserving Biodiversity Hot Spots

In deciding which areas are of highest conservation priority, biologists often focus on hot spots of biodiversity. A **biodiversity hot spot** is a relatively small area with numerous endemic species (species found nowhere else in the world) and a large number of endangered and threatened species (Figure 56.20). Nearly 30% of all bird species can be found in hot spots that make up only about 2% of Earth's land area. Together, the "hottest" of the terrestrial biodiversity hot spots total less than 1.5% of Earth's land but are home to more than a third of all species of plants, amphibians, reptiles (including birds), and mammals. Aquatic

ecosystems also have hot spots, such as coral reefs and certain river systems.

Biodiversity hot spots are good choices for nature reserves, but identifying them is not always simple. One problem is that a hot spot for one taxonomic group, such as butterflies, may not be a hot spot for some other taxonomic group, such as birds. Designating an area as a biodiversity hot spot is often biased toward saving vertebrates and plants, with less attention paid to invertebrates and microorganisms. Some biologists are also concerned that the hot-spot strategy places too much emphasis on such a small fraction of Earth's surface.

Global change makes the task of preserving hot spots even more challenging because the conditions that favor a particular community may not be found in the same location in the future. The biodiversity hot spot in the southwest corner of Australia (see Figure 56.20) holds thousands of species of endemic plants and numerous endemic vertebrates. Researchers recently concluded that between 5% and 25% of the plant species they examined may become extinct by 2080 because the plants will be unable to tolerate the increased dryness predicted for this region.

Philosophy of Nature Reserves

Nature reserves are protected "islands" of biodiversity in a sea of habitat altered or degraded by human activity. An earlier policy—that protected areas should be set aside to remain unchanged forever—was based on the concept that ecosystems are balanced, self-regulating units. However, disturbance is common in all ecosystems, and the nonequilibrium model (see Concept 54.3) applies to nature reserves as well as to the larger landscapes around them. Management policies that ignore disturbances or attempt to prevent them have generally failed. For instance, setting aside an area of a fire-dependent community, such as a portion of a tallgrass prairie, chaparral, or dry pine forest, with the intention of saving it is unrealistic if periodic burning is excluded.

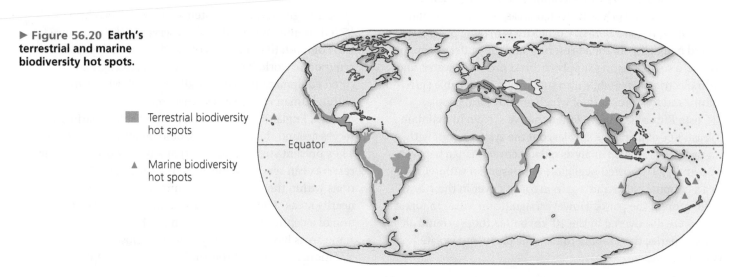

▶ **Figure 56.20 Earth's terrestrial and marine biodiversity hot spots.**

■ Terrestrial biodiversity hot spots

▲ Marine biodiversity hot spots

Equator

Without the dominant disturbance, the fire-adapted species are usually outcompeted and biodiversity is reduced.

An important conservation question is whether to create numerous small reserves or fewer large reserves. Small, unconnected reserves may slow the spread of disease between populations. One argument for large reserves is that large, far-ranging animals with low-density populations, such as the grizzly bear, require extensive habitats. Large reserves also have proportionately smaller perimeters than small reserves and are therefore less affected by edges.

As conservation biologists have learned more about the requirements for achieving minimum viable populations for endangered species, they have realized that most national parks and other reserves are far too small. The area needed for the long-term survival of the Yellowstone grizzly bear population, for instance, is more than ten times the combined area of Yellowstone and Grand Teton National Parks. Areas of private and public land surrounding reserves will likely have to contribute to biodiversity conservation.

Zoned Reserves

Several nations have adopted a zoned reserve approach to landscape management. A **zoned reserve** is an extensive region that includes areas relatively undisturbed by humans surrounded by areas that have been changed by human activity and are used for economic gain. The key challenge of the zoned reserve approach is to develop a social and economic climate in the surrounding lands that is compatible with the long-term viability of the protected core. These surrounding areas continue to support human activities, but regulations prevent the types of extensive alterations likely to harm the protected area. As a result, the surrounding habitats serve as buffer zones against further intrusion into the undisturbed area.

The small Central American nation of Costa Rica has become a world leader in establishing zoned reserves. An agreement initiated in 1987 reduced Costa Rica's international debt in return for land preservation there. The country is now divided into 11 Conservation Areas, which include national parks and other protected areas, both on land and in the ocean (Figure 56.21). Costa Rica is making progress toward managing its zoned reserves, and the buffer zones provide a steady, lasting supply of forest products, water, and hydroelectric power while also supporting sustainable agriculture and tourism, both of which employ local people.

Costa Rica relies on its zoned reserve system to maintain at least 80% of its native species, but the system is not without problems. A 2003 analysis of land cover change between 1960 and 1997 showed negligible deforestation within Costa Rica's national parks and a gain in forest cover in the 1-km buffer around the parks. However, significant losses in forest cover were discovered in the 10-km buffer zones around all national parks, threatening to turn the parks into isolated habitat islands.

(a) Boundaries of the Conservation Areas are indicated by black outlines.

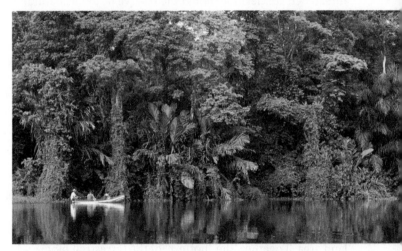

(b) Tourists marvel at the diversity of life in one of Costa Rica's protected areas.

▲ **Figure 56.21 Protected areas in Costa Rica.**

Although marine ecosystems have also been heavily affected by human exploitation, reserves in the ocean are far less common than reserves on land. Many fish populations around the world have collapsed as increasingly sophisticated equipment puts nearly all potential fishing grounds within human reach. In response, scientists at the University of York, England, have proposed establishing marine reserves around the world that would be off-limits to fishing. They present strong evidence that a patchwork of marine reserves can serve as a means of both increasing fish populations within the reserves and improving fishing success in nearby areas. Their proposed system is a modern application of a centuries-old practice in the Fiji Islands in which some areas have historically remained closed to fishing—a traditional example of the zoned reserve concept.

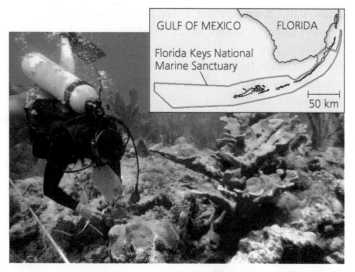

▲ **Figure 56.22** **A diver measuring coral in the Florida Keys National Marine Sanctuary.**

The United States adopted such a system in creating a set of 13 national marine sanctuaries, including the Florida Keys National Marine Sanctuary, which was established in 1990 (**Figure 56.22**). Populations of marine organisms, including fishes and lobsters, recovered quickly after harvests were banned in the 9,500-km^2 reserve. Larger and more abundant fish now produce larvae that help repopulate reefs and improve fishing outside the sanctuary. The increased marine life within the sanctuary also makes it a favorite for recreational divers, increasing the economic value of this zoned reserve.

Urban Ecology

The zoned reserves that you just read about combine habitats that are relatively undisturbed by human activity with those that are used extensively by people for economic gain. Increasingly, ecologists are looking at species preservation even in the context of cities. The field of **urban ecology** examines organisms and their environment in urban settings.

For the first time in history, more than half of the people on Earth live in cities. By the year 2030, 5 billion people are expected to be living in urban environments. As cities expand in number and size, protected areas that were once outside city boundaries become incorporated into urban landscapes. Ecologists are now studying cities as ecological laboratories, seeking to balance species preservation and other ecological needs with the needs of people.

One critical area of research centers on urban streams, including the quality and flow of their water and the organisms living in them. Urban streams tend to rise and fall more quickly after rain than natural streams. This rapid change in water level occurs because of the concrete and other impervious surfaces in cities as well as the drainage systems that route water out of cities as quickly as possible to avoid flooding. Urban streams also tend to have higher concentrations of nutrients and contaminants and are often straightened or even channeled underground.

Near Vancouver, British Columbia, ecologists and volunteers worked to restore a degraded urban stream, Guichon Creek, by planting trees and shrubs along the creek and stabilizing its banks. Their efforts returned the water flow and the communities of invertebrates and fish in the stream much closer to what they had been 50 years before the stream became degraded. A few years ago, ecologists successfully reestablished cutthroat trout in the stream. The trout are now thriving.

As cities continue to expand into the landscapes around them, understanding the ecological effects of this expansion will only increase in importance. Integrating cities into ecological research will grow as a research and conservation field over the coming decades.

CONCEPT CHECK 56.3

1. What is a biodiversity hot spot?
2. How do zoned reserves provide economic incentives for long-term conservation of protected areas?
3. **WHAT IF?** Suppose a developer proposes to clear-cut a forest that serves as a corridor between two parks. To compensate, the developer also proposes to add the same area of forest to one of the parks. As a professional ecologist, how might you argue for retaining the corridor?

For suggested answers, see Appendix A.

CONCEPT 56.4

Earth is changing rapidly as a result of human actions

As we've discussed, landscape and regional conservation help protect habitats and preserve species. However, environmental changes that result from human activities are creating new challenges. As a consequence of human-caused climate change, for example, the place where a vulnerable species is found today may not be the same place that is needed for preservation in the future. What would happen if *many* habitats on Earth changed so quickly that the locations of preserves today were unsuitable for their species in 10, 50, or 100 years? Such a scenario is increasingly possible.

The rest of this section describes four types of environmental change that humans are bringing about: nutrient enrichment, toxin accumulation, climate change, and ozone depletion. The impacts of these and other changes are evident not just in human-dominated ecosystems, such as cities and farms, but also in the most remote ecosystems on Earth.

Nutrient Enrichment

Human activity often removes nutrients from one part of the biosphere and adds them to another. Someone eating strawberries in Washington, DC, consumes nutrients that only days before were in the soil in California; a short time later, some of these nutrients will be in the Potomac River, having passed through the person's digestive system and a local sewage treatment facility.

Farming is an example of how human activities are altering the environment through the enrichment of nutrients, particularly ones containing nitrogen. After vegetation is cleared from an area, the existing reserve of nutrients in the soil is depleted as nutrients are exported from the area in crop biomass. The "free" period for crop production—when there is no need to replenish nutrients by adding fertilizer to the soil—varies greatly. When some of the early North American prairie lands were first tilled, good crops could be produced for decades because the large store of organic materials in the soil continued to decompose and provide nutrients. By contrast, some cleared land in the tropics can be farmed for only one or two years because so little of the ecosystems' nutrient load is contained in the soil. Despite such variations, in any area under intensive agriculture, the natural store of nutrients eventually becomes exhausted.

Nitrogen is the main nutrient lost through agriculture (see Figure 55.14). Plowing mixes the soil and speeds up decomposition of organic matter, releasing nitrogen that is then removed when crops are harvested. Applied fertilizers make up for the loss of usable nitrogen from agricultural ecosystems (Figure 56.23). However, without plants to take up nitrates from the soil, the nitrates are likely to be leached from the ecosystem (see Figure 55.16).

Recent studies indicate that human activities have more than doubled Earth's supply of fixed nitrogen available to primary producers. Industrial fertilizers provide the largest

▲ **Figure 56.23 Fertilization of a corn (maize) crop.** To replace the nutrients removed in crops, farmers must apply fertilizers—either organic, such as manure or mulch, or synthetic, as shown here.

additional nitrogen source. Fossil fuel combustion also releases nitrogen oxides, which enter the atmosphere and dissolve in rainwater; the nitrogen ultimately enters ecosystems as nitrate. Increased cultivation of legumes, with their nitrogen-fixing symbionts, is a third way in which humans increase the amount of fixed nitrogen in the soil.

A problem arises when the nutrient level in an ecosystem exceeds the **critical load**, the amount of added nutrient, usually nitrogen or phosphorus, that can be absorbed by plants without damaging ecosystem integrity. For example, nitrogenous minerals in the soil that exceed the critical load eventually leach into groundwater or run off into freshwater and marine ecosystems, contaminating water supplies and killing fish. Nitrate concentrations in groundwater are increasing in most agricultural regions, sometimes reaching levels that are unsafe for drinking.

Many rivers contaminated with nitrates and ammonium from agricultural runoff and sewage drain into the Atlantic Ocean, with the highest inputs coming from northern Europe and the central United States. The Mississippi River carries nitrogen pollution to the Gulf of Mexico, fueling a phytoplankton bloom each summer. When the phytoplankton die, their decomposition by oxygen-using organisms creates an extensive "dead zone" of low oxygen levels along the coast (Figure 56.24). Fish and other marine animals disappear from some of the most economically important waters in the United States. To reduce the size of the dead zone, farmers have begun using fertilizers more efficiently, and managers are restoring wetlands in the Mississippi watershed, two changes stimulated by the results of ecosystem experiments.

Nutrient runoff can also lead to the eutrophication of lakes (see Concept 55.2). The bloom and subsequent die-off of algae and cyanobacteria and the ensuing depletion of oxygen are similar to what occurs in a marine dead zone. Such conditions threaten the survival of organisms. For example, eutrophication of Lake Erie coupled with overfishing wiped out commercially important fishes such as blue pike, whitefish, and lake trout by the 1960s. Since then, tighter regulations on the dumping of sewage and other wastes into the lake have enabled some fish populations to rebound, but many native species of fish and invertebrates have not recovered.

▶ **Figure 56.24 A phytoplankton bloom arising from nitrogen pollution in the Mississippi basin that leads to a dead zone.** In this satellite image from 2004, red and orange represent high concentrations of phytoplankton in the Gulf of Mexico.

Toxins in the Environment

Humans release an immense variety of toxic chemicals, including thousands of synthetic compounds previously unknown in nature, with little regard for the ecological consequences. Organisms acquire toxic substances from the environment along with nutrients and water. Some of the poisons are metabolized or excreted, but others accumulate in specific tissues, often fat. One of the reasons accumulated toxins are particularly harmful is that they become more concentrated in successive trophic levels of a food web. This phenomenon, called **biological magnification**, occurs because the biomass at any given trophic level is produced from a much larger biomass ingested from the level below (see Concept 55.3). Thus, top-level carnivores tend to be most severely affected by toxic compounds in the environment.

Chlorinated hydrocarbons are a class of industrially synthesized compounds that have demonstrated biological magnification. Chlorinated hydrocarbons include the industrial chemicals called PCBs (polychlorinated biphenyls) and many pesticides, such as DDT. Current research implicates many of these compounds in endocrine system disruption in a large number of animal species, including humans. Biological magnification of PCBs has been found in the food web of the Great Lakes, where the concentration of PCBs in herring gull eggs, at the top of the food web, is nearly 5,000 times that in phytoplankton, at the base of the food web (Figure 56.25).

An infamous case of biological magnification that harmed top-level carnivores involved DDT, a chemical used to control insects such as mosquitoes and agricultural pests. In the decade after World War II, the use of DDT grew rapidly; its ecological consequences were not yet fully understood. By the 1950s, scientists were learning that DDT persists in the environment and is transported by water to areas far from where it is applied. One of the first signs that DDT was a serious environmental problem was a decline in the populations of pelicans, ospreys, and eagles, birds that feed at the top of food webs. The accumulation of DDT (and DDE, a product of its breakdown) in the tissues of these birds interfered with the deposition of calcium in their eggshells. When the birds tried to incubate their eggs, the weight of the parents broke the shells of affected eggs, resulting in catastrophic declines in the birds' reproduction rates. Rachel Carson's book *Silent Spring* helped bring the problem to public attention in the 1960s (Figure 56.26), and DDT was banned in the United States in 1971. A dramatic recovery in populations of the affected bird species followed.

In much of the tropics, DDT is still used to control the mosquitoes that spread malaria and other diseases. Societies there face a trade-off between saving human lives and protecting other species. The best approach seems to be to apply DDT sparingly and to couple its use with mosquito

▲ Figure 56.25 **Biological magnification of PCBs in a Great Lakes food web.** (ppm = parts per million)

INTERPRET THE DATA *If a typical smelt weighs 225 g, what is the total mass of PCBs in a smelt in the Great Lakes? If an average lake trout weighs 4,500 g, what is the total mass of PCBs in a trout in the Great Lakes? Assume that a lake trout from an unpolluted source is introduced into the Great Lakes and smelt are the only source of PCBs in the trout's diet. The new trout would have the same level of PCBs as the existing trout after eating how many smelt? (Assume that the trout retains 100% of the PCBs it consumes.)*

netting and other low-technology solutions. The complicated history of DDT illustrates the importance of understanding the ecological connections between diseases and communities (see Concept 54.5).

Pharmaceuticals make up another group of toxins in the environment, one that is a growing concern among ecologists. The use of over-the-counter and prescription drugs has risen in recent years, particularly in industrialized nations.

◀ Figure 56.26 **Rachel Carson.** Through her writing and her testimony before the U.S. Congress, biologist and author Carson helped promote a new environmental ethic. Her efforts led to a ban on DDT use in the United States and stronger controls on the use of other chemicals.

People who consume such products excrete residual chemicals in their waste and may also dispose of unused drugs improperly, such as in their toilets or sinks. Drugs that are not broken down in sewage treatment plants may then enter rivers and lakes with the material discharged from these plants. Growth-promoting drugs given to farm animals can also enter rivers and lakes with agricultural runoff. As a consequence, many pharmaceuticals are spreading in low concentrations across the world's freshwater ecosystems (Figure 56.27).

▲ Figure 56.27 **Sources and movements of pharmaceuticals in the environment.**

Among the pharmaceuticals that ecologists are studying are the sex steroids, including forms of estrogen used for birth control. Some fish species are so sensitive to certain estrogens that concentrations of a few parts per trillion in their water can alter sexual differentiation and shift the female-to-male sex ratio toward females. Researchers in Ontario, Canada, conducted a seven-year experiment in which they applied the synthetic estrogen used in contraceptives to a lake in very low concentrations (5–6 ng/L). They found that chronic exposure of the fathead minnow (*Pimephales promelas*) to the estrogen led to feminization of males and a near extinction of the species from the lake.

Many toxins cannot be degraded by microorganisms and persist in the environment for years or even decades. In other cases, chemicals released into the environment may be relatively harmless but are converted to more toxic products by reaction with other substances, by exposure to light, or by the metabolism of microorganisms. Mercury, a by-product of plastic production and coal-fired power generation, has been routinely expelled into rivers and the sea in an insoluble form. Bacteria in the bottom mud convert the waste to methylmercury (CH_3Hg^+), an extremely toxic water-soluble compound that accumulates in the tissues of organisms, including humans who consume fish from the contaminated waters.

Greenhouse Gases and Climate Change

Human activities release a variety of gaseous waste products. People once thought that the vast atmosphere could absorb these materials indefinitely, but we now know that such additions can cause fundamental changes to the atmosphere and to its interactions with the rest of the biosphere. In this section, we'll examine how increasing concentrations of carbon dioxide and other greenhouse gases may affect species and ecosystems through a changing climate.

Rising Atmospheric CO_2 Levels

Since the Industrial Revolution, the concentration of CO_2 in the atmosphere has been increasing as a result of the burning of fossil fuels and deforestation. Scientists estimate that the average CO_2 concentration in the atmosphere before 1850 was about 274 ppm. In 1958, a monitoring station began taking very accurate measurements on Hawaii's Mauna Loa peak, a location far from cities and high enough for the atmosphere to be well mixed. At that time, the CO_2 concentration was 316 ppm (Figure 56.28). Today, it is around 400 ppm, an increase of more than 40% since the mid-19th century. In the Scientific Skills Exercise, you can graph and interpret changes in CO_2 concentration that occur during the course of a year and over longer periods.

The marked increase in the concentration of atmospheric CO_2 over the last 150 years concerns scientists because of its link to increased global temperature. Much of the solar radiation that strikes the planet is reflected back into space. Although CO_2, methane, water vapor, and other greenhouse gases in the atmosphere are transparent to visible light, they intercept and absorb much of the infrared radiation Earth emits, re-reflecting some of it back toward Earth. This process retains some of the solar heat. If it were not for this **greenhouse effect**, the average air temperature at Earth's surface would be a frigid −18°C (−0.4°F), and most life as we know it could not exist.

For more than a century, scientists have studied how greenhouse gases warm Earth and how fossil fuel burning could contribute to the warming. Most scientists are convinced that such warming is already occurring and will increase rapidly this century (see Figure 56.28). Global models predict that by the end of the 21st century, the atmospheric

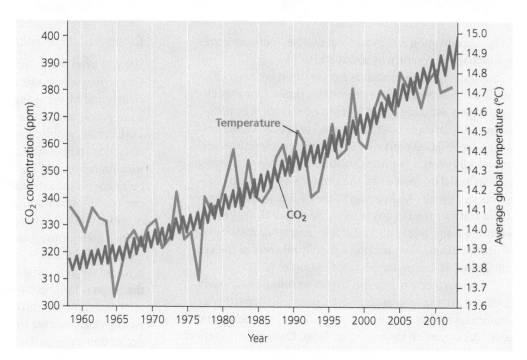

▶ **Figure 56.28 Increase in atmospheric carbon dioxide concentration at Mauna Loa, Hawaii, and average global temperatures.** Aside from normal seasonal fluctuations, the CO_2 concentration (blue curve) has increased steadily from 1958 to 2013. Though average global temperatures (red curve) fluctuated a great deal over the same period, there is a clear warming trend.

SCIENTIFIC SKILLS EXERCISE

Graphing Cyclic Data

How Does the Atmospheric CO_2 Concentration Change During a Year and from Decade to Decade? The blue curve in Figure 56.28 shows how the concentration of CO_2 in Earth's atmosphere has changed over a span of more than 50 years. For each year in that span, two data points are plotted, one in May and one in November. A more detailed picture of the change in CO_2 concentration can be obtained by looking at measurements made at more frequent intervals. In this exercise, you'll graph monthly CO_2 concentrations for three years over three decades.

Data from the Study The data in the table below are average CO_2 concentrations (in parts per million) at the Mauna Loa monitoring station for each month in 1990, 2000, and 2010.

Month	1990	2000	2010
January	353.79	369.25	388.45
February	354.88	369.50	389.82
March	355.65	370.56	391.08
April	356.27	371.82	392.46
May	359.29	371.51	392.95
June	356.32	371.71	392.06
July	354.88	369.85	390.13
August	352.89	368.20	388.15
September	351.28	366.91	386.80
October	351.59	366.91	387.18
November	353.05	366.99	388.59
December	354.27	369.67	389.68

Interpret the Data

1. Plot the data for all three years on one graph. Select a type of graph that is appropriate for these data, and choose a vertical axis scale that

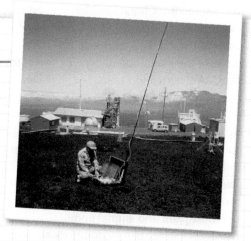

▶ A researcher sampling the air at the Mauna Loa monitoring station, Hawaii.

allows you to clearly see the patterns of CO_2 concentration changes, both during each year and from decade to decade. (For additional information about graphs, see the Scientific Skills Review in Appendix F and in the Study Area in MasteringBiology.)

2. Within each year, what is the pattern of change in CO_2 concentration? Why does this pattern occur?

3. The measurements taken at Mauna Loa represent average atmospheric CO_2 concentrations for the Northern Hemisphere. Suppose you could measure CO_2 concentrations under similar conditions in the Southern Hemisphere. What pattern would you expect to see in those measurements over the course of a year? Explain.

4. In addition to the changes within each year, what changes in CO_2 concentration occurred between 1990 and 2010? Calculate the average CO_2 concentration for the 12 months of each year. By what percentage did this average change from 1990 to 2000 and from 1990 to 2010?

(MB) A version of this Scientific Skills Exercise can be assigned in MasteringBiology.

Data from National Oceanic & Atmospheric Administration, Earth System Research Laboratory, Global Monitoring Division.

CO_2 concentration will more than double, increasing average global temperature by about 3°C (5°F).

Supporting these models is a correlation between CO_2 levels and temperatures in prehistoric times. One way climatologists estimate past CO_2 concentrations is by measuring CO_2 levels in bubbles trapped in glacial ice, some of which are 750,000 years old. Prehistoric temperatures are inferred by several methods, including analysis of past vegetation based on fossils and the chemical isotopes in sediments and corals. An increase of only 1.3°C would make the world warmer than at any time in the past 100,000 years. A warming trend would also alter the geographic distribution of precipitation, likely making agricultural areas of the central United States much drier, for example.

The ecosystems where the largest warming has *already* occurred are those in the far north, particularly northern coniferous forests and tundra. As snow and ice melt and uncover darker, more absorptive surfaces, these systems reflect less radiation back to the atmosphere and warm further. Arctic sea ice in the summer of 2012 covered the smallest area on record. Climate models suggest that there may be no summer ice there within a few decades, decreasing habitat for polar bears, seals, and seabirds. Higher temperatures also increase the likelihood of fires. In boreal forests of western North America and Russia, fires have burned twice the usual area in recent decades.

By studying how past periods of global warming and cooling affected plant communities, ecologists are trying to predict the consequences of future changes in temperature and precipitation. Analysis of fossilized pollen indicates that plant communities change dramatically with changes in temperature. Past climate changes occurred gradually, though, and most plant and animal populations had time to migrate into areas where abiotic conditions allowed them to survive.

Many organisms, especially plants that cannot disperse rapidly over long distances, may not be able to survive the rapid climate change projected to result from global warming. Furthermore, many habitats today are more fragmented than ever (see Concept 56.3), further limiting the ability of many organisms to migrate. For these reasons, ecologists are debating **assisted migration**, the translocation of a species to a favorable habitat beyond its native range to protect the species from human-caused threats. Most ecologists consider such an approach only as a last resort, in part because of the dangers of introducing potentially invasive species to new regions. Although scientists have yet to perform assisted migration, activists in 2008 transplanted seedlings of the endangered tree *Torreya taxifolia* hundreds of kilometers north from its native range in Florida to western North Carolina in anticipation of climate change. This "rewilding," as it is sometimes called, appeared to be driven in part by a desire for publicity; no ecological framework yet exists for deciding if, when, and where assisted migration is desirable.

Climate Change Solutions

We will need many approaches to slow global warming. Quick progress can be made by using energy more efficiently and by replacing fossil fuels with renewable solar and wind power and, more controversially, with nuclear power. Today, coal, gasoline, wood, and other organic fuels remain central to industrialized societies and cannot be burned without releasing CO_2. Stabilizing CO_2 emissions will require concerted international effort and changes in both personal lifestyles and industrial processes. International negotiations have yet to reach a global consensus on how to reduce greenhouse gas emissions.

Another important approach to slowing global warming is to reduce deforestation around the world, particularly in the tropics. Deforestation currently accounts for about 10% of greenhouse gas emissions. Recent research shows that paying countries *not* to cut forests could decrease the rate of deforestation by half within 10 to 20 years. Reduced deforestation would not only slow the buildup of greenhouse gases in our atmosphere, but would also sustain native forests and preserve biodiversity, a positive outcome for all.

Depletion of Atmospheric Ozone

Like carbon dioxide and other greenhouse gases, atmospheric ozone (O_3) has also changed in concentration because of human activities. Life on Earth is protected from the damaging effects of ultraviolet (UV) radiation by a layer of ozone located in the stratosphere 17–25 km above Earth's surface. However, satellite studies of the atmosphere show that the springtime ozone layer over Antarctica has thinned substantially since the mid-1970s (**Figure 56.29**). The

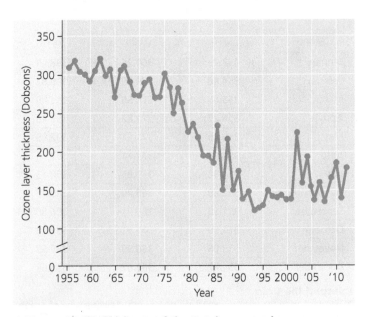

▲ Figure 56.29 **Thickness of the October ozone layer over Antarctica in units called Dobsons.**

① Chlorine from CFCs interacts with ozone (O_3), forming chlorine monoxide (ClO) and oxygen (O_2).

Chlorine atom

Chlorine O_3

O_2

O_2

ClO

ClO

③ Sunlight causes Cl_2O_2 to break down into O_2 and free chlorine atoms. The chlorine atoms can begin the cycle again.

Sunlight

Cl_2O_2

② Two ClO molecules react, forming chlorine peroxide (Cl_2O_2).

▲ **Figure 56.30 How free chlorine in the atmosphere destroys ozone.**

September 1979   September 2012

▲ **Figure 56.31 Erosion of Earth's ozone shield.** The ozone hole over Antarctica is visible as the dark blue patch in these images based on atmospheric data.

destruction of atmospheric ozone results primarily from the accumulation of chlorofluorocarbons (CFCs), chemicals once widely used in refrigeration and manufacturing. In the stratosphere, chlorine atoms released from CFCs react with ozone, reducing it to molecular O_2 **(Figure 56.30)**. Subsequent chemical reactions liberate the chlorine, allowing it to react with other ozone molecules in a catalytic chain reaction.

The thinning of the ozone layer is most apparent over Antarctica in spring, where cold, stable air allows the chain reaction to continue **(Figure 56.31)**. The magnitude of ozone depletion and the size of the ozone hole have been slightly smaller in recent years than the average for the last 20 years, but the hole still sometimes extends as far as the southernmost portions of Australia, New Zealand, and South America. At the more heavily populated middle latitudes, ozone levels have decreased 2–10% during the past 20 years.

Decreased ozone levels in the stratosphere increase the intensity of UV rays reaching Earth's surface. The consequences of ozone depletion for life on Earth may be severe for plants, animals, and microorganisms. Some scientists expect increases in both lethal and nonlethal forms of skin cancer and in cataracts among humans, as well as unpredictable effects on crops and natural communities, especially the phytoplankton that are responsible for a large proportion of Earth's primary production.

To study the consequences of ozone depletion, ecologists have conducted field experiments in which they use filters to decrease or block the UV radiation in sunlight. One such experiment, performed on a scrub ecosystem near the tip of South America, showed that when the ozone hole passed over the area, the amount of UV radiation reaching the ground increased sharply, causing more DNA damage

in plants that were not protected by filters. Scientists have shown similar DNA damage and a reduction in phytoplankton growth when the ozone hole opens over the Southern Ocean (Antarctic Ocean) each year.

The good news about the ozone hole is how quickly many countries have responded to it. Since 1987, at least 197 nations, including the United States, have signed the Montreal Protocol, a treaty that regulates the use of ozone-depleting chemicals. Most nations, again including the United States, have ended the production of CFCs. As a consequence of these actions, chlorine concentrations in the stratosphere have stabilized and ozone depletion is slowing. Even though CFC emissions are close to zero today, however, chlorine molecules already in the atmosphere will continue to influence stratospheric ozone levels for at least 50 years.

The partial destruction of Earth's ozone shield is one more example of how much humans have been able to disrupt the dynamics of ecosystems and the biosphere. It also highlights our ability to solve environmental problems when we set our minds to it.

CONCEPT CHECK 56.4

1. How can the addition of excess mineral nutrients to a lake threaten its fish population?

2. **MAKE CONNECTIONS** There are vast stores of organic matter in the soils of northern coniferous forests and tundra around the world. Suggest an explanation for why scientists who study global warming are closely monitoring these stores (see Figure 55.15).

3. **MAKE CONNECTIONS** Mutagens are chemical and physical agents that induce mutations in DNA (see Concept 17.5). How does reduced ozone concentration in the atmosphere increase the likelihood of mutations in various organisms?

For suggested answers, see Appendix A.

CONCEPT 56.5

Sustainable development can improve human lives while conserving biodiversity

With the increasing loss and fragmentation of habitats, changes in Earth's physical environment and climate, and increasing human population (see Concept 53.6), we face difficult trade-offs in managing the world's resources. Preserving all habitat patches isn't feasible, so biologists must help societies set conservation priorities by identifying which habitat patches are most crucial. Ideally, implementing these priorities should also improve the quality of life for local people. Ecologists use the concept of *sustainability* as a tool to establish long-term conservation priorities.

Sustainable Development

We need to understand the interconnections of the biosphere if we are to protect species from extinction and improve the quality of human life. To this end, many nations, scientific societies, and other groups have embraced the concept of **sustainable development**, economic development that meets the needs of people today without limiting the ability of future generations to meet their needs. The forward-looking Ecological Society of America, the world's largest organization of professional ecologists, endorsed an ongoing research agenda called the Sustainable Biosphere Initiative two decades ago. The goal of this initiative is to define and acquire the basic ecological information needed to develop, manage, and conserve Earth's resources as responsibly as possible. The research agenda includes studies of global change, including interactions between climate and ecological processes; biological diversity and its role in maintaining ecological processes; and the ways in which the productivity of natural and artificial ecosystems can be sustained. This initiative requires a strong commitment of human and economic resources.

Achieving sustainable development is an ambitious goal. To sustain ecosystem processes and stem the loss of biodiversity, we must connect life science with the social sciences, economics, and the humanities. We must also reassess our personal values. Those of us living in wealthier nations have a larger ecological footprint than do people living in developing nations (see Concept 53.6). By including the long-term costs in profit-and-loss calculations, we can learn to value the natural processes that sustain us. The following case study illustrates how the combination of scientific and personal efforts can make a significant difference in creating a truly sustainable world.

Case Study: *Sustainable Development in Costa Rica*

The success of conservation in Costa Rica (see Concept 56.3) has required a partnership between the national government, nongovernment organizations (NGOs), and private citizens. Many nature reserves established by individuals have been recognized by the government as national wildlife reserves and given significant tax benefits. However, conservation and restoration of biodiversity make up only one facet of sustainable development; the other key facet is improving the human condition.

How have the living conditions of the Costa Rican people changed as the country has pursued its conservation goals? Two of the most fundamental indicators of living conditions are infant mortality rate and life expectancy (see Concept 53.6). From 1930 to 2010, the infant mortality rate in Costa Rica declined from 170 to 9 per 1,000 live births; over the same period, life expectancy increased from about 43 years to 79 years **(Figure 56.32)**. Another indicator of living conditions is the literacy rate. The 2004 literacy rate in Costa Rica was 96%, compared to 97% in the United States. Such statistics show that living conditions in Costa Rica have improved greatly over the period in which the country has dedicated itself to conservation and restoration. While this result does not prove that conservation *causes* an improvement in human welfare, we can say with certainty that development in Costa Rica has attended to both nature *and* people.

Costa Rica still faces a number of challenges, particularly a human population growing rapidly at 1.5% per year. Nonetheless, if recent success is any guide, the people of Costa Rica will overcome the challenge of population growth in their quest for sustainable development.

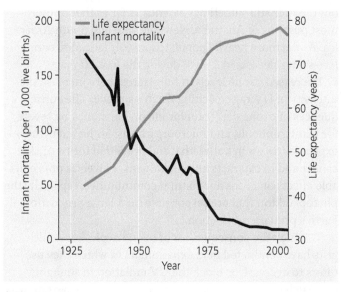

▲ **Figure 56.32 Infant mortality and life expectancy at birth in Costa Rica.**

The Future of the Biosphere

Our modern lives are very different from those of early humans, who hunted and gathered to survive. Their reverence for the natural world is evident in the early murals of wildlife they painted on cave walls **(Figure 56.33a)** and in the stylized visions of life they sculpted from bone and ivory **(Figure 56.33b)**.

Our lives reflect remnants of our ancestral attachment to nature and the diversity of life—the concept of *biophilia* that was introduced early in this chapter. We evolved in natural environments rich in biodiversity, and we still have an affinity for such settings **(Figure 56.33 c and d)**. E. O. Wilson makes the case that our biophilia is innate, an evolutionary product of natural selection acting on a brainy species whose survival depended on a close connection to the environment and a practical appreciation of plants and animals.

Our appreciation of life guides the field of biology today. We celebrate life by deciphering the genetic code that makes each species unique. We embrace life by using fossils and DNA to chronicle evolution through time. We preserve life through our efforts to classify and protect the millions of species on Earth. We respect life by using nature responsibly and reverently to improve human welfare.

Biology is the scientific expression of our desire to know nature. We are most likely to protect what we appreciate, and we are most likely to appreciate what we understand. By learning about the processes and diversity of life, we also become more aware of ourselves and our place in the biosphere. We hope this text has served you well in this lifelong adventure.

(a) Detail of animals in a 17,000-year-old cave painting, Lascaux, France

(b) A 30,000-year-old ivory carving of a water bird, found in Germany

---

CONCEPT CHECK 56.5

1. What is meant by the term *sustainable development*?

2. How might biophilia influence us to conserve species and restore ecosystems?

3. **WHAT IF?** Suppose a new fishery is discovered, and you are put in charge of developing it sustainably. What ecological data might you want on the fish population? What criteria would you apply for the fishery's development?

For suggested answers, see Appendix A.

(c) Nature lovers on a wildlife-watching expedition

▲ **Figure 56.33 Biophilia, past and present.**

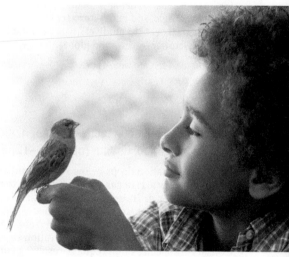

(d) A young biologist holding a songbird

SUMMARY OF KEY CONCEPTS

CONCEPT 56.1

Human activities threaten Earth's biodiversity (pp. 1255–1261)

- Biodiversity can be considered at three main levels:

Genetic diversity: source of variations that enable populations to adapt to environmental changes

Species diversity: important in maintaining structure of communities and food webs

Ecosystem diversity: provides life-sustaining services such as nutrient cycling and waste decomposition

- Our biophilia enables us to recognize the value of biodiversity for its own sake. Other species also provide humans with food, fiber, medicines, and **ecosystem services**.
- Four major threats to biodiversity are habitat loss, **introduced species**, overharvesting, and global change.

? *Give at least three examples of key ecosystem services that nature provides for people.*

CONCEPT 56.2

Population conservation focuses on population size, genetic diversity, and critical habitat (pp. 1261–1265)

- When a population drops below a **minimum viable population (MVP)** size, its loss of genetic variation due to nonrandom mating and genetic drift can trap it in an **extinction vortex**.
- The declining-population approach focuses on the environmental factors that cause decline, regardless of absolute population size. It follows a step-by-step conservation strategy.
- Conserving species often requires resolving conflicts between the habitat needs of **endangered species** and human demands.

? *Why is the minimum viable population size smaller for a genetically diverse population than for a less genetically diverse population?*

CONCEPT 56.3

Landscape and regional conservation help sustain biodiversity (pp. 1265–1269)

- The structure of a landscape can strongly influence biodiversity. As habitat fragmentation increases and edges become more extensive, biodiversity tends to decrease. **Movement corridors** can promote dispersal and help sustain populations.
- **Biodiversity hot spots** are also hot spots of extinction and thus prime candidates for protection. Sustaining biodiversity in parks and reserves requires management to ensure that human activities in the surrounding landscape do not harm the protected habitats. The **zoned reserve** model recognizes that conservation efforts often involve working in landscapes that are greatly affected by human activity.
- **Urban ecology** is the study of organisms and their environment in primarily urban settings.

? *Give two examples that show how habitat fragmentation can harm species in the long term.*

CONCEPT 56.4

Earth is changing rapidly as a result of human actions (pp. 1269–1275)

- Agriculture removes plant nutrients from ecosystems, so large supplements are usually required. The nutrients in fertilizer can pollute groundwater and surface-water aquatic ecosystems, where they can stimulate excess algal growth (eutrophication).
- The release of toxic wastes and pharmaceuticals has polluted the environment with harmful substances that often persist for long periods and become increasingly concentrated in successively higher trophic levels of food webs (**biological magnification**).
- Because of human activities, the atmospheric concentration of CO_2 and other greenhouse gases has been steadily increasing. The ultimate effects include significant climate change.
- The ozone layer reduces the penetration of UV radiation through the atmosphere. Human activities, notably the release of chlorine-containing pollutants, have eroded the ozone layer, but government policies are helping to solve the problem.

? *In the face of biological magnification of toxins, is it healthier to feed at a lower or higher trophic level? Explain.*

CONCEPT 56.5

Sustainable development can improve human lives while conserving biodiversity (pp. 1276–1277)

- The goal of the Sustainable Biosphere Initiative is to acquire the ecological information needed for the development, management, and conservation of Earth's resources.
- Costa Rica's success in conserving tropical biodiversity has involved a partnership among the government, other organizations, and private citizens. Human living conditions in Costa Rica have improved along with ecological conservation.
- By learning about biological processes and the diversity of life, we become more aware of our close connection to the environment and the value of other organisms that share it.

? *Why is sustainability such an important goal for conservation biologists?*

TEST YOUR UNDERSTANDING

LEVEL 1: KNOWLEDGE/COMPREHENSION

1. One characteristic that distinguishes a population in an extinction vortex from most other populations is that
   a. it is a rare, top-level predator.
   b. its effective population size is much lower than its total population size.
   c. its genetic diversity is very low.
   d. it is not well adapted to edge conditions.

2. The main cause of the increase in the amount of CO_2 in Earth's atmosphere over the past 150 years is
   a. increased worldwide primary production.
   b. increased worldwide standing crop.
   c. an increase in the amount of infrared radiation absorbed by the atmosphere.
   d. the burning of larger amounts of wood and fossil fuels.

3. What is the single greatest threat to biodiversity?
   a. overharvesting of commercially important species
   b. habitat alteration, fragmentation, and destruction
   c. introduced species that compete with native species
   d. pollution of Earth's air, water, and soil

LEVEL 2: APPLICATION/ANALYSIS

4. Which of the following is a consequence of biological magnification?
   a. Toxic chemicals in the environment pose greater risk to top-level predators than to primary consumers.
   b. Populations of top-level predators are generally smaller than populations of primary consumers.
   c. The biomass of producers in an ecosystem is generally higher than the biomass of primary consumers.
   d. Only a small portion of the energy captured by producers is transferred to consumers.

5. Which of the following strategies would most rapidly increase the genetic diversity of a population in an extinction vortex?
   a. Establish a reserve that protects the population's habitat.
   b. Introduce new individuals transported from other populations of the same species.
   c. Sterilize the least fit individuals in the population.
   d. Control populations of the endangered population's predators and competitors.

6. Of the following statements about protected areas that have been established to preserve biodiversity, which one is *not* correct?
   a. About 25% of Earth's land area is now protected.
   b. National parks are one of many types of protected areas.
   c. Management of a protected area should be coordinated with management of the land surrounding the area.
   d. It is especially important to protect biodiversity hot spots.

LEVEL 3: SYNTHESIS/EVALUATION

7. **DRAW IT** (a) Referring to Figure 56.28, estimate the average CO_2 concentration in 1975 and in 2012. (b) What was the rate of CO_2 concentration increase (ppm/yr) from 1975 to 2012? (c) Assuming that the CO_2 concentration continues to rise as fast as it did from 1975 to 2012, what will be the approximate CO_2 concentration in 2100? (d) Draw a graph of average CO_2 concentration from 1975 to 2012 and then use a dashed line to extend the graph to the year 2100. (e) What ecological factors and human decisions will influence the actual rise in CO_2 concentration? (f) How might additional scientific data help societies predict this value?

8. **EVOLUTION CONNECTION**
   The fossil record indicates that there have been five mass extinction events in the past 500 million years (see Concept 25.4). Many ecologists think we are currently entering a sixth mass extinction event because of the threats to biodiversity described in this chapter. Briefly discuss the history of mass extinctions and the length of time it typically takes for species diversity to recover through the process of evolution. Explain why this should motivate us to slow the loss of biodiversity today.

9. **SCIENTIFIC INQUIRY**
   DRAW IT Suppose that you are managing a forest reserve, and one of your goals is to protect local populations of woodland birds from parasitism by the brown-headed cowbird. You know that female cowbirds usually do not venture more than about 100 m into a forest and that nest parasitism is reduced when woodland birds nest away from forest edges. The reserve you manage extends about 6,000 m from east to west and 1,000 m from north to south. It is surrounded by a deforested pasture on the west, an agricultural field for 500 m in the southwest corner, and intact forest everywhere else. You must build a road, 10 m by 1,000 m, from the north to the south side of the reserve and construct a maintenance building that will take up 100 m^2 in the reserve. Draw a map of the reserve, showing where you would put the road and the building to minimize cowbird intrusion along edges. Explain your reasoning.

10. **WRITE ABOUT A THEME: INTERACTIONS**
    One factor favoring rapid population growth by an introduced species is the absence of the predators, parasites, and pathogens that controlled its population in the region where it evolved. In a short essay (100–150 words), explain how evolution by natural selection would influence the rate at which native predators, parasites, and pathogens in a region of introduction attack an introduced species.

11. SYNTHESIZE YOUR KNOWLEDGE

Big cats, such as the Siberian tiger (*Panthera tigris altaica*) shown here, are one of the most endangered groups of mammals in the world. Based on what you've learned in this chapter, discuss some of the approaches you would use to help preserve them.

For selected answers, see Appendix A.

MasteringBiology®

Students Go to **MasteringBiology** for assignments, the eText, and the Study Area with practice tests, animations, and activities.

Instructors Go to **MasteringBiology** for automatically graded tutorials and questions that you can assign to your students, plus Instructor Resources.

Chapter 1

Concept Check 1.1

1. Examples: A molecule consists of *atoms* bonded together. Each organelle has an orderly arrangement of *molecules*. Photosynthetic plant cells contain *organelles* called chloroplasts. A tissue consists of a group of similar *cells*. Organs such as the heart are constructed from several *tissues*. A complex multicellular organism, such as a plant, has several types of *organs*, such as leaves and roots. A population is a set of *organisms* of the same species. A community consists of *populations* of the various species inhabiting a specific area. An ecosystem consists of a biological *community* along with the nonliving factors important to life, such as air, soil, and water. The biosphere is made up of all of Earth's *ecosystems*. **2.** (a) New properties emerge at successive levels of biological organization: Structure and function are correlated. (b) Life's processes involve the expression and transmission of genetic information. (c) Life requires the transfer and transformation of energy and matter. **3.** Some possible answers: *Organization (Emergent properties)*: The ability of a human heart to pump blood requires an intact heart; it is not a capability of any of the heart's tissues or cells working alone. *Organization (Structure and function)*: The strong, sharp teeth of a wolf are well suited to grasping and dismembering its prey. *Information*: Human eye color is determined by the combination of genes inherited from the two parents. *Energy and Matter*: A plant, such as a grass, absorbs energy from the sun and transforms it into molecules that act as stored fuel. Animals can eat parts of the plant and use the food for energy to carry out their activities. *Interactions (Ecosystems)*: A mouse eats food, such as nuts or grasses, and deposits some of the food material as wastes (feces and urine). Construction of a nest rearranges the physical environment and may hasten degradation of some of its components. The mouse may also act as food for a predator. *Interactions (Molecules)*: When your stomach is full, it signals your brain to decrease your appetite. *Evolution*: All plants have chloroplasts, indicating their descent from a common ancestor.

Concept Check 1.2

1. An address pinpoints a location by tracking from broader to narrower categories—a state, city, zip, street, and building number. This is analogous to the groups-subordinate-to-groups structure of biological taxonomy. **2.** The naturally occurring heritable variation in a population is "edited" by natural selection because individuals with heritable traits better suited to the environment survive and reproduce more successfully than others. Over time, better-suited individuals persist and their percentage in the population increases, while less well-suited individuals become less prevalent—a type of population editing.

3.

Ancestral eukaryotes
- Plants
- Fungi
- Animals

Concept Check 1.3

1. Inductive reasoning derives generalizations from specific cases; deductive reasoning predicts specific outcomes from general premises. **2.** The fur coat color of the mouse models is the independent variable because this is the variable that was changed intentionally by the researchers. Predation is the dependent variable, measured by the investigators and recorded as the proportion of the total number of attacked models. **3.** Compared to a hypothesis, a scientific theory is usually more general and substantiated by a much greater amount of evidence. Natural selection is an explanatory idea that applies to all kinds of organisms and is supported by vast amounts of evidence of various kinds. **4.** Based on the mouse coloration in Figure 1.25, you might expect that the mice that live on the sandy soil would be lighter in color and those that live on the lava rock would be much darker. And in fact, that is what researchers have found. You would predict that each color of mouse would be less preyed upon in its native habitat than it would be in the other habitat. (Research results also support this prediction.) You could repeat the Hoekstra experiment with colored models, painted to resemble these two types of mouse. Or you could try transplanting some of each population to its non-native habitat and counting how many you can recapture over the next few days, then comparing the four samples as was done in Hoekstra's experiment. (The painted models are easier to recapture, of course!) In the live mouse transplantation experiment, you would have to do controls to eliminate the variable represented by the transplanted mice being in a new, unknown territory. You could control for the transplantation process by transplanting some dark mice from one area of lava rock to one far distant, and some light mice from one area of sandy soil to a distant area.

Concept Check 1.4

1. Science aims to understand natural phenomena and how they work, while technology involves application of scientific discoveries for a particular purpose or to solve a specific problem. **2.** Natural selection could be operating. Malaria is present in sub-Saharan Africa, so there might be an advantage to people with the sickle-cell disease form of the gene that makes them more able to survive and pass on their genes to offspring. Among those of African descent living in the United States, where malaria is absent, there would be no advantage, so they would be selected against more strongly, resulting in fewer individuals with the sickle-cell disease form of the gene.

Summary of Key Concepts Questions

1.1 Evolution explains the most fundamental aspects of all life on Earth. It accounts for the common features shared by all forms of life due to descent from a common ancestor, while also providing an explanation for how the great diversity of living organisms on the planet has arisen. **1.2** Ancestors of the dandelion plant may have exhibited variation in how well their seeds spread to fertile soil for rooting. The variant plants that produced seeds that could travel farther may have had less competition upon reaching fertile soil. They may therefore have survived better and been able to produce more offspring. Over time, a higher and higher proportion of individuals in the population would have had the adaptation of parachute-like structures attached to seeds for seed dispersal. **1.3** Gathering and interpreting data are core activities in the scientific process, and they are affected by, and affect in turn, three other arenas of the scientific process: exploration and discovery, community analysis and feedback, and societal benefits and outcomes. **1.4** Different approaches taken by scientists studying natural phenomena at different levels complement each other, so more is learned about each problem being studied. A diversity of backgrounds among scientists may lead to fruitful ideas in the same way that important innovations have often arisen where a mix of cultures coexist, due to multiple different viewpoints.

Test Your Understanding

1. b **2.** d **3.** a **4.** c **5.** c **6.** c **7.** b **8.** c **9.** a **10.** d
11. Your figure should show: (1) For the biosphere, the Earth with an arrow coming out of a tropical ocean; (2) for the ecosystem, a distant view of a coral reef; (3) for the community, a collection of reef animals and algae, with corals, fishes, some seaweed, and any other organisms you can think of; (4) for the population, a group of fish of the same species; (5) for the organism, one fish from your population; (6) for the organ, the fish's stomach, and for the organ system, the whole digestive tract (see Chapter 41 for help); (7) for a tissue, a group of similar cells from the stomach; (8) for a cell, one cell from the tissue, showing its nucleus and a few other organelles; (9) for an organelle, the nucleus, where most of the cell's DNA is located; and (10) for a molecule, a DNA double helix. Your sketches can be very rough!

Chapter 2

Figure Questions

Figure 2.7 Atomic number = 12; 12 protons, 12 electrons; 3 electron shells; 2 valence electrons **Figure 2.14** One possible answer:

Figure 2.17 The plant is submerged in water (H_2O), in which the CO_2 is dissolved. The sun's energy is used to make sugar, which is found in the plant and can act as food for the plant itself, as well as for animals that eat the plant. The oxygen (O_2) is present in the bubbles.

Concept Check 2.1

1. Table salt (sodium chloride) is made up of sodium and chlorine. We are able to eat the compound, showing that it has different properties from those of a metal (sodium) and a poisonous gas (chlorine). **2.** Yes, because an organism requires trace elements, even though only in small amounts **3.** A person with an iron deficiency will probably show fatigue and other effects of a low oxygen level in the blood. (The condition is called anemia and can also result from too few red blood cells or abnormal hemoglobin.) **4.** Variant ancestral plants that could tolerate elevated levels of the elements in serpentine soils could grow and reproduce there. (Plants that were well adapted to nonserpentine soils would not be expected to survive in serpentine areas.) The offspring of the variants would also vary, with those most capable of thriving under serpentine conditions growing best and reproducing most. Over many generations, this probably led to the serpentine-adapted species we see today.

Concept Check 2.2

1. 7   **2.** $^{15}_{7}N$ **3.** 9 electrons; two electron shells; $1s$, $2s$, $2p$ (three orbitals); 1 electron is needed to fill the valence shell.   **4.** The elements in a row all have the same number of electron shells. In a column, all the elements have the same number of electrons in their valence shells.

Concept Check 2.3

1. Each carbon atom has only three covalent bonds instead of the required four.   **2.** The attraction between oppositely charged ions, forming ionic bonds   **3.** If you could synthesize molecules that mimic these shapes, you might be able to treat diseases or conditions caused by the inability of affected individuals to synthesize such molecules.

Concept Check 2.4

1.

$$2H_2 \qquad O_2 \qquad 2H_2O$$

2. At equilibrium, the forward and reverse reactions occur at the same rate.
3. $C_6H_{12}O_6 + 6 O_2 \rightarrow 6 CO_2 + 6 H_2O + Energy$. Glucose and oxygen react to form carbon dioxide and water, releasing energy. We breathe in oxygen because we need it for this reaction to occur, and we breathe out carbon dioxide because it is a by-product of this reaction. (This reaction is called cellular respiration, and you will learn more about it in Chapter 9.)

Summary of Key Concepts Questions

2.1 Iodine (part of a thyroid hormone) and iron (part of hemoglobin in blood) are both trace elements, required in minute quantities. Calcium and phosphorus (components of bones and teeth) are needed by the body in much greater quantities.
2.2

Neon ($_{10}$Ne)   Argon ($_{18}$Ar)

Both neon and argon have completed valence shells, containing 8 electrons. They do not have unpaired electrons that could participate in chemical bonds.   **2.3** Electrons are shared equally between the two atoms in a nonpolar covalent bond. In a polar covalent bond, the electrons are drawn closer to the more electronegative atom. In the formation of ions, an electron is completely transferred from one atom to a much more electronegative atom.   **2.4** The concentration of products would increase as the added reactants were converted to products. Eventually, an equilibrium would again be reached in which the forward and reverse reactions were proceeding at the same rate and the relative concentrations of reactants and products returned to where they were before the addition of more reactants.

Test Your Understanding

1. a   **2.** d   **3.** b   **4.** a   **5.** d   **6.** b   **7.** c   **8.** d
9.

a.
H :Ö: Ċ: Ċ:: Ö
This structure makes sense because all valence shells are complete, and all bonds have the correct number of electrons.

b.
H :Ċ: H. Ċ:: Ö
This structure doesn't make sense because H has only 1 electron to share, so it cannot form bonds with 2 atoms.

Chapter 3

Figure Questions

Figure 3.2 One possible answer:

Figure 3.6 Without hydrogen bonds, water would behave like other small molecules, and the solid phase (ice) would be denser than liquid water. The ice would sink to the bottom and would no longer insulate the whole body of water, which would eventually freeze because the average annual temperature at the South Pole is $-50°C$. The krill could not survive.   **Figure 3.7** Heating the solution would cause the water to evaporate faster than it is evaporating at room temperature. At a certain point, there wouldn't be enough water molecules to dissolve the salt ions. The salt would start coming out of solution and re-forming crystals. Eventually, all the water would evaporate, leaving behind a pile of salt like the original pile.

Concept Check 3.1

1. Electronegativity is the attraction of an atom for the electrons of a covalent bond. Because oxygen is more electronegative than hydrogen, the oxygen atom in H_2O pulls electrons toward itself, resulting in a partial negative charge on the oxygen atom and partial positive charges on the hydrogen atoms. Atoms in neighboring water molecules with opposite partial charges are attracted to each other, forming a hydrogen bond.   **2.** The hydrogen atoms of one molecule, with their partial positive charges, would repel the hydrogen atoms of the adjacent molecule.   **3.** The covalent bonds of water molecules would not be polar, and water molecules would not form hydrogen bonds with each other.

Concept Check 3.2

1. Hydrogen bonds hold neighboring water molecules together. This cohesion helps chains of water molecules move upward against gravity in water-conducting cells as water evaporates from the leaves. Adhesion between water molecules and the walls of the water-conducting cells also helps counter gravity.   **2.** High humidity hampers cooling by suppressing the evaporation of sweat.   **3.** As water freezes, it expands because water molecules move farther apart in forming ice crystals. When there is water in a crevice of a boulder, expansion due to freezing may crack the boulder.   **4.** The hydrophobic substance repels water, perhaps helping to keep the ends of the legs from becoming coated with water and breaking through the surface. If the legs were coated with a hydrophilic substance, water would be drawn up them, possibly making it more difficult for the water strider to walk on water.

Concept Check 3.3

1. 10^5, or 100,000   **2.** $[H^+] = 0.01 M = 10^{-2} M$, so pH = 2.   **3.** $CH_3COOH \rightarrow CH_3COO^- + H^+$. CH_3COOH is the acid (the H^+ donor), and CH_3COO^- is the base (the H^+ acceptor).   **4.** The pH of the water should decrease from 7 to about 2; the pH of the acetic acid solution will decrease only a small amount, because as a weak acid, it acts as a buffer. The reaction shown for question 3 will shift to the left, with CH_3COO^- accepting the influx of H^+ and becoming CH_3COOH molecules.

Summary of Key Concepts Questions
3.1

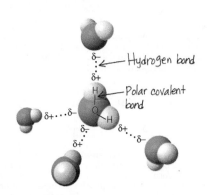

No. A covalent bond is a strong bond in which electrons are shared between two atoms. A hydrogen bond is a weak bond, which does not involve electron sharing, but is simply an attraction between two partial charges on neighboring atoms. **3.2** Ions dissolve in water when polar water molecules form a hydration shell around them. Polar molecules dissolve as water molecules form hydrogen bonds with them and surround them. Solutions are homogeneous mixtures of solute and solvent. **3.3** CO_2 reacts with H_2O to form carbonic acid (H_2CO_3), which dissociates into H^+ and bicarbonate (HCO_3^-). Although the carbonic acid–bicarbonate reaction is a buffering system, adding CO_2 drives the reaction to the right, releasing more H^+ and lowering pH. The excess protons combine with CO_3^{2-} to form bicarbonate ions, lowering the concentration of carbonate ions available for the formation of calcium carbonate (calcification) by corals.

Test Your Understanding
1. c 2. d 3. c 4. a 5. d
6.

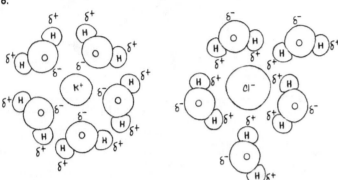

7. Due to intermolecular hydrogen bonds, water has a high specific heat (the amount of heat required to increase the temperature of water by 1°C). When water is heated, much of the heat is absorbed in breaking hydrogen bonds before the water molecules increase their motion and the temperature increases. Conversely, when water is cooled, many H bonds are formed, which releases a significant amount of heat. This release of heat can provide some protection against freezing of the plants' leaves, thus protecting the cells from damage.

Chapter 4

Figure Questions
Figure 4.2 Because the concentration of the reactants influences the equilibrium (as discussed in Chapter 2), there might have been more HCN relative to CH_2O, since there would have been a higher concentration of the reactant gas containing nitrogen.
Figure 4.4

$$Na\cdot \quad \cdot\overset{\displaystyle\cdot}{\underset{\displaystyle\cdot}{P}}\cdot \quad \cdot\overset{\displaystyle\cdot\cdot}{\underset{\displaystyle\cdot\cdot}{S}}: \quad \cdot\overset{\displaystyle\cdot\cdot}{\underset{\displaystyle\cdot\cdot}{Cl}}:$$

Figure 4.6 The tails of fats contain only carbon-hydrogen bonds, which are relatively nonpolar. Because the tails occupy the bulk of a fat molecule, they make the molecule as a whole nonpolar and therefore incapable of forming hydrogen bonds with water.
Figure 4.7

$$\begin{array}{c} H \\ | \\ H-C-H \\ H | \quad | H \\ H-C-C-C-H \\ H | \quad | H \\ H-C-H \\ | \\ H \end{array}$$

Concept Check 4.1
1. Prior to Wöhler's experiment, the prevailing view was that only living organisms could synthesize "organic" compounds. Wöhler made urea, an organic compound, without the involvement of living organisms. **2.** The spark provided energy needed for the inorganic molecules in the atmosphere to react with each other. (You'll learn more about energy and chemical reactions in Chapter 8.)

Concept Check 4.2
1.

$$a.\; \overset{H}{\underset{H}{>}}C=C\overset{H}{\underset{H}{<}} \qquad b.\; \overset{H}{\underset{Cl}{>}}C=C\overset{Cl}{\underset{H}{<}}$$

2. The forms of C_4H_{10} in (b) are structural isomers, as are the butenes in (c). 3. Both consist largely of hydrocarbon chains. **4.** No. There is not enough diversity in the atoms. It can't form structural isomers because there is only one way for three carbons to attach to each other (in a line). There are no double bonds, so *cis-trans* isomers are not possible. Each carbon has at least two hydrogens attached to it, so the molecule is symmetrical and cannot have enantiomers.

Concept Check 4.3
1. It has both an amino group ($-NH_2$), which makes it an amine, and a carboxyl group ($-COOH$), which makes it a carboxylic acid. **2.** The ATP molecule loses

a phosphate, becoming ADP. **3.** A chemical group that can act as a base has been replaced with a group that can act as an acid, increasing the acidic properties of the molecule. The shape of the molecule would also change, likely changing the molecules with which it can interact. The original cysteine molecule has an asymmetric carbon in the center. After replacement of the amino group with a carboxyl group, this carbon is no longer asymmetric.

$$\begin{array}{c} O \quad H \quad O \\ \| \quad | \quad \| \\ C-C-C \\ / \quad | \quad \backslash \\ HO \quad CH_2 \quad OH \\ | \\ SH \end{array}$$

Summary of Key Concepts Questions
4.1 Miller showed that organic molecules could form under the physical and chemical conditions estimated to have been present on early Earth. This abiotic synthesis of organic molecules would have been a first step in the origin of life. **4.2** Acetone and propanal are structural isomers. Acetic acid and glycine have no asymmetric carbons, whereas glycerol phosphate has one. Therefore, glycerol phosphate can exist as forms that are enantiomers, but acetic acid and glycine cannot. **4.3** The methyl group is nonpolar and not reactive. The other six groups are called functional groups because they can participate in chemical reactions. Also, all except the sulfhydryl group are hydrophilic, increasing the solubility of organic compounds in water.

Test Your Understanding
1. b 2. b 3. c 4. c 5. a 6. b 7. a
8. The molecule on the right; the middle carbon is asymmetric.
9. $\cdot\overset{\displaystyle\cdot}{Si}\cdot$ Si has 4 valence electrons, the same number as carbon. Therefore, silicon would be able to form long chains, including branches, that could act as skeletons for large molecules. It would clearly do this much better than neon (with no valence electrons) or aluminum (with 3 valence electrons).

Chapter 5

Figure Questions
Figure 5.3 Glucose and fructose are structural isomers.
Figure 5.4

Linear form   Ring forming   Ring form

Note that the oxygen on carbon 5 lost its proton and that the oxygen on carbon 2, which used to be the carbonyl oxygen, gained a proton. Four carbons are in the fructose ring, and two are not. (The latter two carbons are attached to carbons 2 and 5, which are in the ring.) The fructose ring differs from the glucose ring, which has five carbons in the ring and one that is not. (Note that the orientation of this fructose molecule is flipped horizontally relative to that of the one in Figure 5.5b.)
Figure 5.5

Glucose   Glucose   Maltose

Glucose   Fructose   Sucrose

(Note that fructose is oriented differently from glucose in Figure 5.5b, and from the fructose shown in the answer for Figure 5.4, above.)

Figure 5.11

Figure 5.12

Figure 5.15

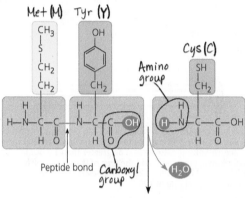

Figure 5.19 The R group on glutamic acid is acidic and hydrophilic, whereas that on valine is nonpolar and hydrophobic. Therefore, it is unlikely that valine and glutamic acid participate in the same intramolecular interactions. A change in these interactions could (and does) cause a disruption of molecular structure.
Figure 5.22 The helical stretches are α helices; these can be seen clearly in many places in the RNA polymerase II model, such as the bottom middle, the upper right, and the lower right areas. Although β pleated sheets may be present, they are not as easy to see.
Figure 5.26 Using a genomics approach allows us to use gene sequences to identify species, and to learn about evolutionary relationships among any two species. This is because all species are related by their evolutionary history, and the evidence is in the DNA sequences. Proteomics—looking at proteins that are expressed—allows us to learn about how organisms or cells are functioning at a given time, or in an association with another species.

Concept Check 5.1
1. The four main classes are proteins, carbohydrates, lipids, and nucleic acids. Lipids are not polymers.   **2.** Nine, with one water molecule required to hydrolyze each connection between adjacent monomers   **3.** The amino acids in the fish protein must be released in hydrolysis reactions and incorporated into other proteins in dehydration reactions.

Concept Check 5.2
1. $C_3H_6O_3$ **2.** $C_{12}H_{22}O_{11}$ **3.** The antibiotic treatment is likely to have killed the cellulose-digesting prokaryotes in the cow's gut. The absence of these prokaryotes would hamper the cow's ability to obtain energy from food and could lead to weight loss and possibly death. Thus, prokaryotic species are reintroduced, in appropriate combinations, in the gut culture given to treated cows.

Concept Check 5.3
1. Both have a glycerol molecule attached to fatty acids. The glycerol of a fat has three fatty acids attached, whereas the glycerol of a phospholipid is attached to two fatty acids and one phosphate group.   **2.** Human sex hormones are steroids, a type of compound that is hydrophobic and thus classified as a lipid.   **3.** The oil droplet membrane could consist of a single layer of phospholipids rather than a bilayer, because an arrangement in which the hydrophobic tails of the membrane phospholipids were in contact with the hydrocarbon regions of the oil molecules would be more stable.

Concept Check 5.4
1. Secondary structure involves hydrogen bonds between atoms of the polypeptide backbone. Tertiary structure involves interactions between atoms of the

side chains of the amino acid subunits.   **2.** The two ring forms of glucose are called α and β, depending on how the glycosidic bond dictates the position of a hydroxyl group. Proteins have α helices and β pleated sheets, two types of repeating structures found in polypeptides due to interactions between the repeating constituents of the chain (not the side chains). The hemoglobin molecule is made up of two types of polypeptides, containing two molecules each of α-globin and β-globin.   **3.** These are all nonpolar, hydrophobic amino acids, so you would expect this region to be located in the interior of the folded polypeptide, where it would not contact the aqueous environment inside the cell.

Concept Check 5.5
1.

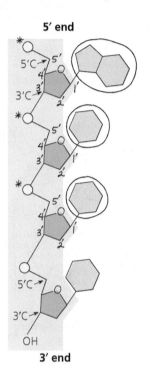

2.

5′–T A G G C C T–3′
3′–A T C C G G A–5′

Concept Check 5.6
1. The DNA of an organism encodes all of its proteins, and proteins are the molecules that carry out the work of cells, whether an organism is unicellular or multicellular. By knowing the DNA sequence of an organism, scientists would be able to catalog the protein sequences as well.   **2.** Ultimately, the DNA sequence carries the information necessary to make the proteins that determine the traits of a particular species. Because the traits of the two species are similar, you would expect the proteins to be similar as well, and therefore the gene sequences should also have a high degree of similarity.

Summary of Key Concepts Questions
Concept 5.1 The polymers of large carbohydrates (polysaccharides), proteins, and nucleic acids are built from three different types of monomers (monosaccharides, amino acids, and nucleotides, respectively).   **Concept 5.2** Both starch and cellulose are polymers of glucose, but the glucose monomers are in the α configuration in starch and the β configuration in cellulose. The glycosidic linkages thus have different geometries, giving the polymers different shapes and thus different properties. Starch is an energy-storage compound in plants; cellulose is a structural component of plant cell walls. Humans can hydrolyze starch to provide energy but cannot hydrolyze cellulose. Cellulose aids in the passage of food through the digestive tract.   **Concept 5.3** Lipids are not polymers because they do not exist as a chain of linked monomers. They are not considered macromolecules because they do not reach the giant size of many polysaccharides, proteins, and nucleic acids.   **Concept 5.4** A polypeptide, which may consist of hundreds of amino acids in a specific sequence (primary structure), has regions of coils and pleats (secondary structure), which are then folded into irregular contortions (tertiary structure) and may be noncovalently associated with other polypeptides (quaternary structure). The linear order of amino acids, with the varying properties of their side chains (R groups), determines what secondary and tertiary structures will form to produce a protein. The resulting unique three-dimensional shapes of proteins are key to their specific and diverse functions.   **Concept 5.5** The complementary base pairing of the two strands of DNA makes possible the precise replication of DNA every time a cell divides, ensuring that genetic information is faithfully transmitted. In some types of RNA, complementary base pairing enables RNA molecules to assume specific three-dimensional shapes that facilitate diverse

functions.   **Concept 5.6** You would expect the human gene sequence to be most similar to that of the mouse (another mammal), then to that of the fish (another vertebrate), and least similar to that of the fruit fly (an invertebrate).

Test Your Understanding
1. d   2. a   3. b   4. a   5. b   6. b   7. c
8.

	Monomers or Components	Polymer or larger molecule	Type of linkage
Carbohydrates	Monosaccharides	Polysaccharides	Glycosidic linkages
Lipids	Fatty acids	Triacylglycerols	Ester linkages
Proteins	Amino acids	Polypeptides	Peptide bonds
Nucleic acids	Nucleotides	Polynucleotides	Phosphodiester linkages

9.

Original Strand   Complementary Strand

Chapter 6

Figure Questions

Figure 6.6 A phospholipid is a lipid consisting of a glycerol molecule joined to two fatty acids and one phosphate group. Together, the glycerol and phosphate end of the phospholipid form the "head," which is hydrophilic, while the hydrocarbon chains on the fatty acids form hydrophobic "tails." The presence in a single molecule of both a hydrophilic and a hydrophobic region makes the molecule ideal as the main building block of a cell or organelle membrane, which is a phospholipid bilayer. In this bilayer, the hydrophobic regions can associate with each other on the inside of the membrane, while the hydrophilic region of each can be in contact with the aqueous solution on either side.   **Figure 6.9** The DNA in a chromosome dictates synthesis of a messenger RNA (mRNA) molecule, which then moves out to the cytoplasm. There, the information is used for the production, on ribosomes, of proteins that carry out cellular functions. **Figure 6.22** Each centriole has 9 sets of 3 microtubules, so the entire centrosome (two centrioles) has 54 microtubules. Each microtubule consists of a helical array of tubulin dimers (as shown in Table 6.1).

1 microtubule

Triplet of microtubules

Figure 6.24

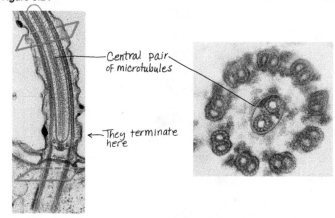

Central pair of microtubules

They terminate here

The two central microtubules terminate above the basal body, so they aren't present at the level of the cross section through the basal body, indicated by the lower red rectangle in (a).

Concept Check 6.1
1. Stains used for light microscopy are colored molecules that bind to cell components, affecting the light passing through, while stains used for electron microscopy involve heavy metals that affect the beams of electrons.   2. (a) Light microscope, (b) scanning electron microscope

Concept Check 6.2
1. See Figure 6.8.
2.

125

1

This cell would have the same volume as the cells in columns 2 and 3 but proportionally more surface area than that in column 2 and less than that in column 3. Thus, the surface-to-volume ratio should be greater than 1.2 but less than 6. To obtain the surface area, you would add the area of the six sides (the top, bottom, sides, and ends): $125 + 125 + 125 + 125 + 1 + 1 = 502$. The surface-to-volume ratio equals 502 divided by a volume of 125, or 4.0.

Concept Check 6.3
1. Ribosomes in the cytoplasm translate the genetic message, carried from the DNA in the nucleus by mRNA, into a polypeptide chain.   2. Nucleoli consist of DNA and the ribosomal RNA (rRNA) made according to its instructions, as well as proteins imported from the cytoplasm. Together, the rRNA and proteins are assembled into large and small ribosomal subunits. (These are exported through nuclear pores to the cytoplasm, where they will participate in polypeptide synthesis.)   3. Each chromosome consists of one long DNA molecule attached to numerous protein molecules, a combination called chromatin. As a cell begins division, each chromosome becomes "condensed" as its diffuse mass of chromatin coils up.

Concept Check 6.4
1. The primary distinction between rough and smooth ER is the presence of bound ribosomes on the rough ER. Both types of ER make phospholipids, but membrane proteins and secretory proteins are all produced by the ribosomes on the rough ER. The smooth ER also functions in detoxification, carbohydrate metabolism, and storage of calcium ions.   2. Transport vesicles move membranes and substances they enclose between other components of the endomembrane system.   3. The mRNA is synthesized in the nucleus and then passes out through a nuclear pore to be translated on a bound ribosome, attached to the rough ER. The protein is synthesized into the lumen of the ER and perhaps modified there. A transport vesicle carries the protein to the Golgi apparatus. After further modification in the Golgi, another transport vesicle carries it back to the ER, where it will perform its cellular function.

Concept Check 6.5
1. Both organelles are involved in energy transformation, mitochondria in cellular respiration and chloroplasts in photosynthesis. They both have multiple membranes that separate their interiors into compartments. In both organelles, the innermost membranes—cristae, or infoldings of the inner membrane, in mitochondria, and the thylakoid membranes in chloroplasts—have large surface areas with embedded enzymes that carry out their main functions.   2. Yes. Plant cells are able to make their own sugar by photosynthesis, but mitochondria in these eukaryotic cells are the organelles that are able to generate energy from sugars, a function required in all cells.   3. Mitochondria and chloroplasts are not derived from the ER, nor are they connected physically or via transport vesicles to organelles of the endomembrane system. Mitochondria and chloroplasts are structurally quite different from vesicles derived from the ER, which are bounded by a single membrane.

Concept Check 6.6

1. Both systems of movement involve long filaments that are moved in relation to each other by motor proteins that grip, release, and grip again adjacent polymers. **2.** Such individuals have defects in the microtubule-based movement of cilia and flagella. Thus, the sperm can't move because of malfunctioning or nonexistent flagella, and the airways are compromised because cilia that line the trachea malfunction or don't exist, and so mucus cannot be cleared from the lungs.

Concept Check 6.7

1. The most obvious difference is the presence of direct cytoplasmic connections between cells of plants (plasmodesmata) and animals (gap junctions). These connections result in the cytoplasm being continuous between adjacent cells. **2.** The cell would not be able to function properly and would probably soon die, as the cell wall or ECM must be permeable to allow the exchange of matter between the cell and its external environment. Molecules involved in energy production and use must be allowed entry, as well as those that provide information about the cell's environment. Other molecules, such as products synthesized by the cell for export and the by-products of cellular respiration, must be allowed to exit. **3.** The parts of the protein that face aqueous regions would be expected to have polar or charged (hydrophilic) amino acids, while the parts that go through the membrane would be expected to have nonpolar (hydrophobic) amino acids. You would predict polar or charged amino acids at each end (tail), in the region of the cytoplasmic loop, and in the regions of the two extracellular loops. You would predict nonpolar amino acids in the four regions that go through the membrane between the tails and loops.

Summary of Key Concepts Questions

6.1 Both light and electron microscopy allow cells to be studied visually, thus helping us understand internal cellular structure and the arrangement of cell components. Cell fractionation techniques separate out different groups of cell components, which can then be analyzed biochemically to determine their function. Performing microscopy on the same cell fraction helps to correlate the biochemical function of the cell with the cell component responsible. **6.2** The separation of different functions in different organelles has several advantages. Reactants and enzymes can be concentrated in one area instead of spread throughout the cell. Reactions that require specific conditions, such as a lower pH, can be compartmentalized. And enzymes for specific reactions are often embedded in the membranes that enclose or partition an organelle. **6.3** The nucleus contains the genetic material of the cell in the form of DNA, which codes for messenger RNA, which in turn provides instructions for the synthesis of proteins (including the proteins that make up part of the ribosomes). DNA also codes for ribosomal RNA, which is combined with proteins in the nucleolus into the subunits of ribosomes. Within the cytoplasm, ribosomes join with mRNA to build polypeptides, using the genetic information in the mRNA. **6.4** Transport vesicles move proteins and membranes synthesized by the rough ER to the Golgi for further processing and then to the plasma membrane, lysosomes, or other locations in the cell, including back to the ER. **6.5** According to the endosymbiont theory, mitochondria originated from an oxygen-using prokaryotic cell that was engulfed by an ancestral eukaryotic cell. Over time, the host and endosymbiont evolved into a single organism. Chloroplasts originated when at least one of these eukaryotic cells containing mitochondria engulfed and then retained a photosynthetic prokaryote. **6.6** Inside the cell, motor proteins interact with components of the cytoskeleton to move cellular parts. Motor proteins "walk" vesicles along microtubules. The movement of cytoplasm within a cell involves interactions of the motor protein myosin and microfilaments (actin filaments). Whole cells can be moved by the rapid bending of flagella or cilia, which is caused by the motor-protein-powered sliding of microtubules within these structures. Cell movement can also occur when pseudopodia form at one end of a cell (caused by actin polymerization into a filamentous network), followed by contraction of the cell toward that end; this is powered by interactions of microfilaments with myosin. Interactions of motor proteins and microfilaments in muscle cells can cause muscle contraction that can propel whole organisms (for example, by walking or swimming). **6.7** A plant cell wall is primarily composed of microfibrils of cellulose embedded in other polysaccharides and proteins. The ECM of animal cells is primarily composed of collagen and other protein fibers, such as fibronectins and other glycoproteins. These fibers are embedded in a network of carbohydrate-rich proteoglycans. A plant cell wall provides structural support for the cell and, collectively, for the plant body. In addition to giving support, the ECM of an animal cell allows for communication of environmental changes into the cell.

Test Your Understanding

1. b **2.** c **3.** b **4.** a **5.** a **6.** c **7.** c **8.** See Figure 6.8.

Chapter 7

Figure Questions

Figure 7.2

Hydrophilic portion

Hydrophobic portion

The hydrophilic portion is in contact with an aqueous environment (cytosol or extracellular fluid), and the hydrophobic portion is in contact with the hydrophobic portions of other phospholipids in the interior of the bilayer. **Figure 7.4** You couldn't rule out movement of proteins within membranes of the same species. You might propose that the membrane lipids and proteins from one species weren't able to mingle with those from the other species because of some incompatibility. **Figure 7.7** A transmembrane protein like the dimer in (f) might change its shape upon binding to a particular ECM molecule. The new shape might enable the interior portion of the protein to bind to a second, cytoplasmic protein that would relay the message to the inside of the cell, as shown in (c). **Figure 7.8** The shape of a protein on the HIV surface is likely to be complementary to the shape of the receptor (CD4) and also to that of the co-receptor (CCR5). A molecule that was a similar shape to the HIV surface protein could bind CCR5, blocking HIV binding. (Another answer would be a molecule that bound to CCR5 and changed the shape of CCR5 so it could no longer bind HIV.) **Figure 7.9**

The protein would contact the extracellular fluid. The protein extends into the ER lumen. Once the vesicle fuses with the plasma membrane, the "inside" of the ER membrane, facing the lumen, will become the "outside" of the plasma membrane, facing the extracellular fluid. **Figure 7.11** The orange dye would be evenly distributed throughout the solution on both sides of the membrane. The solution levels would not be affected because the orange dye can diffuse through the membrane and equalize its concentration. Thus, no additional osmosis would take place in either direction. **Figure 7.16** The diamond solutes are moving into the cell (down), and the round solutes are moving out of the cell (up); both are moving against their concentration gradient.

Concept Check 7.1

1. They are on the inner side of the transport vesicle membrane. **2.** The grasses living in the cooler region would be expected to have more unsaturated fatty acids in their membranes because those fatty acids remain fluid at lower temperatures. The grasses living immediately adjacent to the hot springs would be expected to have more saturated fatty acids, which would allow the fatty acids to "stack" more closely, making the membranes less fluid and therefore helping them to stay intact at higher temperatures. (Cholesterol could not be used to moderate the effects of temperature on membrane fluidity because it is not found within plant cell membranes.)

Concept Check 7.2

1. O_2 and CO_2 are both nonpolar molecules that can easily pass through the hydrophobic interior of a membrane. **2.** Water is a polar molecule, so it cannot pass very rapidly through the hydrophobic region in the middle of a phospholipid bilayer. **3.** The hydronium ion is charged, while glycerol is not. Charge is probably more significant than size as a basis for exclusion by the aquaporin channel.

Concept Check 7.3

1. CO_2 is a nonpolar molecule that can diffuse through the plasma membrane. As long as it diffuses away so that the concentration remains low outside the cell, it will continue to exit the cell in this way. (This is the opposite of the case for O_2, described in this section.) **2.** The activity of *Paramecium caudatum*'s contractile vacuole will decrease. The vacuole pumps out excess water that accumulates in the cell; this accumulation occurs only in a hypotonic environment.

Concept Check 7.4

1. The pump uses ATP. To establish a voltage, ions have to be pumped against their gradients, which requires energy. **2.** Each ion is being transported against its electrochemical gradient. If either ion were transported down its electrochemical gradient, this *would* be considered cotransport. **3.** The internal environment of a lysosome is acidic, so it has a higher concentration of H^+ than does the cytoplasm. Therefore, you might expect the membrane of the lysosome to have a proton pump such as that shown in Figure 7.17 to pump H^+ into the lysosome.

Concept Check 7.5

1. Exocytosis. When a transport vesicle fuses with the plasma membrane, the vesicle membrane becomes part of the plasma membrane.
2.

3. The glycoprotein would be synthesized in the ER lumen, move through the Golgi apparatus, and then travel in a vesicle to the plasma membrane, where it would undergo exocytosis and become part of the ECM.

Summary of Key Concepts Questions

7.1 Plasma membranes define the cell by separating the cellular components from the external environment. This allows conditions inside cells to be controlled by membrane proteins, which regulate entry and exit of molecules and even cell function (see Figure 7.7). The processes of life can be carried out inside the controlled environment of the cell, so membranes are crucial. In eukaryotes, membranes also function to subdivide the cytoplasm into different compartments where distinct processes can occur, even under differing conditions such as pH.   **7.2** Aquaporins are channel proteins that greatly increase the permeability of a membrane to water molecules, which are polar and therefore do not readily diffuse through the hydrophobic interior of the membrane.   **7.3** There will be a net diffusion of water out of a cell into a hypertonic solution. The free water concentration is higher inside the cell than in the solution (where water molecules are not free, but are clustered around the higher concentration of solute particles).   **7.4** One of the solutes moved by the cotransporter is actively transported against its concentration gradient. The energy for this transport comes from the concentration gradient of the other solute, which was established by an electrogenic pump that used energy to transport the other solute across the membrane.   **7.5** In receptor-mediated endocytosis, specific molecules act as ligands when they bind to receptors on the plasma membrane. The cell can acquire bulk quantities of those molecules when a coated pit forms a vesicle and carries the bound molecules into the cell.

Test Your Understanding

1. b   **2.** c   **3.** a   **4.** c   **5.** b
6. (a)

(b) The solution outside is hypotonic. It has less sucrose, which is a nonpenetrating solute. (c) See answer for (a). (d) The artificial cell will become more turgid. (e) Eventually, the two solutions will have the same solute concentrations. Even though sucrose can't move through the membrane, water flow (osmosis) will lead to isotonic conditions.

Chapter 8

Figure Questions

Figure 8.5 With a proton pump (Figure 7.17), the energy stored in ATP is used to pump protons across the membrane and build up a higher (nonrandom) concentration outside of the cell, so this process results in higher free energy. When solute molecules (analogous to H^+ ions) are uniformly distributed, similar to the random distribution in the bottom of (b), the system has less free energy than it does in the top of (b). The system in the bottom can do no work. Because the concentration gradient created by a proton pump (Figure 7.17) represents higher free energy, this system has the potential to do work (as you will see in Chapter 9).
Figure 8.10 Glutamic acid has a carboxyl group at the end of its R group. Glutamine has exactly the same structure as glutamic acid, except that there is an amino group in place of the —OH on the R group. (The O atom on the R group leaves during the synthesis reaction.)

Figure 8.13

Figure 8.16

Figure 8.17

Concept Check 8.1

1. The second law is the trend toward randomization, or increasing entropy. When the concentrations of a substance on both sides of a membrane are equal, the distribution is more random than when they are unequal. Diffusion of a substance to a region where it is initially less concentrated increases entropy, making it an energetically favorable (spontaneous) process as described by the second law. This explains the process seen in Figure 7.10.   **2.** The apple has potential energy in its position hanging on the tree, and the sugars and other nutrients it contains have chemical energy. The apple has kinetic energy as it falls from the tree to the ground. Finally, when the apple is digested and its molecules broken down, some of the chemical energy is used to do work, and the rest is lost as thermal energy.   **3.** The sugar crystals become less ordered (entropy increases) as they dissolve and become randomly spread out in the water. Over time, the water evaporates, and the crystals form again because the water volume is insufficient to keep them in solution. While the reappearance of sugar crystals may represent a "spontaneous" increase in order (decrease in entropy), it is balanced by the decrease in order (increase in entropy) of the water molecules, which changed from a relatively compact arrangement as liquid water to a much more dispersed and disordered form as water vapor.

Concept Check 8.2

1. Cellular respiration is a spontaneous and exergonic process. The energy released from glucose is used to do work in the cell or is lost as heat.   **2.** Catabolism breaks down organic molecules, releasing their chemical energy and resulting in smaller products with more entropy, as when moving from the top to the bottom of part (c). Anabolism consumes energy to synthesize larger molecules from simpler ones, as when moving from the bottom to the top of part (c).   **3.** The reaction is exergonic because it releases energy—in this case, in the form of light. (This is a nonbiological version of the bioluminescence seen in Figure 8.1.)

Concept Check 8.3

1. ATP usually transfers energy to endergonic processes by phosphorylating (adding phosphate groups to) other molecules. (Exergonic processes phosphorylate ADP to regenerate ATP.)   **2.** A set of coupled reactions can transform the first combination into the second. Since this is an exergonic process overall, ΔG is negative and the first combination must have more free energy (see Figure 8.10).
3. Active transport: The solute is being transported against its concentration gradient, which requires energy, provided by ATP hydrolysis.

Concept Check 8.4

1. A spontaneous reaction is a reaction that is exergonic. However, if it has a high activation energy that is rarely attained, the rate of the reaction may be low.
2. Only the specific substrate(s) will fit properly into the active site of an enzyme,

the part of the enzyme that carries out catalysis.   **3.** In the presence of malonate, increase the concentration of the normal substrate (succinate) and see whether the rate of reaction increases. If it does, malonate is a competitive inhibitor.
4. If lactose weren't present in the environment as a source of food and the fucose-containing disaccharide were available, bacteria that could digest the latter would be better able to grow and multiply than those that could not.

Concept Check 8.5
1. The activator binds in such a way that it stabilizes the active form of an enzyme, whereas the inhibitor stabilizes the inactive form.   **2.** A catabolic pathway breaks down organic molecules, generating energy that is stored in ATP molecules. In feedback inhibition of such a pathway, ATP (one product) would act as an allosteric inhibitor of an enzyme catalyzing an early step in the catabolic process. When ATP is plentiful, the pathway would be turned off and no more would be made.

Summary of Key Concepts Questions
8.1 The process of "ordering" a cell's structure is accompanied by an increase in the entropy or disorder of the universe. For example, an animal cell takes in highly ordered organic molecules as the source of matter and energy used to build and maintain its structures. In the same process, however, the cell releases heat and the simple molecules of carbon dioxide and water to the surroundings. The increase in entropy of the latter process offsets the entropy decrease in the former.   **8.2** A spontaneous reaction has a negative ΔG and is exergonic. For a chemical reaction to proceed with a net release of free energy ($-\Delta G$), the enthalpy or total energy of the system must decrease ($-\Delta H$), and/or the entropy or disorder must increase (yielding a more negative term, $-T\Delta S$). Spontaneous reactions supply the energy to perform cellular work.   **8.3** The free energy released from the hydrolysis of ATP may drive endergonic reactions through the transfer of a phosphate group to a reactant molecule, forming a more reactive phosphorylated intermediate. ATP hydrolysis also powers the mechanical and transport work of a cell, often by powering shape changes in the relevant motor proteins. Cellular respiration, the catabolic breakdown of glucose, provides the energy for the endergonic regeneration of ATP from ADP and $\text{\textcircled{P}}_i$.   **8.4** Activation energy barriers prevent the complex molecules of the cell, which are rich in free energy, from spontaneously breaking down to less ordered, more stable molecules. Enzymes permit a regulated metabolism by binding to specific substrates and forming enzyme-substrate complexes that selectively lower the E_A for the chemical reactions in a cell. **8.5** A cell tightly regulates its metabolic pathways in response to fluctuating needs for energy and materials. The binding of activators or inhibitors to regulatory sites on allosteric enzymes stabilizes either the active or inactive form of the subunits. For example, the binding of ATP to a catabolic enzyme in a cell with excess ATP would inhibit that pathway. Such types of feedback inhibition preserve chemical resources within a cell. If ATP supplies are depleted, binding of ADP to the regulatory site of catabolic enzymes would activate that pathway, generating more ATP.

Test Your Understanding
1. b   **2.** c   **3.** b   **4.** a   **5.** c   **6.** d   **7.** c

9.

A. The substrate molecules are entering the cells, so no product is made yet.
B. There is sufficient substrate, so the reaction is proceeding at a maximum rate.
C. As the substrate is used up, the rate decreases (the slope is less steep).
D. The line is flat because no new substrate remains and thus no new product appears.

Chapter 9

Figure Questions
Figure 9.4 The reduced form has an extra hydrogen, along with 2 electrons, bound to the carbon shown at the top of the nicotinamide (opposite the N). There are different numbers and positions of double bonds in the two forms: The oxidized form has three double bonds in the ring, while the reduced form has only two. (In organic chemistry you may have learned, or will learn, that three double bonds in a ring are able to "resonate," or act as a ring of electrons.) In the oxidized form there is a + charge on the N (because it is sharing 4 electron pairs), whereas in the reduced form it is only sharing 3 electron pairs (having a pair of electrons to itself).   **Figure 9.7** Because there is no external source of energy for the reaction, it must be exergonic, and the reactants must be at a higher energy level than the products.   **Figure 9.9** The removal would probably slow glycolysis, or at least slow it down, since it would push the equilibrium for step 5 toward the bottom (toward DHAP). If less (or no) glyceraldehyde 3-phosphate were available, step 6 would slow down (or be unable to occur).   **Figure 9.15** At first, some ATP could be made, since electron transport could proceed as far as complex III, and a small H^+ gradient could be built up. Soon, however, no more electrons could be passed to complex III because it could not be reoxidized by passing its electrons to complex IV.   **Figure 9.16** First, there are 2 NADH from the oxidation of pyruvate plus 6 NADH from the citric acid cycle (CAC); 8 NADH $\times$ 2.5 ATP/NADH = 20 ATP. Second, there are 2 FADH$_2$ from the CAC; 2 FADH$_2$ $\times$ 1.5 ATP/FADH$_2$ = 3 ATP. Third, the 2 NADH from glycolysis enter the mitochondrion through one of two

types of shuttle. They pass their electrons either to 2 FAD, which become FADH$_2$ and result in 3 ATP, or to 2 NAD$^+$, which become NADH and result in 5 ATP. Thus, $20 + 3 + 3 = 26$ ATP, or $20 + 3 + 5 = 28$ ATP from all NADH and FADH$_2$.

Concept Check 9.1
1. Both processes include glycolysis, the citric acid cycle, and oxidative phosphorylation. In aerobic respiration, the final electron acceptor is molecular oxygen (O_2); in anaerobic respiration, the final electron acceptor is a different substance.
2. $C_4H_6O_5$ would be oxidized and NAD$^+$ would be reduced.

Concept Check 9.2
1. NAD$^+$ acts as the oxidizing agent in step 6, accepting electrons from glyceraldehyde 3-phosphate, which thus acts as the reducing agent.

Concept Check 9.3
1. NADH and FADH$_2$; they will donate electrons to the electron transport chain.
2. CO_2 is released from the pyruvate that is the end product of glycolysis, and CO_2 is also released during the citric acid cycle.   **3.** In both cases, the precursor molecule loses a CO_2 molecule and then donates electrons to an electron carrier in an oxidation step. Also, the product has been activated due to the attachment of a CoA group.

Concept Check 9.4
1. Oxidative phosphorylation would eventually stop entirely, resulting in no ATP production by this process. Without oxygen to "pull" electrons down the electron transport chain, H^+ would not be pumped into the mitochondrion's intermembrane space and chemiosmosis would not occur.   **2.** Decreasing the pH means addition of H^+. This would establish a proton gradient even without the function of the electron transport chain, and we would expect ATP synthase to function and synthesize ATP. (In fact, it was experiments like this that provided support for chemiosmosis as an energy-coupling mechanism.)   **3.** One of the components of the electron transport chain, ubiquinone (Q), must be able to diffuse within the membrane. It could not do so if the membrane were locked rigidly into place.

Concept Check 9.5
1. A derivative of pyruvate, such as acetaldehyde during alcohol fermentation, or pyruvate itself during lactic acid fermentation; oxygen   **2.** The cell would need to consume glucose at a rate about 16 times the consumption rate in the aerobic environment (2 ATP are generated by fermentation versus up to 32 ATP by cellular respiration).

Concept Check 9.6
1. The fat is much more reduced; it has many —CH$_2$— units, and in all these bonds the electrons are equally shared. The electrons present in a carbohydrate molecule are already somewhat oxidized (shared unequally in bonds), as quite a few of them are bound to oxygen. Electrons that are equally shared, as in fat, have a higher energy level than electrons that are unequally shared, as in carbohydrates. Thus, fat is a much better fuel than carbohydrate.   **2.** When we consume more food than necessary for metabolic processes, our body synthesizes fat as a way of storing energy for later use.   **3.** AMP will accumulate, stimulating phosphofructokinase, and thus increasing the rate of glycolysis. Since oxygen is not present, the cell will convert pyruvate to lactate in lactic acid fermentation, providing a supply of ATP.   **4.** When oxygen is present, the fatty acid chains containing most of the energy of a fat are oxidized and fed into the citric acid cycle and the electron transport chain. During intense exercise, however, oxygen is scarce in muscle cells, so ATP must be generated by glycolysis alone. A very small part of the fat molecule, the glycerol backbone, can be oxidized via glycolysis, but the amount of energy released by this portion is insignificant compared to that released by the fatty acid chains. (This is why moderate exercise, staying below 70% maximum heart rate, is better for burning fat—because enough oxygen remains available to the muscles.)

Summary of Key Concepts Questions
9.1 Most of the ATP produced in cellular respiration comes from oxidative phosphorylation, in which the energy released from redox reactions in an electron transport chain is used to produce ATP. In substrate-level phosphorylation, an enzyme directly transfers a phosphate group to ADP from an intermediate substrate. All ATP production in glycolysis occurs by substrate-level phosphorylation; this form of ATP production also occurs at one step in the citric acid cycle.
9.2 The oxidation of the three-carbon sugar, glyceraldehyde 3-phosphate, yields energy. In this oxidation, electrons and H^+ are transferred to NAD$^+$, forming NADH, and a phosphate group is attached to the oxidized substrate. ATP is then formed by substrate-level phosphorylation when this phosphate group is transferred to ADP.   **9.3** The release of six molecules of CO_2 represents the complete oxidation of glucose. During the processing of two pyruvates to acetyl CoA, the fully oxidized carboxyl groups (—COO$^-$) are given off as 2 CO_2. The remaining four carbons are released as CO_2 in the citric acid cycle as citrate is oxidized back to oxaloacetate.   **9.4** The flow of H^+ through the ATP synthase complex causes the rotor and attached rod to rotate, exposing catalytic sites in the knob portion that produce ATP from ADP and $\text{\textcircled{P}}_i$. ATP synthases are found in the inner mitochondrial membrane, the plasma membrane of prokaryotes, and membranes within chloroplasts.   **9.5** Anaerobic respiration yields more ATP. The 2 ATP produced by substrate-level phosphorylation in glycolysis represent the total energy yield of fermentation. NADH passes its "high-energy" electrons to pyruvate or a derivative of pyruvate, recycling NAD$^+$ and allowing glycolysis to continue. In anaerobic respiration, the NADH produced during glycolysis, as well as additional molecules of NADH produced as pyruvate is oxidized, are used to generate ATP molecules. An electron transport chain captures the energy of the electrons in NADH via a series of redox reactions; ultimately, the electrons are transferred

to an electronegative molecule other than oxygen. **9.6** The ATP produced by catabolic pathways is used to drive anabolic pathways. Also, many of the intermediates of glycolysis and the citric acid cycle are used in the biosynthesis of a cell's molecules.

Test Your Understanding

1. c   **2.** c   **3.** a   **4.** b   **5.** d   **6.** a   **7.** b
8. Since the overall process of glycolysis results in net production of ATP, it would make sense for the process to slow down when ATP levels have increased substantially. Thus, we would expect ATP to allosterically inhibit phosphofructokinase.   **9.** The proton pump in Figure 7.17 is carrying out active transport, using ATP hydrolysis to pump protons against their concentration gradient. Because ATP is required, this is active transport of protons. The ATP synthase in Figure 9.14 is using the flow of protons down their concentration gradient to power ATP synthesis. Because the protons are moving down their concentration gradient, no energy is required, and this is passive transport.
11.

H^+ would continue to be pumped across the membrane into the intermembrane space, increasing the difference between the matrix pH and the intermembrane space pH. H^+ would not be able to flow back through ATP synthase, since the enzyme is inhibited by the poison, so rather than maintaining a constant difference across the membrane, the difference would continue to increase. (Ultimately, the H^+ concentration in the intermembrane space would be so high that no more H^+ would be able to be pumped against the gradient, but this isn't shown in the graph.)

Chapter 10

Figure Questions

Figure 10.3 Situating containers of algae near sources of CO_2 emissions makes sense because algae need CO_2 to carry out photosynthesis. The higher their rate of photosynthesis, the more plant oil they will produce. At the same time, algae would be absorbing the CO_2 emitted from industrial plants or from car engines, reducing the amount of CO_2 entering the atmosphere.   **Figure 10.12** In the leaf, most of the chlorophyll electrons excited by photon absorption are used to power the reactions of photosynthesis.   **Figure 10.16** The person at the top of the photosystem I tower would not turn to his left and throw his electron into the bucket. Instead, he would throw it onto the top of the ramp at his right, next to the photosystem II tower. The electron would then roll down the ramp, get energized by a photon, and return to him. This cycle would continue as long as light was available. (This is why it's called cyclic electron flow.)   **Figure 10.22** Yes, plants can break down the sugar (in the form of glucose) by cellular respiration, producing ATPs for various cellular processes such as endergonic chemical reactions, transport of substances across membranes, and movement of molecules in the cell. ATPs are also used for the movement of chloroplasts during cellular streaming in some plant cells (see Figure 6.26).   **Figure 10.23** The gene encoding hexokinase is part of the DNA of a chromosome in the nucleus. There, the gene is transcribed into mRNA, which is transported to the cytoplasm where it is translated on a free ribosome into a polypeptide. The polypeptide folds into a functional protein with secondary and tertiary structure. Once functional, it carries out the first reaction of glycolysis in the cytoplasm.

Concept Check 10.1

1. CO_2 enters the leaves via stomata, and water enters via roots and is carried to the leaves through veins.   **2.** Using ^{18}O, a heavy isotope of oxygen, as a label, researchers were able to confirm van Niel's hypothesis that the oxygen produced during photosynthesis comes from water, not from carbon dioxide.   **3.** The light reactions could *not* keep producing NADPH and ATP without the NADP$^+$, ADP, and $\circled{P}_i$ that the Calvin cycle generates. The two cycles are interdependent.

Concept Check 10.2

1. Green, because green light is mostly transmitted and reflected—not absorbed—by photosynthetic pigments   **2.** Water (H_2O) is the initial electron donor; NADP$^+$ accepts electrons at the end of the electron transport chain, becoming reduced to NADPH.   **3.** In this experiment, the rate of ATP synthesis would slow and eventually stop. Because the added compound would not allow a proton gradient to build up across the membrane, ATP synthase could not catalyze ATP production.

Concept Check 10.3

1. 6, 18, 12   **2.** The more potential energy a molecule stores, the more energy and reducing power are required for the formation of that molecule. Glucose is a valuable energy source because it is highly reduced, storing lots of potential energy in its electrons. To reduce CO_2 to glucose, much energy and reducing power are required in the form of large numbers of ATP and NADPH molecules, respectively.   **3.** The light reactions require ADP and NADP$^+$, which would not be formed in sufficient quantities from ATP and NADPH if the Calvin cycle stopped.

4.

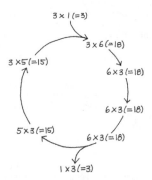

Three carbon atoms enter the cycle, one by one, as individual CO_2 molecules, and leave the cycle in one three-carbon molecule (G3P) per three turns of the cycle.
5. In glycolysis, G3P acts as an intermediate. The 6-carbon sugar fructose 1,6-bisphosphate is cleaved into two 3-carbon sugars, one of which is G3P. The other is an isomer called dihydroxyacetone phosphate (DHAP), which can be converted to G3P by an isomerase. Because G3P is the substrate for the next enzyme, it is constantly removed, and the reaction equilibrium is pulled in the direction of conversion of DHAP to more G3P. In the Calvin cycle, G3P acts as both an intermediate and a product. For every three CO_2 molecules that enter the cycle, six G3P molecules are formed, five of which must remain in the cycle and become rearranged to regenerate three 5-carbon RuBP molecules. The one remaining G3P is a product, which can be thought of as the result of "reducing" the three CO_2 molecules that entered the cycle into a 3-carbon sugar that can later be used to generate energy.

Concept Check 10.4

1. Photorespiration decreases photosynthetic output by adding oxygen, instead of carbon dioxide, to the Calvin cycle. As a result, no sugar is generated (no carbon is fixed), and O_2 is used rather than generated.   **2.** Without PS II, no O_2 is generated in bundle-sheath cells. This avoids the problem of O_2 competing with CO_2 for binding to rubisco in these cells.   **3.** Both problems are caused by a drastic change in Earth's atmosphere due to burning of fossil fuels. The increase in CO_2 concentration affects ocean chemistry by decreasing pH, thus affecting calcification by marine organisms. On land, CO_2 concentration and air temperature are conditions that plants have become adapted to, and changes in these characteristics have a strong effect on photosynthesis by plants. Thus, alteration of these two fundamental factors could have critical effects on organisms all around the planet, in all different habitats.   **4.** C_4 and CAM species would replace many of the C_3 species.

Summary of Key Concepts Questions

10.1 CO_2 and H_2O are the products of respiration; they are the reactants in photosynthesis. In respiration, glucose is oxidized to CO_2 and electrons are passed through an electron transfer chain from glucose to O_2, producing H_2O. In photosynthesis, H_2O is the source of electrons, which are energized by light, temporarily stored in NADPH, and used to reduce CO_2 to carbohydrate.
10.2 The action spectrum of photosynthesis shows that some wavelengths of light that are not absorbed by chlorophyll *a* are still effective at promoting photosynthesis. The light-harvesting complexes of photosystems contain accessory pigments such as chlorophyll *b* and carotenoids, which absorb different wavelengths and pass the energy to chlorophyll *a*, broadening the spectrum of light usable for photosynthesis.
10.3

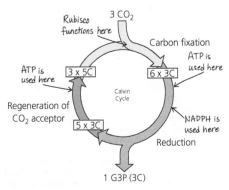

In the reduction phase of the Calvin cycle, ATP phosphorylates a three-carbon compound, and NADPH then reduces this compound to G3P. ATP is also used in the regeneration phase, when five molecules of G3P are converted to three molecules of the five-carbon compound RuBP. Rubisco catalyzes the first step of carbon fixation—the addition of CO_2 to RuBP.   **10.4** Both C_4 photosynthesis and CAM photosynthesis involve initial fixation of CO_2 to produce a four-carbon compound (in mesophyll cells in C_4 plants and at night in CAM plants). These compounds are then broken down to release CO_2 (in the bundle-sheath cells in C_4 plants and during the day in CAM plants). ATP is required for recycling the molecule that is used initially to combine with CO_2. These pathways avoid the photorespiration that consumes ATP and reduces the photosynthetic output of C_3 plants when they close stomata on hot, dry, bright days. Thus, hot, arid climates would favor C_4 and CAM plants.

Test Your Understanding

1. d **2.** b **3.** c **4.** a **5.** c **6.** b **7.** c
10.

The ATP would end up outside the thylakoid. The thylakoids were able to make ATP in the dark because the researchers set up an artificial proton concentration gradient across the thylakoid membrane; thus, the light reactions were not necessary to establish the H^+ gradient required for ATP synthesis by ATP synthase.

Chapter 11

Figure Questions

Figure 11.6 Epinephrine is a signaling molecule; presumably, it binds to a cell-surface receptor protein. **Figure 11.8** This is an example of passive transport. The ion is moving down its concentration gradient, and no energy is required. **Figure 11.9** The aldosterone molecule is hydrophobic and can therefore pass directly through the lipid bilayer of the plasma membrane into the cell. (Hydrophilic molecules cannot do this.) **Figure 11.10** The entire phosphorylation cascade wouldn't operate. Regardless of whether or not the signaling molecule was bound, protein kinase 3 would always be inactive and would not be able to activate the purple-colored protein leading to the cellular response. **Figure 11.11** The signaling molecule (cAMP) would remain in its active form and would continue to signal. **Figure 11.16** 100,000,000 (one hundred million or 10^8) glucose molecules are released. The first step results in 100× amplification (one epinephrine activates 100 G proteins); the next step does not amplify the response; the next step is a 100× amplification (10^2 active adenylyl cyclase molecules to 10^4 cyclic AMPs); the next step does not amplify; the next two steps are each 10× amplifications, and the final step is a 100× amplification. **Figure 11.17** The signaling pathway shown in Figure 11.14 leads to the splitting of PIP_2 into the second messengers DAG and IP_3, which produce different responses. (The response elicited by DAG is mentioned but not shown.) The pathway shown for cell B is similar in that it branches and leads to two responses.

Concept Check 11.1

1. The two cells of opposite mating type (**a** and **α**) each secrete a certain signaling molecule, which can only be bound by receptors carried on cells of the opposite mating type. Thus, the **a** mating factor cannot bind to another **a** cell and cause it to grow toward the first **a** cell. Only an **α** cell can "receive" the signaling molecule and respond by directed growth (see the Scientific Skills Exercise). **2.** Glycogen phosphorylase acts in the third stage, the response to epinephrine signaling.
3. Glucose 1-phosphate is not generated, because the activation of the enzyme requires an intact cell, with an intact receptor in the membrane and an intact signal transduction pathway. The enzyme cannot be activated directly by interaction with the signaling molecule in the test tube.

Concept Check 11.2

1. NGF is water-soluble (hydrophilic), so it cannot pass through the lipid membrane to reach intracellular receptors, as steroid hormones can. Therefore, you'd expect the NGF receptor to be in the plasma membrane—which is, in fact, the case. **2.** The cell with the faulty receptor would not be able to respond appropriately to the signaling molecule when it was present. This would most likely have dire consequences for the cell, since regulation of the cell's activities by this receptor would not occur appropriately. **3.** Binding of a ligand to a receptor changes the shape of the receptor, altering the ability of the receptor to transmit a signal. Binding of an allosteric regulator to an enzyme changes the shape of the enzyme, either promoting or inhibiting enzyme activity. **4.** When the receptor is actively transmitting a signal to the inside of the cell, it is bound to a G protein. To determine a structure corresponding to that state, it might be useful to crystallize the receptor in the presence of many copies of the G protein. (In fact, a research group used this approach successfully with a G protein-coupled receptor related to the one shown in Figure 11.8.)

Concept Check 11.3

1. A protein kinase is an enzyme that transfers a phosphate group from ATP to a protein, usually activating that protein (often a second type of protein kinase). Many signal transduction pathways include a series of such interactions, in which each phosphorylated protein kinase in turn phosphorylates the next protein kinase in the series. Such phosphorylation cascades carry a signal from outside the cell to

the cellular protein(s) that will carry out the response. **2.** Protein phosphatases reverse the effects of the kinases, and unless the signaling molecule is at a high enough concentration that it is continuously rebinding the receptor, the kinase molecules will all be returned to their inactive states by phosphatases. **3.** The signal that is being transduced is the *information* that a signaling molecule is bound to the cell-surface receptor. Information is transduced by way of sequential protein-protein interactions that change protein shapes, causing them to function in a way that passes the signal (the information) along. **4.** The IP_3-gated channel opens, allowing calcium ions to flow out of the ER and into the cytoplasm, which raises the cytosolic Ca^{2+} concentration.

Concept Check 11.4

1. At each step in a cascade of sequential activations, one molecule or ion may activate numerous molecules functioning in the next step. This causes the response to be amplified at each such step and overall results in a large amplification of the original signal. **2.** Scaffolding proteins hold molecular components of signaling pathways in a complex with each other. Different scaffolding proteins would assemble different collections of proteins, leading to different cellular responses in the two cells. **3.** A malfunctioning protein phosphatase would not be able to dephosphorylate a particular receptor or relay protein. As a result, the signaling pathway, once activated, would not be able to be terminated. (In fact, one study found altered protein phosphatases in cells from 25% of colorectal tumors.)

Concept Check 11.5

1. In formation of the hand or paw in mammals, cells in the regions between the digits are programmed to undergo apoptosis. This serves to shape the digits of the hand or paw so that they are not webbed. (A lack of apoptosis in these regions in water birds results in webbed feet.) **2.** If a receptor protein for a death-signaling molecule were defective such that it was activated even in the absence of the death signal, this would lead to apoptosis when it wouldn't normally occur. Similar defects in any of the proteins in the signaling pathway would have the same effect if the defective proteins activated relay or response proteins in the absence of interaction with the previous protein or second messenger in the pathway. Conversely, if any protein in the pathway were defective in its ability to respond to an interaction with an early protein or other molecule or ion, apoptosis would not occur when it normally should. For example, a receptor protein for a death-signaling ligand might not be able to be activated, even when ligand was bound. This would stop the signal from being transduced into the cell.

Summary of Key Concepts Questions

11.1 A cell is able to respond to a hormone only if it has a receptor protein on the cell surface or inside the cell that can bind to the hormone. The response to a hormone depends on the specific signal transduction pathway within the cell, which will lead to the specific cellular response. The response can vary for different types of cells. **11.2** Both GPCRs and RTKs have an extracellular binding site for a signaling molecule (ligand) and one or more α helical regions of the polypeptide that spans the membrane. A GPCR functions singly, while RTKs tend to dimerize or form larger groups of RTKs. GPCRs usually trigger a single transduction pathway, whereas the multiple activated tyrosines on an RTK dimer may trigger several different transduction pathways at the same time. **11.3** A protein kinase is an enzyme that adds a phosphate group to another protein. Protein kinases are often part of a phosphorylation cascade that transduces a signal. A second messenger is a small, nonprotein molecule or ion that rapidly diffuses and relays a signal throughout a cell. Both protein kinases and second messengers can operate in the same pathway. For example, the second messenger cAMP often activates protein kinase A, which then phosphorylates other proteins. **11.4** In G protein-coupled pathways, the GTPase portion of a G protein converts GTP to GDP and inactivates the G protein. Protein phosphatases remove phosphate groups from activated proteins, thus stopping a phosphorylation cascade of protein kinases. Phosphodiesterase converts cAMP to AMP, thus reducing the effect of cAMP in a signal transduction pathway. **11.5** The basic mechanism of controlled cell suicide evolved early in eukaryotic evolution, and the genetic basis for these pathways has been conserved during animal evolution. Such a mechanism is essential to the development and maintenance of all animals.

Test Your Understanding

1. d **2.** a **3.** b **4.** a **5.** c **6.** c **7.** c
8. This is one possible drawing of the pathway. (Similar drawings would also be correct.)

Chapter 12

Figure Questions

Figure 12.4

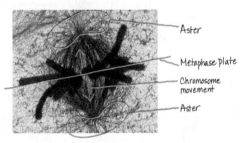

One sister chromatid

Circling the other chromatid instead would also be correct.   **Figure 12.5** The chromosome has four arms.   **Figure 12.7** 12; 2; 2; 1

Figure 12.8

Aster
Metaphase plate
Chromosome movement
Aster

Figure 12.9 The mark would have moved toward the nearer pole. The lengths of fluorescent microtubules between that pole and the mark would have decreased, while the lengths between the chromosomes and the mark would have remained the same.   **Figure 12.14** In both cases, the G_1 nucleus would have remained in G_1 until the time it normally would have entered the S phase. Chromosome condensation and spindle formation would not have occurred until the S and G_2 phases had been completed.   **Figure 12.16** Passing the G_2 checkpoint in the diagram corresponds to the beginning of the "Time" axis of the graph, and entry into the mitotic phase (yellow background on the diagram) corresponds to the peaks of MPF activity and cyclin concentration on the graph (see the yellow M banner over the peaks). During G_1 and S phase in the diagram, Cdk is present without cyclin, so on the graph both cyclin concentration and MPF activity are low. The curved purple arrow in the diagram shows increasing cyclin concentration, seen on the graph during the end of S phase and throughout G_2 phase. Then the cell cycle begins again.   **Figure 12.17** The cell would divide under conditions where it was inappropriate to do so. If the daughter cells and their descendants also ignored either of the checkpoints and divided, there would soon be an abnormal mass of cells. (This type of inappropriate cell division can contribute to the development of cancer.)   **Figure 12.18** The cells in the vessel with PDGF would not be able to respond to the growth factor signal and thus would not divide. The culture would resemble that without the added PDGF.

Concept Check 12.1

1. 1; 1; 2   **2.** 39; 39; 78

Concept Check 12.2

1. 6 chromosomes, duplicated; 12 chromatids   **2.** Following mitosis, cytokinesis results in two genetically identical daughter cells in both plant cells and animal cells. However, the mechanism of dividing the cytoplasm is different in animals and plants. In an animal cell, cytokinesis occurs by cleavage, which divides the parent cell in two with a contractile ring of actin filaments. In a plant cell, a cell plate forms in the middle of the cell and grows until its membrane fuses with the plasma membrane of the parent cell. A new cell wall grows inside the cell plate.   **3.** From the end of S phase in interphase through the end of metaphase in mitosis   **4.** During eukaryotic cell division, tubulin is involved in spindle formation and chromosome movement, while actin functions during cytokinesis. In bacterial binary fission, it's the opposite: Tubulin-like molecules are thought to act in daughter cell separation, and actin-like molecules are thought to move the daughter bacterial chromosomes to opposite ends of the cell.   **5.** A kinetochore connects the spindle (a motor; note that it has motor proteins) to a chromosome (the cargo it will move).   **6.** Microtubules made up of tubulin in the cell provide "rails" along which vesicles and other organelles can travel, based on interactions of motor proteins with tubulin in the microtubules. In muscle cells, actin in microfilaments interacts with myosin filaments to cause muscle contraction.

Concept Check 12.3

1. The nucleus on the right was originally in the G_1 phase; therefore, it had not yet duplicated its chromosomes. The nucleus on the left was in the M phase, so it had already duplicated its chromosomes.   **2.** A sufficient amount of MPF has to exist for a cell to pass the G_2 checkpoint; this occurs through the accumulation of cyclin proteins, which combine with Cdk to form (active) MPF.   **3.** The intracellular estrogen receptor, once activated, would be able to act as a transcription factor in the nucleus, turning on genes that may cause the cell to pass a checkpoint and divide. The HER2 receptor, when activated by a ligand, would form a dimer, and each subunit of the dimer would phosphorylate the other. This would lead to a series of signal transduction steps, ultimately turning on genes in the nucleus. As in the case of the estrogen receptor, the genes would code for proteins necessary to commit the cell to divide.

Summary of Key Concepts Questions

12.1 The DNA of a eukaryotic cell is packaged into structures called *chromosomes*. Each chromosome is a long molecule of DNA, which carries hundreds to thousands of genes, with associated proteins that maintain chromosome structure and help control gene activity. This DNA-protein complex is called *chromatin*. The chromatin of each chromosome is long and thin when the cell is not dividing. Prior to cell division, each chromosome is duplicated, and the resulting sister *chromatids* are attached to each other by proteins at the centromeres and, for many species, all along their lengths (a phenomenon called sister chromatid cohesion).   **12.2** Chromosomes exist as single DNA molecules in G_1 of interphase and in anaphase and telophase of mitosis. During S phase, DNA replication produces sister chromatids, which persist during G_2 of interphase and through prophase, prometaphase, and metaphase of mitosis.   **12.3** Checkpoints allow cellular surveillance mechanisms to determine whether the cell is prepared to go to the next stage. Internal and external signals move a cell past these checkpoints. The G_1 checkpoint, called the "restriction point" in mammalian cells, determines whether a cell will complete the cell cycle and divide or switch into the G_0 phase. The signals to pass this checkpoint often are external—such as growth factors. Passing the G_2 checkpoint requires sufficient numbers of active MPF complexes, which in turn orchestrate several mitotic events. MPF also initiates degradation of its cyclin component, terminating the M phase. The M phase will not begin again until sufficient cyclin is produced during the next S and G_2 phases. The signal to pass the M phase checkpoint is not activated until all chromosomes are attached to kinetochore fibers and are aligned at the metaphase plate. Only then will sister chromatid separation occur.

Test Your Understanding

1. b   **2.** a   **3.** c   **4.** c   **5.** a   **6.** b   **7.** a   **8.** d
9. See Figure 12.7 for a description of major events.

Prometaphase   Prophase   Telophase

Metaphase   Anaphase

Only one cell is indicated for each stage, but other correct answers are also present in this micrograph.

10.

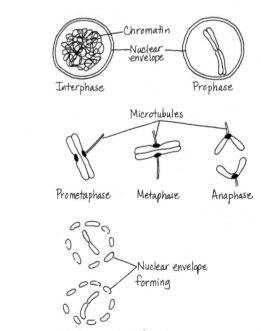

Chromatin
Nuclear envelope
Interphase   Prophase

Microtubules
Prometaphase   Metaphase   Anaphase

Nuclear envelope forming

Telophase and cytokinesis

Chapter 13

Figure Questions

Figure 13.4 Two sets of chromosomes are present. Three pairs of homologous chromosomes are present. **Figure 13.7**

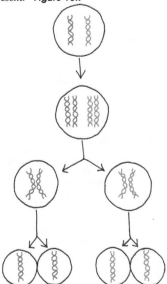

(A short strand of DNA is shown here for simplicity, but each chromosome or chromatid contains a very long coiled and folded DNA molecule.)

Figure 13.8 If a cell with six chromosomes undergoes two rounds of mitosis, each of the four resulting cells will have six chromosomes, while the four cells resulting from meiosis in Figure 13.8 each have three chromosomes. In mitosis, DNA replication (and thus chromosome duplication) precedes each prophase, ensuring that daughter cells have the same number of chromosomes as the parent cell. In meiosis, in contrast, DNA replication occurs only before prophase I (not prophase II). Thus, in two rounds of mitosis, the chromosomes duplicate twice and divide twice, while in meiosis, the chromosomes duplicate once and divide twice. **Figure 13.10** Yes. Each of the six chromosomes (three per cell) shown in telophase I has one nonrecombinant chromatid and one recombinant chromatid. Therefore, eight possible sets of chromosomes can be generated for the cell on the left and eight for the cell on the right.

Concept Check 13.1

1. Parents pass genes to their offspring; by dictating the production of messenger RNAs (mRNAs), the genes program cells to make specific enzymes and other proteins, whose cumulative action produces an individual's inherited traits. **2.** Such organisms reproduce by mitosis, which generates offspring whose genomes are exact copies of the parent's genome (in the absence of mutation). **3.** She should clone it. Cross-breeding it with another plant would generate offspring that have additional variation, which she no longer desires now that she has obtained her ideal orchid.

Concept Check 13.2

1. Each of the six chromosomes is duplicated, so each contains two DNA double helices. Therefore, there are 12 DNA molecules in the cell. The haploid number, n, is 3. One set is always haploid. **2.** 23; 2. **3.** This organism has the life cycle shown in Figure 13.6c. Therefore, it must be a fungus or a protist, perhaps an alga.

Concept Check 13.3

1. The chromosomes are similar in that each is composed of two sister chromatids, and the individual chromosomes are positioned similarly at the metaphase plate. The chromosomes differ in that in a mitotically dividing cell, sister chromatids of each chromosome are genetically identical, but in a meiotically dividing cell, sister chromatids are genetically distinct because of crossing over in meiosis I. Moreover, the chromosomes in metaphase of mitosis can be a diploid set or a haploid set, but the chromosomes in metaphase of meiosis II always consist of a haploid set. **2.** If crossing over did not occur, the two homologs would not be associated in any way. This might result in incorrect arrangement of homologs during metaphase I and ultimately in formation of gametes with an abnormal number of chromosomes.

Concept Check 13.4

1. Mutations in a gene lead to the different versions (alleles) of that gene.
2. Without crossing over, independent assortment of chromosomes during meiosis I theoretically can generate 2^n possible haploid gametes, and random fertilization can produce $2^n \times 2^n$ possible diploid zygotes. Because the haploid number (n) of grasshoppers is 23 and that of fruit flies is 4, two grasshoppers would be expected to produce a greater variety of zygotes than would two fruit flies. **3.** If the segments of the maternal and paternal chromatids that undergo crossing over are genetically identical and thus have the same two alleles for every gene, then the recombinant chromosomes will be genetically equivalent to the parental chromosomes. Crossing over contributes to genetic variation only when it involves the rearrangement of different alleles.

Summary of Key Concepts Questions

13.1 Genes program specific traits, and offspring inherit their genes from each parent, accounting for similarities in their appearance to one or the other parent. Humans reproduce sexually, which ensures new combinations of genes (and thus traits) in the offspring. Consequently, the offspring are not clones of their parents (which would be the case if humans reproduced asexually). **13.2** Animals and plants both reproduce sexually, alternating meiosis with fertilization. Both have haploid gametes that unite to form a diploid zygote, which then goes on to divide mitotically, forming a diploid multicellular organism. In animals, haploid cells become gametes and don't undergo mitosis, while in plants, the haploid cells resulting from meiosis undergo mitosis to form a haploid multicellular organism, the gametophyte. This organism then goes on to generate haploid gametes. (In plants such as trees, the gametophyte is quite reduced in size and not obvious to the casual observer.) **13.3** At the end of meiosis I, the two members of a homologous pair end up in different cells, so they cannot pair up and undergo crossing over. **13.4** First, during independent assortment in metaphase I, each pair of homologous chromosomes lines up independent of each other pair at the metaphase plate, so a daughter cell of meiosis I randomly inherits either a maternal or paternal chromosome. Second, due to crossing over, each chromosome is not exclusively maternal or paternal, but includes regions at the ends of the chromatid from a nonsister chromatid (a chromatid of the other homolog). (The nonsister segment can also be in an internal region of the chromatid if a second crossover occurs beyond the first one before the end of the chromatid.) This provides much additional diversity in the form of new combinations of alleles. Third, random fertilization ensures even more variation, since any sperm of a large number containing many possible genetic combinations can fertilize any egg of a similarly large number of possible combinations.

Test Your Understanding

1. a **2.** b **3.** a **4.** d **5.** c
6. (a)

(b) A haploid set is made up of one long, one medium, and one short chromosome. For example, the chromosomes of one color make up a haploid set. (In cases where crossovers have occurred, a haploid set of one color may include segments of chromatids of the other color.) All red and blue chromosomes together make up a diploid set. (c) Metaphase I **7.** This cell must be undergoing meiosis because homologous chromosomes are associated with each other at the metaphase plate; this does not occur in mitosis.

Chapter 14

Figure Questions

Figure 14.3 All offspring would have purple flowers. (The ratio would be 1 purple : 0 white.) The P generation plants are true-breeding, so mating two purple-flowered plants produces the same result as self-pollination: All the offspring have the same trait.

Figure 14.8

If dependent assortment:

Parents

YyRr × yyrr

Sperm from YyRr plant

1/2 YR · 1/2 yr

Eggs from yyrr plant: yr | YyRr | yyrr

1/2 yellow-round : 1/2 green-wrinkled
1 yellow-round : 1 green-wrinkled
Phenotypic ratio

If independent assortment:

Parents

YyRr × yyrr

Sperm from YyRr plant

1/4 YR · 1/4 Yr · 1/4 yR · 1/4 yr

Eggs from yyrr plant: yr | YyRr | Yyrr | yyRr | yyrr

1/4 yellow-round : 1/4 yellow-wrinkled:
1/4 green-round : 1/4 green-wrinkled

1 yellow-round : 1 yellow-wrinkled : 1 green-round : 1 green-wrinkled
Phenotypic ratio

Yes, this cross would also have allowed Mendel to make different predictions for the two hypotheses, thereby allowing him to distinguish the correct one.
Figure 14.10 Your classmate would probably point out that the F_1 generation hybrids show an intermediate phenotype between those of the homozygous parents, which supports the blending hypothesis. You could respond that crossing the F_1 hybrids results in the reappearance of the white phenotype, rather than identical pink offspring, which fails to support the idea of traits blending during inheritance. **Figure 14.11** Both the I^A and I^B alleles are dominant to the i allele, which results in no attached carbohydrate. The I^A and I^B alleles are codominant; both are expressed in the phenotype of $I^A I^B$ heterozygotes, who have type AB blood.
Figure 14.12 In this cross the final "3" and "1" of a standard cross are lumped together as a single phenotype. This occurs because in dogs that are ee, no pigment is deposited, thus the three dogs that have a B in their genotype (normally black) can no longer be distinguished from the dog who is bb (normally brown).
Figure 14.16 In the Punnett square, two of the three individuals with normal coloration are carriers, so the probability is 2/3. (Note that you must take into account everything you know when you calculate probability: You know she is not aa, so there are only three possible genotypes to consider.)

Concept Check 14.1

1. According to the law of independent assortment, 25 plants (1/16 of the offspring) are predicted to be $aatt$, or recessive for both characters. The actual result is likely to differ slightly from this value.

Parents

AaTt × AaTt

Sperm from AaTt plant

AT · At · aT · at

Eggs from AaTt plant:

	AT	At	aT	at
AT	AATT	AATt	AaTT	AaTt
At	AATt	AAtt	AaTt	Aatt
aT	AaTT	AaTt	aaTT	aaTt
at	AaTt	Aatt	aaTt	aatt

2. The plant could make eight different gametes (*YRI, YRi, YrI, Yri, yRI, yRi, yrI,* and *yri*). To fit all the possible gametes in a self-pollination, a Punnett square would need 8 rows and 8 columns. It would have spaces for the 64 possible unions of gametes in the offspring. **3.** Self-pollination is sexual reproduction because meiosis is involved in forming gametes, which unite during fertilization. As a result, the offspring in self-pollination are genetically different from the parent. (As mentioned in the footnote near the beginning of Concept 14.1, we have simplified the explanation in referring to the single pea plant as a parent. Technically, the gametophytes in the flower are the two "parents.")

Concept Check 14.2

1. 1/2 homozygous dominant (*AA*), 0 homozygous recessive (*aa*), and 1/2 heterozygous (*Aa*)   **2.** 1/4 *BBDD*; 1/4 *BbDD*; 1/4 *BBDd*; 1/4 *BbDd*   **3.** The genotypes that fulfill this condition are *ppyyIi, ppYyii, Ppyyii, ppYYii,* and *ppyyii*. Use the multiplication rule to find the probability of getting each genotype, and then use the addition rule to find the overall probability of meeting the conditions of this problem:

ppyy Ii   1/2 (probability of pp) × 1/4 (yy) × 1/2 (Ii) = 1/16
pp Yy ii   1/2 (pp) × 1/2 (Yy) × 1/2 (ii)   = 1/8
Pp yy ii   1/2 (Pp) × 1/4 (yy) × 1/2 (ii)   = 1/16
pp YY ii   1/2 (pp) × 1/4 (YY) × 1/2 (ii)   = 1/16
pp yy ii   1/2 (pp) × 1/4 (yy) × 1/2 (ii)   = 1/16
_____
Fraction predicted to have at least   = 6/16 or 3/8
two recessive traits

Concept Check 14.3

1. Incomplete dominance describes the relationship between two alleles of a single gene, whereas epistasis relates to the genetic relationship between two genes (and the respective alleles of each).   **2.** Half of the children would be expected to have type A blood and half type B blood.   **3.** The black and white alleles are incompletely dominant, with heterozygotes being gray in color. A cross between a gray rooster and a black hen should yield approximately equal numbers of gray and black offspring.

Concept Check 14.4

1. 1/9 (Since cystic fibrosis is caused by a recessive allele, Beth and Tom's siblings who have CF must be homozygous recessive. Therefore, each parent must be a carrier of the recessive allele. Since neither Beth nor Tom has CF, this means they each have a 2/3 chance of being a carrier. If they are both carriers, there is a 1/4 chance that they will have a child with CF. $2/3 \times 2/3 \times 1/4 = 1/9$); 0 (Both Beth and Tom would have to be carriers to produce a child with the disease.)   **2.** In normal hemoglobin, the sixth amino acid is glutamic acid (Glu), which is acidic (has a negative charge on its side chain). In sickle-cell hemoglobin, Glu is replaced by valine (Val), which is a nonpolar amino acid, very different from Glu. The primary structure of a protein (its amino acid sequence) ultimately determines the shape of the protein and thus its function. The substitution of Val for Glu enables the hemoglobin molecules to interact with each other and form long fibers, leading to the protein's deficient function and the deformation of the red blood cell.
3. Joan's genotype is *Dd*. Because the allele for polydactyly (*D*) is dominant to the allele for five digits per appendage (*d*), the trait is expressed in people with either the *DD* or *Dd* genotype. But because Joan's father does not have polydactyly, his genotype must be *dd*, which means that Joan inherited a *d* allele from him. Therefore Joan, who does have the trait, must be heterozygous.   **4.** In the monohybrid cross involving flower color, the ratio is 3.15 purple : 1 white, while in the human family in the pedigree, the ratio in the third generation is 1 free : 1 attached earlobe. The difference is due to the small sample size (two offspring) in the human family. If the second-generation couple in this pedigree were able to have 929 offspring as in the pea plant cross, the ratio would likely be closer to 3:1. (Note that none of the pea plant crosses in Table 14.1 yielded *exactly* a 3:1 ratio.)

Summary of Key Concepts Questions

14.1 Alternative versions of genes, called alleles, are passed from parent to offspring during sexual reproduction. In a cross between purple- and white-flowered homozygous parents, the F_1 offspring are all heterozygous, each inheriting a purple allele from one parent and a white allele from the other. Because the purple allele is dominant, it determines the phenotype of the F_1 offspring to be purple, and the expression of the white allele is masked. Only in the F_2 generation is it possible for a white allele to exist in a homozygous state, which causes the white trait to be expressed.

14.2

Sperm: 1/2 Y · 1/2 y

Eggs: 1/2 Y | YY | Yy
Eggs: 1/2 y | Yy | yy

3/4 yellow
1/4 green

Sperm: 1/2 R · 1/2 r

Eggs: 1/2 R | RR | Rr
Eggs: 1/2 r | Rr | rr

3/4 round
1/4 wrinkled

3/4 yellow × 3/4 round   = 9/16 yellow-round
3/4 yellow × 1/4 wrinkled = 3/16 yellow-wrinkled
1/4 green × 3/4 round   = 3/16 green-round
1/4 green × 1/4 wrinkled = 1/16 green-wrinkled

= 9 yellow-round : 3 yellow-wrinkled : 3 green-round : 1 green-wrinkled

14.3 The ABO blood group is an example of multiple alleles because this single gene has more than two alleles (I^A, I^B, and i). Two of the alleles, I^A and I^B, exhibit codominance, since both carbohydrates (A and B) are present when these two alleles exist together in a genotype. I^A and I^B each exhibit complete dominance over the i allele. This situation is not an example of incomplete dominance because each allele affects the phenotype in a distinguishable way, so the result is not intermediate between the two phenotypes. Because this situation involves a single gene, it is not an example of epistasis or polygenic inheritance.   **14.4** The chance of the fourth child having cystic fibrosis is 1/4, as it was for each of the other children, because each birth is an independent event. We already know both parents are carriers, so whether their first three children are carriers or not has no bearing on the probability that their next child will have the disease. The parents' genotypes provide the only relevant information.

Test Your Understanding

1.

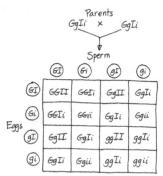

Parents
$GgIi$ × $GgIi$

Sperm

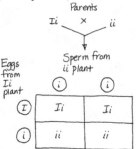

9 green-inflated : 3 green-constricted :
3 yellow-inflated : 1 yellow-constricted

2. Man $I^A i$; woman $I^B i$; child ii. Genotypes for future children are predicted to be $\frac{1}{4} I^A I^B$, $\frac{1}{4} I^A i$, $\frac{1}{4} I^B i$, $\frac{1}{4} ii$. 3. $\frac{1}{2}$ 4. A cross of $Ii \times ii$ would yield offspring with a genotypic ratio of 1 Ii : 1 ii (2:2 is an equivalent answer) and a phenotypic ratio of 1 inflated : 1 constricted (2:2 is equivalent).

Parents
Ii × ii

Sperm from
ii plant

Eggs from Ii plant

	i	i
I	Ii	Ii
i	ii	ii

Genotypic ratio 1 Ii : 1 ii
(2:2 is equivalent)

Phenotypic ratio 1 inflated : 1 constricted
(2:2 is equivalent)

5. (a) $\frac{1}{64}$; (b) $\frac{1}{64}$; (c) $\frac{1}{8}$; (d) $\frac{1}{32}$ 6. (a) $\frac{3}{4} \times \frac{3}{4} \times \frac{3}{4} = \frac{27}{64}$; (b) $1 - \frac{27}{64} = \frac{37}{64}$; (c) $\frac{1}{4} \times \frac{1}{4} \times \frac{1}{4} = \frac{1}{64}$; (d) $1 - \frac{1}{64} = \frac{63}{64}$ 7. (a) $\frac{1}{256}$; (b) $\frac{1}{16}$; (c) $\frac{1}{256}$; (d) $\frac{1}{64}$; (e) $\frac{1}{128}$ 8. (a) 1; (b) $\frac{1}{32}$; (c) $\frac{1}{8}$; (d) $\frac{1}{2}$ 9. $\frac{1}{9}$ 10. Matings of the original mutant cat with true-breeding noncurl cats will produce both curl and noncurl F$_1$ offspring if the curl allele is dominant, but only noncurl offspring if the curl allele is recessive. You would obtain some true-breeding offspring homozygous for the curl allele from matings between the F$_1$ cats resulting from the original curl × noncurl crosses whether the curl trait is dominant or recessive. You know that cats are true-breeding when curl × curl matings produce only curl offspring. As it turns out, the allele that causes curled ears is dominant. 11. 25%, or $\frac{1}{4}$, will be cross-eyed; all (100%) of the cross-eyed offspring will also be white. 12. The dominant allele I is epistatic to the P/p locus, and thus the genotypic ratio for the F$_1$ generation will be 9 $I–P–$ (colorless) : 3 $I–pp$ (colorless) : 3 $iiP–$ (purple) : 1 $iipp$ (red). Overall, the phenotypic ratio is 12 colorless : 3 purple : 1 red. 13. Recessive. All affected individuals (Arlene, Tom, Wilma, and Carla) are homozygous recessive aa. George is Aa, since some of his children with Arlene are affected. Sam, Ann, Daniel, and Alan are each Aa, since they are all unaffected children with one affected parent. Michael also is Aa, since he has an affected child (Carla) with his heterozygous wife Ann. Sandra, Tina, and Christopher can each have either the AA or Aa genotype. 14. $\frac{1}{6}$

Chapter 15

Figure Questions

Figure 15.2 The ratio would be 1 yellow-round : 1 green-round : 1 yellow-wrinkled : 1 green-wrinkled. **Figure 15.4** About $\frac{3}{4}$ of the F$_2$ offspring would have red eyes and about $\frac{1}{4}$ would have white eyes. About half of the white-eyed flies would be female and half would be male; similarly, about half of the red-eyed flies would be female and half would be male. (Note that the homologs with the eye color alleles would be the same shape in the Punnett square, and each offspring would inherit two alleles. The sex of the flies would be determined separately by inheritance of the sex chromosomes. Thus your Punnett square would have four possible combinations in sperm and four in eggs; it would have 16 squares altogether.) **Figure 15.7** All the males would be color-blind, and all the females would be carriers. (Another way to say this is that $\frac{1}{2}$ the offspring would be color-blind males, and $\frac{1}{2}$ the offspring would be carrier females.) **Figure 15.9** The two largest classes would still be the parental-type offspring (offspring with the phenotypes of the true-breeding P generation flies), but now they would be gray-vestigial

and black-normal because those were the specific allele combinations in the P generation. **Figure 15.10** The two chromosomes below, left, are like the two chromosomes inherited by the F$_1$ female, one from each P generation fly. They are passed by the F$_1$ female intact to the offspring and thus could be called "parental" chromosomes. The other two chromosomes result from crossing over during meiosis in the F$_1$ female. Because they have combinations of alleles not seen in either of the F$_1$ female's chromosomes, they can be called "recombinant" chromosomes. (Note that in this example, the alleles on the recombinant chromosomes, $b^+ vg^+$ and $b\ vg$, are the allele combinations that were on the parental chromosomes in the cross shown in Figures 15.9 and 15.10. The basis for calling them parental chromosomes is that they have the combination of alleles that was present on the P generation chromosomes.)

Parental chromosomes   Recombinant chromosomes

Concept Check 15.1

1. The law of segregation relates to the inheritance of alleles for a single character. The law of independent assortment of alleles relates to the inheritance of alleles for two characters. 2. The physical basis for the law of segregation is the separation of homologs in anaphase I. The physical basis for the law of independent assortment is the alternative arrangements of different homologous chromosome pairs in metaphase I. 3. To show the mutant phenotype, a male needs to possess only one mutant allele. If this gene had been on a pair of autosomes, *two* mutant alleles would have had to be present for an individual to show the recessive mutant phenotype, a much less probable situation.

Concept Check 15.2

1. Because the gene for this eye-color character is located on the X chromosome, all female offspring will be red-eyed and heterozygous ($X^{w^+}X^w$); all male offspring will inherit a Y chromosome from the father and be white-eyed ($X^w Y$). (Another way to say this is that $\frac{1}{2}$ the offspring will be red-eyed, heterozygous [carrier] females, and $\frac{1}{2}$ will be white-eyed males.) 2. $\frac{1}{4}$ ($\frac{1}{2}$ chance that the child will inherit a Y chromosome from the father and be male × $\frac{1}{2}$ chance that he will inherit the X carrying the disease allele from his mother). If the child is a boy, there is a $\frac{1}{2}$ chance he will have the disease; a female would have zero chance (but $\frac{1}{2}$ chance of being a carrier). 3. With a disorder caused by a dominant allele, there is no such thing as a "carrier," since those with the allele have the disorder. Because the allele is dominant, the females lose any "advantage" in having two X chromosomes, since one disorder-associated allele is sufficient to result in the disorder. All fathers who have the dominant allele will pass it along to *all* their daughters, who will also have the disorder. A mother who has the allele (and thus the disorder) will pass it to half of her sons and half of her daughters.

Concept Check 15.3

1. Crossing over during meiosis I in the heterozygous parent produces some gametes with recombinant genotypes for the two genes. Offspring with a recombinant phenotype arise from fertilization of the recombinant gametes by homozygous recessive gametes from the double-mutant parent. 2. In each case, the alleles contributed by the female parent (in the egg) determine the phenotype of the offspring because the male in this cross contributes only recessive alleles. Thus, identifying the phenotype of the offspring tells you what alleles were in the egg. 3. No. The order could be *A-C-B* or *C-A-B*. To determine which possibility is correct, you need to know the recombination frequency between *B* and *C*.

Concept Check 15.4

1. In meiosis, a combined 14-21 chromosome will behave as one chromosome. If a gamete receives the combined 14-21 chromosome and a normal copy of chromosome 21, trisomy 21 will result when this gamete combines with a normal gamete during fertilization. 2. No. The child can be either $I^A I^A i$ or $I^A ii$. A sperm of genotype $I^A I^A$ could result from nondisjunction in the father during meiosis II, while an egg with the genotype ii could result from nondisjunction in the mother during either meiosis I or meiosis II. 3. Activation of this gene could lead to the production of too much of this kinase. If the kinase is involved in a signaling pathway that triggers cell division, too much of it could trigger unrestricted cell division, which in turn could contribute to the development of a cancer (in this case, a cancer of one type of white blood cell).

Concept Check 15.5

1. Inactivation of an X chromosome in females and genomic imprinting. Because of X inactivation, the effective dose of genes on the X chromosome is the same in males and females. As a result of genomic imprinting, only one allele of certain genes is phenotypically expressed. 2. The genes for leaf coloration are located in plastids within the cytoplasm. Normally, only the maternal parent transmits plastid genes to offspring. Since variegated offspring are produced only when the female parent is of the B variety, we can conclude that variety B contains both the wild-type and mutant alleles of pigment genes, producing variegated leaves. (Variety A must contain only the wild-type allele of pigment genes.) 3. Each cell contains numerous mitochondria, and in affected individuals, most cells contain a variable mixture of normal and mutant mitochondria. The normal mitochondria carry out enough cellular respiration for survival. (The situation is similar for chloroplasts.)

Summary of Key Concepts Questions

15.1 Because the sex chromosomes are different from each other and because they determine the sex of the offspring, Morgan could use the sex of the offspring as a phenotypic characteristic to follow the parental chromosomes. (He could also have followed them under a microscope, as the X and Y chromosomes look different.) At the same time, he could record eye color to follow the eye-color alleles. **15.2** Males have only one X chromosome, along with a Y chromosome, while females have two X chromosomes. The Y chromosome has very few genes on it, while the X has about 1,000. When a recessive X-linked allele that causes a disorder is inherited by a male on the X from his mother, there isn't a second allele present on the Y (males are hemizygous), so the male has the disorder. Because females have two X chromosomes, they must inherit two recessive alleles in order to have the disorder, a rarer occurrence. **15.3** Crossing over results in new combinations of alleles. Crossing over is a random occurrence, and the more distance there is between two genes, the more chances there are for crossing over to occur, leading to a new allele combination. **15.4** In inversions and reciprocal translocations, the same genetic material is present in the same relative amount but just organized differently. In aneuploidy, duplications, deletions, and nonreciprocal translocations, the balance of genetic material is upset, as large segments are either missing or present in more than one copy. Apparently, this type of imbalance is very damaging to the organism. (Although it isn't lethal in the developing embryo, the reciprocal translocation that produces the Philadelphia chromosome can lead to a serious condition, cancer, by altering the expression of important genes.) **15.5** In these cases, the sex of the parent contributing an allele affects the inheritance pattern. For imprinted genes, either the paternal or the maternal allele is expressed, depending on the imprint. For mitochondrial and chloroplast genes, only the maternal contribution will affect offspring phenotype because the offspring inherit these organelles from the mother, via the egg cytoplasm.

Test Your Understanding

1. 0; $\frac{1}{2}$; $\frac{1}{16}$ **2.** Recessive; if the disorder were dominant, it would affect at least one parent of a child born with the disorder. The disorder's inheritance is sex-linked because it is seen only in boys. For a girl to have the disorder, she would have to inherit recessive alleles from *both* parents. This would be very rare, since males with the recessive allele on their X chromosome die in their early teens. **3.** 17%; yes, it is consistent. In Figure 15.9, the recombination frequency was also 17%. (You'd expect this to be the case since these are the very same two genes, and their distance from each other wouldn't change from one experiment to another.) **4.** Between *T* and *A*, 12%; between *A* and *S*, 5% **5.** Between *T* and *S*, 18%; sequence of genes is *T–A–S* **6.** 6%; wild-type heterozygous for normal wings and red eyes × recessive homozygous for vestigial wings and purple eyes **7.** Fifty percent of the offspring will show phenotypes resulting from crossovers. These results would be the same as those from a cross where *A* and *B* were *not* on the same chromosome, and you would interpret the results to mean that the genes are unlinked. (Further crosses involving other genes on the same chromosome would reveal the genetic linkage and map distances.) **8.** 450 each of blue-oval and white-round (parentals) and 50 each of blue-round and white-oval (recombinants) **9.** About one-third of the distance from the vestigial-wing locus to the brown-eye locus **10.** Because bananas are triploid, homologous pairs cannot line up during meiosis. Therefore, it is not possible to generate gametes that can fuse to produce a zygote with the triploid number of chromosomes. **12.** (a) For each pair of genes, you had to generate an F_1 dihybrid fly; let's use the *A* and *B* genes as an example. You obtained homozygous parental flies, either the first with dominant alleles of the two genes (*AABB*) and the second with recessive alleles (*aabb*), or the first with dominant alleles of gene *A* and recessive alleles of gene *B* (*AAbb*) and the second with recessive alleles of gene *A* and dominant alleles of gene *B* (*aaBB*). Breeding either of these pairs of P generation flies gave you an F_1 dihybrid, which you then testcrossed with a doubly homozygous recessive fly (*aabb*). You classed the offspring as parental or recombinant, based on the genotypes of the P generation parents (either of the two pairs described above). You added up the number of recombinant types and then divided by the total number of offspring. This gave you the recombination percentage (in this case, 8%), which you can translate into map units (8 map units) to construct your map.

(b)

Chapter 16

Figure Questions

Figure 16.2 The living S cells found in the blood sample were able to reproduce to yield more S cells, indicating that the S trait is a permanent, heritable change, rather than just a one-time use of the dead S cells' capsules. **Figure 16.4** The radioactivity would have been found in the pellet when proteins were labeled (batch 1) because proteins would have had to enter the bacterial cells to program them with genetic instructions. It's hard for us to imagine now, but the DNA might have played a structural role that allowed some of the proteins to be injected while it remained outside the bacterial cell (thus no radioactivity in the pellet in batch 2). **Figure 16.11** The tube from the first replication would look the same, with a middle band of hybrid ^{15}N-^{14}N DNA, but the second tube would not have the upper band of two light blue strands. Instead, it would have a bottom band of two dark blue strands, like the bottom band in the result predicted after one replication

in the conservative model. **Figure 16.12** In the bubble at the top in (b), arrows should be drawn pointing left and right to indicate the two replication forks. **Figure 16.14** Looking at any of the DNA strands, we see that one end is called the 5′ end and the other 3′ end. If we proceed from the 5′ end to the 3′ end on the left-most strand, for example, we list the components in this order: phosphate group → 5′ C of the sugar → 3′ C → phosphate → 5′ C → 3′ C. Going in the opposite direction on the same strand, the components proceed in the reverse order: 3′ C → 5′ C → phosphate. Thus, the two directions are distinguishable, which is what we mean when we say that the strands have directionality. (Review Figure 16.5 if necessary.)

Figure 16.17

Figure 16.18

Figure 16.23 The two members of a homologous pair (which would be the same color) would be associated tightly together at the metaphase plate. In metaphase of mitosis, however, each chromosome would be lined up individually, so the two chromosomes of the same color would be in different places at the metaphase plate.

Concept Check 16.1

1. You can't tell which end is the 5′ end. You need to know which end has a phosphate group on the 5′ carbon (the 5′ end) or which end has an —OH group on the 3′ carbon (the 3′ end). **2.** He expected that the mouse injected with the mixture of heat-killed S cells and living R cells would survive, since neither type of cell alone would kill the mouse.

Concept Check 16.2

1. Complementary base pairing ensures that the two daughter molecules are exact copies of the parental molecule. When the two strands of the parental molecule separate, each serves as a template on which nucleotides are arranged, by the base-pairing rules, into new complementary strands. **2.** DNA pol III covalently adds nucleotides to new DNA strands and proofreads each added nucleotide for correct base pairing. **3.** In the cell cycle, DNA synthesis occurs during the S phase, between the G_1 and G_2 phases of interphase. DNA replication is therefore complete before the mitotic phase begins. **4.** Synthesis of the leading strand is initiated by an RNA primer, which must be removed and replaced with DNA, a task that could not be performed if the cell's DNA pol I were nonfunctional. In the overview box in Figure 16.17, just to the left of the top origin of replication, a functional DNA pol I would replace the RNA primer of the leading strand (shown in red) with DNA nucleotides (blue). The nucleotides would be added onto the 3′ end of the final Okazaki fragment of the upper lagging strand (the right half of the replication bubble).

Concept Check 16.3

1. A nucleosome is made up of eight histone proteins, two each of four different types, around which DNA is wound. Linker DNA runs from one nucleosome to the next. **2.** Euchromatin is chromatin that becomes less compacted during interphase and is accessible to the cellular machinery responsible for gene activity. Heterochromatin, on the other hand, remains quite condensed during interphase and contains genes that are largely inaccessible to this machinery. **3.** The nuclear lamina is a netlike array of protein filaments that provides mechanical support just inside the nuclear envelope and thus maintains the shape of the nucleus. Considerable evidence also supports the existence of a nuclear matrix, a framework of protein fibers extending throughout the nuclear interior.

Summary of Key Concepts Questions
16.1 Each strand in the double helix has polarity; the end with a phosphate group on the 5′ carbon of the sugar is called the 5′ end, and the end with an —OH group on the 3′ carbon of the sugar is called the 3′ end. The two strands run in opposite directions, one running 5′ → 3′ and the other alongside it running 3′ → 5′. Thus, each end of the molecule has both a 5′ and a 3′ end. This arrangement is called "antiparallel." If the strands were parallel, they would both run 5′ → 3′ in the same direction, so an end of the molecule would have either two 5′ ends or two 3′ ends. **16.2** On both the leading and lagging strands, DNA polymerase adds onto the 3′ end of an RNA primer synthesized by primase, synthesizing DNA in the 5′ → 3′ direction. Because the parental strands are antiparallel, however, only on the leading strand does synthesis proceed continuously into the replication fork. The lagging strand is synthesized bit by bit in the direction away from the fork as a series of shorter Okazaki fragments, which are later joined together by DNA ligase. Each fragment is initiated by synthesis of an RNA primer by primase as soon as a given stretch of single-stranded template strand is opened up. Although both strands are synthesized at the same rate, synthesis of the lagging strand is delayed because initiation of each fragment begins only when sufficient template strand is available. **16.3** Most of the chromatin in an interphase nucleus is fairly uncondensed. Much is present as the 30-nm fiber, with some in the form of the 10-nm fiber and some as looped domains of the 30-nm fiber. (These different levels of chromatin packing may reflect differences in gene expression occurring in these regions.) Also, a small percentage of the chromatin, such as that at the centromeres and telomeres, is highly condensed heterochromatin.

Test Your Understanding
1. c **2.** c **3.** b **4.** d **5.** a **6.** d **7.** b **8.** a
9. Like histones, the *E. coli* proteins would be expected to contain many basic (positively charged) amino acids, such as lysine and arginine, which can form weak bonds with the negatively charged phosphate groups on the sugar-phosphate backbone of the DNA molecule.

11.

New DNA strand (olive)
Parental DNA strand (purple)
Sliding clamp
DNA pol III
Single-strand binding protein
Direction of replication

Chapter 17

Figure Questions
Figure 17.2 The previously presumed pathway would have been wrong. The new results would support this pathway: precursor → citrulline → ornithine → arginine. They would also indicate that class I mutants have a defect in the second step and class II mutants have a defect in the first step. **Figure 17.4** The mRNA sequence (5′-UGGUUUGGCUCA-3′) is the same as the nontemplate DNA strand sequence (5′-TGGTTTGGCTCA-3′), except there is a U in the mRNA wherever there is a T in the DNA. **Figure 17.7** The processes are similar in that polymerases form polynucleotides complementary to an antiparallel DNA template strand. In replication, however, both strands act as templates, whereas in transcription, only one DNA strand acts as a template. **Figure 17.8** The RNA polymerase would bind directly to the promoter, rather than depending on the previous binding of other factors. **Figure 17.21** It would be packaged in a vesicle, transported to the Golgi apparatus for further processing, and then transported via a vesicle to the plasma membrane. The vesicle would fuse with the membrane, releasing the protein outside the cell. **Figure 17.23** The mRNA farthest to the right (the longest one) started transcription first. The ribosome at the top, closest to the DNA, started translating first and thus has the longest polypeptide.

Concept Check 17.1
1. Recessive **2.** A polypeptide made up of 10 Gly (glycine) amino acids
3.

Template sequence
(from problem):   3′-TTCAGTCGT-5′

Nontemplate sequence: 5′-AAGTCAGCA-3′

mRNA sequence: 5′-AAGUCAGCA-3′

The nontemplate and mRNA nucleotide sequences are the same except that there is a T in the nontemplate strand of DNA wherever there is a U in the mRNA.
4.

"Template sequence" (from nontemplate sequence in problem, written 3′ → 5′):   3′-ACGACTGAA-5′

mRNA sequence: 5′-UGCUGACUU-3′

Translated: Cys-STOP-Leu

(Remember that the mRNA is antiparallel to the DNA strand.) A protein translated from the nontemplate sequence would have a completely different amino acid sequence and would most likely be nonfunctional. (It would also be shorter because of the stop signal shown in the mRNA sequence above—and possibly others earlier in the mRNA sequence.)

Concept Check 17.2
1. A promoter is the region of DNA to which RNA polymerase binds to begin transcription. It is at the upstream end of the gene (transcription unit). **2.** In a bacterial cell, part of the RNA polymerase recognizes the gene's promoter and binds to it. In a eukaryotic cell, transcription factors mediate the binding of RNA polymerase to the promoter. In both cases, sequences in the promoter bind precisely to the RNA polymerase, so the enzyme is in the right location and orientation. **3.** The transcription factor that recognizes the TATA sequence would be unable to bind, so RNA polymerase could not bind and transcription of that gene probably would not occur.

Concept Check 17.3
1. Due to alternative splicing of exons, each gene can result in multiple different mRNAs and can thus direct synthesis of multiple different proteins. **2.** In watching a show recorded with a DVR, you watch segments of the show itself (exons) and fast-forward through the commercials, which are thus like introns. **3.** Once the mRNA has exited the nucleus, the cap prevents it from being degraded by hydrolytic enzymes and facilitates its attachment to ribosomes. If the cap were removed from all mRNAs, the cell would no longer be able to synthesize any proteins and would probably die.

Concept Check 17.4
1. First, each aminoacyl-tRNA synthetase specifically recognizes a single amino acid and attaches it only to an appropriate tRNA. Second, a tRNA charged with its specific amino acid binds only to an mRNA codon for that amino acid. **2.** The structure and function of the ribosome seem to depend more on the rRNAs than on the ribosomal proteins. Because it is single-stranded, an RNA molecule can hydrogen-bond with itself and with other RNA molecules. RNA molecules make up the interface between the two ribosomal subunits, so presumably RNA-RNA binding helps hold the ribosome together. The binding site for mRNA in the ribosome includes rRNA that can bind the mRNA. Also, complementary hydrogen bonding within an RNA molecule allows it to assume a particular three-dimensional shape and, along with the RNA's functional groups, enables rRNA to catalyze peptide bond formation during translation. **3.** A signal peptide on the leading end of the polypeptide being synthesized is recognized by a signal-recognition particle that brings the ribosome to the ER membrane. There the ribosome attaches and continues to synthesize the polypeptide, depositing it in the ER lumen. **4.** Because of wobble, the tRNA could bind to either 5′-GCA-3′ or 5′-GCG-3′, both of which code for alanine (Ala). Alanine would be attached to the tRNA.

Ala
tRNA
3′ CGU 5′
GCA   GCG
5′ ⊥⊥⊥ 3′   5′ ⊥⊥⊥ 3′

5. When one ribosome terminates translation and dissociates, the two subunits would be very close to the cap. This could facilitate their rebinding and initiating synthesis of a new polypeptide, thus increasing the efficiency of translation.

Concept Check 17.5
1. In the mRNA, the reading frame downstream from the deletion is shifted, leading to a long string of incorrect amino acids in the polypeptide, and in most cases, a stop codon will arise, leading to premature termination. The polypeptide will most likely be nonfunctional. **2.** Heterozygous individuals, said to have sickle-cell trait, have a copy each of the wild-type allele and the sickle-cell allele. Both alleles will be expressed, so these individuals will have both normal and sickle-cell hemoglobin molecules. Apparently, having a mix of the two forms of β-globin has no effect under most conditions, but during prolonged periods of low blood oxygen (such as at higher altitudes), these individuals can show some signs of sickle-cell disease.

3.

Normal DNA sequence
(template strand is on top): 3'-TACTTGTCCGATATC-5'
                             5'-ATGAACAGGCTATAG-3'

mRNA sequence: 5'-AUGAACAGGCUAUAG-3'

Amino acid sequence: Met-Asn-Arg-Leu-STOP

Mutated DNA sequence
(template strand is on top): 3'-TACTTGTCCAATATC-5'
                            5'-ATGAACAGGTTATAG-3'

mRNA sequence: 5'-AUGAACAGGUUAUAG-3'

Amino acid sequence: Met-Asn-Arg-Leu-STOP

No effect: The amino acid sequence is Met-Asn-Arg-Leu both before and after the mutation because the mRNA codons 5'-CUA-3' and 5'-UUA-3' both code for Leu. (The fifth codon is a stop codon.)

Summary of Key Concepts Questions

17.1 A gene contains genetic information in the form of a nucleotide sequence. The gene is first transcribed into an RNA molecule, and a messenger RNA molecule is ultimately translated into a polypeptide. The polypeptide makes up part or all of a protein, which performs a function in the cell and contributes to the phenotype of the organism. **17.2** Both bacterial and eukaryotic genes have promoters, regions where RNA polymerase ultimately binds and begins transcription. In bacteria, RNA polymerase binds directly to the promoter; in eukaryotes, transcription factors bind first to the promoter, and then RNA polymerase binds to the transcription factors and promoter together. **17.3** Both the 5' cap and the poly-A tail help the mRNA exit from the nucleus and then, in the cytoplasm, help ensure mRNA stability and allow it to bind to ribosomes. **17.4** tRNAs function as translators between the nucleotide-based language of mRNA and the amino-acid-based language of polypeptides. A tRNA carries a specific amino acid, and the anticodon on the tRNA is complementary to the codon on the mRNA that codes for that amino acid. In the ribosome, the tRNA binds to the A site. Then, the polypeptide being synthesized (currently on the tRNA in the P site) is joined to the new amino acid, which becomes the new (C-terminal) end of the polypeptide. Next, the tRNA in the A site moves to the P site. When the polypeptide is transferred to the new tRNA, thus adding the new amino acid, the now empty tRNA moves from the P site to the E site, where it exits the ribosome. **17.5** When a nucleotide base is altered chemically, its base-pairing characteristics may be changed. When that happens, an incorrect nucleotide is likely to be incorporated into the complementary strand during the next replication of the DNA, and successive rounds of replication will perpetuate the mutation. Once the gene is transcribed, the mutated codon may code for a different amino acid that inhibits or changes the function of a protein. If the chemical change in the base is detected and repaired by the DNA repair system before the next replication, no mutation will result.

Test Your Understanding

1. b **2.** c **3.** a **4.** a **5.** b **6.** c **7.** d
8. No, transcription and translation are separated in space and time in a eukaryotic cell, as a result of the eukaryotyic cell's nuclear membrane.

9.

Type of RNA	Functions
Messenger RNA (mRNA)	Carries information specifying amino acid sequences of proteins from DNA to ribosomes
Transfer RNA (tRNA)	Serves as translator molecule in protein synthesis; translates mRNA codons into amino acids
Ribosomal RNA (rRNA)	Plays catalytic (ribozyme) roles and structural roles in ribosomes
Primary transcript	Is a precursor to mRNA, rRNA, or tRNA, before being processed; also, some of the RNA in introns acts as a ribozyme, catalyzing its own splicing
Small RNAs in the ribosome	Plays structural and catalytic roles in spliceosomes, the complexes of protein and RNA that splice pre-mRNA

Chapter 18

Figure Questions

Figure 18.3 As the concentration of tryptophan in the cell falls, eventually there will be none bound to repressor molecules. These will then change into their inactive shapes and dissociate from the operator, allowing transcription of the operon to resume. The enzymes for tryptophan synthesis will be made, and they will again begin to synthesize tryptophan in the cell. **Figure 18.11** In both types of cell, the albumin gene enhancer has the three control elements colored yellow, gray, and red. The sequences in the liver and lens cells would be identical, since the cells are in the same organism. **Figure 18.18** Even if the mutant MyoD protein couldn't activate the *myoD* gene, it could still turn on genes for the other proteins in the pathway (other transcription factors, which would turn on the genes for muscle-specific proteins, for example). Therefore, some differentiation would occur. But unless there were other activators that could compensate for the loss of the MyoD protein's activation of the *myoD* gene, the cell would not be able to maintain its differentiated state. **Figure 18.22** Normal Bicoid protein would be made in the anterior end and compensate for the presence of mutant *bicoid* mRNA put into the egg by the mother. Development should be normal, with a head present. **Figure 18.25** The mutation is likely to be recessive because it is more likely to have an effect if both copies of the gene are mutated and code for nonfunctional proteins. If one normal copy of the gene is present, its product could inhibit the cell cycle. (However, there are also known cases of dominant *p53* mutations.) **Figure 18.27** Cancer is a disease in which cell division occurs without its usual regulation. Cell division can be stimulated by growth factors (see Figure 12.18), which bind to cell-surface receptors (see Figure 11.8). Cancer cells evade these normal controls and can often divide in the absence of growth factors (see Figure 12.19). This suggests that the receptor proteins or some other components in a signaling pathway are abnormal in some way (see, for example, the mutant Ras protein in Figure 18.24) or are expressed at abnormal levels, as seen for the receptors in this figure. Under some circumstances in the mammalian body, steroid hormones such as estrogen and progesterone can also promote cell division. These molecules also use cell-signaling pathways, as described in Chapter 11 (see Figure 11.9). Because signaling receptors are involved in triggering cells to undergo cell division, it is not surprising that altered genes encoding these proteins might play a significant role in the development of cancer. Genes might be altered either through a mutation that changes the function of the protein product or a mutation that causes the gene to be expressed at abnormal levels that disrupt the overall regulation of the signaling pathway.

Concept Check 18.1

1. Binding by the *trp* corepressor (tryptophan) activates the *trp* repressor, shutting off transcription of the *trp* operon; binding by the *lac* inducer (allolactose) inactivates the *lac* repressor, leading to transcription of the *lac* operon. **2.** When glucose is scarce, cAMP is bound to CAP and CAP is bound to the promoter, favoring the binding of RNA polymerase. However, in the absence of lactose, the repressor is bound to the operator, blocking RNA polymerase binding to the promoter. Therefore, the operon genes are not transcribed. **3.** The cell would continuously produce β-galactosidase and the two other enzymes for lactose utilization, even in the absence of lactose, thus wasting cell resources.

Concept Check 18.2

1. Histone acetylation is generally associated with gene expression, while DNA methylation is generally associated with lack of expression. **2.** General transcription factors function in assembling the transcription initiation complex at the promoters for all genes. Specific transcription factors bind to control elements associated with a particular gene and, once bound, either increase (activators) or decrease (repressors) transcription of that gene. **3.** The three genes should have some similar or identical sequences in the control elements of their enhancers. Because of this similarity, the same specific transcription factors in muscle cells could bind to the enhancers of all three genes and stimulate their expression coordinately. **4.** Regulation of translation initiation, degradation of the mRNA, activation of the protein (by chemical modification, for example), and protein degradation

Concept Check 18.3

1. Both miRNAs and siRNAs are small, single-stranded RNAs that associate with a complex of proteins and then can base-pair with mRNAs that have a complementary sequence. This base pairing leads to either degradation of the mRNA or blockage of its translation. In some yeasts, siRNAs associated with proteins in a different complex can bind back to centromeric chromatin, recruiting enzymes that cause condensation of that chromatin into heterochromatin. Both miRNAs and siRNAs are processed from double-stranded RNA precursors, but have subtle variations in the structure of those precursors. **2.** The mRNA would persist and be translated into the cell division-promoting protein, and the cell would probably divide. If the intact miRNA is necessary for inhibition of cell division, then division of this cell might be inappropriate. Uncontrolled cell division could lead to formation of a mass of cells (tumor) that prevents proper functioning of the organism and could contribute to the development of cancer.

Concept Check 18.4

1. Cells undergo differentiation during embryonic development, becoming different from each other. Therefore, the adult organism is made up of many highly specialized cell types. **2.** By binding to a receptor on the receiving cell's surface and triggering a signal transduction pathway, involving intracellular molecules such as second messengers and transcription factors that affect gene expression **3.** Because their products, made and deposited into the egg by the mother, determine the head and tail ends, as well as the back and belly, of the embryo (and eventually the adult fly) **4.** The lower cell is synthesizing signaling molecules because the gene encoding them is activated, meaning that the appropriate specific transcription factors are binding to the gene's enhancer. The genes encoding these specific transcription factors are also being expressed in this cell because the transcriptional activators that can turn them on were expressed in the precursor to this cell. A similar explanation also applies to the cells expressing the receptor proteins. This scenario began with specific cytoplasmic determinants localized in specific regions of the egg. These cytoplasmic determinants were distributed unevenly to daughter cells, resulting in cells going down different developmental pathways.

Concept Check 18.5

1. Apoptosis is signaled by p53 protein when a cell has extensive DNA damage, so apoptosis plays a protective role in eliminating a cell that might contribute to cancer. If mutations in the genes in the apoptotic pathway blocked apoptosis, a cell with such damage could continue to divide and might lead to tumor formation. **2.** When an individual has inherited an oncogene or a mutant allele of a tumor-suppressor gene **3.** A cancer-causing mutation in a proto-oncogene usually makes the gene product overactive, whereas a cancer-causing mutation in a tumor-suppressor gene usually makes the gene product nonfunctional.

Summary of Key Concepts Questions

18.1 A corepressor and an inducer are both small molecules that bind to the repressor protein in an operon, causing the repressor to change shape. In the case of a corepressor (like tryptophan), this shape change allows the repressor to bind to the operator, blocking transcription. In contrast, an inducer causes the repressor to dissociate from the operator, allowing transcription to begin. **18.2** The chromatin must not be tightly condensed because it must be accessible to transcription factors. The appropriate specific transcription factors (activators) must bind to the control elements in the enhancer of the gene, while repressors must not be bound. The DNA must be bent by a bending protein so the activators can contact the mediator proteins and form a complex with general transcription factors at the promoter. Then RNA polymerase must bind and begin transcription. **18.3** miRNAs do not "code" for the amino acids of a protein—they are never translated. Each miRNA associates with a group of proteins to form a complex. Binding of the complex to an mRNA with a complementary sequence causes that mRNA to be degraded or blocks its translation. This is considered gene regulation because it controls the amount of a particular mRNA that can be translated into a functional protein. **18.4** The first process involves cytoplasmic determinants, including mRNAs and proteins, placed into specific locations in the egg by the mother. The cells that are formed from different regions in the egg during early cell divisions will have different proteins in them, which will direct different programs of gene expression. The second process involves the cell in question responding to signaling molecules secreted by neighboring cells. The signaling pathway in the responding cell also leads to a different pattern of gene expression. The coordination of these two processes results in each cell following a unique pathway in the developing embryo. **18.5** The protein product of a proto-oncogene is usually involved in a pathway that stimulates cell division. The protein product of a tumor-suppressor gene is usually involved in a pathway that inhibits cell division.

Test Your Understanding

1. c **2.** a **3.** b **4.** c **5.** c **6.** d **7.** a **8.** c **9.** b **10.** d
11. (a)

The purple, blue, and red activator proteins would be present.
(b)

Only gene 4 would be transcribed.
(c) In nerve cells, the orange, blue, green, and black activators would have to be present, thus activating transcription of genes 1, 2, and 4. In skin cells, the red, black, purple, and blue activators would have to be present, thus activating genes 3 and 5.

Chapter 19

Figure Questions

Figure 19.2 Beijerinck might have concluded that the agent was a toxin produced by the plant that was able to pass through a filter but that became more and more

dilute. In this case, he would have concluded that the infectious agent could not replicate.
Figure 19.4

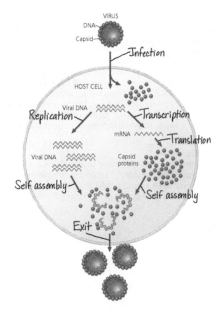

Figure 19.7 Any class V virus, including the viruses that cause influenza (flu), measles, and mumps **Figure 19.8** The main protein on the cell surface that HIV binds to is called CD4. However, HIV also requires a "co-receptor," which in many cases is a protein called CCR5. HIV binds to both of these proteins together and then is taken into the cell. Researchers discovered this requirement by studying individuals who seemed to be resistant to HIV infection, despite multiple exposures. These individuals turned out to have mutations in the gene that encodes CCR5 such that the protein apparently cannot act as a co-receptor, and so HIV can't enter and infect cells.

Concept Check 19.1

1. TMV consists of one molecule of RNA surrounded by a helical array of proteins. The influenza virus has eight molecules of RNA, each surrounded by a helical array of proteins, similar to the arrangement of the single RNA molecule in TMV. Another difference between the viruses is that the influenza virus has an outer envelope and TMV does not. **2.** The T2 phages were an excellent choice for use in the Hershey-Chase experiment because they consist of only DNA surrounded by a protein coat, and DNA and protein were the two candidates for macromolecules that carried genetic information. Hershey and Chase were able to radioactively label each type of molecule alone and follow it during separate infections of *E. coli* cells with T2. Only the DNA entered the bacterial cell during infection, and only labeled DNA showed up in some of the progeny phage. Hershey and Chase concluded that the DNA must carry the genetic information necessary for the phage to reprogram the cell and produce progeny phages.

Concept Check 19.2

1. Lytic phages can only carry out lysis of the host cell, whereas lysogenic phages may either lyse the host cell or integrate into the host chromosome. In the latter case, the viral DNA (prophage) is simply replicated along with the host chromosome. Under certain conditions, a prophage may exit the host chromosome and initiate a lytic cycle. **2.** Both the viral RNA polymerase and the RNA polymerase in Figure 17.9 synthesize an RNA molecule complementary to a template strand. However, the RNA polymerase in Figure 17.9 uses one of the strands of the DNA double helix as a template, whereas the viral RNA polymerase uses the RNA of the viral genome as a template. **3.** HIV is called a retrovirus because it synthesizes DNA using its RNA genome as a template. This is the reverse ("retro") of the usual DNA → RNA information flow. **4.** There are many steps that could be interfered with: binding of the virus to the cell, reverse transcriptase function, integration into the host cell chromosome, genome synthesis (in this case, transcription of RNA from the integrated provirus), assembly of the virus inside the cell, and budding of the virus. (Many of these, if not all, are targets of actual medical strategies to block progress of the infection in HIV-infected people.)

Concept Check 19.3

1. Mutations can lead to a new strain of a virus that can no longer be effectively fought by the immune system, even if an animal had been exposed to the original strain; a virus can jump from one species to a new host; and a rare virus can spread if a host population becomes less isolated. **2.** In horizontal transmission, a plant is infected from an external source of virus, which could enter through a break in the plant's epidermis due to damage by herbivores or other agents. In vertical transmission, a plant inherits viruses from its parent either via infected seeds (sexual reproduction) or via an infected cutting (asexual reproduction). **3.** Humans are not within the host range of TMV, so they can't be infected by the virus. (TMV can't bind human cells and infect them.)

Summary of Key Concepts Questions

19.1 Viruses are generally considered nonliving, because they are not capable of replicating outside of a host cell and are unable to carry out the energy-transforming reactions of metabolism. To replicate and carry out metabolism, they depend completely on host enzymes and resources. **19.2** Single-stranded RNA viruses require an RNA polymerase that can make RNA using an RNA template. (Cellular RNA polymerases make RNA using a DNA template.) Retroviruses require reverse transcriptases to make DNA using an RNA template. (Once the first DNA strand has been made, the same enzyme can promote synthesis of the second DNA strand.) **19.3** The mutation rate of RNA viruses is higher than that of DNA viruses because RNA polymerase has no proofreading function, so errors in replication are not corrected. Their higher mutation rate means that RNA viruses change faster than DNA viruses, leading to their being able to have an altered host range and to evade immune defenses in possible hosts.

Test Your Understanding

1. c **2.** d **3.** c **4.** c **5.** b
6. As shown below, the viral genome would be translated into capsid proteins and envelope glycoproteins directly, rather than after a complementary RNA copy was made. A complementary RNA strand would still be made, however, that could be used as a template for many new copies of the viral genome.

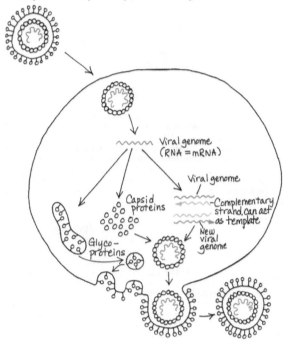

Chapter 20

Figure Questions
Figure 20.6

Figure 20.14 Crossing over, which causes recombination, is a random event. The chance of crossing over occurring between two loci increases as the distance between them increases. The SNP is located very close to an unknown disease-causing allele, and therefore crossing over rarely occurs between the SNP and the allele, so the SNP is a genetic marker indicating the presence of the particular allele. **Figure 20.16** None of the eggs with the transplanted nuclei from the four-cell embryo at the upper left would have developed into a tadpole. Also, the result might include only some of the tissues of a tadpole, which might differ, depending on which nucleus was transplanted. (This assumes that there was some way to tell the four cells apart, as one can in some frog species.) **Figure 20.21** Using converted iPS cells would not carry the same risk, which is its major advantage. Because the donor cells would come from the patient, they would be perfectly matched. The patient's immune system would recognize them as "self" cells and would not mount an attack (which is what leads to rejection). On the other hand, cells that are rapidly dividing might carry a risk of inducing some type of tumor or contributing to development of cancer.

Concept Check 20.1

1. The covalent sugar-phosphate bonds of the DNA strands **2.** Yes, *Pvu*I will cut the molecule.

3. Some human genes are too large to be incorporated into bacterial plasmids. Bacterial cells lack the means to process RNA transcripts into mRNA, and even if the need for RNA processing is avoided by using cDNA, bacteria lack enzymes to catalyze the post-translational processing that many human proteins require to function properly. **4.** During the replication of the ends of linear DNA molecules (see Figure 16.20), an RNA primer is used at the 5′ end of each new strand. The RNA must be replaced by DNA nucleotides, but DNA polymerase is incapable of starting from scratch at the 5′ end of a new DNA strand. During PCR, the primers are made of DNA nucleotides already, so they don't need to be replaced—they just remain as part of each new strand. Therefore, there is no problem with end replication during PCR, and the fragments don't shorten with each replication.

Concept Check 20.2

1. In RT-PCR, the primers must base-pair with their target sequences in the DNA mixture, locating one specific region among many. In DNA microarray analysis, the labeled probe binds only to the specific target sequence due to complementary nucleic acid hybridization (DNA-DNA hybridization). **2.** As a researcher interested in cancer development, you would want to study genes represented by spots that are green or red because these are genes for which the expression level differs between the two types of tissues. Some of these genes may be expressed differently as a result of cancer, while others might play a role in causing cancer, so both would be of interest.

Concept Check 20.3

1. The state of chromatin modification in the nucleus from the intestinal cell was undoubtedly less similar to that of a nucleus from a fertilized egg, explaining why many fewer of these nuclei were able to be reprogrammed. In contrast, the chromatin in a nucleus from a cell at the four-cell stage would have been much more like that of a nucleus in a fertilized egg and therefore much more easily programmed to direct development. **2.** No, primarily because of subtle (and perhaps not so subtle) differences in their environments **3.** The carrot cell has much more potential. The cloning experiment shows that an individual carrot cell can generate all the tissues of an adult plant. The muscle cell, on the other hand, will always remain a muscle cell because of its genetic program (it expresses the *myoD* gene, which ensures continued differentiation). The muscle cell is like other fully differentiated animal cells: It will remain fully differentiated on its own unless it is reprogrammed into an iPS cell using the new techniques described here. (This would be quite difficult to accomplish because a muscle cell has multiple nuclei.)

Concept Check 20.4

1. Stem cells continue to reproduce themselves, ensuring that the corrective gene product will continue to be made. **2.** Herbicide resistance, pest resistance, disease resistance, salinity resistance, drought resistance, and delayed ripening **3.** Because hepatitis A is an RNA virus, you could isolate RNA from the blood and try to detect copies of hepatitis A RNA by RT-PCR. You would first reverse-transcribe the blood mRNA into cDNA and then use PCR to amplify the cDNA, using primers specific to hepatitis A sequences. If you then ran the products on an electrophoretic gel, the presence of a band of the appropriate size would support your hypothesis.

Summary of Key Concepts Questions

20.1 A plasmid vector and a source of foreign DNA to be cloned are both cut with the same restriction enzyme, generating restriction fragments with sticky ends. These fragments are mixed together, ligated, and reintroduced into bacterial cells. The plasmid has a gene for resistance to an antibiotic. That antibiotic is added to the host cells, and only cells that have taken up a plasmid will grow. (Another technique allows researchers to select only the cells that have a recombinant plasmid, rather than the original plasmid without an inserted gene.) **20.2** The genes that are expressed in a given tissue or cell type determine the proteins (and noncoding RNAs) that are the basis of the structure and functions of that tissue or cell type. Understanding which groups of interacting genes establish particular structures and allow certain functions will help us learn how the parts of an organism work together and help us treat diseases that occur when faulty gene expression leads to malfunctioning tissues. **20.3** Cloning a mouse involves transplanting a nucleus from a differentiated mouse cell into a mouse egg cell that has had its own nucleus removed. Fertilizing the egg cell and promoting its development into an embryo in a surrogate mother results in a mouse that is genetically identical to the mouse that donated the nucleus. In this case, the differentiated nucleus has been reprogrammed by factors in the egg cytoplasm. Mouse ES cells are generated from inner cells in mouse blastocysts, so in this case the cells are "naturally" reprogrammed by the process of reproduction and development. (Cloned mouse embryos can also be used as a source of ES cells.) iPS cells can be generated without the use of embryos from a differentiated adult mouse cell, by adding certain transcription factors into the cell. In this case, the transcription factors are reprogramming the cells to become pluripotent. **20.4** First, the disease must be caused by a single gene, and the molecular basis of the problem must be understood. Second, the cells that are going to be introduced into the patient must be cells that will integrate into body tissues and continue to multiply (and provide the needed gene product). Third, the gene must be able to be introduced into the cells in question in a safe way, as there have been instances of cancer resulting from some gene therapy trials. (Note that this will require testing the procedure in mice; moreover, the factors that determine a safe vector are not yet well understood. Maybe one of you will go on to solve this problem!)

Test Your Understanding

1. d **2.** b **3.** c **4.** b **5.** c **6.** b **7.** a **8.** b
9. You would use PCR to amplify the gene. This could be done from genomic DNA. Alternatively, mRNA could be isolated from lens cells and reverse-transcribed by reverse transcriptase to make cDNA. This cDNA could then be used for PCR.
10.

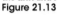

Chapter 21

Figure Questions

Figure 21.2 In stage 2 of this figure, the order of the fragments relative to each other is not known and will be determined later by computer. **Figure 21.8** The transposon would be cut out of the DNA at the original site rather than copied, so the figure would show the original stretch of DNA without the transposon after the mobile transposon had been cut out. **Figure 21.10** The RNA transcripts extending from the DNA in each transcription unit are shorter on the left and longer on the right. This means that RNA polymerase must be starting on the left end of the unit and moving toward the right.
Figure 21.13

Crossover point

Figure 21.14 Pseudogenes are nonfunctional. They could have arisen by any mutations in the second copy that made the gene product unable to function. Examples would be base changes that introduce stop codons in the sequence, alter amino acids, or change a region of the gene promoter so that the gene can no longer be expressed. **Figure 21.15** At position 5, there is an R (arginine) in lysozyme and a K (lysine) in α-lactalbumin; both of these are basic amino acids.

At position 16, there is a G (glutamic acid) in lysozyme and a D (aspartic acid) in α-lactalbumin; both of these are acidic. **Figure 21.16** Let's say a transposable element (TE) existed in the intron to the left of the indicated EGF exon in the EGF gene, and the same TE was present in the intron to the right of the indicated F exon in the fibronectin gene. During meiotic recombination, these TEs could cause nonsister chromatids on homologous chromosomes to pair up incorrectly, as seen in Figure 21.13. One gene might end up with an F exon next to an EGF exon. Further mistakes in pairing over many generations might result in these two exons being separated from the rest of the gene and placed next to a single or duplicated K exon. In general, the presence of repeated sequences in introns and between genes facilitates these processes because it allows incorrect pairing of nonsister chromatids, leading to novel exon combinations. **Figure 21.18** Since you know that chimpanzees do not speak but humans do, you'd probably want to know how many amino acid differences there are between the human wild-type FOXP2 protein and that of the chimpanzee and whether these changes affect the function of the protein. (As we explain later in the text, there are two amino acid differences.) You know that humans with mutations in this gene have severe language impairment. You would want to learn more about the human mutations by checking whether they affect the same amino acids in the gene product that the chimpanzee sequence differences affect. If so, those amino acids might play an important role in the function of the protein in language. Going further, you could analyze the differences between the chimpanzee and mouse FOXP2 proteins. You might ask: Are they more similar than the chimpanzee and human proteins? (It turns out that the chimpanzee and mouse proteins have only one amino acid difference and thus are more similar than the chimpanzee and human proteins, which have two differences, and also more similar than the human and mouse proteins, which have three differences.)

Concept Check 21.1

1. In the whole-genome shotgun approach, short fragments are generated by cutting the genome with multiple restriction enzymes. These fragments are cloned and sequenced and then ordered by computer programs that identify overlapping regions (see Figure 21.2).

Concept Check 21.2

1. The Internet allows centralization of databases such as GenBank and software resources such as BLAST, making them freely accessible. Having all the data in a central database, easily accessible on the Internet, minimizes the possibility of errors and of researchers working with different data. It streamlines the process of science, since all researchers are able to use the same software programs, rather than each having to obtain their own, possibly different, software. It speeds up dissemination of data and ensures as much as possible that errors are corrected in a timely fashion. These are just a few answers; you can probably think of more.
2. Cancer is a disease caused by multiple factors. To focus on a single gene or a single defect would ignore other factors that may influence the cancer and even the behavior of the single gene being studied. The systems approach, because it takes into account many factors at the same time, is more likely to lead to an understanding of the causes and most useful treatments for cancer. **3.** Some of the transcribed region is accounted for by introns. The rest is transcribed into noncoding RNAs, including small RNAs, such as microRNAs (miRNAs) or siRNAs. These RNAs help regulate gene expression by blocking translation, causing degradation of mRNA, binding to the promoter and repressing transcription, or causing remodeling of chromatin structure. The longer noncoding RNAs may also contribute to gene regulation or to chromatin remodeling. **4.** Genome-wide association studies use the systems biology approach in that they consider the correlation of many single nucleotide polymorphisms (SNPs) with particular diseases, such as heart disease and diabetes, in an attempt to find patterns of SNPs that correlate with each disease.

Concept Check 21.3

1. Alternative splicing of RNA transcripts from a gene and post-translational processing of polypeptides **2.** The total number of completed genomes is found by clicking on "Complete Projects"; the number of completed genomes for each domain is indicated at the top of this page. The number of genomes "In Progress" is included under "Incomplete Projects"; click that link to see the number of incomplete genomes, broken down by domain. You can also see the breakdown for genomes "In Progress." (*Note*: You can click on the "Size" column and the table will be re-sorted by genome size. Scroll down to get an idea of relative sizes of genomes in the three domains. Remember, though, that most of the sequenced genomes are bacterial.) **3.** Prokaryotes are generally smaller cells than eukaryotic cells, and they reproduce by binary fission. The evolutionary process involved is natural selection for more quickly reproducing cells: The faster they can replicate their DNA and divide, the more likely they will be able to dominate a population of prokaryotes. The less DNA they have to replicate, then, the faster they will reproduce.

Concept Check 21.4

1. The number of genes is higher in mammals, and the amount of noncoding DNA is greater. Also, the presence of introns in mammalian genes makes them larger, on average, than prokaryotic genes. **2.** In the copy-and-paste transposon mechanism and in retrotransposition **3.** In the rRNA gene family, identical transcription units for all three different RNA products are present in long arrays, repeated one after the other. The large number of copies of the rRNA genes enable organisms to produce the rRNA for enough ribosomes to carry out active protein synthesis, and the single transcription unit for the three rRNAs ensures that the relative amounts of the different rRNA molecules produced are correct—every time one rRNA is made, a copy of each of the other two is made as well. Rather than numerous identical units, each globin gene family consists of a relatively small number of nonidentical genes. The differences in the globin proteins encoded by these genes result in production of hemoglobin molecules adapted to particular developmental stages of the organism.   **4.** The exons would be classified as exons (1.5%); the enhancer region containing the distal control elements, the region closer to the promoter containing the proximal control elements, and the promoter itself would be classified as regulatory sequences (5%); and the introns would be classified as introns (20%).

Concept Check 21.5

1. If meiosis is faulty, two copies of the entire genome can end up in a single cell. Errors in crossing over during meiosis can lead to one segment being duplicated while another is deleted. During DNA replication, slippage backward along the template strand can result in segment duplication.   **2.** For either gene, a mistake in crossing over during meiosis could have occurred between the two copies of that gene, such that one ended up with a duplicated exon. (The other copy would have ended up with a deleted exon.) This could have happened several times, resulting in the multiple copies of a particular exon in each gene.   **3.** Homologous transposable elements scattered throughout the genome provide sites where recombination can occur between different chromosomes. Movement of these elements into coding or regulatory sequences may change expression of genes. Transposable elements also can carry genes with them, leading to dispersion of genes and in some cases different patterns of expression. Transport of an exon during transposition and its insertion into a gene may add a new functional domain to the originally encoded protein, a type of exon shuffling. (For any of these changes to be heritable, they must happen in germ cells, cells that will give rise to gametes.)   **4.** Because more offspring are born to women who have this inversion, it must provide some advantage during the process of reproduction and development. Because proportionally more offspring have this inversion, we would expect it to persist and spread in the population. (In fact, evidence in the study allowed the researchers to conclude that it has been increasing in proportion in the population. You'll learn more about population genetics in the next unit.)

Concept Check 21.6

1. Because both humans and macaques are primates, their genomes are expected to be more similar than the macaque and mouse genomes are. The mouse lineage diverged from the primate lineage before the human and macaque lineages diverged.   **2.** Homeotic genes differ in their *non*homeobox sequences, which determine the interactions of homeotic gene products with other transcription factors and hence which genes are regulated by the homeotic genes. These nonhomeobox sequences differ in the two organisms, as do the expression patterns of the homeobox genes.   **3.** *Alu* elements must have undergone transposition more actively in the human genome for some reason. Their increased numbers may have then allowed more recombination errors in the human genome, resulting in more or different duplications. The divergence of the organization and content of the two genomes presumably made the chromosomes of each genome less homologous to those of the other, thus accelerating divergence of the two species by making matings less and less likely to result in fertile offspring.

Summary of Key Concepts Questions

21.1 One focus of the Human Genome Project was to improve sequencing technology in order to speed up the process. During the project, many advances in sequencing technology allowed faster reactions, which were therefore less expensive.   **21.2** The most significant finding is that more than 75% of the human genome appears to be transcribed at some point in at least one of the cell types studied. Also, at least 80% of the genome contains an element that is functional, participating in gene regulation or maintaining chromatin structure in some way. The project was expanded to include other species to further investigate the functions of these transcribed DNA elements. It is necessary to carry out this type of analysis on the genomes of species that can be used in laboratory experiments.   **21.3** (a) In general, bacteria and archaea have smaller genomes, lower numbers of genes, and higher gene density than eukaryotes. (b) Among eukaryotes, there is no apparent systematic relationship between genome size and phenotype. The number of genes is often lower than would be expected from the size of the genome—in other words, the gene density is often lower in larger genomes. (Humans are an example.)   **21.4** Transposable element–related sequences can move from place to place in the genome, and a subset of these sequences make a new copy of themselves when they do so. Thus, it is not surprising that they make up a significant percentage of the genome, and this percentage might be expected to increase over evolutionary time.   **21.5** Chromosomal rearrangements within a species lead to some individuals having different chromosomal arrangements. Each of these individuals could still undergo meiosis and produce gametes, and fertilization involving gametes with different chromosomal arrangements could result in viable offspring. However, during meiosis in the offspring, the maternal and paternal chromosomes might not be able to pair up, causing gametes with incomplete sets of chromosomes to form. Most often, when zygotes are produced from such gametes, they do not survive. Ultimately, a new species could form if two different chromosomal arrangements became prevalent within a population and individuals could mate successfully only with other individuals having the same arrangement.   **21.6** Comparing the genomes of two closely related species can reveal information about more recent evolutionary events, perhaps events that resulted in the distinguishing characteristics of the two species. Comparing the genomes of very distantly related species can tell us about evolutionary events that occurred a very long time ago. For example, genes that are shared between two distantly related species must have arisen before the two species diverged.

Test Your Understanding

1. b   **2.** a   **3.** c

4.

1. ATETI...PKSSD...TSSTT...NARRD
2. ATETI...PKSSE...TSSTT...NARRD
3. ATETI...PKSSD...TSSTT...NARRD
4. ATETI...PKSSD...TSSNT...SARRD
5. ATETI...PKSSD...TSSTT...NARRD
6. VTETI...PKSSD...TSSTT...NARRD

(a) Lines 1, 3, and 5 are the C, G, R species. (b) Line 4 is the human sequence. See the above figure for the differences between the human and C, G, R sequences—the underlined amino acids at which the human sequence has an N where the C, G, R sequences have a T, and an S where C, G, R have an N. (c) Line 6 is the orangutan sequence. (d) See the above figure. There is one amino acid difference between the mouse (the circled E on line 2) and the C, G, R species (which have a D in that position). There are three amino acid differences between the mouse and the human. (The boxed E, T, and N in the mouse sequence are instead D, N, and S, respectively, in the human sequence.) (e) Because only one amino acid difference arose during the 60–100 million years since the mouse and C, G, R species diverged, it is somewhat surprising that two additional amino acid differences resulted during the 6 million years since chimpanzees and humans diverged. This indicates that the *FOXP2* gene has been evolving faster in the human lineage than in the lineages of other primates.

Chapter 22

Figure Questions

Figure 22.6 The cactus-eater is more closely related to the seed-eater; Figure 1.22 shows that they share a more recent common ancestor (a seed-eater) than the cactus-eater shares with the insect-eater.   **Figure 22.8** The common ancestor lived more than 5.5 million years ago.   **Figure 22.12** The colors and body forms of these mantids allow them to blend into their surroundings, providing an example of how organisms are well matched to life in their environments. The mantids also share features with one another (and with all other mantids), such as six legs, grasping forelimbs, and large eyes. These shared features illustrate another key observation about life: the unity that results from descent from a common ancestor. Over time, as these mantids diverged from a common ancestor, they accumulated different adaptations that made them well suited for life in their different environments. Eventually, these differences became large enough that new species were formed, thus contributing to the great diversity of life.   **Figure 22.13** These results show that being reared from the egg stage on one plant species or the other did not result in the adult having a beak length appropriate for that host; instead, adult beak lengths were determined primarily by the population from which the eggs were obtained. Because an egg from a balloon vine population likely had long-beaked parents, while an egg from a goldenrain tree population likely had short-beaked parents, these results indicate that beak length is an inherited trait.   **Figure 22.14** Both strategies should increase the time that it takes *S. aureus* to become resistant to a new drug. If a drug that harms *S. aureus* does not harm other bacteria, natural selection will not favor resistance to that drug in the other species. This would decrease the chance that *S. aureus* would acquire resistance genes from other bacteria—thus slowing the evolution of resistance. Similarly, selection for resistance to a drug that slows the growth but does not kill *S. aureus* is much weaker than selection for resistance to a drug that kills *S. aureus*—again slowing the evolution of resistance.   **Figure 22.17** Based on this evolutionary tree, crocodiles are more closely related to birds than to lizards because they share a more recent common ancestor with birds (ancestor **5**) than with lizards (ancestor **4**).   **Figure 22.20** Hind limb structure changed first. *Rodhocetus* lacked flukes, but its pelvic bones and hind limbs had changed substantially from how those bones were shaped and arranged in *Pakicetus*. For example, in *Rodhocetus*, the pelvis and hind limbs appear to be oriented for paddling, whereas they were oriented for walking in *Pakicetus*.

Concept Check 22.1

1. Hutton and Lyell proposed that geologic events in the past were caused by the same processes operating today, at the same gradual rate. This principle suggested that Earth must be much older than a few thousand years, the age that was widely accepted at that time. Hutton's and Lyell's ideas also stimulated Darwin to reason that the slow accumulation of small changes could ultimately produce the profound changes documented in the fossil record. In this context, the age of Earth was important to Darwin, because unless Earth was very old, he could not envision how there would have been enough time for evolution to occur.   **2.** By this criterion, Cuvier's explanation of the fossil record and Lamarck's hypothesis of evolution are both scientific. Cuvier thought that species did not evolve over time. He also suggested that sudden, catastrophic events caused extinctions in particular areas and that such regions were later repopulated by a different set of species that immigrated from other areas. These assertions can be tested against the fossil record, and his assertion that species do not evolve has been demonstrated to be incorrect. With respect to Lamarck, his principle of use and disuse can be used to make testable predictions for fossils of groups such as whale ancestors as they adapted to a new habitat. Lamarck's principle of use and disuse and his associated principle of the inheritance of acquired characteristics can also be tested directly in living organisms; these principles have been shown to be incorrect.

Concept Check 22.2

1. Organisms share characteristics (the unity of life) because they share common ancestors; the great diversity of life occurs because new species have repeatedly formed when descendant organisms gradually adapted to different environments, becoming different from their ancestors. **2.** The fossil mammal species (or its ancestors) would most likely have colonized the Andes from within South America, whereas ancestors of mammals currently found in African mountains would most likely have colonized those mountains from other parts of Africa. As a result, the Andes fossil species would share a more recent common ancestor with South American mammals than with mammals in Africa. Thus, for many of its traits, the fossil mammal species would probably more closely resemble mammals that live in South American jungles than mammals that live on African mountains. It is also possible, however, that the fossil mammal species could resemble the African mountain mammals by convergent evolution (even though they were only distantly related to one another). **3.** As long as the white phenotype (encoded by the genotype *pp*) continues to be favored by natural selection, the frequency of the *p* allele will likely increase over time in the population. If the proportion of white individuals increases relative to purple individuals, the frequency of the recessive *p* allele will also increase relative to that of the *P* allele, which only appears in purple individuals (some of which also carry a *p* allele).

Concept Check 22.3

1. An environmental factor such as a drug does not create new traits, such as drug resistance, but rather selects for traits among those that are already present in the population. **2.** (a) Despite their different functions, the forelimbs of different mammals are structurally similar because they all represent modifications of a structure found in the common ancestor. (b) This is a case of convergent evolution. The similarities between the sugar glider and flying squirrel indicate that similar environments selected for similar adaptations despite different ancestry. **3.** At the time that dinosaurs originated, Earth's landmasses formed a single large continent, Pangaea. Because many dinosaurs were large and mobile, it is likely that early members of these groups lived on many different parts of Pangaea. When Pangaea broke apart, fossils of these organisms would have moved with the rocks in which they were deposited. As a result, we would predict that fossils of early dinosaurs would have a broad geographic distribution (this prediction has been upheld).

Summary of Key Concepts Questions

Concept 22.1 Darwin thought that descent with modification occurred as a gradual, steplike process. The age of Earth was important to him because if Earth were only a few thousand years old (as conventional wisdom suggested), there wouldn't have been sufficient time for major evolutionary change. **Concept 22.2** All species have the potential to overreproduce—that is, to produce more offspring than can be supported by the environment. This ensures that there will be what Darwin called a "struggle for existence" in which many of the offspring are eaten, starved, diseased, or unable to reproduce for a variety of other reasons. Members of a population exhibit a range of heritable variations, some of which make it likely that their bearers will leave more offspring than other individuals (for example, the bearer may escape predators more effectively or be more tolerant of the physical conditions of the environment). Over time, natural selection resulting from factors such as predators, lack of food, or the physical conditions of the environment can increase the proportion of individuals with favorable traits in a population (evolutionary adaptation). **Concept 22.3** The hypothesis that cetaceans originated from a terrestrial mammal and are closely related to even-toed ungulates is supported by several lines of evidence. For example, fossils document that early cetaceans had hind limbs, as expected for organisms that descended from a land mammal; these fossils also show that cetacean hind limbs became reduced over time. Other fossils show that early cetaceans had a type of ankle bone that is otherwise found only in even-toed ungulates, providing strong evidence that even-toed ungulates are the land mammals to which cetaceans are most closely related. DNA sequence data also indicate that even-toed ungulates are the land mammals to which cetaceans are most closely related.

Test Your Understanding

1. b **2.** d **3.** c **4.** b **5.** a
7. (a)

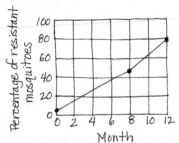

(b) The rapid rise in the percentage of mosquitoes resistant to DDT was most likely caused by natural selection in which mosquitoes resistant to DDT could survive and reproduce while other mosquitoes could not. (c) In India—where DDT resistance first appeared—natural selection would have caused the frequency of resistant mosquitoes to increase over time. If resistant mosquitoes then migrated from India (for example, transported by wind or in planes, trains, or ships) to other parts of the world, the frequency of DDT resistance would increase there as well.

Chapter 23

Figure Questions

Figure 23.4 The genetic code is redundant, meaning that more than one codon can specify the same amino acid. As a result, a substitution at a particular site in a coding region of the *Adh* gene might change the codon but not the translated amino acid, and thus not the resulting protein encoded by the gene. One way an insertion in an exon would not affect the gene produced is if it occurs in an untranslated region of the exon. (This is the case for the insertion at location 1,703.)
Figure 23.8 The predicted frequencies are 36% $C^R C^R$, 48% $C^R C^W$, and 16% $C^W C^W$.
Figure 23.13 Directional selection. Goldenrain tree has smaller fruit than does the native host, balloon vine. Thus, in soapberry bug populations feeding on goldenrain tree, bugs with shorter beaks had an advantage, resulting in directional selection for shorter beak length. **Figure 23.16** Crossing a single female's eggs with both an SC and an LC male's sperm allowed the researchers to directly compare the effects of the males' contribution to the next generation, since both batches of offspring had the same maternal contribution. This isolation of the male's impact enabled researchers to draw conclusions about differences in genetic "quality" between the SC and LC males. **Figure 23.17** Under prolonged low-oxygen conditions, some of the red blood cells of a heterozygote may sickle, leading to harmful effects. This does not occur in individuals with two wild-type hemoglobin alleles, suggesting that there may be selection against heterozygotes in malaria-free regions (where heterozygote advantage does not occur). However, since heterozygotes are healthy under most conditions, selection against them is unlikely to be strong.

Concept Check 23.1

1. Within a population, genetic differences among individuals provide the raw material on which natural selection and other mechanisms can act. Without such differences, allele frequencies could not change over time—and hence the population could not evolve. **2.** Many mutations occur in somatic cells, which do not produce gametes and so are lost when the organism dies. Of mutations that do occur in cell lines that produce gametes, many do not have a phenotypic effect on which natural selection can act. Others have a harmful effect and are thus unlikely to increase in frequency because they decrease the reproductive success of their bearers. **3.** Its genetic variation (whether measured at the level of the gene or at the level of nucleotide sequences) would probably drop over time. During meiosis, crossing over and the independent assortment of chromosomes produce many new combinations of alleles. In addition, a population contains a vast number of possible mating combinations, and fertilization brings together the gametes of individuals with different genetic backgrounds. Thus, via crossing over, independent assortment of chromosomes, and fertilization, sexual reproduction reshuffles alleles into fresh combinations each generation. Without sexual reproduction, the rate of forming new combinations of alleles would be vastly reduced, causing the overall amount of genetic variation to drop.

Concept Check 23.2

1. Each individual has two alleles, so the total number of alleles is 1,400. To calculate the frequency of allele *A*, note that each of the 85 individuals of genotype *AA* has two *A* alleles, each of the 320 individuals of genotype *Aa* has one *A* allele, and each of the 295 individuals of genotype *aa* has zero *A* alleles. Thus, the frequency (*p*) of allele *A* is

$$p = \frac{(2 \times 85) + (1 \times 320) + (0 \times 295)}{1,400} = 0.35$$

There are only two alleles (*A* and *a*) in our population, so the frequency of allele *a* must be $q = 1 - p = 0.65$. **2.** Because the frequency of allele *a* is 0.45, the frequency of allele *A* must be 0.55. Thus, the expected genotype frequencies are $p^2 = 0.3025$ for genotype *AA*, $2pq = 0.495$ for genotype *Aa*, and $q^2 = 0.2025$ for genotype *aa*. **3.** There are 120 individuals in the population, so there are 240 alleles. Of these, there are 124 *V* alleles—32 from the 16 *VV* individuals and 92 from the 92 *Vv* individuals. Thus, the frequency of the *V* allele is $p = 124/240 = 0.52$; hence, the frequency of the *v* allele is $q = 0.48$. Based on the Hardy-Weinberg equation, if the population were not evolving, the frequency of genotype *VV* should be $p^2 = 0.52 \times 0.52 = 0.27$; the frequency of genotype *Vv* should be $2pq = 2 \times 0.52 \times 0.48 = 0.5$; and the frequency of genotype *vv* should be $q^2 = 0.48 \times 0.48 = 0.23$. In a population of 120 individuals, these expected genotype frequencies lead us to predict that there would be 32 *VV* individuals (0.27×120), 60 *Vv* individuals (0.5×120), and 28 *vv* individuals (0.23×120). The actual numbers for the population (16 *VV*, 92 *Vv*, 12 *vv*) deviate from these expectations (fewer homozygotes and more heterozygotes than expected). This indicates that the population is not in Hardy-Weinberg equilibrium and hence may be evolving at this locus.

Concept Check 23.3

1. Natural selection is more "predictable" in that it alters allele frequencies in a nonrandom way: It tends to increase the frequency of alleles that increase the organism's reproductive success in its environment and decrease the frequency of alleles that decrease the organism's reproductive success. Alleles subject to genetic drift increase or decrease in frequency by chance alone, whether or not they are advantageous. **2.** Genetic drift results from chance events that cause allele frequencies to fluctuate at random from generation to generation; within a population, this process tends to decrease genetic variation over time. Gene flow is the transfer of alleles between populations, a process that can introduce new alleles to a population and hence may increase its genetic variation (albeit slightly, since rates of gene flow are often low). **3.** Selection is not important at this locus; furthermore, the populations are not small, and hence the effects of genetic drift should not be pronounced. Gene flow is occurring via the movement of pollen and seeds. Thus, allele and genotype frequencies in these populations should become more similar over time as a result of gene flow.

Concept Check 23.4

1. Zero, because fitness includes reproductive contribution to the next generation, and a sterile mule cannot produce offspring. **2.** Although both gene flow and genetic drift can increase the frequency of advantageous alleles in a population, they can also decrease the frequency of advantageous alleles or increase the frequency of harmful alleles. Only natural selection *consistently* results in an increase in the frequency of alleles that enhance survival or reproduction. Thus, natural selection is the only mechanism that consistently leads to adaptive evolution. **3.** The three modes of natural selection (directional, stabilizing, and disruptive) are defined in terms of the selective advantage of different *phenotypes*, not different genotypes. Thus, the type of selection represented by heterozygote advantage depends on the phenotype of the heterozygotes. In this question, because heterozygous individuals have a more extreme phenotype than either homozygote, heterozygote advantage represents directional selection.

Summary of Key Concepts Questions

23.1 Much of the nucleotide variability at a genetic locus occurs within introns. Nucleotide variation at these sites typically does not affect the phenotype because introns do not code for the protein product of the gene. (Note: In certain circumstances, it is possible that a change in an intron could affect RNA splicing and ultimately have some phenotypic effect on the organism, but such mechanisms are not covered in this introductory text.) There are also many variable nucleotide sites within exons. However, most of the variable sites within exons reflect changes to the DNA sequence that do not change the sequence of amino acids encoded by the gene (and hence may not affect the phenotype). **23.2** No, this is not an example of circular reasoning. Calculating p and q from observed genotype frequencies does not imply that those genotype frequencies must be in Hardy-Weinberg equilibrium. Consider a population that has 195 individuals of genotype AA, 10 of genotype Aa, and 195 of genotype aa. Calculating p and q from these values yields $p = q = 0.5$. Using the Hardy-Weinberg equation, the predicted equilibrium frequencies are $p^2 = 0.25$ for genotype AA, $2pq = 0.5$ for genotype Aa, and $q^2 = 0.25$ for genotype aa. Since there are 400 individuals in the population, these predicted genotype frequencies indicate that there should be 100 AA individuals, 200 Aa individuals, and 100 aa individuals—numbers that differ greatly from the values that we used to calculate p and q. **23.3** It is unlikely that two such populations would evolve in similar ways. Since their environments are very different, the alleles favored by natural selection would probably differ between the two populations. Although genetic drift may have important effects in each of these small populations, drift causes unpredictable changes in allele frequencies, so it is unlikely that drift would cause the populations to evolve in similar ways. Both populations are geographically isolated, suggesting that little gene flow would occur between them (again making it less likely that they would evolve in similar ways). **23.4** Compared to males, it is likely that the females of such species would be larger, more colorful, endowed with more elaborate ornamentation (for example, a large morphological feature such as the peacock's tail), and more apt to engage in behaviors intended to attract mates or prevent other members of their sex from obtaining mates.

Test Your Understanding

1. d **2.** c **3.** b **4.** a **5.** c
7. The frequency of the lap^{94} allele increases as one moves from southwest to northeast across Long Island Sound. The frequency of the lap^{94} allele is higher at sites 9–11 (open ocean) than it is at sites 1–7 (within the Sound); the northeast edge of the Sound (site 8) has about the same frequency of the lap^{94} allele as do the open ocean sites.

Site	1	2	3	4	5	6
lap^{94}%	13	16	16	25	36	37

Site	7	8	9	10	11
lap^{94}%	39	55	59	59	59

A hypothesis that explains the shape of the graph and accounts for the observations stated in the question is that the frequency of the lap^{94} allele at different sites results from an interaction between selection and gene flow. Under this hypothesis, in the southwest portion of the Sound, salinity is relatively low, and selection against the lap^{94} allele is strong. Moving toward the northeast and into the open ocean, where salinity is relatively high, selection favors a high frequency of the lap^{94} allele. However, because mussel larvae disperse long distances, gene flow prevents the lap^{94} allele from becoming fixed in the open ocean or from declining to zero in the southwestern portion of Long Island Sound.

Chapter 24

Figure Questions

Figure 24.7 If this had not been done, the strong preference of "starch flies" and "maltose flies" to mate with like-adapted flies could have occurred simply because the flies could detect (for example, by sense of smell) what their potential mates had

eaten as larvae—and they preferred to mate with flies that had a similar smell to their own. **Figure 24.11** In murky waters where females distinguish colors poorly, females of each species might mate often with males of the other species. Hence, since hybrids between these species are viable and fertile, the gene pools of the two species could become more similar over time. **Figure 24.12** The graph suggests there has been gene flow of some fire-bellied toad alleles into the range of the yellow-bellied toad. Otherwise, all individuals located to the left of the hybrid zone portion of the graph would have allele frequencies close to 1. **Figure 24.13** Because the populations had only just begun to diverge from one another at this point in the process, it is likely that any existing barriers to reproduction would weaken over time. **Figure 24.18** Over time, the chromosomes of the experimental hybrids came to resemble those of *H. anomalus*. This occurred even though conditions in the laboratory differed greatly from conditions in the field, where *H. anomalus* is found, suggesting that selection for laboratory conditions was not strong. Thus, it is unlikely that the observed rise in the fertility of the experimental hybrids was due to selection for life under laboratory conditions. **Figure 24.19** The presence of *M. cardinalis* plants that carry the *M. lewisii yup* allele would make it more likely that bumblebees would transfer pollen between the two monkey flower species. As a result, we would expect the number of hybrid offspring to increase.

Concept Check 24.1

1. (a) All except the biological species concept can be applied to both asexual and sexual species because they define species on the basis of characteristics other than the ability to reproduce. In contrast, the biological species concept can be applied only to sexual species. (b) The easiest species concept to apply in the field would be the morphological species concept because it is based only on the appearance of the organism. Additional information about its ecological habits, evolutionary history, and reproduction is not required. **2.** Because these birds live in fairly similar environments and can breed successfully in captivity, the reproductive barrier in nature is probably prezygotic; given the species' differences in habitat preference, this barrier could result from habitat isolation.

Concept Check 24.2

1. In allopatric speciation, a new species forms while in geographic isolation from its parent species; in sympatric speciation, a new species forms in the absence of geographic isolation. Geographic isolation greatly reduces gene flow between populations, whereas ongoing gene flow is more likely in sympatric populations. As a result, sympatric speciation is less common than allopatric speciation. **2.** Gene flow between subsets of a population that live in the same area can be reduced in a variety of ways. In some species—especially plants—changes in chromosome number can block gene flow and establish reproductive isolation in a single generation. Gene flow can also be reduced in sympatric populations by habitat differentiation (as seen in the apple maggot fly, *Rhagoletis*) and sexual selection (as seen in Lake Victoria cichlids). **3.** Allopatric speciation would be less likely to occur on an island near a mainland than on an isolated island of the same size. The reason we expect this result is that continued gene flow between mainland populations and those on a nearby island reduces the chance that enough genetic divergence will take place for allopatric speciation to occur. **4.** If all of the homologs failed to separate during anaphase I of meiosis, some gametes would end up with an extra set of chromosomes (and others would end up with no chromosomes). If a gamete with an extra set of chromosomes fused with a normal gamete, a triploid would result; if two gametes with an extra set of chromosomes fused with each other, a tetraploid would result.

Concept Check 24.3

1. Hybrid zones are regions in which members of different species meet and mate, producing some offspring of mixed ancestry. Such regions can be viewed as "natural laboratories" in which to study speciation because scientists can directly observe factors that cause (or fail to cause) reproductive isolation. **2.** (a) If hybrids consistently survived and reproduced poorly compared with the offspring of intraspecific matings, reinforcement could occur. If it did, natural selection would cause prezygotic barriers to reproduction between the parent species to strengthen over time, decreasing the production of unfit hybrids and leading to a completion of the speciation process. (b) If hybrid offspring survived and reproduced as well as the offspring of intraspecific matings, indiscriminate mating between the parent species would lead to the production of large numbers of hybrid offspring. As these hybrids mated with each other and with members of both parent species, the gene pools of the parent species could fuse over time, reversing the speciation process.

Concept Check 24.4

1. The time between speciation events includes (1) the length of time that it takes for populations of a newly formed species to begin diverging reproductively from one another and (2) the time it takes for speciation to be complete once this divergence begins. Although speciation can occur rapidly once populations have begun to diverge from one another, it may take millions of years for that divergence to begin. **2.** Investigators transferred alleles at the *yup* locus (which influences flower color) from each parent species to the other. *M. lewisii* plants with an *M. cardinalis yup* allele received many more visits from hummingbirds than usual; hummingbirds usually pollinate *M. cardinalis* but avoid *M. lewisii*. Similarly, *M. cardinalis* plants with an *M. lewisii yup* allele received many more visits from bumblebees than usual; bumblebees usually pollinate *M. lewisii* and avoid *M. cardinalis*. Thus, alleles at the *yup* locus can influence pollinator choice, which in these species provides the primary barrier to interspecific mating. Nevertheless, the experiment does not prove that the *yup* locus alone controls barriers to reproduction between *M. lewisii* and *M. cardinalis*; other genes might enhance the effect of the *yup* locus (by modifying flower color) or cause entirely different barriers to reproduction (for example, gametic isolation or a postzygotic barrier). **3.** Crossing over. If crossing over did not occur, each chromosome in an experimental hybrid would remain as in the F_1 generation: composed entirely of DNA from one parent species or the other.

Summary of Key Concepts Questions

24.1 According to the biological species concept, a species is a group of populations whose members interbreed and produce viable, fertile offspring; thus, gene flow occurs between populations of a species. In contrast, members of different species do not interbreed and hence no gene flow occurs between their populations. Overall, then, in the biological species concept, species can be viewed as designated by the *absence* of gene flow—making gene flow of central importance to the biological species concept. **24.2** Sympatric speciation can be promoted by factors such as polyploidy, sexual selection, and habitat shifts, all of which can reduce gene flow between the subpopulations of a larger population. But such factors can also occur in allopatric populations and hence can also promote allopatric speciation. **24.3** If the hybrids are selected against, the hybrid zone could persist if individuals from the parent species regularly travel into the zone, where they mate to produce hybrid offspring. If hybrids are not selected against, there is no cost to the continued production of hybrids, and large numbers of hybrid offspring may be produced. However, natural selection for life in different environments may keep the gene pools of the two parent species distinct, thus preventing the loss (by fusion) of the parent species and once again causing the hybrid zone to be stable over time. **24.4** As the goatsbeard plant, Bahamas mosquitofish, and apple maggot fly illustrate, speciation continues to happen today. A new species can begin to form whenever gene flow is reduced between populations of the parent species. Such reductions in gene flow can occur in many ways: A new, geographically isolated population may be founded by a few colonists; some members of the parent species may begin to utilize a new habitat; and sexual selection may isolate formerly connected populations or subpopulations. These and many other such events are happening today.

Test Your Understanding

1. b   **2.** c   **3.** b   **4.** a   **5.** d   **6.** c   **7.** d
8. Here is one possibility:

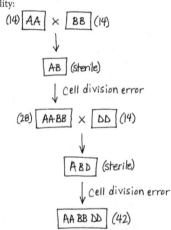

Chapter 25

Figure Questions

Figure 25.2 Proteins are almost always composed of the same 20 amino acids shown in Figure 5.14. However, many other amino acids could potentially form in this or any other experiment. For example, any molecule that had an R group other than those listed in Figure 5.14 yet still contained an α carbon, an amino group, and a carboxyl group would be an amino acid—yet it would not be one of the 20 amino acids commonly found in nature. **Figure 25.6** Because uranium-238 has a half-life of 4.5 billion years, the *x*-axis would be relabeled (in billions of years) as 4.5, 9, 13.5, and 18. **Figure 25.11** You should have circled the node, shown in the tree diagram at approximately 580 million years ago (mya), that leads to the echinoderm/chordate lineage and to the lineage that gave rise to brachiopods, annelids, molluscs, and arthropods. Although the 580 mya date is estimated, this common ancestor must be at least as old as any of its descendants. Since fossil molluscs date to about 560 mya, the common ancestor represented by the circled branch point must be at least 560 million years old. **Figure 25.16** The Australian plate's current direction of movement is roughly similar to the northeasterly direction the continent traveled over the past 65 million years. **Figure 25.26** The coding sequence of the *Pitx1* gene would differ between the marine and lake populations, but patterns of gene expression would not.

Concept Check 25.1

1. The hypothesis that conditions on early Earth could have permitted the synthesis of organic molecules from inorganic ingredients **2.** In contrast to random mingling of molecules in an open solution, segregation of molecular systems by membranes could concentrate organic molecules, assisting biochemical reactions. **3.** Today, genetic information usually flows from DNA to RNA, as when the DNA sequence of a gene is used as a template to synthesize the mRNA encoding a particular protein. However, the life cycle of retroviruses such as HIV shows that genetic information can flow in the reverse direction (from RNA to DNA). In these viruses, the enzyme reverse transcriptase uses RNA as a template for DNA synthesis, suggesting that a similar enzyme could have played a key role in the transition from an RNA world to a DNA world.

Concept Check 25.2

1. 22,920 years (four half-lives: $5,730 \times 4$) **2.** The fossil record shows that different groups of organisms dominated life on Earth at different points in time and that many organisms once alive are now extinct; specific examples of these points can be found in Figure 25.5. The fossil record also indicates that new groups of organisms can arise via the gradual modification of previously existing organisms, as illustrated by fossils that document the origin of mammals from their cynodont ancestors. **3.** The discovery of such a (hypothetical) fossil organism would indicate that aspects of our current understanding of the origin of mammals are not correct because mammals are thought to have originated much more recently (see Figure 25.7). For example, such a discovery could suggest that the dates of previous fossil discoveries are not correct or that the lineages shown in Figure 25.7 shared features with mammals but were not their direct ancestors. Such a discovery would also suggest that radical changes in multiple aspects of the skeletal structure of organisms could arise suddenly—an idea that is not supported by the known fossil record.

Concept Check 25.3

1. Free oxygen attacks chemical bonds and can inhibit enzymes and damage cells. As a result, prokaryotes that had thrived in anaerobic environments would have survived and reproduced poorly in oxygen-rich environments, driving many species to extinction. **2.** All eukaryotes have mitochondria or remnants of these organelles, but not all eukaryotes have plastids. **3.** A fossil record of life today would include many organisms with hard body parts (such as vertebrates and many marine invertebrates), but might not include some species we are very familiar with, such as those that have small geographic ranges and/or small population sizes (for example, endangered species such as the giant panda, tiger, and several rhinoceros species).

Concept Check 25.4

1. The theory of plate tectonics describes the movement of Earth's continental plates, which alters the physical geography and climate of Earth, as well as the extent to which organisms are geographically isolated. Because these factors affect extinction and speciation rates, plate tectonics has a major impact on life on Earth. **2.** Mass extinctions; major evolutionary innovations; the diversification of another group of organisms (which can provide new sources of food); migration to new locations where few competitor species exist **3.** In theory, fossils of both common and rare species would be present right up to the time of the catastrophic event, then disappear. Reality is more complicated because the fossil record is not perfect. So the most recent fossil for a species might be a million years before the mass extinction—even though the species did not become extinct *until* the mass extinction. This complication is especially likely for rare species because few of their fossils will form and be discovered. Hence, for many rare species, the fossil record would not document that the species was alive immediately before the extinction (even if it was).

Concept Check 25.5

1. Heterochrony can cause a variety of morphological changes. For example, if the onset of sexual maturity changes, a retention of juvenile characteristics (paedomorphosis) may result. Paedomorphosis can be caused by small genetic changes that result in large changes in morphology, as seen in the axolotl salamander. **2.** In animal embryos, *Hox* genes influence the development of structures such as limbs and feeding appendages. As a result, changes in these genes—or in the regulation of these genes—are likely to have major effects on morphology. **3.** From genetics, we know that gene regulation is altered by how well transcription factors bind to noncoding DNA sequences called control elements. Thus, if changes in morphology are often caused by changes in gene regulation, portions of noncoding DNA that contain control elements are likely to be strongly affected by natural selection.

Concept Check 25.6

1. Complex structures do not evolve all at once, but in increments, with natural selection selecting for adaptive variants of the earlier versions. **2.** Although the myxoma virus is highly lethal, initially some of the rabbits are resistant (0.2% of infected rabbits are not killed). Thus, assuming resistance is an inherited trait, we would expect the rabbit population to show a trend for increased resistance to the virus. We would also expect the virus to show an evolutionary trend toward reduced lethality. We would expect this trend because a rabbit infected with a less lethal virus would be more likely to live long enough for a mosquito to bite it and hence potentially transmit the virus to another rabbit. (A virus that kills its rabbit host before a mosquito transmits the virus to another rabbit dies with its host.)

Summary of Key Concepts Questions

Concept 25.1 Particles of montmorillonite clay may have provided surfaces on which organic molecules became concentrated and hence were more likely to react with one another. Montmorillonite clay particles may also have facilitated the transport of key molecules, such as short strands of RNA, into vesicles. These vesicles can form spontaneously from simple precursor molecules, "reproduce" and "grow" on their own, and maintain internal concentrations of molecules that differ from those in the surrounding environment. These features of vesicles represent key steps in the emergence of protocells and (ultimately) the first living cells. **Concept 25.2** One challenge is that organisms do not use radioisotopes that have long half-lives to build their bones or shells. As a result, fossils older than 75,000 years cannot be dated directly. Fossils are often found in sedimentary rock, but those rocks typically contain sediments of different ages, again posing a challenge when trying to date old fossils. To circumvent these challenges, geologists date layers of volcanic rock that surround old fossils and that use radioisotopes with long half-lives. This approach provides minimum and maximum estimates for the ages of fossils sandwiched between two layers of volcanic rock. **Concept 25.3** The "Cambrian explosion" refers to a relatively short interval of time (535–525 million years ago) during which large forms of many present-day animal phyla first appear in the fossil record. The evolutionary changes that occurred during this time, such as the appearance of large predators and well-defended prey, were important because they set the stage for many of the key events in the history of life over the last 500 million years. **Concept 25.4** The broad evolutionary changes documented by the fossil record reflect the rise and fall of major groups of organisms. In turn, the rise or fall of any particular group results from a balance between speciation and extinction rates: A group increases in size when the rate at which its members produce new species is greater than the rate at which its member species are lost to extinction, while a group shrinks in size if extinction rates are greater than speciation rates. **Concept 25.5** A change in the sequence or regulation of a developmental gene can produce major morphological changes. In some cases, such morphological changes may enable organisms to perform new functions or live in new environments—thus potentially leading to an adaptive radiation and the formation of a new group of organisms. **Concept 25.6** Evolutionary change results from interactions between organisms and their current environments. No goal is involved in this process. As environments change over time, the features of organisms favored by natural selection may also change. When this happens, what once may have seemed like a "goal" of evolution (for example, improvements in the function of a feature previously favored by natural selection) may cease to be beneficial or may even be harmful.

Test Your Understanding

1. b **2.** a **3.** d **4.** b **5.** c **6.** c **7.** a

Chapter 26

Figure Questions

Figure 26.4 The branching pattern of the tree indicates that the badger and the wolf share a common ancestor that is more recent than the ancestor these two animals share with the leopard. **Figure 26.5** The new version (shown below) does not alter any of the evolutionary relationships shown in Figure 26.5. For example, B and C remain sister taxa, taxon A is still as closely related to taxon B as it is to taxon C, and so on.

Figure 26.6 Unknown 1b (a portion of sample 1) and Unknowns 9–13 all would have to be located on the branch of the tree that currently leads to Minke (Southern Hemisphere) and Unknowns 1a and 2–8. **Figure 26.11** You should have circled the branch point that is drawn farthest to the left (the common ancestor of all taxa shown). Both cetaceans and seals descended from terrestrial lineages of mammals, indicating that the cetacean-seal common ancestor lacked a streamlined body form and hence would not be part of the cetacean-seal group. **Figure 26.12** You should have circled the frog, turtle, and leopard lineages, along with their most recent common ancestor. **Figure 26.16** The lizard and snake lineage is the most basal taxon shown (closest to the root of the tree). Among the descendants of the common ancestor indicated by the blue dot, the crocodilian lineage is the most basal. **Figure 26.21** This tree indicates that the sequences of rRNA and other genes in mitochondria are most closely related to those of proteobacteria, while the sequences of chloroplast genes are most closely related to those of cyanobacteria. These gene sequence relationships are what would be predicted from endosymbiont theory, which posits that both mitochondria and chloroplasts originated as engulfed prokaryotic cells.

Concept Check 26.1

1. We are classified the same from the domain level to the class level; both the leopard and human are mammals. Leopards belong to order Carnivora, whereas humans do not. **2.** The tree in (c) shows a different pattern of evolutionary relationships. In (c), C and B are sister taxa, whereas C and D are sister taxa in (a) and (b).
3.

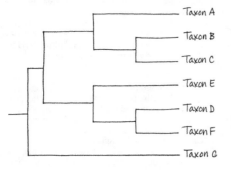

Concept Check 26.2

1. (a) Analogy, since porcupines and cacti are not closely related and since most other animals and plants do not have similar structures; (b) homology, since cats and humans are both mammals and have homologous forelimbs, of which the hand and paw are the lower part; (c) analogy, since owls and hornets are not closely related and since the structure of their wings is very different **2.** Species B and C are more likely to be closely related. Small genetic changes (as between species B and C) can produce divergent physical appearances, but if many genes have diverged greatly (as in species A and B), then the lineages have probably been separate for a long time.

Concept Check 26.3

1. No; hair is a shared ancestral character common to all mammals and thus is not helpful in distinguishing different mammalian subgroups. **2.** The principle of maximum parsimony states that the hypothesis about nature we investigate first should be the simplest explanation found to be consistent with the facts. Actual evolutionary relationships may differ from those inferred by parsimony owing to complicating factors such as convergent evolution. **3.** The traditional classification provides a poor match to evolutionary history, thus violating the basic principle of cladistics—that classification should be based on common descent. Both birds and mammals originated from groups traditionally designated as reptiles, making reptiles (as traditionally delineated) a paraphyletic group. These problems can be addressed by removing *Dimetrodon* and cynodonts from the reptiles and by regarding birds as a group of reptiles (specifically, as a group of dinosaurs).

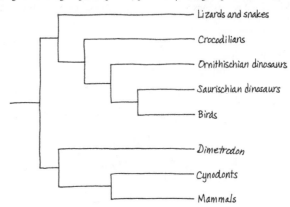

Concept Check 26.4

1. Proteins are gene products. Their amino acid sequences are determined by the nucleotide sequences of the DNA that codes for them. Thus, differences between comparable proteins in two species reflect underlying genetic differences that have accumulated as the species diverged from one another. As a result, differences between the proteins can reflect the evolutionary history of the species.
2. These observations suggest that the evolutionary lineages leading to species 1 and species 2 diverged from one another before a gene duplication event in species 1 produced gene B from gene A. **3.** In RNA processing, the exons or coding regions of a gene can be spliced together in different ways, yielding different mRNAs and hence different protein products. As a result, different proteins could potentially be produced from the same gene in different tissues, thereby enabling the gene to perform different functions in these different tissues.

Concept Check 26.5

1. A molecular clock is a method of estimating the actual time of evolutionary events based on numbers of base changes in orthologous genes. It is based on the assumption that the regions of genomes being compared evolve at constant rates. **2.** There are many portions of the genome that do not code for genes; mutations that alter the sequence of bases in such regions could accumulate through drift without affecting an organism's fitness. Even in coding regions of the genome, some mutations may not have a critical effect on genes or proteins. **3.** The gene (or genes) used for the molecular clock may have evolved more slowly in these two taxa than in the species used to calibrate the clock; as a result, the clock would underestimate the time at which the taxa diverged from each other.

Concept Check 26.6

1. The kingdom Monera included bacteria and archaea, but we now know that these organisms are in separate domains. Kingdoms are subsets of domains, so a single kingdom (like Monera) that includes taxa from different domains is not valid. **2.** Because of horizontal gene transfer, some genes in eukaryotes are more closely related to bacteria, while others are more closely related to archaea; thus, depending on which genes are used, phylogenetic trees constructed from DNA data can yield conflicting results.
3.

The fossil record indicates that prokaryotes originated long before eukaryotes. This suggests that the third tree, in which the eukaryotic lineage diverged first, is not accurate and hence is not likely to receive support from genetic data.

26.1 The fact that humans and chimpanzees are sister species indicates that we share a more recent common ancestor with chimpanzees than we do with any other living primate species. But that does not mean that humans evolved from chimpanzees, or vice versa; instead, it indicates that both humans and chimpanzees are descendants of that common ancestor. **26.2** Homologous characters result from shared ancestry. As organisms diverge over time, some of their homologous characters will also diverge. The homologous characters of organisms that diverged long ago typically differ more than do the homologous characters of organisms that diverged more recently. As a result, differences in homologous characters can be used to infer phylogeny. In contrast, analogous characters result from convergent evolution, not shared ancestry, and hence can give misleading estimates of phylogeny. **26.3** All features of organisms arose at some point in the history of life. In the group in which a new feature first arose, that feature is a shared derived character that is unique to that clade. The group in which each shared derived character first appeared can be determined, and the resulting nested pattern can be used to infer evolutionary history. **26.4** Orthologous genes should be used; for such genes, the homology results from speciation and hence reflects evolutionary history. **26.5** A key assumption of molecular clocks is that nucleotide substitutions occur at fixed rates and hence the number of nucleotide differences between two DNA sequences is proportional to the time since the sequences diverged from each other. Some limitations of molecular clocks: No gene marks time with complete precision; natural selection can favor certain DNA changes over others; nucleotide substitution rates can change over long periods of time (causing molecular clock estimates of when events in the distant past occurred to be highly uncertain); and the same gene can evolve at different rates in different organisms. **26.6** Genetic data indicated that many prokaryotes differed as much from each other as they did from eukaryotes. This indicated that organisms should be grouped into three "super-kingdoms," or domains (Archaea, Bacteria, Eukarya). These data also indicated that the previous kingdom Monera (which had contained all the prokaryotes) did not make biological sense and should be abandoned. Later genetic and morphological data also indicated that the former kingdom Protista (which had primarily contained single-celled organisms) should be abandoned because some protists are more closely related to plants, fungi, or animals than they are to other protists.

Test Your Understanding

1. a 2. c 3. b 4. c 5. d 6. a 7. d
9.

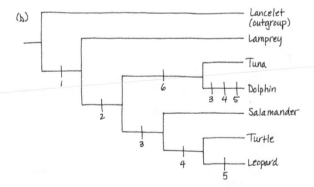

(c) The tree in (a) requires seven evolutionary changes, while the tree in (b) requires nine evolutionary changes. Thus, the tree in (a) is more parsimonious, since it requires fewer evolutionary changes.

Chapter 27

Figure Questions

Figure 27.10 It is likely that the expression or sequence of genes that affect glucose metabolism may have changed; genes for metabolic processes no longer needed by the cell also may have changed. **Figure 27.11** Transduction results in horizontal gene transfer when the host and recipient cells are members of different species. **Figure 27.15** Eukarya **Figure 27.17** Thermophiles live in very hot

environments, so it is likely that their enzymes can continue to function normally at much higher temperatures than can the enzymes of other organisms. At low temperatures, however, the enzymes of thermophiles may not function as well as the enzymes of other organisms. **Figure 27.18** From the graph, plant uptake can be estimated as 0.7, 0.6, and 0.95 mg K^+ for strains 1, 2, and 3, respectively. These values average to 0.75 mg K^+. If bacteria had no effect, the average plant uptake of K^+ for strains 1, 2, and 3 should be close to 0.5 mg K^+, the value observed for plants grown in bacteria-free soil.

Concept Check 27.1

1. Adaptations include the capsule (shields prokaryotes from the host's immune system) and endospores (enable cells to survive harsh conditions and to revive when the environment becomes favorable). 2. Prokaryotic cells lack the complex compartmentalization associated with the membrane-enclosed organelles of eukaryotic cells. Prokaryotic genomes have much less DNA than eukaryotic genomes, and most of this DNA is contained in a single ring-shaped chromosome located in the nucleoid rather than within a true membrane-enclosed nucleus. In addition, many prokaryotes also have plasmids, small ring-shaped DNA molecules containing a few genes. 3. Plastids such as chloroplasts are thought to have evolved from an endosymbiotic photosynthetic prokaryote. More specifically, the phylogenetic tree shown in Figure 26.21 indicates that plastids are closely related to cyanobacteria. Hence, we can hypothesize that the thylakoid membranes of chloroplasts resemble those of cyanobacteria because chloroplasts evolved from a cyanobacterium endosymbiont.

Concept Check 27.2

1. Prokaryotes can have extremely large population sizes, in part because they often have short generation times. The large number of individuals in prokaryotic populations makes it likely that in each generation there will be many individuals that have new mutations at any particular gene, thereby adding considerable genetic diversity to the population. 2. In transformation, naked, foreign DNA from the environment is taken up by a bacterial cell. In transduction, phages carry bacterial genes from one bacterial cell to another. In conjugation, a bacterial cell directly transfers plasmid or chromosomal DNA to another cell via a mating bridge that temporarily connects the two cells. 3. The population that includes individuals capable of conjugation would probably be more successful, since some of its members could form recombinant cells whose new gene combinations might be advantageous in a novel environment. 4. Yes. Genes for antibiotic resistance could be transferred (by transformation, transduction, or conjugation) from the nonpathogenic bacterium to a pathogenic bacterium; this could make the pathogen an even greater threat to human health. In general, transformation, transduction, and conjugation tend to increase the spread of resistance genes.

Concept Check 27.3

1. A phototroph derives its energy from light, while a chemotroph gets its energy from chemical sources. An autotroph derives its carbon from CO_2, HCO_3^-, or related compounds, while a heterotroph gets its carbon from organic nutrients such as glucose. Thus, there are four nutritional modes: photoautotrophic, photoheterotrophic (unique to prokaryotes), chemoautotrophic (unique to prokaryotes), and chemoheterotrophic. 2. Chemoheterotrophy; the bacterium must rely on chemical sources of energy, since it is not exposed to light, and it must be a heterotroph if it requires a source of carbon other than CO_2 (or a related compound, such as HCO_3^-). 3. If humans could fix nitrogen, we could build proteins using atmospheric N_2 and hence would not need to eat high-protein foods such as meat, fish, or soy. Our diet would, however, need to include a source of carbon, along with minerals and water. Thus, a typical meal might consist of carbohydrates as a carbon source, along with fruits and vegetables to provide essential minerals (and additional carbon).

Concept Check 27.4

1. Molecular systematic studies indicate that organisms once classified as bacteria are more closely related to eukaryotes and belong in a domain of their own: Archaea. Such studies have also shown that horizontal gene transfer is common and plays an important role in the evolution of prokaryotes. By not requiring that organisms be cultured in the laboratory, metagenomic studies have revealed an immense diversity of previously unknown prokaryotic species. Over time, the ongoing discovery of new species by metagenomic analyses may alter our understanding of prokaryotic phylogeny greatly. 2. At present, all known methanogens are archaea in the clade Euryarchaeota; this suggests that this unique metabolic pathway probably arose in ancestral species within Euryarchaeota. Since Bacteria and Archaea have been separate evolutionary lineages for billions of years, the discovery of a methanogen from the domain Bacteria would suggest that adaptations that enabled the use of CO_2 to oxidize H_2 may have evolved twice—once in Archaea (within Euryarchaeota) and once in Bacteria. (It is also possible that a newly discovered bacterial methanogen could have acquired the genes for this metabolic pathway by horizontal gene transfer from a methanogen in domain Archaea. However, horizontal gene transfer is not a likely explanation because of the large number of genes involved and because gene transfers between species in different domains are rare.)

Concept Check 27.5

1. Although prokaryotes are small, their large numbers and metabolic abilities enable them to play key roles in ecosystems by decomposing wastes, recycling chemicals, and affecting the concentrations of nutrients available to other organisms. 2. Cyanobacteria produce oxygen when water is split in the light reactions of photosynthesis. The Calvin cycle incorporates CO_2 from the air into organic molecules, which are then converted to sugars.

Concept Check 27.6

1. Sample answers: eating fermented foods such as yogurt, sourdough bread, or cheese; receiving clean water from sewage treatment; taking medicines produced by bacteria   **2.** No. If the poison is secreted as an exotoxin, live bacteria could be transmitted to another person. But the same is true if the poison is an endotoxin—only in this case, the live bacteria that are transmitted may be descendants of the (now-dead) bacteria that produced the poison.   **3.** Some of the many different species of prokaryotes that live in the human gut compete with one another for resources (from the food that you eat). Because different prokaryotic species have different adaptations, a change in diet may alter which species can grow most rapidly, thus altering species abundance.

Summary of Key Concepts Questions

27.1 Specific structural features that enable prokaryotes to thrive in diverse environments include their cell walls (which provide shape and protection), flagella (which function in directed movement), and ability to form capsules or endospores (both of which can protect against harsh conditions). Prokaryotes also possess biochemical adaptations for growth in varied conditions, such as those that enable them to tolerate extremely hot or salty environments.   **27.2** Many prokaryotic species can reproduce extremely rapidly, and their populations can number in the trillions. As a result, even though mutations are rare, every day many offspring are produced that have new mutations at particular gene loci. In addition, even though prokaryotes reproduce asexually and hence the vast majority of offspring are genetically identical to their parent, the genetic variation of their populations can be increased by transduction, transformation, and conjugation. Each of these (nonreproductive) processes can increase genetic variation by transferring DNA from one cell to another—even among cells that are of different species.   **27.3** Prokaryotes have an exceptionally broad range of metabolic adaptations. As a group, prokaryotes perform all four modes of nutrition (photoautotrophy, chemoautotrophy, photoheterotrophy, and chemoheterotrophy), whereas eukaryotes perform only two of these (photoautotrophy and chemoheterotrophy). Prokaryotes are also able to metabolize nitrogen in a wide variety of forms (again unlike eukaryotes), and they frequently cooperate with other prokaryotic cells of the same or different species.   **27.4** Phenotypic criteria such as shape, motility, and nutritional mode do not provide a clear picture of the evolutionary history of the prokaryotes. In contrast, molecular data have elucidated relationships among major groups of prokaryotes. Molecular data have also allowed researchers to sample genes directly from the environment; using such genes to construct phylogenies has led to the discovery of major new groups of prokaryotes.   **27.5** Prokaryotes play key roles in the chemical cycles on which life depends. For example, prokaryotes are important decomposers, breaking down corpses and waste materials, thereby releasing nutrients to the environment where they can be used by other organisms. Prokaryotes also convert inorganic compounds to forms that other organisms can use. With respect to their ecological interactions, many prokaryotes form life-sustaining mutualisms with other species. In some cases, such as hydrothermal vent communities, the metabolic activities of prokaryotes provide an energy source on which hundreds of other species depend; in the absence of the prokaryotes, the community collapses.   **27.6** Human well-being depends on our associations with mutualistic prokaryotes, such as the many species that live in our intestines and digest food that we cannot. Humans also can harness the remarkable metabolic capabilities of prokaryotes to produce a wide range of useful products and to perform key services such as bioremediation. Negative effects of prokaryotes result primarily from bacterial pathogens that cause disease.

Test Your Understanding

1. d   **2.** a   **3.** c   **4.** c   **5.** b   **6.** a

Chapter 47

Figure Questions

Figure 47.4 You could inject the compound into an unfertilized egg, expose the egg to sperm, and see whether the fertilization envelope forms.   **Figure 47.22** When the researchers allowed normal cortical rotation to occur, the "back-forming" determinants were activated. When they then forced the opposite rotation to occur, the back was established on the opposite side as well. Because the molecules on the normal side were already activated, forcing the opposite rotation apparently did not "cancel out" the establishment of the back side by the first rotation.   **Figure 47.23** In Spemann's control, the two blastomeres were physically separated, and each grew into a whole embryo. In Roux's experiment, remnants of the dead blastomere were still contacting the live blastomere, which developed into a half-embryo. Therefore, molecules present in the dead cell's remnants may have been signaling to the live cell, inhibiting it from making all the embryonic structures.   **Figure 47.24** You could inject the isolated protein (or an mRNA encoding it) into ventral cells of an earlier gastrula. If dorsal structures form on the ventral side, that would support the idea that the protein is the signaling molecule secreted or presented by the dorsal lip. You should also do a control experiment to make sure the injection process alone did not cause dorsal structures to form.   **Figure 47.26** Either Sonic hedgehog mRNA or protein can serve as a marker of the ZPA. If either was absent after removal of the AER, that would support your hypothesis. You could also block FGF function and see whether the ZPA formed (by looking for Sonic hedgehog).

Concept Check 47.1

1. The fertilization envelope forms after cortical granules release their contents outside the egg, causing the vitelline membrane to rise and harden. The fertiliza-

tion envelope serves as a barrier to fertilization by more than one sperm.   **2.** The increased Ca^{2+} concentration in the egg would cause the cortical granules to fuse with the plasma membrane, releasing their contents and causing a fertilization envelope to form, even though no sperm had entered. This would prevent fertilization.   **3.** You would expect it to fluctuate. The fluctuation of MPF drives the transition between DNA replication (S phase) and mitosis (M phase), which is still required in the abbreviated cleavage cell cycle.

Concept Check 47.2

1. The cells of the notochord migrate toward the midline of the embryo (converge), rearranging themselves so there are fewer cells across the notochord, which thus becomes longer overall (extends; see Figure 47.17).   **2.** Because microfilaments would not be able to contract and decrease the size of one end of the cell, both the inward bending in the middle of the neural tube and the outward bending of the hinge regions at the edges would be blocked. Therefore, the neural tube probably would not form.   **3.** Dietary intake of the vitamin folic acid dramatically reduces the frequency of neural tube defects.

Concept Check 47.3

1. Axis formation establishes the location and polarity of the three axes that provide the coordinates for development. Pattern formation positions particular tissues and organs in the three-dimensional space defined by those coordinates.   **2.** Morphogen gradients act by specifying cell fates across a field of cells through variation in the level of a determinant. Morphogen gradients thus act more globally than cytoplasmic determinants or inductive interactions between pairs of cells.   **3.** Yes, a second embryo could develop because inhibiting BMP-4 activity would have the same effect as transplanting an organizer.   **4.** The limb that developed probably would have a mirror-image duplication, with the most posterior digits in the middle and the most anterior digits at either end.

Summary of Key Concepts Questions

47.1 The binding of a sperm to a receptor on the egg surface is very specific and likely would not occur if the two gametes were from different species. Without sperm binding, the sperm and egg membranes would not fuse.   **47.2** The neural tube forms when the neural plate, a band of ectodermal tissue oriented along the anterior-posterior axis on the dorsal side of the embryo, rolls into a tube and pinches off from the rest of the ectoderm. Neural crest cells arise as groups of cells in the regions between the edges of the neural tube and the surrounding ectoderm migrate away from the neural tube.   **47.3** Mutations that affected both limb and kidney development would be more likely to alter the function of monocilia because these organelles are important in several signaling pathways. Mutations that affected limb development but not kidney development would more likely alter a single pathway, such as Hedgehog signaling.

Test Your Understanding

1. a   **2.** b   **3.** d   **4.** a   **5.** d   **6.** c   **7.** b
8.

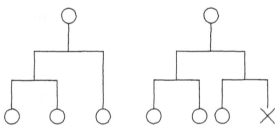

Chapter 52

Figure Questions

Figure 52.7 Dispersal limitations, the activities of people (such as a broad-scale conversion of forests to agriculture or selective harvesting), or many other factors, including those discussed later in the chapter (see Figure 52.16)   **Figure 52.16** Some factors, such as fire, are relevant only for terrestrial systems. At first glance, water availability is primarily a terrestrial factor, too. However, species living along the intertidal zone of oceans or along the edge of lakes also suffer desiccation. Salinity stress is important for species in some aquatic and terrestrial systems. Oxygen availability is an important factor primarily for species in some aquatic systems and in soils and sediments.

Concept Check 52.1

1. In the tropics, high temperatures evaporate water and cause warm, moist air to rise. The rising air cools and releases much of its water as rain over the tropics. The remaining dry air descends at approximately 30° north and south, causing deserts to occur in those regions.   **2.** The microclimate around the stream will be cooler, moister, and shadier than that around the unplanted agricultural field.   **3.** Trees that require a long time to reach reproductive age are likely to evolve more slowly than annual plants in response to climate change, constraining the potential ability of such trees to respond to rapid climate change.   **4.** Plants with C_4 photosynthesis are likely to expand their range globally as Earth's climate warms. C_4 photosynthesis minimizes photorespiration and enhances sugar production, an advantage that is especially useful in warmer regions where C_4 plants are found today.

Concept Check 52.2

2. Answers will vary by location but should be based on the information and maps in Figure 52.11. How much your local area has been altered from its natural state will influence how much it reflects the expected characteristics of your biome, particularly the expected plants and animals. **3.** Northern coniferous forest is likely to replace tundra along the boundary between these biomes. To see why, note that northern coniferous forest is adjacent to tundra throughout North America, northern Europe, and Asia (see Figure 52.8) and that the temperature range for northern coniferous forest is just above that for tundra (see Figure 52.9).

Concept Check 52.3

1. In the oceanic pelagic zone, the ocean bottom lies below the photic zone, so there is too little light to support benthic algae or rooted plants. **2.** Aquatic organisms either gain or lose water by osmosis if the osmolarity of their environment differs from their internal osmolarity. Water gain can cause cells to swell, and water loss can cause them to shrink. To avoid excessive changes in cell volume, organisms that live in estuaries must be able to compensate for both water gain (under freshwater conditions) and water loss (under saltwater conditions). **3.** In a river below a dam, the fish are more likely to be species that prefer colder water. In summer, the deep layers of a reservoir are colder than the surface layers, so a river below a dam will be colder than an undammed river.

Concept Check 52.4

1. (a) Humans might transplant a species to a new area that it could not previously reach because of a geographic barrier. (b) Humans might eliminate a predator or herbivore species, such as sea urchins, from an area. **2.** One test would be to build a fence around a plot of land in an area that has trees of that species, excluding all deer from the plot. You could then compare the abundance of tree seedlings inside and outside the fenced plot over time. **3.** Because the ancestor of the silverswords reached isolated Hawaii early in the islands' existence, it likely faced little competition and was able to occupy many unfilled niches. The cattle egret, in contrast, arrived in the Americas only recently and has to compete with a well-established group of species. Thus, its opportunities for adaptive radiation have probably been much more limited.

Summary of Key Concepts Questions

52.1 Because dry air would descend at the equator instead of at 30° north and south latitude (where deserts exist today), deserts would be more likely to exist along the equator (see Figure 52.3). **52.2** The dominant plants in savanna ecosystems tend to be adapted to fire and tolerant of seasonal droughts. The savanna biome is maintained by periodic fires, both natural and set by humans, but humans are also clearing savannas for agriculture and other uses. **52.3** An aphotic zone is most likely to be found in the deep waters of a lake, the oceanic pelagic zone, or the marine benthic zone. **52.4** You might arrange a flowchart that begins with abiotic limitations—first determining the physical and chemical conditions under which a species could survive—and then moves through the other factors listed in the flowchart.

Test Your Understanding

1. b **2.** b **3.** c **4.** c **5.** d **6.** c **7.** a **8.** a **9.** b

Chapter 53

Figure Questions

Figure 53.4 The dispersion of the penguins would likely appear clumped as you flew over densely populated islands and sparsely populated ocean.
Figure 53.7 #109
Figure 53.16

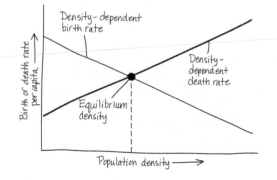

Concept Check 53.1

1.

A Type III survivorship curve is most likely because very few of the young probably survive. **2.** If an animal is captured by attracting it with food, it may be more likely to be recaptured if it seeks the same food. The number of marked animals captured (x) would be an overestimate, and because the population size (N) is equal to sn/x, N would be an underestimate. Alternatively, if an animal has a negative experience during capture and learns from that experience, it may be less likely to be recaptured. In this case, x would be an underestimate and N would be an overestimate. **3.** Male sticklebacks would likely have a uniform pattern of dispersion, with antagonistic interactions maintaining a relatively constant spacing between them.

Concept Check 53.2

1. Though r_{inst} is constant, N, the population size, is increasing. As r_{inst} is applied to an increasingly large N, population growth ($r_{inst}N$) accelerates, producing the J-shaped curve. **2.** Exponential growth is more likely in the area where a forest was destroyed by fire. The first plants that found suitable habitat there would encounter an abundance of space, nutrients, and light. In the undisturbed forest, competition among plants for these resources would be intense. **3.** The net population growth is $\Delta N/\Delta t = bN - mN$. The annual per capita birth rate, b, equals 14/1,000, or 0.014, and the per capita death rate, m, equals 8/1,000, or 0.008. Therefore, the net population growth in 2011 was

$$\frac{\Delta N}{\Delta t} = (0.014 \times 311,000,000) - (0.008 \times 311,000,000)$$

or 1.87 million people. To determine whether the population is growing exponentially, you would need to determine whether $r_{inst} > 0$ and if it is constant through time (across multiple years).

Concept Check 53.3

1. When N (population size) is small, there are relatively few individuals producing offspring. When N is large, near the carrying capacity, the per capita growth rate is relatively small because it is limited by available resources. The steepest part of the logistic growth curve corresponds to a population with a number of reproducing individuals that is substantial but not yet near carrying capacity. **2.** All else being equal, you would expect a plant species to have a larger carrying capacity at the equator than at high latitudes because there is more incident sunlight near the equator. **3.** If a population becomes too crowded, the likelihood of disease and mortality may increase because of the effects of pathogens. Thus, pathogens can reduce the long-term carrying capacity of a population.

Concept Check 53.4

1. The constant, spring-fed stream. In more constant physical conditions, populations are more stable and competition for resources is more likely. In such conditions, larger, well-provisioned young typical of iteroparous species have a better chance of surviving. **2.** By preferentially investing in the eggs it lays in the nest, the peacock wrasse increases their probability of survival. The eggs it disperses widely and does not provide care for are less likely to survive, at least some of the time, but require a lower investment by the adults. (In this sense, the adults avoid the risk of placing all their eggs in one basket.) **3.** If a parent's survival is compromised greatly by bearing young during times of stress, the animal's fitness may increase if it abandons its current young and survives to produce healthier young at a later time.

Concept Check 53.5

1. Three attributes are the size, quality, and isolation of patches. A patch that is larger or of higher quality is more likely to attract individuals and to be a source of individuals for other patches. A patch that is relatively isolated will undergo fewer exchanges of individuals with other patches. **2.** You would need to study the population for more than one cycle (longer than 10 years and probably at least 20) before having sufficient data to examine changes through time. Otherwise, it would be impossible to know whether an observed decrease in the population size reflected a long-term trend or was part of the normal cycle. **3.** In negative feedback, the output, or product, of a process slows that process. In populations that have a density-dependent birth rate, such as dune fescue grass, an accumulation of product (more individuals, resulting in a higher population density) slows the process (population growth) by decreasing the birth rate.

Concept Check 53.6

1. A bottom-heavy age structure, with a disproportionate number of young people, portends continuing growth of the population as these young people begin reproducing. In contrast, a more evenly distributed age structure predicts a more stable population size, and a top-heavy age structure predicts a decrease in population size because relatively fewer young people are reproducing.   **2.** The growth rate of Earth's human population has dropped by half since the 1960s, from 2.2% in 1962 to 1.1% today. Nonetheless, growth has not slowed much because the smaller growth rate is counterbalanced by increased population size; the number of extra people on Earth each year remains enormous—approximately 78 million.   **3.** Each of us influences our ecological footprint by how we live—what we eat, how much energy we use, and the amount of waste we generate—as well as by how many children we have. Making choices that reduce our demand for resources makes our ecological footprint smaller.

Summary of Key Concepts Questions

53.1 Ecologists can potentially estimate birth rates by counting the number of young born each year, and they can estimate death rates by seeing how the number of adults changes each year.   **53.2** Under the exponential model, both populations will continue to grow to infinite size, regardless of the specific value of r_{inst} (see Figure 53.8).   **53.3** There are many things you can do to increase the carrying capacity of the species, including increasing its food supply, protecting it from predators, and providing more sites for nesting or reproduction.   **53.4** Two key factors appear to be the survival rate of the offspring and the chance that adults will live long enough to reproduce again.   **53.5** An example of a biotic factor would be disease caused by a pathogen; natural disasters, such as floods and storms, are examples of abiotic factors.   **53.6** Humans are unique in our potential ability to reduce global population through contraception and family planning. Humans also are capable of consciously choosing their diet and personal lifestyle, and these choices influence the number of people Earth can support.

Test Your Understanding

1. b   **2.** a   **3.** a   **4.** d   **5.** c   **6.** b   **7.** c   **8.** d   **9.** a   **10.** a

Chapter 54

Figure Questions

Figure 54.3 Its realized and fundamental niches would be similar, unlike those of *Chthamalus*.   **Figure 54.15** The number of other organism types eaten is zero for phytoplankton; one for copepods, crab-eater seals, baleen whales, and sperm whales; two for krill, carnivorous plankton, and elephant seals; three for squids, fishes, leopard seals, and humans; and five for birds and smaller toothed whales. The two groups that both consume and are consumed by each other are fishes and squids.   **Figure 54.18** The death of individuals of *Mytilus*, a dominant species, should open up space for other species and increase species richness even in the absence of *Pisaster*.   **Figure 54.23** At the earliest stages of primary succession, free-living prokaryotes in the soil would reduce atmospheric N_2 to NH_3. Symbiotic nitrogen fixation could not occur until plants were present at the site.
Figure 54.26 Other factors not included in the model must contribute to the number of species.   **Figure 54.28** Shrew populations in different locations and habitats might show substantial genetic variation in their susceptibility to the Lyme pathogen. Further studies would be needed to test the generality of the study's results.

Concept Check 54.1

1. Interspecific competition has negative effects on both species (−/−). In predation, the predator population benefits at the expense of the prey population (+/−). Mutualism is a symbiosis in which both species benefit (+/+).   **2.** One of the competing species will become locally extinct because of the greater reproductive success of the more efficient competitor.   **3.** By specializing in eating seeds of a single plant species, individuals of the two finch species may be less likely to come into contact in the separate habitats, reinforcing a reproductive barrier to hybridization.

Concept Check 54.2

1. Species richness, the number of species in the community, and relative abundance, the proportions of the community represented by the various species, both contribute to species diversity. Compared to a community with a very high proportion of one species, one with a more even proportion of species is considered more diverse.   **2.** A food chain presents a set of one-way transfers of food energy up to successively higher trophic levels. A food web documents how food chains are linked together, with many species weaving into the web at more than one trophic level.   **3.** According to the bottom-up model, adding extra predators would have little effect on lower trophic levels, particularly vegetation. If the top-down model applied, increased bobcat numbers would decrease raccoon numbers, increase snake numbers, decrease mouse numbers, and increase grass biomass.

Concept Check 54.3

1. High levels of disturbance are generally so disruptive that they eliminate many species from communities, leaving the community dominated by a few tolerant species. Low levels of disturbance permit competitively dominant species to exclude other species from the community. But moderate levels of disturbance can facilitate coexistence of a greater number of species in a community by preventing competitively dominant species from becoming abundant enough to eliminate other species from the community.   **2.** Early successional species can facilitate the arrival of other species in many ways, including increasing the fertility or water-holding capacity of soils or providing shelter to seedlings from wind and intense sunlight.   **3.** The absence of fire for 100 years would represent a change to a low level of disturbance. According to the intermediate disturbance hypothesis, this change should cause diversity to decline as competitively dominant species gain sufficient time to exclude less competitive species.

Concept Check 54.4

1. Ecologists propose that the greater species richness of tropical regions is the result of their longer evolutionary history and the greater solar energy input and water availability in tropical regions.   **2.** Immigration of species to islands declines with distance from the mainland and increases with island area. Extinction of species is lower on larger islands and on less isolated islands. Since the number of species on islands is largely determined by the difference between rates of immigration and extinction, the number of species will be highest on large islands near the mainland and lowest on small islands far from the mainland.   **3.** Because of their greater mobility, birds disperse to islands more often than snakes and lizards, so birds should have greater richness.

Concept Check 54.5

1. Pathogens are microorganisms, viruses, viroids, or prions that cause disease.   **2.** To keep the rabies virus out, you could ban imports of all mammals, including pets. Potentially, you could also attempt to vaccinate all dogs in the British Isles against the virus. A more practical approach might be to quarantine all pets brought into the country that are potential carriers of the disease, the approach the British government actually takes.

Summary of Key Concepts Questions

54.1 Note: Sample answers follow; other answers could also be correct. Competition: a fox and a bobcat competing for prey. Predation: an orca eating a sea otter. Herbivory: a bison grazing in a prairie. Parasitism: a parasitoid wasp that lays its eggs on a caterpillar. Mutualism: a fungus and an alga that make up a lichen. Commensalism: a remora attached to a whale. Facilitation: a flowering plant and its pollinator.   **54.2** Not necessarily if the more species-rich community is dominated by only one or a few species   **54.3** Because of the presence of species initially, the disturbance would initiate secondary succession in spite of its severe appearance.   **54.4** Glaciations have severely reduced diversity in northern temperate, boreal, and Arctic ecosystems, compared to tropical ecosystems.
54.5 A host is required to complete the pathogen's life cycle, but a vector is not. Vectors are intermediate species that merely transport a pathogen to its host.

Test Your Understanding

1. d   **2.** c   **3.** c   **4.** c   **5.** b   **6.** c   **7.** d   **8.** b
9. Community 1: $H = -(0.05 \ln 0.05 + 0.05 \ln 0.05 + 0.85 \ln 0.85 + 0.05 \ln 0.05) = 0.59$. Community 2: $H = -(0.30 \ln 0.30 + 0.40 \ln 0.40 + 0.30 \ln 0.30) = 1.1$. Community 2 is more diverse.   **10.** Crab numbers should increase, reducing the abundance of eelgrass.

Chapter 55

Figure Questions

Figure 55.6 Wetlands, coral reefs, and coastal zones cover areas too small to show up clearly on global maps.   **Figure 55.7** The availability of nutrients, particularly nitrogen, phosphorus, and iron, as well as temperature, is likely to limit primary production in the oceans.   **Figure 55.8** If the new duck farms made nitrogen available in rich supply, as phosphorus already is, then adding extra nitrogen in the experiment would not increase phytoplankton density.   **Figure 55.13** The lichen symbiosis allows the photosynthetic symbiont to photosynthesize and, in cases where it is a cyanobacterium, to fix nitrogen. The fungal symbiont provides the photosynthetic symbiont with a protective environment as well as phosphorus and other soil nutrients. Lichens are particularly abundant in nutrient-poor habitats such as those found in the Arctic tundra.   **Figure 55.15** Water availability is probably another factor that varied across the sites. Such factors not included in the experimental design could make the results more difficult to interpret. Multiple factors can also covary in nature, so ecologists must be careful that the factor they are studying is actually causing the observed response and is not just correlated with it.

Concept Check 55.1

1. Energy passes through an ecosystem, entering as sunlight and leaving as heat. It is not recycled within the ecosystem.   **2.** You would need to know how much biomass the wildebeests ate from your plot and how much nitrogen was contained in that biomass. You would also need to know how much nitrogen they deposited in urine or feces.   **3.** The second law states that in any energy transfer or transformation, some of the energy is dissipated to the surroundings as heat. This "escape" of energy from an ecosystem is offset by the continuous influx of solar radiation.

Concept Check 55.2

1. Only a fraction of solar radiation strikes plants or algae, only a portion of that fraction is of wavelengths suitable for photosynthesis, and much energy is lost as a result of reflection or heating of plant tissue.   **2.** By manipulating the level of the factors of interest, such as phosphorus availability or soil moisture, and measuring responses by primary producers   **3.** The enzyme rubisco, which catalyzes the first step in the Calvin cycle, is the most abundant protein on Earth. Photosynthetic organisms require considerable nitrogen to make rubisco. Phosphorus is also needed as a component of several metabolites in the Calvin cycle and as a component of both ATP and NADPH (see Figure 10.19).

Concept Check 55.3

1. 20 J; 40%   **2.** Nicotine protects the plant from herbivores.   **3.** Total net production is $10{,}000 + 1{,}000 + 100 + 10$ J $= 11{,}110$ J. At steady state, this is the amount of energy theoretically available to detritivores.

Concept Check 55.4

1. For example, for the carbon cycle:

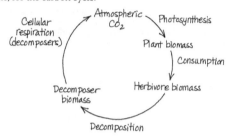

Cycling of a carbon atom

2. Removal of the trees stops nitrogen uptake from the soil, allowing nitrate to accumulate there. The nitrate is washed away by precipitation and enters the streams.   **3.** Most of the nutrients in a tropical rain forest are contained in the trees, so removing the trees by logging rapidly depletes nutrients from the ecosystem. The nutrients that remain in the soil are quickly carried away into streams and groundwater by the abundant precipitation.

Concept Check 55.5

1. The main goal is to restore degraded ecosystems to a more natural state.
2. The Kissimmee River project returns the flow of water to the original channel and restores natural flow, a self-sustaining outcome. Ecologists at the Maungatautari reserve will need to maintain the integrity of the fence indefinitely, an outcome that is not self-sustaining in the long term.

Summary of Key Concepts Questions

55.1 Because energy conversions are inefficient, with some energy inevitably lost as heat, you would expect that a given mass of primary producers would support a smaller biomass of secondary producers.   **55.2** For estimates of NEP, you need to measure the respiration of all organisms in an ecosystem, not just the respiration of primary producers. In a sample of ocean water, primary producers and other organisms are usually mixed together, making their respective respirations hard to separate.   **55.3** Runners use much more energy in respiration when they are running than when they are sedentary, reducing their production efficiency.
55.4 Factors other than temperature, including a shortage of water and nutrients, slow decomposition in hot deserts.   **55.5** If the topsoil and deeper soil are kept separate, you could return the deeper soil to the site first and then apply the more fertile topsoil to improve the success of revegetation and other restoration efforts.

Test Your Understanding

1. c   **2.** b   **3.** a   **4.** c   **5.** a   **6.** b   **7.** d   **8.** d

Chapter 56

Figure Questions

Figure 56.4 You would need to know the complete range of the species and that it is missing across all of that range. You would also need to be certain that the species isn't hidden, as might be the case for an animal that is hibernating underground or a plant that is present in the form of seeds or spores.   **Figure 56.9** The two examples are similar in that segments of DNA from the harvested samples were analyzed and compared with segments from specimens of known origin. One difference is that the whale researchers investigated relatedness at species and population levels to determine whether illegal activity had occurred, whereas the elephant investigators determined relatedness at the population level to determine the precise location of the poaching. Another difference is that mtDNA was used for the whale study, whereas nuclear DNA was used for the elephant study. The primary limitations of such approaches are the need to have (or generate) a reference database and the requirement that the organisms have sufficient variation

in their DNA to reveal the relatedness of samples.   **Figure 56.11** The higher the pH, the lower the acidity. Thus, the precipitation in this forest is becoming less acidic.   **Figure 56.14** Because the population of Illinois birds has a different genetic makeup than birds in other regions, you would want to maintain to the greatest extent possible the frequency of beneficial genes or alleles found only in that population. In restoration, preserving genetic diversity in a species is as important as increasing organism numbers.   **Figure 56.16** The natural disturbance regime in this habitat includes frequent fires that clear undergrowth but do not kill mature pine trees. Without these fires, the undergrowth quickly fills in and the habitat becomes unsuitable for red-cockaded woodpeckers.   **Figure 56.17** The photo shows edges between forest and grassland ecosystems, grassland and river ecosystems, and grassland and lake ecosystems.

Concept Check 56.1

1. In addition to species loss, the biodiversity crisis includes the loss of genetic diversity within populations and species and the degradation of entire ecosystems.   **2.** Habitat destruction, such as deforestation, channelizing of rivers, or conversion of natural ecosystems to agriculture or cities, deprives species of places to live. Introduced species, which are transported by humans to regions outside their native range, where they are not controlled by their natural pathogens or predators, often reduce the population sizes of native species through competition or predation. Overharvesting has reduced populations of plants and animals or driven them to extinction. Finally, global change is altering the environment to the extent that it reduces the capacity of Earth to sustain life.   **3.** If both populations breed separately, then gene flow between the populations would not occur and genetic differences between them would be greater. As a result, the loss of genetic diversity would be greater than if the populations interbreed.

Concept Check 56.2

1. Reduced genetic variation decreases the capacity of a population to evolve in the face of change.   **2.** The effective population size, N_e, would be $4(30 \times 10)/(30 + 10) = 30$ birds.   **3.** Because millions of people use the greater Yellowstone ecosystem each year, it would be impossible to eliminate all contact between people and bears. Instead, you might try to reduce the kinds of encounters where bears are killed. You might recommend lower speed limits on roads in the park, adjust the timing or location of hunting seasons (where hunting is allowed outside the park) to minimize contact with mother bears and cubs, and provide financial incentives for livestock owners to try alternative means of protecting livestock, such as using guard dogs.

Concept Check 56.3

1. A small area supporting numerous endemic species as well as a large number of endangered and threatened species   **2.** Zoned reserves may provide sustained supplies of forest products, water, hydroelectric power, educational opportunities, and income from tourism.   **3.** Habitat corridors can increase the rate of movement or dispersal of organisms between habitat patches and thus the rate of gene flow between subpopulations. They thus help prevent a decrease in fitness attributable to inbreeding. They can also minimize interactions between organisms and humans as the organisms disperse; in cases involving potential predators, such as bears or large cats, minimizing such interactions is desirable.

Concept Check 56.4

1. Adding nutrients causes population explosions of algae and the organisms that feed on them. Increased respiration by algae and consumers, including detritivores, depletes the lake's oxygen, which the fish require.   **2.** Because higher temperatures lead to faster decomposition, organic matter in these soils could be quickly decomposed to CO_2, speeding up global warming.   **3.** Reduced concentrations of ozone in the atmosphere increase the amount of UV radiation that reaches Earth's surface and the organisms living there. UV radiation can cause mutations by producing disruptive thymine dimers in DNA.

Concept Check 56.5

1. Sustainable development is an approach to development that works toward the long-term prosperity of human societies and the ecosystems that support them, which requires linking the biological sciences with the social sciences, economics, and humanities.   **2.** Biophilia, our sense of connection to nature and all forms of life, may act as a significant motivation for the development of an environmental ethic that resolves not to allow species to become extinct or ecosystems to be destroyed. Such an ethic is necessary if we are to become more attentive and effective custodians of the environment.   **3.** At a minimum, you would want to know the size of the population and the average reproductive rate of individuals in it. To develop the fishery sustainably, you would seek a harvest rate that maintains the population near its original size and maximizes its harvest in the long term rather than the short term.

Summary of Key Concepts Questions

56.1 Nature provides us with many beneficial services, including a supply of reliable, clean water, the production of food and fiber, and the dilution and detoxification of our pollutants.   **56.2** A more genetically diverse population is better able to withstand pressures from disease or environmental change, making it less likely to become extinct over a given period of time.   **56.3** Habitat fragmentation can isolate populations, leading to inbreeding and genetic drift, and it can make populations more susceptible to local extinctions resulting from the effects of pathogens, parasites, or predators.   **56.4** It's healthier to feed at a lower trophic level because biological magnification increases the concentration of toxins at higher levels. **56.5** One goal of conservation biology is to preserve as many species as possible. Sustainable approaches that maintain the quality of habitats are required for the long-term survival of organisms.

Test Your Understanding
1. c **2.** d **3.** b **4.** a **5.** b **6.** a
7. (a) The average CO_2 concentration was approximately 330 ppm in 1975 and approximately 394 ppm in 2012. (b) The rate of CO_2 concentration increase was (394 ppm − 330 ppm)/(2012 − 1975) = 64 ppm/37 years = 1.73 ppm/yr. (c) If this rate continues, the concentration in 2100 will be approximately 550 ppm (1.73 ppm/yr × 88 yr = 152 ppm for the increase from 2012–2100 + 394 ppm in 2012 = 546 ppm, rounded off to 550 ppm).
(d)

(e) The actual rise in CO_2 concentration could be larger or smaller, depending on Earth's human population, per capita energy use, and the extent to which societies take steps to reduce CO_2 emissions, including replacing fossil fuels with renewable or nuclear fuels. (f) Additional scientific data will be important for many reasons, such as determining how quickly greenhouse gases such as CO_2 are removed from the atmosphere by the biosphere.

9.

To minimize the area of forest into which the cowbirds penetrate, you should locate the road along one edge of the reserve. Any other location would increase the area of affected habitat. Similarly, the maintenance building should be in a corner of the reserve to minimize the area susceptible to cowbirds.

Atomic number (number of protons)
Element symbol
Atomic mass (number of protons plus number of neutrons averaged over all isotopes)

| 6 |
| C |
| 12.01 |

Metals   Metalloids   Nonmetals

── Representative elements ──

Groups: Elements in a vertical column have the same number of electrons in their valence (outer) shell and thus have similar chemical properties.

Periods: Each horizontal row contains elements with the same total number of electron shells. Across each period, elements are ordered by increasing atomic number.

Alkali metals   Alkaline earth metals

Halogens   Noble gases

Period number

Period 1: Group 1A — H 1.008 ; Group 2A ; Group 3A ; Group 4A ; Group 5A ; Group 6A ; Group 7A ; Group 8A — He 4.003

── Transition elements ──

1	H 1.008																He 4.003
2	Li 6.941	Be 9.012										B 10.81	C 12.01	N 14.01	O 16.00	F 19.00	Ne 20.18
3	Na 22.99	Mg 24.31	3B	4B	5B	6B	7B	──8B──			1B	2B	Al 26.98	Si 28.09	P 30.97	S 32.07	Cl 35.45	Ar 39.95
4	K 39.10	Ca 40.08	Sc 44.96	Ti 47.87	V 50.94	Cr 52.00	Mn 54.94	Fe 55.85	Co 58.93	Ni 58.69	Cu 63.55	Zn 65.41	Ga 69.72	Ge 72.64	As 74.92	Se 78.96	Br 79.90	Kr 83.80
5	Rb 85.47	Sr 87.62	Y 88.91	Zr 91.22	Nb 92.91	Mo 95.94	Tc (98)	Ru 101.1	Rh 102.9	Pd 106.4	Ag 107.9	Cd 112.4	In 114.8	Sn 118.7	Sb 121.8	Te 127.6	I 126.9	Xe 131.3
6	Cs 132.9	Ba 137.3	57* La 138.9	Hf 178.5	Ta 180.9	W 183.8	Re 186.2	Os 190.2	Ir 192.2	Pt 195.1	Au 197.0	Hg 200.6	Tl 204.4	Pb 207.2	Bi 209.0	Po (209)	At (210)	Rn (222)
7	Fr (223)	Ra (226)	89† Ac (227)	Rf (261)	Db (262)	Sg (266)	Bh (264)	Hs (269)	Mt (268)	Ds (271)	Rg (272)	Cn (285)	113 — (284)	Fl (289)	115 — (288)	Lv (293)	117 (292)	118 — (294)

*Lanthanides

58 Ce 140.1	59 Pr 140.9	60 Nd 144.2	61 Pm (145)	62 Sm 150.4	63 Eu 152.0	64 Gd 157.3	65 Tb 158.9	66 Dy 162.5	67 Ho 164.9	68 Er 167.3	69 Tm 168.9	70 Yb 173.0	71 Lu 175.0

†Actinides

90 Th 232.0	91 Pa 231.0	92 U 238.0	93 Np (237)	94 Pu (244)	95 Am (243)	96 Cm (247)	97 Bk (247)	98 Cf (251)	99 Es 252	100 Fm 257	101 Md 258	102 No 259	103 Lr 260

Name (Symbol)	Atomic Number	Name (Symbol)	Atomic Number	Name (Symbol)	Atomic Number	Name (Symbol)	Atomic Number	Name (Symbol)	Atomic Number
Actinium (Ac)	89	Copernicium (Cn)	112	Iodine (I)	53	Osmium (Os)	76	Silicon (Si)	14
Aluminum (Al)	13	Copper (Cu)	29	Iridium (Ir)	77	Oxygen (O)	8	Silver (Ag)	47
Americium (Am)	95	Curium (Cm)	96	Iron (Fe)	26	Palladium (Pd)	46	Sodium (Na)	11
Antimony (Sb)	51	Darmstadtium (Ds)	110	Krypton (Kr)	36	Phosphorus (P)	15	Strontium (Sr)	38
Argon (Ar)	18	Dubnium (Db)	105	Lanthanum (La)	57	Platinum (Pt)	78	Sulfur (S)	16
Arsenic (As)	33	Dysprosium (Dy)	66	Lawrencium (Lr)	103	Plutonium (Pu)	94	Tantalum (Ta)	73
Astatine (At)	85	Einsteinium (Es)	99	Lead (Pb)	82	Polonium (Po)	84	Technetium (Tc)	43
Barium (Ba)	56	Erbium (Er)	68	Lithium (Li)	3	Potassium (K)	19	Tellurium (Te)	52
Berkelium (Bk)	97	Europium (Eu)	63	Livermorium (Lv)	116	Praseodymium (Pr)	59	Terbium (Tb)	65
Beryllium (Be)	4	Fermium (Fm)	100	Lutetium (Lu)	71	Promethium (Pm)	61	Thallium (Tl)	81
Bismuth (Bi)	83	Flerovium (Fl)	114	Magnesium (Mg)	12	Protactinium (Pa)	91	Thorium (Th)	90
Bohrium (Bh)	107	Fluorine (F)	9	Manganese (Mn)	25	Radium (Ra)	88	Thulium (Tm)	69
Boron (B)	5	Francium (Fr)	87	Meitnerium (Mt)	109	Radon (Rn)	86	Tin (Sn)	50
Bromine (Br)	35	Gadolinium (Gd)	64	Mendelevium (Md)	101	Rhenium (Re)	75	Titanium (Ti)	22
Cadmium (Cd)	48	Gallium (Ga)	31	Mercury (Hg)	80	Rhodium (Rh)	45	Tungsten (W)	74
Calcium (Ca)	20	Germanium (Ge)	32	Molybdenum (Mo)	42	Roentgenium (Rg)	111	Uranium (U)	92
Californium (Cf)	98	Gold (Au)	79	Neodymium (Nd)	60	Rubidium (Rb)	37	Vanadium (V)	23
Carbon (C)	6	Hafnium (Hf)	72	Neon (Ne)	10	Ruthenium (Ru)	44	Xenon (Xe)	54
Cerium (Ce)	58	Hassium (Hs)	108	Neptunium (Np)	93	Rutherfordium (Rf)	104	Ytterbium (Yb)	70
Cesium (Cs)	55	Helium (He)	2	Nickel (Ni)	28	Samarium (Sm)	62	Yttrium (Y)	39
Chlorine (Cl)	17	Holmium (Ho)	67	Niobium (Nb)	41	Scandium (Sc)	21	Zinc (Zn)	30
Chromium (Cr)	24	Hydrogen (H)	1	Nitrogen (N)	7	Seaborgium (Sg)	106	Zirconium (Zr)	40
Cobalt (Co)	27	Indium (In)	49	Nobelium (No)	102	Selenium (Se)	34		

Metric Prefixes: 10^9 = giga (G) 10^{-2} = centi (c) 10^{-9} = nano (n)
10^6 = mega (M) 10^{-3} = milli (m) 10^{-12} = pico (p)
10^3 = kilo (k) 10^{-6} = micro (μ) 10^{-15} = femto (f)

Measurement	Unit and Abbreviation	Metric Equivalent	Metric-to-English Conversion Factor	English-to-Metric Conversion Factor
Length	1 kilometer (km)	= 1,000 (10^3) meters	1 km = 0.62 mile	1 mile = 1.61 km
	1 meter (m)	= 100 (10^2) centimeters = 1,000 millimeters	1 m = 1.09 yards 1 m = 3.28 feet 1 m = 39.37 inches	1 yard = 0.914 m 1 foot = 0.305 m
	1 centimeter (cm)	= 0.01 (10^{-2}) meter	1 cm = 0.394 inch	1 foot = 30.5 cm 1 inch = 2.54 cm
	1 millimeter (mm)	= 0.001 (10^{-3}) meter	1 mm = 0.039 inch	
	1 micrometer (μm) (formerly micron, μ)	= 10^{-6} meter (10^{-3} mm)		
	1 nanometer (nm) (formerly millimicron, mμ)	= 10^{-9} meter (10^{-3} μm)		
	1 angstrom (Å)	= 10^{-10} meter (10^{-4} μm)		
Area	1 hectare (ha)	= 10,000 square meters	1 ha = 2.47 acres	1 acre = 0.405 ha
	1 square meter (m^2)	= 10,000 square centimeters	1 m^2 = 1.196 square yards 1 m^2 = 10.764 square feet	1 square yard = 0.8361 m^2 1 square foot = 0.0929 m^2
	1 square centimeter (cm^2)	= 100 square millimeters	1 cm^2 = 0.155 square inch	1 square inch = 6.4516 cm^2
Mass	1 metric ton (t)	= 1,000 kilograms	1 t = 1.103 tons	1 ton = 0.907 t
	1 kilogram (kg)	= 1,000 grams	1 kg = 2.205 pounds	1 pound = 0.4536 kg
	1 gram (g)	= 1,000 milligrams	1 g = 0.0353 ounce 1 g = 15.432 grains	1 ounce = 28.35 g
	1 milligram (mg)	= 10^{-3} gram	1 mg = approx. 0.015 grain	
	1 microgram (μg)	= 10^{-6} gram		
Volume (solids)	1 cubic meter (m^3)	= 1,000,000 cubic centimeters	1 m^3 = 1.308 cubic yards 1 m^3 = 35.315 cubic feet	1 cubic yard = 0.7646 m^3 1 cubic foot = 0.0283 m^3
	1 cubic centimeter (cm^3 or cc)	= 10^{-6} cubic meter	1 cm^3 = 0.061 cubic inch	1 cubic inch = 16.387 cm^3
	1 cubic millimeter (mm^3)	= 10^{-9} cubic meter = 10^{-3} cubic centimeter		
Volume (liquids and gases)	1 kiloliter (kL or kl)	= 1,000 liters	1 kL = 264.17 gallons	
	1 liter (L or l)	= 1,000 milliliters	1 L = 0.264 gallon 1 L = 1.057 quarts	1 gallon = 3.785 L 1 quart = 0.946 L
	1 milliliter (mL or ml)	= 10^{-3} liter = 1 cubic centimeter	1 mL = 0.034 fluid ounce 1 mL = approx. ¼ teaspoon 1 mL = approx. 15–16 drops (gtt.)	1 quart = 946 mL 1 pint = 473 mL 1 fluid ounce = 29.57 mL 1 teaspoon = approx. 5 mL
	1 microliter (μL or μl)	= 10^{-6} liter (10^{-3} milliliter)		
Pressure	1 megapascal (MPa)	= 1,000 kilopascals	1 MPa = 10 bars	1 bar = 0.1 MPa
	1 kilopascal (kPa)	= 1,000 pascals	1 kPa = 0.01 bar	1 bar = 100 kPa
	1 pascal (Pa)	= 1 newton/m^2 (N/m^2)	1 Pa = 1.0×10^{-5} bar	1 bar = 1.0×10^5 Pa
Time	1 second (s or sec)	= 1/60 minute		
	1 millisecond (ms or msec)	= 10^{-3} second		
Temperature	Degrees Celsius (°C) (0 K [Kelvin] = −273.15°C)		°F = 9/5°C + 32	°C = 5/9 (°F − 32)

Light Microscope

In light microscopy, light is focused on a specimen by a glass condenser lens; the image is then magnified by an objective lens and an ocular lens for projection on the eye, digital camera, digital video camera, or photographic film.

Electron Microscope

In electron microscopy, a beam of electrons (top of the microscope) is used instead of light, and electromagnets are used instead of glass lenses. The electron beam is focused on the specimen by a condenser lens; the image is magnified by an objective lens and a projector lens for projection on a digital detector, fluorescent screen, or photographic film.

This appendix presents a taxonomic classification for the major extant groups of organisms discussed in this text; not all phyla are included. The classification presented here is based on the three-domain system, which assigns the two major groups of prokaryotes, bacteria and archaea, to separate domains (with eukaryotes making up the third domain).

Various alternative classification schemes are discussed in Unit Five of the text. The taxonomic turmoil includes debates about the number and boundaries of kingdoms and about the alignment of the Linnaean classification hierarchy with the findings of modern cladistic analysis. In this review, asterisks (*) indicate currently recognized phyla thought by some systematists to be paraphyletic.

DOMAIN BACTERIA

- **Proteobacteria**
- **Chlamydia**
- **Spirochetes**
- **Gram-Positive Bacteria**
- **Cyanobacteria**

DOMAIN ARCHAEA

- **Korarchaeota**
- **Euryarchaeota**
- **Crenarchaeota**
- **Nanoarchaeota**

DOMAIN EUKARYA

In the phylogenetic hypothesis we present in Chapter 28, major clades of eukaryotes are grouped together in the four "supergroups" listed in bold type below and on the facing page. Formerly, all the eukaryotes generally called protists were assigned to a single kingdom, Protista. However, advances in systematics have made it clear that some protists are more closely related to plants, fungi, or animals than they are to other protists. As a result, the kingdom Protista has been abandoned.

Excavata
- Diplomonadida (diplomonads)
- Parabasala (parabasalids)
- Euglenozoa (euglenozoans)
  - Kinetoplastida (kinetoplastids)
  - Euglenophyta (euglenids)

"SAR" Clade
- Stramenopila (stramenopiles)
  - Chrysophyta (golden algae)
  - Phaeophyta (brown algae)
  - Bacillariophyta (diatoms)

- Alveolata (alveolates)
  - Dinoflagellata (dinoflagellates)
  - Apicomplexa (apicomplexans)
  - Ciliophora (ciliates)
- Rhizaria (rhizarians)
  - Radiolaria (radiolarians)
  - Foraminifera (forams)
  - Cercozoa (cercozoans)

Archaeplastida
- Rhodophyta (red algae)
- Chlorophyta (green algae: chlorophytes)
- Charophyta (green algae: charophytes)
- Plantae
  - Phylum Hepatophyta (liverworts) ⎫ Nonvascular
  - Phylum Bryophyta (mosses) ⎬ plants (bryophytes)
  - Phylum Anthocerophyta (hornworts) ⎭
  - Phylum Lycophyta (lycophytes) ⎫ Seedless vascular
  - Phylum Monilophyta (ferns, horsetails, ⎬ plants
    whisk ferns) ⎭
  - Phylum Ginkgophyta (ginkgo) ⎫
  - Phylum Cycadophyta (cycads) ⎬ Gymnosperms ⎫
  - Phylum Gnetophyta (gnetophytes) ⎪   ⎬ Seed
  - Phylum Coniferophyta (conifers) ⎭   ⎪ plants
  - Phylum Anthophyta (flowering ⎫   ⎭
    plants) ⎬ Angiosperms

Unikonta

- Amoebozoa (amoebozoans)
  - Myxogastrida (plasmodial slime molds)
  - Dictyostelida (cellular slime molds)
  - Tubulinea (tubulinids)
  - Entamoeba (entamoebas)
- Nucleariida (nucleariids)
- Fungi
  - *Phylum Chytridiomycota (chytrids)
  - *Phylum Zygomycota (zygomycetes)
  - Phylum Glomeromycota (glomeromycetes)
  - Phylum Ascomycota (ascomycetes)
  - Phylum Basidiomycota (basidiomycetes)

- Choanoflagellata (choanoflagellates)
- Animalia
  - Phylum Porifera (sponges)
  - Phylum Ctenophora (comb jellies)
  - Phylum Cnidaria (cnidarians)
    - Medusozoa (hydrozoans, jellies, box jellies)
    - Anthozoa (sea anemones and most corals)
  - Phylum Acoela (acoel flatworms)
  - Phylum Placozoa (placozoans)
  - <u>Lophotrochozoa (lophotrochozoans)</u>
  - Phylum Platyhelminthes (flatworms)
    - Catenulida (chain worms)
    - Rhabditophora (planarians, flukes, tapeworms)
  - Phylum Nemertea (proboscis worms)
  - Phylum Ectoprocta (ectoprocts)
  - Phylum Brachiopoda (brachiopods)
  - Phylum Rotifera (rotifers)
  - Phylum Cycliophora (cycliophorans)
  - Phylum Mollusca (molluscs)
    - Polyplacophora (chitons)
    - Gastropoda (gastropods)
    - Bivalvia (bivalves)
    - Cephalopoda (cephalopods)
  - Phylum Annelida (segmented worms)
    - Errantia (errantians)
    - Sedentaria (sedentarians)
  - Phylum Acanthocephala (spiny-headed worms)

<u>Ecdysozoa (ecdysozoans)</u>
- Phylum Loricifera (loriciferans)
- Phylum Priapula (priapulans)
- Phylum Nematoda (roundworms)
- Phylum Arthropoda (This survey groups arthropods into a single phylum, but some zoologists now split the arthropods into multiple phyla.)
  - Chelicerata (horseshoe crabs, arachnids)
  - Myriapoda (millipedes, centipedes)
  - Pancrustacea (crustaceans, insects)
- Phylum Tardigrada (tardigrades)
- Phylum Onychophora (velvet worms)

<u>Deuterostomia (deuterostomes)</u>
- Phylum Hemichordata (hemichordates)
- Phylum Echinodermata (echinoderms)
  - Asteroidea (sea stars, sea daisies)
  - Ophiuroidea (brittle stars)
  - Echinoides (sea urchins, sand dollars)
  - Crinoidea (sea lilies)
  - Holothuroidea (sea cucumbers)
- Phylum Chordata (chordates)
  - Cephalochordata (cephalochordates: lancelets)
  - Urochordata (urochordates: tunicates)
  - Cyclostomata (cyclostomes)
    - Myxini (hagfishes)
    - Petromyzontida (lampreys)
  - Gnathostomata (gnathostomes)
    - Chondrichthyes (sharks, rays, chimaeras)
    - Actinopterygii (ray-finned fishes)
    - Actinistia (coelacanths)
    - Dipnoi (lungfishes)
    - Amphibia (amphibians: frogs, salamanders, caecilians)
    - Reptilia (reptiles: tuataras, lizards, snakes, turtles, crocodilians, birds)
    - Mammalia (mammals)

} Vertebrates

CREDITS

Photo Credits

Cover Image Martin Turner/Flickr/Getty Images

New Content Unit I Mark J. Winter/Science Source; **Unit II** Thomas Deerinck and Mark Ellisman, NCMIR; **p. xxxiii cell** Thomas Deerinck; **Unit III** Andrey Prokhorov/E+/Getty Images; **p. xxxiii cell** Thomas Deerinck; **Unit IV** Richard Bizley/Science Source; **Unit V** DOE Photo; **Unit VI** Giuseppe Mazza; **Unit VII** Matthias Wittlinger; **Unit VIII** Jordi Bas Casas/NHPA/Photoshot.

Detailed Contents p xxxii dandelions Carola Koserowsky/AGE Fotostock; **gecko** Martin Harvey/Peter Arnold/Getty Images; **p. xxxiii cell** Thomas Deerinck and Mark Ellisman, NCMIR; **ribbon model** Mark J. Winter/Science Source; **p. xxxiv giraffe** Uryadnikov/Shutterstock; **tree** Aflo/Nature Picture Library; **p. xxxv mitosis** George von Dassow; **flower** John Swithinbank/Garden World Images/AGE Fotostock; **p. xxxvi DNA** Andrey Prokhorov/E+/Getty Images; **ribosome** Venki Ramakirshnan; **p. xxxvii viruses** Richard Bizley/Science Source; **membrane model** Dr. Ian Derrington; **pxxxviii caterpillar** Robert Sisson/National Geographic Stock; **tortoise** Pete Oxford/Nature Picture Library; **p. xxxix hot spring** Shaeri Mukherjee; **stentors** Eric V. Grave/Science Source; **p. xl fireweed** Lyn Topinka/USGS; **lizard** Stephen Dalton/Nature Picture Library; **p. xli coral reef** Image Quest Marine; **p. xlii bee** GFC Collection/Alamy; **snowflake plant** Giuseppe Mazza; **p. xliii otter** Jeff Foott/Discovery Channel Images/Getty Images; **p. xliv macrophage** O.Bellini/Shutterstock; **elephant seals** Phillip Colla/Oceanlight.com; **p. xlv lizard** Pete Oxford/Nature Picture Library; **synapses** Image by Sebastian Jessberger, Fred H. Gage, Laboratory of Genetics LOG-G, The Salk Institute for Biological Studies; **p. xlvi fox** Harpe/Robert Harding World Imagery; **p. xlvii fox** Jordi Bas Casas/NHPA/Photoshot.

Unit Opening Interviews UNIT I p. 27 portrait Courtesy of Venki Ramakrishnan; **ribosome model** Courtesy of Venki Ramakrishnan. From V. Ramakrishnan, What we have learned from ribosome structures (The Heatley Medal Lecture), *Biochem. Soc. Trans.* 2008 Aug;36(4):567–574 (2008). **UNIT II p. 92 portrait** Haifan Lin; **Piwi protein** Haifan Lin; **UNIT III p. 251 portrait** National Human Genome Research Institute; **villagers** Nigel Pavitt/John Warburton-Lee Photography/Alamy; **UNIT IV p. 461 portrait** Josh Frost, Pearson Education; **mouse** J. B. Miller/Florida Park Service; **UNIT V p. 546 portrait** Josh Frost, Pearson Education; **choanoflagellates** Nicole King; **UNIT VI p. 751 portrait** Jeff Dangl Lab; *Arabidopsis* Daniel Aviv, Jeff Dangl Lab; **UNIT VII p. 866 portrait** Ulrike Heberlein; **laboratory setup** Ulrike Heberlein; **UNIT VIII p. 1157 portrait** Josh Frost, Pearson Education; **recovery after fire** Courtesy of Monica Turner.

Chapter 1 Carola Koserowsky/AGE Fotostock; **p. xlviii** Steve Bloom Images/Alamy; **1.2 sunflower** ImageState Media Partners Limited; **seahorse** R. Dirscherl/FLPA; **rabbit** Joe McDonald/Corbis; **butterfly** Toshiaki Ono/amana images/Alamy; **plant** Frederic Didillon/Garden Picture Library/Getty Images; **Venus flytrap** Kim Taylor and Jane Burton/DK Images; **giraffes** Malcolm Schuyl/FLPA; **1.3.1** WorldSat International/Science Source; **1.3.2** Bill Brooks/Alamy; **1.3.3** Linda Freshwaters/Alamy; **1.3.4** Michael Orton/Photographer's Choice/Getty Images; **1.3.5** Ross M. Horowitz/Iconica/Getty Images; **1.3.6** Photodisc/Getty Images; **1.3.7** Jeremy Burgess/Science Source; **1.3.8** Texas A and M University; **1.3.9** E.H. Newcomb and W.P. Wergin/Biological Photo Service; **p. 4** Jim Zipp/Science Source; **1.4 eukaryotic** Steve Gschmeissner/Science Source; **1.4 prokaryotic** S. C. Holt/Biological Photo Service; **1.5** Conly L. Rieder, Ph.D.; **1.6** Camille Tokerud/Getty Images; **1.8a left** Carol Yepes/Flickr RF/Getty Images; **right** Ralf Dahm, Max Planck Institute for Developmental Biology, Tübingen, Germany; **1.10** James Balog/Getty Images; **1.13a** Oliver Meckes, Nicole Ottawa/Science Source; **1.13b** Eye of Science/Science Source; **1.13c left to right** Kunst and Scheidulin/AGE Fotostock; daksel/Fotolia; Anup Shah/Nature Picture Library; D.P. Wilson/Science Source; **1.14 pond** basel101658/Shutterstock; **paramecium** VVG/SPL/Science Source; **cross section** W. L. Dentler/Biological Photo Service; **cilia** OMIKRON/Science Source; **1.15** Dede Randrianarisata, Macalester College; **1.16 left** American Museum of Natural History; **right** ARCHIV/Science Source; **1.17 left to right** zhaoyan/Shutterstock; Sebastian Knight/Shutterstock; Volodymyr Goinyk/Shutterstock; **1.19** Frank Greenaway/DK Images; **1.21** Karl Ammann/Corbis Images; **inset** Tim Ridley/DK Images; **1.23 girl** Martin Shields/Alamy; **woman** EightFish/The Image Bank/Getty Images; **canoe** Rolf Hicker Photography/All Canada Photos/Alamy; **group** Seelevel.com; **1.24 white mouse** Courtesy of Hopi Hoekstra, Harvard University; **sand dunes** From Darwin to DNA: The genetic basis of color adaptations. In *In the Light of Evolution: Essays from the Laboratory and Field* ed. J. Losos, Roberts and Co. Photo by Sacha Vignieri; **field** Sacha Vignieri; **brown mouse** Shawn P. Carey, Migration Productions; **1.25** From S. N. Vignieri, J. Larson, and H. E. Hoekstra, The selective advantage of cryptic coloration in mice. *Evolution* 64:2153–2158 (2010). Fig. 1; **p. 22** Imagebroker/FLPA; **1.26** Jay Janner/Austin American-Statesman/AP Photo; **p. 26** Chris Mattison/Alamy.

Chapter 2 2.1 Kim Taylor/Nature Picture Library; **p. 28** Kim Taylor/Nature Picture Library; **2.2 sodium** Chip Clark; **chlorine, sodium chloride** Pearson Education; **2.3 landscape** Michael C. Hogan; **flower** CNPS California Native Plant Society; **rock** Andrew Alden; **2.5** National Library of Medicine; **p. 33** Pascal Goetgheluck/Science Source; **2.13** Pearson Education; **p. 39** Martin Harvey/Peter Arnold/Getty Images; **2.17** Nigel Cattlin/Science Source; **p. 43 top** Rolf Nussbaumer/Nature Picture Library; **bottom** Thomas Eisner.

Chapter 3 3.1 Teiji Saga/Science Source; **p. 44** Datacraft/UIG. Collection: Universal Images Group/AGE Fotostock; **3.4** iStockphoto; **3.6** Jan van Franeker/Alfred-Wegener-Institut fur Polar-und Meeresforschung; **3.9** NASA/JPL-Caltech/University of Arizona; **3.10 top to bottom** Jakub Semeniuk/iStockphoto; Feng Yu/iStockphoto; Monika Wisniewska/iStockphoto; Beth Van Trees/Shutterstock; **p. 54** The University of Queensland; **p. 56** Eric Guilloret/Biosphoto/Science Source.

Chapter 4 4.1 Florian Möllers/Nature Picture Library; **p. 58 notes** The Register of Stanley Miller Papers 1952 to 2010 in the Mandeville Special Collection Library, Laboratory Notebook 2, page 114, Serial number 655, MSS642, Box 25, Mandeville Collections, Geisel Library; **vials** Robert Benson, courtesy of Jeffrey Bada; **4.6** David M. Phillips/Science Source; **p. 65** George Sanker/Nature Picture Library.

Chapter 5 5.1 Mark J. Winter/Science Source; **p. 66** T. Naeser/Ludwig-Maximilians-Universitat Munchen; **5.6 potatoes** Dougal Waters/Getty Images; **plant cell** John Durham/Science Source; **starch** John N. A. Lott/Biological Photo Service; **glycogen** Dr. Paul B. Lazarow, Ph.D. Professor and Chairman; **cellulose** Biophoto Associates/Science Source; **5.8 top** F. Collet/Science Source; **bottom** Corbis; **5.10a** DK Images; **5.10b** David Murray/DK Images; **5.13 eggs** Andrey Stratilatov/Shutterstock; **muscle tissue** Nina Zanetti; **connective tissue** Nina Zanetti; **5.16c** Clive Freeman/Science Source; **5.17** Peter M. Colman; **5.18** Dieter Hopf/AGE Fotostock; **5.19** Eye of Science/Science Source; **5.21** Reprinted by permission from Nature. P. B. Sigler from Z. Xu, A. L. Horwich, and P. B. Sigler. 388:741–750 Copyright © 1997 Macmillan Magazines Limited; **5.22** Dave Bushnell; **5.26 DNA** Alfred Pasieka/Science Source; **Neanderthal** Viktor Deak; **doctor** CHASSENET/BSIP SA/Alamy; **hippo** Frontline Photography/Alamy; **whale** WaterFrame/Alamy; **elephants** ImageBroker/FLPA; **plant** David Read, Department of Animal and Plant Sciences, University of Sheffield; **p. 89 human** lanych/Shutterstock; **monkey** David Bagnall/Alamy; **gibbon** Eric Isselee/Shutterstock; **p. 91 chick** Africa Studio/Shutterstock.

Chapter 6 6.1 Don W. Fawcett/Science Source; **6.3 brightfield, phase-contrast, DIC** Elisabeth Pierson, FNWI-Radboud University Nijmegen, Pearson Education; **6.3 fluorescence** Michael W. Davidson, The Florida State University Research Foundation/Molecular Expressions; **confocal** Karl Garsha, Beckman Institute for Advanced Science and Technology, University of Illinois; **deconvolution** Dr. James G. Evans, Whitehead Institute, MIT, Boston, MA, USA; **super-resolution** From K. I. Willig et al., STED microscopy reveals that synaptotagmin remains clustered after synaptic vesicle exocytosis, *Nature* 440(13) (2006), doi:10.1038/nature04592, Letters; **SEM** From A. S. Shah et al., Motile cilia of human airway epithelia are chemosensory, Science Express, 23 July 2009, *Science* 325(5944):1131–1134 (2009). Pseudocolored scanning electron micrograph by Tom Moninger (epithelia generated by Phil Karp); **TEM** William Dentler, Biological Photo Service; **6.5b** S. C. Holt, University of Texas Health Center/Biological Photo Service; **6.6** Daniel S. Friend; **p. 99** Kelly Tatchell; **6.8 p. 100 left to right** S. Cinti/Science Source; SPL/Science Source; A. Barry Dowsett/Science Source; **6.8 p. 101 left to right** Biophoto Associates/Science Source; SPL/Science Source; William Dentler, Center for Bioinformatics, University of Kansas: From W. L. Dentler and C. Adams, Flagellar microtubule dynamics in chlamydomonas: cytochalasin d induces periods of microtubule shortening and elongation; and colchicine induces disassembly of the distal, but not proximal, half of the flagellum, *The Journal of Cell Biology* 117(6):1289–1298, Copyright © 1992 by The Rockefeller University Press; **p. 102** Thomas Deerinck and Mark Ellisman, NCMIR; **6.9 top left** Reproduced by permission from L. Orci and A. Perelet, *Freeze-Etch Histology*, Springer-Verlag, Heidelberg (1975). Copyright ©1975 by Springer-Verlag GmbH & Co KG; **6.9 lower left** Reproduced by permission from A. C. Faberge, *Cell Tiss. Res.* 151 Copyright © 1974 by Springer-Verlag GmbH & Co KG; **6.9 lower right** Reprinted by permission from U. Aebi et al., *Nature* 323:560–564 (1996), Copyright © 1996, figure 1a. Used with permission. Macmillan Magazines Limited; **6.10 left** D. W. Fawcett/Science Source; **6.10 right** Courtesy Harry Noller, UCSC; **6.11** R. Bolender, Don Fawcett/Science Source; **6.12** D. W. Fawcett/Science Source; **6.13** Daniel S. Friend; **6.14** Eldon H. Newcomb; **6.17a** Daniel S. Friend; **6.17b** From Y. Hayashi and K. Ueda, The shape of mitochondria and the number of mitochondrial nucleoids during the cell cycle of *Euglena gracilis*, *Journal of Cell Science* 93:565–570 (1989), Copyright © 1989 by Company of Biologists; **6.18a** Courtesy of W. P. Wergin and E. H. Newcomb, University of Wisconsin/Biological Photo Service; **6.18b** Franz Grolig, Philipps-University Marburg, Germany. Image acquired with the confocal microscope Leica TCS SP2; **6.19** From S. E. Fredrick and E. H. Newcomb, *The Journal of Cell Biology* 43:343 (1969). Provided by E. H. Newcomb; **6.20** Albert Tousson, High Resolution Imaging Facility, University of Alabama at Birmingham; **6.21** Bruce J. Schnapp; **Table 6.1 left** Mary Osborn; **middle** Frank Solomon; **right** Mark S. Ladinsky and J. Richard McIntosh, University of Colorado; **6.22** Kent L. McDonald; **6.23a** Biophoto Associates/Science Source; **6.23b** Oliver Meckes and Nicole Ottawa/Science Source; **6.24a** OMIKRON/Science Source; **6.24b** W. L. Dentler/Biological Photo Service; **6.24c** R. W. Linck and R. E. Stephens, Functional protofilament numbering of ciliary, flagellar, and centriolar microtubules, *Cell Motil. Cytoskeleton* 64(7):489–495 (2007); cover. Micrograph by D. Woodrum Hensley; **6.25** From H. Nobutaka, *The Journal of Cell Biology* 94:425 (1982) by copyright permission of The Rockefeller University Press; **6.26a** Clara Franzini-Armstrong, University of Pennsylvania; **6.26b** M. I. Walker/Photo Researchers; **6.26c** Michael Clayton, University of Wisconsin-Madison; **6.27** G. F. Leedale/Science Source; **6.29** Micrograph by W. P. Wergin, provided by E. H. Newcomb; **6.30 top** From D. J. Kelly, *The Journal of Cell Biology* 28:51 (1966), Fig.17. Reproduced by copyright permission of The Rockefeller University Press; **6.30 center** Reproduced by permission from L. Orci and A. Perelet, *Freeze-Etch Histology*, Springer-Verlag, Heidelberg (1975). Copyright © 1975 by Springer-Verlag GmbH & Co KG; **6.30 bottom** From C. Peracchia and A. F. Dulhunty, *The Journal of Cell Biology* 70:419 (1976) by copyright permission of The Rockefeller University Press; **6.31** Lennart Nilsson/Scanpix Sweden AB; **p. 123** Susumu Nishinaga/Science Source.

Chapter 7 7.1 B. L. de Groot; **p. 124** Roderick Mackinnon; **7.13** Michael Abbey/Science Source; **7.19 left** H. S. Pankratz, T. C. Beaman, and P. Gerhardt/Biological Photo Service; **7.19 center** D. W. Fawcett/Photo Researchers; **7.19 right** M. M. Perry and A. B. Gilbert, *J. Cell Science* 39:257 (1979). Copyright 1979 by The Company of Biologists Ltd.; **p. 140** Kristoffer Tripplaar/Alamy.

Chapter 8 **8.1** Doug Perrine/Nature Picture Library; **p. 141** Lance@ancelpics/Flickr/Getty Images; **8.2** Thinkstock; **8.3** Robert N. Johnson/RnJ Photography; **8.4 left** Brandon Blinkenberg/iStockphoto; **right** asharkyu/Shutterstock; **8.15** Thomas A. Steitz, Yale University; **p. 155** Fer Gregory/Shutterstock; **8.22** Nicolae Simionescu; **p. 161** Flickr/Getty Images.

Chapter 9 **9.1** Uryadnikov Sergey/Shutterstock; **9.4** Dionisvera/Fotolia; **p. 177** Kitchin and Hurst/AGE fotostock; **p. 184** Michael Neelon/Alamy.

Chapter 10 **10.1** Aflo/Nature Picture Library; **p. 185** Martha Marks/Shutterstock; **10.2a** Jean-Paul Nacivet/AGE fotostock; **10.2b** Lawrence Naylor/Science Source; **10.2c** M. I. Walker/Science Source; **10.2d** Susan M. Barns, Ph.D.; **10.2e** National Library of Medicine; **10.3** Qiang Hu, ASU; **10.4 mesophyll** Image courtesy Andreas Holzenburg and Stanislav Vitha, Dept. of Biology and Microscopy & Imaging Center, Texas A&M University; **chloroplast** E. H. Newcomb & W. P. Wergin/Biological Photo Service; **10.12** Christine L. Case; **p. 203** Dennis Barnes/Agstockusa/AGE fotostock; **10.21a** Doukdouk/Alamy; **10.21b** Keysurfing/Shutterstock; **p. 209** Gary Yim/Shutterstock.

Chapter 11 **11.1** Federico Veronesi/Gallo Images/Alamy; **p. 210** molekuul.be/Shutterstock; **11.3 top 3** A. Dale Kaiser, Stanford University; **11.3 bottom** Michiel Vos; **11.7** From V. Cherezov et al., High-resolution crystal structure of an engineered human beta2-adrenergic G protein-coupled receptor, *Science* 318(5854):1258–1265 (2007). Epub 2007 Oct 25; **p. 226** D. Matheos et al., Pheromone-induced polarization is dependent on the Fus3p MAPK acting through the formin Bni1p. *J Cell Biol.* 165(1):99–109 (2004); Fig. 9. Reproduced by copyright permission of The Rockefeller University Press; **11.19** Gopal Murti/Science Source; **11.21** From W. Wood et al., Mesenchymal cells engulf and clear apoptotic footplate cells in macrophageless PU.1 null mouse embryos. *Development* 127:5245–5252 (2000); **p. 231** Seelevel.com.

Chapter 12 **12.1** George von Dassow; **p. 232** Jane Stout and Claire Walczak, Indiana University, Winner of the GE Healthcare Life Sciences' 2012 Cell Imaging Competition; Biophoto Associates/Science Source; **12.2b** Biology Pics/Science Source; **12.2c** Biophoto/Science Source; **12.3** John Murray; **12.4** Biophoto/Science Source; **12.5** Biophoto/Science Source; **12.7** Conly L. Rieder, Ph.D.; **12.8 left** J. Richard McIntosh, University of Colorado at Boulder; **12.8 right** Reproduced by permission from Matthew Schibler, from *Protoplasma* 137. Copyright © 1987: 29–44 by Springer-Verlag GmbH & Co KG; **12.10a** Don W. Fawcett/Science Source; **12.10b** Eldon H. Newcomb; **12.11** Elisabeth Pierson, FNWI-Radboud University Nijmegen, Pearson Education; **12.18** Lan Bo Chen; **12.19** Lan Bo Chen; **12.20** Anne Weston, LRI, CRUK, Wellcome Images; **p. 248** Michael Davidson; **p. 250 left** J. L. Carson/Medical Stock Photo; **right** Steve Gschmeissner/Science Source.

Chapter 13 **13.1** Mango Productions/Corbis; **p. 252** Don W. Fawcett/Science Source; **13.2a** Roland Birke/OKAPIA/Science Source; **13.2b** George Ostertag/SuperStock; **13.3 top** Ermakoff/Science Source; **bottom** CNRI/Science Source; **p. 262** Sci-MAT/Science Source; **13.12** Mark Petronczki and Maria Siomos; **13.13** John Walsh, Micrographia.com; **p. 266** Randy Ploetz.

Chapter 14 **14.1** John Swithinbank/Garden World Images/AGE Fotostock; **p. 267** Mendel Museum, Augustinian Abbey Brno; **14.14 left** Mark Turner/Alamy; **right** Paul Dymond/Alamy; **p. 281** Alberto Pomares/E+/Getty Images; **14.15a** PhotoDisc/Getty Images; **14.15b** Anthony Loveday; **14.16** Rick Guidotti/Positive Exposure; **14.18** Michael Ciesielski Photography; **14.19** CNRI/Science Source; **p. 291 cat** Norma Jubinville; **family** Rene Maltete/Gamma-Rapho/Getty Images.

Chapter 15 **15.1** Peter Menzel/Science Source; **p. 292** From Zellsubstanz, Kern und Zelltheilung. Walther Flemming (1882). Courtesy of Yale University, Harvey Cushing/John Hay Whitney Medical Library; **15.3** From J. Childress, R. Behringer, and G. Halder, Learning to fly: Phenotypic markers in *Drosophila*. A poster of common phenotypic markers used in *Drosophila* genetics, *Genesis* 43(1) (2005); **15.5** Andrew Syred/Science Source; **15.6a** stockyimages/Shutterstock; **15.6b** li jingwang/E+/Getty Image; **15.6c** kosam/Shutterstock; **15.6d** Creative images/Fotolia; **15.8** Jagodka/Shutterstock; **p. 302** Oliver911119/Shutterstock; **15.15 left** SPL/Science Source; **right** Lauren Shear/SPL/Science Source; **15.18** phomphan/Shutterstock; **p. 311** James K. Adams, Biology, Dalton State College, Dalton, Georgia.

Chapter 16 **16.1** Andrey Prokhorov/E+/Getty Images; **p. 312** National Institutes of Health; **16.3** Oliver Meckes/Science Source; **16.6a** Library of Congress; **16.6b** From J. D. Watson, *The Double Helix*, Atheneum Press, NY (1968), p. 215. © 1968. Courtesy CSHL Archive; **16.12a** Jerome Vinograd; **16.12b** From D. J. Burks and P. J. Stambrook, *The Journal of Cell Biology* 77:762 (1978), fig. 6 by copyright permission of The Rockefeller University Press. Photo provided by P. J. Stambrook; **16.21** Peter Lansdorp; **16.22 left to right** Stanley C. Holt/Biological Photo Service; Dr. Victoria E. Foe; From J. R. Paulsen and U. K. Laemmli, *Cell* 12:817–828 (1977); Barbara Hamkalo; Biophoto/Photo Researchers; **16.23a** From E. Schröck et al., Multicolor spectral karyotyping of human chromosomes, *Science* 273(5274):494–497 (1996); **16.23b** From M. R. Speicher and N. P. Carter, The new cytogenetics: Blurring the boundaries with molecular biology, *Nat. Rev. Genet.* 6(10):782–792 (2005); **p. 332 left** Thomas A. Steitz; **right** Barry Stoddard, Ph.D., Fred Hutchinson Cancer Research Center.

Chapter 17 **17.1** S. Meyers/Blickwinkel/AGE Fotostock; **p. 333** Richard Stockwell; **17.6a** Keith V. Wood; **17.6b** Simon Lin/AP Images; **17.16** Joachim Frank; **17.22** Barbara Hamkalo and O. Miller, Jr.; **17.23** Reprinted with permission from O. L. Miller, Jr., B. A. Hamkalo, and C. A Thomas, Jr., *Science* 169:392 (1970). Copyright ©1970 American Association for the Advancement of Science; **17.25** Eye of Science/Science Source; **p. 359** Vasiliy Koval/Shutterstock.

Chapter 18 **18.1** Andreas Werth; **p. 360** gallimaufry/Shutterstock; **p. 370** Amanda Rohde/Getty Images; **18.12** From M. R. Speicher and N. P. Carter, The new cytogenetics: Blurring the boundaries with molecular biology, *Nat. Rev. Genet.* 6(10):782–792 (2005); **18.16** Mike Wu; **18.20** F. Rudolf Turner, Indiana University; **18.21** Wolfgang Driever, University of Freiburg, Freiburg, Germany; **18.22** Ruth Lahmann, The Whitehead Institute; **p. 391** Peter Herring/Image Quest Marine.

Chapter 19 **19.1** Richard Bizley/Science Source; **p. 392** Thomas Deerinck, NCMIR/Science Source; **19.2** Peter von Sengbusch; **19.3a** Robley C. Williams-TMV/Biological Photo Service; **19.3b** Valentine/Biological Photo Service; **19.3c** Hazel Appleton/Science Source; **19.3d** Robley C. Williams, Jr./Biological Photo Service; **19.8** C. Dauguet/Institute Pasteur/Science Source; **19.9a** NIBSC/Science Source; **19.9b** Seo Myung-gon/AP Photo; **p. 404** Dong Yanjun/Imaginechina/AP Images; **p. 405** Thomas A. Zitter; **p. 407** Nelson Hale/Shutterstock.

Chapter 20 **20.1** Dr. Ian Derrington; **p. 408** John Elk III/Alamy; **20.2a** Javier Larrea/AGE Fotostock; **20.2b** Volker Steger/Science Source; **20.7** Repligen Corporation; **20.10** Ethan Bier; **p. 420** Thomas Montavon; **20.13** George S. Watts and Bernard W. Futscher, University of Arizona Cancer Center; **20.18** Pat Sullivan/AP Photo; **20.19 left to right** Steve Gschmeissner/Science Source; SPL/Science Source; Steve Gschmeissner/Science Source; **20.23** Brad DeCecco Photography; **20.24** Steve Helber/AP Images; **p. 435** Galyna Andrushko/Shutterstock.

Chapter 21 **21.1** Karen Huntt/Corbis Images; **p. 436** Digital Zoo/Getty Images; **21.4** From M. Costanzo et al., The genetic landscape of a cell, *Science* 327(5964):425–431 (2010); **21.5** GeneChip Human Genome U133 Plus 2.0 Array, image courtesy of Affymetrix; **21.7 left** AP Images; **right** Virginia Walbot, Stanford University; **21.10** Oscar L. Miller Jr., Dept. of Biology, University of Virginia; **21.18** FOXP2 images From W. Shu et al., Altered ultrasonic vocalization in mice with a disruption in the Foxp2 gene, *Proc. Natl. Acad. Sci. U S A* 102(27):9643–9648 (2005); Fig. 3. Image supplied by Joseph Buxbaum; **mice** Nicholas Bergkessel, Jr./Science Source; **p. 458** WaterFrame/Alamy; **p. 460** Patrick Landmann/Science Source.

Chapter 22 **22.1** Robert Sisson/National Geographic Stock; **p. 462** Corinne Lamontagne; **22.2 fossils** PD image: Skeleton of the Rhinoceros unicorne de Java in the Paris Museum of Natural History. From G. Cuvier, *Recherches sur les ossemens fossiles*, Atlas, pl. 17 (1836); **frog** Alfred Russel Wallace Memorial Fund; **Wallace** The Natural History Museum, London/Alamy; **iguana** Wayne Lynch/AGE Fotostock; **book page** American Museum of Natural History; **22.4** Karen Moskowitz/Stone/Getty Images; **22.5 left** ARCHIV/Science Source; **right** Stanley Owen; **22.6a** Michael Gunther/Science Source; **22.6b** David Hosking/Frank Lane Picture Agency; **22.6c** David Hoskin/Alamy; **22.7** Wikimedia Commons; **22.9 brussels sprouts** Paul Rapson/Alamy; **cabbage** Izaokas Sapiro/iStockphoto; **broccoli** YinYang/iStockphoto; **kale** Robert Sarno/IStockphoto; **kohlrabi** floricica buzlea/iStockphoto; **22.10** Laura Jesse; **22.11** Richard Packwood/Oxford Scientific/Getty Images; **22.12 top to bottom** Edward S. Ross; Gallo Images/the Agency Collection/Getty Images; Mark Taylor/Nature Picture Library; **22.13** Scott P. Carroll; **22.16a** Dr. Keith Wheeler/Science Source; **22.16b** Lennart Nilsson/Scanpix Sweden AB; **22.18 left** ANT Photo Library/Science Source; **right** Joe McDonald/Steve Bloom Images/Alamy; **22.19** Chris Linz, Thewissen Lab, Northeastern Ohio University College of Medicine; **p. 479** John Cancalosi/Nature Picture Library.

Chapter 23 **23.1** Sylvain Cordier/Biosphoto/Science Source; **p. 480** Rosemary B. Grant; **23.3** David Stoecklein/AGE fotostock; **23.5** Erick Greene, University of Montana; **23.6 left** Gary Schultz/Photoshot Holdings; **right** James L. and Roxie Davis; **p. 487** Scott Sinklier/AgStock Images, Inc./Alamy; **23.11** William Ervin/Science Source; **23.12** Jan Visser; **23.14** Bruce Coleman/Photoshot Holdings; **23.15** Dave Blackey/AGE fotostock; **23.17 people** Caroline Penn/Alamy; **blood cells** Eye of Science/Science Source; **mosquito** Kletr/Shutterstock; **p. 499** Thomas & Pat Leeson/Science Source.

Chapter 24 **24.1** Mark Jones/AGE Fotostock; **p. 500** Pete Oxford/Nature Picture Library; **24.2a left** Malcolm Schuyl/Alamy; **right** Wave RF/Getty Images; **24.2b top left to right** Robert Kneschke/iStockphoto; Justin Horrocks/iStockphoto; Ryan McVay/Getty Images; **bottom left to right** Photodisc/Getty Images; Photodisc/Getty Images; Masterfile; **24.3a,b** Joe McDonald/Photoshot; **24.3c** Hogle Zoo; **24.3d** APHIS/USDA; **24.3e** Michael Dietrich/Alamy; **24.3f** Takahiro Asami; **24.3g** William E. Furguson; **24.3h** Charles W. Brown; **24.3i** EyeWire Collection/Getty Images; **23.3j** Corbis; **24.3k** Dawn YL/Fotolia; **24.3l** Kazutoshi Okuno; **24.4 grizzly** CLFProductions/Shutterstock; **polar** Boris Karpinski/Alamy; **hybrid** Troy Maben/AP Images; **24.6** From R. B. Langerhans, Morphology, performance, fitness: Functional insight into a post-Pleistocene radiation of mosquitofish, *Biology Letters* 5(4):488–491 (2009); **24.8 map** Visible Earth (http://visibleearth.nasa.gov/), NASA; **shrimp** Arthur Anker; **p. 507** John Shaw/NHPA/Photoshot; **24.11** Ole Seehausen; **p. 510** Phil Huntley-Franck; **24.12** Jeroen Speybroeck, Research Institute for Nature and Forest, Belgium; **24.15** Ole Seehausen; **24.17** Jason Rick and Loren Rieseberg; **24.19** Reprinted by permission from H. D. Bradshaw and D. W. Schemske, Allele substitution at a flower colour locus produces a pollinator shift in monkeyflowers, *Nature* 426(6963):176–178 (2003), Copyright © 2003. Macmillan Magazines Limited; **p. 518** Thomas Marent/Rolf Nussbaumer Photography/Alamy.

Chapter 25 **25.1** Gerhard Boeggemann; **p. 519** Rebecca Hunt; **25.3** D. S. Kelley, University of Washington; **25.4b** F. M. Menger and Kurt Gabrielson, Emory University; **25.4c** M. Hanczyc; **25.5 left top to bottom** Seelevel.com; Roger Jones; S. M. Awramik/Biological Photo Service; Sinclair Stammers/Science Source; **25.5 right top to bottom** Specimen No. 12478, Markus Moser, Staatliches Museum fur Naturkunde Stuttgart; Ted Daeschler/Academy of Natural Sciences/VIREO; Chip Clark; Lisa-Ann Gershwin, University of California, Berkeley, Museum of Paleontology; Andrew H. Knoll, Harvard University; **25.12** Remy W., Taylor T. N., Hass H., Kerp H./*Proceedings of the National Academy of Sciences*; **p. 532** Biophoto Associates/Science Source; **25.22 top center** Bruce G. Baldwin; **all others** Gerald D. Carr; **25.23** Jean Kern; **25.24** Juniors Bildarchiv/Alamy; **25.26 top** David Horsley; **bottom** Mike Shapiro; **25.27** Sinclair Stammers/Science Source; **p. 545** Solent News/Splash News/Newscom.

Chapter 26 **26.1** John Cancalosi/AGE Fotostock; **26.17a** Courtesy Dept. of Library Services, American Museum of Natural History; **26.17b** Ed Heck; **26.22** Ilias Strachinis/Shutterstock; **p. 564** Nigel Cattlin/Alamy; **p. 566** David Fleetham/Nature Picture Library. Solent News/Splash News/Newscom.

Chapter 27 **27.1** Zastolskiy Victor/Shutterstock; **27.2a** Centers for Disease Control and Prevention (CDC); **27.2b** Kari Lounatmaa/Science Source; **27.2c** Stem Jems/Science Source; **27.3** L. Brent Selinger; **27.4** Dr. Immo Rantala/SPL/Science Source; **27.5** H. S. Pankratz, T. C. Beaman/Biological Photo Service; **27.6** Kwangshin Kim/Science Source; **27.7** Julius Adler; **27.8a** S. W. Watson; **27.8b** N. J. Lang/Biological Photo Service; **27.9** Huntington Potter; **27.12** Charles C. Brinton, Jr.; **27.14** Susan M. Barns, Ph.D.; **27.16 p. 578 top to bottom** L. Evans/Biological Photo Service; Yuichi Suwa; National Library of Medicine; From P. L. Grilione and J. Pangborn, Scanning electron microscopy of fruiting body formation by myxobacteria, *J. Bacteriol.* 124(3):1558–1565 (1975); Science Source; **27.16 p. 579 top to bottom** Moredon Animal Health/SPL/Science Source; CNRI/SPL/Science Source; Culture Collection CCALA, Institute of Botany, Academy of Sciences Dukelska, Czech Republic; Paul Hoskisson, Strathclyde Institute of Pharmacy and Biomedical Sciences, Glasgow, Scotland; David M. Phillips/Science Source; **27.17** Shaeri Mukherjee; **27.18** Pascale Frey-Klett; **27.19** Ken Lucas/Biological Photo Service; **27.20 left to right** Scott Camazine/Science Source; David M. Phillips/Science Source; James Gathany/CDC; **27.21** Metabolix Media; **27.22** ExxonMobil Corporation; **p. 584** igor.stevanovic/Shutterstock; **27.23** Kathleen Spuhler; **p. 586** G. Wanner/ScienceFoto/Getty Images.

Chapter 47 47.1 Scanpix Sweden AB; **p. 1037** Oxford Scientific/Getty Images; **47.4 top** From V. D. Vacquier and J. E. Payne, Methods for quantitating sea urchin sperm-egg binding, *Exp. Cell Res.* 82(1):227–235 (1973); **bottom** From M. Hafner et al., Wave of free calcium at fertilization in the sea urchin egg visualized with Fura-2, *Cell Motil. Cytoskel.* 9:271–277 (1988); **47.6** George von Dassow; **47.7a** Jurgen Berger, SpemanMax Planck Campus Tubingen; **47.7b** Andrew J. Ewald, Johns Hopkins Medical School; **47.8** Charles A. Ettensohn; **47.14a** Huw Williams; **47.14c** Thomas Poole, SUNY Health Science Center; **47.15b** Dr. Keith Wheeler/Science Source; **47.18b** From H. Nishida, *Developmental Biology* 121: 526 (1987). Reprinted by permission of Academic Press; **47.20** Adapted from Strome, *International Review of Cytology* 114:81–123 (1989); **47.21** Adapted from Strome, *International Review of Cytology* 114:81–123 (1989); **47.25** Kathryn W. Tosney, University of Michigan; **47.26** Dennis Summerbell; **p. 1060** James Gerholdt/Peter Arnold/Getty Images.

Chapter 52 52.1 Christopher C. Austin; **p. 1158** Christopher C. Austin; **52.2 top to bottom** NASA; William D. Bachman/Science Source; B. Tharp/Science Source; Susan Lee Powell; Barrie Britton/Nature Picture Library; James D. Watt/Alamy; **p. 1164 left** Dr. Randall Rosiere; **p. 1164 right** Rick Koval; **52.9 clockwise from top left** Joseph Sohm/AGE Fotostock; David Halbakken/AGE Fotostock; gary718/Shutterstock; Siepmann/Alamy; Bent Nordeng/Shutterstock; Juan Carlos Munoz/Nature Picture Library; **52.10 left** JTB Photo Communications, Inc./Alamy; **right** Krystyna Szulecka/Alamy; **52.11 tropical forest** Siepmann/Alamy; **desert** Joseph Sohm/AGE Fotostock; **savanna** Robert Harding Picture Library Ltd/Alamy; **chaparral** The California Chaparral Institute; **grassland** David Halbakken/AGE Fotostock; **coniferous** Bent Nordeng/Shutterstock; **broadleaf** gary718/Shutterstock; **tundra** Juan Carlos Munoz/Nature Picture Library; **52.14 oligotrophic** Susan Lee Powell; **eutrophic** AfriPics.com/Alamy; **wetland** David Tipling/Nature Picture Library; **stream** Ron Watts/Corbis; **river** Photononstop/SuperStock; **estuary** Juan Carlos Muñoz/AGE Fotostock; **intertidal** Stuart Westmorland/Corbis; **ocean** Tatonka/Shutterstock; **reef** Digital Vision/Getty Images; **benthic** William Lange/Woods Hole Oceanographic Institute; **52.15** JLV Image Works/Fotolia; **52.17** Peter Llewellyn/Alamy; **52.18 sea urchin** Dr. Scott D. Ling, Institute for Marine and Antarctic Studies; **limpet** Simon Grove; **52.19** Daniel Mosquin; **p. 1181 left** John W. Bova/Science Source; **right** Dave Bevan/Alamy; **p. 1183** Daryl Balfour/Stone/Getty Images.

Chapter 53 53.1 Harpe/Robert Harding World Imagery; **p. 1184** Luiz Claudio Marigo/Nature Picture Library; **53.2** Todd Pusse/Nature Picture Library; **53.4a** Bernard Castelein/Nature Picture Library/Alamy; **53.4b** Fritz Polking/Frank Lane Picture Agency/Corbis; **53.4c** Niali Benvie/Corbis; **p. 1187 center** Jill M. Mateo; **bottom** Scott Nunes, University of San Francisco; **53.9** Hansjoerg Richter/iStockphoto; **p. 1194** Laguna Design/Science Source; **53.12** Photodisc/Getty Images; **53.13a** Stone Nature Photography/Alamy; **53.13b** ableimages/Alamy; **53.14** Dietmar Nill/Nature Picture Library; **53.15a** Steve Bloom Images/Alamy; **53.15b left** Fernanda Preta/Alamy; **right** Edward Parker/Alamy; **53.17 left** Chris Menjou; **right** Peter Brueggeman; **53.18 wheat** fotoVoyager/iStockphoto; **crowd** Reuters; **owl** Hellio and Van Ingen/NHPA/Photoshot Holdings Ltd.; **cheetah** Gregory G. Dimijian/Science Source; **mice** Nicholas Bergkessel, Jr./Science Source; **yeast** Andrew Syred/Science Source; **53.20** Joe McDonald/Corbis; **53.21** Niclas Fritzen; **53.25** Circuit boards #2, New Orleans 2005 by Chris Jordan; **p. 1207** Stringer/Reuters.

Chapter 54 54.1 Jurgen Freund/Nature Picture Library; **p. 1208** Jurgen Freund/Nature Picture Library; **p. 1209** M. I. Walker/Science Source; **54.4 left** Joseph T. Collins/Science Source; **right** National Museum of Natural History/Smithsonian Institution; **p. 1210** Frank W. Lane/Frank Lane Picture Agency Limited; **p. 1211** Johan Larson/Shutterstock; **54.5a** Tony Heald/Nature Picture Library; **54.5b** Tom Vezo/Nature Picture Library; **54.5c** Danté Fenolio/Science Source; **54.5d** Barry Mansell/Nature Picture Library; **54.5e left** Danté Fenolio/Science Source; **right** Robert Pickett/Alamy; **54.5f left** Edward S. Ross, California Academy of Sciences; **right** James K. Lindsey; **54.6** Roger Steene/Image Quest Marine; **54.7** Douglas Faulkner/Science Source; **54.8a** Raul Gonzalez Perez/Science Source; **54.8b** Nicholas Smythe/Science Source; **54.9** Daryl Balfour/Photoshot Holdings; **54.10** Sally D. Hacker; **p. 1216** Dr. Gary W. Saunders; **54.12** Dung Vo Trung/Science Source; **54.13** Cedar Creek Ecosystem Science Reserve, University of Minnesota; **54.18** Genny Anderson; **54.19** Adam Welz; **p. 1221** DEA/T e G BALDIZZ/AGE Fotostock; **54.21a** Ron Landis Photography; **54.21b** Thomas and Pat Leeson/Science Source; **54.22 clockwise from top left** Charles D. Winters/Science Source; Douglas W. Veltre, Ph.D.; Mary Liz Austin and Terry Donnelly; Glacier Bay National Park and Preserve; **54.23 left to right** Charles D. Winters/Science Source; Douglas W. Veltre, Ph.D.; Mary Liz Austin and Terry Donnelly; Glacier Bay National Park and Preserve; **54.24** Elliott A. Norse; **54.27** Tim Laman/National Geographic Creative; **54.28** Bates Magazine, Bates College; **54.29** Josh Spice; **p. 1231** Jacques Rosès/Science Source.

Chapter 55 55.1 Jordi Bas Casas/NHPA/Photoshot Holdings Ltd.; **p. 1232** Steven Kazlowski/Nature Picture Library; **55.2 top** Anne Morkill, U.S. Fish and Wildlife Service; **bottom** Stone Nature Photography/Alamy; **55.3 left** Scimat/Science Source;

right Justus de Cuveland/AGE Fotostock; **p. 1239** Biophoto Associates/Science Source; **p. 1240** David R. Frazier Photolibrary/Science Source; **p. 1247** USDA Forest Service; **55.16a** USDA Forest Service; **55.17** Mark Gallagher; **55.18** U.S. Department of Energy; **55.19 Kissimmee** South Florida Water Management District; **Truckee** Stewart B. Rood, University of Lethbridge; **Costa Rica** Daniel H. Janzen, University of Pennsylvania; **Rhine** Bert Boekhoven; **South Africa** Jean Hall/Holt Studio/Science Source; **Japan** Kenji Morita, Environment Division, Tokyo Kyuei Co., Ltd.; **New Zealand** Tim Day, Xcluder Pest Proof Fencing Ltd.; **p. 1253** Eckart Pott/NHPA/Photoshot Holdings Ltd.

Chapter 56 56.1 L. Lee Grismer; **p. 1254** Thomas Geissmann/Fauna & Flora International; **56.2** Tran Cao Bao Long – UNEP/Robert Harding World Imagery; **56.4 top** Neil Lucas/Nature Picture Library; **bottom** Mark Carwardine/Getty Images; **56.5** Merlin D. Tuttle, Bat Conservation International, www.batcon.org; **56.6** Scott Camazine/Science Source; **56.7** Michael Edwards/Getty Images; **56.8** Robert Ginn/PhotoEdit, Inc.; **56.9** Benezeth Mutayoba, photo provided by the University of Washington; **56.10** Pictures Colour Library/Travel Picture/Alamy; **56.12** F. Latreille/Mammuthus/H.C.E.; **56.14** William Ervin/Science Source; **56.15** Craighead Environmental Research Institute; **56.16a left** William Leaman/Alamy; **right** Chuck Bargeron, The University of Georgia; **56.16b** William D. Boyer, USDA Forest Service; **56.17** Guido Alberto Rossi/TIPS IMAGES/AGE Fotostock; **56.18** R. O. Bierregaard, Jr., Biology Dept., University of North Carolina, Charlotte; **56.19** SPL/Science Source; **56.21** Edwin Giesbers/Nature Picture Library; **56.22** Mark Chiappone and Steven Miller, Center for Marine Science, University of North Carolina-Wilmington, Key Largo, FL; **56.23** Nigel Cattlin/Science Source; **56.24** NASA; **56.26** Erich Hartmann/Magnum Photos, Inc.; **p. 1273** Hank Morgan/Science Source; **56.31** NASA; **56.33a** Serge de Sazo/Science Source; **56.33b** Hilde Jensen/AP Images; **56.33c** Gabriel Rojo/Nature Picture Library; **56.33d** Titus Lacoste/Getty Images; **p. 1279** Edwin Giesbers/Nature Picture Library.

Appendix A p. A-5 left OMIKRON/Science Source; **right** W. L. Dentler/Biological Photo Service; **p. A-11 top left** Biophoto/Science Source; **bottom left** J. Richard McIntosh, University of Colorado at Boulder; **right** J. L. Carson/Custom Medical Stock Photo; **p. A-34** Peter Kitin.

Appendix E p. E-1 top left Oliver Meckes/Nicole Ottawa/Science Source; **bottom left** Eye of Science/Science Source; **middle** M. I. Walker/NHPA/Photoshot; **right** Howard Rice/DK Images; **p. E-2 left** Phil Dotson/Science Source; **right** Oliver Wien/epa European Pressphoto Agency creative account/Alamy.

Illustration and Text Credits

Chapter 1 1.23 Adaptation of figure from "The real process of science," from Understanding Science website. Copyright © 2013 by The University of California Museum of Paleontology, Berkeley, and the Regents of the University of California. Material used courtesy of the UC Museum of Paleontology. ucmp.berkeley.edu; **1.25** Adaptation of figure 3 from "From Darwin to DNA: The Genetic Basis of Color Adaptations" by Hopi E. Hoekstra, edited by Jonathan Losos, from *In the Light of Evolution: Essays from the Laboratory and Field.* Copyright © 2011 by Roberts Company Publishers, Inc. Reprinted with permission. Adaptation of Figure 1b from "The Selective Advantage of Crypsis in Mice" by Sacha N. Vignieri et al., from *Evolution*, July 2010, Volume 64(7). Copyright © 2010 by Society for the Study of Evolution. Reprinted with permission of John Wiley & Sons Ltd.; **p. 21 Quote** Source: Isaac Newton quoted in *Never at Rest: A Biography of Isaac Newton* by Richard Westfall. Cambridge University Press, 1983; **1 SSE** Source: Data from "Adaptive Coloration in *Peromyscus polionotus*: Experimental Selection by Owls" by Donald W. Kaufman, from *Journal of Mammology*, May 1974, Volume 55(2).

Chapter 2 2 SSE Source: Data from "Revised Age of Late Neanderthal Occupation and the End of the Middle Paleolithic in the Northern Caucasus" by Ron Pinhasi et al., *Proceedings of the National Academy of Sciences of the United States of America*, 2011, Volume 108(21).

Chapter 3 3.8 Source: Based on "Stimulating Water and the Molecules of Life" by Mark Gerstein and Michael Levitt, from *Scientific American*, November 1998; **03. Un04** Adaptation of figure 5 from "Effect of Calcium Carbonate Saturation State on the Calcification Rate of an Experimental Coral Reef" by C. Langdon et al., from *Global Biogeochemical Cycles*, June 2000, Volume 14(2). Copyright © 2000 by American Geophysical Union. Reprinted with permission of Wiley Inc.; **3 SSE** Source: Data from "Effect of Calcium Carbonate Saturation State on the Calcification Rate of an Experimental Coral Reef" by Chris Langdon, et al., from *Global Biogeochemical Cycles*, June 2000, Volume 14(2).

Chapter 4 4.2 Source: Based on "A Production of Amino Acids under Possible Primitive Earth Conditions" by Stanley L. Miller, from *Science*, New Series, May 15, 1953, Volume 117(3046); **4 SSE** Source: Data from "Primordial Synthesis of Amines and Amino Acids in a 1958 Miller H_2S-rich Spark Discharge Experiment" by Eric T. Parker et al., from PNAS, March 22, 2012, Volume 108(12); **4.6b** Figure adapted from *Biochemistry*, 2nd Edition, by Christopher K. Mathews and Kensal E. Van Holde. Copyright © 1996 by Pearson Education, Inc. Adapted and electronically reproduced by permission of Pearson Education, Inc., Upper Saddle River, New Jersey; **4.7** Figure adapted from *The World Of The Cell*, 3rd Edition, by Wayne M. Becker, Jane B. Reece, and Martin F. Poenie. Copyright © 1996 by Pearson Education, Inc. Adapted and electronically reproduced by permission of Pearson Education, Inc., Upper Saddle River, New Jersey.

Chapter 5 5.11 Figure adapted from *Biology: The Science of Life*, 3rd Edition, by Robert Wallace, Gerald Sanders, and Robert Ferl. Copyright © 1991 by Pearson Education, Inc. Adapted and electronically reproduced by permission of Pearson Education, Inc., Upper Saddle River, New Jersey; **5.13h, 5.18f** Source: Protein Data Bank ID 1CGD: "Hydration Structure of a Collagen Peptide" by Jordi Bella et al., from *Structure*, September 1995, Volume 3(9); **5.16a, b** Figure adapted from "How Amino-Acid Insertions Are Allowed in an Alpha-helix of T4 Lysozyme" by D. W. Heinz et al., from

Nature, February 1993, Volume 362(6412). Copyright © 1993 by Macmillan Publishers Ltd. Reprinted with permission; **5.18d** Source: Protein Data Bank ID 3GS0: "Novel Transthyretin Amyloid Fibril Formation Inhibitors: Synthesis, Biological Evaluation, and X-ray Structural Analysis" by Satheesh K. Palaninathan et al., from PLOS ONE, July 21, 2009, Volume 4(7); **5.18g** Source: Protein Data Bank ID 2HHB: "The Crystal Structure of Human Deoxyhaemoglobin at 1.74 A Resolution" by G. Fermi et al., from *Journal of Molecular Biology*, May 1984, Volume 175(2); **5.22b** Adaptation of figure 2c from "Structural Basis of Transcription: An RNA Polymerase II Elongation Complex at 3.3 Resolution" by Averell L. Gnatt et al., from *Science*, June 2001, Volume 292(5523). Copyright © 2001 by AAAS. Reprinted with permission; **5 SSE** Source: Data for human from "Molecular and Population Genetic Analysis of Allelic Sequence Diversity at the Human Beta-globin Locus" by S. M. Fullerton et al., from *Proceedings of the National Academy of Sciences USA*, March 1994, Volume 91(5); Data for rhesus from "The Primary Structure of the Alpha and Beta Polypeptide Chains of Adult Hemoglobin of the Rhesus Monkey (*Macaca mulatta*). Biochemical Studies on Hemoglobins and Myoglobins. IV" by Genji Matsuda et al., from *International Journal of Protein Research*, December 1970, Volume 2(1–4); data for gibbon from "Primate Hemoglobins: Some Sequences and Some Proposals Concerning the Character of Evolution and Mutation" by Samuel H. Boyer et al., from *Biochemical Genetics*, October 1971, Volume 5(5).

Chapter 6 6.6b Figure adapted from *The World of the Cell*, 3rd Edition, by Wayne M. Becker, Jane B. Reece, and Martin F. Poenie. Copyright © 1996 by Pearson Education, Inc. Adapted and electronically reproduced by permission of Pearson Education, Inc., Upper Saddle River, New Jersey; **6.8** Adaptation of figure 3.2 from *Human Anatomy and Physiology*, 8th Edition, by Elaine N. Marieb and Katja N. Hoehn, 2010. Copyright © 2010 by Pearson Education, Inc. Reprinted and electronically reproduced by permission of Pearson Education, Inc. Upper Saddle River, New Jersey; **6.9** Adaptation of figure 3.29 from *Human Anatomy and Physiology*, 8th Edition, by Elaine N. Marieb and Katja N. Hoehn, 2010. Copyright © 2010 by Pearson Education, Inc. Reprinted and electronically reproduced by permission of Pearson Education, Inc. Upper Saddle River, New Jersey; **6.10** Adaptation of figure 3.2 from *Human Anatomy and Physiology*, 8th Edition, by Elaine N. Marieb and Katja N. Hoehn, 2010. Copyright © 2010 by Pearson Education, Inc. Reprinted and electronically reproduced by permission of Pearson Education, Inc. Upper Saddle River, New Jersey; **6.11** Adaptation of figure 3.18 from *Human Anatomy and Physiology*, 8th Edition, by Elaine N. Marieb and Katja N. Hoehn, 2010. Copyright © 2010 by Pearson Education, Inc. Reprinted and electronically reproduced by permission of Pearson Education, Inc. Upper Saddle River, New Jersey; **6.12** Adaptation of figure 3.19 from *Human Anatomy and Physiology*, 8th Edition, by Elaine N. Marieb and Katja N. Hoehn, 2010. Copyright © 2010 by Pearson Education, Inc. Reprinted and electronically reproduced by permission of Pearson Education, Inc. Upper Saddle River, New Jersey; **6.13a** Adaptation of figure 3.2 from *Human Anatomy and Physiology*, 8th Edition, by Elaine N. Marieb and Katja N. Hoehn, 2010. Copyright © 2010 by Pearson Education, Inc. Reprinted and electronically reproduced by permission of Pearson Education, Inc. Upper Saddle River, New Jersey; **6.15** Adaptation of figure 3.20 from *Human Anatomy and Physiology*, 8th Edition, by Elaine N. Marieb and Katja N. Hoehn, 2010. Copyright © 2010 by Pearson Education, Inc. Reprinted and electronically reproduced by permission of Pearson Education, Inc. Upper Saddle River, New Jersey; **6.17** Adaptation of figure 3.17 from *Human Anatomy and Physiology*, 8th Edition, by Elaine N. Marieb and Katja N. Hoehn, 2010. Copyright © 2010 by Pearson Education, Inc. Reprinted and electronically reproduced by permission of Pearson Education, Inc. Upper Saddle River, New Jersey; **Table 6.1** Adaptation of table 15.1 from *Becker's World of the Cell*, 8th Edition, by Jeff Hardin et al. Copyright © 1996 by Pearson Education, Inc. Reprinted and electronically reproduced by permission of Pearson Education, Inc. Upper Saddle River, New Jersey; **6.22** Adaptation of figure 3.25 from *Human Anatomy and Physiology*, 8th Edition, by Elaine N. Marieb and Katja N. Hoehn, 2010. Copyright © 2010 by Pearson Education, Inc. Reprinted and electronically reproduced by permission of Pearson Education, Inc. Upper Saddle River, New Jersey; **6.24** Adaptation of figures 3.2 and 3.26 from *Human Anatomy and Physiology*, 8th Edition, by Elaine N. Marieb and Katja N. Hoehn, 2010. Copyright © 2010 by Pearson Education, Inc. Reprinted and electronically reproduced by permission of Pearson Education, Inc. Upper Saddle River, New Jersey; **6.EOC01, 6.EOC03, 6.EOC04** Adaptation of figure 3.2 from *Human Anatomy and Physiology*, 8th Edition, by Elaine N. Marieb and Katja N. Hoehn, 2010. Copyright © 2010 by Pearson Education, Inc. Reprinted and electronically reproduced by permission of Pearson Education, Inc. Upper Saddle River, New Jersey.

Chapter 7 7.4 Source: Based on "The Rapid Intermixing of Cell Surface Antigens After Formation of Mouse-Human Heterokaryons" by L. D. Frye and M. Edidin, from *Journal of Cell Science*, September 1970, Volume 7; **7.6** Source: Protein Data Bank ID 3HAO: "Similar Energetic Contributions of Packing in the Core of Membrane and Water-Soluble Proteins" by Nathan H. Joh et al., from *Journal of the American Chemical Society*, Volume 131(31); **7 SSE** Adaptation of Figure 1 from "Developmental Changes in Glucose Transport of Guinea Pig Erythrocytes" by Takahito Kondo and Ernest Beutler, from *Journal of Clinical Investigation*, January 1980, Volume 65(1). Copyright © by American Society for Clinical Investigation. Permission to reprint conveyed through Copyright Clearance Center, Inc.

Chapter 8 8 SSE Source: Data from "Diets Enriched in Sucrose or Fat Increase Gluconeogenesis and G-6-Pase but Not Basal Glucose Production in Rats" by S. R. Commerford et al., from *American Journal of Physiology–Endocrinology and Metabolism*, September 2002, Volume 283(3); **8.19** Source: Protein Data Bank ID 3e1f: "Direct and Indirect Roles of His-418 in Metal Binding and in the Activity of Beta-Galactosidase (*E. coli*)" by Douglas H. Juers et al., from *Protein Science*, June 2009, Volume 18(6); **8.20** Source: Protein Data Bank ID 1MDYO: "Crystal Structure of MyoD bHLH Domain-DNA Complex: Perspectives on DNA Recognition and Implications for Transcriptional Activation" from *Cell*, May 1994, Volume 77(3); **8.22** Adaptation of figure 3.2 from *Human Anatomy and Physiology*, 8th Edition, by Elaine N. Marieb and Katja N. Hoehn, 2010. Copyright © 2010 by Pearson Education, Inc. Reprinted and electronically reproduced by permission of Pearson Education, Inc. Upper Saddle River, New Jersey.

Chapter 9 9.5 Adaptation of figure 2.69 from *Molecular Biology of the Cell*, 4th Edition, by Bruce Alberts et al. Copyright © 2002 by Garland Science/Taylor & Francis

LLC. Reprinted with permission; **9.9** Figure adapted from *Biochemistry*, 4th Edition, by Christopher K. Mathews et al. Copyright 2013 by Pearson Education, Inc. Adapted and electronically reproduced by permission of Pearson Education, Inc., Upper Saddle River, New Jersey; **9 SSE** Source: Data from "The Quantitative Contributions of Mitochondrial Proton Leak and ATP Turnover Reactions to the Changed Respiration Rates of Hepatocytes from Rats of Different Thyroid Status" by Mary-Ellen Harper and Martin D. Brand, from *Journal of Biological Chemistry*, July 1993, Volume 268(20); **p. 184 Quote** Source: Pharmavite LLC., 2012.

Chapter 10 10.10 Source: Based on "*Bacterium photometricum. Ein Beitrag zur vergteiehenden Physiologie des Licht- und Farbensinnes*" by Theodore W. Engelmann, from *Archive Für Die Gesamte Physiologie Des Menschen Und Der Tiere*, 1883, Volume 30(1); **10.13b** Adaptation of figure 1a from "Architecture of the Photosynthetic Oxygen-Evolving Center" by Kristina N. Ferreira et al., from *Science*, March 2004, Volume 303(5665). Copyright © 2004 by AAAS. Reprinted with permission; **10.15** Adaptation of Figure 4.1 from *Energy, Plants, and Man*, by Richard Walker and David Alan Walker. Copyright © 1992 by Richard Walker and David Alan Walker. Reprinted with permission of Richard Walker; **10 SSE** Source: Data from "Potential Effects of Global Atmospheric CO_2 Enrichment on the Growth and Competitiveness of C_3 and C_4 Weed and Crop Plants" by D. T. Patterson and E. P. Flint, from *Weed Science*, 1980, Volume 28.

Chapter 11 11.8 *The World of the Cell*, 3rd Edition, by Wayne M. Becker, Jane B. Reece, and Martin F. Poenie. Copyright © 1996 by Pearson Education. Reprinted and electronically reproduced by permission of Pearson Education, Inc., Upper Saddle River, New Jersey; **11.12** Figure adapted from *The World of the Cell*, 3rd Edition, by Wayne M. Becker, Jane B. Reece, and Martin F. Poenie. Copyright © 1996 by Pearson Education, Inc. Adapted and electronically reproduced by permission of Pearson Education, Inc., Upper Saddle River, New Jersey; **p. 232 Quote** Source: Rudolf Virchow.

Chapter 12 12.9 Source: Based on "Chromosomes Move Poleward in Anaphase along Stationary Microtubules That Coordinately Disassemble from Their Kinetochore Ends" by Gary J. Gorbsky et al., from *Journal of Cell Biology*, January 1987, Volume 104(1); **12.13** Adaptation of figure 18.41 from *Molecular Biology of the Cell*, 4th Edition, by Bruce Alberts et al. Copyright © 2002 by Garland Science/Taylor & Francis LLC. Reprinted with permission; **12.14** Source: Based on "Mammalian Cell Fusion: Induction of Premature Chromosome Condensation in Interphase Nuclei" by R. T. Johnson and P. N. Rao, from *Nature*, May 1970, Volume 226(5247); **12 SSE** Adaptation of Figure 3A from "Regulation of Glioblastoma Progression by Cord Blood Stem Cells Is Mediated by Downregulation of Cyclin D1" by Kiran K. Velpula et al., from PLoS ONE, March 24, 2011, Volume 6(3). Copyright © 2011 by Kiran K. Velpula et al. Article is open-access and distributed under the terms of the Creative Commons Attribution License, which permits unrestricted use, distribution, and reproduction in any medium, provided the original author and source are credited.

Chapter 14 14.3 Source: Based on "Experiments in Plant Hybridization" by Gregor Mendel, from *Proceedings of the Natural History Society of Brunn*, 1866, Volume 4; **14.8** Source: Based on "Experiments in Plant Hybridization" by Gregor Mendel, from *Proceedings of the Natural History Society of Brunn*, 1866, Volume 4; **p. 294 Quote** Source: Thomas Hunt Morgan quoted in "Embryology and Its Relations" by Ross G. Harrison, from *Science*, April 16, 1937, Volume 85(2207).

Chapter 15 15.4 Source: Based on "Sex Limited Inheritance in *Drosophila*" by Thomas Hunt Morgan, from *Science*, New Series, July 1910, Volume 32(812); **15.9** Source: Based on "The Linkage of Two Factors in *Drosophila* That Are Not Sex-Linked" by Thomas Hunt Morgan and Clara J. Lynch, from *Biological Bulletin*, August 1912, Volume 23(3).

Chapter 16 16.2 Source: Based on "The Significance of Pneumococcal Types" by Fred Griffith, from *Journal of Hygiene*, January 1928, Volume 27(2); **16.4** Source: Based on "Independent Functions of Viral Protein and Nucleic Acid in Growth of Bacteriophage" by Alfred D. Hershey and Martha Chase, from *Journal of General Physiology*, May 1952, Volume 36(1); **16 SSE** Source: Data from "Composition of the Desoxypentose Nucleic Acids of Four Genera of Sea-urchin" by Erwin Chargaff et al., from *Biochemistry*, 1952, Volume 195; **p. 318 Quote** Source: "Molecular Structure of Nucleic Acids: A Structure for Deoxyribose Nucleic Acid" by James D. Watson and Francis H. Crick, from *Nature*, April 1953, Volume 171(4356); **p. 318 Quote** Source: J. D. Watson and F. H. C. Crick, Genetical implications of the structure of deoxyribonucleic acid, *Nature* 171:964–967 (1953); **16.11** Source: Based on "The Replication of DNA in *Escherichia coli*" by Matthew Meselson and Franklin W. Stahl, from PNAS, July 1958, Volume 44(7).

Chapter 17 17.2 Source: Based on "The Ornithine Cycle in Neurospora and Its Genetic Control" by Adrian M. Srb and N. H. Horowitz, from *Biochemistry*, June 1944, Volume 154(1); **17.11** *The World of the Cell*, 3rd Edition, by Wayne M. Becker, Jane B. Reece, and Martin F. Poenie. Copyright © 1996 by Pearson Education. Reprinted and electronically reproduced by permission of Pearson Education, Inc., Upper Saddle River, New Jersey; **17.13** *Principles of Cell and Molecular Biology*, 2nd Edition, by Lewis J. Kleinsmith and Valerie M. Kish. Copyright © 1995 by Pearson Education. Reprinted and electronically reproduced by permission of Pearson Education, Inc., Upper Saddle River, New Jersey; **17 SSE** Material provided courtesy of Dr. Thomas Schneider, National Cancer Institute, National Institutes of Health, 2012.

Chapter 18 18 SSE Source: Based on "Regulation of Human Microsomal Prostaglandin E Synthase-1 Requires a Distal Enhancer Element with a Unique Role for C/EBPb" by Jewell N. Walters et al., from *Biochemical Journal*, April 15, 2012, Volume 443(2); **18.26** Figure adapted from *The World of the Cell*, 3rd Edition, by Wayne M. Becker, Jane B. Reece, and Martin F. Poenie. Copyright © 1996 by Pearson Education, Inc. Adapted and electronically reproduced by permission of Pearson Education, Inc., Upper Saddle River, New Jersey.

Chapter 19 19.2 Source: Based on "Concerning a Contagium Vivum Fluidum as Cause of the Spot Disease of Tobacco Leaves" by M. W. Beijerinck, from *Verhandelingen Der Koninkyke Akademie Wettenschappen Te Amsterdam*, 1898, Volume 65. Translation published in English as *Phytopathological Classics*, Number 7. American Phytopathological Society Press, 1942; **19 SSE 01** Adaptation of Figure 2B from "New Variants and Age Shift to High Fatality Groups Contribute to Severe Successive

Waves in the 2009 Influenza Pandemic in Taiwan" by Ji-Rong Yang et al., from PLOS ONE, November 30, 2011, Volume 6(11). Copyright © 2011 Yang et al. This is an open-access article distributed under the terms of the Creative Commons Attribution License, which permits unrestricted use, distribution, and reproduction in any medium, provided the original author and source are credited; **19 SSE 02** Adaptation of Figure 3A from "New Variants and Age Shift to High Fatality Groups Contribute to Severe Successive Waves in the 2009 Influenza Pandemic in Taiwan" by Ji-Rong Yang et al., from PLOS ONE, November 30, 2011, Volume 6(11). Copyright © 2011 Yang et al. This is an open-access article distributed under the terms of the Creative Commons Attribution License, which permits unrestricted use, distribution, and reproduction in any medium, provided the original author and source are credited.

Chapter 20 **20.8** Figure adapted from *The World of the Cell*, 3rd Edition, by Wayne M. Becker, Jane B. Reece, and Martin F. Poenie. Copyright © 1996 by Pearson Education, Inc. Adapted and electronically reproduced by permission of Pearson Education, Inc., Upper Saddle River, New Jersey; **20 SSE** Source: Data from "A Regulatory Archipelago Controls Hox Genes Transcription in Digits" by Thomas Montavon et al., from CELL, November 23, 2011, Volume 147(5); **20.16** Source: Based on "The Developmental Capacity of Nuclei Transplanted from Keratinized Skin Cells of Adult Frogs" by John B. Gurdon et al., from *Journal of Embryology and Experimental Morphology*, August 1975, Volume 34(1).

Chapter 21 **21.3** Source: Simulated screen shots based on Mac OS X and from data found at NCBI, U.S. National Library of Medicine using Conserved Domain Database, Sequence Alignment Viewer, and Cn3D; **21.8** Figure adapted from *The World of the Cell*, 3rd Edition, by Wayne M. Becker, Jane B. Reece, and Martin F. Poenie. Copyright © 1996 by Pearson Education, Inc. Adapted and electronically reproduced by permission of Pearson Education, Inc., Upper Saddle River, New Jersey; **21.9** Figure adapted from *The World of the Cell*, 3rd Edition, by Wayne M. Becker, Jane B. Reece, and Martin F. Poenie. Copyright © 1996 by Pearson Education, Inc. Adapted and electronically reproduced by permission of Pearson Education, Inc., Upper Saddle River, New Jersey; **21 SSE and 21.Un01** Source: Data from the NCBI database; **21.18b** Adapted from figure 4(c) in "Altered Ultrasonic Vocalization in Mice with a Disruption in the *Foxp2* Gene" by Weiguo Shu et al., from PNAS, July 2005, Volume 102(27). Copyright © 2005 by National Academy of Sciences, U.S.A. Reprinted with permission; **21.20** Adaptation of figure 3 from "Hox Genes and the Evolution of Diverse Body Plans" by Michael Akam, from *Philosophical Transactions of the Royal Society B: Biological Sciences*, September 29, 1995, Volume 349(1329): 313–319. Copyright © 1995 by the Royal Society. Reprinted with permission.

Chapter 22 **22.8** Figure adapted from artwork by Utako Kikutani (as appeared in "What Can Make a Four-Ton Mammal a Most Sensitive Beast?" by Jeheskel Shoshani, from *Natural History*, November 1997, Volume 106(1), 36–45). Copyright © 1997 by Utako Kikutani. Reprinted with permission of the artist; **22.13b** Adaptation of Figure 4 from "Host Race Radiation in the Soapberry Bug: Natural History with the History" by Scott P. Carroll and Christin Boyd, from *Evolution*, 1992, Volume 46(4). Copyright © 1992 by Society for the Study of Evolution. Reprinted with permission of John Wiley & Sons Ltd. Adaptation of Figure 6.11 from *Ecology* by Michael L. Cain et al. Copyright © 2008 by Sinauer Associates, Inc. Reprinted with permission; **22.14a** Figure created by Dr. Binh Diep on request of Michael Cain. Copyright © 2011 by Binh Diep. Reprinted with permission; **22.14b** Source: Based on Figure 1 of "Statistical Brief #35: Infections with Methicillin-Resistant *Staphylococcus aureus* (MRSA) in U.S. Hospitals, 1993–2005" by Anne Elixhauser and Claudia Steiner. Healthcare Cost and Utilization Project. Agency for Healthcare Research and Quality, 2007; **22 SSE** Graphs adapted from Figure 4 of "Natural Selection on Color Patterns in *Poecilia reticulata*" by John A. Endler, from *Evolution*, January 1980, Volume 34(1). Copyright © 1980 by Society for the Study of Evolution. Reprinted with permission of John Wiley & Sons Ltd.; **Question 7 Table** Source: Data from "Selection for and Against Insecticide Resistance and Possible Methods of Inhibiting the Evolution of Resistance in Mosquitoes" by C. F. Curtis et al., from *Ecological Entomology*, November 1978, Volume 3(4).

Chapter 23 **23.4** Source: Data from figure 9.14 of *Evolution*, 1st edition, by Douglas J. Futuyma. Sinauer Associates, 2006; and "Nucleotide Polymorphism at the Alcohol Dehydrogenase Locus of *Drosophila melanogaster*" by Martin Kreitman, from *Nature*, August 1983, Volume 304(5925); **23.11a** Adaptation of figure 20.6 (maps only) from *Discover Biology*, 2nd Edition, edited by Michael L. Cain, Hans Damman, Robert A. Lue, and Carol Kaesuk Loon. Copyright © 2002 by Sinauer Associates, Inc. Adapted with permission of W. W. Norton & Company, Inc.; **23.12** Figure adapted from "Gene Flow Maintains a Large Genetic Difference in Clutch Size at a Small Spatial Scale" by Erik Postma and Arie van Noordwijk, from *Nature*, January 6, 2005, Volume 433(7021). Copyright © 2005 by Macmillan Publishers Ltd. Reprinted with permission; **23.14** Sources: Based on many sources including figure 11.3 from *Evolution* by Douglas J. Futuyma. Sinauer Associates 2005; and *Vertebrate Paleontology and Evolution* by Robert L. Carroll. W.H. Freeman & Co. 1988; **23.16** Source: Based on "Call Duration as an Indicator of Genetic Quality in Male Gray Tree Frogs" by Allison M. Welch, Raymond D. Semlitsch, and H. Carl Gerhardt, from *Science*, June 19, 2008, Volume 280(5371); **23.18** Adaptation of figure 2(A) from "Frequency-Dependent Natural Selection in the Handedness of Scale-Eating Cichlid Fish" by Michio Hori, from *Science*, April 1993, Volume 260(5105). Copyright © 1993 by AAAS. Reprinted with permission; **23.EOC03 Question 7** Source: Data from "The Adaptive Importance of Genetic Variance" by Richard K. Koehn and Thomas J. Hilbish, from *American Scientist*, March–April 1987, Volume 75(2).

Chapter 24 **24.6** Adaptation of Figure 3 from "Ecological Speciation in *Gambusia* Fishes" by R. B. Langerhans et al., from *Evolution*, September 2007, Volume 61(9). Copyright © 2007 by Society for the Study of Evolution. Reprinted with permission of John Wiley & Sons Ltd.; **24.7** Source: Based on "Reproductive Isolation as a Consequence of Adaptive Divergence in *Drosophila pseudoobscura*" by Diane M. B. Dodd, from *Evolution*, September 1989, Volume 43(6); **24 SSE** Source: Data from "Correspondence between Sexual Isolation and Allozyme Differentiation: A Test in the Salamander *Desmognathus ochrophaeus*" by Stephen G. Tilley et al., from PNAS, April 1990, Volume 87(7); **24.11** Source: Based on "The Effect of Male Coloration on Female Mate Choice in Closely Related Lake Victoria Cichlids (*Haplochromis nyererei* Complex)" by Ole Seehausen and Jacques J. M. van Alpen, from *Behavioral Ecology*

and Sociobiology, 1998, Volume 42(1); **24.12** Adaptation of figure 10.8 from *Hybrid Zone and the Evolutionary Process*, edited by Richard G. Harrison. Copyright © 1993 by Oxford University Press. Reprinted with permission; **24.14** Adaptation of Figure 2 from "A Sexually Selected Character Displacement in Flycatchers Reinforces Premating Isolation" by Glenn-Peter Saetre et al., from *Nature*, June 1997, Volume 387(6633). Copyright © 1997 by Macmillan Publishers Ltd. Reprinted with permission; **24.18b** Adaptation of figure 2 from "Role of Gene Interactions in Hybrid Speciation: Evidence from Ancient and Experimental Hybrids" by Loren H. Rieseberg et al., from *Science*, May 1996, Volume 272(5262). Copyright © 1996 by AAAS. Reprinted with permission.

Chapter 25 **25.2** Source: Data from "The Miller Volcanic Spark Discharge Experiment" by Adam P. Johnson et al., from *Science*, October 2008, Volume 322(5900); **25.4a** Figure adapted from "Experimental Models of Primitive Cellular Compartments: Encapsulation, Growth, and Division" by Martin M. Hanczyc, Shelly M. Fujikawa, and Jack W. Szostak from *Science*, October 2003, Volume 302(5645). Copyright © 2003 by AAAS. Reprinted with permission; **25.6** Figure adapted from *Geological Time*, 2nd Edition, by Don L. Eicher. Copyright © 1976 by Pearson Education, Inc. Adapted and electronically reproduced by permission of Pearson Education, Inc., Upper Saddle River, New Jersey; **25.7a–d** Sources: Based on many sources including figure 4.10 from *Evolution*, by Douglas J. Futuyma. Sinauer Associates 2005; and *Vertebrate Paleontology and Evolution* by Robert L. Carroll. W.H. Freeman & Co. 1988; **25.7e** Figure adapted from "A New Mammaliaform from the Early Jurassic and Evolution of Mammalian Characteristics" by Zhe-Xi Luo, Alfred W. Crompton, and Ai-Lin Sun from *Science*, May 2001, Volume 292(5521). Copyright © 2001 by AAAS. Reprinted with permission; **25.8** Source: Adapted from "When Did Photosynthesis Emerge on Earth?" by David J. Des Marais, from *Science*, September 2000, Volume 289(5485); **25.9** Adaptation of Figure 2 from "The Rise of Atmospheric Oxygen" by Lee R. Kump, from *Nature*, January 2008, Volume 451(7176). Copyright © 2008 by Macmillan Publishers Ltd. Reprinted with permission; **25 SSE** Adaptation of figure 1 from "Larval Dispersal and Species Longevity in Lower Tertiary Gastropods" by Thor A. Hansen, from *Science*, February 1978, Volume 199(4331). Copyright © 1978 by AAAS. Reprinted with permission; **25.15** Source: Based on *Earthquake Information Bulletin*, December 1977, Volume 9(6), edited by Henry Spall; **25.17** Adaptation of figures 1 and 2 from "Mass Extinctions in the Marine Fossil Record" by David M. Raup and J. John Sepkoski, Jr., from *Science*, March 1982, Volume 215(4539). Figure also based on: Figure 1 from "A Kinetic Model of Phanerozoic Taxonomic Diversity. III. Post-Paleozoic Families and Mass Extinctions" by J. John Sepkoski, Jr., from *Paleobiology* Volume 10(2); and Figures 7.3a and 7.6 from *Evolution*, by Douglas J. Futuyma. Sinauer Associates, Inc., 2006; **25.19** Adaptation of Figure 3b from "A Long-Term Association between Global Temperature and Biodiversity, Origination and Extinction in the Fossil Record" by Peter J. Mayhew et al., from *Proceedings of the Royal Society B: Biological Sciences*, January 2008, Volume 275(1630): 47–53. Copyright © 2008 by the Royal Society. Reprinted with permission; **25.20** Adaptation of Figure 3 from "Anatomical and Ecological Constraints on Phanerozoic Animal Diversity in the Marine Realm" by Richard K. Bambach et al., from PNAS, May 2002, Volume 99(10). Copyright © 2002 by National Academy of Sciences. Reprinted with permission; **25.25** Adaptation of Figure 1a from "Hox Protein Mutation and Macroevolution of the Insect Body Plan" by Matthew Ronshaugen et al., from *Nature*, February 2002, Volume 415(6874). Copyright © 2002 by Macmillan Publishers Ltd. Reprinted with permission; **25.26** Source: Based on "Genetic and Developmental Basis of Evolutionary Pelvic Reduction in Threespine Sticklebacks" by Michael D. Shapiro et al., from *Nature*, April 2004, Volume 428(6984); **25.28** Adaptations of figure 3-1(a–d, f) from *Evolution*, 3rd Edition, by Monroe W. Strickberger. Copyright © 2005 by Jones & Bartlett Learning, Burlington, MA. Adapted with permission.

Chapter 26 **26.6** Adaptation of Figure 1 from "Which Whales Are Hunted? A Molecular Genetic Approach to Monitoring Whaling" by C. S. Baker and S. R. Palumbi, from *Science*, September 1994, Volume 265(5178). Copyright © 1994 by AAAS. Reprinted with permission; **26.13** Source: Based on Figure 3 from "The Evolution of the Hedgehog Gene Family in Chordates: Insights from Amphioxus Hedgehog" by Sebastian M. Shimeld, from *Developmental Genes and Evolution*, January 1999, Volume 209(1); **26.19** Adaptation of figure 4.3C from *Molecular Markers, Natural History, and Evolution*, 2nd Edition, by John C. Avise. Copyright © 2004 by Sinauer Associates, Inc. Reprinted with permission; **26.20** Adaptation of figure 1b from "Timing the Ancestor of the HIV-1 Pandemic Strains" by B. Korber et al., from *Science*, June 2000, Volume 288(5472). Copyright © 2000 by AAAS. Reprinted with permission; **26 SSE** Source: Based on "Lateral Transfer of Genes from Fungi Underlies Carotenoid Production in Aphids" by Nancy A. Moran and Tyler Jarvik, from *Science*, April 30, 2010, Volume 328(5978); **26.23** Adaptation of figure 3 from "Phylogenetic Classification and the Universal Tree" by W. Ford Doolittle, from *Science*, June 1999, Volume 284(5423). Copyright © 1999 by AAAS. Reprinted with permission.

Chapter 27 **27.10b** Adaptation of Figure 1 from "The Population Genetics of Ecological Specialization in Evolving *Escherichia coli* Populations" by Vaughn S. Cooper and Richard E. Lenski, from *Nature*, October 12, 2000, Volume 407(679). Copyright © 2000 by Macmillan Publishers Ltd. Reprinted with permission; **27.18** Source: Data from "Root-Associated Bacteria Contribute to Mineral Weathering and to Mineral Nutrition in Trees: A Budgeting Analysis" by Christophe Calvaruso et al., *Applied and Environmental Microbiology*, February 2006, Volume 72(2); **27.UnTable01** Source: Data from "Variation in the Effectiveness of Symbiotic Associations between Native Rhizobia and Temperate Australian *Acacia*: Within-Species Interactions" by J. J. Burdon et al., from *Journal of Applied Ecology*, June 1999, Volume 36(3); **p. 587 Quote** Source: *The Collected Letters of Antoni Van Leeuwenhoek* by Antoni van Leeuwenhoek, edited by a Committee of Dutch scientists. Swets & Zeitlinger, 1939.

Chapter 47 **47.4** Source: Based on "Intracellular Calcium Release at Fertilization in the Sea Urchin Egg" by R. Steinhardt et al., from *Developmental Biology*, July 1977, Volume 58(1); **47.10(b) and 47.14** Figures adapted from "Cell Commitment and Gene Expression in the Axolotl Embryo" by T. J. Mohun, et al., from *Cell*, November 1980, Volume 22(1); **47.17** Adaptation from figure 1.9 and Box 8c from *Principles of Development*, 4th Edition, by Lewis Wolpert. Copyright © 2011 by Oxford University Press. Reprinted with permission; **47.19** Adaptation of figure 21.17 from *Molecular Biology of the Cell*, 4th Edition, by Bruce Alberts et al. Copyright © 2002 by Garland

Science/Taylor & Francis LLC. Reprinted with permission; **47.23** Source: Based on *Embryonic Development and Induction* by Hans Spemann. Yale University Press, 1938; **47.24a, b** Adaptation from figure 1.9 and Box 8c from *Principles of Development*, 4th Edition, by Lewis Wolpert. Copyright © 2011 by Oxford University Press. Reprinted with permission; **47.24b** Adaptation of Figure 15.12 from *Developmental Biology* by Scott F. Gilbert. Copyright © 1997 by Sinauer Associates, Inc. Reprinted with permission; **47.26** Source: Based on "Maps of Strength of Positional Signalling Activity in the Developing Chick Wing Bud" by Lawrence S. Honig and Dennis Summerbell, from *Journal of Embryology and Experimental Morphology*, June 1985, Volume 87(1); **47.27** Figure adapted from *Human Anatomy and Physiology*, 8th Edition, by Elaine N. Marieb and Katja Hoehn. Copyright © 2010 by Pearson Education, Inc. Adapted and electronically reproduced by permission of Pearson Education, Inc., Upper Saddle River, New Jersey.

Chapter 52 52.7 Adaptation of figure 2 from "How Fast Can Trees Migrate?" by Leslie Roberts, from *Science*, February 1989, Volume 243(4892). Copyright © 1989 by AAAS. Reprinted with permission; **52.17** Sources: Based on figure 11.19 from *Ecology and Field Biology* by Robert L. Smith. Pearson Education, 1974; and *Sibley Guide to Birds* by David Allen Sibley. Random House, 2000; **52.18** Source: Data from "Interactions Among Subtidal Australian Sea Urchins, Gastropods, and Algae: Effects of Experimental Removals" by W. J. Fletcher, from *Ecological Monographs*, March 1987, Volume 57(1); **52 SSE** Source: Data from "Physical and Biotic Drivers of Plant Distribution across 116 Estuarine Salinity Gradients" by Caitlin M Crain et al., from *Ecology*, September 2004, Volume 85(9); **52.EOC02** Source: Data from *Experimental Studies on the Nature of Species: Iii: Environmental Responses of Climatic Races of Achillea* by Jens C. Clausen et al. Carnegie Institution of Washington, 1948.

Chapter 53 53.2 Source: Based on "Capture-Recapture Estimates of Hector's Dolphin Abundance at Banks Peninsula, New Zealand" by Andrew M. Gormley et al., from *Marine Mammal Science*, April 2005, Volume 21(2); **Table 53.1** Source: Data from "Demography of Belding's Ground Squirrels" by Paul W. Sherman and Martin L. Morton, from *Ecology*, October 1984, Volume 65(5); **Table 53.2** Adaptation of figure 1a from "Demography of Belding's Ground Squirrels" by Paul W. Sherman and Martin L. Morton, from *Ecology*, October 1984, Volume 65(5). Copyright © 1984 by Ecological Society of America. Reprinted with permission; **Table 53.2** Source: Data from "Demography of Belding's Ground Squirrels" by Paul W. Sherman and Martin L. Morton, from *Ecology*, October 1984, Volume 65(5); **53.14** Source: Based on "Brood Size Manipulations in the Kestrel (*Falco tinnunculus*): Effects on Offspring and Parent Survival" by C. Dijkstra et al., from *Journal of Animal Ecology*, 1990, Volume 59(1); **53.16** Figure adapted from "Climate and Population Regulation: The Biogeographer's Dilemma" by J. T. Enright, from Oecologia, 1976, Volume 24(4). Copyright © 1976 by Springer. Reprinted with permission of Springer Science+Business Media; **53.19** Source: Data provided by Dr. Rolf O. Peterson; **53.22** Source: Based on U.S. Census Bureau International Data Base; **53.23** Source: Data from U.S. Census Bureau International Data Base; **53.24** Source: Data from U.S. Census Bureau International Data Base; **53.26** Adaptation of map from *Vital Waste Graphics 2* by Emmanuelle Bournay and Claudia Heberlein. UNEP-GRID/Arendal, 2006. Used by permission.

Chapter 54 54.2 Adaptation of figure 1 from "The Anoles of La Palma: Aspects of Their Ecological Relationships" by A. Stanley Rand and Ernest E. Williams, from BREVIORA, Volume 327: 1–19. Copyright © 1969 by Museum of Comparative Zoology, Harvard University. Reprinted with permission; **54.3** Source: Based on "The Influence of Interspecific Competition and Other Factors on the Distribution of the Barnacle *Chthamalus stellatus*" by Joseph H. Connell, from *Ecology*, October 1961, Volume 42(4); **54 SSE** Source: Data from "An Invasive Species Induces Rapid Adaptive Change in a Native Predator: Cane Toads and Black Snakes in Australia" by Ben L. Phillips and Richard Shine, *Proceedings of the Royal Society B: Biological Sciences*, June 22, 2006, Volume (273)1593; **54.10** Source: Data from "Experimental Evidence for Factors Maintaining Plant Species Diversity in a New England Salt Marsh" by Sally D. Hacker and Mark D. Bertness, from *Ecology*, September 1999, Volume 80(6); **54.12** Adaptation of Figure 1A from "The Diversity and Biogeography of Soil Bacterial Communities" by Noah Fierer and Robert B. Jackson, from PNAS, January 2006, Volume 103(3). Copyright © 2006 by National Academy of Sciences. Reprinted with permission; **54.15** Source: Based on "Antarctic Marine Ecosystems" by George A. Knox, from *Antarctic Ecology*, Volume 1, edited by Martin W. Holdgate. Academic Press, 1970; **54.16** Figure adapted from "Varying Effects of Low Dissolved Oxygen on Trophic Interactions in an Estuarine Food Web" by Denise L. Breitburg et al., from *Ecological Monographs*, November 1997, Volume 67(4). Copyright © 1997 by Ecological Society

of America. Reprinted with permission; **54.17** Source: Based on "Productivity, Disturbance and Food Web Structure at a Local Spatial Scale in Experimental Container Habitats" by B. Jenkins et al., from OIKOS, November 1992, Volume 65(2); **54.18b** Source: Based on "Food Web Complexity and Species Diversity" by Robert T. Paine, from *The American Naturalist*, January-February 1966, Volume 100(910); **54.20** Adaptation of figure 2a from "The Intermediate Disturbance Hypothesis, Refugia, and Biodiversity in Streams" by Colin R. Townsend et al., from *Limnology and Oceanography*, 1997, Volume 42(5): 944. Copyright © 1997 by Association for the Sciences of Limnology and Oceanography, Inc.; **54.22** Source: Based on "Soil Development in Relation to Vegetation and Surface Age at Glacier Bay, Alaska" by Robert L. Crocker and Jack Major, from *Journal of Ecology*, July 1955, Volume 43(2); **54.23** Adaptation of figure 6(e) from "Mechanisms of Primary Succession Following Deglaciation at Glacier Bay" by F. Stuart Chapin et al., from *Ecological Monographs*, May 1994, Volume 64(2). Copyright © 1994 by the Ecological Society of America. Reprinted with permission; **54.25** Adaptation of Figure 7 from " Energy and Large-Scale Patterns of Animal- and Plant-Species Richness" by D. J. Currie, from *American Naturalist*, January 1991, Volume 137(1): 27–49. Copyright © 1991 by the University of Chicago Press. Reprinted with permission; **54.26** Adaptation of figure 1 from "An Equilibrium Theory of Insular Zoogeography" by Robert H. MacArthur and Edward O. Wilson, from *Evolution*, December 1963, Volume 17(4). Copyright © 1963 by Society for the Study of Evolution. Reprinted with permission of John Wiley & Sons Ltd.

Chapter 55 55.4, 55.EOC01 Source: Based on figure 1.2 from *Dynamics of Nutrient Cycling and Food Webs* by Donald L. DeAngelis. Taylor & Francis, 1992; **55.7** Figure adapted from "Argo Operation," from Southampton Oceanography Centre website, June 10, 2002. Copyright © 2002 by University of Southampton, National Oceanographic Centre. Reprinted with permission; **55.8** Adaptation of figure 2 from "Nitrogen, Phosphorus, and Eutrophication in the Coastal Marine Environment" by John H. Ryther and William M. Dunstan, from *Science*, March 1971, Volume 171(3975). Copyright © 1971 by AAAS. Reprinted with permission; **55.9** Figure adapted from *Communities and Ecosystems*, 1st Edition, by Robert H. Whittaker. Copyright © 1970 by Pearson Education, Inc. Adapted and electronically reproduced by permission of Pearson Education, Inc., Upper Saddle River, New Jersey; **55 SSE** Source: Data from "Energy Flow in the Salt Marsh Ecosystem of Georgia" by John M. Teal, from *Ecology*, October 1962, Volume 43(4); **55.14** Adaptation of figure 7.4 from *The Economy of Nature*, 5th edition, by Robert E. Ricklefs. Copyright © 2001 by W.H. Freeman and Company. Reprinted with permission; **55.15a** Figure adapted from "The Canadian Intersite Decomposition Experiment: Project and Site Establishment Report" (Information Report BC-X-378) by J. A. Trofymow and the CIDET Working Group. Copyright © 1998 by Natural Resources Canada, Canadian Forest Service, Pacific Forestry Centre; and "Ecoclimatic Regions of Canada," from *Ecological Land Classification Series*, Number 23, Copyright © 1989 by Environment Canada. Reprinted with permission from the Minister of Public Works and Government Services, Canada, 2013; **55.15b** Adaptation of figure 2 from "Litter Decomposition Rates in Canadian Forests" by T. R. Moore, from *Global Change Biology*, January 1999, Volume 5(1). Copyright © 1999 by John Wiley & Sons Ltd. Reprinted with permission; **p. 1257 Quote** Source: "The Scientific Underpinning of Policy" by Gro Harlem Brundtland, from *Science*, July 1997, Volume 277(5325);

Chapter 56 56.13 *Ecology: The Experimental Analysis of Distribution and Abundance*, 5th Edition, by Charles J. Krebs. Copyright © 2001 by Pearson Education Inc. Adapted and electronically reproduced by permission of Pearson Education, Inc., Upper Saddle River, New Jersey; **56.14** Adaptation of Figure 2 from "Tracking the Long-Term Decline and Recovery of an Isolated Population" by Ronald L. Westemeier et al., from *Science*, November 1998, Volume 282(5394). Copyright © 1998 by AAAS. Reprinted with permission; **56.20** Adaptation of Figure 1 from "Biodiversity Hotspots for Conservation Priorities" by Norman Myers et al., from *Nature*, February 24, 2000, Volume 403(6772). Copyright © 2000 by Macmillan Publishers Ltd. Reprinted with permission; **56 SSE** Source: Earth System Research Laboratory, Global Monitoring Division. NOAA, 2012; **56.28** CO2 data from http://www.esrl.noaa.gov/gmd/ccgg/trends/mlo.html#mlo_full. Temperature data from http://data.giss.nasa.gov/gistemp/graphs_v3/ ; **56.29** Source: Data from "History of the Ozone Hole," from NASA website, February 26, 2013; and "Antarctic Ozone," from British Antarctic Society website, June 7, 2013; **56.31** Source: Ozone Hole Watch website. NASA, 2012; **56.32** Source: Data from Instituto Nacional de Estadistica y Censos de Costa Rica and Centro Centroamericano de Poblacion, Universidad de Costa Rica.

Pronunciation Key

ā	ace
a/ah	ash
ch	chose
ē	meet
e/eh	bet
g	game
ī	ice
i	hit
ks	box
kw	quick
ng	song
ō	robe
o	ox
oy	boy
s	say
sh	shell
th	thin
ū	boot
u/uh	up
z	zoo

′ = primary accent

′ = secondary accent

5′ cap A modified form of guanine nucleotide added onto the 5′ end of a pre-mRNA molecule.

ABC hypothesis A model of flower formation identifying three classes of organ identity genes that direct formation of the four types of floral organs.

abiotic (ā′-bī-ot′-ik) Nonliving; referring to the physical and chemical properties of an environment.

abortion The termination of a pregnancy in progress.

abscisic acid (ABA) (ab-sis′-ik) A plant hormone that slows growth, often antagonizing the actions of growth hormones. Two of its many effects are to promote seed dormancy and facilitate drought tolerance.

absorption The third stage of food processing in animals: the uptake of small nutrient molecules by an organism's body.

absorption spectrum The range of a pigment's ability to absorb various wavelengths of light; also a graph of such a range.

abyssal zone (uh-bis′-ul) The part of the ocean's benthic zone between 2,000 and 6,000 m deep.

acanthodian (ak′-an-thō′-dē-un) Any of a group of ancient jawed aquatic vertebrates from the Silurian and Devonian periods.

accessory fruit A fruit, or assemblage of fruits, in which the fleshy parts are derived largely or entirely from tissues other than the ovary.

acclimatization (uh-klī′-muh-tī-zā′-shun) Physiological adjustment to a change in an environmental factor.

acetyl CoA Acetyl coenzyme A; the entry compound for the citric acid cycle in cellular respiration, formed from a two-carbon fragment of pyruvate attached to a coenzyme.

acetylcholine (as′-uh-til-kō′-lēn) One of the most common neurotransmitters; functions by binding to receptors and altering the permeability of the postsynaptic membrane to specific ions, either depolarizing or hyperpolarizing the membrane.

acid A substance that increases the hydrogen ion concentration of a solution.

acoelomate (uh-sē′-lō-māt) A solid-bodied animal lacking a cavity between the gut and outer body wall.

acquired immunodeficiency syndrome (AIDS) The symptoms and signs present during the late stages of HIV infection, defined by a specified reduction in the number of T cells and the appearance of characteristic secondary infections.

acrosomal reaction (ak′-ruh-sōm′-ul) The discharge of hydrolytic enzymes from the acrosome, a vesicle in the tip of a sperm, when the sperm approaches or contacts an egg.

acrosome (ak′-ruh-sōm) A vesicle in the tip of a sperm containing hydrolytic enzymes and other proteins that help the sperm reach the egg.

actin (ak′-tin) A globular protein that links into chains, two of which twist helically about each other, forming microfilaments (actin filaments) in muscle and other kinds of cells.

action potential An electrical signal that propagates (travels) along the membrane of a neuron or other excitable cell as a nongraded (all-or-none) depolarization.

action spectrum A graph that profiles the relative effectiveness of different wavelengths of radiation in driving a particular process.

activation energy The amount of energy that reactants must absorb before a chemical reaction will start; also called free energy of activation.

activator A protein that binds to DNA and stimulates gene transcription. In prokaryotes, activators bind in or near the promoter; in eukaryotes, activators generally bind to control elements in enhancers.

active immunity Long-lasting immunity conferred by the action of B cells and T cells and the resulting B and T memory cells specific for a pathogen. Active immunity can develop as a result of natural infection or immunization.

active site The specific region of an enzyme that binds the substrate and that forms the pocket in which catalysis occurs.

active transport The movement of a substance across a cell membrane against its concentration or electrochemical gradient, mediated by specific transport proteins and requiring an expenditure of energy.

adaptation Inherited characteristic of an organism that enhances its survival and reproduction in a specific environment.

adaptive evolution Evolution that results in a better match between organisms and their environment.

adaptive immunity A vertebrate-specific defense that is mediated by B lymphocytes (B cells) and T lymphocytes (T cells) and that exhibits specificity, memory, and self-nonself recognition; also called acquired immunity.

adaptive radiation Period of evolutionary change in which groups of organisms form many new species whose adaptations allow them to fill different ecological roles in their communities.

addition rule A rule of probability stating that the probability of any one of two or more mutually exclusive events occurring can be determined by adding their individual probabilities.

adenosine triphosphate *See* ATP (adenosine triphosphate).

adenylyl cyclase (uh-den′-uh-lil) An enzyme that converts ATP to cyclic AMP in response to an extracellular signal.

adhesion The clinging of one substance to another, such as water to plant cell walls by means of hydrogen bonds.

adipose tissue A connective tissue that insulates the body and serves as a fuel reserve; contains fat-storing cells called adipose cells.

adrenal gland (uh-drē′-nul) One of two endocrine glands located adjacent to the kidneys in mammals. Endocrine cells in the outer portion (cortex) respond to adrenocorticotropic hormone (ACTH) by secreting steroid hormones that help maintain homeostasis during long-term stress. Neurosecretory cells in the central portion (medulla) secrete epinephrine and norepinephrine in response to nerve signals triggered by short-term stress.

aerobic respiration A catabolic pathway for organic molecules, using oxygen (O_2) as the final electron acceptor in an electron transport chain and ultimately producing ATP. This is the most efficient catabolic pathway and is carried out in most eukaryotic cells and many prokaryotic organisms.

age structure The relative number of individuals of each age in a population.

aggregate fruit A fruit derived from a single flower that has more than one carpel.

AIDS (acquired immunodeficiency syndrome) The symptoms and signs present during the late stages of HIV infection, defined by a specified reduction in the number of T cells and the appearance of characteristic secondary infections.

alcohol fermentation Glycolysis followed by the reduction of pyruvate to ethyl alcohol, regenerating NAD^+ and releasing carbon dioxide.

aldosterone (al-dos'-tuh-rōn) A steroid hormone that acts on tubules of the kidney to regulate the transport of sodium ions (Na^+) and potassium ions (K^+).

alga (plural, **algae**) A member of a diverse collection of photosynthetic protists that includes both unicellular and multicellular forms. Algal species are included in three eukaryote supergroups (Excavata, "SAR" clade, and Archaeplastida).

alimentary canal (al'-uh-men'-tuh-rē) A complete digestive tract, consisting of a tube running between a mouth and an anus.

alkaline vent A deep-sea hydrothermal vent that releases water that is warm (40–90°C) rather than hot and that has a high pH (is basic). These vents consist of tiny pores lined with iron and other catalytic minerals that some scientists hypothesize might have been the location of the earliest abiotic synthesis of organic compounds.

allele (uh-lē'-ul) Any of the alternative versions of a gene that may produce distinguishable phenotypic effects.

allopatric speciation (al'-uh-pat'-rik) The formation of new species in populations that are geographically isolated from one another.

allopolyploid (al'-ō-pol'-ē-ployd) A fertile individual that has more than two chromosome sets as a result of two different species interbreeding and combining their chromosomes.

allosteric regulation The binding of a regulatory molecule to a protein at one site that affects the function of the protein at a different site.

alpha (α) helix (al'-fuh hē'-liks) A coiled region constituting one form of the secondary structure of proteins, arising from a specific pattern of hydrogen bonding between atoms of the polypeptide backbone (not the side chains).

alternation of generations A life cycle in which there is both a multicellular diploid form, the sporophyte, and a multicellular haploid form, the gametophyte; characteristic of plants and some algae.

alternative RNA splicing A type of eukaryotic gene regulation at the RNA-processing level in which different mRNA molecules are produced from the same primary transcript, depending on which RNA segments are treated as exons and which as introns.

altruism (al'-trū-iz-um) Selflessness; behavior that reduces an individual's fitness while increasing the fitness of another individual.

alveolates (al-vē'-uh-lets) One of the three major subgroups for which the "SAR" eukaryotic supergroup is named. This clade arose by secondary endosymbiosis; alveolate protists have membrane-enclosed sacs (alveoli) located just under the plasma membrane.

alveolus (al-vē'-uh-lus) (plural, **alveoli**) One of the dead-end air sacs where gas exchange occurs in a mammalian lung.

Alzheimer's disease (alts'-hī-merz) An age-related dementia (mental deterioration) characterized by confusion and memory loss.

amino acid (uh-mēn'-ō) An organic molecule possessing both a carboxyl and an amino group. Amino acids serve as the monomers of polypeptides.

amino group (uh-mēn'-ō) A chemical group consisting of a nitrogen atom bonded to two hydrogen atoms; can act as a base in solution, accepting a hydrogen ion and acquiring a charge of 1+.

aminoacyl-tRNA synthetase An enzyme that joins each amino acid to the appropriate tRNA.

ammonia A small, toxic molecule (NH_3) produced by nitrogen fixation or as a metabolic waste product of protein and nucleic acid metabolism.

ammonite A member of a group of shelled cephalopods that were important marine predators for hundreds of millions of years until their extinction at the end of the Cretaceous period (65.5 million years ago).

amniocentesis (am'-nē-ō-sen-tē'-sis) A technique associated with prenatal diagnosis in which amniotic fluid is obtained by aspiration from a needle inserted into the uterus. The fluid and the fetal cells it contains are analyzed to detect certain genetic and congenital defects in the fetus.

amniote (am'-nē-ōt) A member of a clade of tetrapods named for a key derived character, the amniotic egg, which contains specialized membranes, including the fluid-filled amnion, that protect the embryo. Amniotes include mammals as well as birds and other reptiles.

amniotic egg An egg that contains specialized membranes that function in protection, nourishment, and gas exchange. The amniotic egg was a major evolutionary innovation, allowing embryos to develop on land in a fluid-filled sac, thus reducing the dependence of tetrapods on water for reproduction.

amoeba (uh-mē'-buh) A protist characterized by the presence of pseudopodia.

amoebocyte (uh-mē'-buh-sīt') An amoeba-like cell that moves by pseudopodia and is found in most animals. Depending on the species, it may digest and distribute food, dispose of wastes, form skeletal fibers, fight infections, or change into other cell types.

amoebozoan (uh-mē'-buh-zō'-an) A protist in a clade that includes many species with lobe- or tube-shaped pseudopodia.

amphibian A member of the clade of tetrapods that includes salamanders, frogs, and caecilians.

amphipathic (am'-fē-path'-ik) Having both a hydrophilic region and a hydrophobic region.

amplification The strengthening of stimulus energy during transduction.

amygdala (uh-mig'-duh-luh) A structure in the temporal lobe of the vertebrate brain that has a major role in the processing of emotions.

amylase (am'-uh-lās') An enzyme that hydrolyzes starch (a glucose polymer from plants) and glycogen (a glucose polymer from animals) into smaller polysaccharides and the disaccharide maltose.

anabolic pathway (an'-uh-bol'-ik) A metabolic pathway that consumes energy to synthesize a complex molecule from simpler molecules.

anaerobic respiration (an-er-ō'-bik) A catabolic pathway in which inorganic molecules other than oxygen accept electrons at the "downhill" end of electron transport chains.

analogous Having characteristics that are similar because of convergent evolution, not homology.

analogy (an-al'-uh-jē) Similarity between two species that is due to convergent evolution rather than to descent from a common ancestor with the same trait.

anaphase The fourth stage of mitosis, in which the chromatids of each chromosome have separated and the daughter chromosomes are moving to the poles of the cell.

anatomy The structure of an organism.

anchorage dependence The requirement that a cell must be attached to a substratum in order to initiate cell division.

androgen (an'-drō-jen) Any steroid hormone, such as testosterone, that stimulates the development and maintenance of the male reproductive system and secondary sex characteristics.

aneuploidy (an'-yū-ploy'-dē) A chromosomal aberration in which one or more chromosomes are present in extra copies or are deficient in number.

angiosperm (an'-jē-ō-sperm) A flowering plant, which forms seeds inside a protective chamber called an ovary.

angiotensin II A peptide hormone that stimulates constriction of precapillary arterioles and increases reabsorption of NaCl and water by the proximal tubules of the kidney, increasing blood pressure and volume.

anhydrobiosis (an-hī'-drō-bī-ō'-sis) A dormant state involving loss of almost all body water.

animal pole The point at the end of an egg in the hemisphere where the least yolk is concentrated; opposite of vegetal pole.

anion (an'-ī-on) A negatively charged ion.

anterior Pertaining to the front, or head, of a bilaterally symmetrical animal.

anterior pituitary A portion of the pituitary gland that develops from nonneural tissue; consists of endocrine cells that synthesize and secrete several tropic and nontropic hormones.

anther In an angiosperm, the terminal pollen sac of a stamen, where pollen grains containing sperm-producing male gametophytes form.

antheridium (an-thuh-rid'-ē-um) (plural, **antheridia**) In plants, the male gametangium, a moist chamber in which gametes develop.

anthropoid (an'-thruh-poyd) A member of a primate group made up of the monkeys and the apes (gibbons, orangutans, gorillas, chimpanzees, bonobos, and humans).

antibody A protein secreted by plasma cells (differentiated B cells) that binds to a particular antigen; also called immunoglobulin. All antibodies have the same Y-shaped structure and in their monomer form consist of two identical heavy chains and two identical light chains.

anticodon (an'-tī-kō'-don) A nucleotide triplet at one end of a tRNA molecule that base-pairs with a particular complementary codon on an mRNA molecule.

antidiuretic hormone (ADH) (an'-tī-dī-yū-ret'-ik) A peptide hormone, also called vasopressin, that promotes water retention by the kidneys. Produced in the hypothalamus and released from the posterior pituitary, ADH also functions in the brain.

antigen (an'-ti-jen) A substance that elicits an immune response by binding to receptors of B or T cells.

antigen presentation (an'-ti-jen) The process by which an MHC molecule binds to a fragment of an intracellular protein antigen and carries it to the cell surface, where it is displayed and can be recognized by a T cell.

antigen-presenting cell (an'-ti-jen) A cell that upon ingesting pathogens or internalizing pathogen proteins generates peptide fragments that are bound by class II MHC molecules and subsequently displayed on the cell surface to T cells. Macrophages, dendritic cells, and B cells are the primary antigen-presenting cells.

antigen receptor (an'-ti-jen) The general term for a surface protein, located on B cells and T cells, that binds to antigens, initiating adaptive immune responses. The antigen receptors on B cells are called B cell receptors, and the antigen receptors on T cells are called T cell receptors.

antiparallel Referring to the arrangement of the sugar-phosphate backbones in a DNA double helix (they run in opposite 5′ → 3′ directions).

aphotic zone (ā'-fō'-tik) The part of an ocean or lake beneath the photic zone, where light does not penetrate sufficiently for photosynthesis to occur.

apical bud (ā'-pik-ul) A bud at the tip of a plant stem; also called a terminal bud.

apical dominance (ā'-pik-ul) Tendency for growth to be concentrated at the tip of a plant shoot, because the apical bud partially inhibits axillary bud growth.

apical ectodermal ridge (AER) (ā'-pik-ul) A thickened area of ectoderm at the tip of a limb bud that promotes outgrowth of the limb bud.

apical meristem (ā'-pik-ul mār'-uh-stem) Embryonic plant tissue in the tips of roots and buds of shoots. The dividing cells of an apical meristem enable the plant to grow in length.

apicomplexan (ap'-ē-kom-pleks'-un) A protist in a clade that includes many species that parasitize animals. Some apicomplexans cause human disease.

apomixis (ap'-uh-mik'-sis) The ability of some plant species to reproduce asexually through seeds without fertilization by a male gamete.

apoplast (ap'-ō-plast) Everything external to the plasma membrane of a plant cell, including cell walls, intercellular spaces, and the space within dead structures such as xylem vessels and tracheids.

apoptosis (ā-puh-tō'-sus) A type of programmed cell death, which is brought about by activation of enzymes that break down many chemical components in the cell.

aposematic coloration (ap'-ō-si-mat'-ik) The bright warning coloration of many animals with effective physical or chemical defenses.

appendix A small, finger-like extension of the vertebrate cecum; contains a mass of white blood cells that contribute to immunity.

aquaporin A channel protein in a cellular membrane that specifically facilitates osmosis, the diffusion of free water across the membrane.

aqueous solution (ā'-kwē-us) A solution in which water is the solvent.

arachnid A member of a subgroup of the major arthropod clade Chelicerata. Arachnids have six pairs of appendages, including four pairs of walking legs, and include spiders, scorpions, ticks, and mites.

arbuscular mycorrhiza (ar-bus'-kyū-lur mī'-kō-rī'-zuh) Association of a fungus with a plant root system in which the fungus causes the invagination of the host (plant) cells' plasma membranes.

arbuscular mycorrhizal fungus (ar-bus'-kyū-lur) A symbiotic fungus whose hyphae grow through the cell wall of plant roots and extend into the root cell (enclosed in tubes formed by invagination of the root cell plasma membrane).

Archaea (ar-kē'-uh) One of two prokaryotic domains, the other being Bacteria.

Archaeplastida (ar'-kē-plas'-tid-uh) One of four supergroups of eukaryotes proposed in a current hypothesis of the evolutionary history of eukaryotes. This monophyletic group, which includes red algae, green algae, and land plants, descended from an ancient protist ancestor that engulfed a cyanobacterium. *See also* Excavata, "SAR" clade, and Unikonta.

archegonium (ar-ki-gō'-nē-um) (plural, **archegonia**) In plants, the female gametangium, a moist chamber in which gametes develop.

archenteron (ar-ken'-tuh-ron) The endoderm-lined cavity, formed during gastrulation, that develops into the digestive tract of an animal.

archosaur (ar'-kō-sōr) A member of the reptilian group that includes crocodiles, alligators and dinosaurs, including birds.

arteriole (ar-ter'-ē-ōl) A vessel that conveys blood between an artery and a capillary bed.

artery A vessel that carries blood away from the heart to organs throughout the body.

arthropod A segmented ecdysozoan with a hard exoskeleton and jointed appendages. Familiar examples include insects, spiders, millipedes, and crabs.

artificial selection The selective breeding of domesticated plants and animals to encourage the occurrence of desirable traits.

ascocarp The fruiting body of a sac fungus (ascomycete).

ascomycete (as'-kuh-mī'-sēt) A member of the fungal phylum Ascomycota, commonly called sac fungus. The name comes from the saclike structure in which the spores develop.

ascus (plural, **asci**) A saclike spore capsule located at the tip of a dikaryotic hypha of a sac fungus.

asexual reproduction The generation of offspring from a single parent that occurs without the fusion of gametes (by budding, division of a single cell, or division of the entire organism into two or more parts). In most cases, the offspring are genetically identical to the parent.

A site One of a ribosome's three binding sites for tRNA during translation. The A site holds the tRNA carrying the next amino acid to be added to the polypeptide chain. (A stands for aminoacyl tRNA.)

assisted migration The translocation of a species to a favorable habitat beyond its native range for the purpose of protecting the species from human-caused threats.

associative learning The acquired ability to associate one environmental feature (such as a color) with another (such as danger).

aster A radial array of short microtubules that extends from each centrosome toward the plasma membrane in an animal cell undergoing mitosis.

astrocyte A glial cell with diverse functions, including providing structural support for neurons, regulating the interstitial environment, facilitating synaptic transmission, and assisting in regulating the blood supply to the brain.

atherosclerosis A cardiovascular disease in which fatty deposits called plaques develop in the inner walls of the arteries, obstructing the arteries and causing them to harden.

atom The smallest unit of matter that retains the properties of an element.

atomic mass The total mass of an atom, numerically equivalent to the mass in grams of 1 mole of the atom. (For an element with more than one isotope, the atomic mass is the average mass of the naturally occurring isotopes, weighted by their abundance.)

atomic nucleus An atom's dense central core, containing protons and neutrons.

atomic number The number of protons in the nucleus of an atom, unique for each element and designated by a subscript.

ATP (adenosine triphosphate) (a-den'-ō-sēn trī-fos'-fāt) An adenine-containing nucleoside triphosphate that releases free energy when its phosphate bonds are hydrolyzed. This energy is used to drive endergonic reactions in cells.

ATP synthase A complex of several membrane proteins that functions in chemiosmosis with adjacent electron transport chains, using the energy of a hydrogen ion (proton) concentration gradient to make ATP. ATP synthases are found in the inner mitochondrial membranes of eukaryotic cells and in the plasma membranes of prokaryotes.

atrial natriuretic peptide (ANP) (ā'-trē-ul na'-trē-yū-ret'-ik) A peptide hormone secreted by cells of the atria of the heart in response to high blood pressure. ANP's effects on the kidney alter ion and water movement and reduce blood pressure.

atrioventricular (AV) node A region of specialized heart muscle tissue between the left and right atria where electrical impulses are delayed for about 0.1 second before spreading to both ventricles and causing them to contract.

atrioventricular (AV) valve A heart valve located between each atrium and ventricle that prevents a backflow of blood when the ventricle contracts.

atrium (ā′-trē-um) (plural, **atria**) A chamber of the vertebrate heart that receives blood from the veins and transfers blood to a ventricle.

autocrine Referring to a secreted molecule that acts on the cell that secreted it.

autoimmune disease An immunological disorder in which the immune system turns against self.

autonomic nervous system (ot′-ō-nom′-ik) An efferent branch of the vertebrate peripheral nervous system that regulates the internal environment; consists of the sympathetic, parasympathetic, and enteric divisions.

autopolyploid (ot′-ō-pol′-ē-ployd) An individual that has more than two chromosome sets that are all derived from a single species.

autosome (ot′-ō-sōm) A chromosome that is not directly involved in determining sex; not a sex chromosome.

autotroph (ot′-ō-trōf) An organism that obtains organic food molecules without eating other organisms or substances derived from other organisms. Autotrophs use energy from the sun or from oxidation of inorganic substances to make organic molecules from inorganic ones.

auxin (ôk′-sin) A term that primarily refers to indoleacetic acid (IAA), a natural plant hormone that has a variety of effects, including cell elongation, root formation, secondary growth, and fruit growth.

axillary bud (ak′-sil-ār-ē) A structure that has the potential to form a lateral shoot, or branch. The bud appears in the angle formed between a leaf and a stem.

axon (ak′-son) A typically long extension, or process, of a neuron that carries nerve impulses away from the cell body toward target cells.

B cells The lymphocytes that complete their development in the bone marrow and become effector cells for the humoral immune response.

Bacteria One of two prokaryotic domains, the other being Archaea.

bacteriophage (bak-tēr′-ē-ō-fāj) A virus that infects bacteria; also called a phage.

bacteroid A form of the bacterium *Rhizobium* contained within the vesicles formed by the root cells of a root nodule.

balancing selection Natural selection that maintains two or more phenotypic forms in a population.

bar graph A graph in which the independent variable represents groups or nonnumerical categories and the values of the dependent variable(s) are shown by bars.

bark All tissues external to the vascular cambium, consisting mainly of the secondary phloem and layers of periderm.

Barr body A dense object lying along the inside of the nuclear envelope in cells of female mammals, representing a highly condensed, inactivated X chromosome.

basal angiosperm A member of one of three clades of early-diverging lineages of extant flowering plants. Examples are *Amborella*, water lilies, and star anise and its relatives.

basal body (bā′-sul) A eukaryotic cell structure consisting of a "9 + 0" arrangement of microtubule triplets. The basal body may organize the microtubule assembly of a cilium or flagellum and is structurally very similar to a centriole.

basal metabolic rate (BMR) The metabolic rate of a resting, fasting, and nonstressed endotherm at a comfortable temperature.

basal taxon In a specified group of organisms, a taxon whose evolutionary lineage diverged early in the history of the group.

base A substance that reduces the hydrogen ion concentration of a solution.

basidiocarp Elaborate fruiting body of a dikaryotic mycelium of a club fungus.

basidiomycete (buh-sid′-ē-ō-mī′-sēt) A member of the fungal phylum Basidiomycota, commonly called club fungus. The name comes from the club-like shape of the basidium.

basidium (plural, **basidia**) (buh-sid′-ē-um, buh-sid′-ē-ah) A reproductive appendage that produces sexual spores on the gills of mushrooms (club fungi).

Batesian mimicry (bāt′-zē-un mim′-uh-krē) A type of mimicry in which a harmless species looks like a species that is poisonous or otherwise harmful to predators.

behavior Individually, an action carried out by muscles or glands under control of the nervous system in response to a stimulus; collectively, the sum of an animal's responses to external and internal stimuli.

behavioral ecology The study of the evolution of and ecological basis for animal behavior.

benign tumor A mass of abnormal cells with specific genetic and cellular changes such that the cells are not capable of surviving at a new site and generally remain at the site of the tumor's origin.

benthic zone The bottom surface of an aquatic environment.

benthos (ben′-thōz) The communities of organisms living in the benthic zone of an aquatic biome.

beta (β) pleated sheet One form of the secondary structure of proteins in which the polypeptide chain folds back and forth. Two regions of the chain lie parallel to each other and are held together by hydrogen bonds between atoms of the polypeptide backbone (not the side chains).

beta oxidation A metabolic sequence that breaks fatty acids down to two-carbon fragments that enter the citric acid cycle as acetyl CoA.

bicoid A maternal effect gene that codes for a protein responsible for specifying the anterior end in *Drosophila melanogaster*.

bilateral symmetry Body symmetry in which a central longitudinal plane divides the body into two equal but opposite halves.

bilaterian (bī′-luh-ter′-ē-uhn) A member of a clade of animals with bilateral symmetry and three germ layers.

bile A mixture of substances that is produced in the liver and stored in the gallbladder; enables formation of fat droplets in water as an aid in the digestion and absorption of fats.

binary fission A method of asexual reproduction by "division in half." In prokaryotes, binary fission does not involve mitosis, but in single-celled eukaryotes that undergo binary fission, mitosis is part of the process.

binomial A common term for the two-part, latinized format for naming a species, consisting of the genus and specific epithet; also called a binomen.

biodiversity hot spot A relatively small area with numerous endemic species and a large number of endangered and threatened species.

bioenergetics (1) The overall flow and transformation of energy in an organism. (2) The study of how energy flows through organisms.

biofilm A surface-coating colony of one or more species of prokaryotes that engage in metabolic cooperation.

biofuel A fuel produced from biomass.

biogenic amine A neurotransmitter derived from an amino acid.

biogeochemical cycle Any of the various chemical cycles, which involve both biotic and abiotic components of ecosystems.

biogeography The scientific study of the past and present geographic distributions of species.

bioinformatics The use of computers, software, and mathematical models to process and integrate biological information from large data sets.

biological augmentation An approach to restoration ecology that uses organisms to add essential materials to a degraded ecosystem.

biological clock An internal timekeeper that controls an organism's biological rhythms. The biological clock marks time with or without environmental cues but often requires signals from the environment to remain tuned to an appropriate period. *See also* circadian rhythm.

biological magnification A process in which retained substances become more concentrated at each higher trophic level in a food chain.

biological species concept Definition of a species as a group of populations whose members have the potential to interbreed in nature and produce viable, fertile offspring but do not produce viable, fertile offspring with members of other such groups.

biology The scientific study of life.

biomanipulation An approach that applies the top-down model of community organization to alter ecosystem characteristics. For example, ecologists can prevent algal blooms and eutrophication by altering the density of higher-level consumers in lakes instead of by using chemical treatments.

biomass The total mass of organic matter comprising a group of organisms in a particular habitat.

biome (bī′-ōm) Any of the world's major ecosystem types, often classified according to the predominant vegetation for terrestrial biomes and the physical environment for aquatic biomes and characterized by adaptations of organisms to that particular environment.

bioremediation The use of organisms to detoxify and restore polluted and degraded ecosystems.

biosphere The entire portion of Earth inhabited by life; the sum of all the planet's ecosystems.

biotechnology The manipulation of organisms or their components to produce useful products.

biotic (bī-ot'-ik) Pertaining to the living factors—the organisms—in an environment.

bipolar disorder A depressive mental illness characterized by swings of mood from high to low; also called manic-depressive disorder.

birth control pill A hormonal contraceptive that inhibits ovulation, retards follicular development, or alters a woman's cervical mucus to prevent sperm from entering the uterus.

blade (1) A leaflike structure of a seaweed that provides most of the surface area for photosynthesis. (2) The flattened portion of a typical leaf.

blastocoel (blas'-tuh-sēl) The fluid-filled cavity that forms in the center of a blastula.

blastocyst (blas'-tuh-sist) The blastula stage of mammalian embryonic development, consisting of an inner cell mass, a cavity, and an outer layer, the trophoblast. In humans, the blastocyst forms 1 week after fertilization.

blastomere An early embryonic cell arising during the cleavage stage of an early embryo.

blastopore (blas'-tō-pōr) In a gastrula, the opening of the archenteron that typically develops into the anus in deuterostomes and the mouth in protostomes.

blastula (blas'-tyū-luh) A hollow ball of cells that marks the end of the cleavage stage during early embryonic development in animals.

blood A connective tissue with a fluid matrix called plasma in which red blood cells, white blood cells, and cell fragments called platelets are suspended.

blue-light photoreceptor A type of light receptor in plants that initiates a variety of responses, such as phototropism and slowing of hypocotyl elongation.

body cavity A fluid- or air-filled space between the digestive tract and the body wall.

body plan In multicellular eukaryotes, a set of morphological and developmental traits that are integrated into a functional whole—the living organism.

Bohr shift A lowering of the affinity of hemoglobin for oxygen, caused by a drop in pH. It facilitates the release of oxygen from hemoglobin in the vicinity of active tissues.

bolus A lubricated ball of chewed food.

bone A connective tissue consisting of living cells held in a rigid matrix of collagen fibers embedded in calcium salts.

book lung An organ of gas exchange in spiders, consisting of stacked plates contained in an internal chamber.

bottleneck effect Genetic drift that occurs when the size of a population is reduced, as by a natural disaster or human actions. Typically, the surviving population is no longer genetically representative of the original population.

bottom-up model A model of community organization in which mineral nutrients influence community organization by controlling plant or phytoplankton numbers, which in turn control herbivore numbers, which in turn control predator numbers.

Bowman's capsule (bō'-munz) A cup-shaped receptacle in the vertebrate kidney that is the initial, expanded segment of the nephron, where filtrate enters from the blood.

brachiopod (bra'-kē-uh-pod') A marine lophophorate with a shell divided into dorsal and ventral halves; also called lamp shells.

brain Organ of the central nervous system where information is processed and integrated.

brainstem A collection of structures in the vertebrate brain, including the midbrain, the pons, and the medulla oblongata; functions in homeostasis, coordination of movement, and conduction of information to higher brain centers.

branch point The representation on a phylogenetic tree of the divergence of two or more taxa from a common ancestor. A branch point is usually shown as a dichotomy in which a branch representing the ancestral lineage splits (at the branch point) into two branches, one for each of the two descendant lineages.

brassinosteroid A steroid hormone in plants that has a variety of effects, including inducing cell elongation, retarding leaf abscission, and promoting xylem differentiation.

breathing Ventilation of the lungs through alternating inhalation and exhalation.

bronchiole (brong'-kē-ōl') A fine branch of the bronchi that transports air to alveoli.

bronchus (brong'-kus) (plural, **bronchi**) One of a pair of breathing tubes that branch from the trachea into the lungs.

brown alga A multicellular, photosynthetic protist with a characteristic brown or olive color that results from carotenoids in its plastids. Most brown algae are marine, and some have a plantlike body.

bryophyte (brī'-uh-fīt) An informal name for a moss, liverwort, or hornwort; a nonvascular plant that lives on land but lacks some of the terrestrial adaptations of vascular plants.

buffer A solution that contains a weak acid and its corresponding base. A buffer minimizes changes in pH when acids or bases are added to the solution.

bulk feeder An animal that eats relatively large pieces of food.

bulk flow The movement of a fluid due to a difference in pressure between two locations.

bundle-sheath cell In C_4 plants, a type of photosynthetic cell arranged into tightly packed sheaths around the veins of a leaf.

C_3 plant A plant that uses the Calvin cycle for the initial steps that incorporate CO_2 into organic material, forming a three-carbon compound as the first stable intermediate.

C_4 plant A plant in which the Calvin cycle is preceded by reactions that incorporate CO_2 into a four-carbon compound, the end product of which supplies CO_2 for the Calvin cycle.

calcitonin (kal'-si-tō'-nin) A hormone secreted by the thyroid gland that lowers blood calcium levels by promoting calcium deposition in bone and calcium excretion from the kidneys; nonessential in adult humans.

callus A mass of dividing, undifferentiated cells growing in culture.

calorie (cal) The amount of heat energy required to raise the temperature of 1 g of water by 1°C; also the amount of heat energy that 1 g of water releases when it cools by 1°C. The Calorie (with a capital C), usually used to indicate the energy content of food, is a kilocalorie.

Calvin cycle The second of two major stages in photosynthesis (following the light reactions), involving fixation of atmospheric CO_2 and reduction of the fixed carbon into carbohydrate.

Cambrian explosion A relatively brief time in geologic history when many present-day phyla of animals first appeared in the fossil record. This burst of evolutionary change occurred about 535–525 million years ago and saw the emergence of the first large, hard-bodied animals.

CAM plant A plant that uses crassulacean acid metabolism, an adaptation for photosynthesis in arid conditions. In this process, CO_2 entering open stomata during the night is converted to organic acids, which release CO_2 for the Calvin cycle during the day, when stomata are closed.

canopy The uppermost layer of vegetation in a terrestrial biome.

capillary (kap'-il-ār'-ē) A microscopic blood vessel that penetrates the tissues and consists of a single layer of endothelial cells that allows exchange between the blood and interstitial fluid.

capillary bed (kap'-il-ār'-ē) A network of capillaries in a tissue or organ.

capsid The protein shell that encloses a viral genome. It may be rod-shaped, polyhedral, or more complex in shape.

capsule (1) In many prokaryotes, a dense and well-defined layer of polysaccharide or protein that surrounds the cell wall and is sticky, protecting the cell and enabling it to adhere to substrates or other cells. (2) The sporangium of a bryophyte (moss, liverwort, or hornwort).

carbohydrate (kar'-bō-hī'-drāt) A sugar (monosaccharide) or one of its dimers (disaccharides) or polymers (polysaccharides).

carbon fixation The initial incorporation of carbon from CO_2 into an organic compound by an autotrophic organism (a plant, another photosynthetic organism, or a chemoautotrophic prokaryote).

carbonyl group (kar-buh-nēl') A chemical group present in aldehydes and ketones and consisting of a carbon atom double-bonded to an oxygen atom.

carboxyl group (kar-bok'-sil) A chemical group present in organic acids and consisting of a single carbon atom double-bonded to an oxygen atom and also bonded to a hydroxyl group.

cardiac cycle (kar'-dē-ak) The alternating contractions and relaxations of the heart.

cardiac muscle (kar′-dē-ak) A type of striated muscle that forms the contractile wall of the heart. Its cells are joined by intercalated disks that relay the electrical signals underlying each heartbeat.

cardiac output (kar′-dē-ak) The volume of blood pumped per minute by each ventricle of the heart.

cardiovascular system A closed circulatory system with a heart and branching network of arteries, capillaries, and veins. The system is characteristic of vertebrates.

carnivore An animal that mainly eats other animals.

carotenoid (kuh-rot′-uh-noyd′) An accessory pigment, either yellow or orange, in the chloroplasts of plants and in some prokaryotes. By absorbing wavelengths of light that chlorophyll cannot, carotenoids broaden the spectrum of colors that can drive photosynthesis.

carpel (kar′-pul) The ovule-producing reproductive organ of a flower, consisting of the stigma, style, and ovary.

carrier In genetics, an individual who is heterozygous at a given genetic locus for a recessively inherited disorder. The heterozygote is generally phenotypically normal for the disorder but can pass on the recessive allele to offspring.

carrying capacity The maximum population size that can be supported by the available resources, symbolized as K.

cartilage (kar′-til-ij) A flexible connective tissue with an abundance of collagenous fibers embedded in chondroitin sulfate.

Casparian strip (ka-spär′-ē-un) A water-impermeable ring of wax in the endodermal cells of plants that blocks the passive flow of water and solutes into the stele by way of cell walls.

catabolic pathway (kat′-uh-bol′-ik) A metabolic pathway that releases energy by breaking down complex molecules to simpler molecules.

catalyst (kat′-uh-list) A chemical agent that selectively increases the rate of a reaction without being consumed by the reaction.

catecholamine (kat′-uh-kōl′-uh-mēn) Any of a class of neurotransmitters and hormones, including the hormones epinephrine and norepinephrine, that are synthesized from the amino acid tyrosine.

cation (cat′-ī′-on) A positively charged ion.

cation exchange (cat′-ī′-on) A process in which positively charged minerals are made available to a plant when hydrogen ions in the soil displace mineral ions from the clay particles.

cecum (sē′-kum) (plural, **ceca**) The blind pouch forming one branch of the large intestine.

cell body The part of a neuron that houses the nucleus and most other organelles.

cell cycle An ordered sequence of events in the life of a cell, from its origin in the division of a parent cell until its own division into two. The eukaryotic cell cycle is composed of interphase (including G_1, S, and G_2 subphases) and M phase (including mitosis and cytokinesis).

cell cycle control system A cyclically operating set of molecules in the eukaryotic cell that both triggers and coordinates key events in the cell cycle.

cell division The reproduction of cells.

cell fractionation The disruption of a cell and separation of its parts by centrifugation at successively higher speeds.

cell-mediated immune response The branch of adaptive immunity that involves the activation of cytotoxic T cells, which defend against infected cells.

cell plate A membrane-bounded, flattened sac located at the midline of a dividing plant cell, inside which the new cell wall forms during cytokinesis.

cellular respiration The catabolic pathways of aerobic and anaerobic respiration, which break down organic molecules and use an electron transport chain for the production of ATP.

cellulose (sel′-yū-lōs) A structural polysaccharide of plant cell walls, consisting of glucose monomers joined by β glycosidic linkages.

cell wall A protective layer external to the plasma membrane in the cells of plants, prokaryotes, fungi, and some protists. Polysaccharides such as cellulose (in plants and some protists), chitin (in fungi), and peptidoglycan (in bacteria) are important structural components of cell walls.

central nervous system (CNS) The portion of the nervous system where signal integration occurs; in vertebrate animals, the brain and spinal cord.

central vacuole In a mature plant cell, a large membranous sac with diverse roles in growth, storage, and sequestration of toxic substances.

centriole (sen′-trē-ōl) A structure in the centrosome of an animal cell composed of a cylinder of microtubule triplets arranged in a "9 + 0" pattern. A centrosome has a pair of centrioles.

centromere (sen′-trō-mēr) In a duplicated chromosome, the region on each sister chromatid where it is most closely attached to the other chromatid by proteins that bind to the centromeric DNA. Other proteins condense the chromatin in that region, so it appears as a narrow "waist" on the duplicated chromosome. (An unduplicated chromosome has a single centromere, identified by the proteins bound there.)

centrosome (sen′-trō-sōm) A structure present in the cytoplasm of animal cells that functions as a microtubule-organizing center and is important during cell division. A centrosome has two centrioles.

cercozoan An amoeboid or flagellated protist that feeds with threadlike pseudopodia.

cerebellum (sar′-ruh-bel′-um) Part of the vertebrate hindbrain located dorsally; functions in unconscious coordination of movement and balance.

cerebral cortex (suh-rē′-brul) The surface of the cerebrum; the largest and most complex part of the mammalian brain, containing nerve cell bodies of the cerebrum; the part of the vertebrate brain most changed through evolution.

cerebral hemisphere (suh-rē′-brul) The right or left side of the cerebrum.

cerebrum (suh-rē′-brum) The dorsal portion of the vertebrate forebrain, composed of right and left hemispheres; the integrating center for memory, learning, emotions, and other highly complex functions of the central nervous system.

cervix (ser′-viks) The neck of the uterus, which opens into the vagina.

chaparral A scrubland biome of dense, spiny evergreen shrubs found at midlatitudes along coasts where cold ocean currents circulate offshore; characterized by mild, rainy winters and long, hot, dry summers.

chaperonin (shap′-er-ō′-nin) A protein complex that assists in the proper folding of other proteins.

character An observable heritable feature that may vary among individuals.

character displacement The tendency for characteristics to be more divergent in sympatric populations of two species than in allopatric populations of the same two species.

checkpoint A control point in the cell cycle where stop and go-ahead signals can regulate the cycle.

chelicera (kē-lih′-suh-ruh) (plural, **chelicerae**) One of a pair of clawlike feeding appendages characteristic of chelicerates.

chelicerate (kē-lih-suh′-rāte) An arthropod that has chelicerae and a body divided into a cephalothorax and an abdomen. Living chelicerates include sea spiders, horseshoe crabs, scorpions, ticks, and spiders.

chemical bond An attraction between two atoms, resulting from a sharing of outer-shell electrons or the presence of opposite charges on the atoms. The bonded atoms gain complete outer electron shells.

chemical energy Energy available in molecules for release in a chemical reaction; a form of potential energy.

chemical equilibrium In a chemical reaction, the state in which the rate of the forward reaction equals the rate of the reverse reaction, so that the relative concentrations of the reactants and products do not change with time.

chemical reaction The making and breaking of chemical bonds, leading to changes in the composition of matter.

chemiosmosis (kem′-ē-oz-mō′-sis) An energy-coupling mechanism that uses energy stored in the form of a hydrogen ion gradient across a membrane to drive cellular work, such as the synthesis of ATP. Under aerobic conditions, most ATP synthesis in cells occurs by chemiosmosis.

chemoautotroph (kē′-mō-ot′-ō-trōf) An organism that obtains energy by oxidizing inorganic substances and needs only carbon dioxide as a carbon source.

chemoheterotroph (kē′-mō-het′-er-ō-trōf) An organism that requires organic molecules for both energy and carbon.

chemoreceptor A sensory receptor that responds to a chemical stimulus, such as a solute or an odorant.

chiasma (plural, **chiasmata**) (kī-az′-muh, kī-az′-muh-tuh) The X-shaped, microscopically visible region where crossing over has occurred earlier in prophase I between homologous nonsister chromatids. Chiasmata become visible after synapsis ends, with the two homologs remaining associated due to sister chromatid cohesion.

chitin (kī'-tin) A structural polysaccharide, consisting of amino sugar monomers, found in many fungal cell walls and in the exoskeletons of all arthropods.

chlorophyll (klōr'-ō-fil) A green pigment located in membranes within the chloroplasts of plants and algae and in the membranes of certain prokaryotes. Chlorophyll *a* participates directly in the light reactions, which convert solar energy to chemical energy.

chlorophyll *a* (klōr'-ō-fil) A photosynthetic pigment that participates directly in the light reactions, which convert solar energy to chemical energy.

chlorophyll *b* (klōr'-ō-fil) An accessory photosynthetic pigment that transfers energy to chlorophyll *a*.

chloroplast (klōr'-ō-plast) An organelle found in plants and photosynthetic protists that absorbs sunlight and uses it to drive the synthesis of organic compounds from carbon dioxide and water.

choanocyte (kō-an'-uh-sīt) A flagellated feeding cell found in sponges. Also called a collar cell, it has a collar-like ring that traps food particles around the base of its flagellum.

cholesterol (kō-les'-tuh-rol) A steroid that forms an essential component of animal cell membranes and acts as a precursor molecule for the synthesis of other biologically important steroids, such as many hormones.

chondrichthyan (kon-drik'-thē-an) A member of the clade Chondrichthyes, vertebrates with skeletons made mostly of cartilage, such as sharks and rays.

chordate A member of the phylum Chordata, animals that at some point during their development have a notochord; a dorsal, hollow nerve cord; pharyngeal slits or clefts; and a muscular, post-anal tail.

chorionic villus sampling (CVS) (kōr'-ē-on'-ik vil'-us) A technique associated with prenatal diagnosis in which a small sample of the fetal portion of the placenta is removed for analysis to detect certain genetic and congenital defects in the fetus.

chromatin (krō'-muh-tin) The complex of DNA and proteins that makes up eukaryotic chromosomes. When the cell is not dividing, chromatin exists in its dispersed form, as a mass of very long, thin fibers that are not visible with a light microscope.

chromosome (krō'-muh-sōm) A cellular structure consisting of one DNA molecule and associated protein molecules. (In some contexts, such as genome sequencing, the term may refer to the DNA alone.) A eukaryotic cell typically has multiple, linear chromosomes, which are located in the nucleus. A prokaryotic cell often has a single, circular chromosome, which is found in the nucleoid, a region that is not enclosed by a membrane. *See also* chromatin.

chromosome theory of inheritance (krō'-muh-sōm) A basic principle in biology stating that genes are located at specific positions (loci) on chromosomes and that the behavior of chromosomes during meiosis accounts for inheritance patterns.

chylomicron (kī'-lō-mī'-kron) A lipid transport globule composed of fats mixed with cholesterol and coated with proteins.

chyme (kīm) The mixture of partially digested food and digestive juices formed in the stomach.

chytrid (kī'-trid) A member of the fungal phylum Chytridiomycota, mostly aquatic fungi with flagellated zoospores that represent an early-diverging fungal lineage.

ciliate (sil'-ē-it) A type of protist that moves by means of cilia.

cilium (sil'-ē-um) (plural, **cilia**) A short appendage containing microtubules in eukaryotic cells. A motile cilium is specialized for locomotion or moving fluid past the cell; it is formed from a core of nine outer doublet microtubules and two inner single microtubules (the "9 + 2" arrangement) ensheathed in an extension of the plasma membrane. A primary cilium is usually nonmotile and plays a sensory and signaling role; it lacks the two inner microtubules (the "9 + 0" arrangement).

circadian rhythm (ser-kā'-dē-un) A physiological cycle of about 24 hours that persists even in the absence of external cues.

***cis-trans* isomer** One of several compounds that have the same molecular formula and covalent bonds between atoms but differ in the spatial arrangements of their atoms owing to the inflexibility of double bonds; formerly called a geometric isomer.

citric acid cycle A chemical cycle involving eight steps that completes the metabolic breakdown of glucose molecules begun in glycolysis by oxidizing acetyl CoA (derived from pyruvate) to carbon dioxide; occurs within the mitochondrion in eukaryotic cells and in the cytosol of prokaryotes; together with pyruvate oxidation, the second major stage in cellular respiration.

clade (klayd) A group of species that includes an ancestral species and all of its descendants. A clade is equivalent to a monophyletic group.

cladistics (kluh-dis'-tiks) An approach to systematics in which organisms are placed into groups called clades based primarily on common descent.

class In Linnaean classification, the taxonomic category above the level of order.

cleavage (1) The process of cytokinesis in animal cells, characterized by pinching of the plasma membrane. (2) The succession of rapid cell divisions without significant growth during early embryonic development that converts the zygote to a ball of cells.

cleavage furrow The first sign of cleavage in an animal cell; a shallow groove around the cell in the cell surface near the old metaphase plate.

climate The long-term prevailing weather conditions at a given place.

climograph A plot of the temperature and precipitation in a particular region.

clitoris (klit'-uh-ris) An organ at the upper intersection of the labia minora that engorges with blood and becomes erect during sexual arousal.

cloaca (klō-ā'-kuh) A common opening for the digestive, urinary, and reproductive tracts found in many nonmammalian vertebrates but in few mammals.

clonal selection The process by which an antigen selectively binds to and activates only those lymphocytes bearing receptors specific for the antigen. The selected lymphocytes proliferate and differentiate into a clone of effector cells and a clone of memory cells specific for the stimulating antigen.

clone (1) A lineage of genetically identical individuals or cells. (2) In popular usage, an individual that is genetically identical to another individual. (3) As a verb, to make one or more genetic replicas of an individual or cell. *See also* gene cloning.

cloning vector In genetic engineering, a DNA molecule that can carry foreign DNA into a host cell and replicate there. Cloning vectors include plasmids and bacterial artificial chromosomes (BACs), which move recombinant DNA from a test tube back into a cell, and viruses that transfer recombinant DNA by infection.

closed circulatory system A circulatory system in which blood is confined to vessels and is kept separate from the interstitial fluid.

cnidocyte (nī'-duh-sīt) A specialized cell unique to the phylum Cnidaria; contains a capsule-like organelle housing a coiled thread that, when discharged, explodes outward and functions in prey capture or defense.

cochlea (kok'-lē-uh) The complex, coiled organ of hearing that contains the organ of Corti.

codominance The situation in which the phenotypes of both alleles are exhibited in the heterozygote because both alleles affect the phenotype in separate, distinguishable ways.

codon (kō'-don) A three-nucleotide sequence of DNA or mRNA that specifies a particular amino acid or termination signal; the basic unit of the genetic code.

coefficient of relatedness The fraction of genes that, on average, are shared by two individuals.

coelom (sē'-lōm) A body cavity lined by tissue derived only from mesoderm.

coelomate (sē'-lō-māt) An animal that possesses a true coelom (a body cavity lined by tissue completely derived from mesoderm).

coenocytic fungus (sē'-no-si'-tic) A fungus that lacks septa and hence whose body is made up of a continuous cytoplasmic mass that may contain hundreds or thousands of nuclei.

coenzyme (kō-en'-zīm) An organic molecule serving as a cofactor. Most vitamins function as coenzymes in metabolic reactions.

coevolution The joint evolution of two interacting species, each in response to selection imposed by the other.

cofactor Any nonprotein molecule or ion that is required for the proper functioning of an enzyme. Cofactors can be permanently bound to the active site or may bind loosely and reversibly, along with the substrate, during catalysis.

cognition The process of knowing that may include awareness, reasoning, recollection, and judgment.

cognitive map A neural representation of the abstract spatial relationships between objects in an animal's surroundings.

cohesion The linking together of like molecules, often by hydrogen bonds.

cohesion-tension hypothesis The leading explanation of the ascent of xylem sap. It states that transpiration exerts pull on xylem sap, putting the sap under negative pressure, or tension, and that the cohesion of water molecules transmits this pull along the entire length of the xylem from shoots to roots.

cohort A group of individuals of the same age in a population.

coleoptile (kō′-lē-op′-tul) The covering of the young shoot of the embryo of a grass seed.

coleorhiza (kō′-lē-uh-rī′-zuh) The covering of the young root of the embryo of a grass seed.

collagen A glycoprotein in the extracellular matrix of animal cells that forms strong fibers, found extensively in connective tissue and bone; the most abundant protein in the animal kingdom.

collecting duct The location in the kidney where processed filtrate, called urine, is collected from the renal tubules.

collenchyma cell (kō-len′-kim-uh) A flexible plant cell type that occurs in strands or cylinders that support young parts of the plant without restraining growth.

colon (kō′-len) The largest section of the vertebrate large intestine; functions in water absorption and formation of feces.

commensalism (kuh-men′-suh-lizm) A symbiotic relationship in which one organism benefits but the other is neither helped nor harmed.

communication In animal behavior, a process involving transmission of, reception of, and response to signals. The term is also used in connection with other organisms, as well as individual cells of multicellular organisms.

community All the organisms that inhabit a particular area; an assemblage of populations of different species living close enough together for potential interaction.

community ecology The study of how interactions between species affect community structure and organization.

companion cell A type of plant cell that is connected to a sieve-tube element by many plasmodesmata and whose nucleus and ribosomes may serve one or more adjacent sieve-tube elements.

competitive exclusion The concept that when populations of two similar species compete for the same limited resources, one population will use the resources more efficiently and have a reproductive advantage that will eventually lead to the elimination of the other population.

competitive inhibitor A substance that reduces the activity of an enzyme by entering the active site in place of the substrate, whose structure it mimics.

complement system A group of about 30 blood proteins that may amplify the inflammatory response, enhance phagocytosis, or directly lyse extracellular pathogens.

complementary DNA (cDNA) A double-stranded DNA molecule made *in vitro* using mRNA as a template and the enzymes reverse transcriptase and DNA polymerase. A cDNA molecule corresponds to the exons of a gene.

complete dominance The situation in which the phenotypes of the heterozygote and dominant homozygote are indistinguishable.

complete flower A flower that has all four basic floral organs: sepals, petals, stamens, and carpels.

complete metamorphosis The transformation of a larva into an adult that looks very different, and often functions very differently in its environment, than the larva.

compound A substance consisting of two or more different elements combined in a fixed ratio.

compound eye A type of multifaceted eye in insects and crustaceans consisting of up to several thousand light-detecting, focusing ommatidia.

concentration gradient A region along which the density of a chemical substance increases or decreases.

conception The fertilization of an egg by a sperm in humans.

cone A cone-shaped cell in the retina of the vertebrate eye, sensitive to color.

conformer An animal for which an internal condition conforms to (changes in accordance with) changes in an environmental variable.

conidium (plural, **conidia**) A haploid spore produced at the tip of a specialized hypha in ascomycetes during asexual reproduction.

conifer A member of the largest gymnosperm phylum. Most conifers are cone-bearing trees, such as pines and firs.

conjugation (kon′-jū-gā′-shun) (1) In prokaryotes, the direct transfer of DNA between two cells that are temporarily joined. When the two cells are members of different species, conjugation results in horizontal gene transfer. (2) In ciliates, a sexual process in which two cells exchange haploid micronuclei but do not reproduce.

connective tissue Animal tissue that functions mainly to bind and support other tissues, having a sparse population of cells scattered through an extracellular matrix.

conodont An early, soft-bodied vertebrate with prominent eyes and dental elements.

conservation biology The integrated study of ecology, evolutionary biology, physiology, molecular biology, and genetics to sustain biological diversity at all levels.

consumer An organism that feeds on producers, other consumers, or nonliving organic material.

contraception The deliberate prevention of pregnancy.

contractile vacuole A membranous sac that helps move excess water out of certain freshwater protists.

control element A segment of noncoding DNA that helps regulate transcription of a gene by serving as a binding site for a transcription factor. Multiple control elements are present in a eukaryotic gene's enhancer.

control group In a controlled experiment, a set of subjects that lacks (or does not receive) the specific factor being tested. Ideally, the control group should be identical to the experimental group in other respects.

controlled experiment An experiment in which an experimental group is compared with a control group that varies only in the factor being tested.

convergent evolution The evolution of similar features in independent evolutionary lineages.

convergent extension A process in which the cells of a tissue layer rearrange themselves in such a way that the sheet of cells becomes narrower (converges) and longer (extends).

cooperativity A kind of allosteric regulation whereby a shape change in one subunit of a protein caused by substrate binding is transmitted to all the other subunits, facilitating binding of additional substrate molecules to those subunits.

coral reef Typically a warm-water, tropical ecosystem dominated by the hard skeletal structures secreted primarily by corals. Some coral reefs also exist in cold, deep waters.

corepressor A small molecule that binds to a bacterial repressor protein and changes the protein's shape, allowing it to bind to the operator and switch an operon off.

cork cambium (kam′-bē-um) A cylinder of meristematic tissue in woody plants that replaces the epidermis with thicker, tougher cork cells.

corpus callosum (kor′-pus kuh-lō′-sum) The thick band of nerve fibers that connects the right and left cerebral hemispheres in mammals, enabling the hemispheres to process information together.

corpus luteum (kor′-pus lū′-tē-um) A secreting tissue in the ovary that forms from the collapsed follicle after ovulation and produces progesterone.

cortex (1) The outer region of cytoplasm in a eukaryotic cell, lying just under the plasma membrane, that has a more gel-like consistency than the inner regions due to the presence of multiple microfilaments. (2) In plants, ground tissue that is between the vascular tissue and dermal tissue in a root or eudicot stem.

cortical nephron In mammals and birds, a nephron with a loop of Henle located almost entirely in the renal cortex.

cotransport The coupling of the "downhill" diffusion of one substance to the "uphill" transport of another against its own concentration gradient.

cotyledon (kot′-uh-lē′-dun) A seed leaf of an angiosperm embryo. Some species have one cotyledon, others two.

countercurrent exchange The exchange of a substance or heat between two fluids flowing in opposite directions. For example, blood in a fish gill flows in the opposite direction of water passing over the gill, maximizing diffusion of oxygen into and carbon dioxide out of the blood.

countercurrent multiplier system A counter-current system in which energy is expended in active transport to facilitate exchange of materials and generate concentration gradients.

covalent bond (kō-vā′-lent) A type of strong chemical bond in which two atoms share one or more pairs of valence electrons.

crassulacean acid metabolism (CAM) An adaptation for photosynthesis in arid conditions, first discovered in the family Crassulaceae. In this process, a plant takes up CO_2 and incorporates it into a variety of organic acids at night; during the day, CO_2 is released from organic acids for use in the Calvin cycle.

crista (plural, **cristae**) (kris′-tuh, kris′-tē) An infolding of the inner membrane of a mitochondrion. The inner membrane houses electron transport chains and molecules of the enzyme catalyzing the synthesis of ATP (ATP synthase).

critical load The amount of added nutrient, usually nitrogen or phosphorus, that can be absorbed by plants without damaging ecosystem integrity.

crop rotation The practice of growing different crops in succession on the same land chiefly to preserve the productive capacity of the soil.

cross-fostering study A behavioral study in which the young of one species are placed in the care of adults from another species.

crossing over The reciprocal exchange of genetic material between nonsister chromatids during prophase I of meiosis.

cross-pollination In angiosperms, the transfer of pollen from an anther of a flower on one plant to the stigma of a flower on another plant of the same species.

cryptic coloration Camouflage that makes a potential prey difficult to spot against its background.

culture A system of information transfer through social learning or teaching that influences the behavior of individuals in a population.

cuticle (kyū′-tuh-kul) (1) A waxy covering on the surface of stems and leaves that prevents desiccation in terrestrial plants. (2) The exoskeleton of an arthropod, consisting of layers of protein and chitin that are variously modified for different functions. (3) A tough coat that covers the body of a nematode.

cyclic AMP (cAMP) Cyclic adenosine monophosphate, a ring-shaped molecule made from ATP that is a common intracellular signaling molecule (second messenger) in eukaryotic cells. It is also a regulator of some bacterial operons.

cyclic electron flow A route of electron flow during the light reactions of photosynthesis that involves only one photosystem and that produces ATP but not NADPH or O_2.

cyclin (sī′-klin) A cellular protein that occurs in a cyclically fluctuating concentration and that plays an important role in regulating the cell cycle.

cyclin-dependent kinase (Cdk) (sī′-klin) A protein kinase that is active only when attached to a particular cyclin.

cyclostome A member of the vertebrate subgroup lacking jaws. Cyclostomes include hagfishes and lampreys.

cystic fibrosis (sis′-tik fī-brō′-sis) A human genetic disorder caused by a recessive allele for a chloride channel protein; characterized by an excessive secretion of mucus and consequent vulnerability to infection; fatal if untreated.

cytochrome (sī′-tō-krōm) An iron-containing protein that is a component of electron transport chains in the mitochondria and chloroplasts of eukaryotic cells and the plasma membranes of prokaryotic cells.

cytokinesis (sī′-tō-kuh-nē′-sis) The division of the cytoplasm to form two separate daughter cells immediately after mitosis, meiosis I, or meiosis II.

cytokinin (sī′-tō-kī′-nin) Any of a class of related plant hormones that retard aging and act in concert with auxin to stimulate cell division, influence the pathway of differentiation, and control apical dominance.

cytoplasm (sī′-tō-plaz-um) The contents of the cell bounded by the plasma membrane; in eukaryotes, the portion exclusive of the nucleus.

cytoplasmic determinant A maternal substance, such as a protein or RNA, that when placed into an egg influences the course of early development by regulating the expression of genes that affect the developmental fate of cells.

cytoplasmic streaming A circular flow of cytoplasm, involving interactions of myosin and actin filaments, that speeds the distribution of materials within cells.

cytoskeleton A network of microtubules, microfilaments, and intermediate filaments that extend throughout the cytoplasm and serve a variety of mechanical, transport, and signaling functions.

cytosol (sī′-tō-sol) The semifluid portion of the cytoplasm.

cytotoxic T cell A type of lymphocyte that, when activated, kills infected cells as well as certain cancer cells and transplanted cells.

dalton A measure of mass for atoms and subatomic particles; the same as the atomic mass unit, or amu.

data Recorded observations.

day-neutral plant A plant in which flower formation is not controlled by photoperiod or day length.

decomposer An organism that absorbs nutrients from nonliving organic material such as corpses, fallen plant material, and the wastes of living organisms and converts them to inorganic forms; a detritivore.

deductive reasoning A type of logic in which specific results are predicted from a general premise.

deep-sea hydrothermal vent A dark, hot, oxygen-deficient environment associated with volcanic activity on or near the seafloor. The producers in a vent community are chemoautotrophic prokaryotes.

de-etiolation The changes a plant shoot undergoes in response to sunlight; also known informally as greening.

dehydration reaction A chemical reaction in which two molecules become covalently bonded to each other with the removal of a water molecule.

deletion (1) A deficiency in a chromosome resulting from the loss of a fragment through breakage. (2) A mutational loss of one or more nucleotide pairs from a gene.

demographic transition In a stable population, a shift from high birth and death rates to low birth and death rates.

demography The study of changes over time in the vital statistics of populations, especially birth rates and death rates.

denaturation (dē-nā′-chur-ā′-shun) In proteins, a process in which a protein loses its native shape due to the disruption of weak chemical bonds and interactions, thereby becoming biologically inactive; in DNA, the separation of the two strands of the double helix. Denaturation occurs under extreme (noncellular) conditions of pH, salt concentration, or temperature.

dendrite (den′-drīt) One of usually numerous, short, highly branched extensions of a neuron that receive signals from other neurons.

dendritic cell An antigen-presenting cell, located mainly in lymphatic tissues and skin, that is particularly efficient in presenting antigens to helper T cells, thereby initiating a primary immune response.

density The number of individuals per unit area or volume.

density dependent Referring to any characteristic that varies with population density.

density-dependent inhibition The phenomenon observed in normal animal cells that causes them to stop dividing when they come into contact with one another.

density independent Referring to any characteristic that is not affected by population density.

deoxyribonucleic acid (DNA) (dē-ok′-sē-rī′-bō-nū-klā′-ik) A nucleic acid molecule, usually a double-stranded helix, in which each polynucleotide strand consists of nucleotide monomers with a deoxyribose sugar and the nitrogenous bases adenine (A), cytosine (C), guanine (G), and thymine (T); capable of being replicated and determining the inherited structure of a cell's proteins.

deoxyribose (dē-ok′-si-rī′-bōs) The sugar component of DNA nucleotides, having one fewer hydroxyl group than ribose, the sugar component of RNA nucleotides.

dependent variable A variable whose value is measured during an experiment or other test to see whether it is influenced by changes in another variable (the independent variable).

depolarization A change in a cell's membrane potential such that the inside of the membrane is made less negative relative to the outside. For example, a neuron membrane is depolarized if a stimulus decreases its voltage from the resting potential of −70 mV in the direction of zero voltage.

dermal tissue system The outer protective covering of plants.

desert A terrestrial biome characterized by very low precipitation.

desmosome A type of intercellular junction in animal cells that functions as a rivet, fastening cells together.

determinate cleavage A type of embryonic development in protostomes that rigidly casts the developmental fate of each embryonic cell very early.

determinate growth A type of growth characteristic of most animals and some plant organs, in which growth stops after a certain size is reached.

determination The progressive restriction of developmental potential in which the possible fate of each cell becomes more limited as an embryo develops. At the end of determination, a cell is committed to its fate.

detritivore (deh-trī'-tuh-vōr) A consumer that derives its energy and nutrients from nonliving organic material such as corpses, fallen plant material, and the wastes of living organisms; a decomposer.

detritus (di-trī'-tus) Dead organic matter.

deuteromycete (dū'-tuh-rō-mī'-sēt) Traditional classification for a fungus with no known sexual stage.

deuterostome development (dū'-tuh-rō-stōm') In animals, a developmental mode distinguished by the development of the anus from the blastopore; often also characterized by radial cleavage and by the body cavity forming as outpockets of mesodermal tissue.

Deuterostomia (dū'-tuh-rō-stōm'-ē-uh) One of the three main lineages of bilaterian animals. *See also* Ecdysozoa and Lophotrochozoa.

development The events involved in an organism's changing gradually from a simple to a more complex or specialized form.

diabetes mellitus (dī'-uh-bē'-tis mel'-uh-tus) An endocrine disorder marked by an inability to maintain glucose homeostasis. The type 1 form results from autoimmune destruction of insulin-secreting cells; treatment usually requires daily insulin injections. The type 2 form most commonly results from reduced responsiveness of target cells to insulin; obesity and lack of exercise are risk factors.

diacylglycerol (DAG) (dī-a'-sil-glis'-er-ol) A second messenger produced by the cleavage of the phospholipid PIP$_2$ in the plasma membrane.

diaphragm (dī'-uh-fram') (1) A sheet of muscle that forms the bottom wall of the thoracic cavity in mammals. Contraction of the diaphragm pulls air into the lungs. (2) A dome-shaped rubber cup fitted into the upper portion of the vagina before sexual intercourse. It serves as a physical barrier to the passage of sperm into the uterus.

diapsid (dī-ap'-sid) A member of an amniote clade distinguished by a pair of holes on each side of the skull. Diapsids include the lepidosaurs and archosaurs.

diastole (dī-as'-tō-lē) The stage of the cardiac cycle in which a heart chamber is relaxed and fills with blood.

diastolic pressure Blood pressure in the arteries when the ventricles are relaxed.

diatom Photosynthetic protist in the stramenopile clade; diatoms have a unique glass-like wall made of silicon dioxide embedded in an organic matrix.

dicot A term traditionally used to refer to flowering plants that have two embryonic seed leaves, or cotyledons. Recent molecular evidence indicates that dicots do not form a clade; species once classified as dicots are now grouped into eudicots, magnoliids, and several lineages of basal angiosperms.

differential gene expression The expression of different sets of genes by cells with the same genome.

differentiation The process by which a cell or group of cells becomes specialized in structure and function.

diffusion The random thermal motion of particles of liquids, gases, or solids. In the presence of a concentration or electrochemical gradient, diffusion results in the net movement of a substance from a region where it is more concentrated to a region where it is less concentrated.

digestion The second stage of food processing in animals: the breaking down of food into molecules small enough for the body to absorb.

dihybrid (dī'-hī'-brid) An organism that is heterozygous with respect to two genes of interest. All the offspring from a cross between parents doubly homozygous for different alleles are dihybrids. For example, parents of genotypes *AABB* and *aabb* produce a dihybrid of genotype *AaBb*.

dihybrid cross (dī'-hī'-brid) A cross between two organisms that are each heterozygous for both of the characters being followed (or the self-pollination of a plant that is heterozygous for both characters).

dikaryotic (dī'-kār-ē-ot'-ik) Referring to a fungal mycelium with two haploid nuclei per cell, one from each parent.

dinoflagellate (dī'-nō-flaj'-uh-let) A member of a group of mostly unicellular photosynthetic algae with two flagella situated in perpendicular grooves in cellulose plates covering the cell.

dinosaur A member of an extremely diverse clade of reptiles varying in body shape, size, and habitat. Birds are the only extant dinosaurs.

dioecious (dī-ē'-shus) In plant biology, having the male and female reproductive parts on different individuals of the same species.

diploblastic Having two germ layers.

diploid cell (dip'-loyd) A cell containing two sets of chromosomes ($2n$), one set inherited from each parent.

diplomonad A protist that has modified mitochondria, two equal-sized nuclei, and multiple flagella.

directional selection Natural selection in which individuals at one end of the phenotypic range survive or reproduce more successfully than do other individuals.

disaccharide (dī-sak'-uh-rīd) A double sugar, consisting of two monosaccharides joined by a glycosidic linkage formed by a dehydration reaction.

dispersal The movement of individuals or gametes away from their parent location. This movement sometimes expands the geographic range of a population or species.

dispersion The pattern of spacing among individuals within the boundaries of a population.

disruptive selection Natural selection in which individuals on both extremes of a phenotypic range survive or reproduce more successfully than do individuals with intermediate phenotypes.

distal tubule In the vertebrate kidney, the portion of a nephron that helps refine filtrate and empties it into a collecting duct.

disturbance A natural or human-caused event that changes a biological community and usually removes organisms from it. Disturbances, such as fires and storms, play a pivotal role in structuring many communities.

disulfide bridge A strong covalent bond formed when the sulfur of one cysteine monomer bonds to the sulfur of another cysteine monomer.

DNA (deoxyribonucleic acid) (dē-ok'-sē-rī'-bō-nū-klā'-ik) A nucleic acid molecule, usually a double-stranded helix, in which each polynucleotide strand consists of nucleotide monomers with a deoxyribose sugar and the nitrogenous bases adenine (A), cytosine (C), guanine (G), and thymine (T); capable of being replicated and determining the inherited structure of a cell's proteins.

DNA cloning The production of multiple copies of a specific DNA segment.

DNA ligase (lī'-gās) A linking enzyme essential for DNA replication; catalyzes the covalent bonding of the 3' end of one DNA fragment (such as an Okazaki fragment) to the 5' end of another DNA fragment (such as a growing DNA chain).

DNA methylation The presence of methyl groups on the DNA bases (usually cytosine) of plants, animals, and fungi. (The term also refers to the process of adding methyl groups to DNA bases.)

DNA microarray assay A method to detect and measure the expression of thousands of genes at one time. Tiny amounts of a large number of single-stranded DNA fragments representing different genes are fixed to a glass slide and tested for hybridization with samples of labeled cDNA.

DNA polymerase (puh-lim'-er-ās) An enzyme that catalyzes the elongation of new DNA (for example, at a replication fork) by the addition of nucleotides to the 3' end of an existing chain. There are several different DNA polymerases; DNA polymerase III and DNA polymerase I play major roles in DNA replication in *E. coli*.

DNA replication The process by which a DNA molecule is copied; also called DNA synthesis.

DNA sequencing Determining the complete nucleotide sequence of a gene or DNA segment.

DNA technology Techniques for sequencing and manipulating DNA.

domain (1) A taxonomic category above the kingdom level. The three domains are

Archaea, Bacteria, and Eukarya. (2) A discrete structural and functional region of a protein.

dominant allele An allele that is fully expressed in the phenotype of a heterozygote.

dominant species A species with substantially higher abundance or biomass than other species in a community. Dominant species exert a powerful control over the occurrence and distribution of other species.

dopamine A neurotransmitter that is a catecholamine, like epinephrine and norepinephrine.

dormancy A condition typified by extremely low metabolic rate and a suspension of growth and development.

dorsal Pertaining to the top of an animal with radial or bilateral symmetry.

dorsal lip The region above the blastopore on the dorsal side of the amphibian embryo.

double bond A double covalent bond; the sharing of two pairs of valence electrons by two atoms.

double circulation A circulatory system consisting of separate pulmonary and systemic circuits, in which blood passes through the heart after completing each circuit.

double fertilization A mechanism of fertilization in angiosperms in which two sperm cells unite with two cells in the female gametophyte (embryo sac) to form the zygote and endosperm.

double helix The form of native DNA, referring to its two adjacent antiparallel polynucleotide strands wound around an imaginary axis into a spiral shape.

Down syndrome A human genetic disease usually caused by the presence of an extra chromosome 21; characterized by developmental delays and heart and other defects that are generally treatable or non-life-threatening.

Duchenne muscular dystrophy (duh-shen') A human genetic disease caused by a sex-linked recessive allele; characterized by progressive weakening and a loss of muscle tissue.

duodenum (dū'-uh-dēn'-um) The first section of the small intestine, where chyme from the stomach mixes with digestive juices from the pancreas, liver, and gallbladder as well as from gland cells of the intestinal wall.

duplication An aberration in chromosome structure due to fusion with a fragment from a homologous chromosome, such that a portion of a chromosome is duplicated.

dynein (dī'-nē-un) In cilia and flagella, a large motor protein extending from one microtubule doublet to the adjacent doublet. ATP hydrolysis drives changes in dynein shape that lead to bending of cilia and flagella.

E site One of a ribosome's three binding sites for tRNA during translation. The E site is the place where discharged tRNAs leave the ribosome. (E stands for exit.)

Ecdysozoa (ek'-dē-sō-zō'-uh) One of the three main lineages of bilaterian animals; many ecdysozoans are molting animals. *See also* Deuterostomia and Lophotrochozoa.

echinoderm (i-kī'-nō-derm) A slow-moving or sessile marine deuterostome with a water vascular system and, in larvae, bilateral symmetry. Echinoderms include sea stars, brittle stars, sea urchins, feather stars, and sea cucumbers.

ecological footprint The aggregate land and water area required by a person, city, or nation to produce all of the resources it consumes and to absorb all of the wastes it generates.

ecological niche (nich) The sum of a species' use of the biotic and abiotic resources in its environment.

ecological species concept Definition of a species in terms of ecological niche, the sum of how members of the species interact with the nonliving and living parts of their environment.

ecological succession Transition in the species composition of a community following a disturbance; establishment of a community in an area virtually barren of life.

ecology The study of how organisms interact with each other and their environment.

ecosystem All the organisms in a given area as well as the abiotic factors with which they interact; one or more communities and the physical environment around them.

ecosystem ecology The study of energy flow and the cycling of chemicals among the various biotic and abiotic components in an ecosystem.

ecosystem engineer An organism that influences community structure by causing physical changes in the environment.

ecosystem service A function performed by an ecosystem that directly or indirectly benefits humans.

ecotone The transition from one type of habitat or ecosystem to another, such as the transition from a forest to a grassland.

ectoderm (ek'-tō-durm) The outermost of the three primary germ layers in animal embryos; gives rise to the outer covering and, in some phyla, the nervous system, inner ear, and lens of the eye.

ectomycorrhiza (plural, **ectomycorrhizae**) (ek'-tō-mī'-kō-rī'-zuh, ek'-tō-mī'-kō-rī'-zē) Association of a fungus with a plant root system in which the fungus surrounds the roots but does not cause invagination of the host (plant) cell's plasma membrane.

ectomycorrhizal fungus A symbiotic fungus that forms sheaths of hyphae over the surface of plant roots and also grows into extracellular spaces of the root cortex.

ectoparasite A parasite that feeds on the external surface of a host.

ectopic Occurring in an abnormal location.

ectoproct A sessile, colonial lophophorate; also called a bryozoan.

ectothermic Referring to organisms for which external sources provide most of the heat for temperature regulation.

Ediacaran biota (ē'-dē-uh-keh'-run bī-ō'-tuh) An early group of macroscopic, soft-bodied, multicellular eukaryotes known from fossils that range in age from 635 million to 535 million years old.

effective population size An estimate of the size of a population based on the numbers of females and males that successfully breed; generally smaller than the total population.

effector Pathogen-encoded protein that cripples the host's innate immune system.

effector cell (1) A muscle cell or gland cell that carries out the body's response to stimuli as directed by signals from the brain or other processing center of the nervous system. (2) A lymphocyte that has undergone clonal selection and is capable of mediating an adaptive immune response.

egg The female gamete.

egg-polarity gene A gene that helps control the orientation (polarity) of the egg; also called a maternal effect gene.

ejaculation The propulsion of sperm from the epididymis through the muscular vas deferens, ejaculatory duct, and urethra.

electrocardiogram (ECG or EKG) A record of the electrical impulses that travel through heart muscle during the cardiac cycle.

electrochemical gradient The diffusion gradient of an ion, which is affected by both the concentration difference of an ion across a membrane (a chemical force) and the ion's tendency to move relative to the membrane potential (an electrical force).

electrogenic pump An active transport protein that generates voltage across a membrane while pumping ions.

electromagnetic receptor A receptor of electromagnetic energy, such as visible light, electricity, or magnetism.

electromagnetic spectrum The entire spectrum of electromagnetic radiation, ranging in wavelength from less than a nanometer to more than a kilometer.

electron A subatomic particle with a single negative electrical charge and a mass about 1/2,000 that of a neutron or proton. One or more electrons move around the nucleus of an atom.

electron microscope (EM) A microscope that uses magnets to focus an electron beam on or through a specimen, resulting in a practical resolution that is 100-fold greater than that of a light microscope using standard techniques. A transmission electron microscope (TEM) is used to study the internal structure of thin sections of cells. A scanning electron microscope (SEM) is used to study the fine details of cell surfaces.

electron shell An energy level of electrons at a characteristic average distance from the nucleus of an atom.

electron transport chain A sequence of electron carrier molecules (membrane proteins) that shuttle electrons down a series of redox reactions that release energy used to make ATP.

electronegativity The attraction of a given atom for the electrons of a covalent bond.

electroporation A technique to introduce recombinant DNA into cells by applying a brief electrical pulse to a solution containing the cells. The pulse creates temporary holes in the cells' plasma membranes, through which DNA can enter.

element Any substance that cannot be broken down to any other substance by chemical reactions.

elimination The fourth and final stage of food processing in animals: the passing of undigested material out of the body.

embryo sac (em´-brē-ō) The female gametophyte of angiosperms, formed from the growth and division of the megaspore into a multicellular structure that typically has eight haploid nuclei.

embryonic lethal A mutation with a phenotype leading to death of an embryo or larva.

embryophyte Alternate name for land plants that refers to their shared derived trait of multicellular, dependent embryos.

emergent properties New properties that arise with each step upward in the hierarchy of life, owing to the arrangement and interactions of parts as complexity increases.

emigration The movement of individuals out of a population.

enantiomer (en-an´-tē-ō-mer) One of two compounds that are mirror images of each other and that differ in shape due to the presence of an asymmetric carbon.

endangered species A species that is in danger of extinction throughout all or a significant portion of its range.

endemic (en-dem´-ik) Referring to a species that is confined to a specific geographic area.

endergonic reaction (en´-der-gon´-ik) A nonspontaneous chemical reaction in which free energy is absorbed from the surroundings.

endocrine gland (en´-dō-krin) A ductless gland that secretes hormones directly into the interstitial fluid, from which they diffuse into the bloodstream.

endocrine system (en´-dō-krin) In animals, the internal system of communication involving hormones, the ductless glands that secrete hormones, and the molecular receptors on or in target cells that respond to hormones; functions in concert with the nervous system to effect internal regulation and maintain homeostasis.

endocytosis (en´-dō-sī-tō´-sis) Cellular uptake of biological molecules and particulate matter via formation of vesicles from the plasma membrane.

endoderm (en´-dō-durm) The innermost of the three primary germ layers in animal embryos; lines the archenteron and gives rise to the liver, pancreas, lungs, and the lining of the digestive tract in species that have these structures.

endodermis In plant roots, the innermost layer of the cortex that surrounds the vascular cylinder.

endomembrane system The collection of membranes inside and surrounding a eukaryotic cell, related either through direct physical contact or by the transfer of membranous vesicles; includes the plasma membrane, the nuclear envelope, the smooth and rough endoplasmic reticulum, the Golgi apparatus, lysosomes, vesicles, and vacuoles.

endometriosis (en´-dō-mē-trē-ō´-sis) The condition resulting from the presence of endometrial tissue outside of the uterus.

endometrium (en´-dō-mē´-trē-um) The inner lining of the uterus, which is richly supplied with blood vessels.

endoparasite A parasite that lives within a host.

endophyte A harmless fungus, or occasionally another organism, that lives between cells of a plant part or multicellular alga.

endoplasmic reticulum (ER) (en´-dō-plaz´-mik ruh-tik´-yū-lum) An extensive membranous network in eukaryotic cells, continuous with the outer nuclear membrane and composed of ribosome-studded (rough) and ribosome-free (smooth) regions.

endorphin (en-dōr´-fin) Any of several hormones produced in the brain and anterior pituitary that inhibit pain perception.

endoskeleton A hard skeleton buried within the soft tissues of an animal.

endosperm In angiosperms, a nutrient-rich tissue formed by the union of a sperm with two polar nuclei during double fertilization. The endosperm provides nourishment to the developing embryo in angiosperm seeds.

endospore A thick-coated, resistant cell produced by some bacterial cells when they are exposed to harsh conditions.

endosymbiont theory The theory that mitochondria and plastids, including chloroplasts, originated as prokaryotic cells engulfed by a host cell. The engulfed cell and its host cell then evolved into a single organism. *See also* endosymbiosis.

endosymbiosis A relationship between two species in which one organism lives inside the cell or cells of another organism. *See also* endosymbiont theory.

endothelium (en´-dō-thē´-lē-um) The simple squamous layer of cells lining the lumen of blood vessels.

endothermic Referring to organisms that are warmed by heat generated by their own metabolism. This heat usually maintains a relatively stable body temperature higher than that of the external environment.

endotoxin A toxic component of the outer membrane of certain gram-negative bacteria that is released only when the bacteria die.

energetic hypothesis The concept that the length of a food chain is limited by the inefficiency of energy transfer along the chain.

energy The capacity to cause change, especially to do work (to move matter against an opposing force).

energy coupling In cellular metabolism, the use of energy released from an exergonic reaction to drive an endergonic reaction.

enhancer A segment of eukaryotic DNA containing multiple control elements, usually located far from the gene whose transcription it regulates.

enteric division One of three divisions of the autonomic nervous system; consists of networks of neurons in the digestive tract, pancreas, and gallbladder; normally regulated by the sympathetic and parasympathetic divisions of the autonomic nervous system.

entropy A measure of disorder, or randomness.

enzyme (en´-zīm) A macromolecule serving as a catalyst, a chemical agent that increases the rate of a reaction without being consumed by the reaction. Most enzymes are proteins.

enzyme-substrate complex (en´-zīm) A temporary complex formed when an enzyme binds to its substrate molecule(s).

epicotyl (ep´-uh-kot´-ul) In an angiosperm embryo, the embryonic axis above the point of attachment of the cotyledon(s) and below the first pair of miniature leaves.

epidemic A widespread outbreak of a disease.

epidermis (1) The dermal tissue system of nonwoody plants, usually consisting of a single layer of tightly packed cells. (2) The outermost layer of cells in an animal.

epididymis (ep´-uh-did´-uh-mus) A coiled tubule located adjacent to the mammalian testis where sperm are stored.

epigenetic inheritance Inheritance of traits transmitted by mechanisms that do not involve the nucleotide sequence.

epinephrine (ep´-i-nef´-rin) A catecholamine that, when secreted as a hormone by the adrenal medulla, mediates "fight-or-flight" responses to short-term stresses; also released by some neurons as a neurotransmitter; also called adrenaline.

epiphyte (ep´-uh-fīt) A plant that nourishes itself but grows on the surface of another plant for support, usually on the branches or trunks of trees.

epistasis (ep´-i-stā´-sis) A type of gene interaction in which the phenotypic expression of one gene alters that of another independently inherited gene.

epithelial tissue (ep´-uh-thē´-lē-ul) Sheets of tightly packed cells that line organs and body cavities as well as external surfaces.

epithelium An epithelial tissue.

epitope A small, accessible region of an antigen to which an antigen receptor or antibody binds.

equilibrium potential (E_{ion}) The magnitude of a cell's membrane voltage at equilibrium; calculated using the Nernst equation.

erythrocyte (eh-rith´-ruh-sīt) A blood cell that contains hemoglobin, which transports oxygen; also called a red blood cell.

erythropoietin (EPO) (eh-rith´-rō-poy´-uh-tin) A hormone that stimulates the production of erythrocytes. It is secreted by the kidney when body tissues do not receive enough oxygen.

esophagus (eh-sof´-uh-gus) A muscular tube that conducts food, by peristalsis, from the pharynx to the stomach.

essential amino acid An amino acid that an animal cannot synthesize itself and must be obtained from food in prefabricated form.

essential element A chemical element required for an organism to survive, grow, and reproduce.

essential fatty acid An unsaturated fatty acid that an animal needs but cannot make.

essential nutrient A substance that an organism cannot synthesize from any other material and therefore must absorb in preassembled form.

estradiol (es´-truh-dī´-ol) A steroid hormone that stimulates the development and maintenance of the female reproductive system and secondary sex characteristics; the major estrogen in mammals.

estrogen (es'-trō-jen) Any steroid hormone, such as estradiol, that stimulates the development and maintenance of the female reproductive system and secondary sex characteristics.

estrous cycle (es'-trus) A reproductive cycle characteristic of female mammals except humans and certain other primates, in which the nonpregnant endometrium is reabsorbed rather than shed, and sexual response occurs only during mid-cycle at estrus.

estuary The area where a freshwater stream or river merges with the ocean.

ethylene (eth'-uh-lēn) A gaseous plant hormone involved in responses to mechanical stress, programmed cell death, leaf abscission, and fruit ripening.

etiolation Plant morphological adaptations for growing in darkness.

euchromatin (yū-krō'-muh-tin) The less condensed form of eukaryotic chromatin that is available for transcription.

eudicot (yū-dī'-kot) A member of a clade that contains the vast majority of flowering plants that have two embryonic seed leaves, or cotyledons.

euglenid (yū'-glen-id) A protist, such as *Euglena* or its relatives, characterized by an anterior pocket from which one or two flagella emerge.

euglenozoan A member of a diverse clade of flagellated protists that includes predatory heterotrophs, photosynthetic autotrophs, and pathogenic parasites.

Eukarya (yū-kar'-ē-uh) The domain that includes all eukaryotic organisms.

eukaryotic cell (yū'-ker-ē-ot'-ik) A type of cell with a membrane-enclosed nucleus and membrane-enclosed organelles. Organisms with eukaryotic cells (protists, plants, fungi, and animals) are called eukaryotes.

eumetazoan (yū'-met-uh-zō'-un) A member of a clade of animals with true tissues. All animals except sponges and a few other groups are eumetazoans.

eurypterid (yur-ip'-tuh-rid) An extinct carnivorous chelicerate; also called a water scorpion.

Eustachian tube (yū-stā'-shun) The tube that connects the middle ear to the pharynx.

eutherian (yū-thēr'-ē-un) Placental mammal; mammal whose young complete their embryonic development within the uterus, joined to the mother by the placenta.

eutrophic lake (yū-trōf'-ik) A lake that has a high rate of biological productivity supported by a high rate of nutrient cycling.

eutrophication A process by which nutrients, particularly phosphorus and nitrogen, become highly concentrated in a body of water, leading to increased growth of organisms such as algae or cyanobacteria.

evaporative cooling The process in which the surface of an object becomes cooler during evaporation, a result of the molecules with the greatest kinetic energy changing from the liquid to the gaseous state.

evapotranspiration The total evaporation of water from an ecosystem, including water transpired by plants and evaporated from a landscape, usually measured in millimeters and estimated for a year.

evo-devo Evolutionary developmental biology; a field of biology that compares developmental processes of different multicellular organisms to understand how these processes have evolved and how changes can modify existing organismal features or lead to new ones.

evolution Descent with modification; the idea that living species are descendants of ancestral species that were different from the present-day ones; also defined more narrowly as the change in the genetic composition of a population from generation to generation.

evolutionary tree A branching diagram that reflects a hypothesis about evolutionary relationships among groups of organisms.

Excavata (ex'-kuh-vah'-tuh) One of four supergroups of eukaryotes proposed in a current hypothesis of the evolutionary history of eukaryotes. Excavates have unique cytoskeletal features, and some species have an "excavated" feeding groove on one side of the cell body. *See also* "SAR" clade, Archaeplastida, and Unikonta.

excitatory postsynaptic potential (EPSP) An electrical change (depolarization) in the membrane of a postsynaptic cell caused by the binding of an excitatory neurotransmitter from a presynaptic cell to a postsynaptic receptor; makes it more likely for a postsynaptic cell to generate an action potential.

excretion The disposal of nitrogen-containing metabolites and other waste products.

exergonic reaction (ek'-ser-gon'-ik) A spontaneous chemical reaction in which there is a net release of free energy.

exocytosis (ek'-sō-sī-tō'-sis) The cellular secretion of biological molecules by the fusion of vesicles containing them with the plasma membrane.

exon A sequence within a primary transcript that remains in the RNA after RNA processing; also refers to the region of DNA from which this sequence was transcribed.

exoskeleton A hard encasement on the surface of an animal, such as the shell of a mollusc or the cuticle of an arthropod, that provides protection and points of attachment for muscles.

exotoxin (ek'-sō-tok'-sin) A toxic protein that is secreted by a prokaryote or other pathogen and that produces specific symptoms, even if the pathogen is no longer present.

expansin Plant enzyme that breaks the cross-links (hydrogen bonds) between cellulose microfibrils and other cell wall constituents, loosening the wall's fabric.

experiment A scientific test, carried out under controlled conditions, involving manipulation of one or more factors in a system in order to see the effects of those changes.

experimental group A set of subjects that has (or receives) the specific factor being tested in a controlled experiment.

exponential population growth Growth of a population in an ideal, unlimited environment, represented by a J-shaped curve when population size is plotted over time.

expression vector A cloning vector that contains a highly active bacterial promoter just upstream of a restriction site where a eukaryotic gene can be inserted, allowing the gene to be expressed in a bacterial cell. Expression vectors are also available that have been genetically engineered for use in specific types of eukaryotic cells.

extinction vortex A downward population spiral in which inbreeding and genetic drift combine to cause a small population to shrink and, unless the spiral is reversed, become extinct.

extracellular matrix (ECM) The meshwork surrounding animal cells, consisting of glycoproteins, polysaccharides, and proteoglycans synthesized and secreted by cells.

extraembryonic membrane One of four membranes (yolk sac, amnion, chorion, and allantois) located outside the embryo that support the developing embryo in reptiles and mammals.

extreme halophile An organism that lives in a highly saline environment, such as the Great Salt Lake or the Dead Sea.

extreme thermophile An organism that thrives in hot environments (often 60–80°C or hotter).

extremophile An organism that lives in environmental conditions so extreme that few other species can survive there. Extremophiles include extreme halophiles ("salt lovers") and extreme thermophiles ("heat lovers").

F_1 generation The first filial, hybrid (heterozygous) offspring arising from a parental (P generation) cross.

F_2 generation The offspring resulting from interbreeding (or self-pollination) of the hybrid F_1 generation.

facilitated diffusion The passage of molecules or ions down their electrochemical gradient across a biological membrane with the assistance of specific transmembrane transport proteins, requiring no energy expenditure.

facilitation An interaction in which one species has a positive effect on the survival and reproduction of another species without the intimate association of a symbiosis.

facultative anaerobe (fak'-ul-tā'-tiv an'-uh-rōb) An organism that makes ATP by aerobic respiration if oxygen is present but that switches to anaerobic respiration or fermentation if oxygen is not present.

family In Linnaean classification, the taxonomic category above genus.

fast block to polyspermy The depolarization of the egg plasma membrane that begins within 1–3 seconds after a sperm binds to an egg membrane protein. The depolarization lasts about 1 minute and prevents additional sperm from fusing with the egg during that time.

fast-twitch fiber A muscle fiber used for rapid, powerful contractions.

fat A lipid consisting of three fatty acids linked to one glycerol molecule; also called a triacylglycerol or triglyceride.

fate map A territorial diagram of embryonic development that displays the future derivatives of individual cells and tissues.

fatty acid A carboxylic acid with a long carbon chain. Fatty acids vary in length and in the number and location of double bonds; three fatty acids linked to a glycerol molecule form a fat molecule, also called triacylglycerol or triglyceride.

feces (fē′-sēz) The wastes of the digestive tract.

feedback inhibition A method of metabolic control in which the end product of a metabolic pathway acts as an inhibitor of an enzyme within that pathway.

feedback regulation The regulation of a process by its output or end product.

fermentation A catabolic process that makes a limited amount of ATP from glucose (or other organic molecules) without an electron transport chain and that produces a characteristic end product, such as ethyl alcohol or lactic acid.

fertilization (1) The union of haploid gametes to produce a diploid zygote. (2) The addition of mineral nutrients to the soil.

fetus (fē′-tus) A developing mammal that has all the major structures of an adult. In humans, the fetal stage lasts from the 9th week of gestation until birth.

F factor In bacteria, the DNA segment that confers the ability to form pili for conjugation and associated functions required for the transfer of DNA from donor to recipient. The F factor may exist as a plasmid or be integrated into the bacterial chromosome.

fiber A lignified cell type that reinforces the xylem of angiosperms and functions in mechanical support; a slender, tapered sclerenchyma cell that usually occurs in bundles.

fibroblast (fī′-brō-blast) A type of cell in loose connective tissue that secretes the protein ingredients of the extracellular fibers.

fibronectin An extracellular glycoprotein secreted by animal cells that helps them attach to the extracellular matrix.

filament In an angiosperm, the stalk portion of the stamen, the pollen-producing reproductive organ of a flower.

filter feeder An animal that feeds by using a filtration mechanism to strain small organisms or food particles from its surroundings.

filtrate Cell-free fluid extracted from the body fluid by the excretory system.

filtration In excretory systems, the extraction of water and small solutes, including metabolic wastes, from the body fluid.

fimbria (plural, **fimbriae**) A short, hairlike appendage of a prokaryotic cell that helps it adhere to the substrate or to other cells.

first law of thermodynamics The principle of conservation of energy: Energy can be transferred and transformed, but it cannot be created or destroyed.

fission The separation of an organism into two or more individuals of approximately equal size.

fixed action pattern In animal behavior, a sequence of unlearned acts that is essentially unchangeable and, once initiated, usually carried to completion.

flaccid (flas′-id) Limp. Lacking turgor (stiffness or firmness), as in a plant cell in surroundings where there is a tendency for water to leave the cell. (A walled cell becomes flaccid if it has a higher water potential than its surroundings, resulting in the loss of water.)

flagellum (fluh-jel′-um) (plural, **flagella**) A long cellular appendage specialized for locomotion. Like motile cilia, eukaryotic flagella have a core with nine outer doublet microtubules and two inner single microtubules (the "9 + 2" arrangement) ensheathed in an extension of the plasma membrane. Prokaryotic flagella have a different structure.

florigen A flowering signal, probably a protein, that is made in leaves under certain conditions and that travels to the shoot apical meristems, inducing them to switch from vegetative to reproductive growth.

flower In an angiosperm, a specialized shoot with up to four sets of modified leaves, bearing structures that function in sexual reproduction.

fluid feeder An animal that lives by sucking nutrient-rich fluids from another living organism.

fluid mosaic model The currently accepted model of cell membrane structure, which envisions the membrane as a mosaic of protein molecules drifting laterally in a fluid bilayer of phospholipids.

follicle (fol′-uh-kul) A microscopic structure in the ovary that contains the developing oocyte and secretes estrogens.

follicle-stimulating hormone (FSH) (fol′-uh-kul) A tropic hormone that is produced and secreted by the anterior pituitary and that stimulates the production of eggs by the ovaries and sperm by the testes.

food chain The pathway along which food energy is transferred from trophic level to trophic level, beginning with producers.

food vacuole A membranous sac formed by phagocytosis of microorganisms or particles to be used as food by the cell.

food web The interconnected feeding relationships in an ecosystem.

foot (1) The portion of a bryophyte sporophyte that gathers sugars, amino acids, water, and minerals from the parent gametophyte via transfer cells. (2) One of the three main parts of a mollusc; a muscular structure usually used for movement. *See also* mantle and visceral mass.

foraging The seeking and obtaining of food.

foram (foraminiferan) An aquatic protist that secretes a hardened shell containing calcium carbonate and extends pseudopodia through pores in the shell.

forebrain One of three ancestral and embryonic regions of the vertebrate brain; develops into the thalamus, hypothalamus, and cerebrum.

fossil A preserved remnant or impression of an organism that lived in the past.

founder effect Genetic drift that occurs when a few individuals become isolated from a larger population and form a new population whose gene pool composition is not reflective of that of the original population.

fovea (fō′-vē-uh) The place on the retina at the eye's center of focus, where cones are highly concentrated.

F plasmid The plasmid form of the F factor.

fragmentation A means of asexual reproduction whereby a single parent breaks into parts that regenerate into whole new individuals.

frameshift mutation A mutation occurring when nucleotides are inserted in or deleted from a gene and the number inserted or deleted is not a multiple of three, resulting in the improper grouping of the subsequent nucleotides into codons.

free energy The portion of a biological system's energy that can perform work when temperature and pressure are uniform throughout the system. The change in free energy of a system (ΔG) is calculated by the equation $\Delta G = \Delta H - T\Delta S$, where ΔH is the change in enthalpy (in biological systems, equivalent to total energy), ΔT is the absolute temperature, and ΔS is the change in entropy.

frequency-dependent selection Selection in which the fitness of a phenotype depends on how common the phenotype is in a population.

fruit A mature ovary of a flower. The fruit protects dormant seeds and often functions in their dispersal.

functional group A specific configuration of atoms commonly attached to the carbon skeletons of organic molecules and involved in chemical reactions.

G_0 phase A nondividing state occupied by cells that have left the cell cycle, sometimes reversibly.

G_1 phase The first gap, or growth phase, of the cell cycle, consisting of the portion of interphase before DNA synthesis begins.

G_2 phase The second gap, or growth phase, of the cell cycle, consisting of the portion of interphase after DNA synthesis occurs.

gallbladder An organ that stores bile and releases it as needed into the small intestine.

game theory An approach to evaluating alternative strategies in situations where the outcome of a particular strategy depends on the strategies used by other individuals.

gametangium (gam′-uh-tan′-jē-um) (plural, **gametangia**) Multicellular plant structure in which gametes are formed. Female gametangia are called archegonia, and male gametangia are called antheridia.

gamete (gam′-ēt) A haploid reproductive cell, such as an egg or sperm. Gametes unite during sexual reproduction to produce a diploid zygote.

gametogenesis (guh-mē′-tō-gen′-uh-sis) The process by which gametes are produced.

gametophore (guh-mē′-tō-fōr) The mature gamete-producing structure of a moss gametophyte.

gametophyte (guh-mē′-tō-fīt) In organisms (plants and some algae) that have alternation of generations, the multicellular haploid form that produces haploid gametes by mitosis. The haploid gametes unite and develop into sporophytes.

gamma-aminobutyric acid (GABA) An amino acid that functions as a CNS neurotransmitter in the central nervous system of vertebrates.

ganglion (gang'-glē-uhn) (plural, **ganglia**) A cluster (functional group) of nerve cell bodies in a centralized nervous system.

gap junction A type of intercellular junction in animal cells, consisting of proteins surrounding a pore that allows the passage of materials between cells.

gas exchange The uptake of molecular oxygen from the environment and the discharge of carbon dioxide to the environment.

gastric juice A digestive fluid secreted by the stomach.

gastrovascular cavity A central cavity with a single opening in the body of certain animals, including cnidarians and flatworms, that functions in both the digestion and distribution of nutrients.

gastrula (gas'-trū-luh) An embryonic stage in animal development encompassing the formation of three layers: ectoderm, mesoderm, and endoderm.

gastrulation (gas'-trū-lā'-shun) In animal development, a series of cell and tissue movements in which the blastula-stage embryo folds inward, producing a three-layered embryo, the gastrula.

gated channel A transmembrane protein channel that opens or closes in response to a particular stimulus.

gated ion channel A gated channel for a specific ion. The opening or closing of such channels may alter a cell's membrane potential.

gel electrophoresis (ē-lek'-trō-fōr-ē'-sis) A technique for separating nucleic acids or proteins on the basis of their size and electrical charge, both of which affect their rate of movement through an electric field in a gel made of agarose or another polymer.

gene A discrete unit of hereditary information consisting of a specific nucleotide sequence in DNA (or RNA, in some viruses).

gene annotation Analysis of genomic sequences to identify protein-coding genes and determine the function of their products.

gene cloning The production of multiple copies of a gene.

gene expression The process by which information encoded in DNA directs the synthesis of proteins or, in some cases, RNAs that are not translated into proteins and instead function as RNAs.

gene flow The transfer of alleles from one population to another, resulting from the movement of fertile individuals or their gametes.

gene pool The aggregate of all copies of every type of allele at all loci in every individual in a population. The term is also used in a more restricted sense as the aggregate of alleles for just one or a few loci in a population.

gene therapy The introduction of genes into an afflicted individual for therapeutic purposes.

genetic drift A process in which chance events cause unpredictable fluctuations in allele frequencies from one generation to the next. Effects of genetic drift are most pronounced in small populations.

genetic engineering The direct manipulation of genes for practical purposes.

genetic map An ordered list of genetic loci (genes or other genetic markers) along a chromosome.

genetic profile An individual's unique set of genetic markers, detected most often today by PCR or, previously, by electrophoresis and nucleic acid probes.

genetic recombination General term for the production of offspring with combinations of traits that differ from those found in either parent.

genetic variation Differences among individuals in the composition of their genes or other DNA segments.

genetically modified (GM) organism An organism that has acquired one or more genes by artificial means; also called a transgenic organism.

genetics The scientific study of heredity and hereditary variation.

genome (jē'-nōm) The genetic material of an organism or virus; the complete complement of an organism's or virus's genes along with its noncoding nucleic acid sequences.

genome-wide association study (jē'-nōm) A large-scale analysis of the genomes of many people having a certain phenotype or disease, with the aim of finding genetic markers that correlate with that phenotype or disease.

genomic imprinting (juh-nō'-mik) A phenomenon in which expression of an allele in offspring depends on whether the allele is inherited from the male or female parent.

genomics (juh-nō'-miks) The systematic study of whole sets of genes (or other DNA) and their interactions within a species, as well as genome comparisons between species.

genotype (jē'-nō-tīp) The genetic makeup, or set of alleles, of an organism.

genus (jē'-nus) (plural, **genera**) A taxonomic category above the species level, designated by the first word of a species' two-part scientific name.

geologic record A standard time scale dividing Earth's history into time periods, grouped into four eons—Hadean, Archaean, Proterozoic, and Phanerozoic—and further subdivided into eras, periods, and epochs.

germ layer One of the three main layers in a gastrula that will form the various tissues and organs of an animal body.

gestation (jes-tā'-shun) *See* pregnancy.

gibberellin (jib'-uh-rel'-in) Any of a class of related plant hormones that stimulate growth in the stem and leaves, trigger the germination of seeds and breaking of bud dormancy, and (with auxin) stimulate fruit development.

glans The rounded structure at the tip of the clitoris or penis that is involved in sexual arousal.

glia (glial cells) Cells of the nervous system that support, regulate, and augment the functions of neurons.

global ecology The study of the functioning and distribution of organisms across the biosphere and how the regional exchange of energy and materials affects them.

glomeromycete (glō'-mer-ō-mī'-sēt) A member of the fungal phylum Glomeromycota, characterized by a distinct branching form of mycorrhizae called arbuscular mycorrhizae.

glomerulus (glō-mār'-yū-lus) A ball of capillaries surrounded by Bowman's capsule in the nephron and serving as the site of filtration in the vertebrate kidney.

glucocorticoid A steroid hormone that is secreted by the adrenal cortex and that influences glucose metabolism and immune function.

glucagon (glū'-kuh-gon) A hormone secreted by pancreatic alpha cells that raises blood glucose levels. It promotes glycogen breakdown and release of glucose by the liver.

glutamate An amino acid that functions as a neurotransmitter in the central nervous system.

glyceraldehyde 3-phosphate (G3P) (glis'-er-al'-de-hīd) A three-carbon carbohydrate that is the direct product of the Calvin cycle; it is also an intermediate in glycolysis.

glycogen (glī'-kō-jen) An extensively branched glucose storage polysaccharide found in the liver and muscle of animals; the animal equivalent of starch.

glycolipid A lipid with one or more covalently attached carbohydrates.

glycolysis (glī-kol'-uh-sis) A series of reactions that ultimately splits glucose into pyruvate. Glycolysis occurs in almost all living cells, serving as the starting point for fermentation or cellular respiration.

glycoprotein A protein with one or more covalently attached carbohydrates.

glycosidic linkage A covalent bond formed between two monosaccharides by a dehydration reaction.

gnathostome (na'-thu-stōm) A member of the vertebrate subgroup possessing jaws. The gnathostomes include sharks and rays, ray-finned fishes, coelacanths, lungfishes, amphibians, reptiles, and mammals.

golden alga A biflagellated, photosynthetic protist named for its color, which results from its yellow and brown carotenoids.

Golgi apparatus (gol'-jē) An organelle in eukaryotic cells consisting of stacks of flat membranous sacs that modify, store, and route products of the endoplasmic reticulum and synthesize some products, notably noncellulose carbohydrates.

gonad (gō'-nad) A male or female gamete-producing organ.

G protein A GTP-binding protein that relays signals from a plasma membrane signal receptor, known as a G protein-coupled receptor, to other signal transduction proteins inside the cell.

G protein-coupled receptor (GPCR) A signal receptor protein in the plasma membrane that responds to the binding of a signaling molecule by activating a G protein. Also called a G protein-linked receptor.

graded potential In a neuron, a shift in the membrane potential that has an amplitude proportional to signal strength and that decays as it spreads.

Gram stain A staining method that distinguishes between two different kinds of bacterial cell walls; may be used to help determine medical response to an infection.

gram-negative Describing the group of bacteria that have a cell wall that is structurally more complex and contains less peptidoglycan than the cell wall of gram-positive bacteria. Gram-negative bacteria are often more toxic than gram-positive bacteria.

gram-positive Describing the group of bacteria that have a cell wall that is structurally less complex and contains more peptidoglycan than the cell wall of gram-negative bacteria. Gram-positive bacteria are usually less toxic than gram-negative bacteria.

granum (gran'-um) (plural, **grana**) A stack of membrane-bounded thylakoids in the chloroplast. Grana function in the light reactions of photosynthesis.

gravitropism (grav'-uh-trō'-pizm) A response of a plant or animal to gravity.

gray matter Regions of clustered neuron cell bodies within the CNS.

green alga A photosynthetic protist, named for green chloroplasts that are similar in structure and pigment composition to the chloroplasts of land plants. Green algae are a paraphyletic group; some members are more closely related to land plants than they are to other green algae.

greenhouse effect The warming of Earth due to the atmospheric accumulation of carbon dioxide and certain other gases, which absorb reflected infrared radiation and reradiate some of it back toward Earth.

gross primary production (GPP) The total primary production of an ecosystem.

ground tissue system Plant tissues that are neither vascular nor dermal, fulfilling a variety of functions, such as storage, photosynthesis, and support.

growth factor (1) A protein that must be present in the extracellular environment (culture medium or animal body) for the growth and normal development of certain types of cells. (2) A local regulator that acts on nearby cells to stimulate cell proliferation and differentiation.

growth hormone (GH) A hormone that is produced and secreted by the anterior pituitary and that has both direct (nontropic) and tropic effects on a wide variety of tissues.

guard cells The two cells that flank the stomatal pore and regulate the opening and closing of the pore.

gustation The sense of taste.

guttation The exudation of water droplets from leaves, caused by root pressure in certain plants.

gymnosperm (jim'-nō-sperm) A vascular plant that bears naked seeds—seeds not enclosed in protective chambers.

hair cell A mechanosensory cell that alters output to the nervous system when hairlike projections on the cell surface are displaced.

half-life The amount of time it takes for 50% of a sample of a radioactive isotope to decay.

halophile *See* extreme halophile.

Hamilton's rule The principle that for natural selection to favor an altruistic act, the benefit to the recipient, devalued by the coefficient of relatedness, must exceed the cost to the altruist.

haploid cell (hap'-loyd) A cell containing only one set of chromosomes (*n*).

Hardy-Weinberg equilibrium The state of a population in which frequencies of alleles and genotypes remain constant from generation to generation, provided that only Mendelian segregation and recombination of alleles are at work.

haustorium (plural, **haustoria**) (ho-stōr'-ē-um, ho-stōr'-ē-uh) In certain symbiotic fungi, a specialized hypha that can penetrate the tissues of host organisms.

heart A muscular pump that uses metabolic energy to elevate the hydrostatic pressure of the circulatory fluid (blood or hemolymph). The fluid then flows down a pressure gradient through the body and eventually returns to the heart.

heart attack The damage or death of cardiac muscle tissue resulting from prolonged blockage of one or more coronary arteries.

heart murmur A hissing sound that most often results from blood squirting backward through a leaky valve in the heart.

heart rate The frequency of heart contraction (in beats per minute).

heat Thermal energy in transfer from one body of matter to another.

heat of vaporization The quantity of heat a liquid must absorb for 1 g of it to be converted from the liquid to the gaseous state.

heat-shock protein A protein that helps protect other proteins during heat stress. Heat-shock proteins are found in plants, animals, and microorganisms.

heavy chain One of the two types of polypeptide chains that make up an antibody molecule and B cell receptor; consists of a variable region, which contributes to the antigen-binding site, and a constant region.

helicase An enzyme that untwists the double helix of DNA at replication forks, separating the two strands and making them available as template strands.

helper T cell A type of T cell that, when activated, secretes cytokines that promote the response of B cells (humoral response) and cytotoxic T cells (cell-mediated response) to antigens.

hemoglobin (hē'-mō-glō'-bin) An iron-containing protein in red blood cells that reversibly binds oxygen.

hemolymph (hē'-mō-limf') In invertebrates with an open circulatory system, the body fluid that bathes tissues.

hemophilia (hē'-muh-fil'-ē-uh) A human genetic disease caused by a sex-linked recessive allele resulting in the absence of one or more blood-clotting proteins; characterized by excessive bleeding following injury.

hepatic portal vein A large vessel that conveys nutrient-laden blood from the small intestine to the liver, which regulates the blood's nutrient content.

herbivore (hur'-bi-vōr') An animal that mainly eats plants or algae.

herbivory An interaction in which an organism eats part of a plant or alga.

heredity The transmission of traits from one generation to the next.

hermaphrodite (hur-maf'-ruh-dīt') An individual that functions as both male and female in sexual reproduction by producing both sperm and eggs.

hermaphroditism (hur-maf'-rō-dī-tizm) A condition in which an individual has both female and male gonads and functions as both a male and a female in sexual reproduction by producing both sperm and eggs.

heterochromatin (het'-er-ō-krō'-muh-tin) Eukaryotic chromatin that remains highly compacted during interphase and is generally not transcribed.

heterochrony (het'-uh-rok'-ruh-nē) Evolutionary change in the timing or rate of an organism's development.

heterocyst (het'-er-ō-sist) A specialized cell that engages in nitrogen fixation in some filamentous cyanobacteria; also called a heterocyte.

heterokaryon (het'-er-ō-kâr'-ē-un) A fungal mycelium that contains two or more haploid nuclei per cell.

heteromorphic (het'-er-ō-mōr'-fik) Referring to a condition in the life cycle of plants and certain algae in which the sporophyte and gametophyte generations differ in morphology.

heterosporous (het-er-os'-pōr-us) Referring to a plant species that has two kinds of spores: microspores, which develop into male gametophytes, and megaspores, which develop into female gametophytes.

heterotroph (het'-er-ō-trōf) An organism that obtains organic food molecules by eating other organisms or substances derived from them.

heterozygote advantage Greater reproductive success of heterozygous individuals compared with homozygotes; tends to preserve variation in a gene pool.

heterozygous (het'-er-ō-zī'-gus) Having two different alleles for a given gene.

hibernation A long-term physiological state in which metabolism decreases, the heart and respiratory system slow down, and body temperature is maintained at a lower level than normal.

high-density lipoprotein (HDL) A particle in the blood made up of thousands of cholesterol molecules and other lipids bound to a protein. HDL scavenges excess cholesterol.

hindbrain One of three ancestral and embryonic regions of the vertebrate brain; develops into the medulla oblongata, pons, and cerebellum.

histamine (his'-tuh-mēn) A substance released by mast cells that causes blood vessels to dilate and become more permeable in inflammatory and allergic responses.

histogram A variant of a bar graph that is made for numeric data by first grouping, or "binning," the variable plotted on the *x*-axis into intervals of equal width. The "bins" may be integers or ranges of numbers. The height of each bar shows the percent or number of experimental subjects whose characteristics can be described by one of the intervals plotted on the *x*-axis.

histone (his'-tōn) A small protein with a high proportion of positively charged amino acids that binds to the negatively charged DNA and plays a key role in chromatin structure.

histone acetylation (his'-tōn) The attachment of acetyl groups to certain amino acids of histone proteins.

HIV (human immunodeficiency virus) The infectious agent that causes AIDS. HIV is a retrovirus.

holdfast A rootlike structure that anchors a seaweed.

holoblastic (hō'-lō-blas'-tik) Referring to a type of cleavage in which there is complete division of the egg; occurs in eggs that have little yolk (such as those of the sea urchin) or a moderate amount of yolk (such as those of the frog).

homeobox (hō'-mē-ō-boks') A 180-nucleotide sequence within homeotic genes and some other developmental genes that is widely conserved in animals. Related sequences occur in plants and yeasts.

homeostasis (hō'-mē-ō-stā'-sis) The steady-state physiological condition of the body.

homeotic gene (hō-mē-o'-tik) Any of the master regulatory genes that control placement and spatial organization of body parts in animals, plants, and fungi by controlling the developmental fate of groups of cells.

hominin (hō'-mi-nin) A member of the human branch of the evolutionary tree. Hominins include *Homo sapiens* and our ancestors, a group of extinct species that are more closely related to us than to chimpanzees.

homologous chromosomes (or **homologs**) (hō-mol'-uh-gus) A pair of chromosomes of the same length, centromere position, and staining pattern that possess genes for the same characters at corresponding loci. One homologous chromosome is inherited from the organism's father, the other from the mother. Also called a homologous pair.

homologous structures (hō-mol'-uh-gus) Structures in different species that are similar because of common ancestry.

homology (hō-mol'-ō-jē) Similarity in characteristics resulting from a shared ancestry.

homoplasy (hō'-muh-play'-zē) A similar (analogous) structure or molecular sequence that has evolved independently in two species.

homosporous (hō-mos'-puh-rus) Referring to a plant species that has a single kind of spore, which typically develops into a bisexual gametophyte.

homozygous (hō'-mō-zī'-gus) Having two identical alleles for a given gene.

horizontal gene transfer The transfer of genes from one genome to another through mechanisms such as transposable elements, plasmid exchange, viral activity, and perhaps fusions of different organisms.

hormone In multicellular organisms, one of many types of secreted chemicals that are formed in specialized cells, travel in body fluids, and act on specific target cells in other parts of the organism, changing the target cells' functioning.

hornwort A small, herbaceous, nonvascular plant that is a member of the phylum Anthocerophyta.

host The larger participant in a symbiotic relationship, often providing a home and food source for the smaller symbiont.

host range The limited number of species whose cells can be infected by a particular virus.

Human Genome Project An international collaborative effort to map and sequence the DNA of the entire human genome.

human immunodeficiency virus (HIV) The infectious agent that causes AIDS (acquired immunodeficiency syndrome). HIV is a retrovirus.

humoral immune response (hyū'-mer-ul) The branch of adaptive immunity that involves the activation of B cells and that leads to the production of antibodies, which defend against bacteria and viruses in body fluids.

humus (hyū'-mus) Decomposing organic material that is a component of topsoil.

Huntington's disease A human genetic disease caused by a dominant allele; characterized by uncontrollable body movements and degeneration of the nervous system; usually fatal 10 to 20 years after the onset of symptoms.

hybrid Offspring that results from the mating of individuals from two different species or from two true-breeding varieties of the same species.

hybrid zone A geographic region in which members of different species meet and mate, producing at least some offspring of mixed ancestry.

hybridization In genetics, the mating, or crossing, of two true-breeding varieties.

hydration shell The sphere of water molecules around a dissolved ion.

hydrocarbon An organic molecule consisting only of carbon and hydrogen.

hydrogen bond A type of weak chemical bond that is formed when the slightly positive hydrogen atom of a polar covalent bond in one molecule is attracted to the slightly negative atom of a polar covalent bond in another molecule or in another region of the same molecule.

hydrogen ion A single proton with a charge of 1+. The dissociation of a water molecule (H_2O) leads to the generation of a hydroxide ion (OH^-) and a hydrogen ion (H^+); in water, H^+ is not found alone but associates with a water molecule to form a hydronium ion.

hydrolysis (hī-drol'-uh-sis) A chemical reaction that breaks bonds between two molecules by the addition of water; functions in disassembly of polymers to monomers.

hydronium ion A water molecule that has an extra proton bound to it; H_3O^+, commonly represented as H^+.

hydrophilic (hī'-drō-fil'-ik) Having an affinity for water.

hydrophobic (hī'-drō-fō'-bik) Having no affinity for water; tending to coalesce and form droplets in water.

hydrophobic interaction (hī'-drō-fō'-bik) A type of weak chemical interaction caused when molecules that do not mix with water coalesce to exclude water.

hydroponic culture A method in which plants are grown in mineral solutions rather than in soil.

hydrostatic skeleton A skeletal system composed of fluid held under pressure in a closed body compartment; the main skeleton of most cnidarians, flatworms, nematodes, and annelids.

hydrothermal vent An area on the deep seafloor where heated water and minerals from Earth's interior gush into the seawater.

hydroxide ion A water molecule that has lost a proton; OH^-.

hydroxyl group (hī-drok'-sil) A chemical group consisting of an oxygen atom joined to a hydrogen atom. Molecules possessing this group are soluble in water and are called alcohols.

hyperpolarization A change in a cell's membrane potential such that the inside of the membrane becomes more negative relative to the outside. Hyperpolarization reduces the chance that a neuron will transmit a nerve impulse.

hypersensitive response A plant's localized defense response to a pathogen, involving the death of cells around the site of infection.

hypertension A disorder in which blood pressure remains abnormally high.

hypertonic Referring to a solution that, when surrounding a cell, will cause the cell to lose water.

hypha (plural, **hyphae**) (hī'-fuh, hī'-fē) One of many connected filaments that collectively make up the mycelium of a fungus.

hypocotyl (hī'-puh-cot'-ul) In an angiosperm embryo, the embryonic axis below the point of attachment of the cotyledon(s) and above the radicle.

hypothalamus (hī'-pō-thal'-uh-mus) The ventral part of the vertebrate forebrain; functions in maintaining homeostasis, especially in coordinating the endocrine and nervous systems; secretes hormones of the posterior pituitary and releasing factors that regulate the anterior pituitary.

hypothesis (hī-poth'-uh-sis) A testable explanation for a set of observations based on the available data and guided by inductive reasoning. A hypothesis is narrower in scope than a theory.

hypotonic Referring to a solution that, when surrounding a cell, will cause the cell to take up water.

imbibition The physical adsorption of water onto the internal surfaces of structures.

immigration The influx of new individuals into a population from other areas.

immune system An organism's system of defenses against agents that cause disease.

immunization The process of generating a state of immunity by artificial means. In vaccination, an inactive or weakened form of a pathogen is administered, inducing B and T cell responses and immunological memory. In passive immunization, antibodies specific for a particular pathogen are administered, conferring immediate but temporary protection.

immunoglobulin (Ig) (im′-yū-nō-glob′-yū-lin) *See* antibody.

imprinting In animal behavior, the formation at a specific stage in life of a long-lasting behavioral response to a specific individual or object. *See also* genomic imprinting.

inclusive fitness The total effect an individual has on proliferating its genes by producing its own offspring and by providing aid that enables other close relatives to increase production of their offspring.

incomplete dominance The situation in which the phenotype of heterozygotes is intermediate between the phenotypes of individuals homozygous for either allele.

incomplete flower A flower in which one or more of the four basic floral organs (sepals, petals, stamens, or carpels) are either absent or nonfunctional.

incomplete metamorphosis A type of development in certain insects, such as grasshoppers, in which the young (called nymphs) resemble adults but are smaller and have different body proportions. The nymph goes through a series of molts, each time looking more like an adult, until it reaches full size.

independent variable A variable whose value is manipulated or changed during an experiment or other test to reveal possible effects on another variable (the dependent variable).

indeterminate cleavage A type of embryonic development in deuterostomes in which each cell produced by early cleavage divisions retains the capacity to develop into a complete embryo.

indeterminate growth A type of growth characteristic of plants, in which the organism continues to grow as long as it lives.

induced fit Caused by entry of the substrate, the change in shape of the active site of an enzyme so that it binds more snugly to the substrate.

inducer A specific small molecule that binds to a bacterial repressor protein and changes the repressor's shape so that it cannot bind to an operator, thus switching an operon on.

induction A process in which a group of cells or tissues influences the development of another group through close-range interactions.

inductive reasoning A type of logic in which generalizations are based on a large number of specific observations.

inflammatory response An innate immune defense triggered by physical injury or infection of tissue involving the release of substances that promote swelling, enhance the infiltration of white blood cells, and aid in tissue repair and destruction of invading pathogens.

inflorescence A group of flowers tightly clustered together.

ingestion The first stage of food processing in animals: the act of eating.

ingroup A species or group of species whose evolutionary relationships are being examined in a given analysis.

inhibitory postsynaptic potential (IPSP) An electrical change (usually hyperpolarization) in the membrane of a postsynaptic neuron caused by the binding of an inhibitory neurotransmitter from a presynaptic cell to a postsynaptic receptor; makes it more difficult for a postsynaptic neuron to generate an action potential.

innate behavior Animal behavior that is developmentally fixed and under strong genetic control. Innate behavior is exhibited in virtually the same form by all individuals in a population despite internal and external environmental differences during development and throughout their lifetimes.

innate immunity A form of defense common to all animals that is active immediately upon exposure to a pathogen and that is the same whether or not the pathogen has been encountered previously.

inner cell mass An inner cluster of cells at one end of a mammalian blastocyst that subsequently develops into the embryo proper and some of the extraembryonic membranes.

inositol trisphosphate (IP$_3$) (in-ō′-suh-tol) A second messenger that functions as an intermediate between certain signaling molecules and a subsequent second messenger, Ca^{2+}, by causing a rise in cytoplasmic Ca^{2+} concentration.

inquiry The search for information and explanation, often focusing on specific questions.

insertion A mutation involving the addition of one or more nucleotide pairs to a gene.

in situ hybridization A technique using nucleic acid hybridization with a labeled probe to detect the location of a specific mRNA in an intact organism.

insulin (in′-suh-lin) A hormone secreted by pancreatic beta cells that lowers blood glucose levels. It promotes the uptake of glucose by most body cells and the synthesis and storage of glycogen in the liver and also stimulates protein and fat synthesis.

integral protein A transmembrane protein with hydrophobic regions that extend into and often completely span the hydrophobic interior of the membrane and with hydrophilic regions in contact with the aqueous solution on one or both sides of the membrane (or lining the channel in the case of a channel protein).

integrin (in′-tuh-grin) In animal cells, a transmembrane receptor protein with two subunits that interconnects the extracellular matrix and the cytoskeleton.

integument (in-teg′-yū-ment) Layer of sporophyte tissue that contributes to the structure of an ovule of a seed plant.

integumentary system The outer covering of a mammal's body, including skin, hair, and nails, claws, or hooves.

intercalated disk (in-ter′-kuh-lā′-ted) A specialized junction between cardiac muscle cells that provides direct electrical coupling between the cells.

interferon (in′-ter-fēr′-on) A protein that has antiviral or immune regulatory functions. Interferon-α and interferon-β, secreted by virus-infected cells, help nearby cells resist viral infection; interferon-γ, secreted by T cells, helps activate macrophages.

intermediate disturbance hypothesis The concept that moderate levels of disturbance can foster greater species diversity than low or high levels of disturbance.

intermediate filament A component of the cytoskeleton that includes filaments intermediate in size between microtubules and microfilaments.

interneuron An association neuron; a nerve cell within the central nervous system that forms synapses with sensory and/or motor neurons and integrates sensory input and motor output.

internode A segment of a plant stem between the points where leaves are attached.

interphase The period in the cell cycle when the cell is not dividing. During interphase, cellular metabolic activity is high, chromosomes and organelles are duplicated, and cell size may increase. Interphase often accounts for about 90% of the cell cycle.

intersexual selection A form of natural selection in which individuals of one sex (usually the females) are choosy in selecting their mates from the other sex; also called mate choice.

interspecific competition Competition for resources between individuals of two or more species when resources are in short supply.

interspecific interaction A relationship between individuals of two or more species in a community.

interstitial fluid The fluid filling the spaces between cells in most animals.

intertidal zone The shallow zone of the ocean adjacent to land and between the high- and low-tide lines.

intrasexual selection A form of natural selection in which there is direct competition among individuals of one sex for mates of the opposite sex.

introduced species A species moved by humans, either intentionally or accidentally, from its native location to a new geographic region; also called non-native or exotic species.

intron (in′-tron) A noncoding, intervening sequence within a primary transcript that is removed from the transcript during RNA processing; also refers to the region of DNA from which this sequence was transcribed.

invasive species A species, often introduced by humans, that takes hold outside its native range.

inversion An aberration in chromosome structure resulting from reattachment of a chromosomal fragment in a reverse orientation to the chromosome from which it originated.

invertebrate An animal without a backbone. Invertebrates make up 95% of animal species.

in vitro fertilization (IVF) (vē′-trō) Fertilization of oocytes in laboratory containers followed by artificial implantation of the early embryo in the mother's uterus.

in vitro mutagenesis A technique used to discover the function of a gene by cloning it, introducing specific changes into the cloned gene's sequence, reinserting the mutated gene into a cell, and studying the phenotype of the mutant.

ion (ī'-on) An atom or group of atoms that has gained or lost one or more electrons, thus acquiring a charge.

ion channel (ī'-on) A transmembrane protein channel that allows a specific ion to diffuse across the membrane down its concentration or electrochemical gradient.

ionic bond (ī-on'-ik) A chemical bond resulting from the attraction between oppositely charged ions.

ionic compound (ī-on'-ik) A compound resulting from the formation of an ionic bond; also called a salt.

iris The colored part of the vertebrate eye, formed by the anterior portion of the choroid.

isomer (ī'-sō-mer) One of several compounds with the same molecular formula but different structures and therefore different properties. The three types of isomers are structural isomers, *cis-trans* isomers, and enantiomers.

isomorphic Referring to alternating generations in plants and certain algae in which the sporophytes and gametophytes look alike, although they differ in chromosome number.

isotonic (ī'-sō-ton'-ik) Referring to a solution that, when surrounding a cell, causes no net movement of water into or out of the cell.

isotope (ī'-sō-tōp') One of several atomic forms of an element, each with the same number of protons but a different number of neutrons, thus differing in atomic mass.

iteroparity Reproduction in which adults produce offspring over many years; also called repeated reproduction.

jasmonate Any of a class of plant hormones that regulate a wide range of developmental processes in plants and play a key role in plant defense against herbivores.

joule (J) A unit of energy: 1 J = 0.239 cal; 1 cal = 4.184 J.

juxtaglomerular apparatus (JGA) (juks'-tuh-gluh-mār'-yū-ler) A specialized tissue in nephrons that releases the enzyme renin in response to a drop in blood pressure or volume.

juxtamedullary nephron In mammals and birds, a nephron with a loop of Henle that extends far into the renal medulla.

karyogamy (kār'-ē-og'-uh-mē) In fungi, the fusion of haploid nuclei contributed by the two parents; occurs as one stage of sexual reproduction, preceded by plasmogamy.

karyotype (kār'-ē-ō-tīp) A display of the chromosome pairs of a cell arranged by size and shape.

keystone species A species that is not necessarily abundant in a community yet exerts strong control on community structure by the nature of its ecological role or niche.

kidney In vertebrates, one of a pair of excretory organs where blood filtrate is formed and processed into urine.

kilocalorie (kcal) A thousand calories; the amount of heat energy required to raise the temperature of 1 kg of water by 1°C.

kinetic energy (kuh-net'-ik) The energy associated with the relative motion of objects.

Moving matter can perform work by imparting motion to other matter.

kinetic energy (kuh-net'-ik) The energy associated with the relative motion of objects. Moving matter can perform work by imparting motion to other matter.

kinetochore (kuh-net'-uh-kōr) A structure of proteins attached to the centromere that links each sister chromatid to the mitotic spindle.

kinetoplastid A protist, such as a trypanosome, that has a single large mitochondrion that houses an organized mass of DNA.

kingdom A taxonomic category, the second broadest after domain.

kin selection Natural selection that favors altruistic behavior by enhancing the reproductive success of relatives.

***K*-selection** Selection for life history traits that are sensitive to population density; also called density-dependent selection.

labia majora A pair of thick, fatty ridges that encloses and protects the rest of the vulva.

labia minora A pair of slender skin folds that surrounds the openings of the vagina and urethra.

lacteal (lak'-tē-ul) A tiny lymph vessel extending into the core of an intestinal villus and serving as the destination for absorbed chylomicrons.

lactic acid fermentation Glycolysis followed by the reduction of pyruvate to lactate, regenerating NAD$^+$ with no release of carbon dioxide.

lagging strand A discontinuously synthesized DNA strand that elongates by means of Okazaki fragments, each synthesized in a 5' → 3' direction away from the replication fork.

lancelet A member of the clade Cephalochordata, small blade-shaped marine chordates that lack a backbone.

landscape An area containing several different ecosystems linked by exchanges of energy, materials, and organisms.

landscape ecology The study of how the spatial arrangement of habitat types affects the distribution and abundance of organisms and ecosystem processes.

large intestine The portion of the vertebrate alimentary canal between the small intestine and the anus; functions mainly in water absorption and the formation of feces.

larva (lar'-vuh) (plural, **larvae**) A free-living, sexually immature form in some animal life cycles that may differ from the adult animal in morphology, nutrition, and habitat.

larynx (lār'-inks) The portion of the respiratory tract containing the vocal cords; also called the voice box.

lateralization Segregation of functions in the cortex of the left and right cerebral hemispheres.

lateral line system A mechanoreceptor system consisting of a series of pores and receptor units along the sides of the body in fishes and aquatic amphibians; detects water movements made by the animal itself and by other moving objects.

lateral meristem (mār'-uh-stem) A meristem that thickens the roots and shoots of woody

plants. The vascular cambium and cork cambium are lateral meristems.

lateral root A root that arises from the pericycle of an established root.

law of conservation of mass A physical law stating that matter can change form but cannot be created or destroyed. In a closed system, the mass of the system is constant.

law of independent assortment Mendel's second law, stating that each pair of alleles segregates, or assorts, independently of each other pair during gamete formation; applies when genes for two characters are located on different pairs of homologous chromosomes or when they are far enough apart on the same chromosome to behave as though they are on different chromosomes.

law of segregation Mendel's first law, stating that the two alleles in a pair segregate (separate from each other) into different gametes during gamete formation.

leading strand The new complementary DNA strand synthesized continuously along the template strand toward the replication fork in the mandatory 5' → 3' direction.

leaf The main photosynthetic organ of vascular plants.

leaf primordium (plural, **primordia**) A finger-like projection along the flank of a shoot apical meristem, from which a leaf arises.

learning The modification of behavior as a result of specific experiences.

lens The structure in an eye that focuses light rays onto the photoreceptors.

lenticel (len'-ti-sel) A small raised area in the bark of stems and roots that enables gas exchange between living cells and the outside air.

lepidosaur (leh-pid'-uh-sōr) A member of the reptilian group that includes lizards, snakes, and two species of New Zealand animals called tuataras.

leukocyte (lū'-kō-sīt') A blood cell that functions in fighting infections; also called a white blood cell.

lichen The mutualistic association between a fungus and a photosynthetic alga or cyanobacterium.

life cycle The generation-to-generation sequence of stages in the reproductive history of an organism.

life history The traits that affect an organism's schedule of reproduction and survival.

life table An age-specific summary of the survival pattern of a population.

ligament A fibrous connective tissue that joins bones together at joints.

ligand (lig'-und) A molecule that binds specifically to another molecule, usually a larger one.

ligand-gated ion channel (lig'-und) A transmembrane protein containing a pore that opens or closes as it changes shape in response to a signaling molecule (ligand), allowing or blocking the flow of specific ions; also called an ionotropic receptor.

light chain One of the two types of polypeptide chains that make up an antibody molecule and B cell receptor; consists of a variable region, which contributes to the antigen-binding site, and a constant region.

light-harvesting complex A complex of proteins associated with pigment molecules (including chlorophyll *a*, chlorophyll *b*, and carotenoids) that captures light energy and transfers it to reaction-center pigments in a photosystem.

light microscope (LM) An optical instrument with lenses that refract (bend) visible light to magnify images of specimens.

light reactions The first of two major stages in photosynthesis (preceding the Calvin cycle). These reactions, which occur on the thylakoid membranes of the chloroplast or on membranes of certain prokaryotes, convert solar energy to the chemical energy of ATP and NADPH, releasing oxygen in the process.

lignin (lig'-nin) A strong polymer embedded in the cellulose matrix of the secondary cell walls of vascular plants that provides structural support in terrestrial species.

limiting nutrient An element that must be added for production to increase in a particular area.

limnetic zone In a lake, the well-lit, open surface waters far from shore.

linear electron flow A route of electron flow during the light reactions of photosynthesis that involves both photosystems (I and II) and produces ATP, NADPH, and O_2. The net electron flow is from H_2O to $NADP^+$.

line graph A graph in which each data point is connected to the next point in the data set with a straight line.

linkage map A genetic map based on the frequencies of recombination between markers during crossing over of homologous chromosomes.

linked genes Genes located close enough together on a chromosome that they tend to be inherited together.

lipid (lip'-id) Any of a group of large biological molecules, including fats, phospholipids, and steroids, that mix poorly, if at all, with water.

littoral zone In a lake, the shallow, well-lit waters close to shore.

liver A large internal organ in vertebrates that performs diverse functions, such as producing bile, maintaining blood glucose level, and detoxifying poisonous chemicals in the blood.

liverwort A small, herbaceous, nonvascular plant that is a member of the phylum Hepatophyta.

loam The most fertile soil type, made up of roughly equal amounts of sand, silt, and clay.

lobe-fin A member of the vertebrate clade Sarcopterygii, osteichthyans with rod-shaped muscular fins, including coelacanths, lungfishes, and tetrapods.

local regulator A secreted molecule that influences cells near where it is secreted.

locomotion Active motion from place to place.

locus (lō'-kus) (plural, **loci**) (lō'-sī) A specific place along the length of a chromosome where a given gene is located.

logistic population growth Population growth that levels off as population size approaches carrying capacity.

long-day plant A plant that flowers (usually in late spring or early summer) only when the light period is longer than a critical length.

long-term memory The ability to hold, associate, and recall information over one's lifetime.

long-term potentiation (LTP) An enhanced responsiveness to an action potential (nerve signal) by a receiving neuron.

loop of Henle (hen'-lē) The hairpin turn, with a descending and ascending limb, between the proximal and distal tubules of the vertebrate kidney; functions in water and salt reabsorption.

lophophore (lof'-uh-fōr) In some lophotrochozoan animals, including brachiopods, a crown of ciliated tentacles that surround the mouth and function in feeding.

Lophotrochozoa (lo-phah'-truh-kō-zō'-uh) One of the three main lineages of bilaterian animals; lophotrochozoans include organisms that have lophophores or trochophore larvae. *See also* Deuterostomia and Ecdysozoa.

low-density lipoprotein (LDL) A particle in the blood made up of thousands of cholesterol molecules and other lipids bound to a protein. LDL transports cholesterol from the liver for incorporation into cell membranes.

lung An infolded respiratory surface of a terrestrial vertebrate, land snail, or spider that connects to the atmosphere by narrow tubes.

luteinizing hormone (LH) (lū'-tē-uh-nī'-zing) A tropic hormone that is produced and secreted by the anterior pituitary and that stimulates ovulation in females and androgen production in males.

lycophyte (lī'-kuh-fīt) An informal name for a member of the phylum Lycophyta, which includes club mosses, spike mosses, and quillworts.

lymph The colorless fluid, derived from interstitial fluid, in the lymphatic system of vertebrates.

lymph node An organ located along a lymph vessel. Lymph nodes filter lymph and contain cells that attack viruses and bacteria.

lymphatic system A system of vessels and nodes, separate from the circulatory system, that returns fluid, proteins, and cells to the blood.

lymphocyte A type of white blood cell that mediates immune responses. The two main classes are B cells and T cells.

lysogenic cycle (lī'-sō-jen'-ik) A type of phage replicative cycle in which the viral genome becomes incorporated into the bacterial host chromosome as a prophage, is replicated along with the chromosome, and does not kill the host.

lysosome (lī'-suh-sōm) A membrane-enclosed sac of hydrolytic enzymes found in the cytoplasm of animal cells and some protists.

lysozyme (lī'-sō-zīm) An enzyme that destroys bacterial cell walls; in mammals, it is found in sweat, tears, and saliva.

lytic cycle (lit'-ik) A type of phage replicative cycle resulting in the release of new phages by lysis (and death) of the host cell.

macroclimate Large-scale patterns in climate; the climate of an entire region.

macroevolution Evolutionary change above the species level. Examples of macroevolutionary change include the origin of a new group of organisms through a series of speciation events and the impact of mass extinctions on the diversity of life and its subsequent recovery.

macromolecule A giant molecule formed by the joining of smaller molecules, usually by a dehydration reaction. Polysaccharides, proteins, and nucleic acids are macromolecules.

macronutrient An essential element that an organism must obtain in relatively large amounts. *See also* micronutrient.

macrophage (mak'-rō-fāj) A phagocytic cell present in many tissues that functions in innate immunity by destroying microbes and in acquired immunity as an antigen-presenting cell.

magnoliid A member of the angiosperm clade that is most closely related to the combined eudicot and monocot clades. Extant examples are magnolias, laurels, and black pepper plants.

major depressive disorder A mood disorder characterized by feelings of sadness, lack of self-worth, emptiness, or loss of interest in nearly all things.

major histocompatibility complex (MHC) molecule A host protein that functions in antigen presentation. Foreign MHC molecules on transplanted tissue can trigger T cell responses that may lead to rejection of the transplant.

malignant tumor A cancerous tumor containing cells that have significant genetic and cellular changes and are capable of invading and surviving in new sites. Malignant tumors can impair the functions of one or more organs.

Malpighian tubule (mal-pig'-ē-un) A unique excretory organ of insects that empties into the digestive tract, removes nitrogenous wastes from the hemolymph, and functions in osmoregulation.

mammal A member of the clade Mammalia, amniotes that have hair and mammary glands (glands that produce milk).

mammary gland An exocrine gland that secretes milk for nourishing the young. Mammary glands are characteristic of mammals.

mantle One of the three main parts of a mollusc; a fold of tissue that drapes over the mollusc's visceral mass and may secrete a shell. *See also* foot and visceral mass.

mantle cavity A water-filled chamber that houses the gills, anus, and excretory pores of a mollusc.

map unit A unit of measurement of the distance between genes. One map unit is equivalent to a 1% recombination frequency.

marine benthic zone The ocean floor.

mark-recapture method A sampling technique used to estimate the size of animal populations.

marsupial (mar-sū'-pē-ul) A mammal, such as a koala, kangaroo, or opossum, whose young complete their embryonic development inside a maternal pouch called the marsupium.

mass extinction The elimination of a large number of species throughout Earth, the result of global environmental changes.

mass number The sum of the number of protons and neutrons in an atom's nucleus.

mast cell A vertebrate body cell that produces histamine and other molecules that trigger inflammation in response to infection and in allergic reactions.

mate-choice copying Behavior in which individuals in a population copy the mate choice of others, apparently as a result of social learning.

maternal effect gene A gene that, when mutant in the mother, results in a mutant phenotype in the offspring, regardless of the offspring's genotype. Maternal effect genes, also called egg-polarity genes, were first identified in *Drosophila melanogaster*.

matter Anything that takes up space and has mass.

maximum likelihood As applied to DNA sequence data, a principle that states that when considering multiple phylogenetic hypotheses, one should take into account the hypothesis that reflects the most likely sequence of evolutionary events, given certain rules about how DNA changes over time.

maximum parsimony A principle that states that when considering multiple explanations for an observation, one should first investigate the simplest explanation that is consistent with the facts.

mean The sum of all data points in a data set divided by the number of data points.

mechanoreceptor A sensory receptor that detects physical deformation in the body's environment associated with pressure, touch, stretch, motion, or sound.

medulla oblongata (meh-dul'-uh ōb'-long-go'-tuh) The lowest part of the vertebrate brain, commonly called the medulla; a swelling of the hindbrain anterior to the spinal cord that controls autonomic, homeostatic functions, including breathing, heart and blood vessel activity, swallowing, digestion, and vomiting.

medusa (plural, **medusae**) (muh-dū'-suh) The floating, flattened, mouth-down version of the cnidarian body plan. The alternate form is the polyp.

megapascal (MPa) (meg'-uh-pas-kal') A unit of pressure equivalent to about 10 atmospheres of pressure.

megaphyll (meh'-guh-fil) A leaf with a highly branched vascular system, characteristic of the vast majority of vascular plants. *See also* microphyll.

megaspore A spore from a heterosporous plant species that develops into a female gametophyte.

meiosis (mī-ō'-sis) A modified type of cell division in sexually reproducing organisms consisting of two rounds of cell division but only one round of DNA replication. It results in cells with half the number of chromosome sets as the original cell.

meiosis I (mī-ō'-sis) The first division of a two-stage process of cell division in sexually reproducing organisms that results in cells with half the number of chromosome sets as the original cell.

meiosis II (mī-ō'-sis) The second division of a two-stage process of cell division in sexually reproducing organisms that results in cells with half the number of chromosome sets as the original cell.

melanocyte-stimulating hormone (MSH) A hormone produced and secreted by the anterior pituitary with multiple activities, including regulating the behavior of pigment-containing cells in the skin of some vertebrates.

melatonin A hormone that is secreted by the pineal gland and that is involved in the regulation of biological rhythms and sleep.

membrane potential The difference in electrical charge (voltage) across a cell's plasma membrane due to the differential distribution of ions. Membrane potential affects the activity of excitable cells and the transmembrane movement of all charged substances.

memory cell One of a clone of long-lived lymphocytes, formed during the primary immune response, that remains in a lymphoid organ until activated by exposure to the same antigen that triggered its formation. Activated memory cells mount the secondary immune response.

menopause The cessation of ovulation and menstruation marking the end of a human female's reproductive years.

menstrual cycle (men'-strū-ul) *See* uterine cycle.

menstruation The shedding of portions of the endometrium during a uterine (menstrual) cycle.

meristem (mār'-uh-stem) Plant tissue that remains embryonic as long as the plant lives, allowing for indeterminate growth.

meristem identity gene (mār'-uh-stem) A plant gene that promotes the switch from vegetative growth to flowering.

meroblastic (mār'-ō-blas'-tik) Referring to a type of cleavage in which there is incomplete division of a yolk-rich egg, characteristic of avian development.

mesoderm (mez'-ō-derm) The middle primary germ layer in a triploblastic animal embryo; develops into the notochord, the lining of the coelom, muscles, skeleton, gonads, kidneys, and most of the circulatory system in species that have these structures.

mesohyl (mez'-ō-hīl) A gelatinous region between the two layers of cells of a sponge.

mesophyll (mez'-ō-fil) Leaf cells specialized for photosynthesis. In C_3 and CAM plants, mesophyll cells are located between the upper and lower epidermis; in C_4 plants, they are located between the bundle-sheath cells and the epidermis.

messenger RNA (mRNA) A type of RNA, synthesized using a DNA template, that attaches to ribosomes in the cytoplasm and specifies the primary structure of a protein. (In eukaryotes, the primary RNA transcript must undergo RNA processing to become mRNA.)

metabolic pathway A series of chemical reactions that either builds a complex molecule (anabolic pathway) or breaks down a complex molecule to simpler molecules (catabolic pathway).

metabolic rate The total amount of energy an animal uses in a unit of time.

metabolism (muh-tab'-uh-lizm) The totality of an organism's chemical reactions, consisting of catabolic and anabolic pathways, which manage the material and energy resources of the organism.

metagenomics The collection and sequencing of DNA from a group of species, usually an environmental sample of microorganisms. Computer software sorts partial sequences and assembles them into genome sequences of individual species making up the sample.

metamorphosis (met'-uh-mōr'-fuh-sis) A developmental transformation that turns an animal larva into either an adult or an adult-like stage that is not yet sexually mature.

metanephridium (met'-uh-nuh-frid'-ē-um) (plural, **metanephridia**) An excretory organ found in many invertebrates that typically consists of tubules connecting ciliated internal openings to external openings.

metaphase The third stage of mitosis, in which the spindle is complete and the chromosomes, attached to microtubules at their kinetochores, are all aligned at the metaphase plate.

metaphase plate An imaginary structure located at a plane midway between the two poles of a cell in metaphase on which the centromeres of all the duplicated chromosomes are located.

metapopulation A group of spatially separated populations of one species that interact through immigration and emigration.

metastasis (muh-tas'-tuh-sis) The spread of cancer cells to locations distant from their original site.

methanogen (meth-an'-ō-jen) An organism that produces methane as a waste product of the way it obtains energy. All known methanogens are in domain Archaea.

methyl group A chemical group consisting of a carbon bonded to three hydrogen atoms. The methyl group may be attached to a carbon or to a different atom.

microclimate Climate patterns on a very fine scale, such as the specific climatic conditions underneath a log.

microevolution Evolutionary change below the species level; change in the allele frequencies in a population over generations.

microfilament A cable composed of actin proteins in the cytoplasm of almost every eukaryotic cell, making up part of the cytoskeleton and acting alone or with myosin to cause cell contraction; also called an actin filament.

micronutrient An essential element that an organism needs in very small amounts. *See also* macronutrient.

microphyll (mī'-krō-fil) In lycophytes, a small leaf with a single unbranched vein. *See also* megaphyll.

micropyle A pore in the integuments of an ovule.

microRNA (miRNA) A small, single-stranded RNA molecule, generated from a double-stranded RNA precursor. The miRNA associates with one or more proteins in a complex that can degrade or prevent translation of an mRNA with a complementary sequence.

microspore A spore from a heterosporous plant species that develops into a male gametophyte.

microtubule A hollow rod composed of tubulin proteins that makes up part of the cytoskeleton in all eukaryotic cells and is found in cilia and flagella.

microvillus (plural, **microvilli**) One of many fine, finger-like projections of the epithelial cells in the lumen of the small intestine that increase its surface area.

midbrain One of three ancestral and embryonic regions of the vertebrate brain; develops into sensory integrating and relay centers that send sensory information to the cerebrum.

middle lamella (luh-mel´-uh) In plants, a thin layer of adhesive extracellular material, primarily pectins, found between the primary walls of adjacent young cells.

migration A regular, long-distance change in location.

mineral In nutrition, a simple nutrient that is inorganic and therefore cannot be synthesized in the body.

mineralocorticoid A steroid hormone secreted by the adrenal cortex that regulates salt and water homeostasis.

minimum viable population (MVP) The smallest population size at which a species is able to sustain its numbers and survive.

mismatch repair The cellular process that uses specific enzymes to remove and replace incorrectly paired nucleotides.

missense mutation A nucleotide-pair substitution that results in a codon that codes for a different amino acid.

mitochondrial matrix The compartment of the mitochondrion enclosed by the inner membrane and containing enzymes and substrates for the citric acid cycle, as well as ribosomes and DNA.

mitochondrion (mī´-tō-kon´-drē-un) (plural, **mitochondria**) An organelle in eukaryotic cells that serves as the site of cellular respiration; uses oxygen to break down organic molecules and synthesize ATP.

mitosis (mī-tō´-sis) A process of nuclear division in eukaryotic cells conventionally divided into five stages: prophase, prometaphase, metaphase, anaphase, and telophase. Mitosis conserves chromosome number by allocating replicated chromosomes equally to each of the daughter nuclei.

mitotic (M) phase The phase of the cell cycle that includes mitosis and cytokinesis.

mitotic spindle An assemblage of microtubules and associated proteins that is involved in the movement of chromosomes during mitosis.

mixotroph An organism that is capable of both photosynthesis and heterotrophy.

model A physical or conceptual representation of a natural phenomenon.

model organism A particular species chosen for research into broad biological principles because it is representative of a larger group and usually easy to grow in a lab.

molarity A common measure of solute concentration, referring to the number of moles of solute per liter of solution.

mold Informal term for a fungus that grows as a filamentous fungus, producing haploid spores by mitosis and forming a visible mycelium.

mole (mol) The number of grams of a substance that equals its molecular or atomic mass in daltons; a mole contains Avogadro's number of the molecules or atoms in question.

molecular clock A method for estimating the time required for a given amount of evolutionary change, based on the observation that some regions of genomes evolve at constant rates.

molecular mass The sum of the masses of all the atoms in a molecule; sometimes called molecular weight.

molecule Two or more atoms held together by covalent bonds.

molting A process in ecdysozoans in which the exoskeleton is shed at intervals, allowing growth by the production of a larger exoskeleton.

monilophyte An informal name for a member of the phylum Monilophyta, which includes ferns, horsetails, and whisk ferns and their relatives.

monoclonal antibody (mon´-ō-klōn´-ul) Any of a preparation of antibodies that have been produced by a single clone of cultured cells and thus are all specific for the same epitope.

monocot A member of a clade consisting of flowering plants that have one embryonic seed leaf, or cotyledon.

monogamous (muh-nog´-uh-mus) Referring to a type of relationship in which one male mates with just one female.

monohybrid An organism that is heterozygous with respect to a single gene of interest. All the offspring from a cross between parents homozygous for different alleles are monohybrids. For example, parents of genotypes *AA* and *aa* produce a monohybrid of genotype *Aa*.

monohybrid cross A cross between two organisms that are heterozygous for the character being followed (or the self-pollination of a heterozygous plant).

monomer (mon´-uh-mer) The subunit that serves as the building block of a polymer.

monophyletic (mon´-ō-fī-let´-ik) Pertaining to a group of taxa that consists of a common ancestor and all of its descendants. A monophyletic taxon is equivalent to a clade.

monosaccharide (mon´-ō-sak´-uh-rīd) The simplest carbohydrate, active alone or serving as a monomer for disaccharides and polysaccharides. Also called simple sugars, monosaccharides have molecular formulas that are generally some multiple of CH_2O.

monosomic Referring to a diploid cell that has only one copy of a particular chromosome instead of the normal two.

monotreme An egg-laying mammal, such as a platypus or echidna. Like all mammals, monotremes have hair and produce milk, but they lack nipples.

morphogen A substance, such as Bicoid protein in *Drosophila*, that provides positional information in the form of a concentration gradient along an embryonic axis.

morphogenesis (mōr´-fō-jen´-uh-sis) The development of the form of an organism and its structures.

morphological species concept Definition of a species in terms of measurable anatomical criteria.

moss A small, herbaceous, nonvascular plant that is a member of the phylum Bryophyta.

motor neuron A nerve cell that transmits signals from the brain or spinal cord to muscles or glands.

motor protein A protein that interacts with cytoskeletal elements and other cell components, producing movement of the whole cell or parts of the cell.

motor system An efferent branch of the vertebrate peripheral nervous system composed of motor neurons that carry signals to skeletal muscles in response to external stimuli.

motor unit A single motor neuron and all the muscle fibers it controls.

movement corridor A series of small clumps or a narrow strip of quality habitat (usable by organisms) that connects otherwise isolated patches of quality habitat.

MPF Maturation-promoting factor (or M-phase-promoting factor); a protein complex required for a cell to progress from late interphase to mitosis. The active form consists of cyclin and a protein kinase.

mucus A viscous and slippery mixture of glycoproteins, cells, salts, and water that moistens and protects the membranes lining body cavities that open to the exterior.

Müllerian mimicry (myū-lār´-ē-un mim´-uh-krē) Reciprocal mimicry by two unpalatable species.

multifactorial Referring to a phenotypic character that is influenced by multiple genes and environmental factors.

multigene family A collection of genes with similar or identical sequences, presumably of common origin.

multiple fruit A fruit derived from an entire inflorescence.

multiplication rule A rule of probability stating that the probability of two or more independent events occurring together can be determined by multiplying their individual probabilities.

muscle tissue Tissue consisting of long muscle cells that can contract, either on its own or when stimulated by nerve impulses.

mutagen (myū´-tuh-jen) A chemical or physical agent that interacts with DNA and can cause a mutation.

mutation (myū-tā´-shun) A change in the nucleotide sequence of an organism's DNA or in the DNA or RNA of a virus.

mutualism (myū´-chū-ul-izm) A symbiotic relationship in which both participants benefit.

mycelium (mī-sē´-lē-um) The densely branched network of hyphae in a fungus.

mycorrhiza (plural, **mycorrhizae**) (mī′-kō-rī′-zuh, mī′-kō-rī′-zē) A mutualistic association of plant roots and fungus.

mycosis (mī-kō′-sis) General term for a fungal infection.

myelin sheath (mī′-uh-lin) Wrapped around the axon of a neuron, an insulating coat of cell membranes from Schwann cells or oligodendrocytes. It is interrupted by nodes of Ranvier, where action potentials are generated.

myofibril (mī′-ō-fī′-bril) A longitudinal bundle in a muscle cell (fiber) that contains thin filaments of actin and regulatory proteins and thick filaments of myosin.

myoglobin (mī′-uh-glō′-bin) An oxygen-storing, pigmented protein in muscle cells.

myosin (mī′-uh-sin) A type of motor protein that associates into filaments that interact with actin filaments to cause cell contraction.

myriapod (mir′-ē-uh-pod′) A terrestrial arthropod with many body segments and one or two pairs of legs per segment. Millipedes and centipedes are the two major groups of living myriapods.

NAD⁺ Nicotinamide adenine dinucleotide, a coenzyme that cycles easily between oxidized (NAD⁺) and reduced (NADH) states, thus acting as an electron carrier.

NADP⁺ Nicotinamide adenine dinucleotide phosphate, an electron acceptor that, as NADPH, temporarily stores energized electrons produced during the light reactions.

natural killer cell A type of white blood cell that can kill tumor cells and virus-infected cells as part of innate immunity.

natural selection A process in which individuals that have certain inherited traits tend to survive and reproduce at higher rates than other individuals because of those traits.

negative feedback A form of regulation in which accumulation of an end product of a process slows the process; in physiology, a primary mechanism of homeostasis, whereby a change in a variable triggers a response that counteracts the initial change.

negative pressure breathing A breathing system in which air is pulled into the lungs.

nematocyst (nem′-uh-tuh-sist′) In a cnidocyte of a cnidarian, a capsule-like organelle containing a coiled thread that when discharged can penetrate the body wall of the prey.

nephron (nef′-ron) The tubular excretory unit of the vertebrate kidney.

neritic zone The shallow region of the ocean overlying the continental shelf.

nerve A fiber composed primarily of the bundled axons of neurons.

nervous system In animals, the fast-acting internal system of communication involving sensory receptors, networks of nerve cells, and connections to muscles and glands that respond to nerve signals; functions in concert with the endocrine system to effect internal regulation and maintain homeostasis.

nervous tissue Tissue made up of neurons and supportive cells.

net ecosystem production (NEP) The gross primary production of an ecosystem minus the energy used by all autotrophs and heterotrophs for respiration.

net primary production (NPP) The gross primary production of an ecosystem minus the energy used by the producers for respiration.

neural crest In vertebrates, a region located along the sides of the neural tube where it pinches off from the ectoderm. Neural crest cells migrate to various parts of the embryo and form pigment cells in the skin and parts of the skull, teeth, adrenal glands, and peripheral nervous system.

neural tube A tube of infolded ectodermal cells that runs along the anterior-posterior axis of a vertebrate, just dorsal to the notochord. It will give rise to the central nervous system.

neurohormone A molecule that is secreted by a neuron, travels in body fluids, and acts on specific target cells, changing their functioning.

neuron (nyūr′-on) A nerve cell; the fundamental unit of the nervous system, having structure and properties that allow it to conduct signals by taking advantage of the electrical charge across its plasma membrane.

neuronal plasticity The capacity of a nervous system to change with experience.

neuropeptide A relatively short chain of amino acids that serves as a neurotransmitter.

neurotransmitter A molecule that is released from the synaptic terminal of a neuron at a chemical synapse, diffuses across the synaptic cleft, and binds to the postsynaptic cell, triggering a response.

neutral variation Genetic variation that does not provide a selective advantage or disadvantage.

neutron A subatomic particle having no electrical charge (electrically neutral), with a mass of about 1.7×10^{-24} g, found in the nucleus of an atom.

neutrophil The most abundant type of white blood cell. Neutrophils are phagocytic and tend to self-destruct as they destroy foreign invaders, limiting their life span to a few days.

nitric oxide (NO) A gas produced by many types of cells that functions as a local regulator and as a neurotransmitter.

nitrogen cycle The natural process by which nitrogen, either from the atmosphere or from decomposed organic material, is converted by soil bacteria to compounds assimilated by plants. This incorporated nitrogen is then taken in by other organisms and subsequently released, acted on by bacteria, and made available again to the nonliving environment.

nitrogen fixation The conversion of atmospheric nitrogen (N_2) to ammonia (NH_3). Biological nitrogen fixation is carried out by certain prokaryotes, some of which have mutualistic relationships with plants.

nociceptor (nō′-si-sep′-tur) A sensory receptor that responds to noxious or painful stimuli; also called a pain receptor.

node A point along the stem of a plant at which leaves are attached.

node of Ranvier (ron′-vē-ā′) Gap in the myelin sheath of certain axons where an action potential may be generated. In saltatory conduction, an action potential is regenerated at each node, appearing to "jump" along the axon from node to node.

nodule A swelling on the root of a legume. Nodules are composed of plant cells that contain nitrogen-fixing bacteria of the genus *Rhizobium*.

noncompetitive inhibitor A substance that reduces the activity of an enzyme by binding to a location remote from the active site, changing the enzyme's shape so that the active site no longer effectively catalyzes the conversion of substrate to product.

nondisjunction An error in meiosis or mitosis in which members of a pair of homologous chromosomes or a pair of sister chromatids fail to separate properly from each other.

nonequilibrium model A model that maintains that communities change constantly after being buffeted by disturbances.

nonpolar covalent bond A type of covalent bond in which electrons are shared equally between two atoms of similar electronegativity.

nonsense mutation A mutation that changes an amino acid codon to one of the three stop codons, resulting in a shorter and usually nonfunctional protein.

norepinephrine A catecholamine that is chemically and functionally similar to epinephrine and acts as a hormone or neurotransmitter; also called noradrenaline.

northern coniferous forest A terrestrial biome characterized by long, cold winters and dominated by cone-bearing trees.

no-till agriculture A plowing technique that minimally disturbs the soil, thereby reducing soil loss.

notochord (nō′-tuh-kord′) A longitudinal, flexible rod made of tightly packed mesodermal cells that runs along the anterior-posterior axis of a chordate in the dorsal part of the body.

nuclear envelope In a eukaryotic cell, the double membrane that surrounds the nucleus, perforated with pores that regulate traffic with the cytoplasm. The outer membrane is continuous with the endoplasmic reticulum.

nuclear lamina A netlike array of protein filaments that lines the inner surface of the nuclear envelope and helps maintain the shape of the nucleus.

nucleariid A member of a group of unicellular, amoeboid protists that are more closely related to fungi than they are to other protists.

nuclease An enzyme that cuts DNA or RNA, either removing one or a few bases or hydrolyzing the DNA or RNA completely into its component nucleotides.

nucleic acid (nū-klā′-ik) A polymer (polynucleotide) consisting of many nucleotide monomers; serves as a blueprint for proteins and, through the actions of proteins, for all cellular activities. The two types are DNA and RNA.

nucleic acid hybridization (nū-klā′-ik) The base pairing of one strand of a nucleic acid to the complementary sequence on a strand from *another* nucleic acid molecule.

nucleic acid probe (nū-klā′-ik) In DNA technology, a labeled single-stranded nucleic acid molecule used to locate a specific nucleotide sequence in a nucleic acid sample. Molecules of the probe hydrogen-bond to the complementary sequence wherever it occurs; radioactive, fluorescent, or other labeling of the probe allows its location to be detected.

nucleoid (nū′-klē-oyd) A non-membrane-enclosed region in a prokaryotic cell where its chromosome is located.

nucleolus (nū-klē′-ō-lus) (plural, **nucleoli**) A specialized structure in the nucleus, consisting of chromosomal regions containing ribosomal RNA (rRNA) genes along with ribosomal proteins imported from the cytoplasm; site of rRNA synthesis and ribosomal subunit assembly. *See also* ribosome.

nucleosome (nū′-klē-ō-sōm′) The basic, bead-like unit of DNA packing in eukaryotes, consisting of a segment of DNA wound around a protein core composed of two copies of each of four types of histone.

nucleotide (nū′-klē-ō-tīd′) The building block of a nucleic acid, consisting of a five-carbon sugar covalently bonded to a nitrogenous base and one or more phosphate groups.

nucleotide excision repair (nū′-klē-ō-tīd′) A repair system that removes and then correctly replaces a damaged segment of DNA using the undamaged strand as a guide.

nucleotide-pair substitution (nū′-klē-ō-tīd′) A type of point mutation in which one nucleotide in a DNA strand and its partner in the complementary strand are replaced by another pair of nucleotides.

nucleus (1) An atom's central core, containing protons and neutrons. (2) The organelle of a eukaryotic cell that contains the genetic material in the form of chromosomes, made up of chromatin. (3) A cluster of neurons.

nutrition The process by which an organism takes in and makes use of food substances.

obligate aerobe (ob′-lig-et ār′-ōb) An organism that requires oxygen for cellular respiration and cannot live without it.

obligate anaerobe (ob′-lig-et an′-uh-rōb) An organism that carries out only fermentation or anaerobic respiration. Such organisms cannot use oxygen and in fact may be poisoned by it.

ocean acidification Decreasing pH of ocean waters due to absorption of excess atmospheric CO_2 from the burning of fossil fuels.

oceanic pelagic zone Most of the ocean's waters far from shore, constantly mixed by ocean currents.

odorant A molecule that can be detected by sensory receptors of the olfactory system.

Okazaki fragment (ō′-kah-zah′-kē) A short segment of DNA synthesized away from the replication fork on a template strand during DNA replication. Many such segments are joined together to make up the lagging strand of newly synthesized DNA.

olfaction The sense of smell.

oligodendrocyte A type of glial cell that forms insulating myelin sheaths around the axons of neurons in the central nervous system.

oligotrophic lake A nutrient-poor, clear lake with few phytoplankton.

ommatidium (ōm′-uh-tid′-ē-um) (plural, **ommatidia**) One of the facets of the compound eye of arthropods and some polychaete worms.

omnivore An animal that regularly eats animals as well as plants or algae.

oncogene (on′-kō-jēn) A gene found in viral or cellular genomes that is involved in triggering molecular events that can lead to cancer.

oocyte (ō′-uh-sīt) A cell in the female reproductive system that differentiates to form an egg.

oogenesis (ō′-uh-jen′-uh-sis) The process in the ovary that results in the production of female gametes.

oogonium (ō′-uh-gō′-nē-em) (plural, **oogonia**) A cell that divides mitotically to form oocytes.

open circulatory system A circulatory system in which fluid called hemolymph bathes the tissues and organs directly and there is no distinction between the circulating fluid and the interstitial fluid.

operator In bacterial and phage DNA, a sequence of nucleotides near the start of an operon to which an active repressor can attach. The binding of the repressor prevents RNA polymerase from attaching to the promoter and transcribing the genes of the operon.

operculum (ō-per′-kyuh-lum) In aquatic osteichthyans, a protective bony flap that covers and protects the gills.

operon (op′-er-on) A unit of genetic function found in bacteria and phages, consisting of a promoter, an operator, and a coordinately regulated cluster of genes whose products function in a common pathway.

opisthokont (uh-pis′-thuh-kont′) A member of an extremely diverse clade of eukaryotes that includes fungi, animals, and several closely-related groups of protists.

opposable thumb A thumb that can touch the ventral surface of the fingertips of all four fingers.

opsin A membrane protein bound to a light-absorbing pigment molecule.

optimal foraging model The basis for analyzing behavior as a compromise between feeding costs and feeding benefits.

oral cavity The mouth of an animal.

orbital The three-dimensional space where an electron is found 90% of the time.

order In Linnaean classification, the taxonomic category above the level of family.

organ A specialized center of body function composed of several different types of tissues.

organ identity gene A plant homeotic gene that uses positional information to determine which emerging leaves develop into which types of floral organs.

organ of Corti (kor′-tē) The actual hearing organ of the vertebrate ear, located in the floor of the cochlear duct in the inner ear; contains the receptor cells (hair cells) of the ear.

organ system A group of organs that work together in performing vital body functions.

organelle (ōr-guh-nel′) Any of several membrane-enclosed structures with specialized functions, suspended in the cytosol of eukaryotic cells.

organic chemistry The study of carbon compounds (organic compounds).

organismal ecology The branch of ecology concerned with the morphological, physiological, and behavioral ways in which individual organisms meet the challenges posed by their biotic and abiotic environments.

organogenesis (ōr-gan′-ō-jen′-uh-sis) The process in which organ rudiments develop from the three germ layers after gastrulation.

origin of replication Site where the replication of a DNA molecule begins, consisting of a specific sequence of nucleotides.

orthologous genes Homologous genes that are found in different species because of speciation.

osculum (os′-kyuh-lum) A large opening in a sponge that connects the spongocoel to the environment.

osmoconformer An animal that is isoosmotic with its environment.

osmolarity (oz′-mō-lār′-uh-tē) Solute concentration expressed as molarity.

osmoregulation Regulation of solute concentrations and water balance by a cell or organism.

osmoregulator An animal that controls its internal osmolarity independent of the external environment.

osmosis (oz-mō′-sis) The diffusion of free water across a selectively permeable membrane.

osteichthyan (os′-tē-ik′-thē-an) A member of a vertebrate clade with jaws and mostly bony skeletons.

outgroup A species or group of species from an evolutionary lineage that is known to have diverged before the lineage that contains the group of species being studied. An outgroup is selected so that its members are closely related to the group of species being studied, but not as closely related as any study-group members are to each other.

oval window In the vertebrate ear, a membrane-covered gap in the skull bone, through which sound waves pass from the middle ear to the inner ear.

ovarian cycle (ō-vār′-ē-un) The cyclic recurrence of the follicular phase, ovulation, and the luteal phase in the mammalian ovary, regulated by hormones.

ovary (ō′-vuh-rē) (1) In flowers, the portion of a carpel in which the egg-containing ovules develop. (2) In animals, the structure that produces female gametes and reproductive hormones.

oviduct (ō′-vuh-duct) A tube passing from the ovary to the vagina in invertebrates or to the uterus in vertebrates, where it is also called a fallopian tube.

oviparous (ō-vip′-uh-rus) Referring to a type of development in which young hatch from eggs laid outside the mother's body.

ovoviviparous (ō′-vō-vī-vip′-uh-rus) Referring to a type of development in which young hatch from eggs that are retained in the mother's uterus.

ovulation The release of an egg from an ovary. In humans, an ovarian follicle releases an egg during each uterine (menstrual) cycle.

ovule (o′-vyūl) A structure that develops within the ovary of a seed plant and contains the female gametophyte.

oxidation The complete or partial loss of electrons from a substance involved in a redox reaction.

oxidative phosphorylation (fos'-fōr-uh-lā'-shun) The production of ATP using energy derived from the redox reactions of an electron transport chain; the third major stage of cellular respiration.

oxidizing agent The electron acceptor in a redox reaction.

oxytocin (ok'-si-tō'-sen) A hormone produced by the hypothalamus and released from the posterior pituitary. It induces contractions of the uterine muscles during labor and causes the mammary glands to eject milk during nursing.

p53 gene A tumor-suppressor gene that codes for a specific transcription factor that promotes the synthesis of proteins that inhibit the cell cycle.

paedomorphosis (pē'-duh-mōr'-fuh-sis) The retention in an adult organism of the juvenile features of its evolutionary ancestors.

pain receptor A sensory receptor that responds to noxious or painful stimuli; also called a nociceptor.

paleoanthropology The study of human origins and evolution.

paleontology (pā'-lē-un-tol'-ō-jē) The scientific study of fossils.

pancreas (pan'-krē-us) A gland with exocrine and endocrine tissues. The exocrine portion functions in digestion, secreting enzymes and an alkaline solution into the small intestine via a duct; the ductless endocrine portion functions in homeostasis, secreting the hormones insulin and glucagon into the blood.

pancrustacean A member of a diverse arthropod clade that includes lobsters, crabs, barnacles and other crustaceans, as well as insects and their six-legged terrestrial relatives.

pandemic A global epidemic.

Pangaea (pan-jē'-uh) The supercontinent that formed near the end of the Paleozoic era, when plate movements brought all the landmasses of Earth together.

parabasalid A protist, such as a trichomonad, with modified mitochondria.

paracrine Referring to a secreted molecule that acts on a neighboring cell.

paralogous genes Homologous genes that are found in the same genome as a result of gene duplication.

paraphyletic (pār'-uh-fī-let'-ik) Pertaining to a group of taxa that consists of a common ancestor and some, but not all, of its descendants.

parareptile A basal group of reptiles, consisting mostly of large, stocky quadrupedal herbivores. Parareptiles died out in the late Triassic period.

parasite (pār'-uh-sīt) An organism that feeds on the cell contents, tissues, or body fluids of another species (the host) while in or on the host organism. Parasites harm but usually do not kill their host.

parasitism (pār'-uh-sit-izm) A symbiotic relationship in which one organism, the parasite, benefits at the expense of another, the host, by living either within or on the host.

parasympathetic division One of three divisions of the autonomic nervous system; generally enhances body activities that gain and conserve energy, such as digestion and reduced heart rate.

parathyroid gland One of four small endocrine glands, embedded in the surface of the thyroid gland, that secrete parathyroid hormone.

parathyroid hormone (PTH) A hormone secreted by the parathyroid glands that raises blood calcium level by promoting calcium release from bone and calcium retention by the kidneys.

parenchyma cell (puh-ren'-ki-muh) A relatively unspecialized plant cell type that carries out most of the metabolism, synthesizes and stores organic products, and develops into a more differentiated cell type.

parental type An offspring with a phenotype that matches one of the true-breeding parental (P generation) phenotypes; also refers to the phenotype itself.

Parkinson's disease A progressive brain disease characterized by difficulty in initiating movements, slowness of movement, and rigidity.

parthenogenesis (par'-thuh-nō'-jen'-uh-sis) A form of asexual reproduction in which females produce offspring from unfertilized eggs.

partial pressure The pressure exerted by a particular gas in a mixture of gases (for instance, the pressure exerted by oxygen in air).

passive immunity Short-term immunity conferred by the transfer of antibodies, as occurs in the transfer of maternal antibodies to a fetus or nursing infant.

passive transport The diffusion of a substance across a biological membrane with no expenditure of energy.

pathogen An organism or virus that causes disease.

pathogen-associated molecular patterns (PAMPs) Short molecular sequences that typify certain groups of pathogens and that are recognized by cells of the innate immune system.

pattern formation The development of a multicellular organism's spatial organization, the arrangement of organs and tissues in their characteristic places in three-dimensional space.

peat Extensive deposits of partially decayed organic material often formed primarily from the wetland moss *Sphagnum*.

pedigree A diagram of a family tree with conventional symbols, showing the occurrence of heritable characters in parents and offspring over multiple generations.

pelagic zone The open-water component of aquatic biomes.

penis The copulatory structure of male mammals.

PEP carboxylase An enzyme that adds CO_2 to phosphoenolpyruvate (PEP) to form oxaloacetate in mesophyll cells of C_4 plants. It acts prior to photosynthesis.

pepsin An enzyme present in gastric juice that begins the hydrolysis of proteins.

pepsinogen The inactive form of pepsin secreted by chief cells located in gastric pits of the stomach.

peptide bond The covalent bond between the carboxyl group on one amino acid and the amino group on another, formed by a dehydration reaction.

peptidoglycan (pep'-tid-ō-glī'-kan) A type of polymer in bacterial cell walls consisting of modified sugars cross-linked by short polypeptides.

perception The interpretation of sensory system input by the brain.

pericycle The outermost layer in the vascular cylinder, from which lateral roots arise.

periderm (pār'-uh-derm') The protective coat that replaces the epidermis in woody plants during secondary growth, formed of the cork and cork cambium.

peripheral nervous system (PNS) The sensory and motor neurons that connect to the central nervous system.

peripheral protein A protein loosely bound to the surface of a membrane or to part of an integral protein and not embedded in the lipid bilayer.

peristalsis (pār'-uh-stal'-sis) (1) Alternating waves of contraction and relaxation in the smooth muscles lining the alimentary canal that push food along the canal. (2) A type of movement on land produced by rhythmic waves of muscle contractions passing from front to back, as in many annelids.

peristome (pār'-uh-stōme') A ring of interlocking, tooth-like structures on the upper part of a moss capsule (sporangium), often specialized for gradual spore discharge.

peritubular capillary One of the tiny blood vessels that form a network surrounding the proximal and distal tubules in the kidney.

peroxisome (puh-rok'-suh-sōm') An organelle containing enzymes that transfer hydrogen atoms from various substrates to oxygen (O_2), producing and then degrading hydrogen peroxide (H_2O_2).

petal A modified leaf of a flowering plant. Petals are the often colorful parts of a flower that advertise it to insects and other pollinators.

petiole (pet'-ē-ōl) The stalk of a leaf, which joins the leaf to a node of the stem.

P generation The true-breeding (homozygous) parent individuals from which F_1 hybrid offspring are derived in studies of inheritance; P stands for "parental."

pH A measure of hydrogen ion concentration equal to $-\log [H^+]$ and ranging in value from 0 to 14.

phage (fāj) A virus that infects bacteria; also called a bacteriophage.

phagocytosis (fag'-ō-sī-tō'-sis) A type of endocytosis in which large particulate substances or small organisms are taken up by a cell. It is carried out by some protists and by certain immune cells of animals (in mammals, mainly macrophages, neutrophils, and dendritic cells).

pharyngeal cleft (fuh-rin′-jē-ul) In chordate embryos, one of the grooves that separate a series of arches along the outer surface of the pharynx and may develop into a pharyngeal slit.

pharyngeal slit (fuh-rin′-jē-ul) In chordate embryos, one of the slits that form from the pharyngeal clefts and open into the pharynx, later developing into gill slits in many vertebrates.

pharynx (fãr′-inks) (1) An area in the vertebrate throat where air and food passages cross. (2) In flatworms, the muscular tube that protrudes from the ventral side of the worm and ends in the mouth.

phase change (1) A shift from one developmental phase to another. (2) In plants, a morphological change that arises from a transition in shoot apical meristem activity.

phenotype (fē′-nō-tīp) The observable physical and physiological traits of an organism, which are determined by its genetic makeup.

pheromone (fãr′-uh-mōn) In animals and fungi, a small molecule released into the environment that functions in communication between members of the same species. In animals, it acts much like a hormone in influencing physiology and behavior.

phloem (flō′-em) Vascular plant tissue consisting of living cells arranged into elongated tubes that transport sugar and other organic nutrients throughout the plant.

phloem sap (flō′-em) The sugar-rich solution carried through a plant's sieve tubes.

phosphate group A chemical group consisting of a phosphorus atom bonded to four oxygen atoms; important in energy transfer.

phospholipid (fos′-fō-lip′-id) A lipid made up of glycerol joined to two fatty acids and a phosphate group. The hydrocarbon chains of the fatty acids act as nonpolar, hydrophobic tails, while the rest of the molecule acts as a polar, hydrophilic head. Phospholipids form bilayers that function as biological membranes.

phosphorylated intermediate (fos′-fōr-uh-lā′-ted) A molecule (often a reactant) with a phosphate group covalently bound to it, making it more reactive (less stable) than the unphosphorylated molecule.

phosphorylation cascade (fos′-fōr-uh-lā′-shun) A series of protein phosphorylations occurring sequentially in which each protein kinase phosphorylates the next, activating it; often found in signaling pathways.

photic zone (fō′-tic) The narrow top layer of an ocean or lake, where light penetrates sufficiently for photosynthesis to occur.

photoautotroph (fō′-tō-ot′-ō-trōf) An organism that harnesses light energy to drive the synthesis of organic compounds from carbon dioxide.

photoheterotroph (fō′-tō-het′-er-ō-trōf) An organism that uses light to generate ATP but must obtain carbon in organic form.

photomorphogenesis Effects of light on plant morphology.

photon (fō′-ton) A quantum, or discrete quantity, of light energy that behaves as if it were a particle.

photoperiodism (fō′-tō-pēr′-ē-ō-dizm) A physiological response to photoperiod, the interval in a 24-hour period during which an organism is exposed to light. An example of photoperiodism is flowering.

photophosphorylation (fō′-tō-fos′-fōr-uh-lā′-shun) The process of generating ATP from ADP and phosphate by means of chemiosmosis, using a proton-motive force generated across the thylakoid membrane of the chloroplast or the membrane of certain prokaryotes during the light reactions of photosynthesis.

photoreceptor An electromagnetic receptor that detects the radiation known as visible light.

photorespiration A metabolic pathway that consumes oxygen and ATP, releases carbon dioxide, and decreases photosynthetic output. Photorespiration generally occurs on hot, dry, bright days, when stomata close and the O_2/CO_2 ratio in the leaf increases, favoring the binding of O_2 rather than CO_2 by rubisco.

photosynthesis (fō′-tō-sin′-thi-sis) The conversion of light energy to chemical energy that is stored in sugars or other organic compounds; occurs in plants, algae, and certain prokaryotes.

photosystem A light-capturing unit located in the thylakoid membrane of the chloroplast or in the membrane of some prokaryotes, consisting of a reaction-center complex surrounded by numerous light-harvesting complexes. There are two types of photosystems, I and II; they absorb light best at different wavelengths.

photosystem I (PS I) A light-capturing unit in a chloroplast's thylakoid membrane or in the membrane of some prokaryotes; it has two molecules of P700 chlorophyll *a* at its reaction center.

photosystem II (PS II) One of two light-capturing units in a chloroplast's thylakoid membrane or in the membrane of some prokaryotes; it has two molecules of P680 chlorophyll *a* at its reaction center.

phototropism (fō′-tō-trō′-pizm) Growth of a plant shoot toward or away from light.

phyllotaxy (fil′-uh-tak′-sē) The pattern of leaf attachment to the stem of a plant.

phylogenetic species concept Definition of a species as the smallest group of individuals that share a common ancestor, forming one branch on the tree of life.

phylogenetic tree A branching diagram that represents a hypothesis about the evolutionary history of a group of organisms.

phylogeny (fī-loj′-uh-nē) The evolutionary history of a species or group of related species.

phylum (fī′-lum) (plural, **phyla**) In Linnaean classification, the taxonomic category above class.

physiology The processes and functions of an organism.

phytochrome (fī′-tuh-krōm) A type of light receptor in plants that mostly absorbs red light and regulates many plant responses, such as seed germination and shade avoidance.

phytoremediation An emerging technology that seeks to reclaim contaminated areas by taking advantage of some plant species' ability to extract heavy metals and other pollutants from the soil and to concentrate them in easily harvested portions of the plant.

pilus (plural, **pili**) (pī′-lus, pī′-lī) In bacteria, a structure that links one cell to another at the start of conjugation; also called a sex pilus or conjugation pilus.

pineal gland (pī′-nē-ul) A small gland on the dorsal surface of the vertebrate forebrain that secretes the hormone melatonin.

pinocytosis (pī′-nō-sī-tō′-sis) A type of endocytosis in which the cell ingests extracellular fluid and its dissolved solutes.

pistil A single carpel or a group of fused carpels.

pith Ground tissue that is internal to the vascular tissue in a stem; in many monocot roots, parenchyma cells that form the central core of the vascular cylinder.

pituitary gland (puh-tū′-uh-tār′-ē) An endocrine gland at the base of the hypothalamus; consists of a posterior lobe, which stores and releases two hormones produced by the hypothalamus, and an anterior lobe, which produces and secretes many hormones that regulate diverse body functions.

placenta (pluh-sen′-tuh) A structure in the uterus of a pregnant eutherian mammal that nourishes the fetus with the mother's blood supply; formed from the uterine lining and embryonic membranes.

placoderm A member of an extinct group of fishlike vertebrates that had jaws and were enclosed in a tough outer armor.

planarian A free-living flatworm found in ponds and streams.

plasma (plaz′-muh) The liquid matrix of blood in which the blood cells are suspended.

plasma cell (plaz′-muh) The antibody-secreting effector cell of humoral immunity. Plasma cells arise from antigen-stimulated B cells.

plasma membrane (plaz′-muh) The membrane at the boundary of every cell that acts as a selective barrier, regulating the cell's chemical composition.

plasmid (plaz′-mid) A small, circular, double-stranded DNA molecule that carries accessory genes separate from those of a bacterial chromosome; in DNA cloning, plasmids are used as vectors carrying up to about 10,000 base pairs (10 kb) of DNA. Plasmids are also found in some eukaryotes, such as yeasts.

plasmodesma (plaz′-mō-dez′-muh) (plural, **plasmodesmata**) An open channel through the cell wall that connects the cytoplasm of adjacent plant cells, allowing water, small solutes, and some larger molecules to pass between the cells.

plasmogamy (plaz-moh′-guh-mē) In fungi, the fusion of the cytoplasm of cells from two individuals; occurs as one stage of sexual reproduction, followed later by karyogamy.

plasmolysis (plaz-mol′-uh-sis) A phenomenon in walled cells in which the cytoplasm shrivels and the plasma membrane pulls away from the cell wall; occurs when the cell loses water to a hypertonic environment.

plastid One of a family of closely related organelles that includes chloroplasts, chromoplasts, and amyloplasts. Plastids are found in cells of photosynthetic eukaryotes.

plate tectonics The theory that the continents are part of great plates of Earth's crust that float on the hot, underlying portion of the mantle. Movements in the mantle cause the continents to move slowly over time.

platelet A pinched-off cytoplasmic fragment of a specialized bone marrow cell. Platelets circulate in the blood and are important in blood clotting.

pleiotropy (plī′-o-truh-pē) The ability of a single gene to have multiple effects.

pluripotent Describing a cell that can give rise to many, but not all, parts of an organism.

point mutation A change in a single nucleotide pair of a gene.

polar covalent bond A covalent bond between atoms that differ in electronegativity. The shared electrons are pulled closer to the more electronegative atom, making it slightly negative and the other atom slightly positive.

polar molecule A molecule (such as water) with an uneven distribution of charges in different regions of the molecule.

polarity A lack of symmetry; structural differences in opposite ends of an organism or structure, such as the root end and shoot end of a plant.

pollen grain In seed plants, a structure consisting of the male gametophyte enclosed within a pollen wall.

pollen tube A tube that forms after germination of the pollen grain and that functions in the delivery of sperm to the ovule.

pollination (pol′-uh-nā′-shun) The transfer of pollen to the part of a seed plant containing the ovules, a process required for fertilization.

poly-A tail A sequence of 50–250 adenine nucleotides added onto the 3′ end of a pre-mRNA molecule.

polygamous Referring to a type of relationship in which an individual of one sex mates with several of the other.

polygenic inheritance (pol′-ē-jen′-ik) An additive effect of two or more genes on a single phenotypic character.

polymer (pol′-uh-mer) A long molecule consisting of many similar or identical monomers linked together by covalent bonds.

polymerase chain reaction (PCR) (puh-lim′-uh-rās) A technique for amplifying DNA *in vitro* by incubating it with specific primers, a heat-resistant DNA polymerase, and nucleotides.

polynucleotide (pol′-ē-nū′-klē-ō-tīd) A polymer consisting of many nucleotide monomers in a chain. The nucleotides can be those of DNA or RNA.

polyp The sessile variant of the cnidarian body plan. The alternate form is the medusa.

polypeptide (pol′-ē-pep′-tīd) A polymer of many amino acids linked together by peptide bonds.

polyphyletic (pol′-ē-fī-let′-ik) Pertaining to a group of taxa that includes distantly related organisms but does not include their most recent common ancestor.

polyploidy (pol′-ē-ploy′-dē) A chromosomal alteration in which the organism possesses more than two complete chromosome sets. It is the result of an accident of cell division.

polyribosome (polysome) (pol′-ē-rī′-buh-sōm′) A group of several ribosomes attached to, and translating, the same messenger RNA molecule.

polysaccharide (pol′-ē-sak′-uh-rīd) A polymer of many monosaccharides, formed by dehydration reactions.

polytomy (puh-lit′-uh-mē) In a phylogenetic tree, a branch point from which more than two descendant taxa emerge. A polytomy indicates that the evolutionary relationships between the descendant taxa are not yet clear.

pons A portion of the brain that participates in certain automatic, homeostatic functions, such as regulating the breathing centers in the medulla.

population A group of individuals of the same species that live in the same area and interbreed, producing fertile offspring.

population dynamics The study of how complex interactions between biotic and abiotic factors influence variations in population size.

population ecology The study of populations in relation to their environment, including environmental influences on population density and distribution, age structure, and variations in population size.

positional information Molecular cues that control pattern formation in an animal or plant embryonic structure by indicating a cell's location relative to the organism's body axes. These cues elicit a response by genes that regulate development.

positive feedback A form of regulation in which an end product of a process speeds up that process; in physiology, a control mechanism in which a change in a variable triggers a response that reinforces or amplifies the change.

positive pressure breathing A breathing system in which air is forced into the lungs.

posterior Pertaining to the rear, or tail end, of a bilaterally symmetrical animal.

posterior pituitary An extension of the hypothalamus composed of nervous tissue that secretes oxytocin and antidiuretic hormone made in the hypothalamus; a temporary storage site for these hormones.

postzygotic barrier (pōst′-zī-got′-ik) A reproductive barrier that prevents hybrid zygotes produced by two different species from developing into viable, fertile adults.

potential energy The energy that matter possesses as a result of its location or spatial arrangement (structure).

predation An interaction between species in which one species, the predator, eats the other, the prey.

prediction In deductive reasoning, a forecast that follows logically from a hypothesis. By testing predictions, experiments may allow certain hypotheses to be rejected.

pregnancy The condition of carrying one or more embryos in the uterus; also called gestation.

prepuce (prē′-pyūs) A fold of skin covering the head of the clitoris or penis.

pressure potential (Ψ_p) A component of water potential that consists of the physical pressure on a solution, which can be positive, zero, or negative.

prezygotic barrier (prē-zī-got′-ik) A reproductive barrier that impedes mating between species or hinders fertilization if interspecific mating is attempted.

primary cell wall In plants, a relatively thin and flexible layer that surrounds the plasma membrane of a young cell.

primary consumer An herbivore; an organism that eats plants or other autotrophs.

primary electron acceptor In the thylakoid membrane of a chloroplast or in the membrane of some prokaryotes, a specialized molecule that shares the reaction-center complex with a pair of chlorophyll *a* molecules and that accepts an electron from them.

primary growth Growth produced by apical meristems, lengthening stems and roots.

primary immune response The initial adaptive immune response to an antigen, which appears after a lag of about 10–17 days.

primary oocyte (ō′-uh-sīt) An oocyte prior to completion of meiosis I.

primary producer An autotroph, usually a photosynthetic organism. Collectively, autotrophs make up the trophic level of an ecosystem that ultimately supports all other levels.

primary production The amount of light energy converted to chemical energy (organic compounds) by the autotrophs in an ecosystem during a given time period.

primary structure The level of protein structure referring to the specific linear sequence of amino acids.

primary succession A type of ecological succession that occurs in an area where there were originally no organisms present and where soil has not yet formed.

primary transcript An initial RNA transcript from any gene; also called pre-mRNA when transcribed from a protein-coding gene.

primase An enzyme that joins RNA nucleotides to make a primer during DNA replication, using the parental DNA strand as a template.

primer A short stretch of RNA with a free 3′ end, bound by complementary base pairing to the template strand and elongated with DNA nucleotides during DNA replication.

primitive streak A thickening along the future anterior-posterior axis on the surface of an early avian or mammalian embryo, caused by a piling up of cells as they congregate at the midline before moving into the embryo.

prion An infectious agent that is a misfolded version of a normal cellular protein. Prions appear to increase in number by converting correctly folded versions of the protein to more prions.

problem solving The cognitive activity of devising a method to proceed from one state to another in the face of real or apparent obstacles.

producer An organism that produces organic compounds from CO_2 by harnessing light energy (in photosynthesis) or by oxidizing inorganic chemicals (in chemosynthetic reactions carried out by some prokaryotes).

product A material resulting from a chemical reaction.

production efficiency The percentage of energy stored in assimilated food that is not used for respiration or eliminated as waste.

progesterone A steroid hormone that prepares the uterus for pregnancy; the major progestin in mammals.

progestin Any steroid hormone with progesterone-like activity.

prokaryotic cell (prō'-kār'-ē-ot'-ik) A type of cell lacking a membrane-enclosed nucleus and membrane-enclosed organelles. Organisms with prokaryotic cells (bacteria and archaea) are called prokaryotes.

prolactin A hormone produced and secreted by the anterior pituitary with a great diversity of effects in different vertebrate species. In mammals, it stimulates growth of and milk production by the mammary glands.

prometaphase The second stage of mitosis, in which the nuclear envelope fragments and the spindle microtubules attach to the kinetochores of the chromosomes.

promoter A specific nucleotide sequence in the DNA of a gene that binds RNA polymerase, positioning it to start transcribing RNA at the appropriate place.

prophage (prō'-fāj) A phage genome that has been inserted into a specific site on a bacterial chromosome.

prophase The first stage of mitosis, in which the chromatin condenses into discrete chromosomes visible with a light microscope, the mitotic spindle begins to form, and the nucleolus disappears but the nucleus remains intact.

prostaglandin (pros'-tuh-glan'-din) One of a group of modified fatty acids that are secreted by virtually all tissues and that perform a wide variety of functions as local regulators.

prostate gland (pros'-tāt) A gland in human males that secretes an acid-neutralizing component of semen.

protease (prō'-tē-āz) An enzyme that digests proteins by hydrolysis.

protein (prō'-tēn) A biologically functional molecule consisting of one or more polypeptides folded and coiled into a specific three-dimensional structure.

protein kinase (prō'-tēn) An enzyme that transfers phosphate groups from ATP to a protein, thus phosphorylating the protein.

protein phosphatase (prō'-tēn) An enzyme that removes phosphate groups from (dephosphorylates) proteins, often functioning to reverse the effect of a protein kinase.

proteoglycan (prō'-tē-ō-glī'-kan) A large molecule consisting of a small core protein with many carbohydrate chains attached, found in the extracellular matrix of animal cells. A proteoglycan may consist of up to 95% carbohydrate.

proteome The entire set of proteins expressed by a given cell or group of cells.

proteomics (prō'-tē-ō'-miks) The systematic study of sets of proteins and their properties, including their abundance, chemical modifications, and interactions.

protist An informal term applied to any eukaryote that is not a plant, animal, or fungus. Most protists are unicellular, though some are colonial or multicellular.

protocell An abiotic precursor of a living cell that had a membrane-like structure and that maintained an internal chemistry different from that of its surroundings.

proton (prō'-ton) A subatomic particle with a single positive electrical charge, with a mass of about 1.7×10^{-24} g, found in the nucleus of an atom.

protonema (prō'-tuh-nē'-muh) (plural, **protonemata**) A mass of green, branched, one-cell-thick filaments produced by germinating moss spores.

protonephridium (prō'-tō-nuh-frid'-ē-um) (plural, **protonephridia**) An excretory system, such as the flame bulb system of flatworms, consisting of a network of tubules lacking internal openings.

proton-motive force (prō'-ton) The potential energy stored in the form of a proton electrochemical gradient, generated by the pumping of hydrogen ions (H^+) across a biological membrane during chemiosmosis.

proton pump (prō'-ton) An active transport protein in a cell membrane that uses ATP to transport hydrogen ions out of a cell against their concentration gradient, generating a membrane potential in the process.

proto-oncogene (prō'-tō-on'-kō-jēn) A normal cellular gene that has the potential to become an oncogene.

protoplast The living part of a plant cell, which also includes the plasma membrane.

protostome development In animals, a developmental mode distinguished by the development of the mouth from the blastopore; often also characterized by spiral cleavage and by the body cavity forming when solid masses of mesoderm split.

provirus A viral genome that is permanently inserted into a host genome.

proximal tubule In the vertebrate kidney, the portion of a nephron immediately downstream from Bowman's capsule that conveys and helps refine filtrate.

pseudocoelomate (sū-dō-sē'-lō-māt) An animal whose body cavity is lined by tissue derived from mesoderm and endoderm.

pseudogene (sū'-dō-jēn) A DNA segment that is very similar to a real gene but does not yield a functional product; a DNA segment that formerly functioned as a gene but has become inactivated in a particular species because of mutation.

pseudopodium (sū'-dō-pō'-dē-um) (plural, **pseudopodia**) A cellular extension of amoeboid cells used in moving and feeding.

P site One of a ribosome's three binding sites for tRNA during translation. The P site holds the tRNA carrying the growing polypeptide chain. (P stands for peptidyl tRNA.)

pterosaur Winged reptile that lived during the Mesozoic era.

pulse The rhythmic bulging of the artery walls with each heartbeat.

punctuated equilibria In the fossil record, long periods of apparent stasis, in which a species undergoes little or no morphological change, interrupted by relatively brief periods of sudden change.

Punnett square A diagram used in the study of inheritance to show the predicted genotypic results of random fertilization in genetic crosses between individuals of known genotype.

pupil The opening in the iris, which admits light into the interior of the vertebrate eye. Muscles in the iris regulate its size.

purine (pyū'-rēn) One of two types of nitrogenous bases found in nucleotides, characterized by a six-membered ring fused to a five-membered ring. Adenine (A) and guanine (G) are purines.

pyrimidine (puh-rim'-uh-dēn) One of two types of nitrogenous bases found in nucleotides, characterized by a six-membered ring. Cytosine (C), thymine (T), and uracil (U) are pyrimidines.

quantitative character A heritable feature that varies continuously over a range rather than in an either-or fashion.

quaternary structure (kwot'-er-nār'-ē) The particular shape of a complex, aggregate protein, defined by the characteristic three-dimensional arrangement of its constituent subunits, each a polypeptide.

radial cleavage A type of embryonic development in deuterostomes in which the planes of cell division that transform the zygote into a ball of cells are either parallel or perpendicular to the vertical axis of the embryo, thereby aligning tiers of cells one above the other.

radial symmetry Symmetry in which the body is shaped like a pie or barrel (lacking a left side and a right side) and can be divided into mirror-imaged halves by any plane through its central axis.

radicle An embryonic root of a plant.

radioactive isotope An isotope (an atomic form of a chemical element) that is unstable; the nucleus decays spontaneously, giving off detectable particles and energy.

radiolarian A protist, usually marine, with a shell generally made of silica and pseudopodia that radiate from the central body.

radiometric dating A method for determining the absolute age of rocks and fossils, based on the half-life of radioactive isotopes.

radula A straplike scraping organ used by many molluscs during feeding.

***ras* gene** A gene that codes for Ras, a G protein that relays a growth signal from a growth factor receptor on the plasma membrane to a cascade of protein kinases, ultimately resulting in stimulation of the cell cycle.

ratite (rat'-īt) A member of the group of flightless birds.

ray-finned fish A member of the clade Actinopterygii, aquatic osteichthyans with fins supported by long, flexible rays, including tuna, bass, and herring.

reabsorption In excretory systems, the recovery of solutes and water from filtrate.

reactant A starting material in a chemical reaction.

reaction-center complex A complex of proteins associated with a special pair of chlorophyll *a* molecules and a primary electron acceptor. Located centrally in a photosystem, this complex triggers the light reactions of photosynthesis. Excited by light energy, the pair of chlorophylls donates an electron to the primary electron acceptor, which passes an electron to an electron transport chain.

reading frame On an mRNA, the triplet grouping of ribonucleotides used by the translation machinery during polypeptide synthesis.

receptacle The base of a flower; the part of the stem that is the site of attachment of the floral organs.

reception In cellular communication, the first step of a signaling pathway in which a signaling molecule is detected by a receptor molecule on or in the cell.

receptor-mediated endocytosis (en'-dō-sī-tō'-sis) The movement of specific molecules into a cell by the infolding of vesicles containing proteins with receptor sites specific to the molecules being taken in; enables a cell to acquire bulk quantities of specific substances.

receptor potential An initial response of a receptor cell to a stimulus, consisting of a change in voltage across the receptor membrane proportional to the stimulus strength.

receptor tyrosine kinase (RTK) A receptor protein spanning the plasma membrane, the cytoplasmic (intracellular) part of which can catalyze the transfer of a phosphate group from ATP to a tyrosine on another protein. Receptor tyrosine kinases often respond to the binding of a signaling molecule by dimerizing and then phosphorylating a tyrosine on the cytoplasmic portion of the other receptor in the dimer.

recessive allele An allele whose phenotypic effect is not observed in a heterozygote.

reciprocal altruism Altruistic behavior between unrelated individuals, whereby the altruistic individual benefits in the future when the beneficiary reciprocates.

recombinant chromosome A chromosome created when crossing over combines DNA from two parents into a single chromosome.

recombinant DNA A DNA molecule made *in vitro* with segments from different sources.

recombinant type (recombinant) An offspring whose phenotype differs from that of the true-breeding P generation parents; also refers to the phenotype itself.

rectum The terminal portion of the large intestine, where the feces are stored prior to elimination.

red alga A photosynthetic protist, named for its color, which results from a red pigment that masks the green of chlorophyll. Most red algae are multicellular and marine.

redox reaction (rē'-doks) A chemical reaction involving the complete or partial transfer of one or more electrons from one reactant to another; short for **red**uction-**ox**idation reaction.

reducing agent The electron donor in a redox reaction.

reduction The complete or partial addition of electrons to a substance involved in a redox reaction.

reflex An automatic reaction to a stimulus, mediated by the spinal cord or lower brain.

refractory period (rē-frakt'-ōr-ē) The short time immediately after an action potential in which the neuron cannot respond to another stimulus, owing to the inactivation of voltage-gated sodium channels.

regulator An animal for which mechanisms of homeostasis moderate internal changes in a particular variable in the face of external fluctuation of that variable.

regulatory gene A gene that codes for a protein, such as a repressor, that controls the transcription of another gene or group of genes.

reinforcement In evolutionary biology, a process in which natural selection strengthens prezygotic barriers to reproduction, thus reducing the chances of hybrid formation. Such a process is likely to occur only if hybrid offspring are less fit than members of the parent species.

relative abundance The proportional abundance of different species in a community.

relative fitness The contribution an individual makes to the gene pool of the next generation, relative to the contributions of other individuals in the population.

renal cortex The outer portion of the vertebrate kidney.

renal medulla The inner portion of the vertebrate kidney, beneath the renal cortex.

renal pelvis The funnel-shaped chamber that receives processed filtrate from the vertebrate kidney's collecting ducts and is drained by the ureter.

renin-angiotensin-aldosterone system (RAAS) A hormone cascade pathway that helps regulate blood pressure and blood volume.

repetitive DNA Nucleotide sequences, usually noncoding, that are present in many copies in a eukaryotic genome. The repeated units may be short and arranged tandemly (in series) or long and dispersed in the genome.

replication fork A Y-shaped region on a replicating DNA molecule where the parental strands are being unwound and new strands are being synthesized.

repressor A protein that inhibits gene transcription. In prokaryotes, repressors bind to the DNA in or near the promoter. In eukaryotes, repressors may bind to control elements within enhancers, to activators, or to other proteins in a way that blocks activators from binding to DNA.

reproductive isolation The existence of biological factors (barriers) that impede members of two species from producing viable, fertile offspring.

reproductive table An age-specific summary of the reproductive rates in a population.

reptile A member of the clade of amniotes that includes tuataras, lizards, snakes, turtles, crocodilians, and birds.

residual volume The amount of air that remains in the lungs after forceful exhalation.

resource partitioning The division of environmental resources by coexisting species such that the niche of each species differs by one or more significant factors from the niches of all coexisting species.

respiratory pigment A protein that transports oxygen in blood or hemolymph.

response (1) In cellular communication, the change in a specific cellular activity brought about by a transduced signal from outside the cell. (2) In feedback regulation, a physiological activity triggered by a change in a variable.

resting potential The membrane potential characteristic of a nonconducting excitable cell, with the inside of the cell more negative than the outside.

restriction enzyme An endonuclease (type of enzyme) that recognizes and cuts DNA molecules foreign to a bacterium (such as phage genomes). The enzyme cuts at specific nucleotide sequences (restriction sites).

restriction fragment A DNA segment that results from the cutting of DNA by a restriction enzyme.

restriction site A specific sequence on a DNA strand that is recognized and cut by a restriction enzyme.

retina (ret'-i-nuh) The innermost layer of the vertebrate eye, containing photoreceptor cells (rods and cones) and neurons; transmits images formed by the lens to the brain via the optic nerve.

retinal The light-absorbing pigment in rods and cones of the vertebrate eye.

retrotransposon (re'-trō-trans-pō'-zon) A transposable element that moves within a genome by means of an RNA intermediate, a transcript of the retrotransposon DNA.

retrovirus (re'-trō-vī'-rus) An RNA virus that replicates by transcribing its RNA into DNA and then inserting the DNA into a cellular chromosome; an important class of cancer-causing viruses.

reverse transcriptase (tran-skrip'-tās) An enzyme encoded by certain viruses (retroviruses) that uses RNA as a template for DNA synthesis.

reverse transcriptase–polymerase chain reaction (RT-PCR) A technique for determining expression of a particular gene. It uses reverse transcriptase and DNA polymerase to synthesize cDNA from all the mRNA in a sample and then subjects the cDNA to PCR amplification using primers specific for the gene of interest.

Rhizaria (rī-za'-rē-uh) One of the three major subgroups for which the "SAR" eukaryotic supergroup is named. Many species in this clade are amoebas characterized by threadlike pseudopodia.

rhizobacterium A soil bacterium whose population size is much enhanced in the rhizosphere, the soil region close to a plant's roots.

rhizoid (rī'-zoyd) A long, tubular single cell or filament of cells that anchors bryophytes to the ground. Unlike roots, rhizoids are not composed of tissues, lack specialized conducting cells, and do not play a primary role in water and mineral absorption.

rhizosphere The soil region close to plant roots and characterized by a high level of microbiological activity.

rhodopsin (rō-dop'-sin) A visual pigment consisting of retinal and opsin. Upon absorbing light, the retinal changes shape and dissociates from the opsin.

ribonucleic acid (RNA) (rī'-bō-nū-klā'-ik) A type of nucleic acid consisting of a polynucleotide made up of nucleotide monomers with a ribose sugar and the nitrogenous bases adenine (A), cytosine (C), guanine (G), and uracil (U); usually single-stranded; functions in protein synthesis, in gene regulation, and as the genome of some viruses.

ribose The sugar component of RNA nucleotides.

ribosomal RNA (rRNA) (rī'-buh-sō'-mul) RNA molecules that, together with proteins, make up ribosomes; the most abundant type of RNA.

ribosome (rī'-buh-sōm) A complex of rRNA and protein molecules that functions as a site of protein synthesis in the cytoplasm; consists of a large and a small subunit. In eukaryotic cells, each subunit is assembled in the nucleolus. *See also* nucleolus.

ribozyme (rī'-buh-zīm) An RNA molecule that functions as an enzyme, such as an intron that catalyzes its own removal during RNA splicing.

RNA interference (RNAi) A mechanism for silencing the expression of specific genes. In RNAi, double-stranded RNA molecules that match the sequence of a particular gene are processed into siRNAs that either block translation or trigger the degradation of the gene's messenger RNA. This happens naturally in some cells, and can be carried out in laboratory experiments as well.

RNA polymerase An enzyme that links ribonucleotides into a growing RNA chain during transcription, based on complementary binding to nucleotides on a DNA template strand.

RNA processing Modification of RNA primary transcripts, including splicing out of introns, joining together of exons, and alteration of the 5' and 3' ends.

RNA splicing After synthesis of a eukaryotic primary RNA transcript, the removal of portions of the transcript (introns) that will not be included in the mRNA and the joining together of the remaining portions (exons).

rod A rodlike cell in the retina of the vertebrate eye, sensitive to low light intensity.

root An organ in vascular plants that anchors the plant and enables it to absorb water and minerals from the soil.

root cap A cone of cells at the tip of a plant root that protects the apical meristem.

root hair A tiny extension of a root epidermal cell, growing just behind the root tip and increasing surface area for absorption of water and minerals.

root pressure Pressure exerted in the roots of plants as the result of osmosis, causing exudation from cut stems and guttation of water from leaves.

root system All of a plant's roots, which anchor it in the soil, absorb and transport minerals and water, and store food.

rooted Describing a phylogenetic tree that contains a branch point (often, the one farthest to the left) representing the most recent common ancestor of all taxa in the tree.

rough ER That portion of the endoplasmic reticulum with ribosomes attached.

round window In the mammalian ear, the point of contact where vibrations of the stapes create a traveling series of pressure waves in the fluid of the cochlea.

R plasmid A bacterial plasmid carrying genes that confer resistance to certain antibiotics.

r-selection Selection for life history traits that maximize reproductive success in uncrowded environments; also called density-independent selection.

rubisco (rū-bis'-kō) Ribulose bisphosphate (RuBP) carboxylase-oxygenase, the enzyme that normally catalyzes the first step of the Calvin cycle (the addition of CO_2 to RuBP). When excess O_2 is present or CO_2 levels are low, rubisco can bind oxygen, resulting in photorespiration.

saccule In the vertebrate ear, a chamber in the vestibule behind the oval window that participates in the sense of balance.

salicylic acid (sal'-i-sil'-ik) A signaling molecule in plants that may be partially responsible for activating systemic acquired resistance to pathogens.

salivary gland A gland associated with the oral cavity that secretes substances that lubricate food and begin the process of chemical digestion.

salt A compound resulting from the formation of an ionic bond; also called an ionic compound.

saltatory conduction (sol'-tuh-tōr'-ē) Rapid transmission of a nerve impulse along an axon, resulting from the action potential jumping from one node of Ranvier to another, skipping the myelin-sheathed regions of membrane.

"SAR" clade One of four supergroups of eukaryotes proposed in a current hypothesis of the evolutionary history of eukaryotes. This supergroup contains a large, extremely diverse collection of protists from three major subgroups: stramenopiles, alveolates, and rhizarians. *See also* Excavata, Archaeplastida, and Unikonta.

sarcomere (sar'-kō-mēr) The fundamental, repeating unit of striated muscle, delimited by the Z lines.

sarcoplasmic reticulum (SR) (sar'-kō-plaz'-mik ruh-tik'-yū-lum) A specialized endoplasmic reticulum that regulates the calcium concentration in the cytosol of muscle cells.

saturated fatty acid A fatty acid in which all carbons in the hydrocarbon tail are connected by single bonds, thus maximizing the number of hydrogen atoms that are attached to the carbon skeleton.

savanna A tropical grassland biome with scattered individual trees and large herbivores and maintained by occasional fires and drought.

scaffolding protein A type of large relay protein to which several other relay proteins are simultaneously attached, increasing the efficiency of signal transduction.

scanning electron microscope (SEM) A microscope that uses an electron beam to scan the surface of a sample, coated with metal atoms, to study details of its topography.

scatter plot A graph in which each piece of data is represented by a point. A scatter plot is used when the data for all variables are numerical and continuous.

schizophrenia (skit'-suh-frē'-nē-uh) A severe mental disturbance characterized by psychotic episodes in which patients have a distorted perception of reality.

Schwann cell A type of glial cell that forms insulating myelin sheaths around the axons of neurons in the peripheral nervous system.

science An approach to understanding the natural world.

scion (sī'-un) The twig grafted onto the stock when making a graft.

sclereid (sklār'-ē-id) A short, irregular sclerenchyma cell in nutshells and seed coats. Sclereids are scattered throughout the parenchyma of some plants.

sclerenchyma cell (skluh-ren'-kim-uh) A rigid, supportive plant cell type usually lacking a protoplast and possessing thick secondary walls strengthened by lignin at maturity.

scrotum A pouch of skin outside the abdomen that houses the testes; functions in maintaining the testes at the lower temperature required for spermatogenesis.

second law of thermodynamics The principle stating that every energy transfer or transformation increases the entropy of the universe. Usable forms of energy are at least partly converted to heat.

second messenger A small, nonprotein, water-soluble molecule or ion, such as a calcium ion (Ca^{2+}) or cyclic AMP, that relays a signal to a cell's interior in response to a signaling molecule bound by a signal receptor protein.

secondary cell wall In plant cells, a strong and durable matrix that is often deposited in several laminated layers around the plasma membrane and provides protection and support.

secondary consumer A carnivore that eats herbivores.

secondary endosymbiosis A process in eukaryotic evolution in which a heterotrophic eukaryotic cell engulfed a photosynthetic eukaryotic cell, which survived in a symbiotic relationship inside the heterotrophic cell.

secondary growth Growth produced by lateral meristems, thickening the roots and shoots of woody plants.

secondary immune response The adaptive immune response elicited on second or subsequent exposures to a particular antigen. The secondary immune response is more rapid, of greater magnitude, and of longer duration than the primary immune response.

secondary oocyte (ō′-uh-sīt) An oocyte that has completed meiosis I.

secondary production The amount of chemical energy in consumers' food that is converted to their own new biomass during a given time period.

secondary structure Regions of repetitive coiling or folding of the polypeptide backbone of a protein due to hydrogen bonding between constituents of the backbone (not the side chains).

secondary succession A type of succession that occurs where an existing community has been cleared by some disturbance that leaves the soil or substrate intact.

secretion (1) The discharge of molecules synthesized by a cell. (2) The active transport of wastes and certain other solutes from the body fluid into the filtrate in an excretory system.

seed An adaptation of some terrestrial plants consisting of an embryo packaged along with a store of food within a protective coat.

seed coat A tough outer covering of a seed, formed from the outer coat of an ovule. In a flowering plant, the seed coat encloses and protects the embryo and endosperm.

seedless vascular plant An informal name for a plant that has vascular tissue but lacks seeds. Seedless vascular plants form a paraphyletic group that includes the phyla Lycophyta (club mosses and their relatives) and Monilophyta (ferns and their relatives).

selective permeability A property of biological membranes that allows them to regulate the passage of substances across them.

self-incompatibility The ability of a seed plant to reject its own pollen and sometimes the pollen of closely related individuals.

semelparity (seh′-mel-pār′-i-tē) Reproduction in which an organism produces all of its offspring in a single event; also called big-bang reproduction.

semen (sē′-mun) The fluid that is ejaculated by the male during orgasm; contains sperm and secretions from several glands of the male reproductive tract.

semicircular canals A three-part chamber of the inner ear that functions in maintaining equilibrium.

semiconservative model Type of DNA replication in which the replicated double helix consists of one old strand, derived from the parental molecule, and one newly made strand.

semilunar valve A valve located at each exit of the heart, where the aorta leaves the left ventricle and the pulmonary artery leaves the right ventricle.

seminal vesicle (sem′-i-nul ves′-i-kul) A gland in males that secretes a fluid component of semen that lubricates and nourishes sperm.

seminiferous tubule (sem′-i-nif′-er-us) A highly coiled tube in the testis in which sperm are produced.

senescence (se-nes′-ens) The growth phase in a plant or plant part (as a leaf) from full maturity to death.

sensitive period A limited phase in an animal's development when learning of particular behaviors can take place; also called a critical period.

sensor In homeostasis, a receptor that detects a stimulus.

sensory adaptation The tendency of sensory neurons to become less sensitive when they are stimulated repeatedly.

sensory neuron A nerve cell that receives information from the internal or external environment and transmits signals to the central nervous system.

sensory reception The detection of a stimulus by sensory cells.

sensory receptor A specialized structure or cell that responds to a stimulus from an animal's internal or external environment.

sensory transduction The conversion of stimulus energy to a change in the membrane potential of a sensory receptor cell.

sepal (sē′-pul) A modified leaf in angiosperms that helps enclose and protect a flower bud before it opens.

septum (plural, **septa**) One of the cross-walls that divide a fungal hypha into cells. Septa generally have pores large enough to allow ribosomes, mitochondria, and even nuclei to flow from cell to cell.

serial endosymbiosis A hypothesis for the origin of eukaryotes consisting of a sequence of endosymbiotic events in which mitochondria, chloroplasts, and perhaps other cellular structures were derived from small prokaryotes that had been engulfed by larger cells.

serotonin (ser′-uh-tō′-nin) A neurotransmitter, synthesized from the amino acid tryptophan, that functions in the central nervous system.

set point In homeostasis in animals, a value maintained for a particular variable, such as body temperature or solute concentration.

seta (sē′-tuh) (plural, **setae**) The elongated stalk of a bryophyte sporophyte.

sex chromosome A chromosome responsible for determining the sex of an individual.

sex-linked gene A gene located on either sex chromosome. Most sex-linked genes are on the X chromosome and show distinctive patterns of inheritance; there are very few genes on the Y chromosome.

sexual dimorphism (dī-mōr′-fizm) Differences between the secondary sex characteristics of males and females of the same species.

sexual reproduction A type of reproduction in which two parents give rise to offspring that have unique combinations of genes inherited from both parents via the gametes.

sexual selection A form of natural selection in which individuals with certain inherited characteristics are more likely than other individuals to obtain mates.

Shannon diversity An index of community diversity symbolized by H and represented by the equation $H = -(p_A \ln p_A + p_B \ln p_B + p_C \ln p_C + \ldots)$, where A, B, C . . . are species,

p is the relative abundance of each species, and ln is the natural logarithm.

shared ancestral character A character, shared by members of a particular clade, that originated in an ancestor that is not a member of that clade.

shared derived character An evolutionary novelty that is unique to a particular clade.

shoot system The aerial portion of a plant body, consisting of stems, leaves, and (in angiosperms) flowers.

short tandem repeat (STR) Simple sequence DNA containing multiple tandemly repeated units of two to five nucleotides. Variations in STRs act as genetic markers in STR analysis, used to prepare genetic profiles.

short-day plant A plant that flowers (usually in late summer, fall, or winter) only when the light period is shorter than a critical length.

short-term memory The ability to hold information, anticipations, or goals for a time and then release them if they become irrelevant.

sickle-cell disease A recessively inherited human blood disorder in which a single nucleotide change in the β-globin gene causes hemoglobin to aggregate, changing red blood cell shape and causing multiple symptoms in afflicted individuals.

sieve plate An end wall in a sieve-tube element, which facilitates the flow of phloem sap in angiosperm sieve tubes.

sieve-tube element A living cell that conducts sugars and other organic nutrients in the phloem of angiosperms; also called a sieve-tube member. Connected end to end, they form sieve tubes.

sign stimulus An external sensory cue that triggers a fixed action pattern by an animal.

signal In animal behavior, transmission of a stimulus from one animal to another. The term is also used in the context of communication in other kinds of organisms and in cell-to-cell communication in all multicellular organisms.

signal peptide A sequence of about 20 amino acids at or near the leading (amino) end of a polypeptide that targets it to the endoplasmic reticulum or other organelles in a eukaryotic cell.

signal-recognition particle (SRP) A protein-RNA complex that recognizes a signal peptide as it emerges from a ribosome and helps direct the ribosome to the endoplasmic reticulum (ER) by binding to a receptor protein on the ER.

signal transduction The linkage of a mechanical, chemical, or electromagnetic stimulus to a specific cellular response.

signal transduction pathway A series of steps linking a mechanical, chemical, or electrical stimulus to a specific cellular response.

silent mutation A nucleotide-pair substitution that has no observable effect on the phenotype; for example, within a gene, a mutation that results in a codon that codes for the same amino acid.

simple fruit A fruit derived from a single carpel or several fused carpels.

simple sequence DNA A DNA sequence that contains many copies of tandemly repeated short sequences.

single bond A single covalent bond; the sharing of a pair of valence electrons by two atoms.

single circulation A circulatory system consisting of a single pump and circuit, in which blood passes from the sites of gas exchange to the rest of the body before returning to the heart.

single-lens eye The camera-like eye found in some jellies, polychaete worms, spiders, and many molluscs.

single nucleotide polymorphism (SNP) A single base-pair site in a genome where nucleotide variation is found in at least 1% of the population.

single-strand binding protein A protein that binds to the unpaired DNA strands during DNA replication, stabilizing them and holding them apart while they serve as templates for the synthesis of complementary strands of DNA.

sinoatrial (sī′-nō-ā′-trē-uhl) **(SA) node** A region in the right atrium of the heart that sets the rate and timing at which all cardiac muscle cells contract; the pacemaker.

sister chromatids Two copies of a duplicated chromosome attached to each other by proteins at the centromere and, sometimes, along the arms. While joined, two sister chromatids make up one chromosome. Chromatids are eventually separated during mitosis or meiosis II.

sister taxa Groups of organisms that share an immediate common ancestor and hence are each other's closest relatives.

skeletal muscle A type of striated muscle that is generally responsible for the voluntary movements of the body.

sliding-filament model The idea that muscle contraction is based on the movement of thin (actin) filaments along thick (myosin) filaments, shortening the sarcomere, the basic unit of muscle organization.

slow block to polyspermy The formation of the fertilization envelope and other changes in an egg's surface that prevent fusion of the egg with more than one sperm. The slow block begins about 1 minute after fertilization.

slow-twitch fiber A muscle fiber that can sustain long contractions.

small interfering RNA (siRNA) One of multiple small, single-stranded RNA molecules generated by cellular machinery from a long, linear, double-stranded RNA molecule. The siRNA associates with one or more proteins in a complex that can degrade or prevent translation of an mRNA with a complementary sequence.

small intestine The longest section of the alimentary canal, so named because of its small diameter compared with that of the large intestine; the principal site of the enzymatic hydrolysis of food macromolecules and the absorption of nutrients.

smooth ER That portion of the endoplasmic reticulum that is free of ribosomes.

smooth muscle A type of muscle lacking the striations of skeletal and cardiac muscle because of the uniform distribution of myosin filaments in the cells; responsible for involuntary body activities.

social learning Modification of behavior through the observation of other individuals.

sociobiology The study of social behavior based on evolutionary theory.

sodium-potassium pump A transport protein in the plasma membrane of animal cells that actively transports sodium out of the cell and potassium into the cell.

soil horizon A soil layer with physical characteristics that differ from those of the layers above or beneath.

solute (sol′-yūt) A substance that is dissolved in a solution.

solute potential (Ψ_S) A component of water potential that is proportional to the molarity of a solution and that measures the effect of solutes on the direction of water movement; also called osmotic potential, it can be either zero or negative.

solution A liquid that is a homogeneous mixture of two or more substances.

solvent The dissolving agent of a solution. Water is the most versatile solvent known.

somatic cell (sō-mat′-ik) Any cell in a multicellular organism except a sperm or egg or their precursors.

somite One of a series of blocks of mesoderm that exist in pairs just lateral to the notochord in a vertebrate embryo.

soredium (suh-rē′-dē-um) (plural, **soredia**) In lichens, a small cluster of fungal hyphae with embedded algae.

sorus (plural, **sori**) A cluster of sporangia on a fern sporophyll. Sori may be arranged in various patterns, such as parallel lines or dots, which are useful in fern identification.

spatial learning The establishment of a memory that reflects the environment's spatial structure.

spatial summation A phenomenon of neural integration in which the membrane potential of the postsynaptic cell is determined by the combined effect of EPSPs or IPSPs produced nearly simultaneously by different synapses.

speciation (spē′-sē-ā′-shun) An evolutionary process in which one species splits into two or more species.

species (spē′-sēz) A population or group of populations whose members have the potential to interbreed in nature and produce viable, fertile offspring but do not produce viable, fertile offspring with members of other such groups.

species-area curve (spē′-sēz) The biodiversity pattern that shows that the larger the geographic area of a community is, the more species it has.

species diversity (spē′-sēz) The number and relative abundance of species in a biological community.

species richness (spē′-sēz) The number of species in a biological community.

specific heat The amount of heat that must be absorbed or lost for 1 g of a substance to change its temperature by 1°C.

spectrophotometer An instrument that measures the proportions of light of different wavelengths absorbed and transmitted by a pigment solution.

sperm The male gamete.

spermatheca (sper′-muh-thē′-kuh) (plural, **spermathecae**) In many insects, a sac in the female reproductive system where sperm are stored.

spermatogenesis (sper-ma′-tō-gen′-uh-sis) The continuous and prolific production of mature sperm in the testis.

spermatogonium (sper-ma′-tō-gō′-nē-um) (plural, **spermatogonia**) A cell that divides mitotically to form spermatocytes.

S phase The synthesis phase of the cell cycle; the portion of interphase during which DNA is replicated.

sphincter (sfink′-ter) A ringlike band of muscle fibers that controls the size of an opening in the body, such as the passage between the esophagus and the stomach.

spiral cleavage A type of embryonic development in protostomes in which the planes of cell division that transform the zygote into a ball of cells are diagonal to the vertical axis of the embryo. As a result, the cells of each tier sit in the grooves between cells of adjacent tiers.

spliceosome (splī′-sō-sōm) A large complex made up of proteins and RNA molecules that splices RNA by interacting with the ends of an RNA intron, releasing the intron and joining the two adjacent exons.

spongocoel (spon′-jō-sēl) The central cavity of a sponge.

spontaneous process A process that occurs without an overall input of energy; a process that is energetically favorable.

sporangium (spōr-an′-jē-um) (plural, **sporangia**) A multicellular organ in fungi and plants in which meiosis occurs and haploid cells develop.

spore (1) In the life cycle of a plant or alga undergoing alternation of generations, a haploid cell produced in the sporophyte by meiosis. A spore can divide by mitosis to develop into a multicellular haploid individual, the gametophyte, without fusing with another cell. (2) In fungi, a haploid cell, produced either sexually or asexually, that produces a mycelium after germination.

sporophyll (spō′-ruh-fil) A modified leaf that bears sporangia and hence is specialized for reproduction.

sporophyte (spō-ruh-fīt′) In organisms (plants and some algae) that have alternation of generations, the multicellular diploid form that results from the union of gametes. The sporophyte produces haploid spores by meiosis that develop into gametophytes.

sporopollenin (spōr-uh-pol′-eh-nin) A durable polymer that covers exposed zygotes of charophyte algae and forms the walls of plant spores, preventing them from drying out.

stabilizing selection Natural selection in which intermediate phenotypes survive or reproduce more successfully than do extreme phenotypes.

stamen (stā′-men) The pollen-producing reproductive organ of a flower, consisting of an anther and a filament.

standard deviation A measure of the variation found in a set of data points.

standard metabolic rate (SMR) Metabolic rate of a resting, fasting, and nonstressed ectotherm at a particular temperature.

starch A storage polysaccharide in plants, consisting entirely of glucose monomers joined by α glycosidic linkages.

start point In transcription, the nucleotide position on the promoter where RNA polymerase begins synthesis of RNA.

statocyst (stat′-uh-sist′) A type of mechanoreceptor that functions in equilibrium in invertebrates by use of statoliths, which stimulate hair cells in relation to gravity.

statolith (stat′-uh-lith′) (1) In plants, a specialized plastid that contains dense starch grains and may play a role in detecting gravity. (2) In invertebrates, a dense particle that settles in response to gravity and is found in sensory organs that function in equilibrium.

stele (stēl) The vascular tissue of a stem or root.

stem A vascular plant organ consisting of an alternating system of nodes and internodes that support the leaves and reproductive structures.

stem cell Any relatively unspecialized cell that can produce, during a single division, one identical daughter cell and one more specialized daughter cell that can undergo further differentiation.

steroid A type of lipid characterized by a carbon skeleton consisting of four fused rings with various chemical groups attached.

sticky end A single-stranded end of a double-stranded restriction fragment.

stigma (plural, **stigmata**) The sticky part of a flower's carpel, which receives pollen grains.

stimulus In feedback regulation, a fluctuation in a variable that triggers a response.

stipe A stemlike structure of a seaweed.

stock The plant that provides the root system when making a graft.

stoma (stō′-muh) (plural, **stomata**) A microscopic pore surrounded by guard cells in the epidermis of leaves and stems that allows gas exchange between the environment and the interior of the plant.

stomach An organ of the digestive system that stores food and performs preliminary steps of digestion.

Stramenopila (strah′-men-ō′-pē-lah) One of the three major subgroups for which the "SAR" eukaryotic supergroup is named. This clade arose by secondary endosymbiosis and includes diatoms and brown algae.

stratum (strah′-tum) (plural, **strata**) A rock layer formed when new layers of sediment cover older ones and compress them.

strigolactone Any of a class of plant hormones that inhibit shoot branching, trigger the germination of parasitic plant seeds, and stimulate the association of plant roots with mycorrhizal fungi.

strobilus (strō-bī′-lus) (plural, **strobili**) The technical term for a cluster of sporophylls known commonly as a cone, found in most gymnosperms and some seedless vascular plants.

stroke The death of nervous tissue in the brain, usually resulting from rupture or blockage of arteries in the head.

stroke volume The volume of blood pumped by a heart ventricle in a single contraction.

stroma (strō′-muh) The dense fluid within the chloroplast surrounding the thylakoid membrane and containing ribosomes and DNA; involved in the synthesis of organic molecules from carbon dioxide and water.

stromatolite Layered rock that results from the activities of prokaryotes that bind thin films of sediment together.

structural isomer One of several compounds that have the same molecular formula but differ in the covalent arrangements of their atoms.

style The stalk of a flower's carpel, with the ovary at the base and the stigma at the top.

substrate The reactant on which an enzyme works.

substrate feeder An animal that lives in or on its food source, eating its way through the food.

substrate-level phosphorylation The enzyme-catalyzed formation of ATP by direct transfer of a phosphate group to ADP from an intermediate substrate in catabolism.

sugar sink A plant organ that is a net consumer or storer of sugar. Growing roots, shoot tips, stems, and fruits are examples of sugar sinks supplied by phloem.

sugar source A plant organ in which sugar is being produced by either photosynthesis or the breakdown of starch. Mature leaves are the primary sugar sources of plants.

sulfhydryl group A chemical group consisting of a sulfur atom bonded to a hydrogen atom.

suprachiasmatic nucleus (SCN) (sūp′-ruh-kē′-as-ma-tik) A group of neurons in the hypothalamus of mammals that functions as a biological clock.

surface tension A measure of how difficult it is to stretch or break the surface of a liquid. Water has a high surface tension because of the hydrogen bonding of surface molecules.

surfactant A substance secreted by alveoli that decreases surface tension in the fluid that coats the alveoli.

survivorship curve A plot of the number of members of a cohort that are still alive at each age; one way to represent age-specific mortality.

suspension feeder An animal that feeds by removing suspended food particles from the surrounding medium by a capture, trapping, or filtration mechanism.

sustainable agriculture Long-term productive farming methods that are environmentally safe.

sustainable development Development that meets the needs of people today without limiting the ability of future generations to meet their needs.

swim bladder In aquatic osteichthyans, an air sac that enables the animal to control its buoyancy in the water.

symbiont (sim′-bē-ont) The smaller participant in a symbiotic relationship, living in or on the host.

symbiosis An ecological relationship between organisms of two different species that live together in direct and intimate contact.

sympathetic division One of three divisions of the autonomic nervous system; generally increases energy expenditure and prepares the body for action.

sympatric speciation (sim-pat′-rik) The formation of new species in populations that live in the same geographic area.

symplast In plants, the continuum of cytoplasm connected by plasmodesmata between cells.

synapse (sin′-aps) The junction where a neuron communicates with another cell across a narrow gap via a neurotransmitter or an electrical coupling.

synapsid (si-nap′-sid) A member of an amniote clade distinguished by a single hole on each side of the skull. Synapsids include the mammals.

synapsis (si-nap′-sis) The pairing and physical connection of duplicated homologous chromosomes during prophase I of meiosis.

synaptonemal (si-nap′-tuh-nē′-muhl) **complex** A zipper-like structure composed of proteins, which connects two homologous chromosomes tightly along their lengths.

systematics A scientific discipline focused on classifying organisms and determining their evolutionary relationships.

systemic acquired resistance A defensive response in infected plants that helps protect healthy tissue from pathogenic invasion.

systemic circuit The branch of the circulatory system that supplies oxygenated blood to and carries deoxygenated blood away from organs and tissues throughout the body.

systems biology An approach to studying biology that aims to model the dynamic behavior of whole biological systems based on a study of the interactions among the system's parts.

systole (sis′-tō-lē) The stage of the cardiac cycle in which a heart chamber contracts and pumps blood.

systolic pressure Blood pressure in the arteries during contraction of the ventricles.

taproot A main vertical root that develops from an embryonic root and gives rise to lateral (branch) roots.

tastant Any chemical that stimulates the sensory receptors in a taste bud.

taste bud A collection of modified epithelial cells on the tongue or in the mouth that are receptors for taste in mammals.

TATA box A DNA sequence in eukaryotic promoters crucial in forming the transcription initiation complex.

taxis (tak′-sis) An oriented movement toward or away from a stimulus.

taxon (plural, **taxa**) A named taxonomic unit at any given level of classification.

taxonomy (tak-son′-uh-mē) A scientific discipline concerned with naming and classifying the diverse forms of life.

Tay-Sachs disease A human genetic disease caused by a recessive allele for a dysfunctional enzyme, leading to accumulation of certain lipids in the brain. Seizures, blindness, and degeneration of motor and mental performance usually become manifest a few months after birth, followed by death within a few years.

T cells The class of lymphocytes that mature in the thymus; they include both effector cells for the cell-mediated immune response and helper cells required for both branches of adaptive immunity.

technology The application of scientific knowledge for a specific purpose, often involving industry or commerce but also including uses in basic research.

telomere (tel′-uh-mēr) The tandemly repetitive DNA at the end of a eukaryotic chromosome's DNA molecule. Telomeres protect the organism's genes from being eroded during successive rounds of replication. *See also* repetitive DNA.

telophase The fifth and final stage of mitosis, in which daughter nuclei are forming and cytokinesis has typically begun.

temperate broadleaf forest A biome located throughout midlatitude regions where there is sufficient moisture to support the growth of large, broadleaf deciduous trees.

temperate grassland A terrestrial biome that exists at midlatitude regions and is dominated by grasses and forbs.

temperate phage A phage that is capable of replicating by either a lytic or lysogenic cycle.

temperature A measure in degrees of the average kinetic energy (thermal energy) of the atoms and molecules in a body of matter.

template strand The DNA strand that provides the pattern, or template, for ordering, by complementary base pairing, the sequence of nucleotides in an RNA transcript.

temporal summation A phenomenon of neural integration in which the membrane potential of the postsynaptic cell in a chemical synapse is determined by the combined effect of EPSPs or IPSPs produced in rapid succession.

tendon A fibrous connective tissue that attaches muscle to bone.

terminator In bacteria, a sequence of nucleotides in DNA that marks the end of a gene and signals RNA polymerase to release the newly made RNA molecule and detach from the DNA.

territoriality A behavior in which an animal defends a bounded physical space against encroachment by other individuals, usually of its own species.

tertiary consumer (ter′-shē-ār′-ē) A carnivore that eats other carnivores.

tertiary structure (ter′-shē-ār′-ē) The overall shape of a protein molecule due to interactions of amino acid side chains, including hydrophobic interactions, ionic bonds, hydrogen bonds, and disulfide bridges.

test In foram protists, a porous shell that consists of a single piece of organic material hardened with calcium carbonate.

testcross Breeding an organism of unknown genotype with a homozygous recessive individual to determine the unknown genotype. The ratio of phenotypes in the offspring reveals the unknown genotype.

testis (plural, **testes**) The male reproductive organ, or gonad, in which sperm and reproductive hormones are produced.

testosterone A steroid hormone required for development of the male reproductive system, spermatogenesis, and male secondary sex characteristics; the major androgen in mammals.

tetanus (tet′-uh-nus) The maximal, sustained contraction of a skeletal muscle, caused by a very high frequency of action potentials elicited by continual stimulation.

tetrapod A vertebrate clade whose members have limbs with digits. Tetrapods include mammals, amphibians, and birds and other reptiles.

thalamus (thal′-uh-mus) An integrating center of the vertebrate forebrain. Neurons with cell bodies in the thalamus relay neural input to specific areas in the cerebral cortex and regulate what information goes to the cerebral cortex.

theory An explanation that is broader in scope than a hypothesis, generates new hypotheses, and is supported by a large body of evidence.

thermal energy Kinetic energy due to the random motion of atoms and molecules; energy in its most random form. *See also* heat.

thermocline A narrow stratum of abrupt temperature change in the ocean and in many temperate-zone lakes.

thermodynamics (ther′-mō-dī-nam′-iks) The study of energy transformations that occur in a collection of matter. *See also* first law of thermodynamics and second law of thermodynamics.

thermophile *See* extreme thermophile.

thermoreceptor A receptor stimulated by either heat or cold.

thermoregulation The maintenance of internal body temperature within a tolerable range.

theropod A member of a group of dinosaurs that were bipedal carnivores.

thick filament A filament composed of staggered arrays of myosin molecules; a component of myofibrils in muscle fibers.

thigmomorphogenesis (thig′-mō-mor′-phō-gen′-uh-sis) A response in plants to chronic mechanical stimulation, resulting from increased ethylene production. An example is thickening stems in response to strong winds.

thigmotropism (thig-mō′-truh-pizm) A directional growth of a plant in response to touch.

thin filament A filament consisting of two strands of actin and two strands of regulatory protein coiled around one another; a component of myofibrils in muscle fibers.

threatened species A species that is considered likely to become endangered in the foreseeable future.

threshold The potential that an excitable cell membrane must reach for an action potential to be initiated.

thrombus A fibrin-containing clot that forms in a blood vessel and blocks the flow of blood.

thylakoid (thī′-luh-koyd) A flattened, membranous sac inside a chloroplast. Thylakoids often exist in stacks called grana that are interconnected; their membranes contain molecular "machinery" used to convert light energy to chemical energy.

thymus (thī′-mus) A small organ in the thoracic cavity of vertebrates where maturation of T cells is completed.

thyroid gland An endocrine gland, located on the ventral surface of the trachea, that secretes two iodine-containing hormones, triiodothyronine (T_3) and thyroxine (T_4), as well as calcitonin.

thyroid hormone Either of two iodine-containing hormones (triiodothyronine and thyroxine) that are secreted by the thyroid gland and that help regulate metabolism, development, and maturation in vertebrates.

thyroxine (T_4) One of two iodine-containing hormones that are secreted by the thyroid gland and that help regulate metabolism, development, and maturation in vertebrates.

tidal volume The volume of air a mammal inhales and exhales with each breath.

tight junction A type of intercellular junction between animal cells that prevents the leakage of material through the space between cells.

tissue An integrated group of cells with a common structure, function, or both.

tissue system One or more tissues organized into a functional unit connecting the organs of a plant.

Toll-like receptor (TLR) A membrane receptor on a phagocytic white blood cell that recognizes fragments of molecules common to a set of pathogens.

tonicity The ability of a solution surrounding a cell to cause that cell to gain or lose water.

top-down model A model of community organization in which predation influences community organization by controlling herbivore numbers, which in turn control plant or phytoplankton numbers, which in turn control nutrient levels; also called the trophic cascade model.

topoisomerase A protein that breaks, swivels, and rejoins DNA strands. During DNA replication, topoisomerase helps to relieve strain in the double helix ahead of the replication fork.

topsoil A mixture of particles derived from rock, living organisms, and decaying organic material (humus).

torpor A physiological state in which activity is low and metabolism decreases.

totipotent (tō′-tuh-pōt′-ent) Describing a cell that can give rise to all parts of the embryo and adult, as well as extraembryonic membranes in species that have them.

trace element An element indispensable for life but required in extremely minute amounts.

trachea (trā′-kē-uh) The portion of the respiratory tract that passes from the larynx to the bronchi; also called the windpipe.

Glossary

tracheal system In insects, a system of branched, air-filled tubes that extends throughout the body and carries oxygen directly to cells.

tracheid (trā′-kē-id) A long, tapered water-conducting cell found in the xylem of nearly all vascular plants. Functioning tracheids are no longer living.

trait One of two or more detectable variants in a genetic character.

trans fat An unsaturated fat, formed artificially during hydrogenation of oils, containing one or more *trans* double bonds.

transcription The synthesis of RNA using a DNA template.

transcription factor A regulatory protein that binds to DNA and affects transcription of specific genes.

transcription initiation complex The completed assembly of transcription factors and RNA polymerase bound to a promoter.

transcription unit A region of DNA that is transcribed into an RNA molecule.

transduction (1) A process in which phages (viruses) carry bacterial DNA from one bacterial cell to another. When these two cells are members of different species, transduction results in horizontal gene transfer. (2) In cellular communication, the conversion of a signal from outside the cell to a form that can bring about a specific cellular response; also called signal transduction.

transfer RNA (tRNA) An RNA molecule that functions as a translator between nucleic acid and protein languages by carrying specific amino acids to the ribosome, where they recognize the appropriate codons in the mRNA.

transformation (1) The conversion of a normal cell into a cell that is able to divide indefinitely in culture, thus behaving like a cancer cell. (Malignant transformation may also describe the series of changes in a normal cell in an organism that change it into a malignant (cancerous) cell.) (2) A change in genotype and phenotype due to the assimilation of external DNA by a cell. When the external DNA is from a member of a different species, transformation results in horizontal gene transfer.

transgenic Pertaining to an organism whose genome contains a gene introduced from another organism of the same or a different species.

translation The synthesis of a polypeptide using the genetic information encoded in an mRNA molecule. There is a change of "language" from nucleotides to amino acids.

translocation (1) An aberration in chromosome structure resulting from attachment of a chromosomal fragment to a nonhomologous chromosome. (2) During protein synthesis, the third stage in the elongation cycle, when the RNA carrying the growing polypeptide moves from the A site to the P site on the ribosome. (3) The transport of organic nutrients in the phloem of vascular plants.

transmission The passage of a nerve impulse along axons.

transmission electron microscope (TEM) A microscope that passes an electron beam through very thin sections stained with metal atoms and is primarily used to study the internal ultrastructure of cells.

transpiration The evaporative loss of water from a plant.

transport epithelium One or more layers of specialized epithelial cells that carry out and regulate solute movement.

transport protein A transmembrane protein that helps a certain substance or class of closely related substances to cross the membrane.

transport vesicle A small membranous sac in a eukaryotic cell's cytoplasm carrying molecules produced by the cell.

transposable element A segment of DNA that can move within the genome of a cell by means of a DNA or RNA intermediate; also called a transposable genetic element.

transposon A transposable element that moves within a genome by means of a DNA intermediate.

transverse (T) tubule An infolding of the plasma membrane of skeletal muscle cells.

triacylglycerol (trī-as′-ul-glis′-uh-rol) A lipid consisting of three fatty acids linked to one glycerol molecule; also called a fat or triglyceride.

triple response A plant growth maneuver in response to mechanical stress, involving slowing of stem elongation, thickening of the stem, and a curvature that causes the stem to start growing horizontally.

triplet code A genetic information system in which sets of three-nucleotide-long words specify the amino acids for polypeptide chains.

triploblastic Possessing three germ layers: the endoderm, mesoderm, and ectoderm. All bilaterian animals are triploblastic.

trisomic Referring to a diploid cell that has three copies of a particular chromosome instead of the normal two.

trochophore larva (trō′-kuh-fōr) Distinctive larval stage observed in some lophotrochozoan animals, including some annelids and molluscs.

trophic efficiency The percentage of production transferred from one trophic level to the next higher trophic level.

trophic structure The different feeding relationships in an ecosystem, which determine the route of energy flow and the pattern of chemical cycling.

trophoblast The outer epithelium of a mammalian blastocyst. It forms the fetal part of the placenta, supporting embryonic development but not forming part of the embryo proper.

tropic hormone A hormone that has an endocrine gland or endocrine cells as a target.

tropical dry forest A terrestrial biome characterized by relatively high temperatures and precipitation overall but with a pronounced dry season.

tropical rain forest A terrestrial biome characterized by relatively high precipitation and temperatures year-round.

tropics Latitudes between 23.5° north and south.

tropism A growth response that results in the curvature of whole plant organs toward or away from stimuli due to differential rates of cell elongation.

tropomyosin The regulatory protein that blocks the myosin-binding sites on actin molecules.

troponin complex The regulatory proteins that control the position of tropomyosin on the thin filament.

true-breeding Referring to organisms that produce offspring of the same variety over many generations of self-pollination.

tubal ligation A means of sterilization in which a woman's two oviducts (fallopian tubes) are tied closed and a segment of each is removed to prevent eggs from reaching the uterus.

tube foot One of numerous extensions of an echinoderm's water vascular system. Tube feet function in locomotion and feeding.

tumor-suppressor gene A gene whose protein product inhibits cell division, thereby preventing the uncontrolled cell growth that contributes to cancer.

tundra A terrestrial biome at the extreme limits of plant growth. At the northernmost limits, it is called arctic tundra, and at high altitudes, where plant forms are limited to low shrubby or matlike vegetation, it is called alpine tundra.

tunicate A member of the clade Urochordata, sessile marine chordates that lack a backbone.

turgid (ter′-jid) Swollen or distended, as in plant cells. (A walled cell becomes turgid if it has a lower water potential than its surroundings, resulting in entry of water.)

turgor pressure The force directed against a plant cell wall after the influx of water and swelling of the cell due to osmosis.

turnover The mixing of waters as a result of changing water-temperature profiles in a lake.

turnover time The time required to replace the standing crop of a population or group of populations (for example, of phytoplankton), calculated as the ratio of standing crop to production.

twin study A behavioral study in which researchers compare the behavior of identical twins raised apart with that of identical twins raised in the same household.

tympanic membrane Another name for the eardrum, the membrane between the outer and middle ear.

Unikonta (yū′-ni-kon′-tuh) One of four supergroups of eukaryotes proposed in a current hypothesis of the evolutionary history of eukaryotes. This clade, which is supported by studies of myosin proteins and DNA, consists of amoebozoans and opisthokonts. *See also* Excavata, "SAR" clade, and Archaeplastida.

unsaturated fatty acid A fatty acid that has one or more double bonds between carbons in the hydrocarbon tail. Such bonding reduces the number of hydrogen atoms attached to the carbon skeleton.

urban ecology The study of organisms and their environment in urban and suburban settings.

urea A soluble nitrogenous waste produced in the liver by a metabolic cycle that combines ammonia with carbon dioxide.

ureter (yū-rē′-ter) A duct leading from the kidney to the urinary bladder.

urethra (yū-rē′-thruh) A tube that releases urine from the mammalian body near the vagina in females and through the penis in males; also serves in males as the exit tube for the reproductive system.

uric acid A product of protein and purine metabolism and the major nitrogenous waste product of insects, land snails, and many reptiles. Uric acid is relatively nontoxic and largely insoluble in water.

urinary bladder The pouch where urine is stored prior to elimination.

uterine cycle In humans and certain other primates, a type of reproductive cycle in which the nonpregnant endometrium is shed through the cervix into the vagina; also called the menstrual cycle.

uterus A female organ where eggs are fertilized and/or development of the young occurs.

utricle (yū′-trih-kuhl) In the vertebrate ear, a chamber in the vestibule behind the oval window that opens into the three semicircular canals.

vaccine A harmless variant or derivative of a pathogen that stimulates a host's immune system to mount defenses against the pathogen.

vacuole (vak′-yū-ōl′) A membrane-bounded vesicle whose specialized function varies in different kinds of cells.

vagina Part of the female reproductive system between the uterus and the outside opening; the birth canal in mammals. During copulation, the vagina accommodates the male's penis and receives sperm.

valence The bonding capacity of a given atom; usually equals the number of unpaired electrons required to complete the atom's outermost (valence) shell.

valence electron An electron in the outermost electron shell.

valence shell The outermost energy shell of an atom, containing the valence electrons involved in the chemical reactions of that atom.

van der Waals interactions Weak attractions between molecules or parts of molecules that result from transient local partial charges.

variable A factor that varies in an experiment or other test.

variation Differences between members of the same species.

vas deferens In mammals, the tube in the male reproductive system in which sperm travel from the epididymis to the urethra.

vasa recta The capillary system in the kidney that serves the loop of Henle.

vascular cambium A cylinder of meristematic tissue in woody plants that adds layers of secondary vascular tissue called secondary xylem (wood) and secondary phloem.

vascular plant A plant with vascular tissue. Vascular plants include all living plant species except liverworts, mosses, and hornworts.

vascular tissue Plant tissue consisting of cells joined into tubes that transport water and nutrients throughout the plant body.

vascular tissue system A transport system formed by xylem and phloem throughout a vascular plant. Xylem transports water and minerals; phloem transports sugars, the products of photosynthesis.

vasectomy The cutting and sealing of each vas deferens to prevent sperm from entering the urethra.

vasoconstriction A decrease in the diameter of blood vessels caused by contraction of smooth muscles in the vessel walls.

vasodilation An increase in the diameter of blood vessels caused by relaxation of smooth muscles in the vessel walls.

vector An organism that transmits pathogens from one host to another.

vegetal pole The point at the end of an egg in the hemisphere where most yolk is concentrated; opposite of animal pole.

vegetative propagation Asexual reproduction in plants that is facilitated or induced by humans.

vegetative reproduction Asexual reproduction in plants.

vein (1) In animals, a vessel that carries blood toward the heart. (2) In plants, a vascular bundle in a leaf.

ventilation The flow of air or water over a respiratory surface.

ventral Pertaining to the underside, or bottom, of an animal with radial or bilateral symmetry.

ventricle (ven′-tri-kul) (1) A heart chamber that pumps blood out of the heart. (2) A space in the vertebrate brain, filled with cerebrospinal fluid.

venule (ven′-yūl) A vessel that conveys blood between a capillary bed and a vein.

vernalization The use of cold treatment to induce a plant to flower.

vertebrate A chordate animal with vertebrae, the series of bones that make up the backbone.

vesicle (ves′-i-kul) A membranous sac in the cytoplasm of a eukaryotic cell.

vessel A continuous water-conducting micropipe found in most angiosperms and a few nonflowering vascular plants.

vessel element A short, wide water-conducting cell found in the xylem of most angiosperms and a few nonflowering vascular plants. Dead at maturity, vessel elements are aligned end to end to form micropipes called vessels.

vestigial structure A feature of an organism that is a historical remnant of a structure that served a function in the organism's ancestors.

villus (plural, **villi**) (1) A finger-like projection of the inner surface of the small intestine. (2) A finger-like projection of the chorion of the mammalian placenta. Large numbers of villi increase the surface areas of these organs.

viral envelope A membrane, derived from membranes of the host cell, that cloaks the capsid, which in turn encloses a viral genome.

viroid (vī′-royd) A plant pathogen consisting of a molecule of naked, circular RNA a few hundred nucleotides long.

virulent phage A phage that replicates only by a lytic cycle.

virus An infectious particle incapable of replicating outside of a cell, consisting of an RNA or DNA genome surrounded by a protein coat (capsid) and, for some viruses, a membranous envelope.

visceral mass One of the three main parts of a mollusc; the part containing most of the internal organs. *See also* foot and mantle.

visible light That portion of the electromagnetic spectrum that can be detected as various colors by the human eye, ranging in wavelength from about 380 nm to about 750 nm.

vital capacity The maximum volume of air that a mammal can inhale and exhale with each breath.

vitamin An organic molecule required in the diet in very small amounts. Many vitamins serve as coenzymes or parts of coenzymes.

viviparous (vī-vip′-uh-rus) Referring to a type of development in which the young are born alive after having been nourished in the uterus by blood from the placenta.

voltage-gated ion channel A specialized ion channel that opens or closes in response to changes in membrane potential.

vulva Collective term for the female external genitalia.

water potential (Ψ) The physical property predicting the direction in which water will flow, governed by solute concentration and applied pressure.

water vascular system A network of hydraulic canals unique to echinoderms that branches into extensions called tube feet, which function in locomotion and feeding.

wavelength The distance between crests of waves, such as those of the electromagnetic spectrum.

wetland A habitat that is inundated by water at least some of the time and that supports plants adapted to water-saturated soil.

white matter Tracts of axons within the CNS.

whole-genome shotgun approach Procedure for genome sequencing in which the genome is randomly cut into many overlapping short segments that are sequenced; computer software then assembles the complete sequence.

wild type The phenotype most commonly observed in natural populations; also refers to the individual with that phenotype.

wilting The drooping of leaves and stems as a result of plant cells becoming flaccid.

wobble Flexibility in the base-pairing rules in which the nucleotide at the 5′ end of a tRNA anticodon can form hydrogen bonds with more than one kind of base in the third position (3′ end) of a codon.

xerophyte (zir′-ō-fīt′) A plant adapted to an arid climate.

X-linked gene A gene located on the X chromosome; such genes show a distinctive pattern of inheritance.

X-ray crystallography A technique used to study the three-dimensional structure of molecules. It depends on the diffraction of an X-ray beam by the individual atoms of a crystallized molecule.

xylem (zī′-lum) Vascular plant tissue consisting mainly of tubular dead cells that conduct most of the water and minerals upward from the roots to the rest of the plant.

xylem sap (zī′-lum) The dilute solution of water and minerals carried through vessels and tracheids.

yeast Single-celled fungus. Yeasts reproduce asexually by binary fission or by the pinching of small buds off a parent cell. Many fungal species can grow both as yeasts and as a network of filaments; relatively few species grow only as yeasts.

yolk Nutrients stored in an egg.

zero population growth (ZPG) A period of stability in population size, when additions to the population through births and immigration are balanced by subtractions through deaths and emigration.

zona pellucida The extracellular matrix surrounding a mammalian egg.

zoned reserve An extensive region that includes areas relatively undisturbed by humans surrounded by areas that have been changed by human activity and are used for economic gain.

zone of polarizing activity (ZPA) A block of mesoderm located just under the ectoderm where the posterior side of a limb bud is attached to the body; required for proper pattern formation along the anterior-posterior axis of the limb.

zoonotic pathogen A disease-causing agent that is transmitted to humans from other animals.

zoospore Flagellated spore found in chytrid fungi and some protists.

zygomycete (zī′-guh-mī′-sēt) A member of the fungal phylum Zygomycota, characterized by the formation of a sturdy structure called a zygosporangium during sexual reproduction.

zygosporangium (zī′-guh-spōr-an′-jē-um) (plural, **zygosporangia**) In zygomycete fungi, a sturdy multinucleate structure in which karyogamy and meiosis occur.

zygote (zī′-gōt) The diploid cell produced by the union of haploid gametes during fertilization; a fertilized egg.

DNA replication in, 320–325f
evidence for DNA in research on, 313f–314f, 315
evolution of cell division in, 241–242f
evolution of glycolysis in, 179–180
expressing cloned eukaryotic genes in, 416, 417
flagellum, movement of, 987f
genome sizes and number of genes for, 442t–443
G proteins and infections by, 215f
Gram staining of, 568–569f
land colonization by, 530
as model organism (see Escherichia coli (E. coli) bacteria)
mutualistic and pathogenic, 582–583f
nitrogen-fixing, and plants, 807f–809f, 810
origin of photosynthesis in, 528
origins of mitochondria and chloroplasts, 109–110f
in Permian mass extinction, 534–535
photosynthesis of, 186f, 187, 197
phylogeny of, 577f–579f, 580
plant defenses against, 860
in polymerase chain reaction, 415–416f
as prokaryotes, 97 (see also Prokaryotes)
prokaryotic cells of, 4f–5 (see also Prokaryotic cells)
protecting fruit flies from infection by, 948f, 949f
regulation of transcription in, 361f–364f
relatedness of, to mitochondria, 589
soil, 801, 1217f
transcription and translation in, 336–337f, 353f
transcription in, 340f–342f
translation in (see Translation)
viral infections of (see Phages)
Bacteria, domain, 11f, 562–563f, 577f–579f, 580t
Bacteriophages (phages), 313, 395
capsids of, 394f–395
in DNA research, 313f–314f, 315
prophages and temperate, 397f–398
replicative cycles of, 396f–397f, 398
in transduction, 573f
virulent, 396f–397f
Bacteriorhodopsin, 127f
Bacteroides thetaiotaomicron, 582–583
Bacteroids, 809f–810
Bada, Jeffrey, 58
Bait-and-switch defense, 594
Baker, C. S., 551f
Baker's yeast. See Saccharomyces cerevisiae (yeast)
Balance, body, 1106f–1110f, 1129
Balancing selection, 494–495f, 496f–497f
Baleen, 898f
Ball-and-socket joints, 1128f
Ball-and-stick models, 39f, 59f
Ballooning, spider, 702
Ball pythons, 886
Barbiturates, 104–105
Barbs, 639f
Bar graphs in Scientific Skills Exercises, 22, 177, 370, 420, 477, 584, 623, 694, 756, 858, 1144, 1181, 1211
Bark, 768
Barley, 644f, 845f
Barnacles, 704f, 1210f
Barr, Murray, 298
Barr body, 298f
Barrier contraceptives, 1032f
Barrier defenses, 946f–947f, 948–949
Barrier reefs, 1176f
Basal angiosperms, 642, 643f–644f
Basal animals, 676–677f, 684
Basal body, 115, 116f
Basal cells, 822f
Basal lamina, 923
Basal-like breast cancer, 387f
Basal metabolic rate (BMR), 884f–885f, 886
Basal nuclei, 1087f
Basal surface, epithelial, 871f
Basal taxon, 550f
Base pairing, DNA and RNA, 86–87f, 317–318f, 319f–320f
Bases, 51–52f, 53, 76–77f
Basidiocarps, 660f
Basidiomycetes, 651, 655f, 659f–661f

Basidiospores, 660f
Basidium, 659
Basilar membrane, 1107f
Basin wetlands, 1173f
Basking, reptilian, 729–730
Basophils, 928f, 930f
Bass fishes, 875f
Bassham, James, 189
Batesian mimicry, 1212f–1213
Batrachochytrium dendrobatidis, 663–664f
Bats, 14f, 552, 821f, 985f–986, 1256f
B cells, 952–953f, 954f–955f, 956–957f, 960f
Bdelloid rotifers, 264–265f, 692
Beach mouse (Peromyscus polionotus), 19f, 20f, 461f
Beadle, George, 334–335f, 336
Beagle, Charles Darwin's voyage on H.M.S., 465–466f
Beaks
finch, 466–467f, 480f–481f
shapes of bird, 734f
soapberry bug, 471f–472
Beans, 823f–824f, 851–852f, 893
Bears, 10f, 143f, 504f, 1263f, 1268
Beavers, 1220f
Bed bugs, 706f
Beech trees, 1164f
Bees, 296f, 706f, 815f–816, 820f, 881
Beetles, 469f, 706f
Behavior, 1133. See also Animal behavior
Behavioral ecology, 1134
Behavioral isolation, 502f
Beijerinck, Martinus, 393
Belding's ground squirrels, 1151–1152, 1153f, 1187t–1188f, 1189t–1190
Beluga whales, 1105f
Benign tumors, 247
Benson, Andrew, 189
Benthic zone, 1171f
Benthos, 1171
Berthold, Peter, 1151f
β_2-adrenergic receptor, 214f, 217
β-amyloid, 1098
Beta-carotene, 832f, 896
Beta cells, 910f
β chain, 954f
β-galactosidase, 157f, 363f
β-globin, 89
β-globin gene family, 447f
β-keratin, bird feathers and, 732f
Beta oxidation, 181
β pleated sheat, 80f
Beta proteobacteria, 578f
BGI (formerly Beijing Genome Institute), 438
bicoid gene, 381f–382f, 457
Biennials, 761
Big-bang reproduction, 1195
Bilateral symmetry, 673
animal, 673f–674f, 676
axis formation and, 1054
flower, 638f, 643f, 817f
Bilaterians, 671
chordates, 713f
invertebrates, 680f
Lophotrochozoans, 688
origin of, 671
phylogeny of, 676–677f
Bilayers, phospholipid. See Phospholipid bilayers
Bile, 903
Binary fission, 240–241f, 571–572, 600f–601
Binding sites, ribosome, 347f–348
Binomials (nomenclature), 464, 548–549f
Biochemical pathways. See Metabolic pathways
Biochemistry, 96
Biodiesel, 186f
Biodiversity
angiosperm, 643f–644f (see also Angiosperms)
animal (see Animal(s))
of bacteria and archaea (see Archaea; Bacteria)
classification of, 464
conservation biology and, 1255 (see also Conservation biology)
effects of mass extinctions on, 534f–536f
evolution and, 12f–15f, 462f, 467 (see also Evolution)

of fungi (see Fungi)
gymnosperm, 635, 636f–637f
habitat loss and fragmentation and, 1257–1258
human welfare and, 1257f
invertebrate (see Invertebrates)
landscape ecology and regional conservation to sustain, 1265–1266f, 1267f–1269f
levels of, 1255f–1256f
plant (see Plant(s))
potential resurrection of extinct species for, 1260–1261f
protist (see Protists)
within species, 501f
taxonomy and classification of, 10f–11f
threats to, 1254f–1255f, 1258f–1260f
tree of life and, 14f–15f (see also Phylogenetic trees; Phylogenies; Tree of life)
tropical deforestation as threat to, 645f–646
unity in, 12f, 13f, 462f, 467
vertebrate (see Vertebrates)
Biodiversity hot spots, 1267f
Bioenergetics, 142, 883. See also Metabolism
energy allocation and use in, 883–884f
energy budgets in, 886
energy costs of foraging in, 1143–1144
influences on metabolic rate in, 885f–886
of locomotion, 1130
metabolic rates and thermoregulation in, 884–885
of osmoregulation, 974–975
thyroid regulation of, 1004f–1005f
torpor, hibernation, and energy conservation in, 886–887f
of urea and uric acid wastes, 977
Biofilms, 212, 576
Biofuels, 186f, 665f, 832
Biogenic amines, 1075t
Biogeochemical cycles, 1244f–1245f, 1246–1247f, 1248f. See also Energy flow and chemical cycling
Biogeographic factors, community diversity and, 1225–1226f, 1227f–1228
Biogeography, 476–477
Bioinformatics, 7, 437
in analysis of protein structure, 83
centralized resources of, for genome analysis, 438–439f
genome analysis using genomics and, 437
genomics, proteomics, and, 87–88f
identifying protein-coding genes using gene annotation in, 439–440
in study of genomes, 7
systems biology and proteomics in study of genes and gene expression in, 440–441f, 442
Biological augmentation, 1250
Biological clocks, 851–852f, 853f–854f, 855, 1088–1089. See also Circadian rhythms
Biological Dynamics of Forest Fragments Project, 1266
Biological magnification, 1271f–1272
Biological molecules. See also Organic compounds
analyzing polypeptide sequence data of, 89
carbohydrates as (see Carbohydrates)
four classes of, 66
genomics and proteomics in study of, 87–88f
lipids as, 72–73f, 74f–75f
macromolecules as polymers of monomers and, 66f–67f
as measures of evolution, 89
nucleic acids as, 84–85f, 86–87f
proteins as (see Proteins)
Biological species concept, 501f–504f
Biology, 1 (facing page)
astrobiology in, 50f
biodiversity in (see Animal(s); Biodiversity; Plant(s))
biophilia and, 1277f
cells in (see Cell(s))
classification in (see Cladistics; Phylogenies; Systematics; Taxonomy)
common unifying themes of, 2f–9f
connection of, to chemistry, 28 (see also Chemistry)
conservation biology in (see Conservation biology)

Index

Human population
    biosphere carrying capacity for global, 1201*f*–1204*f*, 1205
    density-dependent population regulation of, by diseases, 1198*f*
    survivorship curves for, 1188*f*
Human reproduction. *See also* Animal reproduction
    conception, embryonic development, and birth in, 1028*f*–1031*f*
    contraception and abortion in, 1032*f*–1033
    endocrine disruptors and, 1009
    female reproductive organs of, 1020–1021*f*
    hormonal regulation of, 1024*f*–1027*f*
    as iteroparity, 1195*f*
    male reproductive organs of, 1019*f*–1020
    maternal immune tolerance of embryo and fetus in, 1031
    oogenesis in, 1023*f*
    prostaglandins and, 999
    reproductive technologies and, 1033–1034*f*
    sexual response in, 1027–1028
    spermatogenesis in, 1022*f*
Hummingbird hawkmoth, 706*f*
Hummingbirds, 4, 516, 734*f*, 821*f*
Humoral immune response, 947*f*, **958***f*–959*f*
Humpback whales, 898*f*
Humus, **800**, 801
Hundred Heartbeat Club species, 1256*f*
Hunger, transgenic crops and reducing human, 831–832*f*
Huntington's disease, **285**, 426
Hurricane Katrina, 1166
Hutton, James, 463*f*, 464
Huxley, Andrew, 1068
Hybrid breakdown, 503*f*
Hybridization, **269**, 831, 833–834
Hybrid orbitals, 39*f*–40
Hybrids, **501**
    bears, 504*f*
    reproductive barriers and sterility of, 503*f*
    speciation rates and, 514–515*f*
    sterility of, 516
Hybrid zones, **510**–511*f*, 512*f*–513*f*
Hydrangea, 280*f*
Hydras, 253*f*, 685–686*f*, 687*f*, 899*f*, 1080*f*
Hydration shells, **49**
Hydrocarbons, **60**–61*f*, 665*f*
Hydrocarbon tail, chlorophyll, 192*f*
Hydrochloric acid, 51, 901–902*f*
Hydrogen
    covalent bonding and, 36*f*–37*f*
    as essential element, 29*t*, 56, 64
    in organic compounds, 59*f*
    oxidation of organic molecules containing, 164–165*f*
    in plant composition, 803
    in saturated and unsaturated fats, 73*f*–74
Hydrogen bonds, **39***f*
    in DNA structure, 86–87*f*
    floating of ice and, 48
    in water molecules, 45*f*
    as weak chemical bonds, 39*f*
Hydrogen ions, **51**–52*f*, 53
Hydrogenosomes, 593
Hydrogen peroxide, 111
Hydrogen sulfide gas, 534–535
Hydrolysis, **67**
    of ATP, 149*f*–151*f*
    disassembling of polymers to monomers by, 67*f*
    enzymatic, 897
    by lysosomes, 107*f*–108
Hydrolytic enzymes, fungal, 649
Hydronium ions, **51**–52*f*, 53
Hydrophilic substances, **49**, 76–77*f*, 125*f*–126
Hydrophobic interaction, **81***f*
Hydrophobic substances, **49**, 76–77*f*, 125*f*–126
Hydroponic culture, **804***f*
Hydrostatic skeletons, **1127***f*
Hydrothermal vents, **520**–21*f*, 580, 582, 908*f*
Hydroxide ions, **51**–52*f*, 53
Hydroxyl group, **63***f*
Hydrozoans, 686*f*–687*f*
Hymen, 1020
Hymenoptera, 706*f*

Hypercholesterolemia, 137
Hypermastigote, 608*f*
Hyperosmotic solutions, 972*f*, 985
Hyperpolarization, **1066***f*–1067*f*
Hypersensitive response, plant, **860**, 861
Hypertension, **932**
Hypertonic solutions, **132***f*
Hyphae, fungal, **649***f*–650*f*, 651, 811
Hypoblast cells, 1046*f*–1047*f*
Hypocotyl, **822**–823*f*, 824*f*
Hypoosmotic solutions, 972*f*
Hypothalamus, **882**, **1002**, **1087**
    in homeostasis, 1084
    in human brain, 1087*f*
    in human endocrine system, 999*f*
    in kidney regulation, 988*f*–989*f*
    in neuroendocrine signaling, 1002*f*–1005*f*
    in regulation of mammalian reproduction, 1024*f*–1026*f*, 1027
    in sex hormone cascades, 1009
    in stress responses, 1007*f*
    suparchiasmatic nucleus (SCN) in, 1088–1089
    in thermoregulation, 882–883*f*
Hypotheses, **16**. *See also* Inquiry Figures; Scientific Skills Exercises
    forming and testing of, in science, 16–17*f*, 18*f*–19
    phylogenetic trees as, 558*f*
    theories and, 21, 477–478
Hypothyroidism, 1004
Hypotonic solutions, **132***f*
Hyraciodea, 739*f*
Hyracotherium, 542–543*f*

Ibex, 1260–1261
Ibuprofen, 62*f*, 1008, 1106
Ice
    floating of, on liquid water, 48*f*
    on Mars, 50*f*
    as solid water, 44
Icosahedral viruses, 394*f*–395
Identical DNA sequences, 447*f*
Identical twins, 1030, 1055
Idioblasts, 862*f*
IgE antibodies, 964
Iguanas, 883
Ileum, 904
Imaging, brain, 1079*f*–1080, 1090*f*
Imaging techniques, fetal testing, 287
Imatinib, 429–430
Imbibition, **823**
Immigration, population dynamics of, **1186***f*, 1190–1191*f*, 1200–1201*f*, 1227
Immune defenses, plant, 751, 859–860
Immune response
    primary and secondary, 956–957*f*
    trypanosome evasion of, 594
Immune systems, **946**
    adaptations of pathogens to evade, 965–968*f*
    diseases of, 227
    disruptions of, 964–965*f*, 966
    HIV/AIDS and, 392*f*, 400 (*see also* AIDS (acquired immunodeficiency syndrome); HIV (human immunodeficiency virus))
    immune rejection by, 962–963
    immune responses by adaptive immunity in, 958*f*–963*f*, 964
    immune responses by innate immunity in, 947–948*f*, 949*f*–951*f*, 952
    immunization and, 961–962, 967*f*
    leukocytes in, 929
    lymphatic systems and, 927*f*
    maternal immune tolerance of embryo and fetus during pregnancy, 1031
    membrane carbohydrate cell-cell recognition in, 128–129
    pathogen-specific recognition by adaptive immunity in, 952–953*f*, 954*f*–955*f*, 956–957*f*
    in plants, 751, 859–860
    prostaglandins in, 995
    recognition and response functions of innate and adaptive immunity in, 946*f*–947*f*
    stem cells and, 426
    trematode camouflage and, 690*f*

Immunity
    active and passive, and immunization, 962–963
    maternal immune tolerance of embryo and fetus during pregnancy, 1031
Immunization, **963**
Immunodeficiency diseases, 966
Immunoglobulin (Ig), **953***f*, 955*f*–956*f*, 961
Immunological memory, 954, 956–957*f*
Impala, 219*f*
Imprinting, **1138**–1139*f*, 1146*f*–1147*f*
Inactivation, cell-signaling, 227
Inborn immunodeficiency, 966
Inclusive fitness, **1152***f*–1153*f*
Incomplete dominance, **277***f*
Incomplete flowers, **638***f*, 816
Incomplete metamorphosis, **705**, 706*f*
Independent assortment, law of, 272–273, 274*f*, 293*f*–294, 300
Independent assortment of chromosomes, 263*f*
Independent variables, **21**, 507
Indeterminate cleavage, **675***f*–676
Indeterminate growth, **760***f*–761*f*
Indian corn, 445*f*
Indian Ocean Subtropical Gyre, 1162*f*
Indian pipe, 812*f*
Indian rice, 1257
Indoleacetic acid (IAA), 842. *See also* Auxin
Indolebutyric acid (IBA), 843
Induced fit, 153*f*–**154**
Induced pluripotent stem cells, 426–427*f*
Inducers, **363***f*–364
Inducible enzymes, 363*f*–364
Inducible innate immune response, 948*f*, 949*f*
Inducible operons, 363*f*–364
Induction, 377*f*–**378**, **1048**
Inductive reasoning, **16**
Inductive signals, cell fate determination and pattern formation by, 1055–1056*f*, 1057*f*–1058
Industrialization, human population growth and, 1201*f*–1202
Inert elements, 35
Infant mortality, 1203, 1276*f*
Infection
    bacterial, 215*f*
    cytotoxic T cell response to, 959*f*
    fungal, 664
    inflammatory response and, 951–952
Infection thread, bacterial, 809*f*
Inferences, 1025
Infertility, 1033–1034*f*
Inflammation, 578*f*, 931*f*–932, 1008, 1106
Inflammatory response, **951***f*–952
Inflorescences, **816**
Influenza viruses
    antibody proteins and, 79*f*
    antigenic variation of, 966
    in density-dependent population regulation, 1198*f*
    as emerging viruses, 402–403*f*, 404–405
    structure of, 394*f*–395
    as zoonotic, 1228–1229*f*
Information, as theme of biology, 2, 5*f*–6*f*, 7
Information processing
    cerebral cortex in, 1090–1091*f*
    ion movements and gradients and, 987*f*
    neuron, 1061–1062, 1063*f*
    problem solving and, 1141*f*
Infrared receptors, 1104–1105*f*
Ingestion, **897***f*
Ingroups, 555
Inhalation, 938–939*f*, 940*f*
Inheritance. *See also* Mendelian inheritance; Sexual life cycles
    blending hypothesis vs. particulate hypothesis on, 267–68
    of cancer predisposition, 388
    chromosomal basis of (*see* Chromosomal basis of inheritance)
    of chromosomes and genes, 253
    C. Darwin on, 13*f*–15*f*
    Darwinian theory on, 469*f*–470
    epigenetic, 367
    expression and transmission of genetic information in, 5*f*–6*f*, 7

evolution of animal, 671*f*
insects as, 707
mass extinctions and, 536
plant recruitment of, as herbivore defense, 863*f*
Predictions, scientific, 16–17*f*, 18*f*, 487
Predisposition, cancer and inherited, 388
Preganglionic neurons, 1084
Pregnancy, human, **1029**
conception and trimesters of, 1028*f*–1031*f*
detecting disorders during, 1033
detecting human, 963
endocrine disruptors and, 1009
prevention of, 1032*f*–1033
Pre-mRNA, 337*f*, 343*f*–344*f*, 367*f*
Prenatally and Postnatally Diagnosed Conditions
Awareness Act, 307
Preprophase band, 770–771*f*
Prepuce, 1019*f*–**1020**
Pressure
hearing and, 1108
receptors for, 1104*f*
root, 787–788*f*
water potential and, 782–784
Pressure-flow hypothesis, 794–795*f*
Pressure potential, **783**
Presynaptic cells, 1062
Presynaptic neurons, 1073, 1074*f*, 1095*f*
Prey
adaptations of native predators to introduced,
1211
defensive adaptations of, 1211–1212*f*, 1213*f*
genetic variation in selection of, 1150*f*
Prezygotic barriers, 502*f*–503*f*, **504**
Priapula, 682*f*
Primary cell walls, **118**
Primary cilium, 114
Primary consumers, **1234**–1235*f*
Primary electron acceptors, **194**
Primary growth, plant, **760**
meristem generation of cells for, 760*f*–761*f*
of roots, 761*f*–763*f*
of woody stems, 766*f*
Primary immune response, **956**–957*f*
Primary motor cortex, 1091*f*
Primary oocytes, 1023*f*
Primary producers, **1234**–1235*f*
Primary production, **1235**
in aquatic ecosystems, 1237*f*–1238*f*
in Arctic tundra ecosystem, 1242*f*–1243*f*
determining, for oceans, 1237*f*
determining, with satellites, 1236*f*
ecosystem energy budgets in, 1235–1236*f*, 1237*f*
in terrestrial ecosystems, 1238*f*–1239
Primary roots, 753
Primary somatosensory cortex, 1091*f*
Primary structure, protein, **80***f*
Primary succession, **1223**–1224*f*
Primary transcripts, **337**
Primary visual cortex, 1115*f*
Primases, 321*f*–**322**, 324*f*, 325*t*
Primates. *See also* Human(s)
cloning of, 425
derived characters of, 740
HIV in, 561
living, 740*f*–741*f*, 742
in mammalian phylogeny, 739*f*
phylogenetic tree of, 740*f*
Primers, 321*f*–**322**
Primitive streak, 1046*f*
Primordial germ cells, 1023*f*
Principle of conservation of energy, 143*f*–144
Printing press, 23–24
Prions, **405**–406*f*
Probability
laws of, 274–275*f*, 276
principle of maximum likelihood and, 556
Problem solving, **1141***f*
Proboscidea, 739*f*
Proboscis, 682*f*, 706*f*, 821
Process, evolutionary, 463, 477, 547
Producers, 7, 185*f*–186*f*, **608**–609*f*
Production efficiency, 1239*f*–**1240**
Products, **41**, 645

Progesterone, **1009***f*, **1024**
Progestins, 999*f*, 1008–**1009***f*, 1032*f*–1033
Proglottids, 691*f*
Programmed cell death. *See* Apoptosis
Projections, body surface area and, 689*f*
Prokaryotes
adaptive abilities of, 567*f*–568
archaea as, 580*f*–581
bacteria as, 577–578*f*, 579*f*–580
beneficial and harmful impacts of, on humans,
582–583*f*, 584*f*–585*f*
bioremediation using, 1249*f*
cell signaling in, 211*f*–212
cells of (*see* Prokaryotic cells)
chemiosmosis in, 173–174*f*, 175
ecological roles of, in biosphere, 581*f*–582*f*
electron transport chains in, 166
as endosymbionts, 528–529*f*
evolution of glycolysis in, 179–180
fossils of, 523*f*
genetic diversity in, 572–573*f*, 574*f*–575
genome sizes and number of genes for, 442*t*–443
horizontal gene transfer in genomes of, 563
land colonization by, 530
nutritional and metabolic adaptations of,
575–576*f*, 577
origin of, 526, 528*f*
photosynthesis in, 185–186*f*
phylogeny of, 577*f*
in protection of plants from diseases, 584
structural and functional adaptations of, 568*f*–572*f*
taxonomy of, 562, 563*f*
Prokaryotic cells, **5**, **97**. *See also* Cell(s)
cell-surface structures of, 568–569*f*, 570*f*
DNA replication in, 320*f*–325*f*
eukaryotic cells vs., 4*f*–5, 97*f*–98*f*, 99 (*see also*
Eukaryotic cells)
evolution of cell division of, 241–242*f*
programming of, by viral DNA, 313*f*–314*f*, 315
regulation of transcription in, 361*f*–364*f*
structure of, 97*f*
transcription and translation in, 336–337*f*, 353*f*
transcription in, 340*f*–342*f*
translation in (*see* Translation)
Prolactin, 999*f*, **1003**, 1010*f*
Prolactin-releasing hormone, 1003
Proliferative phase, 1027
Proline, 77*f*, 339
Prometaphase, **235**, 236*f*, 241*f*
Promiscuous mating, 1145
Promoters, 340*f*–**341***f*, 806
Proof, hypotheses and, 17
Proofreading, DNA, 325–326*f*
Propanal, **63***f*
Properties, chemical, 34*f*–35
Properties, emergent. *See* Emergent properties
Prophages, 397*f*–398
Prophase, **235**, 236*f*, 241*f*, 261*f*
Prophase I, 258*f*, 260*f*–261*f*, 264*f*
Prophase II, 259*f*
Propithecus verreauxi, 740*f*
Prop roots, 754*f*
Prostaglandins, **995**, 1031*f*, 1106
Prostate glands, 999, 1019*f*–**1020**
Prosthetic groups, 173
Proteases, **901**
Proteasomes, 373
Protected areas, 1267*f*–1269*f*
Protein Data Bank, 439
Protein interaction networks, 440–441*f*
Protein kinases, **219***f*–220, 221*f*, 225–227
Protein phosphatases, **220**
Proteins, **75**. *See also* Amino acids
amino acids of, 67, 75–77*f* (*see also* Amino acids)
antibiotics and prokaryotic synthesis of, 571
antifreeze, 882
in bacterial binary fission, 240–241*f*
biotechnology in production of, 430*f*
blood plasma, 928*f*–929
cadherin in choanoflagellates and animals, 670*f*
in cell-signaling nuclear responses, 223*f*
cell-signaling receptor, 214, 215*f*–217*f*
in cellular membranes, 125*f*–128*f*

cellulose-synthesizing, 613
as composed of polypeptides, 78*f* (*see also*
Polypeptides)
Conserved Domain Database (CDD) of structures
of, 438–439*f*
denaturation and renaturation of, 82*f*–83
digestion of, 903*f*
in DNA replication, 324*f*–325*t*
DNA vs., as genetic material, 313, 314*f*–315
domains of, 344–345*f*
in electron transport chains, 172*f*–173
enzymes as, 8–9*f*, 75–76*f*, 151, 157*f*
essential amino acids in, 893
evolution of genes for, with novel functions, 450,
451*f*
expressing cloned genes for, 417
facilitated diffusion and, 133*f*
florigen as, 855
folding and post-translational modifications of,
351–352*f*
folding of, in cells, 83*f*–84*f*
four levels of structure of, 79, 80*f*–81*f*
as fuel for catabolism, 180*f*
functions of types of, 76*f*
human dietary deficiencies in, 896
identifying genes coding for, 439*f*–440
innate immune reponse and, 951
as macromolecules, 66
as measures of evolution, 89
mediator, 368–369*f*
motor (*see* Motor proteins)
nonenzyme, 336
nucleic acids in gene expression and synthesis of,
84*f*–85
packing of DNA and, into chromosomes,
328*f*–330*f*
phosphorylation of, in cell-signal transduction,
219*f*–220
in photosystems, 194*f*–198*f*, 199
plant antifreeze, 859
plant heat-shock, 858
post-translational modification of, in plant
responses, 839
prions as infectious, 405–406*f*
producing, with gene cloning, 412*f*–413
in prokaryotic flagella, 570*f*–571
proteomics in study of, 7, 87–88*f*, 440
regulation of eukaryotic processing and
degradation of, 373
regulatory, 373, 378–379*f*
in replication of DNA telomeres, 326
repressor, 362*f*
scaffolding, 225*f*–227
separating, with gel electrophoresis, 414*f*
synthesis of (*see* Protein synthesis)
synthesis of, in expression and transmission of
genetic information, 5*f*–6*f*, 7
synthesis of, in plant cells, 206*f*
systems biology in studying networks of, 440–441*f*
transcription factors, 341*f*
translation elongation factors, 350
translation initiation factors, 348*f*, 350
translation release factors, 351*f*
transport (*see* Transport proteins)
in transport and mechanical work, 150*f*
using data on, to test hypotheses on horizontal
gene transfer, 564
viral movement, 796
viruses and, 394–395, 396*f*–397*f*
water-soluble, 49*f*
Protein sequences, 438–439*f*, 440
in Scientific Skills Exercise, 564
Protein synthesis. *See also* Gene expression
evidence for, in study of metabolic defects,
334–335*f*, 336
gene concept and, 357
genetic code in, 337–338*f*, 339*f*–340
mutations during, 355*f*–356*f*, 357
by ribosomes, 102, 103*f*–104
summary of, 354*f*
via transcription, RNA processsing, and
translation, 336–337*f* (*see also* RNA
processing; Transcription; Translation)

Ventral nerve cords
earthworm, 698*f*
planarian, 690*f*
Ventral side, **673**
Ventral tegmental area (VTA), 1097*f*
Ventricles, brain, 1082*f*
Ventricles, heart, **918**–919*f*, 920*f*–921*f*
Venules, **918**, 923*f*–924*f*
Venus flytrap, 796, 812*f*, 856
Vernalization, **854**
Verreaux's sifaka, 740*f*
Vertebrates, **676**, **712**
action potential conduction speed in, 1070
adaptations of digestive systems of, 906*f*–908*f* (*see also* Digestive systems)
amniotes and development of terrestrially adapted eggs in, 727–728*f*, 729*f*–734*f* (*see also* Amniotes)
anatomical homologies in embryos of, 473*f*–474
brains of, 1085*f*–1090*f*, 1093*f* (*see also* Nervous systems)
cardiovascular systems of (*see* Cardiovascular systems)
as chordates, 709, 713*f*–719*f* (*see also* Chordates)
derived characters of, 716–717
embryonic germ layers of, 1045*f*
energy budgets for terrestrial, 886
evolution of, 672
evolution of backbones and diversity vs. disparity in, 712*f*–713
fossils and early evolution of, 718*f*–719*f*
gamete production and delivery in, 1018
gas exchange systems of (*see* Gas exchange systems)
gnathostomes and development of jaws in, 719*f*–723*f*, 724
hominins and humans, 742*f*–744*f*, 745–746*f*, 747*f*–748*f*
innate immunity in, 948–949*f*, 950*f*–951*f*, 952
kidneys in excretory systems of, 980*f*–981*f*, 985–987*f* (*see also* Excretory systems; Kidneys)
limb formation in, 1056*f*–1057*f*, 1058*f*
mammals, 735*f*–741*f*, 742
mechanoreceptors for hearing and equilibrium in, 1106*f*–1110*f* (*see also* Sensory systems)
neuroendocrine signaling in, 1002*f*–1005*f*
organogenesis in, 1049*f*
origins of bone and teeth in, 719
phylogeny of, 676–677*f*
small intestine surface area in, 689*f*
tetrapods and development of limbs in, 724*f*–727*f*
visual systems of, 1112*f*–1116*f*, 1117
Vertical layering, terrestrial biome, 1166
Vertical transmission, viral, 405
Vervet monkeys, 1142*f*
Vesicles, **104**
abiotically produced, as protocells, 521*f*–522
in endomembrane system, 104
in exocytosis and endocytosis, 137–138*f*
in plant cytokinesis, 239–240*f*
self-replicating RNA in, 522
transport, 105–106*f*, 107
Vessel elements, 642, **759***f*
Vessels, 759*f*
Vessels, blood. *See* Blood vessels
Vessels, lymph, 927*f*
Vestibular glands, 1021*f*
Vestigial structures, **474**
Viagra, 221, 995–996, 998, 1020, 1076
Vibrio cholerae, 221, 583
Vietnam, 1254*f*–1255*f*
Viewpoints, science and diverse, 23–24
Villi, 689*f*, **904***f*
Viral envelopes, 394*f*–**395**, 398–399*f*
Viral integration, 388
Viral movement proteins, 796*f*
Virchow, Rudolf, 232
Viroids, **405**
Virtual plants, computer-generated, 770
Virulent phages, 396*f*–397*f*
Viruses, **314**, **392**
analyzing sequence-based phylogenetic trees to understand evolution of, 404

cancer-causing, 968
in cancer development, 388
cellular RNAi pathway and, 375
classes of animal, 398*t*
discovery of, 393*f*
emerging, 402–403*f*, 404–405, 406*f*
evolution of, 400
features of replicative cycles of, 395*f*–396
host range of, 395
importance of, 392*f*–393
infection of bacterial cells by, 313*f*–314*f*, 315
influenza (*see* Influenza viruses)
latency of, 966–967
as pathogens, 392*f*–393, 394*f*, 401*f*, 402–403*f*, 404–405, 406*f*
rapid reproduction of, as source of genetic variation, 483
replicative cycles of animal, 398–399*f*, 400, 401*f*
replicative cycles of phages as, 396*f*–397*f*, 398
structure of, 394*f*–395
viral movement proteins of plant, 796
Visceral mass, **692**–693*f*
Visible light, **190***f*
Visual communication, 1136*f*
Visual cortex, 1115*f*
Visual pigments, 1113*f*, 1116
Visual systems
color vision in, 1115–1116*f*
compound eyes in, 1111*f*–1112
evolution of light detectors in, 1111*f*–1113*f*
gene therapy for vision in, 1116*f*
light-detecting organs in, 1111*f*
sensory transduction in, 1114*f*
single-lens eyes in, 1112–1113
structure of human eyes in, 1112*f*–1113*f*
visual fields and focusing in, 1116*f*–1117
visual information processing in brain in, 1115*f*
visual information processing in retina in, 1114–1115*f*
Vital capacity, **939**
Vital statistics, population, 1186–1187*f*, 1188*f*–1189, 1190
Vitamin A deficiencies, 832, 896
Vitamin C, 894
Vitamin D, 998, 1006*f*
Vitamins, 156, **894**
deficiencies of, 896
effects of supplementation of, on neural tube defects in, 896*f*
essential, 894*t*
as lipid-soluble hormones, 998
parathyroid hormone and, 1006*f*
Vitelline layer, 1039*f*
Vitellogenin, 997*f*–998
Vitreous humor, 1112*f*
Viviparous organisms, **721**
Vocal cords, 936–937
Vocal folds, 936–937
Vocalization, *FOXP2* gene and, 454*f*–455
Vogt, Walther, 1051–1052*f*
Volcanic springs, 580*f*
Volcanism, 630*f*
Volcanoes, 57, 58, 520*f*, 534–535
Voles, 1150*f*–1151
Voltage-gated ion channels, 217*f*, 1066*f*–**1067***f*, 1068*f*–1071*f*
Volume, 99, 1108
Volume–surface area relationships, 98*f*
Voluntary contraception, population growth and, 1202
Volutidae family, 532
Volvox, 591*f*, 603*f*
von Frisch, Karl, 1134, 1136
von Humboldt, Alexander, 1226
Vulva, **1020**–1021*f*

W

Waggle dance, honeybee, 1136–1137*f*
Wagler's pit viper, 731*f*
Waists, chromatid, 234
Walking, 1129
Wallace, Alfred Russel, 463*f*, 467, 1226
Walrus, 878*f*
Warming, global. *See* Global climate change

Warren, Robin, 902
Washington, Earl, 431*f*
Wasps, 706*f*, 863*f*, 1140*f*
Waste, toxic. *See* Toxic waste
Wastes, nitrogenous. *See* Nitrogenous wastes
Water
acidic and basic conditions of, and living organisms, 51–52*f*, 53
acidification as threat to quality of, 53*f*–54
albatross drinking of salty, 971*f*
biomanipulation and quality of, 1221
in blood plasma, 928*f*
cohesion of molecules and transport of, in plants, 45–46*f*
conduction of, in plant cells, 759*f*
conservation of, by kidneys, 983–984*f*, 985*f*–986*f*
covalent bonding of, 36*f*–37*f*, 45*f*
evolution of life on planets with, 50
floating of ice on liquid, 48*f*
forms of, and importance of, to life on Earth, 44
fruit and seed dispersal by, 826*f*
hydrogen bonds and, 39*f*
imbibition of, by seeds, 823
ions in, 38
irrigation with, 802
latitudinal gradients and evapotranspiration of, 1226*f*
as limiting factor on human population size, 1205
maximizing body surface area and uptake of, 689*f*
moderation of temperature by, 46–47*f*, 48
molecular shape of, 39*f*
molluscs and pollution of, 696
plant adaptations for reducing evaporative loss of, 792–793*f*
in plant composition, 803
plant response to submergence in, 857
regulation of transpiration and plant loss of, 790–791*f*, 792
root architecture and acquisition of, 781
seed dispersal by, 639*f*
as solvent of life, 48–49*f*, 50
species distributions and availability of, 1180
splitting of, in photosynthesis, 188*f*
transport of, across plant plasma membranes, 782–84*f*, 785*f*
transport of, from roots to shoots via xylem, 786–787*f*, 788*f*–789*f*, 790
Water balance
effects of osmosis on, 131*f*–133*f*
hormonal regulation of, 988*f*–990*f*
in insects, 979*f*–980
nitrogenous wastes and, 976
osmoregulation of, 972*f*–974*f*, 975–976*f*
Water bears, 683*f*
Water bodies, climate and, 1162*f*–1163*f*
Water bugs, 1017*f*
Water conservation
kidney adaptations for, 985*f*–986*f*
kidney role in, 983–984*f*, 985
Water cycle, 1244*f*
Water fleas, 442*t*, 1015, 1193*f*–1194
Water lily, 644*f*
Water potential, **782**–783*f*, 784–785*f*
Water scorpions, 702*f*
Water-soluble hormones, 996*f*, 997*f*
Water-soluble vitamins, 894*t*
Water vapor, 44
Water vascular system, **707**–708*f*
Watkinson, Andrew, 1197*f*
Watson, James, 3, 23, 312*f*, 316*f*–318*f*, 319*f*
Wavelengths, electromagnetic, **190***f*–192*f*
Wawona Sequoia, 768*f*
WD40 domains, 439*f*–440
Weak acids, 51
Weather, population fluctuations and, 1199*f*–1200. *See also* Climate
Weathering, rock, 623
Web of life, 564*f*
Weddell seals, 943*f*
Weeds, transgene escape and, 833
Weevils, 706*f*
Weight, mass vs., 29*n*
Welch, Allison, 494*f*